WHITCHURCH POSTGRADUATE MEDICAL LIBRARY

DONATED TO

AF740811

THE WHITCHURCH

POSTGRADUATE MEDICAL CENTRE

by

PROFESSOR PETER McGUFFIN

wesca B4716

WITHDRAWN

BIOLOGICAL PSYCHIATRY
Volume 2

BIOLOGICAL PSYCHIATRY

Volume 2

Proceedings of the 5th World Congress of Biological Psychiatry,
Florence, 9–14 June 1991

Editors:

Giorgio Racagni, Ph.D.
Professor of Pharmacology
Director, Center of Neuropharmacology
Institute of Pharmacological Sciences
University of Milan, Milan, Italy

Nicoletta Brunello, Ph.D.
Assistant Professor of Pharmacology
Center of Neuropharmacology
Institute of Pharmacological Sciences
University of Milan, Milan, Italy

Tetsuo Fukuda, M.D., D.med.Sci.
Director, Osaka Institute of Clinical Psychiatry
Takatsuki, and Professor of Psychiatry and Mental Health
Doshisha University, Kyoto, Japan

1991

EXCERPTA MEDICA, AMSTERDAM, LONDON, NEW YORK, TOKYO

© 1991 Elsevier Science Publishers B.V. All rights reserved.

No part of this publication may be reproduced, stored in a retrieval system or transmitted in any form or by any means, electronic, mechanical, photocopying, recording or otherwise without the prior written permission of the publisher, Elsevier Science Publishers B.V., Permissions Department P.O. Box 521, 1000 AM Amsterdam, The Netherlands.

No responsibility is assumed by the Publisher for any injury and/or damage to persons or property as a matter of products liability, negligence or otherwise, or from any use or operation of any methods, products, instructions or ideas contained in the material herein. Because of rapid advances in the medical sciences, the Publisher recommends that independent verification of diagnoses and drug dosages should be made.

Special regulations for readers in the USA – This publication has been registered with the Copyright Clearance Center Inc. (CCC), 27 Congress Street, Salem, MA 01970, USA. Information can be obtained from the CCC about conditions under which photocopies of parts of this publication may be made in the USA. All other copyright questions, including photocopying outside the USA, should be referred to the copyright owner, Elsevier Science Publishers B.V., unless otherwise specified.

International Congress Series No. 968
ISBN 0 444 89295 8

This book is printed on acid-free paper.

Published by:
Elsevier Science Publishers B.V.
P.O. Box 211
1000 AE Amsterdam
The Netherlands

Sole distributors for the USA and Canada:
Elsevier Science Publishing Company Inc.
655 Avenue of the Americas
New York, NY 10010
USA

In order to ensure rapid publication this volume was prepared using a method of electronic text processing known as Optical Character Recognition (OCR). Scientific accuracy and consistency of style were handled by the author. Time did not allow for the usual extensive editing process of the Publisher.

Printed in The Netherlands

Preface

Six years have elapsed since the last World Congress held in Philadelphia in 1985, an unexpectedly long interval – the longest so far – between one congress and the next. This was however unavoidable in order not to interfere with other large scale international congresses being held in the same year.

Thus, the volumes now at the readers disposal comprise an essence, or resumé, of what was undertaken and/or achieved worldwide in the course of the past six years in the highly specialized research domain, biological psychiatry. For the high quality of the volumes, in terms of scientific and practical values, the Editors are indebted to the conscientious work of the Scientific Program Committee who made a selection of the symposia topics and competent experts for each topic. I would like to inform all readers that many of the Free Communications, oral and poster alike, were of an equally high level; exclusion of these from these volumes was warranted solely because of space limitation.

Speaking briefly of the World Federation of Societies of Biological Psychiatry (WFSBP), simple statistics in terms of member (national) societies show a sharp increase from 26 (September 1985) to 38 (June 1991), while the number of attenders to the congress grew from 2500 to 5000. This increase and growth may well be the result in part of the six years interval; colleagues worldwide could hardly wait to get together to learn and discuss what has been brought forward from various centers.

It might be timely to note here how the WFSBP started since only a few people who know of this are still living. Officially, it dates back from 1974 when the 1st World Congress of Biological Psychiatry was held in Buenos Aires. In actuality, however, it dates back even further, i.e. on the occasion of the 5th World Congress of World Psychiatry Association, Mexico City, 1971. I happen to be the person responsible for alluring some number of American biological psychiatrists into forming an international body for biological psychiatry, which was to be named three years later as the WFSBP. Dr. R. Mitsuda, Founder of the Japanese Society of Biological Psychiatry, was my strongest proponent and Dr. George A. Ulett, St. Louis, was also of great help. For further information a short remark can be found in the Preface of C. Shagaas et al. “Biological Psychiatry 1985”. Therefore, taking into account the forming years, the WFSBP may now be looked at as twenty years old.

During all these years, and one way or another, I continuously had something to do with the WFSBP – as I do now – so that every phase of the development of the WFSBP has remained in my memory; the embryo to baby and further to adolescence.... Growth of the WFSBP has been, roughly speaking. proportional to that of biological psychiatry per se, particularly in terms of clinical science; it is best reflected in the issues of the criteria of diagnosis and classification from DSM-I, RDC, DSM-III, DSM-III R, and now DSM-IV. Needless to say, basic sciences are accordingly "growing up" along with the clinical moves, as they both have to be taken into account in our particular expertise.

The volumes that appear in the midst of such background will no doubt provide the readers with a wealth of knowledge and information in learning how far we have come, and which way we should better move, again roughly in proportion to the two decade growth of our discipline. Contributions made by biological psychiatry are now being more appropriately appreciated by fellow colleagues, whatever approaches they may prefer to choose, and general trends today are, unlike sometime ago, towards more cooperation and understanding of different approaches and/or discipline.

To this end, it is my duty to point out that this is the very first time the World Congress has been held outside the country of residence of the President. The two congress chairpersons had to communicate with each other by use of all available means of course, but the actual labor depended exclusively upon the Organizer and his crew. Moreover, the Organizer took care of the heavy work as Secretary-Treasurer of the WFSBP; to which I nominate myself as the best judge of the heavy workload since I myself carried out this task between 1982–1985. My sincere gratitude, therefore, goes to Professor Giorgio Racagni for his tireless work, both as the Congress Organizer and Secretary-Treasurer, and as my right hand of the WFSBP. To Dr. Nicoletta Brunello, my deepest appreciation is due; without her efficient assistance, the present volumes would not have seen the light of day.

I hope the volumes will be duly acknowledged worldwide and assume an important landmark in the history of biological psychiatry, and of psychiatry on the whole, for years to come; hopefully in someway comparable to what Florence, the congress site, and Renaissance have done to the world of art, science and humanity!

Tetsuo Fukuda
Past-President, World Federation of
Societies of Biological Psychiatry
Chairperson, 5th World Congress of
Biological Psychiatry

Introduction

The 5th World Congress of Biological Psychiatry took place in Florence from June 9th to 14th, 1991. It was attended by about 5,000 participants from 70 countries.

The congress included 120 symposia, 40 oral free communication sessions and 2,500 poster presentations. Moreover, 11 satellite symposia were organized.

These volumes contain the papers presented at the symposium sessions of congress.

Biological psychiatry represents a fusion of several scientific disciplines – pharmacology, neurobiology, biochemistry, genetics, physiology, anatomy, biophysics and psychology – all focused on acquiring an ultimate understanding of the relationships between brain and behaviour.

Psychiatric disorders include schizophrenia, affective disorders, the many forms of senile and presenile dementia including Alzheimer's disease, the anxiety disorders, childhood disorders and the variants of eating and sleeping dysfunctions. Each of these illnesses represents a complex interaction of biological, psychological and social variables.

The growing number of neuroscientists adopting the biological approach to neuropsychiatric diseases has resulted in a fast expanding body of knowledge regarding brain function and pathology. The field is exciting because we see complementary advances across a broad front of recently developed research areas.

Psychotherapeutic drugs used to treat psychiatric and neurologic disorders play a crucial role in elucidating the biological bases of these diseases.

Studying the mechanism of action of these compounds should give us important clues about the normal and pathological functioning of the brain.

The objectives of the effort are well reflected in the topics covered by the papers in these two volumes.

This book will be of interest to psychiatrists, neurologists, clinicians and neuropharmacologists.

The Editors

Acknowledgements

The editors acknowledge the following companies for their support in the publication of the proceedings:

Astra Research Centre, Sweden
Bayer A/G, Germany
Bristol-Myers Squibb Company, U.S.A.
Ciba-Geigy A/G, Switzerland
Duphar B.V., The Netherlands
Eli Lilly International Corporation, U.S.A.
FIDIA Research Laboratories, Abano Terme, Italy
Glaxo Holdings p.l.c., U.K.
F. Hoffmann-La Roche Ltd., Switzerland
H. Lundbeck A/S, Denmark
Janssen Pharmaceutica, Belgium
Laboratories Synthélabo, France
Menarini Industrie Farmaceutiche Riunite s.r.l., Italy
Pfizer International Inc., U.S.A.
Sandoz Pharma Ltd., Switzerland
SmithKline Beecham Pharmaceuticals, U.K.
Takeda Italia Farmaceutici, Italy
The Upjohn Company, U.S.A.
Wyeth-Ayerst, U.K.
Zambeletti S.p.A., Italy

The editors gratefully acknowledge the skilful assistance of Mrs. Carla Penza.

Contents

Volume 2

ALCOHOLISM, DRUG DEPENDENCE AND ABUSE

AGING AND DEMENTIA: CLINICAL AND BIOLOGICAL RESEARCH

HIV-1 associated dementia

Cognitive impairment in psychiatric diseases: Basic and clinical investigations

Neuroimmunomodulation in aging

Neurobiology of aging and Alzheimer disease

ANTICONVULSANTS, EPILEPSY AND ORGANIC MENTAL DISORDERS

Pharmacotherapy of brain lesions

Biological basis of ictal, perictal and interictal behavioural changes in epilepsy

Kindling, psychiatry and anticonvulsant drugs

Limbic system surgery in the treatment of severe refractory psychiatric illness

Carbamazepine and other anticonvulsants in the treatment of psychiatric disorders

Psychobiology of eating disorders

Pharmaco-EEG and EEG mapping

GENETICS IN PSYCHIATRY: BASIC AND CLINICAL ASPECTS

Transgenic animals as experimental models in neuroimmunology

Molecular genetics of affective illnesses

Molecular genetics of psychoses

Role of neuropeptides in the pathogenesis of affective disorders

Immunological aspects of psychiatric disorders

Psychoneuroimmunoendocrinology: A new research pathway

NEUROTRANSMITTERS, RECEPTOR MOLECULAR BIOLOGY, BRAIN SIGNAL TRANSDUCTIONS AND BEHAVIOUR

Main directions of WHO strategy in the field of biological research in psychiatry

Animal models of psychiatric and neurological diseases

Substrates for brain function: Morphology and its functional significance

Neurobiology of the nigrostriatal system

Transcriptional regulation of receptors: Structure and function

New trends in molecular biology and pharmacology of dopaminergic transmission

Multiple serotonin receptors: Possible therapeutic applications

The Heuristic value of biological models for predicting the therapeutic activity of 5-HT_{1A} agonists

Excitatory amino acids and signal transduction

Eicosanoids in brain signal transduction

Calcium homeostasis in the brain

Neuronal nicotinic receptors

Alcoholism, drug dependence and abuse

© 1991 Elsevier Science Publishers B.V. All rights reserved.
Biological Psychiatry, Volume 2. G. Racagni et al., editors.

Suppression of dopamine release in alcohol abstinence syndrome: Reversal by ethanol, MK-801 and γ-hydroxybutyrate

Zvani L. Rossetti, Franco Melis, Susanna Carboni and Gian Luigi Gessa
"B.B. Brodie" Department of Neuroscience, University of Cagliari, 09124 Cagliari, Italy

Introduction

Chronic use of ethanol may lead to psychological and physical dependence [1]. Ethanol withdrawal in alcoholics is associated, besides major neurological symptoms, with subjective symptoms such as malaise, dysphoria and lack of reward (anhedonia). The mesolimbic dopaminergic system is considered to play an important role in conveying the rewarding effects elicited by drugs of abuse, including ethanol [2,3]. Accordingly, it has been reported that ethanol stimulates the firing rate of dopaminergic neurons of the ventral tegmental area [4] and that ethanol increases extracellular dopamine (DA) concentrations in the terminal areas innervated by the mesolimbic DA system [5]. Since the aversive symptoms of abstinence might be considered a result of adaptive changes to the initial rewarding effect of ethanol, it is conceivable that the mesolimbic DA system might be affected during withdrawal. Thus we studied the changes in extracellular concentrations of DA in the ventral striatum of rats rendered physically dependent to ethanol after ethanol withdrawal.

The present report shows that ethanol abstinence in rats is associated with a dramatic fall in extraneuronal DA concentration and that this effect is reverted by the non-competitive NMDA receptor antagonist MK-801 and by γ-hydroxybutyrate, two drugs known to revert the ethanol withdrawal symptomatology [6,7].

Material and Methods

Rats were rendered physically dependent on ethanol [8] by administering ethanol orally at the initial dose of 5 g/kg and then once every 6 h for 6 days at doses graded from 2–5 g/kg. On day 6, immediately after the first ethanol dose, animals were implanted with the dialysis fibre under light chloral hydrate anesthesia and received 4 additional doses of ethanol at 6-h intervals, starting 6 h after surgery. One hour following the last treatment, i.e. 5 g/kg, 24 h after the fibre implantation, rats were connected to the perfusion system. Control rats were given water orally in place of ethanol and were implanted with the dialysis probe in the same manner as the ethanol-treated rats. Dialysis fibers (AN69 HF, Hospal, France) were inserted transversely through the ventral striatum with coordinates A: 1.7; V: 6.5 from bregma [9]. Microdialysis was performed in freely behaving rats substantially as described by Imperato and Di Chiara [5], using as perfusing solution a modified Krebs buffer, pH 7.2 (composition, Mm: NaCl 147; KCl 3.0; $CaCl_2$ 2.2; $MgSO_4$ 1.2; KH_2PO_4 0.4). DA, 3,4-di-hydroxyphenylacetic acid and homovanillic acid concentrations in the perfusates were measured in 20-min dialysate samples and at the same time intervals, the withdrawal signs were scored according to the rating scale of Lal et al. [10]. The statistical significance of the results was evaluated by ANOVA followed by Newman-Keuls post hoc test.

Results

One hour following the last treatment, extraneuronal DA concentration was about 70% higher in ethanol-withdrawn rats than in saline-treated control (Fig. 1). Thereafter, whereas in control animals DA output remained relatively constant, in ethanol-withdrawn rats it fell progressively, reaching about 30% of the control value at 8 h after ethanol withdrawal. DA output persisted at such a reduced level throughout the withdrawal period and eventually reverted toward control values at 24 h following ethanol withdrawal. DA metabolites underwent similar, although less pronounced changes (not shown).

As shown in Fig. 1, the scores for withdrawal signs in ethanol-withdrawn rats were inversely proportional to the concentrations of extracellular DA, i.e. they were maximal from 8–12 h after withdrawal.

The oral administration of ethanol (5 g/kg) to 10-h withdrawn rats reverted both the withdrawal symptomatology and the fall in DA output (Fig. 2). Similarly, the

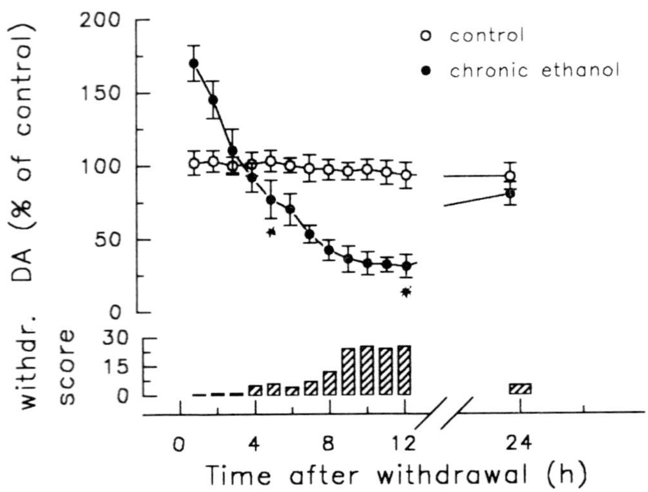

Fig. 1. (Top) Inhibition of extraneuronal DA after ethanol withdrawal in the ventral striatum of dependent rats. (Bottom) behavioral score. Values are means ± S.E.M. from 6 animals per group. *$P < 0.01$ as compared to control group, 2-way ANOVA, followed by Newman-Keuls test.

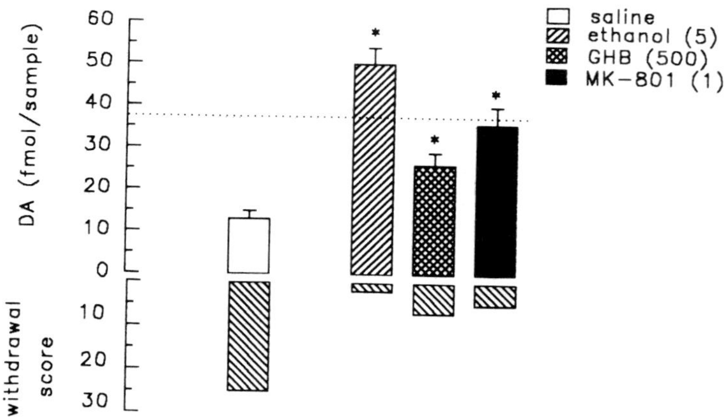

Fig. 2. Reversal of the withdrawal-induced inhibition of DA output and of the abstinence symptomatology by ethanol, MK-801 and GHB. Ethanol was administered intragastrically (5 g/kg), the other drugs at the doses indicated in parentheses (mg/kg i.p.) to dependent rats 10 h after the last ethanol administration. Means ± S.E.M. from 5–6 animals per group. $*P < 0.01$ as compared to saline.

administration of the NMDA receptor antagonist MK-801 (1 mg/kg, i.p.) and of GHB (500 mg/kg i.p.) reverted the fall in DA output and suppressed the withdrawal symptoms within 20 min after treatment (Fig. 2). DA metabolites underwent parallel but less pronounced changes as extraneuronal DA (results not shown).

Discussion

These results show that withdrawal from chronic ethanol results in a progressive, marked reduction in extraneuronal DA and its metabolites in the ventral striatum. The mechanism by which ethanol increases DA output and that underlying the fall in the extraneuronal concentration of DA during withdrawal is not known. Since ethanol has been shown to activate the firing rate of DA neurons [4] one might suggest that the rise and fall on DA output are due to the activation and inhibition of dopaminergic activity, respectively. This interpretation implies that ethanol abstinence may be associated with the suppression of dopaminergic activity in the ventral tegmental area.

The reversal of the inhibition of DA output and of withdrawal symptomatology by MK-801 and GHB confirms and extends previous results [6,7]. GHB has been suggested to act as an alcohol-like compound [7] and recent results from our laboratory indicate that GHB, like ethanol, stimulates the firing of A10 DA neurons (Diana et al., submitted). On the other hand, it has been recently shown that MK-801 potently stimulates the firing activity of DA neurons in this area [11]. Thus the 2 drugs may elicit their effects via the activation of mesolimbic DA neurons, presumably through different primary mechanisms. In addition, these findings suggest that glutamate receptors of the NMDA subtype may have a role in the hedonic response to ethanol, and perhaps to other drugs of abuse as well.

As to the functional relevance of changes in DA output, if one considers that activation of the mesolimbic dopaminergic system may play an important role in the mediation of the reward by different drugs of abuse, including ethanol [3], it is reasonable to conclude that inhibition of DA neurotransmission during abstinence might be responsible for dysphoria and anhedonia during withdrawal.

This conclusion might apply to the abstinence syndrome from other drugs of abuse as well. Indeed we have shown that extraneuronal DA concentrations are reduced during withdrawal from morphine [12] and cocaine (Rossetti et al., in preparation).

Acknowledgements

The skillful technical assistance of Mr. A. Boi is gratefully acknowledged. We thank Dr. R. Hill of MSD Research Laboratories, Harlow, U.K., for the supply of MK-801 and Mr. H. Sugden for secretarial work.

References

1. Jaffe JH (1990) In: Gilman AG, Rall TW, Nies AS and Taylor P (eds.) Goodman and Gilman's The Pharmacological Basis of Therapeutics. Pergamon Press, New York, pp. 522–573.
2. Di Chiara G and Imperato A (1988) Proc. Natl. Acad. Sci. U.S.A. 85: 5274–5278.
3. Wise RA and Rompre PP (1989) Ann. Rev. Psychol. 40: 191–225.
4. Mereu G and Gessa GL (1985) Brain Res. 360: 325–330.
5. Imperato A and Di Chiara G (1986) J. Pharmacol. Exp. Ther. 239: 219–238.
6. Grant KA, Valverius P, Hudspith M and Tabakoff B (1990) Eur. J. Pharmacol. 176: 289–296.
7. Fadda F, Colombo G, Mosca E and Gessa GL (1989) Alcohol Alcohol. 24: 447–451.
8. Majchrovitz E (1975) Psychopharmacologia 43: 245–251.
9. Paxinos G and Watson C (1986) The Rat Brain in Stereotaxic Coordinates. Academic Press Ltd., London, U.K.
10. Lal H, Harris CM, Benjamin D, Springfield AC, Bhadra S and Emmett-Oglesby MW (1988) J. Pharmacol. Exp. Ther. 249: 508–518.
11. French ED and Ceci A (1990) Neurosci. Lett. 119: 159–162.
12. Rossetti ZL, Melis F, Carboni S and Gessa GL (1990) Neurosci. Lett. 39: S184.

© 1991 Elsevier Science Publishers B.V. All rights reserved.
Biological Psychiatry, Volume 2. G. Racagni et al., editors.

The AA and ANA rat lines as a tool for identifying the biological mechanisms of alcohol abuse

K. Kiianmaa[1] and T. Saito[2]
[1]Research Laboratories, Alko Ltd., Helsinki, Finland; and [2]Department of Neuropsychiatry, Sapporo Medical College, Sapporo, Japan

Introduction

A selective breeding program conducted in this laboratory has resulted in the establishment of the alcohol-preferring AA (alko alcohol) and alcohol-avoiding ANA (alko non-alcohol) rat lines [1]. These lines have been used as a tool for attempting to identify the behavioral, neurochemical, and biochemical correlates of differential voluntary ethanol consumption, and thus to determine the genetically-controlled physiological mechanisms responsible for the abuse of ethanol [2].

Ethanol self-administration

In the standard experimental conditions, the rats have a choice between 10% (v/v) ethanol solution and tap water, and free access to food [1]. The lines have been developed on the basis of their ethanol intake during the fourth week of access. The ethanol consumption in the current generation (F_{60}) is in AA males, 8.2 ± 0.4; AA females, 8.1 ± 0.4; ANA males, 0.32 ± 0.06; ANA females, 0.28 ± 0.03 g/kg/d (mean ± S.E.M.). During the peak hours of voluntary ethanol intake the blood ethanol concentration of AA rats approaches 10 mM (median), while many rats have levels as high as 25 mM [3].

The idea that ethanol is a strong reinforcer for the AA rats is supported by findings that they rapidly learn to lever-press in an operant chamber in order to obtain ethanol despite continual free access to food and water [4–6]. AA rats also increase ethanol responding as more presses are required for each drop of ethanol [6].

Ethanol sensitivity

A factor that could contribute to higher ethanol drinking in AA rats may be their relative sensitivity to the stimulatory ethanol effects which are supposedly reinforcing and the depressive effects which supposedly limit ethanol drinking. A low dose (1 g/kg) has been found to produce an increase in locomotor activity in AA rats but not in ANA rats [7].

With regard to the depressive effects, although the AA and ANA rats do not differ in ethanol-induced motor impairment, hypothermia or hypnosis [7–9], there is evidence that the AA rats have a better acquisition of tolerance. For example, the AA rats recover from ethanol-induced impairment of motor performance at a faster rate than the ANA rats [8,9]. Another experiment showed that the AA rats have a better capacity to develop rapid tolerance than do the ANA rats [8]. A third study revealed that following chronic treatment with ethanol for 16 days the AA rats acquired tolerance to the motor impairment, hypothermic, and hypnotic effects of ethanol at a faster rate and to a greater extent than did the ANA rats [8]. The AA rats' greater development of tolerance to the depressive effects of ethanol would permit them to drink more ethanol while more stimulatory effect would make it more reinforcing.

Neurochemistry

Central monoaminergic neurons are believed to be important in the regulation of ethanol consumption. Consequently, the levels of different monoamine neurotransmitters and their major metabolites in the brain of AA and ANA rats have been measured in several studies [2]. Recent measurements in the $F_{55\text{-}57}$ generations, in contrast to earlier studies, showed only a non-significant tendency in the direction of AA having higher levels of brain 5-hydroxytryptamine [10]. The AA rats, however, had significantly higher levels of dopamine in the striatum than did the ANA rats [10]. The levels of noradrenaline in AA and ANA also seemed to differ, too, but in this case with the ANA rats showing higher levels in the cerebral cortex, frontal cortex, limbic forebrain, and hippocampus. In parallel with these findings, the basal level of 3,4-dihydroxyphenylacetic acid (DOPAC) was higher in the striatum of the rats and that of 3-methoxy-4-hydroxy-phenylglycol (MHPG) in the cerebral cortex, frontal cortex, and hippocampus of the ANA rats [10].

In accordance with these findings, the basal activity of adenylate cyclase is higher in striatum of the AA rats compared to ANA rats, while in the frontal cortex the activity of adenylate cyclase is higher in the ANA rats (Table 1). The activity of adenylate cyclase was, however, increased by addition of guanine nucleotide, Gpp(NH)p, in a similar manner in all brain parts in both rat lines.

The activities of the enzymes synthesizing and inactivating catecholamines have been determined in the whole brains of the AA and ANA rats in vitro [11]. The activity of tyrosine hydroxylase was 42% and dopa decarboxylase 24% higher in the AA rats than in the ANA rats. Perhaps in compensation to the higher level of dopamine, the AA rats have a lower maximal number of dopamine D_2 receptors in the striatum than the ANA rats, as measured by the in vitro binding of $[^3H]$spiperone to membrane homogenates [13].

The sensitivity of the monoaminergic neurons to ethanol has been studied using several conventional techniques. Ethanol had little effect on the levels of 5-hydroxyindoleacetic acid, but it increased the levels of DOPAC and MHPG in

Table 1. Effect of ethanol (EtOH), added in vitro, on the adenylate cyclase activity in different brain parts of AA and ANA rats

Additions	Frontal cortex		Striatum	
	AA	ANA	AA	ANA
None (basal)	39.5 ± 1.7	48.1 ± 4.2[a]	337.3 ± 5.3	262.8 ± 16.1[a]
100 mM EtOH	43.2 ± 3.6	50.9 ± 2.4[a]	370.1 ± 6.7	293.2 ± 33.1[a]
250 mM EtOH	52.7 ± 0.9	64.6 ± 7.8[a]	414.1 ± 20.2	354.5 ± 45.7[a]
1 µM Gpp(NH)p	195.8 ± 9.6	220.5 ± 17.8	660.5 ± 34.5	648.4 ± 63.0
+ 100 mM EtOH	236.4 ± 21.4	241.0 ± 25.1	817.7 ± 15.8	764.9 ± 106.3
+ 250 mM EtOH	251.3 ± 1.8	291.3 ± 25.2	946.1 ± 49.7	939.8 ± 107.7

Adenylate cyclase activity is given in µmol cyclic AMP/min/mg protein (mean ± S.D.). For methodological details see [12]; [a]$P < 0.05$, difference from AA line (*t*-test).

various brain parts [10]. Ethanol also enhanced the rate of synthesis of catecholamines in several brain areas [2]. No significant differences between AA and ANA rats were, however, found with any of these ethanol effects.

Conclusions

It seems clear that AA rats drink more ethanol than do the ANA rats because they receive more positive and less negative reinforcement. The differences in reinforcement in turn can be explained, at least partially, by the AA rats developing rapid tolerance to the depressive effects. The neurochemical studies consistently show differences between the lines in the basal functions of different neurotransmitter systems suggesting a role for these neuronal systems in the regulation of ethanol intake. Since no differences in the sensitivity of these systems to ethanol have been observed, the level on which these systems take part in the regulation, however, remains unclear.

References

1. Eriksson K (1969) Ann. Zool. Fenn. 6: 227.
2. Sinclair JD, Lê AD and Kiianmaa K (1989) Experientia 45: 798.
3. Aalto J (1986) Alcohol 3: 73.
4. Sinclair JD (1974) Nature 2: 409.
5. Hyytiä P and Sinclair JD (1989) Alcohol 6: 161.
6. Hyytiä P and Sinclair JD (1990) Alcohol. Clin. Exp. Res. 14: 375.
7. Hilakivi L, Eriksson CJP, Sarviharju M and Sinclair JD (1984) Alcohol 1: 59.
8. Lê AD and Kiianmaa K (1988) Psychopharmacology 94: 479.
9. Lê AD and Kiianmaa K (1988) In: Kuriyama K, Takada A and Ishii H (eds.) Biomedical and Social Aspects of Alcohol and Alcoholism. Elsevier, Amsterdam, pp. 423-426.

10. Kiianmaa K, Stenius K and Sinclair JD (1991) Proc. 5th ISBRA Congr. Alcohol Alcoholism.
11. Pispa JP, Huttunen MO, Sarviharju M and Ylikahri R (1986) Alcohol Alcoholism 21: 181.
12. Saito T, Lee JM and Tabakoff B (1985) J. Neurochem. 44: 1037.
13. Korpi ER, Sinclair JD and Malminen O (1987) Pharmacol. Toxicol. 61: 94.

© 1991 Elsevier Science Publishers B.V. All rights reserved.
Biological Psychiatry, Volume 2. G. Racagni et al., editors.

Blockade of the discriminative stimulus and anxiolytic effects of ethanol with 5-HT$_3$ receptor antagonists

Kathleen A. Grant[1] and James E. Barrett[2]

[1]Section on Receptor Mechanisms, National Institute on Alcohol Abuse and Alcoholism, 12501 Washington Ave., Rockville, MD 20852; and [2]Department of Psychiatry, Uniformed Services University of the Health Sciences, 4301 Jones Bridge Road, Bethesda, MD 20814, U.S.A.

Introduction

Recent evidence from a variety of procedures suggests that the effects of ethanol in the CNS are mediated, in part, by the 5-HT$_3$ receptor/channel complex. Ethanol (25–100 mM) potentiates the actions of 5-HT at this receptor [1] and 5-HT$_3$ receptor antagonists attenuate many effects of ethanol, including ethanol-induced dopamine release in the nucleus accumbens [2,3], and ethanol intakes [4]. The results of these studies imply that ethanol-induced potentiation of 5-HT at 5-HT$_3$ receptors is an important component of the behavioral actions of ethanol.

We have previously used a drug discrimination procedure to study the role of specific receptor-mediated activity in the behavioral actions of ethanol [5,6]. Using this procedure, antagonists of the 5-HT$_3$ receptor complex were found to block the discriminative stimulus effects of ethanol in pigeons [6]. The present study explores whether these finding can be extended to the rat, whether the discriminative stimulus effects of another sedative hypnotic, pentobarbital, are also blocked by a 5-HT$_3$ antagonist, and whether another behavioral effect of ethanol, an anxiolytic effect, is also blocked by a 5-HT$_3$ antagonist.

Materials and Methods

Animals

White Carneau pigeons or Long Evans rats were kept at 85% of their free-feeding weights and housed in accordance with NIH animal care guidelines.

Discrimination training and testing

Subjects were trained to discriminate either ethanol (1.5 g/kg, i.g.) from water or pentobarbital (10 mg/kg, i.p.) from saline. Key pecking (pigeons) or lever pressing (rats) was maintained under fixed-ratio schedules of food reinforcement (see [6] for complete methodology). MDL 72222 (3-tropanyl-3, 5-dichlorobenzoate; RBI, Natick, MA) was administered 20 min prior to the training dose of ethanol or pentobarbital. During these sessions 30 consecutive responses resulted in reinforcer delivery.

Punishment procedure and testing

Pigeons were trained under a "conflict" procedure in which key pecks during the presence of one keylight color produced food, whereas in the presence of a different color responses produced both food and shock [7]. Ethanol was administered by gavage 30 min before the experimental session and MDL 72222 by i.m. injection 40 min prior to the session.

Results

Pretreatment with MDL 72222 resulted in a dose-dependent reduction of ethanol appropriate responding (Table 1). In pigeons and rats, responding on the ethanol key fell from 99% in the absence of MDL 72222 to 11% (pigeons; 17 mg/kg MDL 72222) and 8% (rats; 10 mg/kg MDL 72222) when MDL 72222 was given in combination with the training dose of ethanol.

In contrast to the ethanol data, MDL 72222 did not block the discriminative stimulus effects of 10 mg/kg pentobarbital.

To test the specificity of the blockade within the 5-HT system, various doses (5.6–30 mg/kg) of the 5-HT_2 antagonist ketanserin (RBI, Natick, MA) were administered 15 min prior to the training dose of ethanol. The discriminative stimulus effects of ethanol were not blocked by any dose of ketanserin in either species.

Table 1. Effect of the 5-HT_3 antagonist MDL 72222 on the discriminative stimulus effects of ethanol and pentobarbital

Training drug	MDL 72222 dose (mg/kg)	Drug responses (%)	Responses/s
Ethanol (pigeon, n = 5)	0	99 ± 2	1.7 ± 0.1
	5.6	83 ± 13	1.6 ± 0.2
	10.0	54 ± 10	1.3 ± 0.2
	17.0	11 ± 7	0.6 ± 0.3
Ethanol (rat, n = 6)	0	99 ± 1	1.3 ± 0.2
	3.0	61 ± 15	1.2 ± 0.1
	5.6	11 ± 8	1.1 ± 0.1
	10.0	8 ± 7	0.8 ± 0.2
Pentobarbital (rat, n = 5)	0	100 ± 0	1.5 ± 0.1
	3.0	99 ± 1	1.5 ± 0.2
	5.6	91 ± 7	1.4 ± 0.1
	10.0	80 ± 14	1.1 ± 0.1
	17.0	100 ± 0	0.1 ± 0.1

A dose of 1.0 g/kg ethanol increased punished responding to approximately 200% of control performance levels, with little effect on unpunished responding. Doses of MDL 72222 from 1.0 to 10 mg/kg produced a dose-dependent antagonism of the anticonflict effects of ethanol.

Discussion

The results show that the discriminative stimulus and anxiolytic-like effects of ethanol can be blocked by a 5-HT_3 receptor complex antagonist and suggest that the 5-HT_3 receptor may represent another receptor-linked ionophore that appears to be particularly sensitive to the actions of ethanol. Since the discriminative stimulus properties of pentobarbital are not blocked by MDL 72222, the blockade of the ethanol discriminative stimulus appears to be relatively specific. Blockade of the effects of ethanol on punished responding suggests a role for the 5-HT_3 receptor in anxiety, but one that is different from previous proposals that antagonists at this site may be anxiolytic. Further studies with 5-HT_3 antagonists and ethanol may lead to a better understanding of how ethanol exerts its behavioral effects.

References

1. Lovinger DM (1991) Neurosci. Lett. (in press).
2. Carboni E, Acquas E, Frau R and DiChiara G (1989) Eur. J. Pharmacol. 164: 515.
3. Wozniak K, Pert A and Linnoila M (1990) Eur. J. Pharmacol. 187: 287.
4. Costall BR, Naylor J and Tyers MB (1990) Pharmacol. Ther. 1: 181.
5. Grant KA, Knisely JS, Tabakoff B, Barrett JE and Balster RL (1991) Behav. Pharmacol. (in press).
6. Grant KA and Barrett JE (1991) Psychopharmacology (in press).
7. Barrett JE, Witkin JM, Mansbach RS, Skolnick P and Weissman BA (1986) J. Pharmacol. Exp. Ther. 238: 1009.

© 1991 Elsevier Science Publishers B.V. All rights reserved.
Biological Psychiatry, Volume 2. G. Racagni et al., editors.

The A1 allele of the dopamine D_2 receptor gene as a genetic marker for risk of severe alcoholism*

Kenneth Blum[1], Peter J. Sheridan[2] and Ernest P. Noble[3]
[1]Departments of Pharmacology and [2]Cellular and Structural Biology, University of Texas Health Science Center, San Antonio, Texas and [3]Alcohol Research Center, Neuropsychiatric Institute UCLA, Los Angeles, California, U.S.A.

Introduction

Although alcoholism has been classified as a multigenetic complex disorder consisting of multiple subforms, its genetic roots are still unknown [1]. In response to numerous population studies showing that severe alcoholism is an inheritable entity [2–4], a number of laboratories are beginning to search for specific genes that might modify the risk of developing alcoholism. Currently, the specific mode of inheritance of alcoholism is characterized by incomplete and variable clinical expression [5]. Moreover, linkage analysis has implicated chromosomes 4, 6 and 11, but not specific gene markers, in the genetic risk for alcoholism [6–8]. However, several candidate genes related to heritable variation in neural reward mechanisms affected by alcohol as well as other abusable drugs have been proposed [9–11].

One logical candidate is the dopamine D_2 receptor, since alterations in dopamine availability at its receptors, particularly at the D_2 dopamine receptor (D_2DR), have been implicated in neural reward mechanisms in addiction [12,13]. The recent availability of genomic probes for the human dopamine D_2 receptor locus has allowed direct molecular genetic tests on the involvement of the D_2 receptor in disease states [14,15]. Moreover, the D_2 receptor RNA is alternately spliced to produce 2 RNAs [16–22]. These mRNAs produce 2 receptors which differ by 29 amino acids (D_2A415 and D_2A444). These 2 isoforms, in addition to the recently identified dopamine D_3 receptor [23], bind [^{3}H]spiperone with high affinity and their mRNAs are found in the limbic system. The D_2 receptor locus has been localized to the 11q22–11q23 region of the human genome and a restriction fragment length polymorphism (RFLP) has been found for the endonuclease TaqI [14].

With regard to alcoholism, using the TaqI polymorphism of the D_2 receptor locus of DNA isolated from the cerebral cortex of nonalcoholic and severe alcoholic subjects, our laboratory recently reported an association between severe alcoholism and the minor locus allele (A1) in this population [24]. We found the A1 allele to be present in 64% of 22 white alcoholic and only 16.7% of 24 white

*A full manuscript is to be published in Alcohol, 1991.

non-alcoholic controls and in 77% of 13 black alcoholics and 27% of 11 black non-alcoholic controls. The importance of the allelic association of the A1 allele in alcoholism severity has been similarly observed by Bolos et al. [25]. In that study, using our 2 white groups (non-alcoholics and severe alcoholics) and the 3 groups of Bolos et al. (CEPH "controls" (alcoholics not excluded), less severe and more severe alcoholics) a χ^2 test for linear trend revealed increasing degree of alcoholism severity and was found to correspond with a significant increase (P = 0.0002) of A1 allele prevalence [26].

In the present study we have further characterized a doublet DNA fragment of a Bam H1 digestion of phage DNA (λhD_2G1) as an informative gene probe in recognizing the TaqI polymorphism of the D_2 receptor gene. Moreover, this report represents the largest association study in living subjects to date, which unequivocally supports an association of the Al allele of the D_2DR gene in alcoholism severity.

Materials and Methods

For the present study, high molecular weight DNA was isolated from both brain tissue (cerebral cortex) of previously well-characterized deceased alcoholics and non-alcoholics [24] and from lymphocytes of a large number of different populations categorized for severity of alcoholism using standard methods.

Results

Characterization of 1.5 kb Bam H1 digest

To check the possibility that the original 1.5 kb fragment obtained from a Bam H1 digest as previously utilized by our laboratory was a doublet, a ligation was performed using this fragment by following the procedure given by Sea Plaque GTG agarose. Transformation of DH5α cells was performed following the Hanahan method [27].

In order to differentiate between different clones, minipreps were prepared and the DNA cut with a series of enzymes (Hinf-1, Msp-1, Taq-I, and Hind III) established 2 definite populations containing inserts of the appropriate size (1.73 kb). Two subclones, named #9 and #16 were grown and the DNA purified. The 1.73-kb fragments from each of the clones were labeled with ^{32}P and used as probes to hybridize to human genomic DNA cut with Taq-I using the same procedure described previously by our group.

The 1.73-kb probe from subclone 9 hybridized with human genomic DNA cut with Taq-I at 6.6 kb and 3.7 kb, whereas the 1.73-kb probe from subclone #16 hybridized with a band at 10.5 kb. Thus, the 1.73-kb fragment from clone 9 is informative as a probe for the presence of the A1 allele in human DNA.

Identification of subclone 9

Previous reports indicated that the λhD_2G1 clone with an 18-kb insert contained the entire 3' coding exon, the polyadenylation signal and approximately 16.4 kb of non-coding 3' sequence [16]. We therefore suspected that clone 9 might contain, in part, the coding sequence of the last exon containing the 7th transmembrane domain. In order to quickly establish the possible presence of the last exon, 2 30-base pair oligomers containing the first and last base pair sequence (cDNA) as described by Grandy et al. [16], were synthesized by Genetic Design, Inc. (Houston, TX).

To test these 30-base pair oligomers as probes which would be informative for the A1 allele, the oligomers were hybridized to the 1.73 fragments from subclones 9 and 16 described above. The radiolabeled-synthetic oligomer (3' end of the last exon) was found to hybridize to subclone 9 but not to subclone 16.

The other 30-base pair oligomer corresponding to the first 30-base pairs of the cDNA coding for the last exon of the D_2 receptor gene was tested as a potential probe for the A1 allele. This oligomer consisting of the last 30-base pairs of the last exon, hybridized to subclone 9 and not to subclone 16, indicating that subclone 9 contains the entire last exon of the D_2 receptor gene in addition to a small portion of the 5' intron and about a 1-kb 3' region which includes the polyadenylation signal.

The present investigation includes a total DNA sample size of 348 genotypes obtained from well-characterized subjects divided according to their severity of alcoholism as well as age, sex and race.

Yates χ^2 (one-tailed) analysis of the data revealed that the A1 allele of the dopamine D_2 receptor gene significantly associates with severity of alcoholism in this well-defined population. In this study COAs also showed a significantly greater association with the A1 allele than non-alcoholics, but not when compared to alcoholics. Analysis of risk of alcoholism suggests that it is composed of 2 independent components: family history of alcoholism and the presence of the A1 allele.

Discussion

We will discuss and review the current literature as it relates to the role of the dopaminergic system in neural reward mechanisms and compulsive diseases. These results further emphasize the importance of the A1 allele as a potential genetic marker for risk of these diseases.

Acknowledgements

This study has been funded in part through The Seaver Institute in Los Angeles, CA, and Neurogensis Inc., Houston, TX.

References

1. Devor EJ and Cloniger CR (1989) Annu. Rev. Genet. 23: 19–36.
2. Pickens RW et al. (1991) Arch. Gen. Psychiatry 48: 19–28.
3. Comings EE and Comings BG (1990) J. Clin. Psychiatry 51: 281–287.
4. Tarter RE et al. (1977) Arch. Gen. Psychiatry 34: 761–768.
5. Gilligan SB et al. (1987) Genet. Epidemiol. 4: 395–414.
6. Hill SY et al. (1975) J. Stud. Alcohol. 36: 981–992.
7. Shigeta Y et al. (1980) Pharmacol. Biochem. Behav. 13 (Suppl. 1): 89–94.
8. Hill SY et al. (1987) Alcoholism (N.Y.) 11: 345–348.
9. Blum K and Kozlowski (1990) Prog. Alcohol Res. 2: 131–149.
10. Kornetsky C et al. (1988) Alcoholism 12: 609–616.
11. Wise RA and Rompre PP (1989) Annu. Rev. Psychol. 40: 191–225.
12. DiChiara G and Imperato A (1988) Proc. Natl. Acad. Sci. U.S.A. 85: 5274–5278.
13. Koob GG and Bloom FE (1988) Science 242: 715–723.
14. Grandy DK et al. (1989) Am. J. Hum. Genet. 45: 778–785.
15. O'Malley KL et al. (1990) Biochemistry 29: 1367–1371.
16. Grandy DK et al. (1989) Prod. Natl. Acad. Sci. U.S.A. 86: 9762–9766.
17. Dal Toso R et al. (1989) Embl. J. 8: 4025–4034.
18. Selbie LA et al. (1989) DNA 8: 685–689.
19. Giros B et al. (1989) Nature (Lond.) 342: 923–926.
20. Monsma FJ Jr et al. (1989) Nature (Lond.) 342: 926–929.
21. Chio CL et al. (1990) Nature (Lond.) 343: 266–269.
22. Gandelman KY et al. (1990) J. Neurochemistry (in press).
23. Sokoloff P et al. (1990) Nature (Lond.) 347: 146–151.
24. Blum K et al. (1990) J. Am. Med. Assoc. 263: 2055–2060.
25. Bolos AM et al. (1990) J. Am. Med. Assoc. 264: 3156–3160.
26. Noble EP and Blum K (1990) Letter to the Editor, J. Am. Med. Assoc. (in press).
27. Hanahan S (1983) J. Mol. Biol. 166: 557–580.

© 1991 Elsevier Science Publishers B.V. All rights reserved.
Biological Psychiatry, Volume 2. G. Racagni et al., editors.

Chemical-anatomical circuitry in the brain underlying alcohol drinking: Clinical implications

R.D. Myers

Departments of Pharmacology and Psychiatric Medicine, School of Medicine, East Carolina University, Greenville, NC 27834, U.S.A.

The concept that an unusual metabolite detected in abnormal amounts in the brain is involved in the etiology of alcoholism is based upon two facts. First, a biogenic aldehyde arising from either an alcohol or an amine can react with a monoaminergic neurotransmitter or its precursor to form an aldehyde metabolite, e.g. a tetrahydro-isoquinoline (TIQ) or tetrahydro-β-carboline (THBC). Such a reaction occurs in the brain, adrenal gland or other tissue [1]. Second, one of these aldehyde metabolites, tetrahydropapaveroline (THP), is the biosynthetic precursor of the highly addicting opiate alkaloid, morphine [2].

What is the significance of these two observations? Experimentally, the dopaldehyde-dopamine (DA) metabolite, THP, injected centrally in an efficacious dose enhances dramatically the voluntary drinking of alcohol in the rat and monkey [2]. As reviewed recently, this preference is characterized by drinking of ordinarily aversive concentrations of alcohol, withdrawal symptoms, permanency of preference, elevated levels of blood alcohol and selection of alcohol over other addicting agents or palatable solutions [1,3]. Further, an opiate receptor antagonist, naloxone or naltrexone, attenuates THP-induced drinking of alcohol [5,8]. Equally important is the fact that the endogenous formation of a TIQ or THBC in the brain and peripheral tissue is alcohol contingent. Indeed, prolonged exposure to alcohol is a critical factor in the de novo synthesis and sequestration of a TIQ or THBC in the brain [1,6–8].

Recently, the critical question on the site of action in the brain of a TIQ in evoking drinking of alcohol has been answered. An anatomical survey of limbic midbrain-forebrain structures which react to THP in terms of enhanced alcohol drinking shows that within 48–72 h after micro-injection of THP into structures comprising the mesolimbic "reward" system, individual rats drink alcohol in aversive concentrations as high as 30%. The sites of maximal sensitivity to doses of only 25–50 ng of THP include the n. accumbens, medial forebrain bundle, olfactory tubercle, septum pellucidum and hippocampus [9]. Mapping of these sites reveals a clear-cut "circuitry" of neuronal structures which coalesce with dopaminergic and enkephalinergic pathways [3]. When one of the dominant structures in this circuit, the n. accumbens, is lesioned by the catecholamine neurotoxin, 6-OHDA, alcohol preference of the rat rises sharply [10]. Collectively, therefore, these observations strongly suggest a functional involvement of both the dopaminergic and opioid receptors in abnormal drinking. Included among the potential mechanisms responsible for the addictive property of alcohol are an irreversible perturbation of DA receptors in the n. accumbens and other dopaminergic structures as well as a permanent alteration in synthesis, release or other activity of DA neurons [1,3].

A current analysis of the alcohol drinking patterns of genetically bred alcohol preferring (P) rats unexpectedly showed that the P rat drinks increasing volumes of alcohol similarly to a rat injected with THP centrally or given a 6-OHDA lesion of the n. accumbens [11]. A regression analysis, presented in Fig. 1, depicts the rising slopes of intake of alcohol offered over a range of 3–30% to: P rats; rats in which THP was injected either i.c.v. or into a limbic system site; and rats with a 6-OHDA lesion of the n. accumbens. The conspicuous concordance in their profiles of drinking provides compelling evidence for a commonality in the central mechanism underlying aberrant preference for alcohol. In spite of the diversity in treatments and genetic breeding, the consequence is identical. Surely, one component of a genetic predisposition to alcohol abuse thus could be a neurochemical dysfunction of the mesolimbic dopaminergic system [3,10].

The irreversibility of genetically determined or pharmacologically induced drinking by an animal in itself has profound implications for therapeutic strategies to be adopted for the alcoholic patient. To illustrate, the synthesis, gradual accumulation and sequestration of THP and other metabolites within n. accumbens and other structures of limbic system after prolonged bouts of alcohol drinking clearly produces a disastrous neurochemical consequence. Clinically, such infor-

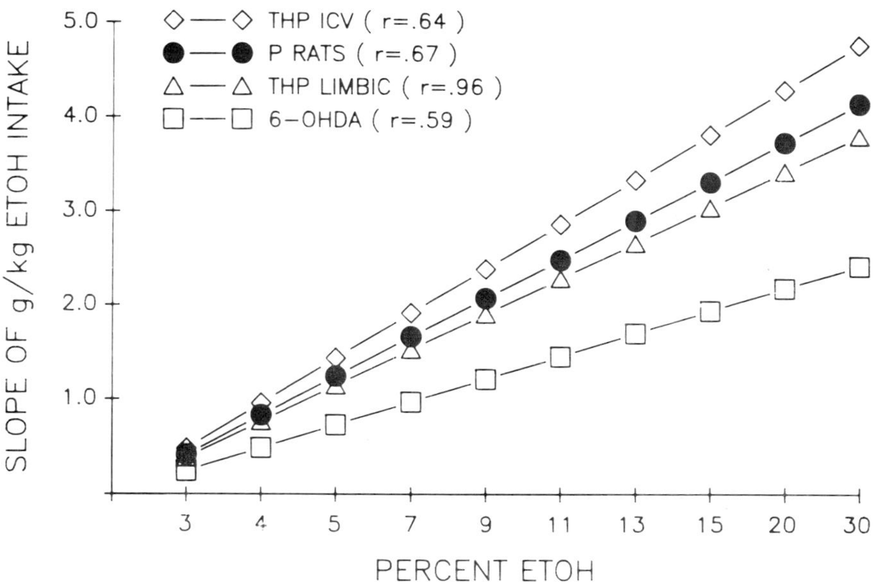

Fig. 1. Lines of best fit with a Y intercept of zero and respective regression coefficients (r) for g/kg intakes of 3–30% alcohol, from Lankford et al. [11].

mation would be extremely worthwhile to the patient who is vitally concerned about the etiology of the disease of alcoholism. In fact, each patient should be provided with a factual account of important highlights of research on rodents and monkeys which has transpired in the last decade. For example, persistent exposure to alcohol can produce a metabolic dysfunction in the body whereby neurochemically active amounts of an aldehyde metabolite are produced. One of these metabolites, THP, is the precursor to the opiate drug, morphine. In addition, the presence of only a tiny amount of THP or THBC in the brain causes intense drinking of alcohol, often in the form of bouts, even in individuals that naturally detest the fluid; thus, an abstinent animal becomes an alcoholic-like individual. Further, alcohol consumption of the THP-treated rat persists for as long as a year after the metabolite is administered, an interval equivalent to 30 years in the life-span of a human being.

In the alcoholic individual, a spree of intense drinking for an extended period ostensibly causes the formation of aldehyde metabolites in the brain. Subsequently, a change in nerve cells is induced that is apparently not only permanent but also enhances the liability to alcohol addiction. The extent to which an individual synthesizes an alkaloid metabolite and the impact of its actions on dopaminergic pathways in the brain depends presumably upon a genetic component and an inherent predisposition to its effect. Finally, the complexity of the addictive state seems to be characterized by self-regenerative mechanism operating in the brain; the more alcohol that is imbibed, the more metabolite is synthesized. In turn, elevated levels of metabolites lead to even greater drinking. When the alcoholic patient grasps the significance of this knowledge on the fundamental basis of recurrent drinking behavior, the therapeutic advantage becomes self-evident.

References

1. Myers RD (1989) Experientia 45: 436–444.
2. Myers RD (1980) In: Rigter H and Crabbe J (eds.) Alcohol Tolerance and Dependence. Elsevier, Amsterdam, pp. 339–370.
3. Myers RD (1990) Alcohol 7(5): 449–459.
4. Critcher EC, Lin CI, Patel J and Myers RD (1983) Pharmacol. Biochem. Behav. 18: 225–229.
5. Myers RD, Borg S and Mossberg R (1986) Alcohol 3(6): 383–388.
6. Collins MA, Ung-Chhun N, Cheng BY and Pronger D (1990) J. Neurochem. 55: 1507–1514.
7. Myers WD, Ng KT, Marzuki S, Myers RD and Singer G (1984) Alcohol 1: 229–236.
8. Rommelspacher H and Schmidt L (1985) Pharmacopsychiatry 18: 153–154.
9. Myers RD and Privette TH (1989) Brain Res. Bull. 22: 899–911.
10. Quarfordt SD, Kalmus GW and Myers RD (1991) Alcohol 8(3): 211–217.
11. Lankford MR, Roscoe AK, Pennington S and Myers RD (1991) Alcohol 8(4): (in press).

© 1991 Elsevier Science Publishers B.V. All rights reserved.
Biological Psychiatry, Volume 2. G. Racagni et al., editors.

Cognitive and sensory evoked potentials in chronic marihuana users

J. Straumanis, F. Struve, G. Patrick and Y. Raz
LSU Medical Center, 1501 Kings Hwy., Shreveport, LA 71130, U.S.A.

Introduction

Numerous electrophysiological studies of CNS effects of acute and chronic marihuana use have been reported since 1945 [1]. Struve et al. [2] reported the following EEG effects of chronic marihuana use: 1) increase of frontal absolute and relative α power; 2) decrease of relative β power; and 3) increase of frontal interhemispheric α coherence. The studies of marihuana (THC) effects on cognitive and sensory evoked potentials (EP's) are fewer in number and the findings are more variable. This study reports on the effects of chronic (years), frequent (daily) use of marihuana on cognitive (P300), somatosensory (SEP), auditory (AEP), brain stem (BAER) and visual (VEP) evoked potentials.

Subjects

Psychiatric patients with (users) and without (non-users) history of chronic marihuana use and normal volunteers (controls): a) *P300:* 15 users, 17 non-users, 14 controls of similar age. Six users and 12 non-users medication free; b) *AEP:* 15 users, non-users and controls (age 31, 32, 26 years). Eight users and 5 non-users medication free; c) *BAER:* 20 users, 28 non-users and 44 controls (age 30, 34, 25 years). Twelve users and 10 non-users medication free; d) *VEP:* 20 users, 19 non-users (age 29, 33, 28 years). Nine users and 13 non-users medication free; e)*SEP:* 16 age and sex-matched users and controls.

The diagnostic composition of groups is shown in Table 1.

Procedure

P300 elicited with auditory "odd ball" paradigm; target tone 15%, rep. rate 0.9 per s, measurements at cz. *VEP* elicited by checkerboard reversal (32 checks, 48 cm screen, 60 cm from eyes) with 0.92 per s rep. rate, measurements at O_1 and O_2. *AEP* elicited by bilateral clicks, 80 db, rep. rate 0.32 per s, measurements at cz. *BAER* elicited by bilateral clicks, 80 db, rep. rate 11.10 per s, measurement at cz. *SEP* elicited by 0.1 ms 10 MA above threshold constant current stimulus over left

Table 1. Diagnostic description

Diagnosis	P300		AEP		BAER		VEP		SEP
	user	non-user	user	non-user	user	non-user	user	non-user	users
Schizophrenia	2	1	2	3	4	8	3	1	3
Affective	4	10	2	7	5	13	4	9	4
Personality	–	3	–	2	5	5	4	5	5
Alcoholism	–	3	3	3	2	2	1	4	–
THC only	9	–	8	–	4	–	8	–	4

median nerve with 0.92 per s rep. rate. Recording was taken from contralateral electrode 2 cm posterior and 1 cm lateral to C4 (C4x). All derivations were in reference to linked ears. Subjects were tested 2–10 days after last exposure to marihuana.

Results

Cognitive (P300)

P300 latencies: Users 353 ms, non-users 325 ms, controls 326 ms. Users differed significantly from non-users (t, $P < 0.01$) and controls (t, $P < 0.01$). Controls did not differ from non-users.

P300 amplitude: This was measured: 1) peak to peak; N_2–P_2; 2) baseline to P_3; and 3) target minus non-target, baseline to P_3.

Results: 1) N_2–P_2 amplitude: users 12.1 u.v., non-users 14.8 u.v., controls 18.6 u.v.; 2) baseline to P_3: users 7.1 u.v., non-users 8.9 u.v., controls 10.3 u.v.; and 3) target minus non-target: users 7.8 u.v., non-users 9.5 u.v., controls 10.4 u.v. Users differed from controls on all 3 measures (t, $P < 0.001$, $P < 0.01$, $P < 0.02$ respectively), all other comparisons were non-significant.

AEP

Latencies and amplitudes of P_1, N_1, P_2 and N_2 were measured. There were no significant latency differences for any peak between users, non-users and controls. The only amplitude that differed between groups was the P_1 amplitude: users 3.63 u.v., non-users 1.84 u.v., controls 1.05 u.v. (ANOVA F, $P < 0.02$).

BAER

Latencies and amplitudes for peaks 1–5 were measured for all 3 groups. The user group had significantly longer latencies for peaks 1, 2 and 3; however, this difference was lost when peak 2 and 3 latencies were covaried for peak 1 latency. Peak 1 latencies were: users 1.92 ms, non-users 1.82 ms, controls 1.79 ms (users vs. controls, t, $P < 0.002$, users vs. non-users. t, $P < 0.07$, non-users vs. controls, N.S.). Interpeak (1–3, 3–5, 1–5) latencies did not differ between groups. Users had significantly ($P < 0.02$) lower amplitudes for peaks 1, 2 and 3 than controls, but not non-users.

VEP

VEP P100 latencies at O_1 and O_2 did not differ between groups. P100 amplitudes at O_1 were: users 5.7 u.v., non-users 4.9 u.v., controls 7.3 u.v. Users and non-users differed from controls ($P < 0.02$), but not between themselves. However, both non-users and controls showed less intersubject latency variability than users. Nine out of 20 users, 3/19 non-users and 1/17 controls had O_1 latencies outside the 90–110 ms window; users vs. controls (χ^2 $P < 0.01$), users vs. non-users (χ^2 $P < 0.05$), controls vs. non-users, N.S.

SEP

N_{18}–P_{30} peak to peak amplitude to left wrist stimulus was measured at C4x. The amplitudes were: users 5.26 u.v., controls 3.24 u.v. (Mann-Whitney, $P < 0.001$).

Discussion

The increased P300 latency with THC exposure could represent early organic cognitive impairment, since patients with senile dementia have significant prolongation of P300 latency [3]. Amplitude reduction is seen both in dementia [3] and schizophrenia [4] and to lesser extent in major depression and may represent altered information processing. The prolongation of BAER peak 1 without effect on interpeak latencies suggests possible damage to eighth nerve or cochlea. This could be a direct ototoxic effect of THC similar to aminoglycoside antibiotics, or exposure of users to loud music with resultant hearing loss. The amplitude reduction does not appear to be a specific effect of THC exposure, but related to being a patient and receiving psychotropic drugs. The greater intersubject VEP latency variability in users might be interpreted as reflecting inconsistent information transmission. The augmented SEP N_{18}–P_{30} amplitude has been observed in dementia, chronic schizophrenia and major depression and might reflect an early filtering defect of incoming information.

References

1. Struve FA and Straumanis JJ (1990) Drug Dev. Res. 20: 369–388.
2. Struve FA, Straumanis JJ, Patrick G and Raz Y (1989) Clin. Electroencephalogr. 20: 6–23.
3. Zappolli R (1988) In: Giannitreponi D and Murri G (eds.) The EEG of Mental Activities. Karger, Basel, pp. 1–25.
4. Straumanis JJ (1990) In: Hall R and Winstead D (eds.) Psychiatric Medicine. Ryandic, Longwood, Florida, pp. 76–96.

© 1991 Elsevier Science Publishers B.V. All rights reserved.
Biological Psychiatry, Volume 2. G. Racagni et al., editors.

Topographic brain mapping during cocaine-induced intoxication and self-administration

Scott E. Lukas
Alcohol and Drug Abuse Research Center, McLean Hospital/Harvard Medical School, Belmont, Massachusetts, U.S.A.

Introduction

Technological advancements in computer-assisted analysis of brain electrical activity now provide a second-by-second view of the brain which permits quantifying cerebral processes involved in the transition between behavioral states. Important neurophysiological events can be missed when recording from only a few electrode sites. However, conventional paper recordings of 18–20 channels of EEG activity provide too much information to detect such paroxysmal events by visual inspection alone. Recently developed topographic mapping procedures consolidate EEG activity from a full array of recording sites into a single display representing the distribution of electrical activity over the entire scalp.

EEG topographic mapping has been gaining widespread use as a diagnostic tool in psychiatry and neurology (cf. [1,2]), but it has only recently been utilized to assess drug-induced alterations in brain electrical activity. Drugs of abuse have three properties in common: they alter behavior, they have discriminative stimulus properties, and they have direct reinforcing properties [3]. While reinforcement per se is frequently thought of as being a mechanism for drug abuse, it is often quantified without measures that are independent of the drug-taking event. In clinical studies, the term "euphoria" is frequently used without an objective measure of a drug's reinforcing efficacy. Our preliminary studies suggest that the distribution of EEG α activity is a strong candidate as a neurophysiological correlate of drug-induced euphoria. Thus, a major reason for conducting the proposed studies using topographic mapping techniques is that the power, predominant frequency, distribution, and time course of brain electrical activity can be simultaneously measured over the entire scalp to provide a complete assessment of paroxysmal neurophysiological events likely to be associated with rapidly changing behavioral states.

The present study was designed to measure these events and to extend our understanding of the processes involved in cocaine abuse. A second aim was to measure the electrophysiological changes of subjects during a cocaine self-administration. Cocaine plasma levels were measured in order to determine if they co-varied with subjective reports of euphoria.

Since achievement of these aims requires precise temporal correlations between

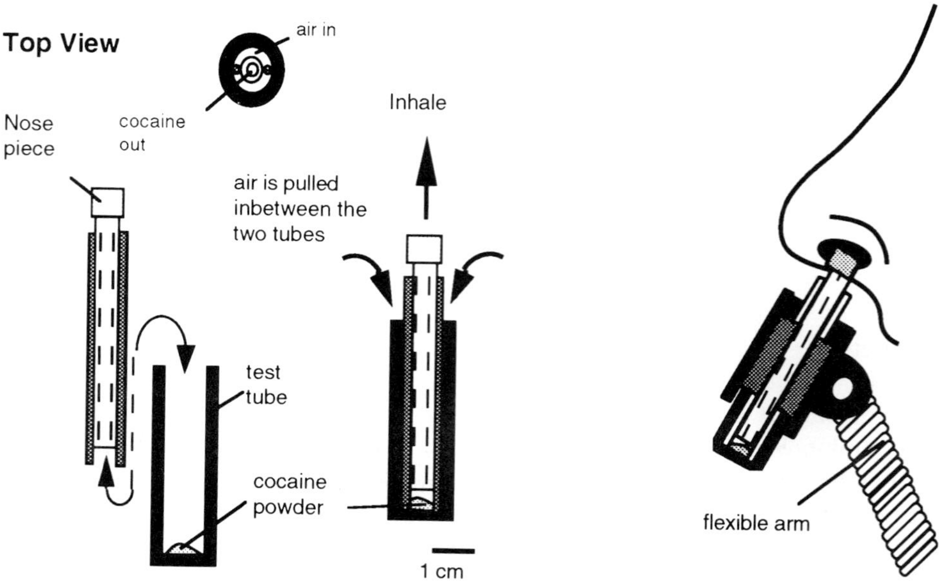

Fig. 1. Device for intranasal delivery of cocaine.

drug administration and its consequences, we have elected to use the auditory P300 ERP *oddball* task. Such measures have obvious advantages in that this wave appears to reflect alterations in memory updating during cognitive processing. Merging the salient properties of these two concepts results in a research strategy that can be applied to explore the neurophysiological concomitants of drug-induced intoxication.

In the second study, P300 amplitude and distribution was larger when subjects were about to receive an active cocaine dose. When placebo was available, P300 amplitude was very small, but no consistent changes in latency were observed.

Discussion

The finding that cocaine causes increases in EEG α during subjective reports of euphoria is interesting in that a similar profile has been demonstrated for ethanol [4,5]. This response may be similar to the reports that increases in EEG α are associated with a pleasurable, free-floating and extremely relaxed state [6,7]. The parallel EEG and behavioral responses suggest that abrupt increases in EEG α activity may be associated with cocaine's reinforcing properties.

The finding that P300 amplitudes were larger during active cocaine self-administration is interesting, but the implications are not, as yet, fully understood. Most studies have demonstrated that P300 amplitude is attenuated in certain conditions such as dementia, depression and schizophrenia [8]. There is an extensive literature on the co-variance between alterations in brain electrical activity and behavior – in both normal and abnormal states (cf. [9,10]). Further, there has been an extensive use of EEG activity to quantify drug effects on central nervous system function (cf. [11,12]). While Herning et al. [13] found no changes in P300 amplitude and latency after *acute* cocaine administration, there have been no reports of using these procedures to monitor the electrophysiological correlates of cocaine-seeking behavior.

Materials and Methods

Subjects

Healthy male recreational drug users (age 21–35 years) provided informed consent to participate in these studies. Subjects received a full physical and psychiatric examination to ensure that they were healthy and that no naive or cocaine-dependent subject was admitted into the protocol. Individuals with a positive family history for alcoholism were excluded. Subjects were prepared with a full set of EEG scalp electrodes using the 10-20 International System and an i.v. catheter for blood sampling and plasma cocaine level determinations.

EEG recording procedure

Subjects sat in a sound-attenuated and electrically-shielded chamber in a semi-supine position. A wired intercom and a closed circuit video camera permitted audio and visual contact with the subjects at all times. EEG and ERP recordings were collected using tin electrodes. A linked ears referential montage was used with a bandpass of 1.0–30 Hz for the EEG studies and 0.01–70 Hz for the ERP studies. EEG studies were conducted with the subjects' eyes closed, but the ERP data were collected during the eyes open condition. A continuous electrocardiogram was also recorded for safety.

Subjective measures of intoxication

Subjects were instructed to report behavioral changes (e.g., detection, euphoria, dysphoria, etc.) by moving an instrumental joystick device [14]. Movement of this device was translated directly onto the paper record and a digital time code was recorded on magnetic tape for subsequent synchronization of off-line data analysis. In addition, an Addiction Research Center Inventory (ARCI) was administered at various times after drug administration.

Experimental procedure

After baseline EEG and behavioral data were collected subjects were given either placebo or 0.45 or 0.9 mg/kg cocaine; EEG and behavioral data were then collected continuously for 2 h. Cocaine was delivered intranasally either as an aqueous spray using an automated airbrush device [15] or via a customized glass straw device (Fig. 1). In a separate protocol subjects smoked a placebo marihuana cigarette and then were required to complete an auditory P300 task in order to obtain a cocaine dose. Subjects were given four such opportunities to snort cocaine (2 placebos, 0.225 and 0.45 mg/kg, i.n.) in the following order: placebo, active, placebo, active. The order of low and moderate cocaine doses was randomized. Subjects were told which dose they were about to receive.

Results

In the first study cocaine produced dose-related increases in the duration and the number of euphoric episodes. These early episodes of euphoria were heralded by pronounced increases in α activity over occipital and parietal areas. Some frontal α was also evident. The α activity disappeared along with the euphoria. After the acute response waned the EEG reverted to a desynchronized state with predominantly β activity. These data suggest that the neurophysiological correlates of euphoria may be linked to EEG α activity.

Conclusions

The data demonstrate the utility of using topographic brain mapping techniques to quantify various behavioral states such as drug-induced intoxication and drug-seeking behavior. Further research using multiple drugs and possible pharmacotherapies may yield important information on the neurophysiological basis of drug abuse.

Acknowledgements

This work was supported by Grant DA03994 and Research Scientist Development Award DA00115 from the National Institute on Drug Abuse. The author gratefully acknowledges the technical assistance of Leslie Amass, Richard Benedikt, Elena Kouri and Michelle Fortin.

References

1. Duffy FH (ed.) (1986) Topographic Mapping of Brain Electrical Activity. Butterworth, Boston.
2. Duffy FH, Burchfield JL and Lombroso CT (1979) Ann. Neurol. 5: 309–321.
3. Henningfield JE, Lukas SE and Bigelow GE (1986) In: Goldberg SR and Stolerman I (eds.) Behavioral Analysis of Drug Dependence. Academic Press, New York, pp. 69–122.
4. Lukas SE, Mendelson JH, Benedikt RA and Jones B (1986b) Pharmacol. Biochem. Behav. 25: 889–895.
5. Lukas SE, Mendelson JH, Woods BT, Mello NK and Tech SK (1989) J. Stud. Alcohol 50: 176–185.
6. Brown BB (1970) Psychophysiology 6: 442–452.
7. Wallace RK (1970) Science 167: 1751–1754.
8. Pfefferbaum A, Wenegrat BG, Ford JM, Roth WT and Kopell BS (1984) Electroencephalogr. Clin. Neurophysiol. 59: 104–124.
9. Begleiter H (ed.) (1977) Evoked Brain Potentials and Behavior. The Downstate Series of Research in Psychiatry and Psychology, Vol. 2. Plenum Press, New York.
10. Callaway E (1975) Brain Electrical Potentials and Individual Psychological Differences. Grune & Stratton, New York.
11. Herrmann WM (ed.) (1982) Electroencephalography in Drug Research. Gustav Fisher, New York.
12. Lukas SE (1991) In: Mello NK (ed.) Advances in Substance Abuse Behavioral and Biological Research, Vol. 4. Jessica Lindsley Publishers, London (in press).
13. Herning RI, Hooker WD and Jones RT (1987) Electroencephalogr. Clin. Neurophysiol. 66: 42–43.
14. Lukas SE, Mendelson JH, Benedikt RA and Jones B (1986a) Psychopharmacology 89: 8–13.
15. Lukas SE, Mendelson JH, Amass L and Benedikt R (1990) In: Harris LS (ed.) Problems of Drug Dependence, 1989. U.S. Govt. Printing Office, NIDA Research Monograph No. 95, DHHS Publication No. (ADM)90-1663, Washington, D.C., pp. 146–151.

© 1991 Elsevier Science Publishers B.V. All rights reserved.
Biological Psychiatry, Volume 2. G. Racagni et al., editors.

Quantitative EEG and THC abuse: Topographic findings and discriminant function analysis

Fred Struve, John Straumanis, Gloria Patrick and Yoram Raz
LSU Medical Center, 1501 Kings Hwy., Shreveport, LA 71130, U.S.A.

Introduction

A recent review of quantitative EEG studies of acute marihuana (THC) exposure [1] suggests that this substance produces transient EEG effects represented primarily by an increase in the amount of α (% relative power), a decrease in α frequency, a decrease in the relative amount of β and possibly a decreased percentage of θ activity as well. Persistent EEG effects following long-term THC abuse have not been reported and the topographic distribution of quantitative EEG findings associated with chronic THC exposure has not been previously explored.

Methods and Results

In a pilot study [2] quantitative EEGs were obtained on 10 chronic THC users, 10 psychiatric patient non-users and 10 normal non-users. Chronic THC use was defined as 1 "joint" per day for 1 year or longer. However, most THC users had smoked 3 to 15 joints per day for 5 to 15 years. All THC users were psychiatric inpatients with no access to THC and negative urines at EEG study. Using 21 scalp electrodes plus ocular monitoring leads, 21 channels of monopolar (linked ear reference) EEG were recorded using a Cadwell Spectrum 32 instrument. Recordings were made with Ss reclined with eyes closed. All Ss were kept awake during EEG recording. Quantitative EEG measures were derived from 40 to 60 2–1/2 s epochs of artifact-free awake EEG activity. At all 21 scalp leads quantitative values for absolute and % relative power were obtained for each of the four traditional EEG frequency bands. Quantitative values for interhemispheric coherence and power asymmetry were also obtained for 8 homologous lead pairs. When the THC group was contrasted with each non-user group, THC users were found to have: 1) significant elevations of absolute power of α over all cortical regions with the most marked elevations over frontal cortex; 2) significant elevations of relative power of α over frontal cortex; and 3) significant elevations of interhemispheric coherence of α confined to the frontal cortex. We referred to these three findings collectively as *hyperfrontality of* α. Chronic THC use was also associated with a less pronounced voltage increase of all frequencies over all cortical regions but without a frontal predominance. We referred to this finding as *generalized power enhancement.* THC use was also associated with significant decreases of relative power of δ activity over prefrontal and frontal cortex and significant elevations of θ coherence over prefrontal, frontal and lateral frontal areas.

A recent replication study (unpublished observations) using new Ss and the same methodology contrasted 17 THC users with 21 patient non-users and 12 normal non-users. The replication was successful and all of the above findings were confirmed. In the replication study, frontal δ coherence was also significantly elevated among THC users.

In both studies intergroup differences in diagnosis and medication could not be controlled. Combining Ss from both studies we contrasted 13 medication-free THC users with 13 medication-free patient non-users (diagnosis uncontrolled) and 8 THC users matched for diagnosis with 8 patient non-users (medication uncontrolled). In both post hoc analyses the above THC effects remained significant.

Current preliminary analyses of quantitative EEGs obtained from normal daily THC users and non-users screened to be free of significant psychiatric disease and current or past medical disease or injury of CNS relevance now provide another replication of the above findings. In addition, data from our current ongoing studies of THC use in normals demonstrate that THC users have a significant decrease in mean α frequency at all recording electrodes as contrasted with non-users.

All 80 Ss in the pilot study and first replication mentioned above were used in an effort to separate THC users from non-users using a discriminant function analysis. The dependent variable was daily use or non-use of THC. Candidate predictors were absolute and relative power, asymmetry and coherence for all four EEG bands at all 21 electrode sites and transformations of these scores. The discrimination function analysis and its jack-knife replication were robust. Only two predictors, Z-scores for absolute power of α at F_3 (AF_3a) and Z-scores for absolute power of α at P_3 (AP_3a), were needed to generate the following successful discriminant formula:

$$D = (1.7416)(AF_3a) - (1.0048)(AP_3a)$$

The classification success using this formula is shown Table 1.

Using both THC group Ss and current or former THC users not qualifying for inclusion in the study chronic THC group, we were able to identify 32 Ss who were

Table 1.

Actual group	n	Predicted		Jack-knife	
		THC	No THC	THC	No THC
THC user	27	27	0	26	1
Non-user	53	4	49	4	49
Classification:		95% Correct		93.8% Correct	

confident in reporting long-term duration of THC use and average number of joints used per day over long time periods. We found significant correlations between discriminant scores (as calculated in Table 1) and the following:

1. duration of THC use in years (r = 0.44, $P = 0.005$);
2. exposure defined as joints/day times duration (r = 0.31, $P = 0.038$);
3. abstinence from THC in years (r = –0.60, $P < 0.001$).

When partial correlations controlling for abstinence effect were calculated, discriminant scores correlated with:

1. average number of joints/day (r = 0.39, $P < 0.015$);
2. duration of THC use in years (r = 0.43, $P = 0.005$);
3. exposure defined as joints/day times duration (r = 0.43, $P = 0.005$);
4. logarithmic transformation of exposure (r = 0.65, $P < 0.001$).

Discussion

Chronic daily THC use appears to be associated with persistent CNS neurophysiological sequelae, as indicated by the topographic quantitative EEG effects described above. Continuing work in this area should focus on potential neuropsychological correlates to these findings, additional quantitative EEG changes that might be seen with excessively long cumulative THC exposure, and the degree of reversal of the described quantitative EEG effect with prolonged abstinence from THC in Ss who are able to stop use of this compound.

References

1. Struve FA and Straumanis JJ (1990) Drug Dev. Res. 20: 369–388.
2. Struve FA, Straumanis JJ, Patrick G and Price L (1989) Clin. Electroencephalogr. 20: 6–23.

© 1991 Elsevier Science Publishers B.V. All rights reserved.
Biological Psychiatry, Volume 2. G. Racagni et al., editors.

Neural substrates mediating the motivational effects of opioids

Toni S. Shippenberg, Albert Herz, Rainer Spanagel and Regine Bals-Kubik

Introduction

Opioids, prototypic drugs of abuse, exert marked effects on motivation. μ-Receptor agonists function as positive reinforcers and it is this action which underlies their abuse liability. In contrast, κ-agonists induce aversive and dysphoric states [1–2]. Although both effects appear to be centrally mediated [3], their site of action and neurochemical basis is unclear. Accordingly a series of studies, employing both a behavioral and neurochemical approach, were conducted to address these issues. The conditioned place preference paradigm, an animal model for the detection of drug-induced motivational states [2,3] was used to examine the neuroanatomical substrates mediating the motivational effects of opioids and the technique of in vivo microdialysis was used to assess the neurochemical basis for such effects.

Material and Methods

Place conditioning was conducted in rats as described previously using an unbiased procedure [3,4]. Animals were implanted with intracerebral guide cannulae aimed at the ventral tegmental area (VTA), nucleus accumbens (NAC), caudate/putamen (CPU), substantia nigra or medial prefrontal cortex (MFC) to permit micro-injection of the conditioning drugs. A map of those sites producing opioid-induced reinforcement of aversion, as indicated by, respectively, conditioned preferences or aversions for the drug-paired place, was then generated. The influence of 6-hydroxydopamine (6-OHDA) lesions or DA receptor antagonists upon the conditioning produced by systemically applied opioids was also examined.

For microdialysis studies, animals were implanted with injection cannulae in the VTA and microdialysis guide cannulae in the NAC. After insertion of the micro-dialysis probe (2.0 mm), which was perfused with Ringer solution (2.2 μl/m), basal and opioid-induced DA release was monitored in 20-min dialysates of anesthetized animals [5]. The effects of the μ-receptor agonists DAMGO and morphine and the κ-opioid agonists U-50488 and 0-69593 were assessed.

Results

Mapping studies demonstrate that the activation of opioid receptors in areas comprising the mesocorticolimbic DA system is sufficient for the induction of the reinforcing and aversive effects of opioids. Microinjection of μ-agonists into the VTA, the site of origin of this DA system produced dose-related preferences for the drug-paired place, whereas injection of κ-agonists into either the VTA, NAC or MFC produced conditioned place aversions. Other injection sites were ineffective. 6-OHDA lesions of the NAC, which resulted in a marked depletion of DA in this brain area, or the specific blockade of NAC DA receptors also attenuated the motivational effects of μ- and κ-agonists (Fig. 1). The same manipulations to other ascending DA systems were without effect.

Systemic or intracerebroventricular (i.c.v.) injection of μ-agonists, at doses producing place preferences, stimulated DA release and metabolism in the NAC. A similar effect was observed in response to their intra-VTA but not NAC application. In contrast to μ-agonists, κ-agonists, at doses which were aversive, inhibited DA release. This inhibition occurred after systemic, i.c.v. or NAC application whereas the VTA administration route was without effect.

Discussion

Data derived from conditioning studies demonstrate that the mesolimbic DA

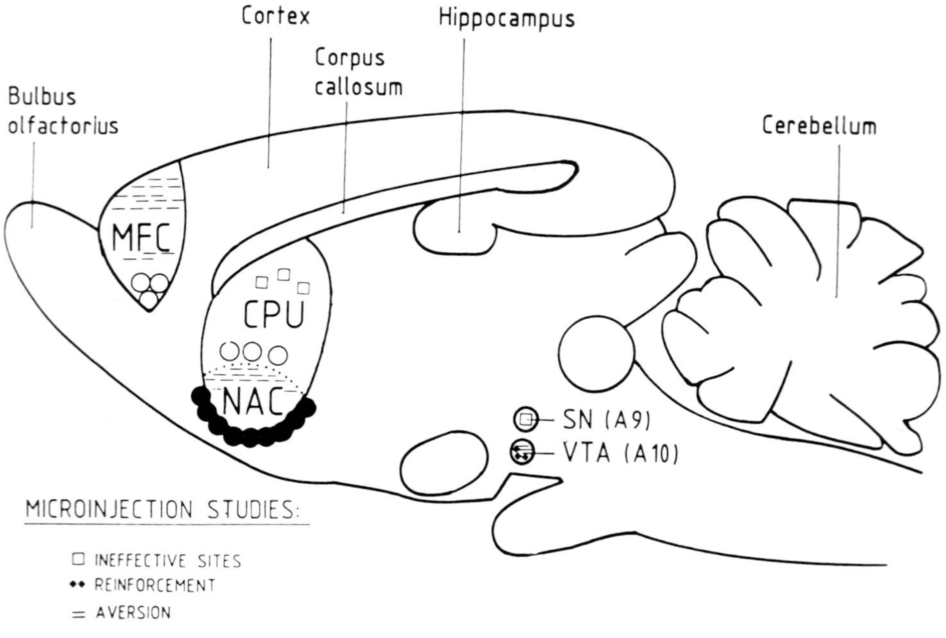

Fig. 1. Results of mapping and lesion studies. Only microinjections of μ-agonists into the VTA or of κ-agonists into the VTA, NAC or MFC produced significant motivational effects. 6-OHDA lesions or D_1 receptor blockade of the NAC (shaded circles) in contrast to the CPU or MFC (open circles) abolished the effects of opioids.

system, specifically the DA neurons projecting from the VTA to the NAC, is critical for the expression of both the reinforcing and aversive effects of opioids. μ-Receptor agonists increased DA release and metabolism in the NAC [5,6], effects which were shown to be mediated at the level of the DA cell body. In contrast, κ-agonists and the activation of opioid receptors located on or in the vicinity of DA nerve terminals inhibited DA release. These data and those demonstrating a preferential stimulation of mesolimbic DA release in response to several drugs of abuse [6] suggest that the opposing effects of μ- and κ-agonists upon DA release and the ensuing changes in activation of NAC DA receptors underlies their opposing motivational effects. Furthermore, the efficacy of D_1 antagonists in attenuating the motivational effects of opioids and other psychoactive drugs together with the finding that the intra-NAC application of D_1 but not D_2 DA receptor antagonists induces aversive states [2,4] suggests a critical role for this DA receptor type in motivational processes.

References

1. Pfeiffer A (1991) In: Almeida OFX and Shippenberg TS (eds.) Neurobiology of Opioids. Springer-Verlag, Heidelberg, pp. 351–362.
2. Shippenberg TS and Bals-Kubik R (1991) In: Almeida OFX and Shippenberg TS (eds.) Neurobiology of Opioids. Springer-Verlag, Heidelberg, pp. 321–350.
3. Bals-Kubik R, Herz A and Shippenberg TS (1989) Psychopharmacology 98: 203.
4. Shippenberg TS, Bals-Kubik R, Huber A and Herz A (1991) Psychopharmacology 103: 209.
5. Spanagel R, Herz A and Shippenberg TS (1990) Eur. J. Pharmacol. 190: 177.
6. DiChiara G and Imperato A (1988) Proc. Natl. Acad. Sci. U.S.A. 85: 5274.

© 1991 Elsevier Science Publishers B.V. All rights reserved.
Biological Psychiatry, Volume 2. G. Racagni et al., editors.

Neurobiological sites for drug dependence

George F. Koob
Department of Neuropharmacology, Research Institute of Scripps Clinic

Classical definitions of dependence emphasize two important phenomena: a compulsion to take the drug with a loss of control in limiting intake and a characteristic withdrawal syndrome that results in physical signs as well as motivational signs of discomfort when the drug is removed. The search for neurobiological substrates for these phenomena has depended on the development of animal models, both for the acute reinforcing or rewarding effects of drugs as well as for the motivational aspects of the withdrawal syndromes associated with the removal of the drug after chronic access or administration.

Neurobiological substrates for the acute reinforcing effects of cocaine

Intravenous self-administration of the drugs has proven a reliable animal model for the acute reinforcing effects of drugs. Rats with limited access to cocaine (3 h/day) will show a stable and regular drug intake over each daily session without any obvious tolerance or dependence. A special aspect of this model is that the rats appear to regulate the amount of drug self-administered. Lowering the dose from the training dose of 0.75 mg/kg per injection increases cocaine self-administration. Increasing the dose decreases cocaine self-administration.

Using this model, dopamine has been strongly implicated in the reinforcing effects of cocaine. Low doses of dopamine receptor antagonists when injected systemically reliably increase cocaine self-administration. Rats appear to compensate for decreases in the magnitude of reinforcement with an increase in cocaine self-administration (or a decrease in the interinjection interval). Similar effects have been observed with direct intracerebral injections of dopamine antagonists. Microinjections of haloperidol and SCH 23390 into the nucleus accumbens also produce an increase in cocaine self-administration [1].

These results are consistent with earlier lesion studies showing that denervation of the dopamine projection to the nucleus accumbens can block cocaine self-administration [2,3]. Similar attenuation of cocaine self-administration has been observed following cell body-specific lesions of the nucleus accumbens itself [4] or the ventral pallidum [5]. These results suggest that the reinforcing actions of cocaine in non-dependent rats may involve activation of neural elements in an accumbens-pallidal circuit that receive afferents from multiple limbic sources.

Neurobiological substrates for the motivational aspects of withdrawal associated with chronic cocaine administration

Cocaine dependence has never been characterized by major opiate-like physical signs of withdrawal during abstinence, but evidence exists to show that following a cocaine binge, severe depressive symptoms combined with irritability and anxiety develop during abstinence [6]. These symptoms characterize the "crash" associated with the cocaine dependence cycle and may last several hours to several days.

In an attempt to develop an animal model of the salient motivational symptom of anhedonia, animals were prepared with both intravenous catheters and electrodes aimed at the medial forebrain bundle for determination of brain stimulation reward threshold using a discrete trials threshold technique [7]. Following exposure to different times of access of cocaine for intravenous self-administration, brain stimulation reward thresholds were elevated during withdrawal when compared to pre-drug baseline levels. The magnitude and duration of the elevation in reward thresholds was proportional to the amount of cocaine self-administered [8]. The effects of cocaine withdrawal on brain stimulation thresholds was the opposite of the effect of acute cocaine on brain stimulation reward [7]. These results suggest that cocaine can alter the function of the medial forebrain bundle during the course of a cocaine bout and withdrawal.

Neurobiological substrates for the acute reinforcing effects of opiates

Opiate drugs such as heroin provided in limited access are readily self-administered intravenously by rats. Again rats will maintain stable levels of drug intake on a daily basis without any major signs of tolerance or dependence. Using this model, both systemic and central administration of competitive opiate antagonists increase heroin self-administration, suggesting that the animals attempt to compensate for the opiate antagonism by increasing the amount of drug injected. The region of the nucleus accumbens appeared to be particularly sensitive to the effects of methylnaloxonium [9]. Injections of methylnaloxonium into the ventral tegmental area produced increases in heroin self-administration only at doses similar to those required by the intracerebroventricular route. These results suggested that neural elements in the region of the nucleus accumbens may be responsible for the reinforcing properties of opiates as well as cocaine. Other work supporting this hypothesis is the observation that rats will self-administer opioid peptides in the region of the nucleus accumbens [10]. The exact neurochemical mechanisms mediating the rewarding effect of opiates in the nucleus accumbens is unknown, but some evidence exists to suggest that it is independent of dopamine release. In rats trained to self-administer cocaine and heroin on alternate days, 6-OHDA lesions of the nucleus accumbens produced a time-dependent decrease or extinction of cocaine self-administration, whereas heroin self-administration returned to near-normal levels [11].

Neurobiological substrates for the motivational aspects of withdrawal associated with chronic opiate administration

In contrast to stimulants, the dependence on opiate drugs is defined by a characteristic withdrawal syndrome that appears with the abrupt termination of opiate administration or with administration of competitive opiate antagonists. Humans report both physical and motivational symptoms such as nausea, gastrointestinal disturbances, chills, sympathetic reactions and a painful flu-like dysphoric state. In rats physical dependence has been characterized by an abstinence syndrome that includes the appearance of ptosis, teeth chattering, wet dog shakes and diarrhea. More motivational measures have included the disruption of trained operant behavior for food reward and the development of place aversions following precipitated withdrawal with systemic opiate antagonist administration. Local intracerebral injections of methylnaloxonium into various brain sites revealed that injections into the region of the nucleus accumbens produced disruption of operant responding on an FR-15 schedule at doses significantly lower than other sites [12]. Confirmation of an aversive stimulus effect for intracerebral methylnaloxonium was shown using the place aversion test and the nucleus accumbens proved to be the most sensitive site for intracerebral injections of methylnaloxonium to produce place aversions [13]. Microinjection of methylnaloxonium into the nucleus accumbens precipitated almost no signs of physical withdrawal (Maldonaldo-Lopez and Koob, unpublished observations).

Summary and Conclusions

The region of the nucleus accumbens appears to be important for processing the cocaine and opiate reinforcing stimulus. This same circuitry may be involved in the aversive stimulus effects associated with cocaine and opiate withdrawal. Thus, the same neural elements responsible for "euphoria" may also be changed in the course of dependence to be responsible for the "dysphoria" associated with drug removal.

Two possible mechanisms have been hypothesized at the molecular and cellular level to explain this change: a "Within Systems" adaptation and a "Between Systems" adaptation [14]. In a Within Systems adaptation, the primary molecular or cellular response to the drug would itself adapt to neutralize the effects of the drug. Persistence of this change in the primary molecular or cellular response after the drug is removed would produce the aversive stimulus effects of withdrawal. In a Between Systems adaptation, a different cellular system and separate molecular apparatus would be triggered by the changes in the primary drug response and again, removal of the drug would unmask the activity of this system to produce the aversive stimulus effects of withdrawal. Identification of the cellular and molecular components of these adaptations may provide the keys to the understanding of the addiction process itself.

Acknowledgements

This work was supported in part by NIDA Grants DA04398 and DA04043. I thank MEM Word Processing for manuscript preparation.

References

1. Maldonaldo R, Robledo P, Clover AJ and Koob GF (1991) Neurosci. Abstr. (abstract).
2. Roberts DCS, Koob GF, Klonoff P and Fibiger HC (1980) Pharmacol. Biochem. Behav. 12: 781.
3. Koob GF, Vaccarino FJ, Amalric M and Bloom FE (1987) In: Engel J and Oreland L (eds.) Brain Reward Systems and Abuse. Raven Press, New York, pp. 35–50.
4. Zito KA, Vickers G and Roberts DCS (1985) Pharmacol. Biochem. Behav. 23: 1029 .
5. Hubner CB and Koob GF (1990) Brain Res. 508: 20.
6. Gawin FH and Kleber HD (1986) Arch. Gen. Psychiatry 43: 107.
7. Kornetsky C and Esposito RU (1981) Brain Res. 209: 496.
8. Markou MA and Koob GF (1991) Neuropsychopharmacology 4: 17.
9. Vaccarino FJ, Bloom FE and Koob GF (1985) Psychopharmacology 86: 37.
10. Goeders NE, Lane JD and Smith JE (1984) Pharmacol. Biochem. Behav. 20: 451.
11. Pettit HO, Ettenberg A, Bloom FE and Koob GF (1984) Psychopharmacology 84: 167.
12. Koob GF, Wall TL and Bloom FE (1989) Psychopharmacology 98: 530.
13. Stinus L, Le Moal M and Koob GF (1990) Neuroscience 37: 767.
14. Koob GF and Bloom FE (1988) Science 242: 715.

© 1991 Elsevier Science Publishers B.V. All rights reserved.
Biological Psychiatry, Volume 2. G. Racagni et al., editors.

Transcutaneous cranial electrical stimulation with high frequency intermittent current (Limoge's) potentiates opiate-induced analgesia and alleviates the opiate abstinence syndrome

Louis Stinus[1], Marc Auriacombe[1], Aymé Limoge[2] and Michel Le Moal[1]
[1]*INSERM U. 259, Université de Bordeaux II, Domaine de Carreire, 33077 Bordeaux Cedex; and* [2]*Laboratoire d'Electrophysiologie, Université René Descartes de Paris, 92120 Montrouge, France*

Introduction

Since the beginning of the century, numerous studies have investigated the possibility of producing sleep and general anesthesia by means of low frequency electric currents. These effects were always associated with severe physiological side-effects. Considerable progress was made by the introduction of a different stimulation method (Limoge current) which facilitated the penetration of electric fields into brain tissue. It consisted of a low frequency envelope (4 ms, 100 Hz) containing high-frequency balanced (zero net charge) pulses (166 kHz, positive for 2 μs and negative for 4 μs) which permitted the increase of current intensity with no reduction of tissue conductivity normally associated with low frequency currents (the 100 mA peak-to-peak stimulation corresponds to 17.5 mA effective current). Transcranial electrical stimulation (TCES) was applied through a frontal cathode and two posterior electrodes at the level of the mastoid bones (positive pole). Under these conditions, electropharmaceutical anesthesia was induced in animals [1]. Subsequently this TCES has been used with very positive results during a variety of human surgery. TCES induced an increase of N_2O anaesthetic potency, a reduction by 60% of the need for opiate analgesics, a better quality of anesthesia, a more rapid recovery from anesthesia followed by a long-lasting post-operative analgesic period [2,3]. Based on the fact that TCES reduces opiate requirement during anesthesia, TCES was used as a treatment for the rapid detoxification of heroin addicts. Its clinical efficacy was confirmed by double-blind experiments [4]. TCES is asymptomatic and no side-effects have ever been reported even after several days of continuous application of TCES.

Recently, several animal studies have confirmed and extended these clinical findings. For the purpose of these experiments three silver electrodes (6 mm in diameter) were connected to a microplug fixed to the calvarium by acrylic cement. The frontal electrode (negative pole) was placed on the mesopic suture between the eyes and the two posterior electrodes (positive pole) behind the mastoid bones on each side.

Table 1. Tail flick maximal latency as percentage of baseline

	Without TCES (%)	With TCES (%)
Morphine s.c. 10 mg/kg	174	306
Morphine i.c.v. 15 μg	152	207
Fentanyl s.c. 30 μg/kg	176	336
Alfentanil s.c. 120 μg/kg	160	215
Dextromoramide s.c. 300 μg/kg	267	392

TCES potentiation of opiate-induced analgesia [5]

Tail flick latency (TFL) test was used to measure pain threshold. TCES was not found to modify the pain threshold in drug-free rats, but it potentiated the efficacy of several opiate analgesic drugs currently used in human surgery (Table 1). To obtain a maximal effect, TCES must be initiated 3 h before the drug injection and be maintained throughout the duration of its pharmacological action. TCES potentiation was found to be dependent on drug dose, current intensity and electrode polarity.

These results were obtained not only after systemic opiate treatment but also after intracerebroventricular (i.c.v.) injection of morphine, suggesting that TCES potentiation of opiate-induced analgesia is centrally mediated.

TCES attenuates opiate abstinence syndrom [6]

Opiate withdrawal was studied in morphine-dependent rats with implanted electrodes as described before. Morphine dependence was induced by injection of increasing doses of the drug (twice daily) for 10 days up to 90 mg/kg i.p. The last injection of morphine took place on the morning of the 11th day. The rats were then placed in cages for TCES, which started 3 h later and lasted for 4 days. Every 6 h, rats were observed for measurement of opiate withdrawal symptoms according to the Gellert's scale [4]. All the rats were connected to the stimulators but only half of them received TCES. The experimentator was blind to the subject's status. In control rats, withdrawal syndrome appeared within 24 h and lasted for at least 3 days with a peak on the third day. TCES did not change the time course but reduced considerably the intensity of the syndrome. The total mean score for the three days was 4.64 for the control group and 2.52 for the stimulated rats (–46%, $P < 0.0001$) and the peak effect was respectively 8.78 and 4.53 (–48%, $P < 0.0001$).

Since TCES failed to attenuate naloxone-precipitated withdrawal syndrome in morphine-dependent rats, we suspect that TCES effects were mediated through the activation of endogenous opioid neuronal systems. Interestingly, the attenuation of opiate abstinence syndrome was also observed during transcranial stimulation with low frequency currents [7], which confirms again the putative therapeutic properties of brain transcutaneous cranial electrical stimulation. However, the duration of the stimulation never exceeded 30 min, presumably due to side-effects and secondly, the evolution of the withdrawal following the termination of the stimulation was never reported.

Behavioural effects of long-term application of TCES

Rats were submitted to a 7-h continuous TCES session and then tested in different behavioral situations under TCES (n = 15). Results were compared to those obtained with non-stimulated rats (control group, n = 15). When locomotor was activity measured in photocell activity cages for the first time (novelty) TCES rats were more active than controls (1 h session, TCES: 796 ± 36 and C: 558 ± 33 counts $P < 0.001$). However, after habituation for several days, locomotor activity was unchanged (TCES: 432 ± 46, C: 340 ± 32). Spontaneous alternation measured in a Y maze for 10 min was not altered by TCES (TCES: 73 ± 3%, C: 80 ± 3%). Finally, after 18 h food deprivation, food and water intake measured for 1 h were similar (TCES: 5.3 ± 0.4 g, C: 5.1 ± 0.4 ml, C: 5.8 ± 0.4 g and 5.9 ± 0.4 ml); however, a subtle difference was observed in eating patterns since TCES rats began to eat less biscuits than controls (TCES: 2.3 ± 0.2, C: 3.6 ± 0.4 biscuits, $P < 0.005$). These results indicate that long-term application of TCES did not alter rats behavior and if anything emerged it could trigger a better interaction of the animal with its environment.

Conclusion

Although neurobiological mechanisms of TCES are unknown, one hypothesis is that it interferes with endogenous opioid systems. This is in agreement with recent findings [8] since halothane anesthesia was potentiated by TCES and this effect was abolished by naloxone pretreatment. TCES with high frequency intermittent currents appears, both from animal and human studies, to be a safe procedure applicable for several days for the alleviation of the opiate abstinence syndrome.

Acknowledgements

Supported by the Bordeaux II University, CNRS, INSERM, Aquitaine Regional Council and Mission Interministérielle pour la Lutte contre la Toxicomanie (MILT).

References

1. Limoge A (ed.) (1975) An Introduction to Electroanesthesia. University Park Press, Baltimore, pp. 1–121.

2. Stanley TH, Cazalaa JA, Atinault A, Coeytaux R, Limoge A and Louville Y (1982) Anesth. Analg. 61: 863–866.
3. Stanley TH, Cazalaa JA and Limoge A (1982) Anesthesiology 57: 293–297.
4. Ellison F, Ellison W, Daulouède JP, Daubech JF, Pautrizel B, Bourgeois M and Tignol J (1987) Encéphale 13: 225–229.
5. Stinus L, Auriacombe M, Tignol J, Limoge A and Le Moal M (1990) Pain 42: 351–363.
6. Auriacombe M, Tignol J, Le Moal M and Stinus L (1990) Biol. Psychiatry 28: 650–656.
7. Malin DH, Murray JB, Crucian GP et al. (1988) Biol. Psychiatry 24: 886–890.
8. Mantz J, Azerad J, Limoge A and Desmonts JM (1991) (submitted).

© 1991 Elsevier Science Publishers B.V. All rights reserved.
Biological Psychiatry, Volume 2. G. Racagni et al., editors.

Involvement of condensation products in the process of alcohol addiction

Hans Rommelspacher and Lutz G. Schmidt

Departments of Neuropsychopharmacology and Psychiatry, Free University of Berlin, Ulmenallee 30, D-1000 Berlin 19, Germany

Introduction

Substances which are formed by condensation of pyruvate or aldehydes with catecholamines (tetrahydroisoquinolines, TIQ) and indolealkylamines (β-carbolines, BC) may induce voluntary ethanol intake in rats and monkeys [1–4]. They could be implicated in the development and maintenance of alcoholism and drug dependence. The original hypothesis concerning the role of condensation products was based on the well known fact that tetrahydropapaveroline (THP) – a complex TIQ – is the requisite intermediate in the biosynthesis of morphine in the opium poppy [5]. At the same time a simple TIQ (salsolinol) was detected in the adrenal gland [6] and only a few years later a simple BC in rat brain [7] (Fig. 1). In the following years numerous TIQs, BCs and even traces of 6-acetyl-morphine, morphine and codeine [8,9] were found in mammalian tissues.

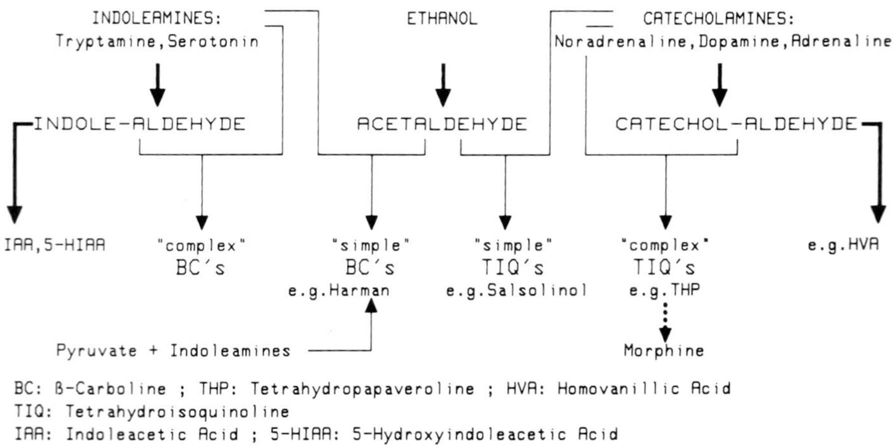

Fig. 1. Formation of β-carbolines and tetrahydroisoquinolines.

Biosynthesis in alcoholics and non-alcoholics

Several studies have shown that the biosynthesis of the simple TIQs and BCs occurs normally by condensation of pyruvate with the respective biogenic amines. Injection of [^{3}H]-tryptamine into the lateral ventricle of rat brain results in the formation of the carboxyl-substituted BC [10]. It is noteworthy that administration of the precursors of both components induces an increase of the level of the condensation products. For example, in rats, the administration of glucose, a precursor of pyruvate causes a significant increase of salsolinol levels in striatum [11]. Likewise, administration of L-dopa leads to an increased excretion of salsolinol in the urine [12,13]. Studies of the enantiomeric composition of (R) and (S) salsolinol in urine suggest that there is no alternative pathway for the formation of salsolinol in healthy subjects [14]. Chronic ingestion of alcoholic beverages however, changes the enantiomeric composition of salsolinol which could mean that there are metabolic alterations as well as that the acetaldehyde serves as precursor in pathological states (Dostert, Strolin Benedetti, Dordain, Vernay, unpublished). Such changes may explain the fact that chronic alcoholics have significantly elevated plasma levels of salsolinol sulfate as compared with non-alcoholics. No correlation can be noted between the concentration of plasma salsolinol sulfate and time of the last alcoholic drink among these subjects [15].

With respect to BCs elevated levels of norharman, a simple BC has been detected in the blood plasma of alcoholics as compared with non-alcoholics, whereas harman levels increased only after a load with ethanol [16,17]. In the subgroup of alcoholics with delirium or hallucinosis, a slight increase of norharman during detoxication could be detected while in alcoholics with vegetative withdrawal symptoms norharman levels dropped slightly over time.

Mechanisms of action

The vivo and in vitro effects of TIQs and BCs are the subject of several studies. Besides those mentioned above, it has been shown that harman binds with high affinity and specificity to the active site of monoamine oxidase subtype A. This suggests a modulatory function which might be disturbed in depressed states [18,19]. Norharman binds to specific binding sites in brain and other tissues of rat and to human platelets as well as erythrocytes. These binding sites are clearly distinct from benzodiazepine receptors and monoamine oxidase [20]. Provided the effects of norharman are mediated by these membrane sites, it would be invaluable in detecting changes in alcoholics.

Conclusions

In conclusion, animal experiments suggest a reinforcing role of TIQs and BCs in the voluntary intake of ethanol. The levels of salsolinol, norharman and possibly other condensation products are elevated in alcoholics. Whether the changes are specific markers of alcoholism, dependence or indicate psychic disturbances remain to be elucidated. The in vivo effects of the BCs seem to be mediated by either modulation of enzymatic activities and/or by activation of receptors.

Acknowledgement

The study was supported by the Deutsche Forschungsgemeinschaft (DFG-AZ: HE 916/7-1).

References

1. Myers RD and Melchior CL (1977) Pharmacol. Biochem. Behav. 7: 381–392.
2. Myers RD and Privette TH (1989) Brain Res. Bull. 22: 899–911.
3. Tuomisto L, Airaksinen MM, Peura P and Eriksson CIP (1982) Pharmacol. Biochem. Behav. 17: 831–836.
4. Rommelspacher H, Büchau C and Weiss J (1987) Pharmacol. Biochem. Behav. 26: 749–755.
5. Davis VE and Walsh MJ (1970) Science 167: 1005–1007.
6. Cohen G and Collins M (1970) Science 167: 1749–1751.
7. Honecker H and Rommelspacher H (1978) Arch. Pharmacol. 305: 135–141.
8. Weitz C, Lowney LI, Faull KF, Feistner G and Goldstein A (1988) Proc. Natl. Acad. Sci. U.S.A. 85: 5335–5338.
9. Collins MA (1988) Rec. Dev. Alcohol. 6: 387–403.
10. Susilo R and Rommelspacher H (1987) Arch. Pharmacol. 335: 70–76.
11. Sjöquist B (1985) Prog. Clin. Biol. Res. 183: 115–124.
12. Dostert P, Strolin Benedetti M, Dordain G and Vernay D (1989) J. Neural Transm. 1: 269–278.
13. Sandler M, Bonhaus Carter S, Hunter KR and Stern GM (1973) Nature 241: 439–443.
14. Dostert P, Strolin Benedetti M, Bellotti V, Allievi C and Dordain G (1990) J. Neural Transm. 81: 215–223.
15. Faraj BA, Camp VM, Davis DC, Lenton JD and Kutner M (1989) Alcohol. Clin. Exp. Res. 13: 155–163.
16. Rommelspacher H, Damm H, Lutter St, Schmidt LG, Otto M, Sachs-Ericsson N and Schmidt G (1990) Alcohol 7: 21–31.
17. Rommelspacher H, Schmidt L and May T (1991) Alcohol. Clin. Exp. Res. 15. (in press).
18. May T, Rommelspacher H and Pawlik M (1991) J. Neurochem. 56: 490–499.
19. May T, Pawlik M and Rommelspacher H (1991) J. Neurochem. 56: 500–508.
20. Pawlik M and Rommelspacher H (1988) Eur. J. Pharmacol. 147: 163–171.

© 1991 Elsevier Science Publishers B.V. All rights reserved.
Biological Psychiatry, Volume 2. G. Racagni et al., editors.

Treatment of compulsivity in alcohol abuse

Enrico Tempesta[1], Luigi Janiri[1] and Massimo Casacchia[2]
[1]Department of Psychiatry, Catholic University, Rome; and [2]Department of Psychiatry, University of Aquila, Italy

Introduction

Compulsivity in alcoholics may result from factors such as primary preference for ethanol, prolonged withdrawal symptoms, re-emerging psychiatric disorders, need for satiation, subclinical deterioration. Therefore clinical trials of drugs found to be effective in reducing ethanol intake in animals should take into account the whole range of possible causes of compulsivity. However, the rationale for treatments of this behavior rely upon animal models. Some drugs inhibiting, at least partly, the consumption of ethanol lead to postulate a role for the GABAergic transmission. Gamma-hydroxybutyric acid (GHB), a constituent of the mammalian brain with a GABA-like activity, has been found to inhibit voluntary ethanol consumption of ethanol-preferring rats [1]. Another GABAergic compound, calcium acetylhomotaurinate (AOTA-Ca), has been demonstrated to induce a dose-dependent suppression of the high alcohol intake of chronically-intoxicated rats [2]. All the other drugs which enhance the actions of GABA system, benzodiazepines included, are effective in the experimental ethanol withdrawal [3]. Calcium antagonists may also be useful in the management of the alcohol withdrawal syndrome, because dihydropyridine-sensitive Ca^{2+} channels in brain are involved in the CNS hyperexcitability associated with alcohol withdrawal states [4]. At present the possible role of anti-withdrawal agents in the treatment of ethanol-oriented compulsive behavior has not been elucidated.

Evidence exists that noradrenaline and GABA brain receptors are co-involved in the voluntary intake of ethanol by rats [5]. Thus noradrenergic drugs may be helpful in the control of compulsivity.

However, since several studies showed that 5-HT uptake inhibitors consistently attenuated ethanol intake in rats [6], these drugs have been the most employed in clinical trials. In fact, data obtained from selectively bred alcohol-preferring and -non-preferring lines of rodents have indicated the involvement of 5-HT in ethanol preference [7].

The present preliminary study was aimed at evaluating the effect of fluoxetine, a selective 5-HT uptake inhibitor, on ethanol-oriented compulsivity of detoxified alcoholics.

Materials and Methods

A double-blind placebo-controlled trial was performed on 30 detoxified alcoholics (M/F : 5, mean age: 42.6 ± 11.1 years, drinking history: 20.45 ± 12 years) who applied for treatment at the alcohol unit of a University General Hospital. Out of them 13 were given fluoxetine (20–40 mg/day p.o.) (F group) and 11 placebo (C group) for 2 months; the other 6 patients dropped out from the study within 15 days from the basal testing time (T_0). Only patients meeting the DSM III-R criteria for alcohol dependence and showing no alcohol withdrawal syndrome at T_0 were admitted to the protocol. Each patient during the early detoxification period underwent a T_0 protocol including: intake assessment, history and specialistic counseling. The following evaluation procedures were applied at T_0 and after 60 days of treatment (T_{60}): physical and neurological examination, routine blood and urine tests, DSM III-R psychiatric examination, Visual Analog Scale on craving for alcohol (VAS), Hamilton Depression Scale (HDS), Brief Psychiatric Rating Scale for Anxiety (BPRS-A), Alcohol Withdrawal Rating Scale (AWRS). Plasma ethanol, a drinking questionnaire on alcohol-related habits and behaviors, and a family interview were scheduled weekly from T_0 up to T_{60}. The T_0–T_{60} comparison for paired data was made by means of the Wilcoxon test.

Results

The T_0–T_{60} comparisons in F and C groups showed similar patterns of change as to depression (decreased HDS score, $P < 0.1$), anxiety (BPRS-A, N.S.) and withdrawal symptoms (decreased AWRS score, $P < 0.1$).

Difference was found between F and C groups regarding drinking behavior and alcohol-oriented compulsivity. In fact, fluoxetine-treated patients showed a more significant reduction ($P < 0.0025$) of the daily amount of alcohol consumed than control alcoholics ($P < 0.025$) (Fig. 1).

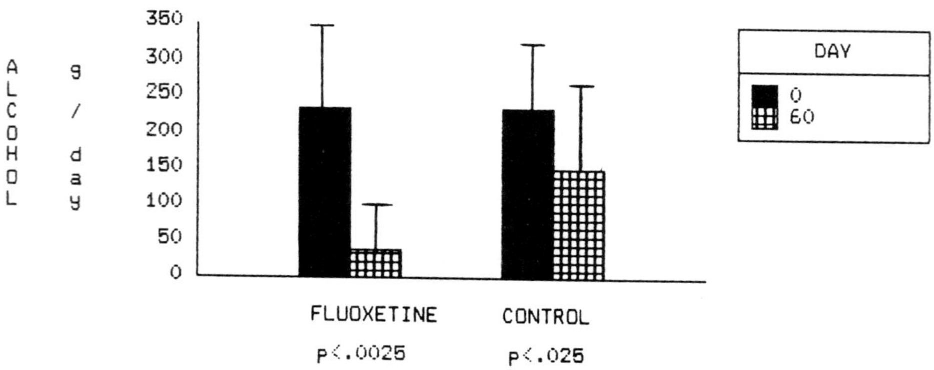

Fig. 1. Drinking behavior expressed as daily amount (g) of alcohol consumed. Fluoxetine and control patients were examined at baseline (T_0) and after 60 days (T_{60}) of treatment.

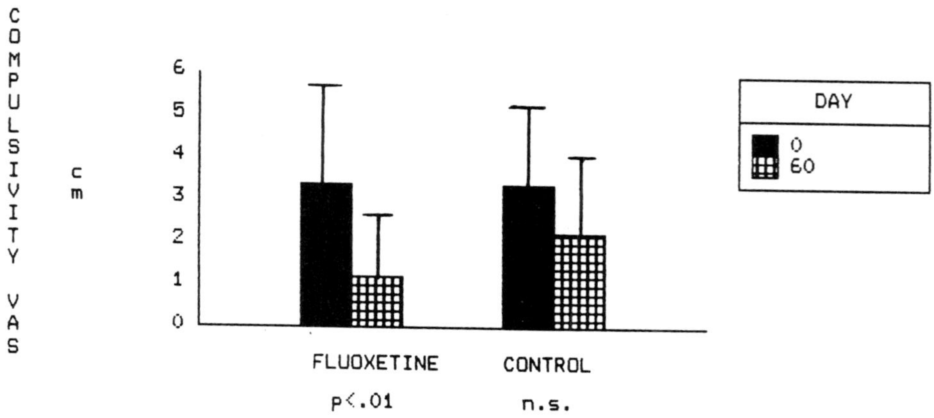

Fig. 2. Alcohol-oriented compulsivity expressed as length (cm) of the Visual Analog Scale on craving for alcohol (VAS). Fluoxetine and control patients were examined at baseline (T_0) and after 60 days (T_{60}) of treatment.

In addition, in fluoxetine-treated patients a significant reduction of the mean VAS length was observed, while in control patients the reduction was not significant (Fig. 2).

Discussion

Pharmacological studies have demonstrated that fluoxetine, a 5-HT uptake inhibitor, reduced the oral consumption or intragastric self-administration of alcohol in alcohol-preferring rats [7]. Clinical studies with fluoxetine have shown attenuation of ethanol intake in early stage problem drinkers [8]. In chronic alcoholics investigated for 4 weeks according to a fixed-interval drinking decision procedure, fluoxetine decreased both alcohol consumption and alcohol craving, but only during the first week [9].

Fluoxetine in the present study was proved to reduce the alcohol-oriented compulsive behavior by decreasing both consumption and craving. This occurred after 2 months of a low-dose treatment regimen. The effect was shown to be independent of antidepressant, anxiolytic or anti-withdrawal effects, as demonstrated by the lack of any correspondence between the results on alcohol-related parameters and those on mood and alcohol withdrawal. In addition to other 5-HT uptake inhibitors (e.g. zimelidine, citalopram) shown to be effective in attenuating ethanol intake also in clinical trials, only AOTA-Ca has been reported to prevent relapse in weaned alcoholics [10]. Comparative studies on drugs acting by various mechanisms (monoamines, GABA, calcium channels) involved in alcohol-related behaviors are needed in order to clarify the nature of compulsivity and to distinguish it from withdrawal and drinking habits.

References

1. Fadda F, Argiolas A, Melis MR, De Montis G and Gessa GL (1983) Life Sci. 32: 1471–1477.
2. Le Magnen J, Tran G, Durlach J and Martin C (1987) Alcohol 4: 97–102.
3. Frye GD, McCown TJ and Breese GR (1983) J. Pharmacol. Exp. Ther. 226: 720–725.
4. Littleton JM and Little HJ (1988) Am. N.Y. Acad. Sci. 513: 109–202.
5. Daoust M, Lhuintre JP, Saligant C, Moore N, Flipo JL and Boismare F (1987) Alcohol S1: 319–322.
6. Naranjo CA, Sellers EM and Lawrin MO (1986) J. Clin. Psychiatry 47: 16–22.
7. Mc Bride WJ, Murphy JM, Lumeng L and Ting-Kai Li (1989) Recent Dev. Alcohol 7: 187–209.
8. Naranjo CA and Sellers EM (1989) Recent Dev. Alcohol 7: 255–266.
9. Gorelick DA (1986) Alcohol Clin. Exp. Res. 10: 13.
10. Lhuintre JP, Daoust M, Moore N, Chretien P, Saligant C, Tran G, Boismare F and Hillemand B (1985) Lancet i: 1014–1016.

© 1991 Elsevier Science Publishers B.V. All rights reserved.
Biological Psychiatry, Volume 2. G. Racagni et al., editors.

The treatment of psychiatric disorders in substance abusers

I. Carta and M. Clerici
Department of Psychiatry, University of Milan, via Ippocrate 45, 20161 Milan, Italy

This paper investigates the psychopathological correlates of drug addiction. A number of studies published, in fact, have clearly reported that the "rate" of psychopathology among drug addicts attending the services is high (between 50 and 90%) and significantly predictive of treatment outcome.

Materials and Methods

The sample investigated consisted of 606 opioid drug addicts divided into two subgroups, according to the service they were referred to for their opioid addiction. The former (233 patients, 36.8%) started a residential program (milieu therapy and group psychotherapy). The latter (383 subjects, 63.2%) followed outpatient treatment offered by two services in the Milan area (individual psychotherapy and/or family therapy plus drug treatment). Statistical analysis revealed that the two subgroups did not differ regarding anamnestic and socio-environmental data. For the psychopathological assessment we followed the DSM III diagnostic criteria [36], while during the follow-up (only 323 of the 606 subjects were included in this study), data was collected by offering some different types of the same "ad hoc" questionnaire (54 areas investigated, 115 items) closely correlated to the preliminary anamnestic and socio-environmental survey.

Discussion

Of the 606 subjects referred to these services (Table 1), 108 (17.8%) did not show any psychiatric opioid-addiction associated pathology, while 160 (26.4%) received an Axis I diagnosis and 338 (55.8%) belonged to Axis II classification. The disorders most frequently detected in our sample, then, are Axis II personality disorders, which was the case for both subgroups. Contrary to Axis I and Axis II-related groups, the statistical analysis highlighted the high significance of distribution differences between inpatients and outpatients according to the presence or absence of a psychiatric diagnosis concomitant to the addictive behaviour. Regarding the relationship between diagnostic groups and treatment outcomes, topology apart, the statistical investigation does not show any significant long-term differences concerning Axis II, Axis I and "pure" addicted subjects (Table 2).

Table 1. Distribution of patients in the two treatment settings according to their DSM III psychopathological diagnosis

Diagnosis	Inpatients		Outpatients		Total	
	No.	%	No.	%	No.	%
"Pure addiction"	21	9.4	87	22.7	108	17.82
Drug addiction + Axis I	65	29.2	95	24.8	160	26.40
Drug addiction + Axis II	137	61.4	201	52.5	338	55.78
Total	223	36.79	383	63.21	606	100.0

X = 17.019; $P < 0.001$.

Axis-II diagnosed patients and outcome distribution according to treatment topology have been investigated in Table 3. Data ($P < 0.001$) show that patients responded well to residential treatment (58.1% vs. 41.9%) while, on the contrary, subjects referred to outpatient treatment had a worse response (18.0% vs. 82%). Table 4 presents data on the population referred to an outpatient service offering only psychotherapy, the subject of investigation being the correlation between treatment compliance and the 3 diagnostic groups (Axis I, Axis II and absence of diagnosis). As to the outpatient intervention, the choice to investigate the variable "compliance" to treatment instead of the "outcome" has a reason. We observed, in fact, that psychotherapy alone cannot approach substance withdrawal as the primary goal of its intervention, as the literature reports. A propaedeutic work should be rather developed for supporting the subject's ability to comply more steadily and completely with a more structured program, either a residential or a multiple outpatient approach (drug therapy + psychotherapy + family therapy). Data show that there is a general trend to drop out within the first 6 months of treatment; the statistical analysis, however, does not differentiate this last element in relation to the three different diagnostic groups investigated. As to the correlations between psychopathological profile and treatment outcome, literature reports have been only partially replicated in this study. Although not statistically signifi-

Table 2. Correlation between DSM III diagnosis and treatment outcomes

Diagnosis	Follow-up				Total	
	Positive		Negative			
	No.	%	No.	%	No.	%
Axis I	39	47.5	43	52.5	82	25.4
Axis II	88	47.3	98	52.7	186	57.5
"Pure addiction"	29	52.7	26	47.3	55	17.1
Total	156	48.3	167	51.7	323	100.0

X = 0.552; $P < 0.05$ N.S.

Table 3. Outcome distribution in different treatment settings for patients with personality disorders

Treatment	Follow-up				Total	
	Positive		Negative			
	No.	%	No.	%	No.	%
Residential	79	58.1	57	41.9	136	73.1
Outpatient	9	18.1	41	83.0	50	26.9
Total	88	47.3	98	52.7	186	100.0

X = 21.898; $P < 0.001$.

cant, our findings indicate, as a result, a trend towards a good outcome among subjects with a lesser degree of psychiatric severity. On the other hand, we noticed the absolute overlapping of Axis I and Axis II values, which ronfutes the assumption that the increased degree of psychopathological severity is inversely proportional to the decreased number of good prognoses. Of particular interest were, on the contrary, the correlations between Axis II diagnostic profiles, treatment topology and its outcome. Our study compared two psychotherapic interventions with either an outpatient or a residential approach, which shows that the response to such treatment differs completely according to the possibilities of offering socio-environmental and psychological management. The psychotherapy delivered in a residential setting, in fact, improves remarkably with equal diagnoses, the chances to succeed in comparison to simple outpatient psychotherapy, either coupled or not with drug treatment.

In conclusion, we warmly support the suitability of applying a clinical therapeutic approach to residential treatments for psychotic drug addicts in "ad hoc" therapeutic communities. The access to such structures, in our opinion, should be carried out differently from intake of "tout court" psychotic subjects because of the additional burden of the substance abuse-related disorder. Its cover-up function, in fact, requires a preliminary outpatient stage during which, – possibly on a one-by-

Table 4. Correlation between diagnosis and compliance to outpatient treatment

Diagnosis	Compliance				Total	
	<6 months		>6 months			
	No.	%	No.	%	No.	%
Axis I	15	60.0	10	40.0	25	16.9
Axis II	56	62.9	33	37.1	89	60.1
"Pure addiction"	24	70.5	10	29.5	34	23.0
Total	95	64.1	53	35.9	148	100.0

X = 0.001; $P < 0.05$ N.S.

one basis – the use of various therapeutic techniques in an integrated project should be planned (drug treatment, individual or group psychotherapy, family therapy and so on).

References

1. Clerici M et al. (1989) Soc. Psychiatr. Pschiatr. Epidemol. 24: 219–226.
2. Clerici M et al. (1986) Psychol. Méd. 18(8): 1237–1242.
3. Khantzian EJ et al. (1985) DSM III Psychiatric diagnosis of narcotic addicts: recent findings. Arch. Gen. Psychiatry, Vol. 42, Nov.
4. McLellan AT et al. (1984) Am. J. Drug Alcohol Abuse 10(1): 77–95.
5. Rounseville BJ et al. (1986) Prognostic significance of psychopathology in treated opiade addicts. A 25-year follow-up study. Arch. Gen. Psychiatry, Vol. 43, Aug.

© 1991 Elsevier Science Publishers B.V. All rights reserved.
Biological Psychiatry, Volume 2. G. Racagni et al., editors.

Naltrexone maintenance programs in opioid addiction

Luis San

Sección de Toxicomanías, Hospital del Mar, Universidad Autónoma de Barcelona, Paseo Marítimo 25-29, 08003 Barcelona, Spain

Introduction

Naltrexone, a potent oral opioid antagonist, has recently been marketed in some countries as an adjunctive chemotherapeutic agent in the management of opioid-dependent patients. It antagonizes heroin effects, produces no dysphoria or euphoria and does not cause tolerance or physical dependence [1]. In blind and non-blind dose-ranging and efficacy studies, oral naltrexone was administered in daily doses of 20 to 200 mg. Overall, complete blockade or attenuation of opioid effects after an intravenous heroin challenge was produced by naltrexone. Naltrexone administration produced a reduction in craving and heroin use. Controlled and non-comparative studies have shown that naltrexone reduces heroin self-administration and opioid craving in detoxified addicts. The use of naltrexone has been assessed in several clinical trials in heroin addicts, patients on methadone maintenance and patients in drug-free programs. Only a few of these trials, however, were controlled and the number of patients included in most of them was small. Studies combining naltrexone with counselling, supportive and psychotherapy or multiple family therapy appear to improve retention times and overall treatment success rates. In double-blind trials, the efficacy of naltrexone was compared with that of cyclazocine or placebo in heroin addicts, detoxified addicts, patients on methadone maintenance and ex-addicts [2].

An unequivocally beneficial effect of naltrexone on rates of recidivism has not been established and thus further studies in selected patient groups combining naltrexone with "high intervention therapy" are required to reaffirm existing clinical evidence of the usefulness of this drug. For this reason we present a study double-blind, controlled clinical trial, naltrexone and placebo were compared in 50 heroin addicts treated on an outpatient basis after inpatient detoxification and naltrexone induction [3].

Patients and Methods

Fifty patients of both sexes who fulfilled DSM III-R [4] criteria for opiate (heroin) dependence were included in the study.

Inpatient program

All patients completed detoxification with clonidine at decreasing dose while hospitalized for 14 days, according to a previously reported schedule [5]. Prior to the first naltrexone dose, naloxone challenge was conducted. On day 1 of naltrexone induction, patients received a single dose of 12.5 mg orally; on day 2, 25 mg; and on day 3, 50 mg. Patients were then discharged.

Outpatient program

From the date of discharge, patients attended the clinic daily to receive a dose of 50 mg up to the end of the first week of treatment with naltrexone (days 4 to 7). From week 2 to week 4, patients attended the clinic three times a week for 100 mg on Monday, 100 mg on Wednesday and 150 mg on Friday of naltrexone on successive visits for a total of 1-month's treatment.

From the second month on, patients were randomly allocated to treatment with naltrexone or placebo. Treatment was administered in a double-blind fashion. Patients underwent pharmacologic treatment for a total of 6 months (6 months of active principle for the naltrexone group and 1 month of active drug plus 5 months of placebo for patients in the placebo group). During the whole of this period, 3 times a week patients had urine screen for opiate, cocaine, cannabinoids and treatment compliance. After a period of drug treatment, outpatient clinical control was continued for a further 6 months. During this period, patients attended schedule visits, when a medical team provided supportive psychotherapy, nursing staff recorded the presence of side-effects, and drug-screening urines were collected. One week prior to naltrexone induction and during weeks 8 and 16 of treatment, biochemical profile and liver function tests were carried out.

Evaluation of efficacy

In order to assess the overall efficacy of treatment, the following four criteria were considered: degree of treatment acceptance, percentage of relapse in heroin consumption, presence of side-effects; and overall retention on naltrexone.

Statistical analysis

The Student's *t*-test was applied for comparisons of means of continuous quantitative variables. The normal approximation was used for comparison of proportions. The levels of statistical significance was established at 5%. Analyses were carried out with SPSS [6].

Results

A total of 55 eligible patients were asked to enter the study and all of them agreed. Five patients, however, were lately excluded: one because of imprisonment and four because of hepatic dysfunction on baseline laboratory tests before naltrexone induction. The study sample consisted of 50 patients. After inpatient detoxification, naloxone challenge was negative in all patients and naltrexone induction was immediately initiated. After the first month of naltrexone maintenance, 28 patients were randomly allocated to the naltrexone group and 22 to the placebo group. Patients in both groups were comparable in terms of baseline data.

Therapeutic success was achieved in 4 of the 28 naltrexone-treated patients and in 8 of the 22 placebo-treated patients. This clinically relevant difference was not statistically significant probably because of the small number of patients included in each category, which gave rise to a β error of 65%. A large number of subjects would have probably shown a statistical difference in favour of placebo-treated patients.

No patient had to discontinue treatment because of liver function impairment or intolerable side-effects. The main reason for dropout (5 patients in the naltrexone group and 2 patients in the placebo group) was the impossibility of attending the schedule treatment because of occupation or moving to geographically distant places. The main reason for therapeutic failure (19 patients in the naltrexone group and 12 patients in the placebo group) was the unjustified lack of attendance to scheduled visits.

The mean duration of drug treatment was 3.7 ± 2.0 months with an average of 8.1 ± 5.3 visits. Patients in the placebo group continued treatment for a longer period and generally attended a large number of visits than patients in the naltrexone group. These differences, however, were neither statistically nor clinically significant.

In the naltrexone group, a decrease in the number of consumers of different drugs was shown except in the case of alcohol intake and benzodiazepines which were mostly prescribed. Six months after completion of pharmacologic treatment, figures were similar and significant differences between both groups were not found. In the naltrexone group, 12.8% and 52.4% were positive for opiates and cannabinoids, whereas in the placebo group 20.3% were positive for cocaine. Drug compliance was 94.4% in patients on naltrexone and 82.2% in those on placebo.

Overall retention rate at 6 months was 27.9% (12/43 patients, dropouts were excluded). Differences between retention rates in the naltrexone group (17.4%) (4/23 patients) and placebo group (40%) (8/20 patients) were not statistically significant. Six months after completion of treatment (1 year after naltrexone induction), the percentage of drug-free patients was 32% in the naltrexone group and 36% in the placebo group. Nevertheless, 13 (46.4%) patients in the naltrexone group and 6 (27.2%) in the placebo group fulfilled criteria for opiate dependence. One patient in the naltrexone group also presented cocaine dependence, and two others alcohol dependence. Two patients in the naltrexone group died during the first-year study period (overdose and suicide).

Discussion

The overall results were similar in both groups. There was even a higher percentage of therapeutic success and a lower number of failures and dropout observed among patients receiving placebo. It would seem that the administration of naltrexone had no advantages over the administration of placebo, although it should be remembered that most patients believed that they were receiving naltrexone. Differences with respect to the number of visits between naltrexone and placebo groups were not observed. An improvement in drug consumption patterns was also noticed in patients of both groups which would be probably related to enrollment in an opioid-free support program. In the present study, 28 (56%) patients (16 naltrexone-treated patients and 12 placebo-treated patients) used opioids.

The tolerance of pharmacological treatment from the second month on was similar in both groups as most side-effects occurring in the placebo group manifested during the first month of treatment during which the patients were receiving naltrexone. Results of laboratory tests were similar in both groups. Anti-HIV antibodies were found in 58% of patients included in the study. All patients consumed heroin by intravenous route and treatment did not have any impact on injecting behaviour.

Results of the drug-screening urines showed a higher percentage of opiate- and cannabinoid-positive urines in naltrexone group patients and a higher percentage of cocaine-positive urines in placebo group patients. The number of habitual consumers of cannabis was higher in the naltrexone group before and during treatment. The proper compliance with treatment guaranteed the elimination of bias induced by incorrect drug intake.

The only differences observed occurred in the retention rates that were always higher in the placebo group. Six months after completion of treatment, however, these differences had practically disappeared and never reached statistical significance. The relatively high retention rate in the placebo group (36% vs. 32% in the naltrexone group) one year after naltrexone induction is similar to that obtained in a previous multicenter study in our country [7].

On the whole, the efficacy of naltrexone was not superior to that of placebo as there were no differences in acceptance of treatment, retention rates, opiate and other drug consumption, or side-effects during the study period. Although statistical power is limited by the small number of patients, from a clinical standpoint, the results obtained were considered relevant.

Acknowledgement

This work was supported by a grant from CITRAN (Centro para la Investigación, Tratamiento y Rehabilitación de Adictos a Narcóticos).

References

1. Resnick R, Volavka J, Freedman AM and Thomas M (1974) Am. J. Psychiatry 131: 646–650.
2. Gonzalez JP and Brogden RN (1988) Drugs 35: 192–213.
3. San L, Pomarol G, Peri JM, Ollé JM and Camí J (1991) Br. J. Addict. (in press).
4. American Psychiatric Association. Diagnosis and Statistical Manual of Mental Disorders, Third Edition Revised (1987) American Psychiatric Association, Washington.
5. San L, Camí J, Peri JM, Mata R and Porta M (1990) Br. J. Addict. 85: 141–147.
6. SPSSx (1986) Users Guide 2nd Edn. McGraw-Hill, New York.
7. García-Alonso F, Gutiérrez M, San L et al. and the Spanish Study Group on Drug Addiction (1989) Drug Alcohol. Depend. 23: 117–121.

© 1991 Elsevier Science Publishers B.V. All rights reserved.
Biological Psychiatry, Volume 2. G. Racagni et al., editors.

Prevention, education and drug therapy in cocaine abuse and dependence

Mark S. Gold
Fair Oaks Hospital, Delray Beach, Florida; and Summit, New Jersey, U.S.A.

Recently, several national surveys have shown that the drug abuse problem in America – once thought to be so rampant that it would defy any efforts to control it – has dramatically declined in response to a broad-based antidrug effort. In 1985 the National Household Survey found that the number of current users of any illicit drug was 23 million (12.1%); in 1988 this number decreased to 14.5 million users (7.3%); in 1990 the number of current users fell to 13 million (6.4%). Among cocaine users, the decline was even more vivid: from 5.8 million current cocaine users to 2.9 million 1988 to 1.6 million in 1990 – a 72% decrease since 1985.

This overall decline in drug use reflects a similar decline in drug use by adolescents. Previously, many experts considered that an antidrug message would be poorly received by a young audience. However, the National Institute on Drug Abuse (NIDA) Surveys of High School Seniors clearly indicate that the majority of adolescents have been positively affected by the antidrug message. For example, in 1985 nearly 30% of the high school seniors admitted to using at least one illegal drug within the past month; by 1990 this number had dropped to just over 17%. A similar drop occurred among seniors who had admitted to using cocaine at least once within their lifetime: 17.3% in 1985 compared to 9.4% in 1990.

The most effective treatment: Education and prevention

The declining number of drug users occurred mainly because of a remarkable change in the American attitude towards drugs in general and cocaine in particular. The publicized deaths of sport celebrities Len Bias and Don Rodgers from cocaine toxicity, combined with the increased suffering of numerous cocaine addicts, the emergence of the new and highly addicting form of cocaine called crack, and the frightening violence of cocaine dealers helped to coalesce the anti-drug movement and emphasize the importance of their message. Government policies combined with educational efforts in our schools and workplaces (often augmented by employee treatment programs and urine screens for drugs) have supported this antidrug movement. In addition, the Partnership for a Drug-Free America used some of the best advertizing and marketing minds in this country to produce a series of powerful and highly visible commercials aimed at reducing the number of first-time drug users by de-mystifying and de-glamorizing drugs.

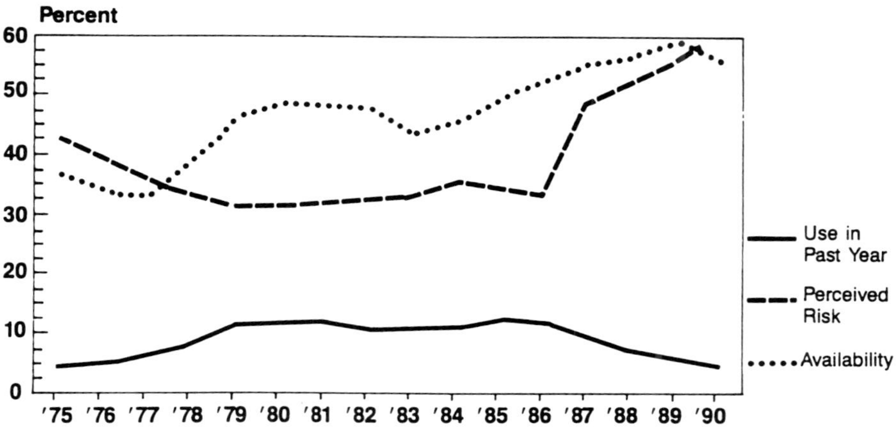

Fig. 1. Trends in cocaine availability. Perceived risk, and use in past year for high school seniors.

The success of this antidrug movement chronicled above has been matched by changes in attitudes towards drugs. In 1985 only 74% of our high school seniors disapproved of adults using cocaine; by 1990, 91.5% disapproved of any cocaine use by adults. In 1978, only 35% of the seniors believed that smoking marijuana posed a great risk; by 1990, this number had soared to 77%. Figure 1 shows that drug use declines when the perceived risk of drug use increases – even when the availability of the drug increases! Clearly, this educational effort has prevented experimental and occasional cocaine use and significantly reduced the number of drug users.

While the overall number of users has declined, the addicts who use drugs on a nearly continuous basis remain a formidable problem. In fact, over the last five years the number of continuous users appears to have increased from 246,000 to 662,000 (some experts, including Senator Joseph Biden, place this number at 2.4 million). Specific education and treatment approaches must be devised and directed at this segment. Similarly, the medical treatment of cocaine addiction must remain a priority.

The pharmacological treatment of cocaine addiction

Currently, the most promising pharmacological treatments for cocaine addiction have been based upon the fact that cocaine depletes levels of the neurotransmitter, dopamine. Cocaine achieves this effect by first stimulating brain cells to secrete dopamine and then by blocking its reabsorption. Without sufficient levels of dopamine, the addict experiences intense symptoms of withdrawal when attempting to stop using cocaine. Bromocriptine medication helps to restore dopamine levels and was previously used in the treatment of Parkinson's disease and amenorrhea-galactorrhea, has been administered successfully by this author and others in the treatment of cocaine withdrawal. By relieving the effects of cocaine withdrawal, bromocriptine has helped numerous cocaine addicts to remain in treatment.

Other medications have also been administered in the treatment of cocaine withdrawal. Some researchers have reported success with the antidepressant desipramine, although Marian Fischman's data at the NIDA Research Center showed only a slight beneficial effect with desipramine while reporting an increased risk of cardiotoxicity, irritability and anger among patients. A dopamine-acting antidepressant, such as buproprion, may ultimately prove to be more effective than desipramine.

Unlike heroin, there is no medical treatment for cocaine overdose or toxicity. In the future, research efforts at identifying cocaine's receptor in the brain may lead to a medication that blocks the acute effects of cocaine and thereby greatly improves our treatment for cocaine overdose and toxicity.

Even with more effective pharmacological treatments for cocaine withdrawal, overdose and toxicity, the most effective treatment will always be prevention through education.

© 1991 Elsevier Science Publishers B.V. All rights reserved.
Biological Psychiatry, Volume 2. G. Racagni et al., editors.

CNS stimulant abuse: Long-lasting symptoms of amphetamine psychosis

Tsukasa Koyama, Akira Muraki, Makoto Nakayama, Junji Ichikawa and Itaru Yamashita

Department of Psychiatry and Neurology, Hokkaido University School of Medicine, Sapporo, Japan

Introduction

Amphetamine abuse is one of the most important problems of substance abuse in Japan. It has long been believed that amphetamine-induced psychosis disappears within a few days or weeks after drug discontinuation and leaves no residual symptoms. However, several long-term follow-up studies in Japan have indicated that the psychic and somatic symptoms induced by methamphetamine abuse may remain in a considerable proportion of patients for not days or months but many years after the overt psychosis has disappeared.

Clinical studies

Connell [1] published a book "Amphetamine Psychosis" in 1958 and described such symptoms as delusions of reference and persecution, and mostly auditory hallucinations of the same nature which are observed in clear consciousness. He stressed that these symptoms disappear about a week after the drug has been withdrawn. On the other hand, many Japanese psychiatrists who had treated many more patients for much longer periods of time had different opinions. Tatetsu et al. [2] published a book on amphetamine abuse in 1956, before Connell, unfortunately in Japanese, in which they described that 17 out of 74 methamphetamine addicts, who had been kept in mental hospitals or in prison, suffered from various symptoms including long-lasting hallucinations and delusions, and personality changes and somatic complaints even 1–6.5 years after the drug discontinuation. At least 12 reports on methamphetamine psychosis in Japan since 1956 support the existence of a long-lasting psychotic state after drug discontinuation of more than 6 months in 7% of 177 cases [3], more than 7 years in 26% of 23 cases [4], more than 8 years in 82% of 114 cases [5].

These residual symptoms include hallucinations and delusions of reference and persecution, usually fluctuating or continuous and often intensified by emotional stress and personality changes exemplified by timid, fearful or often explosive behaviors and such somatic complaints as night-sweat, flushing, insomnia, or headache indicating the existence of autonomic dysfunctions. Differential diagnosis from schizophrenia and pre-existing personality deviation is certainly a matter of great importance and requires a careful scrutinization. It was repeatedly confirmed, however, that they had never shown the symptoms mentioned above before the use of methamphetamine. Some of them appeared autistic because they tended to avoid people on account of delusional ideas. However, in most instances, they were emotionally vivid, communicative to others and not blunted in any sense. All reports cited above contend that these manifestations can be distinguished from schizophrenia and other conditions by careful and long-term observations.

Laboratory studies

The clinical experiences cited above suggest that some neurochemical changes, actually take place in the brain of amphetamine users. Recently, we have been investigating this topic by using radio-receptor binding assay, in vivo microdialysis techniques, etc. Male Wistar-King rats received methamphetamine treatment according to the repeated escalating dose schedule (2.5, 5, 7.5, 10 mg/kg, s.c., $\times$ 2, every other day for a week). The afflux of dopamine was examined in the striatal perfusates from animals pretreated with methamphetamine using in vivo microdialysis. The degree to which dopamine afflux increased following a challenge of methamphetamine was significantly greater in the methamphetamine-treated animals than controls. There was no change in B_{max} of D_1 and D_2 receptors by the methamphetamine-pretreatment. Therefore as a possible explanation for the enhanced dopamine release mechanism, it was speculated that the repeated exposure to abnormally high concentrations of dopamine produced by repeated methamphetamine treatment could change the presynapic regulation mechanism as follows. First, low doses of apomorphine (25–50 μg/kg), decreased striatal dopamine afflux below the predrug basal level in controls, but such decrease was not observed in the methamphetamine-pretreated rats. This finding indicates that prolonged treatment with methamphetamine can induce the subsensitivity of presynaptic dopamine autoreceptor. Next, we examined the DOPA accumulation in the rat striatum for 30 min after NSD 1015, an aromatic 1-amino acid decarboxylase inhibitor. The results indicated a significantly greater accumulation of DOPA in methamphetamine-pretreated rats than in controls. This shows that the long-term methamphetamine treatment increased the activity of tyrosine hydroxylase, which is the rate-limiting enzyme of the dopamine synthesis. Lastly, we examined the dopamine uptake activity using [^{3}H]-GBR 12935 which binds selectively at the reuptake sites of presynaptic cell membrane. The results demonstrated the significant decrease of B_{max} in methamphetamine-pretreated rats 1 week, or even 1 month after the drug discontinuation. [^{3}H]-DA uptake was also found significantly decreased in methamphetamine-pretreated rats.

The above results indicate a lasting change in presynaptic cell membrane, including the 3 mechanisms regulating the release of dopamine. These disturbances may work together and produce the long-lasting increase of dopamine content in the synaptic space. We also found that the coadministration of MK-801 with methamphetamine prevented the occurrence of the neurochemical changes mentioned above. This finding suggest the possible involvement of excitatory amino acids in dopaminergic neuronal disturbances and the possible strategy by MK-801 treatment for preventing amphetamine psychosis.

Both clinical and laboratory findings correspond to each other in that the effects of amphetamine abuse may often produce long-lasting changes in the central nervous system function after the drug has been discontinued.

References

1. Connell PH (1958) Amphetamine Psychosis. Oxford University Press, London.
2. Tatetsu M, Goto A and Fujiwara T (1956) Amphetamine Abuse. Igaku-shoin, Tokyo.
3. Morita S, Ishido M and Miyagishi T (1962) Psychiatr. Neurol. Jpn. 64: 373.
4. Goto T (1960) Psychiatr. Neurol. Jpn. 62: 163–173.
5. Teraoka A (1967) Psychiatr. Neurol. Jpn. 69: 597–619.

© 1991 Elsevier Science Publishers B.V. All rights reserved.
Biological Psychiatry, Volume 2. G. Racagni et al., editors.

Behavioural changes produced by prenatal and early postnatal treatment with neuroleptics

Vinçenzo Cuomo, Raffaele Cagiano, Maria A. de Salvia, Corrado Lacomba, Michele Mazzoccoli and Giuseppe Renna
Institute of Pharmacology, University of Bari, Piazza G. Cesare, I-70124 Bari, Italy

Introduction

The particular period of administration of neuroleptic drugs plays a critical role in producing neurobehavioural changes in rats. Developmental exposure to various neuroleptics can lead to short-and/or long-term neurobehavioural alterations that are not obtained by treating adult animals [1].

Moreover, the timing of developmental administration of some neuroleptic agents seems to be crucial for the induction of selective neurobehavioural changes in rats. In fact, prenatal exposure to haloperidol results in response profiles that are opposite to those produced by early postnatal administration of this neuroleptic (see [2]). For example, a comparative evaluation of the responsiveness to drug challenges used to assess the functional state of the central dopaminergic system has shown that apomorphine-induced stereotyped behaviour was decreased in rats exposed prenatally to haloperidol [3], whereas a behavioural supersensitivity to this dopamine receptor agonist was found in animals treated with haloperidol during neonatal life [4]. Since we have recently found that prenatal treatment with haloperidol markedly affected the ultrasonic vocalizations of male rats during mating activity [5], it was of interest to compare these changes with those produced by postnatal neuroleptic administration.

Ultrasonic calls emitted by adult males during sexual behaviour seem to be a sensitive indicator of subtle changes in sexual motivation [6].

Materials and Methods

Haloperidol (0.5 mg/kg) was administered to male pups (Wistar rats) from post-natal day 1–20. At 90 days of age, male rats were tested for sexual behaviour. Ultrasonic vocalizations were recorded according to the technique described by Cagiano et al. [5].

No differences in mortality or weight gain were observed in rats treated with haloperidol with respect to controls.

Results and Discussion

Early postnatal treatment with haloperidol did not significantly affect any parameter of sexual behaviour in 90-day old males.

Moreover, the latency of emission of the first precopulatory 50 kHz call was not influenced by haloperidol treatment. Conversely, one-way ANOVA has shown that the period of the 22 kHz call emission was shorter in haloperidol-treated animals than in controls ($F = 5.21$, $df = 1/16$, $P < 0.05$).

The comparison of the results of the present study with those of our previous experiments further confirms that the behavioural consequences of developmental treatments with a dopamine receptor blocking agent (haloperidol) depend critically upon the period of its administration.

In fact, the latency of emission of the first precopulatory 50 kHz ultrasound as well as the duration of the period of the 22 kHz post-ejaculatory call emission were significantly increased by prenatal exposure to haloperidol [5,7]. Since we have shown that a subtype of dopamine receptors (dopamine D_2 receptors) is involved in the emission of 22 kHz post-ejaculatory calls [8], the selective alterations in this ultrasonic parameter produced by prenatal and neonatal treatment with haloperidol could be due to interactions with the development of D_2 receptors.

Neurochemical studies have shown a decrease in ^{3}H-spiroperidol binding in the striatum of rats born to mothers treated with haloperidol during gestation [9]. More recently, Scalzo et al. [10] reported that prenatal haloperidol treatment reduced both D_1 and D_2 receptor binding in some regions of the rat forebrain dopamine system. Conversely, an increased ^{3}H-spiroperidol binding was found in the striatum of rats treated with haloperidol during early postnatal life [9].

In conclusion, our data confirms that ultrasonic calling during sexual behaviour is an accurate tool for detecting subtle changes in sexual motivation induced by treatments with psychotropic drugs during development.

Moreover, these results further extend the profile of the behavioural syndrome produced by developmental administration of a dopamine receptor blocking agent such as haloperidol.

Acknowledgement

This research was supported by Grant No. 90/4956 from the MURST (40%).

References

1. Cuomo V (1987) Trends Pharmacol. Sci. 8: 346–350.
2. Spear LP and Scalzo FM (1986) In: Edward PR and Vorhees CV (eds.) Handbook of Behavioural Teratology. Plenum Press, New York, pp. 173–184.

3. Cuomo V , Cagiano R, Renna G, Serinelli A, Brunello N and Racagni G (1985) Neurobehav. Toxicol. Teratol. 7: 489–492.
4. Cuomo V, Cagiano R, Coen E, Mocchetti I, Cattabeni F and Racagni G (1981) Psychopharmacology 74: 166–169.
5. Cagiano R, Barfield RJ, White NR, Pleim ET, Weinstein M and Cuomo V (1988) Eur. J. Pharmacol. 157: 45–50.
6. Barfield RJ, Auerbach P, Geyer LA and McIntosh TK (1979) Am. Zool. 19: 469–476.
7. Cuomo V, Cagiano R, De Salvia MA, Lacomba C and Renna G (1990) Clin. Neuropharmacol. 13 (Suppl. 2): 549–550.
8. Cagiano R, Barfield RJ, White NR, Pleim ET and Cuomo V (1989) Pharmacol. Biochem. Behav. 34: 53–58.
9. Rosengarten H and Friedhoff AJ (1979) Science 203: 1133–1135.
10. Scalzo FM, Holson RR, Gough BJ and Ali SF (1989) Pharmacol. Biochem. Behav. 34: 721–725.

© 1991 Elsevier Science Publishers B.V. All rights reserved.
Biological Psychiatry, Volume 2. G. Racagni et al., editors.

Recent developments in the study of the effects of prenatal exposure to anxiolytics on neurobehavioral development

Giorgio Bignami, Enrico Alleva and Giovanni Laviola
Laboratory of Organ and System Pathophysiology, Instituto Superiore di Sanita, Viale Regina Elena 299, 1-00161 Rome, Italy

Introduction

Substantial progress has been made over the past decade in the assessment of subtle effects on human neurobehavioral development of low-level early exposure to some centrally acting agents (for ethanol and lead, see e.g. [1] and [2], respectively).

As concerns anxiolytics, particularly benzodiazepines (BDZ), recent analyses [3] have questioned previous reports which indicated an absence or scarcity of teratogenic potential [4]. Moreover, there appears to be a lack of longitudinal neuropsychological studies aimed at assessing long-term neurobehavioral effects of a subtle kind in subjects whose mothers took anxiolytics during pregnancy. In fact, some animal data, although far from dramatic, are suggestive of a production of selective changes in some regulatory mechanisms which serve important behavioral functions (see e.g. [3,5–8]).

Selective effects of early benzodiazepine exposure in animals

Changes in activity and in responses to drug challenges

After prenatal BDZ treatment, mouse and rat pups often tend to be hypoactive, particularly around the end of the second postnatal week, that is, at a critical time of rapid transition between the neonatal low level of activity and the appearance of an adult-like profile [9–11].

Moreover, there can be changes in some responses to drug challenges used to assess the functional state of various regulatory systems. For example, our work with mice exposed in utero to oxazepam (15 mg/kg given p.o. twice daily to the mothers on days 12–16 of pregnancy) has shown 2 main types of effect. The first is a reduced hyperactivity response to a monoaminergic stimulant (amphetamine) at 2 weeks of age [10]. The second is a blockade of 2 hyperactivity responses which normally appear around the end of the fourth postnatal week, namely: 1) of morphine hyperactivity [12]; and 2) of the rebound hyperactivity which follows the depression produced by a GABA-α agonist (muscimol) at 28 days, but not at earlier or later ages [13] (for normative data see [14]).

These effects are apparently quite selective. In fact, the former effect is not accompanied by a comparable change in the hyperactivity response to a muscarinic blocker (scopolamine) 1 week later [10], while the latter occurs in the absence of changes in response to pain stimulation and in morphine and muscimol analgesia at any of the ages tested (14–28 days) [12,13].

Changes in social responses

Lactating mice from litters exposed to oxazepam in utero show a marked enhancement of aggressive responses towards male intruders in the nest area. This effect is quite striking, given the high baseline of maternal aggression in control animals. The same females do not show changes in the proaggressive effect of BDZ treatment given shortly before testing [15].

Changes in learning and memory

Substantial long-term deficits in higher associative and cognitive capacities are apparently excluded by the variable results reported for different test situations. Learning and performance changes, when present, are likely due to modifications in other functions which may, or may not, reflect themselves on the acquisition or performance of a particular task. For example, after prenatal exposure to oxazepam young adult mice show a deficit in active avoidance but not in passive avoidance [7,10]. Such a profile is suggestive of a mild impairment in motor response initiation, rather than a more widespread impairment of higher functions.

Discussion

Several of the effects so far summarized are best ascribed to the changes in CNS monoaminergic functions after early BDZ exposure which have been documented by neurochemical studies (e.g. the alterations in norepinephrine-containing neurons in the hypothalamus [16]). This might also apply to the abatement of morphine hyperactivity and perhaps to that of rebound hyperactivity after muscimol depression. In fact, a monoaminergic link is involved in at least the first of these responses; moreover, widespread modifications of opioid and GABAergic behavioral functions are apparently ruled out by the normal development of pain reactivity and of morphine and muscimol analgesia. However, it remains to be ascertained whether the modified activity responses to morphine and muscimol are due at least in part to the changes produced by prenatal BDZ exposure in BDZ and GABA mechanisms, such as the reduced BDZ receptor density [17] and the increased activity of glutamic acid decarboxylase (GAD) [18].

In any event, the animal data point to a need for a more thorough assessment of the long-term effects of early anxiolytic exposure on human neurobehavioral development.

Acknowledgements

This research was supported as part of the Sub-Project on Behavioral Pathophysiology (Project on Non-Infectious Pathology) of the Instituto Superiore di Sanita, and by Grant No. 89.04677.CT04 from the Consiglio Nazionale delle Ricerche.

References

1. Barr HM, Streissguth AP, Darby BL and Sampson PD (1990) Dev. Psychol. 26: 339–348.
2. Needleman HL and Gatsonis CA (1990) J. Am. Med. Assoc. 263: 673–678.
3. Laegreid L, Olegard R, Conradi N, Hagberg G, Wahlstrom J and Abrahamsson L (1990) Dev. Med. Child. Neurol. 32: 432–441.
4. Elia J, Kats IR and Simpson GM (1987) Psychopharmacol. Bull. 23: 531–586.
5. Grimm VE (1984) In: Yanai J (ed.) Neurobehavioral Teratology. Elsevier, Amsterdam, pp. 153–162.
6. Tucker JC (1985) Neurosci. Biobehav. Rev. 9: 101–111.
7. Alleva E and Bignami G (1986) Neurotoxicology 7: 309–323.
8. Kellogg CK (1988) Progr. Brain Res. 73: 207–228.
9. Shore CO, Vorhees CV, Bornschein RL and Stemmer K (1983) Neurobehav. Toxicol. Teratol. 5: 565–570.
10. Alleva E, Laviola G, Tirelli E and Bignami G (1985) Psychopharmacology 87: 434–441.
11. Cagiano R, De Salvia MA, Persichella M, Renna G, Tattoli M and Cuomo V (1990) Eur. J. Pharmacol. 177: 67–74.
12. Alleva E, Laviola G and Bignami G (1987) Psychopharmacology 92: 438–440.
13. Laviola G and Alleva E (1988) Psychopharmacology 96: S34.
14. Laviola G and Alleva E (1990) Psychopharmacology 102: 41–48.
15. Laviola G, De Acetis L, Bignami G and Alleva E (1991) Neurotoxicol. Teratol. 13: 75–81.
16. Simmons RD, Kellogg CK and Miller RE (1984) Brain Res. 293: 73–83.
17. Livezey GT, Radulovacki M, Isaac L and Marczynski TJ (1985) Brain Res. 334: 361–365.
18. Rothe T, Middleton-Price H and Bigl V (1988) Neuropharmacology 27: 661–667.

© 1991 Elsevier Science Publishers B.V. All rights reserved.
Biological Psychiatry, Volume 2. G. Racagni et al., editors.

Effects of paternal alcohol consumption and withdrawal on offspring growth, development and behavior in rats

E.L. Abel

Department of Obstetrics and Gynecology and Fetal Alcohol Research Center, Wayne State University, 275 E. Hancock, Detroit, MI 48237, U.S.A.

Introduction

Although alcoholism and various disorders related to it may be genetically related [1], the chaotic family environment associated with parental alcoholism undoubtedly contributes to many problems occurring in children of alcoholics [2].

We reported that paternal alcohol consumption does not affect birth weight or postpartum weights of animal offspring but does affect their behavior [3–6]. Since these kinds of study were undertaken as "animal models" of potential effects that may occur in offspring of humans that consume alcohol, we undertook the present study to determine if the presence during pregnancy, of a male consuming alcohol and his presence during lactation when he was undergoing withdrawal, would affect the growth or development of offspring or their behavior apart from any impact of alcohol on the genome.

Method

Male Long-Evans rats, 75 days old, were given free access to liquid alcohol diet (6.6% v/v). A control group was pair-fed to these animals with an isocaloric liquid diet. Males were mated to females after six months of diet consumption. During mating, no food or water were present. Pregnant females were subdivided with one group undergoing male "cohabitation" with its mate while the other remained as a "single parent". Males in the "cohabitation" condition were placed for 8 h per day during the gestation period into the pregnant female's cage with the females they had impregnated. During this time, neither the male nor female had access to food or water. In the "single parent" condition, females were not disturbed except that food and water were also removed from their cages. After the daily cohabitation period, males in this condition were placed back into their own cages. Liquid alcohol diets and food and water were then returned to the males and females respectively. On the day of parturition, after females had delivered, males in the "cohabitation" condition were taken off their liquid diet and were placed into the cage with their female mate and remained there throughout the nursing period until weaning at day 21. Thus there were 4 subgroups: alcohol or no alcohol combined with cohabitation or no cohabitation. At birth, offspring were counted and weighed, culled to 6–8 pups and returned to the dams. Offspring were weighed again at 21 and 56 days of age.

At 70 days of age, 1 male and female per group were tested for their immobility response in the forced swimming test.

Results

Paternal alcohol consumption did not significantly affect fertility, litter size, birth weight or weights at 21 or 56 days, or postnatal mortality. Paternal presence (cohabitation/withdrawal) resulted in a significant reduction in body weights of offspring ($F = 8.95$, $df = 1{,}32$, $P < 0.01$) but this was age-related ($F = 5.31$, $df = 2{,}64$, $P < 0.01$). Analysis of each age separately indicated that paternal presence was a significant factor only at 21 and 56 days of age ($F = 5.84, 6.92$, $df = 1{,}32$, $P < 0.05$, respectively). If paternal withdrawal had significantly affected postnatal growth, the paternal alcohol × paternal condition interaction would have been significant, but was not.

Paternal alcohol consumption was associated with a significant decrease in immobility ($F = 18.0$, $df = 1{,}48$, $P < 0.001$). Paternal presence was not significantly associated with differences in immobility. These two factors did not interact significantly.

Discussion

As observed in this study and in our previous studies, paternal alcohol consumption did not significantly affect body weights of offspring but did affect their behavior in the forced swimming test. These observations in offspring support our previous studies and those reported by others [3–7]. Other studies from our laboratory have also found that these offspring ambulate less and groom less in stress-producing situations such as novel environments [3–6]. These animals are also less capable of resisting infection [8,9]. Thus far, the influence of the father's presence during pregnancy or postpartum has received little experimental attention in animal studies, although such influences have been reported [10–13]. The present study indicated that paternal presence can affect offspring growth. Surprisingly, no studies have been conducted with animals to examine the role of withdrawal from alcohol on offspring, although control over alcohol consumption/withdrawal is practical in animals. Although males were withdrawn from alcohol during the cohabitation period, this did not appear to have any effect on the offspring. These results suggest that behavior of animal offspring is affected by paternal alcohol consumption but is not affected by paternal presence or withdrawal from alcohol.

Acknowledgement

Supported by NIAAA Grant P50-AA07606.

References

1. Cloninger CR, Bohman M and Sigvardson S (1981) Arch. Gen. Psychiatry 28: 861–868.
2. Reich W, Earls F and Powell J (1988) Br. J. Addict. 83: 831–839.
3. Abel EL (1991) Alcohol 8: 21–23.
4. Abel EL (1989b) Growth Dev. Aging 53: 195–199.
5. Abel EL and Bilitzke PJ (1990) Psychopharmacology 100: 159–164.
6. Abel EL and Tan SE (1988) Neurotoxicol. Teratol. 10: 187–192.
7. Leichter J (1986) Growth 50: 228–233.
8. Berk RS, Montgomery IN, Hazlett LD and Abel EL (1989) Alcohol. Clin. Exp. Res. 13: 795–798.
9. Hazlett LD, Barrett RP, Berk RS and Abel EL (1989) Ophthal. Res. 21: 381–387.
10. Csermely D (1980) Boll. Zool. 47: 139–142.
11. Mugford RA and Nowell NW (1972) J. Comp. Physiol. Psychol. 79: 30–36.
12. Smith ML and Simmel EC (1977) Dev. Psychobiol. 10: 151–159.
13. Wynne-Edwards KE and Lisk RD (1989) Physiol. Behav. 45: 465–469.

© 1991 Elsevier Science Publishers B.V. All rights reserved.
Biological Psychiatry, Volume 2. G. Racagni et al., editors.

Drug abuse and pregnancy: AIDS and the new methadone dilemma

Donald E. Hutchings and Ann C. Zmitrovich

New York State Psychiatric Institute, Department of Developmental Psychobiology and Columbia University, Department of Psychiatry, New York, NY 10032, U.S.A.

Introduction

The use of methadone to treat pregnant heroin abusers in the early 1970s afforded the unusual circumstance whereby preclinical drug-safety testing in animals would be carried out concurrently with human clinical observations of reproductive and developmental toxicity. Because of the enormous difficulties of studying an addict population with its attendant confounding problems of polydrug abuse, heavy cigarette smoking, medical complications, poor diet, inadequate prenatal care and the like, it was hoped that the animal research could afford more interpretable data. Unfortunately, because of methodological problems in the development of animal models and particularly the lack of dosing techniques that induced physical dependence, a coherent body of basic research data with clear and convincing relevance to the clinical problem never emerged [1,2].

By the early to mid-1980s, results of five longitudinal studies of children exposed to methadone prenatally were published. Of the 4-year-old children tested, no consistent cognitive impairments or deficits in I.Q. were found [3]. Although many of the children appeared to be at risk for developing problems of fine motor coordination and attention deficit disorder, it remained unclear whether or not these effects were related to methadone or the poor quality environments in which they were raised. By and large, these clinical and epidemiological studies demonstrated the relative safety of methadone and there seemed little need for further research.

AIDS and the new methadone dilemma

It is well established that daily methadone maintenance doses in the range of 60–100 mg/day are significantly more successful and of optimal rehabilitative benefit for the prevention of relapse to illicit drug use than daily doses of 30–50 mg/day or lower [see major review, 4]. With low dose regimens, clients begin to complain of withdrawal and are at risk of relapse to excessive alcohol and illicit drug use. A major problem that has evolved in methadone clinics since the late 1970s has been the shift to low maintenance doses in the range of 20–40 mg [5]. Adding to the problem, if clients become pregnant, it had been strongly recommended that clinics reduce the daily maintenance dose even further in order to minimize symptoms of neonatal abstinence. Currently, pregnant clients are routinely maintained at 20–30 mg per day or even lower. A serious health crisis created by these low maintenance doses is that pregnant clients, particularly during the increased weight gain in the third trimester, begin to experience withdrawal as their low dose results in progressively lower plasma levels. Thus, these individuals are at high risk for abusing other illicit substances, including i.v. heroin, alcohol, and cocaine.

One result is that with the advent of AIDS during the 1980s, there has been a substantial increase in HIV infection among clients in methadone maintenance programs [6]. Moreover, this problem is growing by alarming proportions and one that could, in part, be remedied by a higher dosing regimen [7]. The sad paradox of the low dose treatment policy is that pregnant clients are administered suboptimal doses of methadone in order to avoid a manageable risk – i.e., the neonatal abstinence syndrome. By "manageable", we mean a risk that is readily treated with appropriate pharmacotherapy. The tragedy is that by virtue of the likelihood that these mothers will resort to i.v. heroin use, they expose themselves as well as their fetuses to the unacceptable risk of HIV infection [8]. And by "unacceptable", we mean the high risk of AIDS and eventually death for both the mother and child. Current figures from NIDA indicate that 75% of HIV-infected babies are born to i.v. drug abusers or their sexual partners [9]. We emphasize that the pharmacological aspect of treatment is only one of many components of a comprehensive drug treatment program but it does play a major role in the retention of clients in these programs [7] so that they remain available for the psychosocial intervention that is so vital for successful rehabilitation.

Thus, we encourage a renewed effort to study methadone both in humans and animals to aid in providing sound scientific data with respect to the developmental effects of methadone and contribute to a more appropriate and rationally based dosing regimen. This research should be part of a comprehensive approach that re-evaluates methadone treatment for the pregnant client with a view toward the development of an effective public health policy that vigorously addresses the current AIDS epidemic. The testing techniques utilized in developing animal models could prove useful in the discovery of alternative treatment pharmacotherapies both for mothers as well as their infants. We believe this research effort will be a useful preclinical adjunct to the NIDA Medications Development Program, including the development of screening protocols to study potential treatment compounds under consideration for other drug dependencies.

Acknowledgement

Preparation of this manuscript was supported by Grant No. DA03544 from the National Institute on Drug Abuse.

References

1. Hutchings DE (1990) Neuorotoxicol. Teratol. 12: 183–189.
2. Hutchings DE and Fifer WP (1986) In: Riley E and Vorhees C (eds.) Handbook of Behavioral Teratology. Plenum Press, New York, pp. 141–172.
3. Kaltenbach K and Finnegan LP (1984) Neurobehav. Toxicol. Teratol. 6: 271–275.
4. Hargreaves WA (1983) In: Cooper JR et al. (eds.) Research on the Treatment of Narcotic Addiction: State of the Art. DHHS Pub. No. (ADM)83-1281. NIDA, Rockville, MD., pp. 19–79.
5. Schuster CR (1989) NIDA Notes, National Institute on Drug Abuse, Spring/Summer.
6. Selwyn PA, Hartel D, Wasserman W and Drucker E (1989) Am. J. Public Health 79: 1358–1362.
7. Ball GC, Lange WRR, Meyers CP and Friedman SR (1988) J. Health Soc. Behav. 29: 214–226.
8. Pyun KH, Ochs HD, Dufford MTW and Wedgewood RJ (1987) N. Engl. J. Med. 317: 611–614.
9. NIDA Notes (1990) National Institute on Drug Abuse, p. 15.

© 1991 Elsevier Science Publishers B.V. All rights reserved.
Biological Psychiatry, Volume 2. G. Racagni et al., editors.

Stimulant use during pregnancy: Effects on offspring and potential mechanisms

Lawrence D. Middaugh

Department of Psychiatry and Behavioral Sciences, Medical University of South Carolina, 171 Ashley Avenue, Charleston, SC 29425-0742, U.S.A.

Human reports

Reports of babies born with cocaine or amphetamine in their urine or delivered by pregnant women with positive urine samples or histories of stimulant use suggest that a substantial number of fetuses are exposed to stimulants. For example, one report indicated that 25% of the babies delivered at Washington D.C. General Hospital were by mothers who admitted regular use of illegal drugs with "crack" being the most frequent choice [1]. In the San Diego area between January 1987 and July 1988, of 103 infants delivered with positive urine for *illicit* drugs, 41% were exposed to cocaine and 30% to methamphetamine [2]. A study on 1226 mothers from a general prenatal clinic at Boston City Hospital indicated that cocaine was used by 18% of pregnant women based on history and 9% based on positive urine [3]. This study indicates that the method of establishing drug use profoundly influences the "users" number, since 24% of the women with positive urine for cocaine denied ever having used the drug.

Several reports suggest that cocaine or methamphetamine use during pregnancy can be detrimental to the fetus or neonate. Reports from the Prenatal Care Clinic at Northwestern University Medical School's Perinatal Addiction Project indicated that *cocaine* was detrimental to the pregnancy, the fetus, or the neonate [4]. A statistically well designed population-based study on a large sample from Boston City Hospital [3] confirmed that infants of women with urine samples containing cocaine were growth-retarded compared to a drug-free control group, but did not confirm some of the effects of maternal cocaine noted in earlier reports. Reports from the Stockholm Sweden area indicated that *methamphetamine* use was also detrimental to the pregnancy and offspring [5]. Reports from the University of California San Diego Medical Center Hospital [2] indicated that cocaine (n = 13) or methamphetamine (n = 28) use influenced perinatal measures compared to drug-free controls, but that the perinatal measures for the 2 stimulant groups did not differ from each other.

The picture emerging from these reports is that cocaine and amphetamine use during pregnancy can elevate the blood pressure of the mother and promote premature labor associated with *abruptio placentae*. Increased spontaneous abortion and decreased gravidity have been reported but are not consistent findings.

The most extreme reported effects of these stimulants on the offspring include an increased frequency of malformations, increased SIDS and increased cerebral hemorrhagic infarction. These extreme effects were not observed in the study on a larger population-based sample with more rigorous statistical control; hence this might be due to other factors common to a lower socioeconomic drug using population or to the interaction of the stimulant drug with these factors. Intrauterine growth retardation and neurobehavioral abnormalities have been rather consistent findings in both clinical and population-based studies. Most of the perinatal effects of maternal cocaine appear to be eliminated by confining drug use to the first trimester; however, neurobehavioral abnormalities were observed in infants and children of women who presumably did not use drugs after this time.

The conclusions drawn from these reports should be considered tentative. Since cocaine use during pregnancy is correlated with a number of potential risk factors for perinatal outcome, the reported perinatal effects might be due to its interaction with other drugs (e.g. ethanol, nicotine), with nutritional deficiency, with infection, etc. Several studies in progress based on samples from a more affluent population and with more statistical control of socioeconomic status, polydrug use and nutritional factors are not finding the detrimental effects noted in the earlier studies. Thus, the reported effects of maternal cocaine and amphetamine may be due to their interaction with other drugs, with undernutrition, or a number of other variables. In the absence of sufficient sample sizes and controls for these factors, assignment of the above-noted effects to stimulant drugs per second must remain tentative.

Animal models and mechanisms

Animal models to investigate the effects of maternal exposure to stimulant drugs have extended human studies by demonstrating that these drugs can effect the fetus and offspring in the absence of other drugs and/or caloric deficiency, and that some of the effects can extend to the adult. Most of the maternal amphetamine studies were conducted several years ago and have been previously reviewed [5]. Maternal cocaine studies are more recent and are generally better designed than the earlier studies on amphetamines. The current literature is too limited to draw firm conclusions; however, it suggests that maternal exposure to either drug at very high doses can be teratogenic [7,6] and at lower doses can have long-term neurochemical and behavioral consequences for rodent offspring.

Reports on maternal amphetamine exposure indicate that the drug can improve active avoidance but impair passive-avoidance performance of adult offspring. This combination suggests the possibility of hyper-reactivity; and reports consistently indicate that amphetamine exposure throughout or during the last third of pregnancy increased motor activity of adult offspring. Neurochemical studies indicate that brains of newborns have reduced NE levels, suggesting that transplacentally it derived amphetamine can deplete monoamines of the fetus. Other reports indicate an increased synthesis and turnover of DA and NE, and a reduction in the number of adrenergic or dopaminergic receptors in adults prenatally exposed to amphetamines. These studies are provocative, but frequently have not been replicated or lack the controls necessary for ruling out the possible confounding effects of undernutrition and altered maternal care.

Reports on maternal cocaine exposure include both acute and chronic effects. The acute cocaine effects of cocaine on the fetus were examined in pregnant sheep infused with cocaine [9]. Cocaine produced hypertension in the fetus which was due to the drug's direct vasoconstrictive action on the fetal vasculature, or indirectly to hypoxia resulting from the drug's vasoconstrictive action on the uterine arteries. The cerebrovascular hemorrhagic infarction noted above for infants exposed to cocaine or methamphetamine in utero is consistent with this mode of drug action. However, it remains to be established that cocaine induced hypertension or hypoxia produces cerebrovascular hemorrhage in the sheep model or that the cerebrovascular effects are associated with any long-term functional changes.

The effects of more chronic cocaine exposure has been examined in rodents. Maternal cocaine at relative high doses (80–100 mg/kg) decreased gravidity and intrauterine growth, and increased perinatal mortality as noted above for humans [10]. Pair-fed controls were similarly effected, suggesting that these effects could be related to nutritional variables. These doses of cocaine also altered brainstem auditory evoked potentials of young offspring as noted for humans and caused hearing impairments extending into adulthood.

Additional studies indicate that lower doses of cocaine which had no effect on perinatal mortality or intrauterine growth can still produce a number of behavioral and neurochemical effects on the offspring. Young rats prenatally exposed to cocaine had learning and motor deficits [11]. In addition, they were more responsive to DA antagonists and less responsive to DA agonists and had increased D_2 receptor affinity, suggesting that DA systems were compromised. Other reports [12] indicated that adults rats exposed to cocaine during early development had an altered response to amphetamine, altered 2DG utilization in several DA brain areas and an altered number of D_1 receptors. The latter reports indicate that the DA involvement produced by cocaine extended to the fully mature adult and that the specific effect depended upon the sex of the animal and the particular stage of development during which exposure occurred.

In summary, in utero exposure to stimulant drugs can have adverse consequences for both the pregnancy and the offspring. Work using animal models suggests that many of the effects reported for humans might be mediated by nutritional variables. Several studies, however, suggest that in utero stimulant exposure can produce changes in behavior and neural systems which appear to be unrelated to nutritional factors and can be detected in the fully mature adult animal.

References

1. Taylor R (1989) J. NIH Res. 1: 29–32.
2. Dixon S (1989) West. J. Med. 150: 436–442.
3. Zuckerman B et al. (1989) N. Engl. J. Med. 320: 762–768.
4. Chasnoff I et al. (1989) Ann. N.Y. Acad. Sci. 562: 260–266.
5. Eriksson M et al. (1989) Acta Paediatr. Scand. 78: 944–949.
6. Middaugh L (1989) Ann. N.Y. Acad. Sci. 562: 308–318.
7. Fantel AG et al. (1982) Teratology 26: 17–19.
8. Vorhees CV et al. (1990) Neurotoxicol. Teratol. 12: 409.
9. Woods JR et al. (1989) Ann. N.Y. Acad. Sci. 562: 267–279.
10. Church MW et al. (1990) Neurotoxicol. Teratol. 12: 73–79.
11. Spear LP et al. (1989) Ann. N.Y. Acad. Sci. 562: 290–307.
12. Dow-Edwards DL (1989) Ann. N.Y. Acad. Sci. 562: 280–289.

Aging and dementia: Clinical and biological research

© 1991 Elsevier Science Publishers B.V. All rights reserved.
Biological Psychiatry, Volume 2. G. Racagni et al., editors.

Clinical characterization of HIV-1-associated dementia

Jose Catalan
Charing Cross and Westminster Medical School, Westminster Hospital, London SW1, U.K.

Introduction

Nervous system involvement is common in HIV-1 infection and a substantial proportion of individuals with advanced HIV-1 disease suffer acute and/or chronic organic brain syndromes [1]. Postmortem studies have confirmed the presence of central nervous system abnormalities in a majority of AIDS patients [2,3]. HIV-1 can be identified in CSF and neural tissues of infected individuals, which can be used to transmit infection in the laboratory [4]. CNS involvement in HIV-1 disease may be the result of processes secondary to immunodeficiency (opportunistic infections, tumours or other), or may happen in the absence of such processes, and so be attributed to the primary effects of HIV-1 [1]. It is this latter group of syndromes that has led to a good deal of research and clinical interest, focussing both on the organic brain syndromes developing in advanced HIV disease, and in the search for markers of organic brain impairment in early HIV-1 disease.

What's in a name?

Research in this field has been hampered by terminological and conceptual confusion. Many new terms have been introduced to describe what may or may not be similar clinical, neurophysiological, neuropsychological or neuropathological phenomena, making premature assumptions about aetiological mechanisms, syndrome clusters and prognosis. They include, amongst others, subacute encephalitis, HIV-1 encephalopathy, AIDS-dementia complex, HIV-1 associated organic brain disease, and HIV-1 associated neuropsychiatric disorders. This confusion has not helped care providers and patients to make sense of what is a complex issue. Efforts need to be made to unify terminological and conceptual usage.

HIV-1 associated neuropsychiatric disorders in early disease

HIV-1 disease is now regarded as a continuum, from the stage of infection to CDC group IV disease (AIDS) and so it could be argued that CNS involvement would also follow a progressive course, which might not necessarily parallel other clinical or laboratory manifestations. There has been much research into the identification of early markers of neuropsychiatric decline and while early work suggested that asymptomatic individuals had detectable neuropsychological impairment, the current consensus view is that clinically significant impairment is unlikely in individuals whose immune function remains inadequate [5,6]. There are many possible reasons for literature discrepancies, including the role of pre-existing confounding factors. Work continues in the field of experimental neuropsychological testing and other techniques.

HIV-associated dementia

Early work highlighted the complex manifestations of this syndrome [7] and there is consensus about its clinical picture, which is comparable to that found in other dementias, and is characterized by cognitive changes (memory and concentration problems, psychomotor slowing, planning and problem-solving impairment) and behavioural manifestations. Other syndromes including neuromuscular problems may also develop, although not invariably. Early presenting features may be less consistent and show a good deal of vulnerability in relation to course and prognosis, some individuals presenting a fairly stable course. The prognostic significance of early mild impairment remains uncertain. While there is usually agreement about the existence of a severe syndrome of dementia, insufficient attention has been paid until recently to the development of operationally defined and reliable classifications to measure severity of the disorder and to the relationship between clinical classification and neuropsychological testing. Similarly, the relationships between the clinical syndrome, neuropsychological performance and neuropathology is far from settled, so that emphasis on concepts such as "subcortical dementia" may be premature and delay adequate understanding. There is uncertainty about the epidemiology of HIV-1 associated dementia, reports suggesting a lower point prevalence than originally estimated [5]. It has been suggested that the use of anti-retroviral medication may have reduced its prevalence [6]. Differential diagnosis will require exclusion of opportunistic infections, neoplasms and other disorders likely to cause generalized impairment and detailed clinical, neurological, neuroradiological and other investigation will need to be performed [1].

Conclusion

Further work is needed in the development of clinically reliable classification systems, relating clinical to other data and establishing the prevalence of aprognosis of HIV-1 associated dementia. Treatment and practical implications for services and individuals with HIV-1 infection need clarification. The pathophysiological mechanisms remain speculative.

References

1. Rosenblum M, Levy R and Bredesen D (eds.) (1988) AIDS and the Nervous System. Raven Press, New York.
2. Snider W, Simpson D and Nielsen S (1983) Ann. Neurol. 14: 403–418.
3. De la Monte S, Ho D and Schooley R (1987) Neurology 37: 562–569.
4. Gadjusek D, Amyx H and Gibbs C (1985) Lancet i: 55–56.
5. Grant I, Atkinson J and Hesselink J (1987) Ann. Int. Med. 107: 828–836.
6. WHO (1990) Report of the Second Consultation on the Neuropsychiatric Aspects of HIV-2 Infection. Global Programme on AIDS, WHO, Geneva.
7. Portegies P, de Gans J and Lange JMA (1989) Br. Med. J. 299: 819–821.

© 1991 Elsevier Science Publishers B.V. All rights reserved.
Biological Psychiatry, Volume 2. G. Racagni et al., editors.

Neuropsychological and neuroimaging findings in HIV-related disease

Wilfred G. Van Gorp and Charles Hinkin
Department of Psychiatry and Biobehavioural Sciences, University of California, Los Angeles School of Medicine, 760 Westwood Plaza, Los Angeles, CA 90024, U.S.A.

Introduction

Several studies have reported significant neuropsychological dysfunction in a large proportion of symptomatic, HIV-infected individuals with a smaller subset actually meeting criteria for an HIV encephalopathy. Timed, psychomotor and memory tasks appear to be most affected in the earliest stages. Despite these descriptions of neuropsychological dysfunction in HIV-related disease, few studies have attempted to relate the overt cognitive dysfunction with functional neuroimaging techniques, or to study the degree to which depression might affect the neuropsychological test scores in this population. This paper will present new findings from our laboratory which address these questions.

Study I: Cerebral metabolic functioning in HIV-related disease

Positron emission tomography (PET) was coupled with neurological and neuropsychological evaluations to study regional cerebral activity and neurologic status in 2 subject groups: 17 patients with full blown AIDS and 14 seronegative controls were studied with PET using (F-18) 2-deoxy-2-fluoro-D-glucose (FDG) as a tracer in a resting state. Sixteen regions of interest (ROIs) were drawn for each subject by an operator blind to serostatus (AIDS/control) using ROI templates for each of the scanning levels. The bilateral ROIs defined in this study correspond to: a) the cerebellum; b) the brainstem; c) the basal ganglia; d) the thalamus; e) the frontal lobe; f) the parietal lobe; g) the occipital lobe; and h) the temporal lobe.

Regional hypermetabolism was found in the basal ganglia and thalamus for the AIDS group. To examine the *pattern* of cerebral metabolic function in AIDS, a stepwise discriminant function analysis was performed using relative metabolic values to predict group membership (AIDS/controls). At Step 0, the thalamus and basal ganglia were the only regions with an F-to-enter ratio greater than 4 (F values of 9.27 and 6.86, respectively), suggesting that these two regions best discriminate between groups. Following Step 1, however, only the basal ganglia retained sufficient discriminant power to enter the discriminant equation. After the jack-knifing procedure, the resultant discriminant equation correctly classified 70.6% of the AIDS subjects and 71.4% of the controls.

To determine the presence and severity of dementia, subjects were rated on the Sloan Kettering AIDS Dementia Complex Rating Scale (SKRS) by the study neurologist. Seven of the 17 AIDS subjects were rated as 0 (normal, n = 3) or 0.5 (equivocal, n = 4) and 10 were rated as either 1 (mild, n = 6) or 2 (moderate, n = 4). Stepwise multiple regression analyses revealed a significant relationship between temporal lobe metabolism and severity of dementia as measured by the Sloan Kettering Rating Scale (multiple r = −0.50).

These results suggest that the basal ganglia, thalamus and temporal lobes are differentially affected in AIDS.

Study II: Depressed mood and neuropsychological test performance in HIV-infected individuals

This study was conducted to determine whether different patterns of neuropsychological test performance would be present in depressed vs. non-depressed individuals infected by the human immunodeficiency virus (HIV-1). Subjects were 54 mostly symptomatic HIV-1 seropositive homosexual/bisexual males aged 20–60 years. A comprehensive neuropsychological test battery together with the Beck Depression Inventory (BDI) was administered to all subjects.

To determine the relationship between level of depression and neuropsychological performance, a stepwise multiple regression analysis was performed between the neuropsychological measures and the Beck Depression Inventory (BDI) for all subjects regardless of symptom status. This analysis revealed only 2 neuropsychological variables to be significantly associated with BDI scores: the first variable to enter the regression equation was the Grooved Pegboard Test, dominant hand (multiple r = 0.30; $P < 0.01$), a measure of motor speed, dexterity, and hand-eye coordination. The second variable to enter was Trial 6 of the Rey Auditory Verbal Learning Test (RAVLT) (multiple r = 0.41; $P < 0.01$), a task which measures immediate recall, concentration, and sensitivity to proactive interference.

We next dichotomized subjects into those who report a considerable degree of depressive symptomatology vs. those who deny symptoms of depression based upon their score on the BDI. In an effort to maximize the differences between the high and low BDI groups, we included *only* those scoring in the upper and lower thirds of the distribution of BDI scores. This resulted in a low-BDI group (n = 18) with a mean score of 6.3 (S.D. = 2.4) and a high-BDI group (n = 19) with a mean BDI score of 28.9 (S.D. = 6.9). The 2 groups did not differ on mean level of age, education, or CD4 count.

Despite dramatic differences in severity of self-endorsed depressive symptomatology evidenced by these 2 groups, the level of neuropsychological test performance between the 2 groups was remarkably similar. Significant differences were found only on the Grooved Pegboard Test. A trend towards significance was observed in Trial 6 of the RAVLT ($F(1,35) = 0.37$; $P = 0.07$). However, following

Bonferroni correction which resulted in an adjusted α of 0.002, neither of these differences remained significant.

These results suggest that the presence of clinically significant levels of depression in a non-elderly HIV-1 seropositive sample does not necessarily lead to significant neuropsychological dysfunction.

Acknowledgements

This research was supported by the Department of Veteran's Affairs Medical Research Service and by American Foundation for AIDS Research, Grant No. 000947.

© 1991 Elsevier Science Publishers B.V. All rights reserved.
Biological Psychiatry, Volume 2. G. Racagni et al., editors.

Neuropsychological deficits in HIV-infected patients: Relationship to depression

D. Naber, R. Riedel, C. Perro, U. Schick, T. Vieler and J. Binder
Department of Psychiatry, University of Munich, Nußbaumstr. 7, D-8000 Munich 2, Germany

Introduction

Marked neuropsychological deficits in AIDS-patients are well documented, but in asymptomatic HIV-positive subjects, data on incidence, severity and etiology are rather controversial. Several studies showed reduced performance of abstract thinking, learning, memory and information processing [1,2], but others did not reveal deficits [3–7]. An organic etiology is sometimes assumed, but other factors such as education, neuropsychiatric history, drug abuse, depression are often not fully considered [8].

Methods

Two-hundred and five HIV-positive subjects (age 33 ± 8 years) were investigated; 118 patients in early stages, either asymptomatic or with LAS [3–5], 87 were in late stages, ARC or AIDS [1,6,7]. Psychiatric exploration was performed according to the AMDP; depression (SDS), anxiety (STAI) and other mood states (POMS) were self-rated. Neuropsychological examination included "Vocabulary", "Similarities", "Digit-Symbol", "Color-Word-Interference", "Maze", "Benton", "Trail-Making" and "Auditory Verbal Learning". A control group of 115 HIV-negative subjects, matched for to sex, age, education and % of i.v. drug addicts underwent the same tests.

Results

Psychiatric exploration and self-rating revealed a clinically relevant depression in 27% (SDS > 48 pts) and symptoms of major depression (SDS > 55 pts) in 8%. Twenty-four percent suffered from marked anxiety (STAI > 54 pts). Compared to the HIV-negative controls, most tests showed a significant deficit in patient's functioning. Only "Vocabulary" and "Similarities" did not show any significant differences. Controls and patients in early stages differed only slightly, but significantly (Table 1). The relationships of neuropsychological functioning to

Table 1. Neuropsychological functioning of HIV-negative controls and of HIV-infected patients

		Normal (%)	Slight impairment (%)	Marked impairment (%)
HIV-negative	n = 115	81	17	2
HIV-positive [3–5]	n = 118	75	20	5
HIV-positive [1,6,7]	n = 87	57	26	17

psychopathological variables consisted of numerous highly significant correlations (Table 2).

A multiple regression analysis with criterion "neuropsychological total score" showed that severity of central neurological symptoms, CSF level of protein and AMDP depression explained 32% of the variance. Other variables (education, duration of heroin abuse, WR stage, SDS, STAI, CT, EEG, CSF cells, oligoclonal bands) did not increase variance explained.

A subgroup of 68 patients was re-examined after 6–9 months. The whole group did not show any change in psychopathological or neuropsychological variables. However, individually, test scores of 35% worsened significantly, while those of 19% improved. The change in neuropsychological performance correlated with the change in depression, measured by AMDP ($P < 0.005$) as well as by SDS ($P < 0.01$).

Discussion

These results indicate already in early stages of HIV-infection a discrete, but significant reduction in neuropsychological functioning. Moreover, its multifactorial etiology with a psychogenic and a somatogenic component is obvious. Comparing neuropsychological functioning of HIV-infected patients with HIV-negative subjects, one has to consider that one can easily control for age, education a.o., but not for the major difference between both groups: the affective state, the burden of a unique life-threatening illness with enormous social implications.

Table 2. Neuropsychological functioning, relationships to psychopathological variables

	Digit-Symbol	Color-Word-Interference	Auditory Verbal Learning	Trail-Making	Benton	Total Score
Depression (AMDP)	-0.13^{a}	-0.24^{d}	n.s.	-0.19^{b}	n.s.	-0.31^{f}
Depression (SDS)	-0.17^{a}	-0.27^{e}	-0.26^{e}	-0.28^{e}	n.s.	-0.26^{d}
Anxiety (STAI)	n.s.	-0.23^{c}	-0.19^{b}	-0.21^{c}	n.s.	-0.24^{d}
Depression (POMS)	-0.13^{a}	-0.21^{c}	-0.17^{a}	-0.25^{d}	n.s.	-0.20^{b}

n = 205; Pearson's correlation coefficient: $^{a}P < 0.05$; $^{b}P < 0.01$; $^{c}P < 0.005$; $^{d}P < 0.001$; $^{e}P < 0.0005$; $^{f}P < 0.0001$.

References

1. Naber D, Perro C, Schick U, Sadri I, Schmauss M, Fröschl M, Matuschke A, Goebel FD and Hippius H (1989) Nervenarzt 60: 80–85.
2. Silberstein CH, McKegney FP, O'Dowd MA, Selwyn PA, Schoenbaum E, Drucker E, Feiner C, Cox CP and Friedland G (1987) Int. J. Neurosci. 32: 669–676.
3. Clifford BG, Jacoby RG, Miller JP, Seyfried WR and Glicksman M (1990) AIDS 9: 767–774.
4. Egan VG, Crawford JR, Brettle RP and Goodwin GM (1990) AIDS 7: 651–656.
5. Goethe KE, Mitchell JE, Marshall DW, Brey RL, Cahill WT, Leger GD, Hoy LJ and Boswell RN (1989) Arch. Neurol. 46: 129–133.
6. Janssen RS, Saykin AJ, Cannon L, Campbell J, Pinsky PF, Hessol NA, O'Malley PM, Lifson AR, Doll LS, Rutherford GW and Kaplan JE (1989) Ann. Neurol. 26: 592–600.
7. McArthur JC, Cohen BA, Selnes OA, Kumar AJ, Cooper K, McArthur JH, Soucy G, Cornblath DR, Chmiel JS, Wang MC, Starkey DL, Ginzburg H, Ostrow DG, Johnson RT, Phair JP and Polk BF (1989) Ann. Neurol. 26: 601–611.
8. Wilkins JW, Robertson KR, van der Horst C, Robertson WT, Fryer JG and Hall CD (1990) J. Acq. Imm. Def. Syndr. 3: 938–942.

© 1991 Elsevier Science Publishers B.V. All rights reserved.
Biological Psychiatry, Volume 2. G. Racagni et al., editors.

Pathogenesis and biological markers of HIV-1 associated dementia

Rosemay Vazeux[1], Dominique Henin[2], Catherine Lacroix[2], Marc Tardieu[3] and Luc Montagnier[1]

[1]*Viral Oncology Unit and UA CNRS 04 1157, Pasteur Institute, Paris;* [2] *Neuropathology Department, Hopital Pitie-Salpetriere and Hôpital Bicêtre, Le Kremlin-Bicêtre; and* [3]*Pediatrics Neurology Department, Hôpital Bicêtre, Le Kremlin-Bicêtre, France*

Introduction

The human immunodeficiency virus (HIV) induces severe dementia in about 20% of adult AIDS patients. A severe HIV-related encephalopathy occurs in almost all children who are HIV-infected at birth and develop an early and severe immunosuppression. In all cases, the brain monocytes/macrophages and the microglial cells, which are the resident macrophages of the CNS, are the only cells that replicate HIV in the central nervous system (CNS). These cells play a central role in the pathogenesis of AIDS-related encephalopathy.

Adult HIV-related encephalitis

HIV is responsible for severe dementia in about 20% of adult AIDS patients. In the brain of these patients, the neuropathological examination reveals signs of subacute encephalitis with microglial nodules, perivascular infiltrates and astrocytosis. These lesions are associated with perivascular areas of demyelination and diffuse myelin pallor without necrosis. HIV can be demonstrated in these lesions either by the detection of multinucleated cells on formalin fixed tissues, of HIV antigens using immunological staining, of viral particles by electron microscopy, or by the detection of HIV RA or DNA using in situ hybridization. Typically, severe HIV encephalitis in adults is characterized by a multifocal and massive HIV CNS infection. Large numbers of HIV infected cells (either disseminated in the parenchyma or perivascular) can be detected in almost every tissue block studied. Infected cells predominate in basal ganglia, brain stem and white matter. Based on immunological identification, we and others reported the presence of HIV exclusively in the monocyte/macrophage/microglial cells [1–4].

The neurotropism of HIV is related to viral isolates which replicate preferentially in monocytes/macrophages in relation to other isolates which replicate mostly in $CD4^+$ T-lymphocytes. The development of HIV encephalopathy is also related to the appearance of immunosuppression, which is necessary to trigger viral dissemination in the CNS. It is likely that the association with other CNS opportunistic infections triggers HIV brain dissemination by a non-specific mechanism of macrophage recruitment and activation.

There is no direct infection of neurons during HIV CNS infection. Therefore, it is unclear how the virus induces neurological symptoms. There is currently no evidence for a neuronal disappearance and it is very likely that there is an unfavorable interaction between CNS cells and HIV-infected macrophages, either by release of toxic products or by suppression of normal microglial function [5,6].

HIV encephalopathy in children

About 35% of children born to HIV-infected mothers are HIV-infected. A third of HIV-infected children develop an early and severe immunosuppression, usually during the first year of life. A severe encephalopathy characterized by a loss of developmental milestones and severe intellectual deficiency [7] occurs almost exclusively and in the majority of children with severe immunosuppression. We have examined the brain of seven children infected at birth presenting with typical encephalopathy. Very surprisingly, using immunological staining and in situ hybridization we could detect few or no signs of HIV replication in the CNS of four of these patients, despite severe AIDS encephalopathy and typical neuropathological lesions (intra-parenchymal calcifications or gliosis and white matter pallor). Therefore, a severe HIV-related encephalopathy is not necessarily associated with viral replication in the CNS at the time of death. However, in these patients HIV DNA was detected by PCR in all CNS samples, while all controls were negative. Therefore, childhood encephalopathy could be related either to a latent brain infection similar to that induced by other lentiviruses, or to the sequelae of an acute or subacute HIV encephalitis, which would have occurred during the early stages of HIV infection. In this case, the very high incidence of encephalopathy in perinatally-infected children suggests that HIV infection of monocytes/macrophages/microgliae induces severe damage in the developing brain.

Conclusion

HIV infection of microglia is responsible for a severe encephalopathy in adults and children with AIDS. In all cases, HIV replication in the monocytes/macrophages/ microglial cells plays a central role in the development of neurological lesions. Our work in children with AIDS demonstrates that an active replication is not necessary to maintain neurological symptoms and that HIV might induce sequelae after a transient replication. Interestingly, some cases of dementia have been described in adults with AIDS, with few or no signs of HIV replication and no signs of inflammation in the CNS [8,9]. Since it seems possible to improve the patients' neurological condition with antiviral drugs, it is essential to understand the pathogenesis of this neurological disease and the kinetics of HIV replication in brain tissue of children and adults with AIDS encephalopathy in order to determine the best therapeutic strategy.

References

1. Koenig S, Gendelman H, Orenstein J et al. (1986) Science 233: 1089–1093.
2. Vazeux R, Brousse N, Jarry A et al. (1987) Am. J. Pathol. 126: 403–410.
3. Price RW, Brew B, Sidtis J et al. (1988) Science 239: 586–592.
4. Budka H, Costanzi G, Cristina S et al. (1987) Acta Neuropathol. (Berlin) 185–198.
5. Dreyer EB, Kaiser PK, Offerman JT et al. (1990) Science 248: 364–367.
6. Giulian D, Vaca K and Noonan CA (1990) Science 250: 1593–1596.
7. Epstein L, Sharer L and Goudsmit (1988) Ann. Neurol. 23 (Suppl.): S19–S23.
8. Navia B, Cho E, Petito CK et al. (1986) Ann. Neurol. 19: 525–535.
9. McArthur J, Becker P, Parisi J et al. (1989) Ann. Neurol. 26: 681–684.

© 1991 Elsevier Science Publishers B.V. All rights reserved.
Biological Psychiatry, Volume 2. G. Racagni et al., editors.

HIV-associated cognitive impairment: Response to zidovudine

Frederick A. Schmitt, Joseph W. Bigley and AZT Collaborative Group
Department of Neurology, University of Kentucky Medical Center, Lexington, KY 40526-0084, U.S.A.

Introduction

Neurologic and neuropsychological symptoms are well known complications of advanced HIV infection [1–4]. This presentation reviews data from a randomized double-blind treatment study of AIDS and ARC patients [5–7]. Based on the neuropsychological data we were able to estimate the prevalence of cognitive impairment in these patients. In addition, we applied impairment criteria to divide our patients into impaired and non-impaired groups and assessed for the effects of ZDV (zidovudine, azidothymidine, AZT) treatment on functions in "impaired" patients with early AIDS and ARC.

Estimates of cognitive impairment

As reported in several papers [5–7], 281 patients with AIDS or advanced AIDS-related complex were enrolled in a double-blind placebo-controlled trial designed to evaluate the efficacy and safety of orally administered ZDV. This study showed that ZDV therapy reduced both mortality and the frequency and severity of opportunistic infections [5]. Even though ZDV was associated with hematologic toxicity [6], patients showed cognitive improvement as a result of treatment [7].

In reviewing the abnormalities seen on the cognitive and motor tests, Schmitt et al. [7], used a criterion similar to that reported by Grant et al. [8], where patients were considered to be "probably impaired" if they had two screening tests which fell at least 1 S.D. below a normative mean. Additionally, patients were considered to be "probably impaired" if they showed a deficit of 2 S.D. or more on any individual test. Based on this criterion, 41% of the patients with ARC and 55% of AIDS patients were classified as impaired. On the screening exam alone, 76% of the early AIDS and ARC patients were impaired. If the second, or baseline exam was evaluated without reference to screening, 54% of the AIDS and ARC patients showed impairment. When stability of impairment was evaluated by including patients who showed *impairment on both screening and baseline exams*, the frequency of impairment dropped to 49%. Patients demonstrating impairment for only one assessment were excluded from our analyses.

An alternative criterion of impairment from the Multi-Center AIDS Cohort Study (MACS) [9] bases impairment on two cognitive tests that are at least two standard deviations below a normative mean. Applying this criterion to our patients at screening, results in a 31% impairment rate and 22% meet this criterion at baseline; while imposing the MACS criterion for *both screening and baseline* evaluations reduces the rate of impairment to 12%.

Treatment results

The data reported in the original treatment outcome paper [6] were analyzed for change in all patients enrolled in the study. We subsequently used our impairment criterion (at least two tests at 1 S.D. below a standardized mean and/or 1 or more tests at 2 S.D. below a standardized mean for both baseline and screening exams) to investigate treatment effects in impaired patients. This analysis investigated patients similar to the Yarchoan et al. [9] patients with ADC who obtained beneficial effects of ZDV treatment on CNS functions.

The results of treatment for the impaired patients are summarized in Table 1. The data for weeks 8 and 16 show consistent treatment effects across the cognitive measures. Once again, patients receiving ZDV improved while patients in the placebo arm showed stability or decline in their scores.

Discussion

These data demonstrate the efficacy of ZDV in the treatment of HIV-associated cognitive impairment. Treatment effects of ZDV appear to be robust in patients who meet criteria for cognitive impairment while patients on placebo show

Table 1. Mean change from baseline in impaired[a] patients taking ZDV or placebo (PCB) at weeks 8 and 16

	Week 8		Week 16	
Measure : Units	ZDV	PCB	ZDV	PCB
Attention				
Targets correct	33.04 (51)	− 2.04[c] (57)	38.38 (34)	− 3.93[c] (29)
Memory				
Words stored	8.23 (48)	0.50[c] (56)	9.38 (34)	2.33 (30)
Words recalled	9.88 (48)	0.77[c] (56)	12.12 (34)	1.80[c] (30)
Cognition				
Symbol digit (total)	3.53 (51)	− 2.02[c] (56)	5.41 (34)	3.73[c] (30)
Trails A time	− 3.35 (51)	0.30 (56)	− 4.82 (34)	2.37[b] (30)
Trails B time	−29.04 (50)	−11.69 (54)	−29.24 (34)	1.48[c] (29)

[a]Impairment implies at least 2 tests at −1 S.D. or at least 1 test at −2 S.D. Values in parentheses represent the number of patients evaluated; less time for trails is improvement. Wilcoxon sign rank test (two-sided); [b]$P < 0.01$; [c]$P < 0.001$.

declines in cognitive scores that are suggestive of progressive CNS involvement. The mechanisms of CNS-related impairment due to HIV-infection and treatment response in cognition are still unclear at present. There is some suggestion in our data that improvement due to treatment is partially accounted for by improved health, but the changes in cognitive scores are much larger than changes seen in patients' self-ratings of physical health from the SCL90 R [6]. These data suggest that neuropsychological functioning should be included in studies evaluating antiretroviral agents. By adding cognitive measures to outcome measures such as viral titers, mortality, etc., future therapies could be evaluated for their biologic impact, but also for their impact on quality of life.

Acknowledgements

Supported by a grant from Burroughs Wellcome. The authors wish to thank Dr. Joan Drucker, Dr. Ray McKinnis, Dr. Lynn Dix, Ms. Gail Rogers, Ms. Jennifer Stewart and Mr. David Lamb for assistance with this study.

References

1. Boccellari A, Dilley JW and Shore MD (1988) Neurotoxicology 9: 381–390.
2. Navia BA, Jordan BD and Price RW (1986) Ann. Neurol. 19: 517–524.
3. Wilkie FL, Eisdorfer C, Morgan R et al. (1990) Arch. Neurol. 47: 433–440.
4. Maj M (1990) AIDS 4: 831–840.
5. Fischl MA, Richmann DD, Grieco MH et al. (1987) N. Engl. J. Med. 317: 185–191.
6. Richmann DD, Fischl MA, Grieco MH et al. (1987) N. Engl. J. Med. 317: 192–197.
7. Schmitt FA, Bigley JW, McKinnis R et al. (1988) N. Engl. J. Med. 319: 1573–1578.
8. Grant I, Atkinson JH, Hesselink JR et al. (1987) Ann. Intern. Med. 107: 828–836.
9. Miller EN, Selnes OA, McArthur JC et al. (1990) Neurology 40: 197–203.

© 1991 Elsevier Science Publishers B.V. All rights reserved.
Biological Psychiatry, Volume 2. G. Racagni et al., editors.

The WHO cross-cultural study on neuropsychiatric aspects of HIV-1 infection

Mario Maj

Department of Psychiatry, First Medical School, University of Naples, Italy; and World Health Organization, Division of Mental Health/Global Programme on AIDS, Geneva, Switzerland

Introduction

Neurological and psychiatric disorders frequently occur in subjects with acquired immune deficiency syndrome (AIDS) and AIDS-related complex (ARC): about 65% of those who die of AIDS exhibit significant mental and neurological impairment in the terminal phase of the illness [1], and pathological changes in central and peripheral nervous system have been found in the autopsy of up to 90% of AIDS cases [2]. Moreover, acute stress reactions and adjustment disorders are common in otherwise asymptomatic HIV-1-infected subjects, especially immediately after discovery of seropositivity [3].

The World Health Organization, acknowledging the important health care and policy implications of research concerning HIV-1-associated neurological and psychiatric disorders, has launched a large cross-cultural study, aiming to explore the nature and prevalence of these disorders in persons living in different geographic and socio-cultural contexts.

Methods

The study is being performed in Bangkok, Thailand; Kinshasa, Zaire; Los Angeles, California, USA; Munich, Germany; Nairobi, Kenya; and Sao Paulo, Brazil. In each centre, a comprehensive evaluation instrument is administered to HIV-1-seropositive symptomatic and asymptomatic subjects and to age-, sex- and education-matched HIV-1-seronegative individuals, all recruited in outpatient units. The evaluation instrument consists of seven modules:

1. socio-demographic survey;
2. cognitive/neuropsychological assessment;
3. psychiatric assessment;
4. neurological assessment;
5. physical assessment;
6. laboratory tests;
7. summary sheets.

The neuropsychological battery has been validated for use in a cross-cultural context, and includes four newly-developed tests [4]. The psychiatric and neurological modules include two sets of operational diagnostic criteria for HIV-1-associated disorders, developed by the World Health Organization [5] and the American Academy of Neurology [6]. All investigators have been formally trained in the use of the evaluation instrument. The study is ongoing and the relevant results will be available by the end of 1991. A 3-year follow-up is planned in all subjects.

Reliability rating and feasibility testing

The inter-centre reliability in the use of each module of the evaluation instrument was measured by the joint independent assessment of a series of live and video-taped interviews and clinical examinations of patients with HIV-1-related symptoms and signs. It ranged from 89 to 97%. The intra-centre reliability was measured in each centre by the joint independent assessment of at least 5 patients with HIV-1-associated neuropsychiatric manifestations by all the researchers involved in the project. It ranged from 79 to 100%.

The feasibility of the recruitment and assessment procedure was tested in each centre by a pilot study involving 175 subjects. The procedure was found to be feasible. The percentage of dropouts throughout the procedure was 6.8%. The time for administering the evaluation instrument was on average about 2 h. The instrument was well accepted by all subjects.

Comment

It has been repeatedly emphasized [7,8] that currently available information on the neurological and psychiatric aspects of HIV-1 infection is of uncertain generalizability, having been obtained from studies mostly carried out in Western countries and on samples of well-educated, predominantly white, homosexual or bisexual men. In particular, it has been argued [8,9] that subtle cognitive deficits might be more evident in HIV-1-infected subjects with fewer compensatory resources, such as those living in countries where cerebral "reserve" is likely to be reduced in part of the population, due to the high incidence of infectious diseases and obstetric traumas, and to malnutrition, poor education and inadequate health care. Therefore, the need for the assessment of HIV-1-associated neurological and psychiatric abnormalities in different cultural and socioeconomic settings has been stressed by several authors. The WHO cross-cultural study represents a first attempt to address this need.

The pilot phase has shown that such a study is feasible. Of particular interest has been the favourable reception of the battery of neuropsychological tests by all subject groups in all the centres. The use of a set of neuropsychological tests in several different cultures has no precedent, and could pave the way for the investigation of cognitive abnormalities occurring in other infectious or non-infectious diseases which affect the central nervous system and are highly prevalent in developing countries.

References

1. Navia BA, Jordan BD and Price RW (1986) Ann. Neurol. 19: 517–524.
2. Petito CK, Cho ES, Lemann W et al. (1986) Neuropathol. Exp. Neurol. 45: 635–646.
3. Maj M (1990) Psychol. Med. 20: 547–563.
4. Maj M, Janssen R, Satz P et al. (1991) Br. J. Psychiatry (in press).
5. WHO (1990) Report of the Second Consultation on the Neuropsychiatric Aspects of HIV-1 Infection. WHO, Geneva.
6. American Academy of Neurology AIDS Task Force (1990) Nomenclature and Research Case Definitions for the Neurological Manifestations of HIV-1 Infection. Unpublished report.
7. Janssen R, Saykin AJ, Cannon L et al. (1989) Ann. Neurol. 26: 592–600.
8. Perry S, Belsky-Barr D, Barr WB et al. (1989) J. Neuropsychiatry 1: 286–302.
9. Maj M (1990) AIDS 4: 831–840.

© 1991 Elsevier Science Publishers B.V. All rights reserved.
Biological Psychiatry, Volume 2. G. Racagni et al., editors.

Long-term potentiation and its role in memory mechanisms

Serge Laroche

Département de Psychophysiologie, Laboratoire de Physiologie Nerveuse, CNRS, 91198 Gif-sur-Yvette, France

It is widely accepted by many neuroscientists that memory is an emergent property of the collective behaviour of systems of neurons organized into functional networks. According to traditional views, events from the environment are transformed into sets of sensory messages and encoded as spatio-temporal patterns of activity in vast, complex circuits. Experimental studies over the last decades have, however, provided evidence that specific activity patterns – the active state of memory – cannot persist indefinitely. In the line of the dual-trace hypothesis [1], the idea that a static form of memory is encoded as changes in strength or weight of modifiable synapses has long been proposed.

Neuropsychological data demonstrate that the integrity of the hippocampus is essential for the formation of many types of new memories (see [2]). In recent years, electrical recordings in behaving animals have provided evidence of the involvement of hippocampal circuits in associative memory. Since the discovery that certain synapses within the hippocampal formation possess a property, called long-term potentiation, or LTP, of being altered in an activity-dependent manner [3], this phenomenon has attracted much attention as a potential candidate mechanism for selective strengthening of synaptic connections within memory networks. In many hippocampal pathways, LTP is rapidly induced after brief episodes of electrical stimulation, is restricted to activated synapses, lasts for periods of several weeks or months and possesses associative properties postulated by numerous memory models (see [4]).

This paper summarizes experiments designed at investigating whether the neural mechanisms underlying hippocampal long-term potentiation (LTP) are activated during associative learning and whether they are necessary, or at least useful, for the building up and maintenance of a hippocampal component of a neural associative trace.

Experiments are conducted with rats trained to learn an association between a tone as conditioned stimulus (CS) and a footshock as unconditioned stimulus (US). Acquisition and retention of associative learning are measured in a standard conditioned suppression paradigm. During acquisition of this task, neurons in the dentate gyrus and hippocampus show accelerated firing in response to the behaviourally significant CS. The elevated discharge develops in parallel with behavioural conditioning and can be retained for periods of several months. It reflects the formation and activation by the CS of a central representation of the CS-US associative link [5–6]. Electrical recordings of perforant path-evoked dentate responses showed that learning the CS-US association is also accompanied by an increase in synaptic efficacy in the dentate gyrus, as previously found in rats exploring complex environments [7]. Whereas in this experiment conditioning induced a prolonged increase in the slope of the EPSP component of the dentate response, pseudoconditioning resulted in depression of the response. While these changes cannot be detected for long periods of time similar to what is seen after massive LTP induction by repeated tetanization of the perforant path, they suggest that the occurrence of synaptic potentiation or depression can be determined by contingencies between environmental events in a learning task.

Other electrophysiological and neurochemical analyses demonstrate learning-specific, long-lasting changes in synapse properties. First, learning is accompanied by an enduring modification of the capacity of perforant path to dentate granule cell synapses to support LTP [8]. In these experiments, an increase in the amplitude of tetanus-induced LTP in conditioned relative to pseudoconditioned animals was seen 2 days, and more recently 5 days, after learning. Second, over the last few years, we have found that associative learning is correlated with a rapid and sustained increase in the release of amino acids in the dentate gyrus and hippocampus [9–10]. Changes in neurotransmitter release, as estimated by the calcium-dependent component of potassium-stimulated release in slices or synaptosomes preincubated with radiolabelled glutamate, were obtained in the dentate gyrus 1 h, 1 day and as long as 50 days after classical conditioning. Further analyses suggest that the increase in transmitter release after conditioning may implicate activation of phosphoinositol lipid cell-signalling cascade, as indicated by the increased labelling of inositol phosphates and diacylglycerol after conditioning [10]. This cascade may also implicate activation of protein kinase C, as has been shown to occur after classical conditioning in the rabbit [11]. These data indicate a considerable degree of similarity in the changes associated with classical conditioning and LTP and identify a neurochemical mechanism which may at least in part underlie lasting changes in synaptic function built up during learning.

The hypothesis that learning-dependent synaptic potentiation provides a mechanism for selective stabilization and maintenance of memory networks predicts that the apparent strength of the memory trace will depend on the magnitude of synaptic changes in the relevant network. This prediction has been verified in an associative task in which electrical stimulation of the perforant path fibers serves as a signal for learning. In this task, learning performances are linearly correlated with the magnitude of LTP induced in the activated pathway [12]. Moreover, procedures which block the induction of LTP such as chronic infusion into the dentate gyrus of 2-amino-5-phosphonovalerate, a N-methyl-D-aspartate receptor antagonist, produces severe learning deficits [12], as seen by others in spatial learning tasks [13]. Long-term retention of the CS-US association has also been examined. Behavioural performance was found to be linearly correlated with the residual magnitude of LTP maintained just prior to retention, whereas forgetting occurred in conditions of regression of synaptic changes during the learning-to-retention interval [14]. The demonstration that the decay of LTP is associated with forgetting suggests that forgetting itself may involve an actual deterioration of synaptic weights at neural connections originally strengthened during learning, a process which could in principle lead to either information loss, retrieval failure, or both.

To summarize, several findings support the conclusion that learning a simple associative task is accompanied by changes in synapse physiology and chemistry in the dentate gyrus, changes that bear a number of features of an LTP as induced by tetanization of the perforant path. The magnitude of synaptic changes seems to play an important part in the control of the apparent strength of the memory trace; and their decay with time, in forgetting. The data obtained in the hippocampus are compatible with neurobiological models which assert that synaptic potentiation is involved in long-term marking of neural networks during learning so that the network can later be reactivated during the readout of memory (e.g. [15]).

References

1. Hebb DO (1949) In: The Organization of Behaviour. Wiley, New York.
2. Squire LR (1987) In: Memory and Brain. Oxford University Press, Oxford.
3. Bliss TVP and Lomo T (1973) J. Physiol. (London) 232: 331–356.
4. Bliss TVP and Lynch MA (1988) In: Landfield PW and Deadwyler SA (eds.) Long-Term Potentiation: From Biophysics to Behaviour. Alan R. Liss, New York, pp. 3–72.
5. Laroche S, Neuenschwander-El Massioui N, Edeline JM and Dutrieux G (1987) Behav. Neural. Biol. 47: 356–368.
6. Neuenschwander-El Massioui N, Dutrieux G and Edeline JM (1991) Behav. Neurosci. 105: 313–325.
7. Green EJ, McNaughton BL and Barnes C (1990) J. Neurosci. 10: 1455–1471.
8. Bergis OE, Bloch V and Laroche S (1990) Neurosci. Res. Commun. 6: 119–128.
9. Laroche S, Errington ML, Lynch MA and Bliss TVP (1987) Behav. Brain Res. 25: 23–29.
10. Laroche S, Rédini Del Négro C, Clements MP and Lynch MA (1990) Eur. J. Neurosci. 2: 534–543.
11. Bank B, DeWeer A, Kuzirian AM, Rasmusse H and Alkon DL (1988) Proc. Natl. Acad. Sci. U.S.A. 85: 1988–1992.
12. Laroche S, Doyère V and Bloch V (1989) J. Neurosci. 28: 375–386.
13. Morris RGM, Anderson E, Lynch G and Baudry M (1986) Nature 319: 774–776.
14. Laroche S, Doyère V and Rédini Del Négro C (1991) In: Baudry M and Davis J (eds.) Long-Term Potentiation: A Debate of Current Issues. MIT Press, Cambridge, pp. 301–316.
15. Bloch V and Laroche S (1984) In: Lynch G, McGaugh JL and Weinberger NM (eds.) Neurobiology of Learning and Memory. Guilford, New York, pp. 249–260.

© 1991 Elsevier Science Publishers B.V. All rights reserved.
Biological Psychiatry, Volume 2. G. Racagni et al., editors.

Memory disturbances and schizophrenia

Adolfo Pazzagli and Stefano Pallanti
Department of Neurology and Psychiatry, Florence University Medical School, V. le Morgagni, 85 Florence, Italy

Introduction

Memory disturbances are considered both as symptoms in all clinical descriptions of the schizophrenic syndrome and as fundamental or epiphenomenal elements, in various theoretical interpretations of mental activity in schizophrenia. Investigators of memory processes have focused on whether there are specific deficits in schizophrenia (encoding vs. retrieval, verbal vs. visual memory, free recall as compared to recognition memory) that is whether or not "differential deficits" exist (see review in [1]). Memory impairment has also been explored neurophysiologically by measures such as the amplitude of the P300 component of the event-related potential (ERP) which is said to reflect a variety of psychological processes such as attention, effort, and even memory (Donchin et al., 1978; Johnson, 1987).

Compared to normal subjects schizophrenic patients show reduced P300 amplitude, although clinical correlations and meaning of this alteration are unclear [2]. We present preliminary results of a study on the relevance of memory disturbances assessed through ERPs, clinical symptoms, memory tests and subjective experiences of memory impairment.

Subjects and Methods

Sixteen outpatients (11 male, 5 female) according to DSM III-R criteria for schizophrenia, paranoid type and 18 normal individuals (12 male, 6 female) matched for age and educational level within the age range 17–42 years, took part in the study. Fourteen patients were on neuroleptic medication and the other 2 were drug-naive. None had had more than 3 months of cumulative hospitalization to exclude both chronic and severe illness. Their I.Q.s as measured by PM 38 test were normal. They had no record of brain injuries or ECT therapy and no signs of tardive dyskinesia. Severity of psychiatric symptomatology was determined by calculating the mean scores from two trained raters (intraclass correlation = 0.78) on the Brief Psychiatric Rating Scale (BPRS), the Scale for the Assessment of Negative Symptoms (SANS) and the Scale for the Assessment of Positive Symptoms (SAPS) taking into account the acute phase. No patient was in an observable acute or hallucinatory state at the time of memory or ERP testing. Subjective symptoms were also evaluated using the Frankfurter Beschwerde-Fragebogen (FBF) [3].

Test measures

The preliminary tasks measured the subject's memory span for digit and block tapping. The verbal memory tasks [4] measure word recall and word recognition. The visual memory tasks consisted of the Benton Visual Retention Test (BVRT), a measure of visual recall and a second test using BVRT stimuli as a measure of visual recognition.

ERP testing

Auditory ERPs were obtained by means of a simple oddball paradigm. Two successive series of randomly intermixed tones (1000 Hz, overall probability 85%; 2000 Hz, probability 15%) were delivered binaurally through earphones at a rate of one tone every 1.1 s. Subjects were required to keep a mental count of the rare tones and to report the number at the end of each series. Responses were recorded (filter bandpass: 0.1–100 Hz) from Fz, Cz, Pz electrodes, all referred to linked mastoids. Response to frequent ($n = 100$) and rare ($n = 27–30$) tones were averaged separately. Peak latency and amplitude of ERP components N1, P2, N2, P3 obtained in patients were compared with those from 36 age and sex-matched normal controls. A two-tone choice reaction time was also subsequently recorded in all patients.

Statistical procedure

All statistical evaluations were performed using the SPSS package; the *t*-test, Pearson correlation analysis were performed as appropriate.

Results

Clinical ratings: BPRS total score average was 37.62 S.D. 7.35, SAPS total score average was 13.19 S.D. 4.15, SANS total score average was 11.06 S.D. 3.96.

Subjective symptoms: FBF (range 0–98) total score average was 54.81 S.D. 17.77; GED (memory subjective impairment) (range 0–10) score average was 6.5 S.D. 1.77.

Reaction time (RT) and P300: There was no difference in RT between control and schizophrenic subjects, but a significant difference was found ($P < 0.005$) in latency and/or amplitude of P300 late components. Twelve of 16 patients showed alterations in P2, N2, P3 in the Cz and Pz electrodes.

Memory tests: No differences were recorded between patients and healthy controls in digit numeric span performance. Significant differences were recorded compared to healthy controls in block span (t = 3.31; $P < 0.005$), word recall (t = 2.12; $P < 0.05$), word recognition (t = 2.79; $P < 0.01$) and BVRT recognition (t = 7.73; $P < 0.0001$). The main neuropsychological differences was in BVRT recall (t = 5.59; P < 0.0001). Drug-naive patients did not differ from drug-treated schizophrenics either in memory test score or with respect to other clinical variables (duration of illness, clinical severity or prevalence of positive or negative symptoms).

The various clinical ratings were correlated with the P300 parameters in the schizophrenic group and in no case was significant correlation achieved. Schizophrenics with P300 alteration showed difference in FBF score (n = 12; M = 61.33; S.D. = 15.6) compared to the patients with no P300 alteration (n = 4; M = 35.25; S.D. = 2.36) (t = 3.25; $P < 0.01$). Significant correlations were observed, however, with FBF vs. word recall (r = –0.8488; $P < 0.0001$) and FBF vs. visual recall (r = –0.6672; $P < 0.005$).

Discussion

Our study is consistent with the hypothesis of generalized memory impairment in schizophrenics with normal I.Q. Whereas word and visual recall were most impaired, deficits were observed in all tasks.

The main conclusion of this exploratory study is that memory disturbance (documented by the correlation between P300 late component abnormalities, poor memory test scores and "basic symptoms" high scores) may represent a selective criterion for establishing a sub-group in a sample that appears clinically homogeneous.

On the other hand, there is no correlation between symptoms and P300 alterations. These results are discussed in relationship to hypotheses of cognitive processes in schizophrenia as well as at the theoretical level for possibly interesting clinical applications.

References

1. Levin S, Yurgelun-Todd D and Craft S (1989) J. Abnorm. Psychol. 4(98): 341–356.
2. Pfefferbaum A, Ford MJ, White PM and Roth WT (1989) Arch. Gen. Psychiatry 46: 1035–1044.
3. Suellwold L and Huber G (1986) Schizophrene Basisstorungen. Springer Verlag, Berlin.
4. Rosen WG, Mohs RC and Davis KL (1984) Am. J. Psychiatry 141: 13456–13640.

© 1991 Elsevier Science Publishers B.V. All rights reserved.
Biological Psychiatry, Volume 2. G. Racagni et al., editors.

Memory disturbances in aging and depression: Similarities and differences

Milton E. Strauss and Monisha Pasupathi

Department of Psychology, Case Western Reserve University and Cleveland Department of Veterans Affairs Medical Center, Cleveland, OH 44106, U.S.A.

A common reason for psychiatric referral of older adults is the evaluation of suspected memory disorder. A number of researchers have examined the utility of neuropsychological evaluation of memory for making diagnostic discriminations among the underlying causes of memory dysfunction in the elderly. Because disorders of memory have multiple potential causes and associated treatment responses, differential diagnosis is critical. In considering this literature it must be borne in mind that differentiation among the memory disorders due to clinical depression, mild dementia and normal aging is complicated by the absence of unequivocal physical diagnostic criteria for the two clinical groups.

A four-stage model of memory [1] offers a convenient framework for organizing the findings of the studies of memory in aging, dementia and depression (Table 1). In this framework, information is first briefly held in a sensory register (iconic memory), following which attended information is held in consciousness (primary memory), a limited capacity store. Information that passes out of consciousness but is potentially retrievable is considered to be in secondary memory. Remote memory refers to memory for skills, biographical and factual information. Most clinical tests of verbal memory (e.g. paired-associate or list learning) are tests of secondary memory; primary memory is usually assessed by digit span tasks.

Normal aging is characterized by the absence of deficit in any stage of memory. Iconic memory is relatively unimpaired, but has not been studied in demented patients because of the complexities of measurement involved. Primary memory deficits are often seen in clinically depressed patients, but may not be clearly present in early dementia [3–5]. AAMI is defined as secondary memory impairment in the absence of other deficits, and secondary memory impairment is also found in both clinical groups. While remote memory impairments have been reported in dementia, this has been less studied than other aspects of memory in all the groups.

The differences summarized in the table are both qualitative (specific memory processes affected) and quantitative (degree of dysfunction). For example, both depressed and demented patients show reduced memory span (primary memory), but depressed patients are less impaired relative to normals [5]. The magnitude of group differences is variable across studies because of divergence in diagnostic criteria and clinical severity. These characteristics of the literature, together with

Table 1. Memory characteristics of diagnostic groups

	AAMI	Depression	Dementia
Iconic	+	+	+
Primary	+	–	–/?
Secondary	–	–	–
Remote	+	?	–

Note: + = unimpaired; – = impaired; ? = unclear.

the small samples studied, limit confidence in the specificity and sensitivity estimates that may be derived from published studies. Because of overlaps in performance between clinical groups, accurate estimates for sensitivity and specificity, together with knowledge of the base rates of specific diseases, are necessary for evaluation of the diagnostic utility of an instrument or procedure [6].

Assessment is most important early in the course of illness, when differential diagnosis leads to different treatment strategies, but investigations of very mildly cognitively impaired persons are rare in the literature. There is substantial variability in severity of illness at initial examination and in progression; consequently cross-sectional studies are of limited utility for the development of diagnostic indices. Prospective, longitudinal studies of high-risk groups, such as AAMI, will be a more productive strategy, despite requiring large subject samples.

Some studies suggest that the specific forms of memory failure may vary across illnesses. That is, demented and depressed patients may do poorly on a recognition memory test for different reasons: The "pure memory" (d') of dementia patients is much poorer than normals' and depressives', who may not differ from normals. Depressed elderly, on the other hand, are more likely to deny that a word had appeared on the list than either normal elderly or dementia patients (a difference in response bias, β) [7]. Diagnostic differentiation of depression and dementia may be enhanced by evaluating secondary memory deficits against a baseline of primary memory impairment. Secondary memory appears relatively spared in depression, but not in dementia, when compared to a constant primary memory deficit level [5].

An important conceptual distinction is that between performance deficits on a memory task due to "apparent" vs. "genuine" memory impairments [6,8]. Dysfunctions of attention, limited activation of encoding or retrieval strategies, or reduced motivation produce poor task performance but strictly speaking are not memory process impairments in some theoretical views [6,8]. Genuine memory deficits are dysfunctions in retrieval of information from secondary memory when initial memory processing has been experimentally controlled [6,8]. Such deficits reflect storage and retrieval dysfunctions and are a hallmark of dementia. Deficits in memory among normal elderly and, perhaps AAMI, are principally apparent memory deficits [6,8]. This interpretation of AAMI/normal elderly deficits as "apparent" is supported by the success of mnemonic and image elaboration training in obviating the memory deficits of elderly subjects with memory complaints (probable AAMI) [9], and the failure of dementia patients to be helped by semantic encoding strategies [8]. Neither depressed elderly nor mildly demented patients have been studied within this framework, so the sensitivity of the discrimination is unknown.

Despite gaps in the literature, current knowledge about memory disorders among the elderly is useful in differentiating among disorders. Because some differences among groups are qualitative and others are quantitative, the use of multiple tasks to assess aspects of memory is required. A failure of memory or complaint about memory can be due to any of a number of factors. Consequently, it is useful to employ tasks or tests that permit dissociation of component processes. The use of such methods, in conjunction with a sequential testing strategy may increase the utility of memory assessment for clinical diagnosis. Given the overlap of memory deficits among mildly demented and depressed patients, differential diagnosis requires careful evaluation of other neuropsychological functions as well as psychiatric history.

Acknowledgement

We thank John S. Kennedy, M.D., for his constructive comments on this paper.

References

1. Squire LR (1987) Memory and Brain. Oxford University Press, New York.
2. Crook TH, Bartus RT, Ferris SH, Whitehouse P, Cohen GD and Gershon S (1986) Dev. Neuropsychol. 2(4): 261–276.
3. Jolles J (1986) In: Swaab DF, Fliers E, Mirmiran M, Van Gool WA and Van Haaren (eds.) Progress in Brain Research, Vol. 70. Elsevier Science Publishers, Amsterdam, pp. 15–39.
4. La Rue A (1989) J. Clin. Exp. Neuropsychol. 11(4): 409–422.
5. Dannenbaum SE, Parkinson SR and Inman VW (1988) Cognit. Neuropsychol. 5(2): 213–233.
6. Buschke H and Grober E (1986) Dev. Neuropsychol. 2(4): 287–307.
7. Grober E and Buschke H (1987) Dev. Neuropsychol. 3(1): 13–36.
8. Sheikh JI, Hill RD and Yesavage JA (1986) Dev. Neuropsychol. 2(4): 413–421.
9. Brook CD and Simpson WM (1990) Geriatrics 45(10): 37–43.

© 1991 Elsevier Science Publishers B.V. All rights reserved.
Biological Psychiatry, Volume 2. G. Racagni et al., editors.

Effects of phosphatidylserine in age-associated memory impairment

Thomas Crook[1], Jared Tinklenberg[2], Jerome Yesavage[2], William Petrie[3], Maria Grazia Nunzi[4] and Danilo Casadei Massari[4]

[1]*Memory Assessment Clinics, Inc., Bethesda, Maryland;* [2]*Stanford University School of Medicine, Palo Alto, California;* [3]*Vanderbilt University School of Medicine, Nashville, Tennessee, U.S.A.; and* [4]*Fidia, Abano Terme, Italy*

Introduction

Age-associated memory impairment (AAMI) is a diagnostic term describing healthy persons over 50 years of age who have experienced normal developmental changes in learning and memory [1,2]. Multiple neurochemical deficits have been implicated in AAMI [3,4] and treatment studies have been undertaken with a number of compounds. A formulation of phosphatidylserine derived from bovine cortex (BC-PS) is of particular interest because the compound affects multiple neurochemical systems in which declines are seen with advancing age [5,6], and behavioral evidence from both animals [7,8] and humans [9,10] that the compound may reverse age-related cognitive impairments.

Table 1. Significant differences ($P < 0.05$) in drug-placebo ANCOVA comparisons – impaired patients

Variable	Study week	BC-PS	Placebo	F	(Sign.)	Favors	Treatment by clinic interaction
Name face acquistion	3	8.36	6.41	8.14	(0.01)	BC-PS	No
	6	8.51	6.98	4.47	(0.04)	BC-PS	No
	9	9.69	7.87	7.75	(0.01)	BC-PS	No
Name face delayed recall	3	7.17	5.89	3.91	(0.05)	BC-PS	No
	12	8.84	7.58	4.59	(0.04)	BC-PS	No
Facial recognition	3	12.37	9.32	5.22	(0.03)	BC-PS	No
	6	12.20	9.38	5.50	(0.02)	BC-PS	No
	12	13.06	9.68	5.43	(0.02)	BC-PS	No
	16	13.29	9.60	7.38	(0.01)	BC-PS	No
Telephone number recall	12	4.23	3.48	3.38	(0.07)	BC-PS	No
	16	4.54	3.44	8.92	(0.00)	BC-PS	No
Misplaced objects recall	6	14.60	12.53	9.29	(0.00)	BC-PS	No
	16	15.38	13.45	5.30	(0.03)	BC-PS	No

Procedures

We conducted a study of 149 patients meeting AAMI criteria selected from 3 clinical centers in the United States. Patients were treated with 100 mg BC-PS t.i.d. or with placebo for 12 weeks in a fully randomized, double-blind trial. Evaluations were performed every 3 weeks during treatment and 4 weeks after the conclusion of treatment. Five principal measures of efficacy were selected prior to the trial from a computerized battery of learning and memory tests that simulate cognitive tasks of daily life [11,12].

Results

During the course of treatment, significant improvement ($P < 0.05$) was seen in subjects treated with BC-PS relative to those treated with placebo on 3 of the 5 primary measures and a trend ($P < 0.10$) was noted on the fourth. In all 3 cases where significant differences were found, they emerged at the first evaluation period (week 3).

Analysis of clinical subgroups revealed that a subgroup of patients who performed at a relatively low level prior to treatment (57 of 149 patients) were most likely to respond to BC-PS. This distinct subgroup of impaired patients was identified in an earlier study [13] and it was suggested that these patients may be at substantially greater risk of developing dementia. Within this subgroup, significant improvement was seen on BC-PS relative to placebo on all 5 primary measures following treatment. Also, a significant difference was seen at post-treatment on 1 of 3 standard neuropsychological tests (Wechsler Memory Scale – Logical Memory Subtest; $F = 5.38$, $P < 0.03$) administered at screening and the conclusion of treatment. Differences in the computerized cognitive tests that emerged during treatment among the more impaired patients are shown in Table 1. Of considerable importance to clinicians, ratings of clinical global improvement also showed significant differences favoring BC-PS within the subgroup. These differences are shown in Table 2.

Table 2. Significant differences ($P < 0.05$) at the conclusion of treatment in drug-placebo ANOVA comparisons – impaired patients – clinical global improvement

Variable	BC-PS	Placebo	F	(Sign.)	Favors
Memory for names of persons after introduction	4.12	3.96	6.10	(0.02)	BC-PS
Ability to maintain concentration when reading, conversing, or performing tasks	4.32	3.97	5.63	(0.02)	BC-PS
Overall global change in cognitive status	4.25	4.00	4.11	(0.05)	BC-PS
Visual analog scale of global improvement	4.26	3.99	4.18	(0.05)	BC-PS

Conclusion

We believe the results suggest that BC-PS may be a promising candidate for treating AAMI and perhaps other cognitive disorders of later life.

References

1. Crook TH, Bartus RT, Ferris SH, Whitehouse P, Cohen GD and Gershon S (1986) Dev. Neuropsychol. 2(4): 261–276.
2. Crook TH (1989) Semin. Neurol. 9(1): 20–30.
3. McEntee WJ and Crook TH (1990) Neurology 40: 526–530.
4. McEntee WJ and Crook TH (1991) Psychopharmacology 103: 143–149.
5. Calderini G, Bellini F, Bonetti AC, Galbiati E, Rubini R, Zanotti A and Toffano G (1986) In: Horrocks LA, Freysz L and Toffano G (eds.) Phospholipid Research and the Nervous System: Biochemical and Molecular Pharmacology. Liviana Press, Padua.
6. Vannucchi MG and Pepeu G (1987) Neurobiol. Aging 8: 403–407.
7. Corwin J, Dean RL, Bartus RT, Rotrosen J and Watkins DL (1985) Neurobiol. Aging 6: 11–15.
8. Drago F, Canonico PL and Scapagnini U (1981) Neurobiol. Aging 2: 209–213.
9. Delwaide PJ, Gysetynck-Mambourg AM, Hurlet A and Ylieff M (1986) Acta Neurol. Scand. 73: 136–140.
10. Villardita C, Grioli S, Salmeri G, Nicoletti F and Pennisi G (1987) Clin. Trials J. 244: 84–93.
11. Crook TH, Johnson BA and Larrabee GJ (1990) In: Benkert O, Maier W and Rickels K (eds.) Methodology of the Evaluation of Psychotropic Drugs. Springer, Berlin-Heidelberg, pp. 37–55.
12. Crook TH and West RL (1990) Br. J. Psychol. 81: 335–349.
13. Larrabee GJ and Crook TH (1989) Dev. Neuropsychol. 5(4): 267–283.

© 1991 Elsevier Science Publishers B.V. All rights reserved.
Biological Psychiatry, Volume 2. G. Racagni et al., editors.

Recombinant interleukin-6 stimulation of pituitary ACTH secretion requires interleukin-1

S. Lori Brown[1] and J. Edwin Blalock[2]

[1]Department of Surgery, Stanford University School of Medicine, S-067, 300 Pasteur Drive, Stanford, California; and [2]Department of Physiology and Biophysics, University of Alabama at Birmingham, Birmingham, AL 35294, U.S.A.

Abstract

Corticotropin-releasing activity of the monokines hepatocyte stimulating factor and interleukin-1 have been reported previously. The effect of recombinant human interleukin-6 (IL-6) on ACTH release by cultured rat pituitary cells was measured in an ELISA assay. IL-6 did not promote ACTH release when included in culture at concentrations ranging from 0.01–500 U/ml. However, when pituitary cells were treated with IL-6 in conjunction with a low concentration of interleukin-1 (IL-1). the release of ACTH by these cells was observed. Unlike CRF, which causes the rapid release of ACTH by pituitary cells, combinations of IL-6/IL-1 caused the release of ACTH at later times. This study provides further evidence for the direct action of monokines on pituitary cells to cause the release of ACTH.

Introduction

The importance of bidirectional communication between the immune and neuroendocrine systems is becoming increasingly evident. There are numerous reports on the effects of monokines such as hepatocyte stimulating factor (HSF or IL-6) [1,2] and IL-1 [1,3–5] on the secretion of pituitary ACTH. The corticotropin releasing activity of these monocyte-derived cytokines has been observed both in vitro [1,3–5] and in vivo [2,6]. IL-1 enhances the expression of the proopiomelanocortin (POMC) gene in pituitary cells [7] as does the hypothalamic hormone corticotropic releasing factor (CRF) [8]. The gene for IL-6 (formerly hepatocyte stimulating factor, interferon β_2, or B-cell stimulatory factor type-2 [9]) has recently been sequenced [10] and recombinant human IL-6 (rIL-6) is now commercially available as a purified preparation, free of contaminating lymphokines and monokines. We report on the corticotropin-releasing activity of rIL-6 alone and in conjunction with IL-1.

Materials and Methods

Female Sprague-Dawley rats weighing 175–199 g were sacrificed by exposure to chloroform. Anterior pituitary cells were dispersed in 0.25% trypsin (GIBCO) for 90 min, at 37°C with occasional pipetting to assist in dispersion. After washing, pituitary cells were treated for 10 min at 22°C with 10 μg/ml of DNase type I (Sigma). These cells were plated in 24-well plates (Costar) at 5×10^5/ml in Ham's F-10 media supplemented with 15% horse serum (HS), 2.5% fetal calf serum (FCS), 100 U/ml/100 μg/ml penicillin streptomycin and 25 μg/ml nystatin. After 4–5 days at 37°C, 5% CO_2, adherent cells were washed with prewarmed Ham's F-100 containing 1.5% HS and 0.25% FCS (F-10-1.5.25) and resuspended in 0.5 ml of the same. To these cells, the indicated amounts of recombinant human IL-6 (Genzyme, Boston, MA) or of ultrapure human IL-1 (Genzyme) alone or in combination were added. After the indicated times, supernates were harvested and centrifuged to remove free cells or cell debris. Supernates were stored at –20°C until assayed for ACTH.

The ACTH content of supernates was determined by ELISA. Polyvinylchloride microtiter plate (Falcon) wells were coated in duplicate with 100 μl of supernates. Each plate also contained a standard curve, ACTH 1-39 (Sigma Chemical Co.) diluted in F-10-1.5.25. A rabbit antibody to ACTH 1-24 (Chemicon International, Temecula, CA) was used as the primary antisera and a goat antirabbit conjugated to horse radish peroxidase (Cappel, West Chester, PA) was used as the secondary antibody. Plates were developed using the chromogenic substrate 2,2'-azino-bis (3-ethylbenzthiazoline-6'-sulfonic acid) (Sigma) and read at 405 nm on an ELISA reader (Bio-Rad). Values of ACTH in supernates were determined from the standard curve by regression analysis and are expressed as enzyme immunoassay units (EIA units). EIA units reflect the relative amount of ACTH within an assay but cannot be correlated to an absolute amount of ACTH. The content of ACTH in some supernates was measured using an RIA kit (Incstar Corp., Stillwater, MN) to confirm ACTH release by pituitary cells.

Results

Previous studies have demonstrated that natural HSF, a monokine, has corticotropin releasing activity on pituitary cells. However, recombinant purified IL-6 (HSF) appears to have little or negligible corticotropin releasing activity (Fig. 1). In three experiments using adherent cultured rat pituitary cells, doses of rIL-6 ranging from 0.01 U/ml to 500 U/ml (1 pg–50 ng/ml), there was little difference in ACTH content in supernates from untreated cells when compared to IL-6-treated cells. In some cases, supernates from IL-6-treated pituitary cells contained slightly lower concentrations of ACTH than did control supernates. In each experiment, a well containing 0.5 μg/ml of CRF was included as a positive control for ACTH release. In the three experiments shown (Fig. 1), CRF stimulated significant ACTH

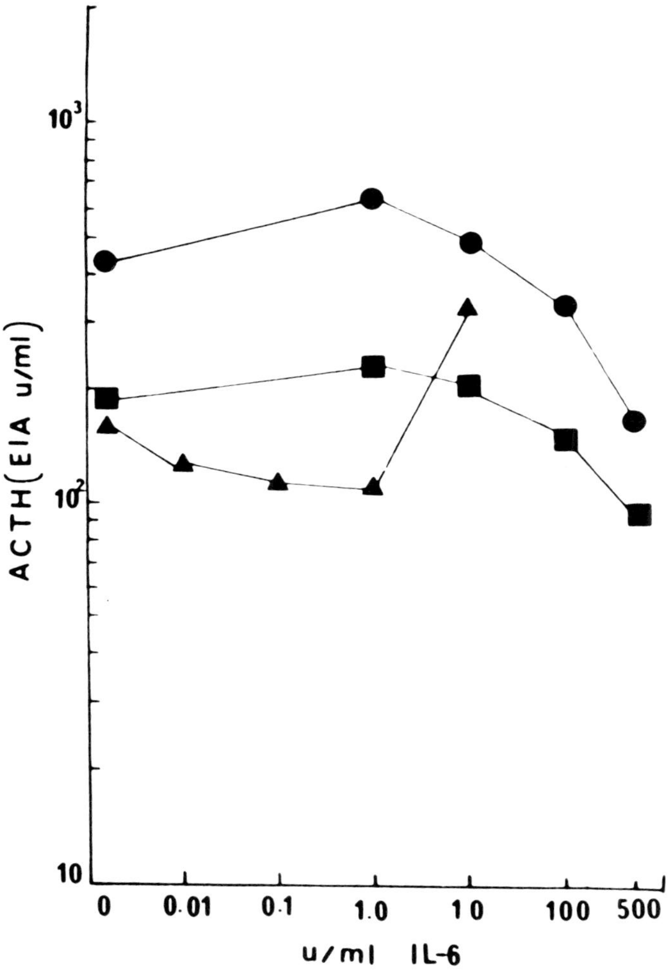

Fig. 1. IL-6-stimulated release of ACTH from rat pituitary cells. ACTH content of supernates after 20–24 h of culture with IL-6. Symbols represent three different experiments.

release ranging from an increase of 4-fold to 150-fold EIA units over spontaneous ACTH release by untreated pituitary cells.

Due to a previous study demonstrating the corticotropin releasing activity of purified natural human HSF (IL-6) [1] on a murine anterior pituitary cell line and because synergistic effects between IL-1 and IL-6 have been reported [11,12], experiments were designed to determine if rIL-6 would cause the release of ACTH in the presence of a suboptimal dose of IL-1. The latter was tested as shown in Fig. 2. When 0.01 U/ml–10 U/ml of rIL-6 was incubated with pituitary cells, very little ACTH release was observed over a 24-h period. However, if 0.1 pg/ml IL-1 was included in these cultures, a dramatic increase in ACTH content was observed. The dose of IL-1 used was one which provokes low or negligible ACTH release alone (Fig. 2) yet in the presence of IL-6, the two monokines enhanced the release of ACTH. The peak response of pituitary cells was seen with doses of IL-6 between 0.1-1.0 U/ml. Table 1 shows the results from four experiments in which rat pituitary cells were treated for 24 h with 1.0 U/ml of IL-6 and 0.1 pg/ml of IL-1. In these experiments the mean ± S.E.M. stimulation of ACTH release by IL-6/IL-1 was 401 ± 85% of spontaneous ACTH EIA units. In contrast, IL-6 or IL-1 caused 97 ± 26% and 159 ± 99% above spontaneous ACTH release, respectively. The ACTH content in these supernates was also measured by RIA. The spontaneous release of ACTH by untreated pituitary cells was 34 ± 6 ng/ml ACTH. IL-6 (1.0 U/ml) or 0.1

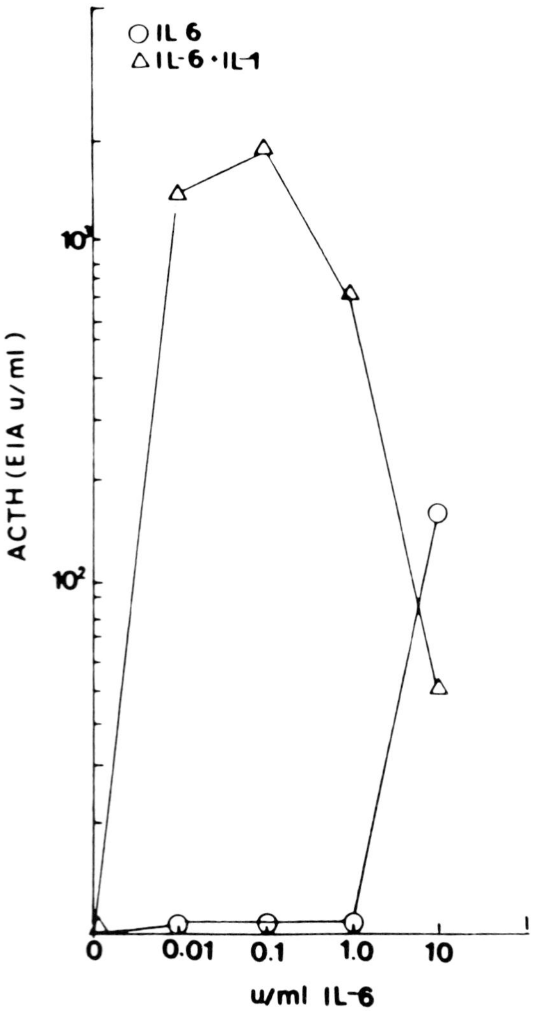

Fig. 2. IL-6 dose response. ACTH content of supernates with 0.1 pg IL-1 and indicated concentrations of IL-6 were measured at 24 h. Control (spontaneous) ACTH release has been subtracted.

Table 1. ACTH release in response to IL-6 and IL-1

Experiment	Spontaneous[a]	ACTH secreted in 24 h		
		1.0 U/ml IL-6	0.1 pg/ml IL-1	IL-6 + IL-1
No. 1	189 (100)[b]	235 (124)	514 (272)	563 (298)
No. 2	420 (100)	652 (155)	372 (89)	909 (216)
No. 3	167 (100)	114 (68)	106 (64)	942 (564)
No. 4	1775 (100)	733 (41)	3731 (210)	9336 (525)
X % ± S.E.M.	(100 ± 0%)	(97 ± 26%)	(159 ± 99%)	(401 ± 85%)

[a]Spontaneous ACTH release by untreated (control) pituitary cells after 24 h (EIA U/ml);
[b]In parentheses, as a percent of spontaneous ACTH release.

pg/ml of IL-1 stimulated release of 33 ± 5 ng/ml and 46 ± 9 ng/ml of ACTH. The combination of IL-6 and IL-1 stimulated release of 56 ± 8 ng/ml of ACTH. For comparison, in these four experiments, treatment with CRF at a concentration of 0.5 μg/ml resulted in the secretion of 88 ± 5 ng/ml of ACTH.

A study of the kinetics of this interaction demonstrated that IL-6/IL-1-stimulated ACTH release can be observed between 8 and 12 h (Fig. 3). Figure 3a depicts an experiment in which IL-1 alone caused some ACTH release. The addition of IL-6 to these cells resulted in enhanced ACTH release. Figure 3b is representative of experiments in which IL-1 alone failed to stimulate ACTH release but when in combination with IL-6 caused the release of ACTH from pituitary cells. The release of ACTH is sustained up until 24 h. By 30 h or later, the ACTH levels begin to decline. This may be due to peptidases in the media or possible to the activation of an enzyme which cleaves the ACTH. In contrast to the late stimulation of ACTH by IL-6/IL-1, CRF was observed to cause rapid release of ACTH between 1–2 h and like IL-6/IL-1 there was a sustained release of ACTH over a 24-h period (data not shown).

Discussion

IL-6, a monokine which plays an important role in the acute phase response, has a minimal corticotropin releasing activity on cultured rat pituitary cells. However, when recombinant IL-6 is included in culture with IL-1, at a concentration which stimulates negligible ACTH release, an enhanced release of ACTH is observed. Previous studies with highly purified natural HSF (IL-6) demonstrated the release of ACTH from AtT-20 cells, the murine anterior pituitary corticotrophs, in a dose-dependent manner [1]. This discrepancy in the corticotropin-releasing activity of natural HSF and recombinant IL-6 may be due to a difference in responsiveness of AtT-20 cells and fresh cultured rat pituitary cells. Another possibility is that natural HSF preparations may have contained minute amounts of IL-1. The

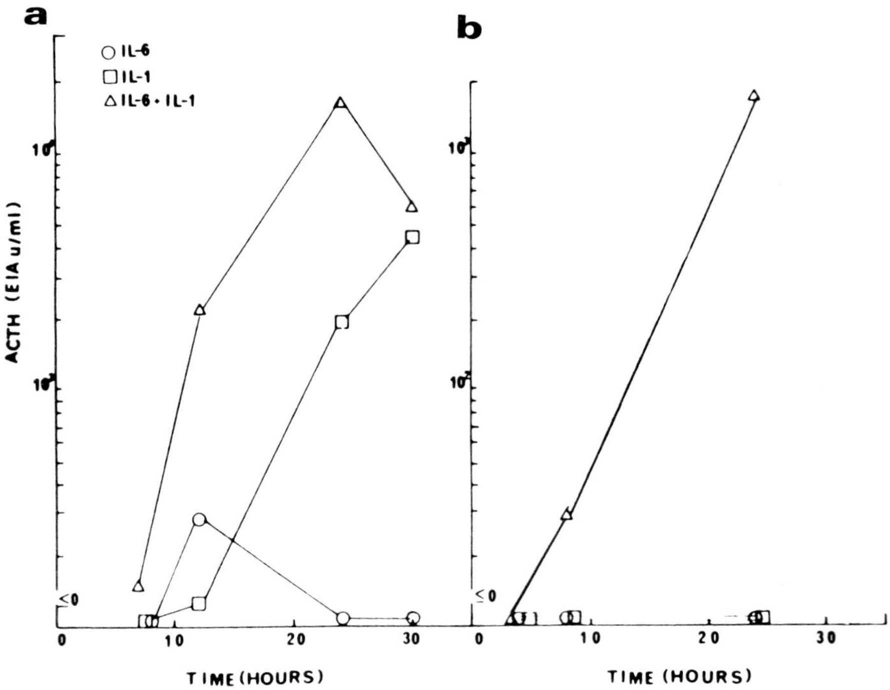

Fig. 3. IL-6 and IL-1-stimulated release of ACTH from rat pituitary cells over time. IL-6 (0.1 u.ml) alone and in combinations. Control (spontaneous) ACTH release has been subtracted. Representative experiments: a) IL-1 alone caused release of ACTH in this experiment but is enhanced in presence of IL-6; and b) neither IL-1 nor IL-6 alone cause ACTH release but together caused release of ACTH.

mechanism of IL-6 and IL-1-mediated ACTH release is not clear from this current study. Whether IL-6 enhances the responsiveness of pituitary cells to IL-1, or whether some other mechanism is responsible for this effect is yet to be determined. However, a synergistic action between IL-1 and HSF on the synthesis of α_1-acid glycoprotein by hepatic cells has been described [11].

Indirect mechanisms of monokine-mediated release of pituitary ACTH via the release of hypothalamic stores of CRF have been proposed [2,6,13–15]. The data presented in the current study strengthens the hypothesis that monokines also act directly on pituitary cells to cause the release of ACTH [1,3–5,7] as does the recent study demonstrating IL-1β innervation of the median eminence of the hypothalamus [16]. Neuroendocrine sources of IL-6 are also likely. IL-6 mRNA was detected in both a glioblastoma cell line and an astrocytoma cell line following treatment with IL-1β [17]. Furthermore, it is interesting to note that IL-6 was recently shown to be produced by [18,19] and active on, with regard to hormones other than ACTH, cells of the anterior pituitary gland [20].

The importance of the immune-pituitary-adrenal axis was recently demonstrated in vivo. IL-1α, IL-1β, and tumor necrosis factor all exhibited anti-inflammatory properties when injected into intact rats. However, the anti-edemic activity of these immune response modifiers was not observed in adrenalectomized rats [21]. This, in conjunction with the known immunomodulatory effects of glucocorticoids [22,23] argues that monokines such as IL-6 and IL-1 play an important role in modulating the immune response through the pituitary-adrenal axis.

Acknowledgements

We gratefully acknowledge Diane Weigent for typing this manuscript. This study was supported in part by NIH Grants GM40176 and DK38024.

References

1. Woloski BMRNJ, Smith EM, Meyer III WJ, Fuller GM and Blalock JE (1985) Science 230:1035.
2. Naitoh Y, Fukata J, Tominaga T, Nakai Y, Tamai S, Mori K and Imura H (1988) Biochem. Biophys. Res. Commun. 155: 1459.
3. Kehrer P, Turnill D, Dayer J-M, Muller AF and Gaillard RC (1988) Neuroendocrinology 48: 160.
4. Bernton EW, Beach JE, Holaday JW, Smallridge RC and Fein HG (1987) Science 238: 519.
5. Uehara A, Gillis S and Arimura A (1987) Neuroendocrinology 45: 343.
6. Besedovsky H, Del Rey A, Sorkin E and Dinarello CA (1986) Science 233: 652.
7. Brown SL, Smith LR and Blalock JE (1987) J. Immunol. 139: 3181.
8. Affolter H-V and Reisine T (1985) J. Biol. Chem. 260: 15477.
9. Gauldie J, Richards C, Harnish D, Lansdorp P and Baumann H (1987) Proc. Natl. Acad. Sci. U.S.A. 84: 7251.
10. Hirano T, Yasukawa K, Harada H, Taga T, Watanabe Y, Matsuda T, Kashiwamura S-i, Nakajima K, Koyama K, Iwamatsu A, Tsunasawa S, Sakiyama F, Matsui H, Takahara Y, Taniguchi T and Kishimoto T (1986) Nature 324: 73.
11. Baumann H, Richards C and Gauldie J (1987) J. Immunol. 139: 4122.
12. McKenzie D (1988) J. Immunol. 141: 2907.
13. Sapolsky R, Rivier C, Yamamoto G, Plotsky P and Vale W (1987) Science 238: 522.
14. Berkenbosch F, van Oers J, Del Rey A, Tilders F and Besedovsky H (1987) Science 238: 524.
15. Uehara A, Gottschall PE, Dahl RR and Arimura A (1987) Endocrinology 121: 1580.
16. Breder CD, Dinarello CA and Saper CB (1988) Science 240: 321.
17. Yasukawa K, Hirano T, Watanabe Y, Muratani K, Matsuda T, Nakai S and Kishimoto T (1987) EMBO J. 6: 2939.
18. Vankelecom H, Carmeliet P, Van Damme J, Billiau A and Denef C (1989) Neuroendocrinology 49: 102.
19. Spangelo BL, MacLeod RM and Isakson PC (1990) Endocrinology 126: 582.
20. Spangelo BL, Judd AM, Isakson PC and MacLeod RM (1989) Endocrinology 125: 575.
21. Nakamura H, Motyoshi S and Kadokawa T (1988) Eur. J. Pharmacol. 151: 67.
22. Cupps TR and Fauci AS (1983) Immunol. Rev. 65: 133.
23. Munck A, Guyre PM and Holbrook NJ (1984) Endocrinol. Rev. 5: 25.

© 1991 Elsevier Science Publishers B.V. All rights reserved.
Biological Psychiatry, Volume 2. G. Racagni et al., editors.

Neuropathological and morphometric aspects of dementia, Alzheimer type

Koho Miyoshi and Masayasu Sato
Department of Neuropsychiatry, Hyogo Medical College, Nishinomiya, Hyogo, Japan

Introduction

As well as the characteristic neuronal changes, like neurofibrillary tangles and senile plaques, neuronal loss in neuronal parenchyma is important pathological features of Alzheimer's disease (AD) [1–3]. In the present study, we tried to evaluate the usefulness of morphometric procedures for the neuropathological studies of AD. So, we estimated neuronal changes quantitatively in cerebral cortex and subcortical gray matter of AD and normal aged brains.

Material and Methods

Brains of 5 cases of AD, and 5 of age-matched controls were studied morphometrically. Ten serial sections, 6-micron thick, stained with cresyl-violet, were used for calculation in each examined areas of the cerebral cortex and subcortical gray matter. Image Analyzing System (Olympus Command 5098) was used for calculation [4].

Macroscopically, ratio of the tissue shrinkage cortical thickness and depth of each cortical layer were calculated. Microscopically. the following items were investigated quantitatively; 1) number of large (>151 μm^2), medium-sized (101–150 μm^2) and small-sized (<100 μm^2) neurons; and 2) number of tangle-bearing neurons and senile plaques in Bodian sections.

Results

Cerebral cortex

Macroscopically, the most conspicuous alteration of the cerebral cortex in AD was shrinkage of cortical layers. Average thickness of total cortical layers in AD reduced to approximately 80 to 75% of control brains. Basic portion of temporal lobe was most severely atrophic. Depth of temporal cortex of most advanced AD reduced to approximately 50% of normal aged brains. Reduction of depth was most conspicuous in the deep cortical layers.

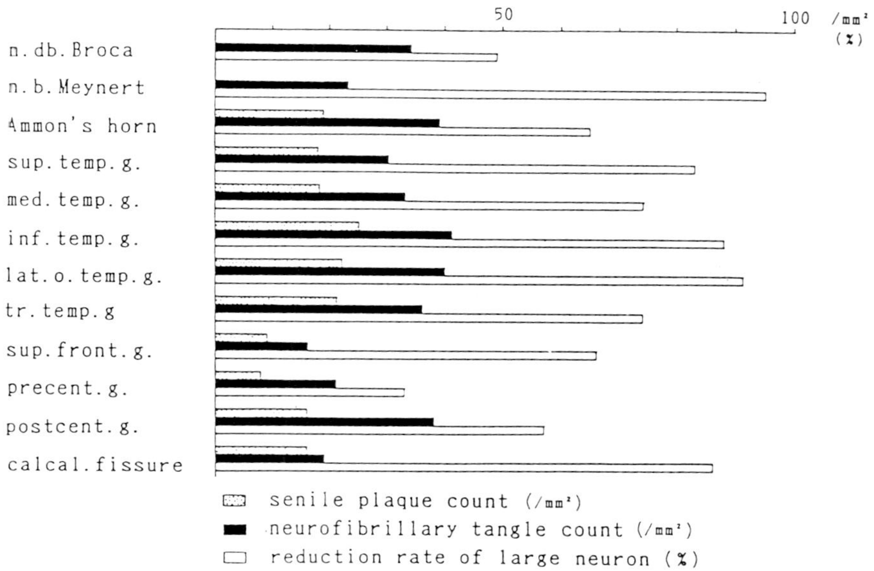

Fig. 1. Correlation of senile plaques, neurofibrillary tangles and reduction of neuronal population.

Neuronal loss was most severe in temporal lobe of AD brains, namely 38–58% of neurons disappeared in the single unit area (Fig. 1). Reduction of number of neurons was most remarkable in the deep cortical layers of the temporal lobe.

Apparently, occipital cortex was not spared from the neuronal loss in AD. In occipital lobe, neuronal population was reduced by 45–52% of control brains. Neuronal loss in frontal cortex and postcentral gyrus was less severe, when compared to that of temporal lobe. Reduction of large sized neurons was especially conspicuous in the temporal and occipital lobe. Cell population diminished by 65% in hippocampus of AD, when compared to age-matched non-demented controls.

The severity of nerve cell loss had direct correlation with the number of neurofibrillary tangles, but did not have positive correlation with the number of senile plaques (Fig. 1).

Subcortical gray matter

Number and size of neurons in the single examined area of subcortical gray matter decreased significantly in AD (Fig. 2). In nucleus basalis of Meynert (nbM), number and size of neurons were most severely decreased. Total number of neurons in nbM of AD decreased to 41.6% of control brains. Average size of neurons in nbM diminished significantly in AD.

In caudate nucleus slight reduction of large-sized neurons and relative increase of small-sized neurons were demonstrated in AD. The same tendencies were also noted in putamen of AD brains. Significant reduction of number of large-sized

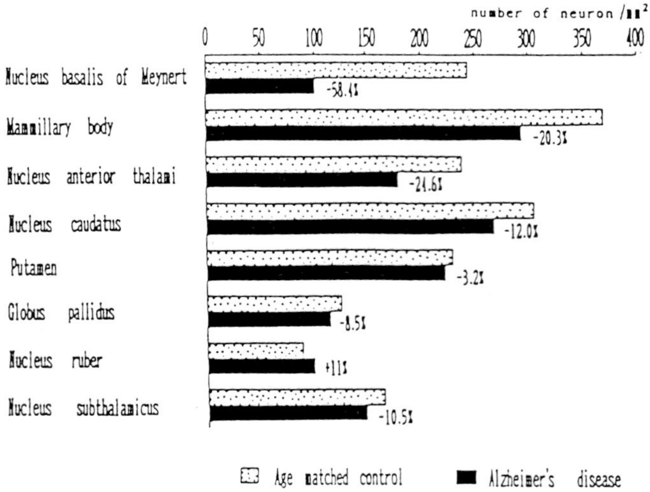

Fig. 2. Total count of neurons in subcortical gray matter.

neurons was demonstrated in globus pallidus in AD; however, no remarkable alteration of population of medium- and small-sized neurons was observed.

In mammillary bodies, diminution of number of medium- to large-sized neurons and relative increase of small sized neurons were demonstrated in AD.

Anterior thalamic nucleus showed a significant reduction of number of large-sized neurons with slight increase in density of cellular component. In subthalamic nucleus, marked reduction of large-sized neurons and relative increase of small-sized cells was demonstrated in AD. Medium-sized neurons appeared to be spared.

Reduction of size and number of neurons was remarkable in locus caeruleus in AD. Morphometric changes in substantia nigra in AD was characterized by reduction of cell size, not by the remarkable neuronal loss. Relative increase of small cell group and slight decrease of number of large-sized neurons were observed in red nucleus.

Conclusion

Distinct neuronal loss, as well as atrophy of neuronal parenchyma, were demonstrated quantitatively in AD brains by the Computer Image Analyzing System. Diminution of neuronal size concurrently occurred in the degenerated areas. The most prominent atrophy and neuronal loss were demonstrated in the temporal lobe of AD. The severity of nerve cell loss had direct correlation with the number of NFT, but did not have positive correlation with the number of senile plaques.

In subcortical gray matter, reduction of size of neurons was most prominent features. Significant loss of large-sized neurons was also demonstrated in the subcortical gray matter of AD. Usefulness of morphometric procedures for the neuropathological studies of AD has been briefly discussed.

References

1. Anderson JM, Hubbard BM, Coghill GR and Slidders W (1983) J. Neurol. Sci. 58: 233–244.
2. Allen SJ, Dawbarn D and Wilcock GX (1988) Brain Res. 454: 275–281.
3. Hansen LA, DeTersa R and Terry RD (1988) Neurology 38: 48–54.
4. Sato M and Miyoshi K (1990) In: Hasegawa K and Homma A (eds.) Psychogeriatrics. Excerpta Medica, Tokyo, pp. 123–127.

© 1991 Elsevier Science Publishers B.V. All rights reserved.
Biological Psychiatry, Volume 2. G. Racagni et al., editors.

Dementia of frontal lobe type

Arne Brun
Department of Pathology, University Hospital, S-221 85 Lund, Sweden

Introduction

Organic dementia, clinically of a degenerative frontal character, constitutes a diagnostically troublesome group of disorders. The present study deals with its magnitude and patho-anatomical composition with emphasis on frontal lobe non-Alzheimer dementia (FLD).

Material and Methods

The material consisted of 23 cases with a frontal symptomatology out of 108 consecutive cases included in a prospective organic dementia study. All brains were studied histopathologically in coronal whole brain semiserial sections and analyzed against the background of a previous study on frontal lobe dementia of non-Alzheimer type [1].

Results

Group 1. This group consisted of 11 cases, 5 male and 6 female, aged 51–75 years, average 63 years. They had in common a clinical picture of frontal dysfunction with loss of insight and expressive speech, disinhibition and a marked frontal flow reduction as in previous reports [2]. Patho-anatomically there was a frontal and in some cases also anterior temporal degeneration of the cortex with microvacuolation, mild gliosis and loss of neurons in laminae I–III. There were no senile plaques or tangles save for a few in 3 of the oldest cases, no amyloid angiopathy but diffuse amyloid deposits in some cases. One case had changes typical of Pick's disease, whereas in the remaining 10 cases the atrophy was mild, non-circumscript and without Pick bodies or inflated neurons. These cases were diagnosed as frontal lobe degeneration of non-Alzheimer type (FLD) in one group combined with amyotrophic lateral sclerosis (ALS).

Group 2. This group consisted of 8 cases, all with a predominantly frontal symptomatology and flow decrease, in 2 cases taken to indicate frontal disease, in 3 a mainly frontal dementia especially in the early phases and in the remaining 3 a frontal disease on top of an Alzheimer dementia. Neuropathologically they all had a dementia of Alzheimer's type with a frontal accent and a varying frontal white matter incomplete infarction. Four were of the presenile type (PDAT), aged 67–70 years and 4 of the senile type (SDAT) aged 77–83 years.

Group 3. This group consisted of 4 cases, 58–83 years of age, clinically with a varying frontal flow decrease and a vague frontal symptomatology with personality changes, disinhibition and emotional lability, insidious and without neurological components. The blood pressure was low. Neuropathologically there were only widespread mainly frontal incomplete white matter infarctions (SIWI).

Discussion

In our recent material of 108 consecutive cases of organic dementia, 23 cases, i.e. more than 20%, were clinically of a degenerative type with pure or prominent frontal symptomatology. About half of these (9%) had an FLD, a figure almost identical to our previous results [1]. This is a presenile dementia, not found in older material and thus entirely absent in a dementia group over 80 years of age that we have analyzed. Both in terms of topography and type of tissue changes, it is entirely different from the dominating mainly posterior form of DAT.

The only exception is the diffuse amyloid deposits which are, however, also seen in normal aging and which thus lack specificity. DAT may, however, have impressive frontal symptoms due to a frontal main accent of the changes, here in about 7% of cases, especially early in the course of the disease, possibly aided by frontal SIWI.

SIWI alone may also, on account of its preference for frontal white matter, produce a frontal dysfunction though with vague symptoms. Through its assumed pathogenesis, multiple mild added lesions, it may appear as a progressive disorder in spite of a likely vascular origin [3]. Other disorders of a character similar enough to merit inclusion in a group together with FLD are ALS with frontal dementia, represented by 1 case in the present material and in addition to Pick's disease, progressive frontal lobe sclerosis [4,5]. In conclusion, frontal dementias are more common than generally recognized and among them especially FLD is an important differential diagnostic alternative to DAT.

References

1. Brun A (1987) Arch. Gerontol. Geriatr. 6: 193–208.
2. Gustafson L (1987) Arch. Gerontol. Geriatr. 6: 209–223.
3. Brun A and Englund E(1986) Ann. Neurol. 19: 253–262.
4. Neary D, Snowden JS, Northen JS and Goulding P (1988) J. Neurol. Neurosurg. Psychiatry 51: 353–356.
5. Neary D, Snowden JS, Mann DMA, Northen B, Goulding PJ and Macdermott N (1990) J. Neurol. Neurosurg. Psychiatry 53: 23–32.

© 1991 Elsevier Science Publishers B.V. All rights reserved.
Biological Psychiatry, Volume 2. G. Racagni et al., editors.

Clinico-pathological studies in frontal non-Alzheimer dementias

S. Brion, J. Plas, G. Masse and A. Jeanneau
Laboratoire Universitaire de Neuropathologie, Hôpital Sainte-Anne, 1 rue Cabanis, 75014 Paris, France

Introduction

Some presenile non-Alzheimer dementias lack clearly defined pathological limits, whereas their clinical aspect shows many common signs of a frontal lobe disturbance.

Moreover, they show roughly similar lesions under the usual histological technique such as hematin-eosin staining: loss of neurons in the cortex, external gliospongiosis of the cortex and gliosis of the adjacent white matter. These lesions have been described in progressive subcortical gliosis (PSG) [1–3], amyotrophic lateral sclerosis (ALS) with dementia [4,5] and Pick's disease (PD) [6]. In ALS and PD, other associated lesions are considered to be more specific, but their limits with other pathologies are not clear-cut in all cases. The cases reported by Brun et al. may belong to this group [7,8].

Lastly, some cases with progressive aphasia [9,10] may be interpreted as belonging to these different entities.

The aim of the study is to gain a better understanding of distinction or similarity between these diseases, using the immuno-cytochemical GFA technique.

GFA staining is known to label glial filaments, which are more abundant in fibrillar than protoplasmic gliosis and when gliosis is proliferating. So, different patterns of GFA labelling of glia may be interpreted as reflecting different types of pathological processes.

In this study, we compare 4 cases of PD of long clinical duration (over 10 years), 1 case of PD of short duration (6 months), 2 cases of PSG, 1 case of ALS + PD, 2 cases of ALS with dementia and another without dementia, and 4 controls either normal senile subjects, or vascular subjects with recent or old necrotic lesions.

All these cases have previously undergone a pathological examination which confirmed the diagnosis with usual histology.

Results

We summarize the results in Table 1, which shows the presence of glia and the intensity of GFA labelling in upper ($C1C_2$) and lower (C_6) cortical layers and in white matter at 3 levels of the brain: the most involved zone (F_2, or motor cortex for ALS), a less involved zone (P_2) and a histologically normal zone.

Table 1. Aspect of glial lesions in frontal non-Alzheimer diseases

	Very involved zones			Little involved zones			Normal zones
	$C1C_2$	C_6 and superficial white matter	Inner white matter	$C1C_2$	C_6 and superficial white matter	Inner white matter	Inner white matter
Pick long course	++	++	G	±	+	++	±
Pick short course	++	++	+	0	+	+	0
Pick ALS	++	++	G	0	+	+	±
PSG	+ S	++	++	±	+	+	±
ALS	+ S	++	+	±	±	±	/
ALS + dementia	+ S	++	++	+ S	+	+	±

GFA staining reference: 0 = no staining; ++ = high density; + = moderate density; ± = low density; S: laminar spongiosis; G: gliosis without GFA staining.

All PD cases show 2 layers of dense GFA stained glia in the cortex of the most atrophied zones: 1 in the upper layers, $C1C_2$ and the other in the lower layers, C_6 [4], whereas the glia in inner white matter is diffuse but does not stain with GFA. In these cases, less atrophied areas show few glia in the cortex, but the profound white matter is intensively stained with GFA, especially in 4 long-lasting PD cases.

This inner white matter glia is quite similar to the lesions seen in the most involved zones of PSG, and in the motor cortex of ALS or frontal cortex of ALS with dementia. In these cases, there is also a laminar spongiosis located in the second cortical layer.

Discussion

PSG was extracted by Neumann [2] from PD because of a lesser atrophy of cortex and the absence of Pick's bodies. Nevertheless, these distinctions are still being discussed. In this study, if we consider the most involved zones of the cortex, differences seem important: strong GFA staining of glia in the cortex and not in the white matter in PD, versus the opposite aspect in PSG. But one could say that glial lesions in PSG are quite similar to those of poorly involved zones of cortex in PD, assuming PSG to be an abortive form of PD, where the processus should have stayed in the white matter. The case of the short duration of PD seems to show that the processus is different, with a precocious involvement of the cortex in this disease and a strong GFA staining in the external cortical layers. So, these aspects and the known clinical differences such as spatial disorientation and EEG disturbances in PSG lead us to consider that PSG and PD may be 2 distinct entities.

The problem is less simple in distinguishing PSG from ALS. In both diseases, usual histology shows superficial laminar glio-spongiosis of the cortex and gliosis of the white matter. In simple ALS, these lesions are located in the motor cortex, but they seem to extend to other cortical areas in the cases where ALS is associated with dementia.

In this study, the aspect of GFA staining is similar in both diseases. The clinical course of mental impairment also is not different, if one excepts motor disturbances. So it is not out of line to consider that the processus may be similar in both diseases, with only a difference in the extension to motor cortex which explains the motor impairment in ALS.

Variations in GFA staining according to the age of lesions have to be considered. In long-lasting PD cases, there are 2 layers of GFA-labelled glia in the cortex, whereas in the frontal inner white matter there is a widely-spread gliosis which does not stain with GFA. This aspect is not encountered in the short-duration PD case or in PSG or ALS cases which lasted a shorter time. Similarly, the aspect of glia in vascular diseases varies with time: recent infarction shows a strong GFA staining, whereas old infarction (over 10 years) shows a dense astroglial reaction which stains little with GFA. But this explanation is not adequate, because in the Pick-ALS case which lasted 5 years, there is also a little GFA staining of the glia in the inner white matter.

References

1. Masse G, Mikol J and Brion S (1981) J. Neurol. Sci. 52: 245–267.
2. Neumann MA (1949) J. Neuropath. Exp. Neurol. 8: 255–282.
3. Neumann MA and Cohn R (1966) J. Neuropath. Exp. Neurol. 25 122–130.
4. Brion S et al. (1980) Encéphale 6: 259–286.
5. Brion S and Plas J (1986) Encéphale 12: 81–87.
6. Escourolle R (1956) La maladie de Pick. Étude d'ensemble et synthèse anatomoclinique. Thèse, Paris, 231 pp.
7. Brun A (1987) Arch. Gerontol. Geriatr. 6: 193–207.
8. Gustafson L (1987) Arch. Gerontol. Geriatr. 6: 209–223.
9. Kirshner HS, Tanridag O, Thurman L and Whetsell WO Jr (1987) Ann. Neurol. 22: 527–532.
10. Morris JC, Cole M, Banker BA and Wright D (1984) Ann. Neurol. 16: 455–466.
11. Neary D, Snowden JS, Northern B and Goulding P (1988) J. Neurol. Neurosurg. Psychiatry 51: 353–361.

© 1991 Elsevier Science Publishers B.V. All rights reserved.
Biological Psychiatry, Volume 2. G. Racagni et al., editors.

Postmortem human brain tissue investigations of neurotransmitters in aging and in AD/SDAT

H. Arai, T. Takahashi, M. Kimura, I. Noguchi, M. Minami and R. Iizuka
Department of Psychiatry, Juntendo University School of Medicine, Bunkyo-ku, Tokyo 113, Japan

Introduction

Alzheimer-type dementia (ATD) is a representative disease which causes dementia in the elderly. Since the etiology is not known, there is no definite treatment for the disease and recovery from disturbance in memory and other higher cerebral functions is very difficult.

Many neurotransmitter candidates have been found in the central nervous system (CNS) and they are likely to be involved in the mechanism to maintain higher cerebral function. Recent developments in biochemical technology have enabled us to investigate changes in neurotransmitters in neurodegenerative disorders and may provide important information for the development of new treatments. Various materials including blood, cerebrospinal fluid, postmortem brain and specimens from brain biopsy may be used for such examinations. However, samples of cerebrospinal fluid and postmortem brain of these materials are more suitable, because blood samples may not reflect the metabolism of neurotransmitters in CNS and from an ethical viewpoint, brain biopsy should not be performed. Studies on postmortem brains also pose problems. Antemortem and postmortem factors may affect the content of transmitters in brains. However, as long as such factors are taken into consideration in interpreting the results, morphological and chemical investigations of postmortem brains are of value.

We have performed neurochemical studies on postmortem brains obtained from patients with ATD. Concentrations of biogenic amines, their metabolites, the activity of synthesizing enzymes, concentrations of amino acids and several neuropeptides have been examined in the brain. In this paper, we focus on changes in the serotonergic system as another dramatic abnormality in ATD brains, although the cholinergic deficit has received most attention in the study of ATD. We also report changes in galanin, an interesting peptide which may affect cholinergic transmission in the CNS.

Subjects and Methods

Autopsied human brains obtained from ATD patients and age-matched normal controls with no neuropsychiatric disorders were studied. All of the brains were

were verified neuropathologically and tissue samples for biochemical examinations were obtained from 22 regions including 7 cortical and 15 subcortical areas. The detailed clinical and postmortem data and the methods for the determination of the biochemical data have already been reported elsewhere [1].

Results and Discussion

Changes in the serotonergic system

Neurochemical investigations have revealed the existence in ATD brains of depleted cholinergic enzyme activity (choline acetyltransferase and acetylcholinesterase), concentration of biogenic amines and their metabolites (noradrenaline, serotonin and 5-hydroxyindole acetic acid (5-HIAA)), several neuropeptide immunoreactivities (somatostatin and vasoactive intestinal polypeptide) and glutamate concentration.

Of these changes in ATD brains, the serotonergic and cholinergic deficits were the most dramatic changes. The concentrations of serotonin and its metabolite, 5-HIAA, were significantly decreased both in the cortical and subcortical areas. The activity of synthesizing enzyme of serotonin, tryptophan hydroxylase, were also depleted in ATD brains [2]. On the other hand, the concentration of tryptophan, the precursor of serotonin, was not depleted in these brains. In addition to these biochemical data, neuropathological studies have shown a loss of neurons in the nucleus of dorsal raphe in ATD brains, where the serotonergic neurons exist. These findings strongly suggest the involvement of the serotonergic system in the pathology of ATD.

Although replacement therapy for the cholinergic deficit has been mainly studied, the results have been disappointing, with no clear effect seen. The existence of the serotonergic deficit may explain the results. In fact, replacement therapy for the serotonergic deficit has not been examined intensely. Based on the present findings, such treatment with serotonergic drugs should be considered. The candidates for such trials are serotonin reuptake blockers or agonists for the serotonergic postsynaptic receptor, rather than the precursor of serotonin.

Changes in galanin

Galanin (GAL) is a 29 amino-acid peptide first isolated from porcine intestine and found to be widely distributed in the mammalian CNS. GAL is a very interesting peptide for ATD research, because GAL has been reported to inhibit the evoked release of acetylcholine from presynaptic terminals. Therefore, we measured GAL-like immunoreactivity (LI) in cortical areas and also stained GAL-containing neurons in ATD brains.

GAL-LI tended to be increased in the ATD brains compared to the control brains and the difference was statistically significant in the frontal cortex. Moreover, although significant correlations of GAL-LI between cortical areas were found in the control brains, no such correlations were found in the ATD brains [3]. The GAL-containing neurons were found mainly in the hypothalamus and the basal nucleus of Mynert. The number of the GAL-containing neurons in both areas did not seem to be decreased in the ATD brains.

This increase in GAL content may be pathogenetically important in producing symptoms in ATD given the relationship between GAL and the cholinergic systems. Since GAL inhibits acetylcholine release, increased GAL may negatively affect the impaired cholinergic transmission in ATD brains. The involvement of GAL in the pathological manifestation of ATD should be taken into consideration when we consider strategies for the treatment of ATD.

References

1. Arai H, Kosaka K and Iizuka R (1984) J. Neurochem. 43: 388–393.
2. Sawada M, Hirata Y, Arai H, Iizuka R and Nagatsu T (1987) J. Neurochem. 48: 760–764.
3. Minami M, Makino Y, Arai H and Iizuka R (1991) J. Neural Transm. (in press).

© 1991 Elsevier Science Publishers B.V. All rights reserved.
Biological Psychiatry, Volume 2. G. Racagni et al., editors.

Pharmacological replacement of cholinergic function in Alzheimer's disease

Ezio Giacobini[1] and Robert Becker[2]

[1]Department of Pharmacology; and [2]Department of Psychiatry, Southern Illinois University School Medicine, P.O. Box 19230, Springfield, IL 62794, U.S.A.

The discovery of a gene mapped to chromosome 21 encoding for the β-amyloid precursor protein (APP) and the identification of a close gene locus (i) segregating with the familial form of Alzheimer's disease (AD) raised hopes for a rapid development of a cure. But, recent genetic analysis of a large number of AD families has demonstrated that the disease is genetically heterogenous, involving two or more genes [1]. Moreover, families with late-onset AD do not show linkage to chromosome markers [1]. In addition, an unequivocal diagnostic test of AD is not available for early detection of AD cases. A rapid "genetic" solution of the AD

Table 1. Strategies for cholinergic interventions in Alzheimer's disease

1. *Cholinergic function enhancers*

   A) *Acetylcholine precursors*
      a) choline, lecithin
      b) acetyl-l-carnitine
      c) L-α-glycerylphosphorylcholine (α-GFC)
      d) phosphatidylcholine

   B) *Acetylcholine release- and storage-modulators*
      a) aminopyridines
      b) phosphatidylserine
      c) piracetam
      d) DuPont 996

   C) *Neuropeptides and neurotrophic factors*
      a) anti-galanin agents
      b) TRH
      c) somatostatin
      d) NGF, NGF inducers, GM_1
      e) other growth factors (aFGF, bFGF, bDNF)

2. *Cholinergic agents*

   A) *Cholinesterase inhibitors (I and II generation)*

   B) *Cholinergic agonists*
      a) muscarinic
      b) nicotinic (incl. nicotine)

Table 2. The "ideal" cholinesterase inhibitor should show:

1. High specificity for AChE including molecular forms;
2. Short half-life;
3. Long AChE activity recovery;
4. Ability to achieve high levels of AChE CNS inhibition;
5. Ability to achieve a long-term steady-state of synaptic ACh levels;
6. Favorable cortical NE/ACh interaction;
7. Minimal side-effects and toxicity;
8. No development of tolerance.

problem does not seem to be in sight; thus, we must limit our expectation to symptomatic amelioration of the disease. Limitation of function, deterioration of daily living, progressive cognitive impairment and high costs of management make even a partial and temporary improvement of the patient conditions of considerable clinical and economical value. A treatment which is able to shift the curve of progressive deterioration or to delay onset in a large number of patients for a 3–5-year period would significantly decrease the need and the costs of care.

Correlations between psychometrics, pathological changes and neurochemical markers of the disease indicate that loss of large cortical neurons and synapses and decrease of cortical choline acetyltransferase (ChAT) activity may be more suggestive of pathogenetic mechanisms than concentrations of plaques and amyloid or density of tangles [2].

Cholinergic deficits in AD have been documented by numerous studies during the last 15 years (c.f. [3]). Most important, the severity of cholinergic cell loss in CNS has been correlated with the extent of the neuropathology and with the severity of memory and cognitive impairment (c.f. [3]). These findings suggest that pharmacological manipulation of the surviving cholinergic system could be efficacious in the symptomatic treatment of AD [4–5].

Both pre- and postsynaptic cholinergic interventions are under investigation (Table 1). Present strategies are directed to enhance cholinergic function three

Table 3. Relationships: inhibition, toxicity and side-effects, selectivity and efficacy[a]

Oral dose (mg/kg)	% Plasma ChE-inhibition	Toxicity side-effects[b]	Selectivity for AChE[c]	Clinical efficacy[d]
THA (0.35-2)	10–30	+++	0.25	+
Physostigmine (0.06)	24	++	6.5	(+)
Heptyl-physostigmine (0.6)	60	+	0.25	N.A.
Metrifonate (5)	60–80	(+)	22.5	++

[a] References [6–9];
[b](+) = very mild, transient; + = mild; ++ = moderate, +++ = severe (hepatotoxicity);
[c]IC_{50} plasma BuChE/IC_{50} RBC AChE;
[d]memory and/or cognitive effects;
N.A. = data not available.

ways: 1) to increase various precursor molecules utilized for acetylcholine (ACh) synthesis; 2) to improve release of ACh; or 3) to maintain function of cholinergic neurons or prolong their survival (Table 1 (1)).

The second group of strategies makes use of various cholinergic agents, mainly cholinesterase inhibitors (ChEI) (I and II generation) and cholinergic (mainly muscarinic) agonists (Table 1 (2)).

Most of the compounds used up to now as anti-AD drugs have not been designed or developed specifically for this treatment, but have been borrowed from other areas of therapy or pharmacology [6].

The most interesting advances are being made in the class of ChEI [6]. Several requirements are necessary in order to achieve an "ideal" ChEI (Table 2).

Table 3 shows the relationship between inhibition of plasma cholinesterase, toxicity and side-effects, selectivity and efficacy of several ChEI presently tested in AD experimental therapy.

Acknowledgements

Supported by NIA AG05416-0161 to E.G. and NIMH AG4182 to R.B.

References

1. St. George-Hyslop P et al. (1990) Nature 347: 194–197.
2. Terry R, Masliah E, Salmon D, Butters N, DeTeresa R, Hansen L and Katzman R (1990) Neurobiol. Aging 11 (3): 267 (#56).
3. Giacobini E (1990) In: Aquilonius S-M and Gillberg P-G (eds.) Progress in Brain Research, Vol. 84. Elsevier, Amsterdam, pp. 321–332.
4. Becker RE and Giacobini E (1988) Drug Dev. Res. 12: 163–195.
5. Becker RE and Giacobini E (1988) Drug Dev. Res. 14: 235–246.
6. Pomponi M, Giacobini E and Brufani M (1990) Aging 2: 125–153.
7. Becker RE, Colliver J, Elble R, Feldman E, Giacobini E, Kumar V, Markwell S, Moriearty P, Parks R, Shillcutt SC, Unni L, Vicari S, Womack C and Zec RF (1990) Drug Dev. Res. 19: 425–434.
8. Unni LK, Becker RE, Hutt V and Imbimbo BP (1990) IUPHAR Congr., Amsterdam.
9. Kumar V and Becker RE (1989) Clin. Pharmacol. Ther. Toxicol. 27 (10): 478–485.

© 1991 Elsevier Science Publishers B.V. All rights reserved.
Biological Psychiatry, Volume 2. G. Racagni et al., editors.

Supplementations of the serotonergic system in aging and AD/SDAT

C.-G. Gottfries and Anna Lena Nyth

Department of Psychiatry and Neurochemistry, University of Göteborg, St. Jörgen Hospital, S-422 03 Hisings-Backa, Sweden

Introduction

Human beings have the longest senium of all species. The human brain is an organ with great reserve capacities, which may explain why cognitive and emotional functions can be maintained well into old age. Data from several sources, however, indicate that there is an involution phase in the brain which has its onset in the 7th decade of life and progresses slowly and continously [1–3]; whether the involution phase of the brain is a genetically determined process or the result of environmental factors is not known. Mainly from postmortem human brain investigations, age-related reductions in the concentrations of neurotransmitters are shown.

The aim of this presentation is to report changes in the metabolism of 5-hydroxytryptamine (5-HT) which takes place in aging and in dementia disorders and how these changes can be manipulated.

Biochemical changes in the 5-HT system in aging

In postmortem human brain investigations it has been shown that there is age-related reduction in the concentration of 5-HT [1,4]. The patients in these investigations were aged 60 years or older. So far no data on significant correlations between 5-hydroxyindoleacetic acid (5-HIAA) and age have been published. 5-HT sensitive imipramine binding is considered a marker of presypnatice 5-HT terminals. A decrease in B_{max} with age was found in the cortex gyrus cinguli [5].

Biochemical changes in the 5-HT system in dementia disorders

There is evidence from several postmortem studies on brains from patients with Alzheimer type dementia (AD/SDAT) that the concentration of both 5-HT and 5-HIAA are reduced in discrete brain areas when compared to age-matched controls [6].

As shown by Wallin [7] pronounced disturbances of the serotonergic and cholinergic systems were found in subcortical and cortical grey matter of patients with non-multi-infarct vascular dementia. In these brains there was a widespread neurotransmitter deficit which hardly could be explained by the localized brain infarcts per se.

The 5-HT sensitive imipramine binding in tissue from AD/SDAT brains and from VD brains show an almost 50% decrease in B_{max} when compared with age-matched controls [5].

The 5-HT synthesizing enzyme, tryptophan hydroxylase (TPH), was also investigated [8]. TPH activity was found to be lower in various areas of the brain for patients with AD/SDAT. Degenerative changes in the raphe nucleus in patients with AD/SDAT have also been reported [9,10]. Thus, there are several postmortem markers for a disturbed 5-HT metabolism in aging, in brains from patients with AD/SDAT and VD.

Treatment with selective 5-HT reuptake blockers

In a multicenter internordic study the clinical efficacy of citalopram, a selective 5-HT reuptake blocker, was investigated in 98 patients with moderate AD/SDAT and VD. Analyses were made for each diagnosis after four weeks of double-blind treatment. Patients with AD/SDAT treated with citalopram showed a significant improvement in emotional bluntness, confusion, irritability, anxiety, fear/panic, depressed mood and restlessness [11].

In another internordic double-blind study, citalopram was given to patients over 65 years of age with depression as recorded with the Hamilton Depression Scale (HDS). Also in this study the active treatment induced an improvement [12].

References

1. Gottfries C-G (1990) Triangle 29: 127–131.
2. Carlsson A and Winblad B (1976) J. Neural Transm. 38: 271–276.
3. Svanborg A, Landahl S and Mellström D (1983) In: Thomas H and Maddox GLZ (eds.) New Perspectives on Old Age: A Message to Decision Makers. Springer Publishing Company, New York, pp. 31–52.
4. Gottfries C-G (1991) In: Sandler M, Coppen A and Harnett S (eds.) 5-Hydroxytryptamine in Psychiatry, A Spectrum of Ideas. pp. 309–323.
5. Marcusson JO, Alafuzoff I, Bäckström, IT, Ericson E, Gottfries CG and Winblad B (1987) Brain. Res. 425: 137–145.
6. Cowburn RF, Hardy JA and Roberts PJ (1989) In: Davies DC (ed.) Alzheimer's Disease: Towards an Understanding of the Etiology and Pathogenesis. John Libbey, London/Paris, pp. 9–32.
7. Wallin A. (1989) Vascular Dementia – Pathogenetic and Clinical Aspects. Doctoral Thesis from Dept. of Psychiatry and Neurochemistry, Gothenburg University, St. Jörgen's Hospital, Sweden.
8. Nagatsu T and Iizuka R (1989) J. Neural Transm. 1: 21.
9. Mann DMA and Yates PO (1983) Serotonin nerve cells in Alzheimer's disease 46: 96.
10. Curcio CA and Kemper T (1984) J. Neuropathol. Exp. Neurol. (1984) 43: 359–368.
11. Nyth AL and Gottfries C-G (1990) Br. J. Psychiatry 157: 894–901.
12. Nyth AL and Gottfries C-G (1991) A controlled, clinical multicentre study of citalopram and placebo in patients over 65 years suffering from depression. (To be published).

© 1991 Elsevier Science Publishers B.V. All rights reserved.
Biological Psychiatry, Volume 2. G. Racagni et al., editors.

Gangliosides and myelin lipids in Alzheimer brains

Lars Svennerholm

Department of Psychiatry and Neurochemistry, University of Göteborg, St. Jörgen's Hospital, S-422 03 Hisings Backa, Sweden

Introduction

The nervous system is unique for its abundance of membranes. The core of these membranes is a double layer of lipids, with a constant lipid composition. In the human brain the membranes will only undergo minor changes during development and under the influence of various environmental factors. The major lipids of both grey and white matter are phospholipids and cholesterol. Except for these 2 major lipid groups, glycosphingo-lipids occur in the brain in much higher concentrations than in any other organ. The characteristic glycosphingolipids of neuronal membranes are gangliosides with a neutral carbohydrate core of 4 sugars to which is bound 1–4 sialic acids:

Galactose β 1-3N-acetylgalactosamine β 1-4-galactose β 1-4-glucose-ceramide	
α2 ¦ 3	α2 | 8
Sialic acid	Sialic acid
α2 ¦ 3	α2 ¦ 8
Sialic acid	Sialic acid

Gangliosides are localized to the outer cell surface of the neuronal membrane and are particularly enriched in synapses [1]. They were already proposed in 1957 to be a biochemical marker for the amount of axons and dendrites [2]. The characteristic component of white matter is the myelin sheath, which is the plasma membrane of oligodendrocytes wrapped around the axon. One oligodendrocyte supplies several axons with a myelin sheath. There is, therefore, a large metabolic demand on the oligodendrocyte and the cell is sensitive to the decreased supply of oxygen, glucose and other nutrients. There is also a continuous loss of myelin membranes in the aging human brain [3]. The characteristic glycosphingolipids of the myelin sheath are cerebrosides and sulfatides. The concentration of sulfatide is only 1/3–1/4 of that of cerebroside and it also occurs in minor amounts in the neuronal membrane. For these 2 reasons cerebroside was suggested to be the optimal lipid marker for myelin sheath [4].

Physiological aging

No comprehensive biochemical study of human brain lipid changes during aging on a well characterized normal material has been performed. For this reason we decided 10 years ago to conduct an extensive investigation of the forebrain membrane lipids during physiological aging. Brain weight and concentrations of water, phospholipids, cholesterol, gangliosides and cerebroside, were determined in frontal and temporal cortex and white matter and the whole brain in more than 100 human brains from early fetal stage to 100 years of age. The results of the study are under publication, but only a minor part of the articles has hitherto appeared [4,5]. The ganglioside concentration reached its highest level in cortical areas before 20 years of age, was relatively constant for 40 years and started to decrease slowly from 60 years of age and more rapidly from 90 years of age [4]. The concentration of cerebroside underwent a similar course but the decline after 60 years of age and especially after 90 years of age was much more pronounced for cerebroside than for gangliosides. The changes were still more pronounced when expressed on a whole brain basis. The amount of cerebroside at 90–100 years of age was only 40% of that at 20 years of age.

Alzheimer disease

Patients dying with late onset senile Alzheimer disease (type II) had a marked loss of cerebroside, particularly pronounced in the temporal lobe [6]. Isolation of myelin from the white matter of semiovale centre demonstrated that the recovery of myelin was significantly reduced but its composition was the same in the Alzheimer brains as in the age-matched control brains. The concentration of gangliosides was also significantly diminished in frontal and temporal white matter, particularly in the macroscopically demyelinated areas [7] which indicates an axonic damage. This biochemical change has also been microscopically confirmed.

In the early onset form, presenile Alzheimer disease (type I), the ganglioside concentration was significantly diminished ($P > 0.001$) in frontal and temporal lobes, hippocampus and caudate nuclei. The ganglioside pattern did not show any significant change. We interpreted our results as demonstrating a serious loss of nerve endings in Alzheimer disease type I. Ultracentrifugal isolation of synaptosomes from frontal and temporal lobes showed a yield of 40–60% in Alzheimer brains of that in age-matched controls. The isolated synaptosomes had the same ganglioside pattern in Alzheimer and age-matched control brains which differ from the starting material (cerebral cortex) by having a higher proportion of GM1 and GD1a and a lower proportion of GT1b. The finding of a severe loss of synaptosomes in Alzheimer brain led us to examine the ganglioside pattern in cerebrospinal fluid, which also showed a significant increase of ganglioside GM1.

Gangliosides of the gangliotetraose series, especially ganglioside GM1, has a neuronotrophic and neurotogenic effect. An open study was performed in which 16 patients with presenile Alzheimer disease received daily subcutaneous injections of ganglioside GM1 for 3 months [8]. Ganglioside GM1 was found to be remarkably stable in blood plasma with a turnover time of 72 h. Brain biopsy was performed in 5 patients which showed that less than 0.05% of the injected dose had been taken up in the brain. Treatment trials are in progress in which ganglioside will be given through implanted catheters into the ventricles of the temporal lobes. The infusion will be continuous through a micropump.

References

1. Hansson HA, Holmgren J and Svennerholm L (1977) Proc. Natl. Acad. Sci. U.S.A. 74: 3782–3796.
2. Svennerholm L (1957) Acta Soc. Med. Upsaliensis 62: 1–16.
3. Svennerholm L, Boström K, Helander CG and Jungbjer B (1991) J. Neurochem. 56: 2051–2059.
4. Svennerholm (1956) J. Neurochem. 1: 42–53.
5. Svennerholm L, Boström K, Fredman P, Månsson JE, Rosengren B and Rynmark BM (1989) Biochim. Biophys. Acta 1005: 109–117.
6. Wallin A, Gottfries CG, Karlsson I and Svennerholm L (1989) Acta Neurol. Scand. 80: 319–323.
7. Englund E, Bruhn A and Svennerholm L (1990) Dementia 1: 286–291.
8. Svennerholm L, Gottfries CG, Blennow K, Fredman P, Karlsson I, Månsson JE, Toffano G and Wallin A (1990) Acta Neurol. Scand. 81: 48–53.

© 1991 Elsevier Science Publishers B.V. All rights reserved.
Biological Psychiatry, Volume 2. G. Racagni et al., editors.

Excitatory amino acids: Trophic influences and neuronal damage in the mammalian central nervous system

M. Favaron, J. Rimland, N. Gabellini, S. Romanello, C. Minozzi, A. Leon and R. Dal Toso

Fidia Research Laboratories, 35031 Abano Terme, Padua, Italy

Introduction

Excitatory amino acid (EAA) receptors are present on virtually every central nervous system (CNS) neuron. Probably more than 30% of the synapses within the vertebrate CNS use glutamate or aspartate or another dicarboxylic amino acid for the synaptic exchange of information [1].

EAAs appear to be operative in mediating morphological changes in the CNS during ontogenesis and neuronal plasticity. In contrast, an excess concentration of EAAs in the extracellular fluid has been implicated as a cause of neuronal death in various chronic and acute neurodegenerative diseases [2]. Thus, in recent years, major research efforts have focused on elucidating the cascade of intracellular events induced by EAA receptor activation leading to neuroplastic or neurotoxic effects. In particular, we have investigated the regulation of c-fos messenger RNA (mRNA) expression which acts as a third messenger molecule, coupling short-term signals elicited by cell surface stimulation to long-term alteration in cellular phenotype [3].

Induction of c-fos mRNA in cerebellar granule cells under conditions of EAA-mediated neurotrophism or neurotoxicity

Primary cultures of cerebellar neurons from 8-day old rat cerebella may serve as a simple in vitro model system. The relatively homogeneous composition of these cultures facilitates the detection of transient and maturation dependent traits. In addition, after 7–10 days in culture, cerebellar granule neurons express a mature and operative glutamatergic neurotransmitter system, indicating that these cells constitute a suitable system to study glutamate-induced neurotoxicity.

Recent work [4] has shown that N-methyl-D-aspartate (NMDA), which acts on a specific subclass of EAA receptors, promotes the survival of cerebellar granule cells in culture. We have investigated the effects of NMDA administration on c-fos mRNA induction in cerebellar granule cells at different days in culture. The expression of c-fos mRNA induced by NMDA is shown in Fig. 1A. By day 2 in vitro, c-fos induction by NMDA already reached maximal expression, compared to the control neurons which show a higher level of c-fos induction starting from day

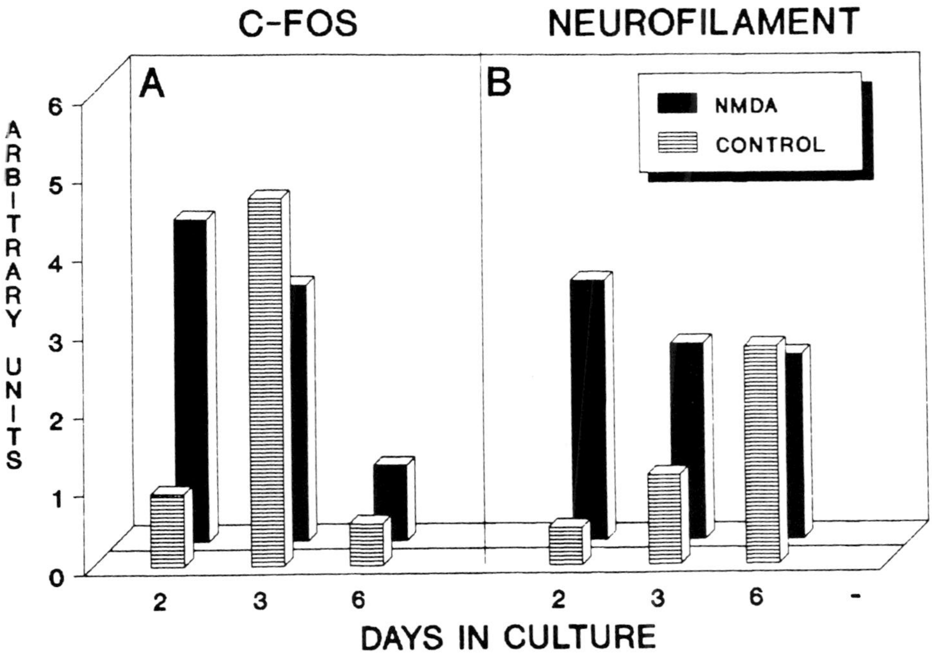

Fig. 1. The influence of NMDA on the expression of an early and late gene at different days in culture. Rat cerebellar granule cells were exposed to 100 μM NMDA at the day of seeding. Cells were collected at the indicated days and RNA was isolated [5]. Northern blots were probed for: A) c-fos; and B) neurofilament mRNA.

3 in vitro. At day 6 in vitro, c-fos expression reaches a plateau in control and NMDA-treated cells. In order to relate the c-fos induction to a marker of neurotrophism, we monitored the expression of neurofilament mRNA. Figure 1B shows that following NMDA addition the neurofilament mRNA content is maintained at a maximal level since day 2 in culture, mimicking the establishment of synaptic connections, that in control conditions will be reached only at a later stage of maturation in vitro.

Treatment of mature cerebellar granule neurons (day 7–10 in culture) with neurotoxic doses of glutamate triggers a completely different response. Fig. 2 shows the time-course of c-fos induction following glutamate treatment of cerebellar granule cells with non-toxic (2 μM) and toxic (50 μM) doses of glutamate. The toxicity of glutamate results in a repressed induction of c-fos mRNA, suggesting a positive role for c-fos induction in the physiological response of neurons to EAAs.

Conclusions

The developmental profile of EAA-induction of c-fos mRNA in cerebellar granule

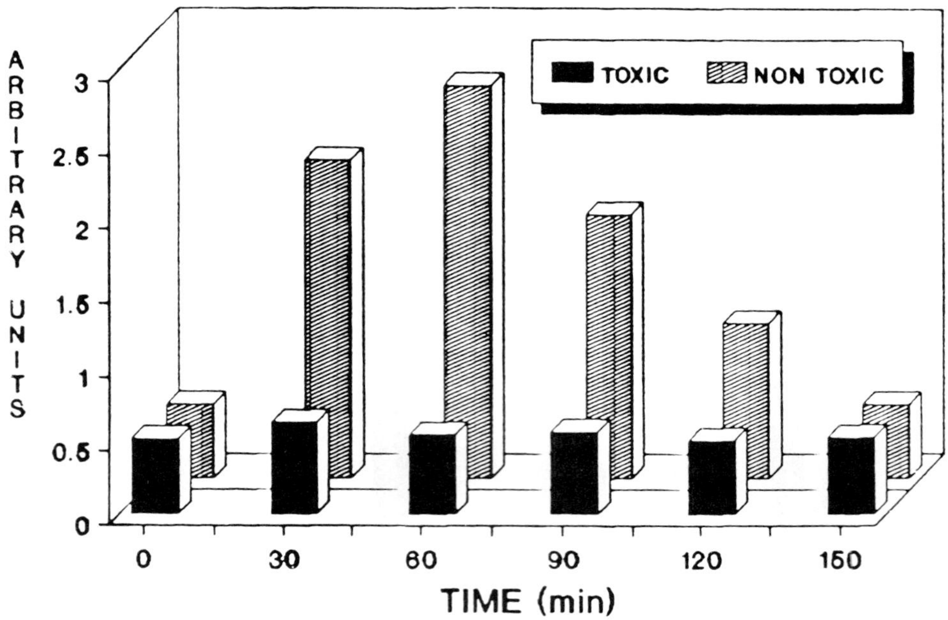

TOXIC: GLUTAMATE 50 μM
NON-TOXIC: GLUTAMATE 2 μm

Fig. 2. The effect of glutamate on cerebellar granule cells. Rat cerebellar granule cells were exposed to the indicated glutamate concentrations at 8 days in culture. Cells were collected at the indicated times after glutamate administration and RNA was isolated [5]. Northern blots were probed for c-fos mRNA.

cells in vitro suggests that the receptor-activated signal transduction pathways leading to early gene activation are linked to the subsequent induction of late genes necessary for the expression of the proper neuronal phenotype. In contrast, stimulation of mature cerebellar granule cells with a dose of glutamate leading to neuronal death impedes c-fos mRNA induction. The latter further supports the possibility that early inducible gene activation plays a critical physiological role mediating neuroplastic responses, either directly or via intermediate neuronotrophic factors.

References

1. Cotman CW, Monaghan DT and Ganong AH (1988) Ann. Rev. Neurosci. 11: 61.
2. Choi DW (1988) Trends Neurosci. 11: 465.
3. Curran T and Franza BR Jr (1988) Cell 55: 395.
4. Balazs R, Jorgensen OS and Hack N (1988) Neuroscience 27: 437.
5. Szekely AM, Barbaccia ML, Alho H and Costa E (1989) Mol. Pharmacol. 35: 401.

© 1991 Elsevier Science Publishers B.V. All rights reserved.
Biological Psychiatry, Volume 2. G. Racagni et al., editors.

Morpho-functional correlations of learning and memory in aged rats: Effects of phosphatidylserine administration

M.G. Nunzi, A. Zanotti, P. Polato, L. Petrelli and D. Guidolin
Fidia Research Laboratories, 35031 Abano Terme, Padua, Italy

Introduction

The search for potential treatments of age-associated cognitive declines has stimulated studies in animal models of neurobiological factors and neuronal pathways underlying specific cognitive dysfunctions. Deficits in spatial memory are common in aged human subjects [1]. Aged rodents likewise develop spatial memory impairments. Furthermore, a strong correlation exists between spatial performance and neuronal dysfunctions in basal forebrain and neocortical pathways, which are also affected in Alzheimer's patients. The aged rat with deficits in spatial memory constitutes a useful model for understanding neurological aspects of human brain aging and evaluating potential therapies for age-related memory disorders.

In this chapter we will describe neuropathological changes in cholinergic basal forebrain nuclei (BFN) and the entorhinodentate pathway of aged memory-impaired rats and the effect of chronic phosphatidylserine (BC-PS) administration (for background information see Nunzi et al. [2]).

Materials and Methods

Young adult (5 months) and old (21–24 months) Sprague-Dawley rats were tested in the Morris water maze to assess spatial memory. The latency to reach the hidden platform was automatically recorded. Old impaired and non-impaired rats were selected according to criteria based on the performance of young adult controls. After the screening test, the memory-impaired rats were divided equally between either the treatment or control groups. Oral BC-PS administration (50 mg/kg/day) started 1 week after the screening test. Animals were retested in the maze 7 and 12 weeks later. After the last behavioral test, rats were perfused with a mixture of aldehydes and the brains processed for choline acetyltransferase (ChAT) and nerve growth factor receptor (NGFR) immunocytochemistry or electron microscopy.

Results

As previously reported [3], only a subpopulation of aged rats displayed a signifi-

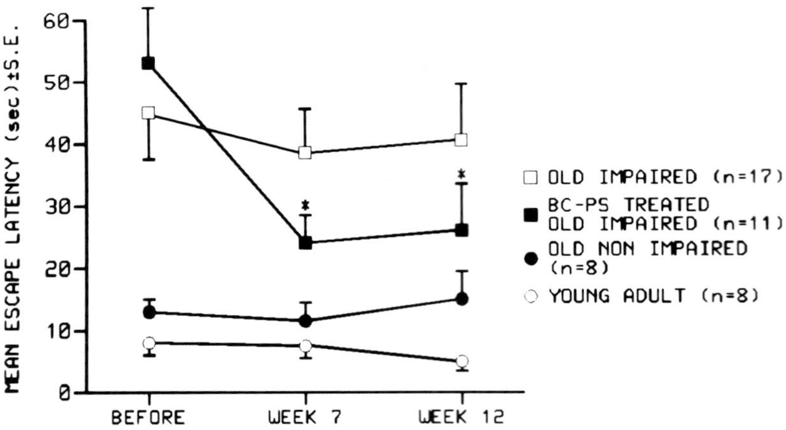

Fig. 1. Effect of chronic BC-PS administration on the performance of old impaired rats in the Morris water maze. * $P < 0.01$ (Dunnett's test) compared to performance before treatment.

cant behavioral impairment compared to young adult animals. Mean escape latencies for all groups across the different testing periods are shown in Fig. 1. Performance of aged impaired control rats did not change on 7th and 12th test weeks. However, BC-PS administration significantly improved the performance of aged impaired animals at both testing weeks.

A densitometric analysis was performed on immunostained sections through the

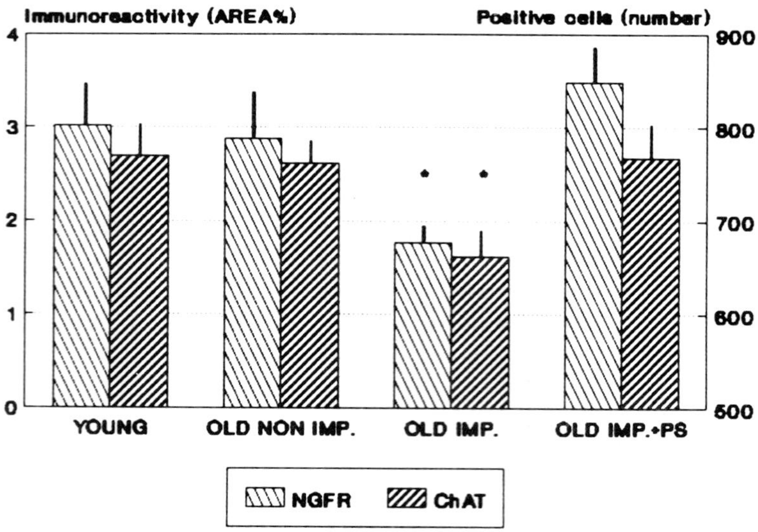

Fig. 2. Effect of chronic BC-PS administration on ChAT-positive cell number and NGFR immunoreactivity of old impaired rats (* $P < 0.05$).

medial septum and diagonal band of Broca. In aged impaired animals, ChAT-positive profiles and NGFR immunoreactivity were significantly reduced, as compared to young adult and aged non-impaired rats. No significant reduction in either parameter was seen in aged impaired rats treated with BC-PS (Fig. 2). Furthermore, single neuron densitometry in non-treated aged impaired rats showed a decrement in optical density of the ChAT immunoreactive end-product and almost normal levels following BC-PS treatment. The apparent loss of cholinergic cell bodies might therefore be indicative of ChAT levels below the limit of immunocytochemical detection, rather than an actual death of these cells.

Aged impaired rats also showed, in the hippocampal formation, a decrease in the percentage of axospinous perforated synapses in the terminal field of the entorhinodentate pathway. Long-term BC-PS administration restored the incidence of perforated synapses to normal values, further supporting a facilitatory role of this phospholipid in neuronal plasticity and metabolic functions.

Conclusions

The beneficial effect of BC-PS on spatial memory in aged rats is very likely related to restoration of morpho-functional properties of the cholinergic neuronal population in BFN and hippocampal synaptic plasticity. Nerve growth factor appears to act in the central nervous system by inducing ChAT activity. The increased density of NGFR in BFN of aged BC-PS treated rats might enhance or facilitate retrograde trophic support of NGF to cholinergic neurons, thereby promoting ChAT activity and cholinergic neurotransmission. This would be consistent with recovery of cortical acetylcholine synthesis and release in aged rats following BC-PS treatment [4]. Enhancement by BC-PS of central neurotransmission and synaptic plasticity might underlay the improvement of cognitive functions in aged subjects after BC-PS treatment [5].

References

1. Ohta RJ, Walsh DA and Krauss I (1981) Exp. Aging Res. 7: 45–63.
2. Nunzi MG, Galbiati E, Milan F, Guidolin D, Zanotti A and Toffano G (1990) In: Battistin L and Gerstenbrand F (eds.) Aging Brain and Dementia: New Trends in Diagnosis and Therapy. Alan R. Liss, Inc., pp. 577–590.
3. Gage FH, Kelly PT and Björklund A (1984) J. Neurosci. 4: 2856–2865.
4. Casamenti F, Scali C and Pepeu G (1991) Eur. J. Pharmacol. 194: 11–16.
5. Delwaide PJ, Hurlet A, Hambourg AM and Klieff M (1986) Acta Neurol. Scand. 73: 136–140.

© 1991 Elsevier Science Publishers B.V. All rights reserved.
Biological Psychiatry, Volume 2. G. Racagni et al., editors.

Brain energy metabolism in aging and in Alzheimer's disease

Siegfried Hoyer
Department of Pathochemistry and General Neurochemistry, University of Heidelberg, P.O. Box 104340, 6900 Heidelberg, Germany

Introduction

An adequate formation and turnover rate of energy in the form of ATP guarantees the maintenance of function and structure of any neuron. In the mature, healthy, non-starved mammalian brain, glucose is the only substrate for oxidation and thus for ATP formation [1–3] to maintain important neuronal functions such as synaptic transmission and calcium homeostasis [4,5]. A total of 10 $NADH_2$ and 2 $FADH_2$ as oxidation equivalents generates from the oxidative breakdown of glucose to form 36 mol ATP. A further 2 mol ATP derives from other processes than oxidation in glycolysis. As a whole, 1 mol glucose yields 38 mol ATP.

Materials and Methods

In this study, the ATP production rate was calculated from the cerebral metabolic rates (CMRs) of oxygen, glucose and lactate, which had been studied earlier in healthy young adult volunteers [1], in healthy middle-aged controls, and in patients with early-onset and late-onset dementia of Alzheimer type (DAT) [6,7]. Values of normal elderly subjects were taken from Dastur [8] for ATP calculation.

Results

The ATP formation rate from the CMRs of oxygen and oxidized glucose is listed in Table 1. It becomes obvious that energy formation was found to be almost undisturbed during normal aging. However, in early-onset and late-onset DAT, brain energy formation from glucose is severely perturbed and reduced to around 50% compared to healthy subjects. However, lacking glucose can obviously be substituted by the oxidation of substrates other than glucose by the utilization of oxygen not used for glucose oxidation. If this is taken into account, total ATP formation increased to 8.70 μmol/g × min in early-onset DAT, and to 7.62 μmol/g × min in late-onset DAT.

Table 1. ATP formation in brain during normal aging and in DAT

	CMRs in μmol/g × min				
	Oxygen (measured)	Oxygen (used)	Oxidized glucose	ATP	Rate of glucose oxidation
HYAV	1.52	1.56	0.26	9.36	0.99
HMAC	1.54	1.56	0.26	9.36	1.01
NES	1.49	1.44	0.24	8.64	0.97
Early-onset DAT	1.45	0.72	0.12	4.32	0.50
Late-onset DAT	1.27	0.84	0.14	5.04	0.66

HYAV: healthy young adult volunteer [6]; HMAC: healthy middle-aged controls [6]; NES: normal elderly subjects [8].

Conclusion

During normal aging, energy formation in the brain is obviously undisturbed at least until the 7th to 8th decade of life. In both, incipient early-onset and incipient late-onset DAT, energy formation from glucose is severely perturbed. However, total energy production is less severely reduced because of the substitution of endogenous substrates other than glucose. This only slight but permanently maintained and progressive reduction in available energy may have detrimental impacts on neuronal function.

References

1. Hoyer S (1970) Klin. Wochenschr. 48: 1239–1243.
2. Erecinska M and Silver IA (1989) Cereb. Blood Flow Metab. 9: 2–19.
3. Siesjö BK (1978) In: Brain Energy Metabolism. Wiley, Chichester, pp. 1–28, 151–209.
4. Lipton P and Whittingham TS (1982) Physiology 325: 51–65.
5. Siesjö BK (1981) Cereb. Blood Flow Metab. 1: 155–185.
6. Hoyer S, Oesterreich K and Wagner O (1988) Neurology 235: 143–148.
7. Hoyer S, Nitsch R and Oesterreich K (1991) Neural Transm. (in press).
8. Dastur DK (1985) Cereb. Blood Flow Metab. 5: 1–9.

© 1991 Elsevier Science Publishers B.V. All rights reserved.
Biological Psychiatry, Volume 2. G. Racagni et al., editors.

A radical view on the pathogenesis of Alzheimer's disease

Peter Riederer, Mario Götz, Albrecht Dirr and Wieland Gsell
Department of Psychiatry, Division of Clinical Neurochemistry, University of Würzburg, Füchsleinstraße 15, D-8700 Würzburg, Germany

Introduction

Alzheimer's disease (AD) and senile dementia of the Alzheimer type (SDAT) are both characterized by multiple deteriorations of neurotransmitter systems in cortical and subcortical regions. This is due to cell degeneration and cell loss in neurotransmitter synthesizing areas of the brain. Neuropathological degenerations show a clear rank order, where nucleus basalis of Meynert (NBM) is severely damaged (about 70% neuronal cell loss as compared to age-matched controls [1–3]), whilst locus coeruleus (LC) and dorsal raphe nucleus (DRN) are moderately (44–68% neuronal cell loss as compared to age-matched controls [4–9]) and substantia nigra is slightly damaged (20–25% neuronal cell loss as compared to age-matched controls [7,8,10,11]). The underlying mechanisms of neurodegeneration are so far unknown and various hypotheses have been proposed. One of the main theories of aging, the "free radical theory of aging" [12] was adopted about 10 years ago by dementia research, as structures affected histopathologically and biochemically in AD and SDAT correspond partly to those affected during normal aging, though changes are much more drastic and accelerated in AD/SDAT. But our knowledge of radical participation in pathogenesis of AD/SDAT is very limited.

Radical theory of neurodegeneration

Production of and damage by free radicals

Many single reactions, reaction chains, organelles and diseases are involved in reactive oxygen production. On a cellular level superoxide anion radical is mainly produced by oxygenation reactions, with NADPH, xanthine, Fenton reagents, etc. as electron donors [13]. Nothing is known about altered superoxide producing reactions in AD/SDAT, although a possible link between one of the other hypothesis, the "decline in energy supply" is obvious. Hydrogen peroxide for example is produced by superoxide detoxication via superoxide dismutase [14] and by biogenic amine degradation via monoamine oxidases (MAO). MAO-B activity is known to increase in platelets and brains of patients with AD/SDAT [15,16]. Hydroxyl radical, which is produced from hydrogen peroxide by Fenton reaction is assumed to be the major membrane toxic oxygen species. There is some indirect evidence that membranes in brains from patients with AD/SDAT are degraded by radicals [17], although we recently found that the usual method, namely the measurement of thiobarbituric acid reactive material or the malondialdehyde production does not reflect "lipid peroxidation" as such. Rather these method describes the *sensitivity* of membrane structures *to be oxidized*. In fact, this parameter is indeed significantly enhanced in various brain regions of AD/SDAT. In agreement with this finding, measurements using the physicochemical approach of "differential scanning calorimetry" show a significant reduction of the thermostability of membrane structures in frontal cortex and NBM of AD/SDAT.

Protection from free radical damage

Protective mechanisms can be divided in protective substances (vitamins C and E, etc.) and into active detoxication reactions (superoxide dismutase, SOD; catalase, CAT; glutathione peroxidase, GSH-Px; glutathione reductase, GSSG-Rd). Very little is known about these mechanisms in brains of patients with AD/SDAT. SOD was found to be unchanged in brains of patients with SDAT [18]. We confirmed these findings in cortical areas, basal ganglia, and limbic regions in SDAT brains. On the other hand, we found a significant reduction in CAT activity in the parietal cortex (25% reduction when compared to age-matched controls), basal ganglia (21% in caudate nucleus and 27% in putamen), and amygdala (20%). Unchanged SOD activity and reduced CAT together with increased MAO activity may cause an increase in membrane-toxic hydrogen peroxide (via hydroxyl radical). Although the enzyme activities of GSH-Px and GSSG-Rd are not known so far and the concentrations of GSH and GSSG have not been detected in the brains of AD/SDAT, it is hypothesized that radicals may accumulate by these and other routes, e.g. via impaired calcium homeostasis. Evidence for this assumption is given by the reduction of CAT, which beside a possible defect in enzyme synthesis or activation may be due to increased concentration of superoxide radicals [19] and hydrogen peroxide [20]. Furthermore, our data obtained with two different methods showing increased sensitivity of membrane structures to be oxidized are in line with the hypothesis that radicals are involved in the pathogenesis of AD/SDAT.

References

1. Mann DMA and Yates PO (1983) Neuropathol. Appl. Neurobiol. 9: 3–19.
2. Gibb WRG and Lees AJ (1987) Acta Neuropathol. 73: 195–201.
3. Hirsch E, Graybiel AM and Agid YA (1988) Nature 334: 345–348.
4. Tomlinson BE, Irving D and Blessed G (1981) J. Neurol. Sci. 49: 419–428.
5. Bondareff N, Mountjoy CQ and Roth M (1982) Neurology 32: 165–168.
6. Tomonaga M (1983) J. Neurol. 230: 231–240.
7. Mann DMA, Yates PO and Hawkes J (1983) Clin. Neuropathol. 2: 1–7.

8. Jellinger K (1987) In: Marsden CD and Fahn S (eds.) Movement Disorders. Butterworth, London, pp. 124–165.
9. Ingram VM, Koenig JH, Miller CH, Moore HE, Blanchard B and Perry DE (1987) In: Wurtman RJ, Corkin SH and Growden JH (eds.) Alzheimer's Disease: Advances in Basic Research and Therapy. Cambridge, pp. 435–440.
10. Gibb WRC (1988) In: Jankovic J and Tolowa E (eds.) Parkinson's Disease and Movement Disorders. Urban and Schwarzenberg, Baltimore, pp. 205–223.
11. Mann DMA, Tucken CM and Yates PO (1987) Neuropathol. Appl. Neurobiol. 13: 123–139.
12. Harman D (1981) PNAS 78: 7124–7128.
13. Weber GF (1990) J. Clin. Chem. Clin. Biochem. 28: 569–603.
14. Fridovich I (1975) Ann. Rev. Biochem. 44: 147–159.
15. Danielczyk W, Streifler M, Konradi C, Riederer P and Moll G (1988) Acta Psychiatr. Scand. 78: 730–736.
16. Adolfsson R, Gottfries CG, Oreland L, Wiberg A and Winblad B (1980) Life Sci. 27: 1029–1034.
17. Subbarao KV, Richardson JS and Ang LC (1990) J. Neurochem. 55: 342–345.
18. Marklund SL, Adolfsson R, Gottfries CG and Winblad B (1985) J. Neurol. Sci. 67: 319–325.
19. Kono Y and Fridovich I (1982) J. Biol. Chem. 257: 5751–5754.
20. Vasudevan PT and Weiland RH (1990) Biotechnol. Bioeng. 36: 783–789.

© 1991 Elsevier Science Publishers B.V. All rights reserved.
Biological Psychiatry, Volume 2. G. Racagni et al., editors.

Analytical epidemiology: Risk factors for Alzheimer's disease

L. Amaducci and A. Lippi
Department of Neurological and Psychiatric Sciences, University of Florence, Florence, Italy

Analytical epidemiology is aimed at stressing an association between a disease and one or more hypothesized risk factors. Hypotheses can be generated from clinical observation, laboratory research and prevalence studies. To test hypotheses two studies designs are available: the retrospective, case-control study and the prospective cohort study.

The present state of knowledge of risk factors for Alzheimer's disease (AD) is briefly discussed.

Age and sex

Epidemiological studies indicated a steep increase of prevalence and incidence rates of AD with age [1]. In some studies the incidence ratio of AD seems to decrease during late old age (after 80 years), but because of the limited number of subjects in this age group the observation has to be considered with caution [2]. Moreover, the age-specific incidence rates are higher in females in almost all the studies [1].

Education

No association has been demonstrated between different levels of education and AD in case-control studies, with the exception of a recent Japanese case-control study [3]. However, some recent prevalence studies on dementia showed an interesting relationship between prevalence rates and education: dementia, AD and vascular dementia were found to be significantly higher in illiterate people than in the educated [4,5].

Although prevalence studies cannot be considered etiologically valuable, the observation of these trends is interesting. Prospective studies could be very useful to demonstrate the possible existence of a relationship between education and dementia.

Presence of dementia among relatives

There has been a long history of reports in the literature on many families in which dementia was present in more than one subject [6]. In some families with early-onset AD, the pattern of inheritance seems to be an autosomal dominant transmission. An increased frequency of AD among relatives of AD patients as compared to the general population was reported in family studies [7]. Similar data have been found comparing relatives of AD patients with those of non-demented controls [8]. Several case-control studies showed a significant association between the presence of dementia among first-degree relatives and AD [9–14]. One case-control study failed to demonstrate such an association in late-onset AD [15].

Supporting the epidemiologic findings, St. George Hyslop and co-workers [16] reported that a gene for familial AD of early onset mapped to the proximal long arm of chromosome 21, while other reports have failed to detect linkage to this location in other families [17].

Recent data, obtained from genetic linkage studies, suggest that AD is not a single entity, but may be the result of genetic defects on chromosome 21 and genetic or non-genetic factors [18].

Down's syndrome

Several observations have reported that patients with Down's syndrome frequently develop dementia when they survive beyond 40 years of age [19]. An increased frequency of Down's syndrome among relatives of AD patients as compared to the general population was reported in the study of Heston and coworkers [7]. Two case-control studies found a significant association between AD and the presence of Down's syndrome in the family [9,14]. In three case-control studies such an association was not observed [10,13,15]. However, because Down's syndrome is a rare condition, it must be taken into account that the simple size of these latter studies appeared insufficient to demonstrate an association with AD.

In conclusion, Down's syndrome in the subject seems to be a risk factor for AD, but there are not sufficient data to consider the presence of Down's syndrome in the family as a risk factor.

Late maternal age at subject's birth

Several studies have investigated late maternal age at the subject's birth as a possible risk factor for AD. Some studies found a significant difference in the mean age of the mother at subject's birth in cases in respect to the controls [20,21]. An Italian case-control study [10] showed a significant association in the comparison of AD cases to population controls, while the association was suggestive but did not reach statistical significance in the comparison with hospital controls. Finally, the association was not demonstrated in other studies [13]. Subgroup analyses of the Italian case-control study indicated that late maternal age may be a specific risk factor for sporadic AD only, but not for familial AD [22].

Head trauma

Head trauma as a risk factor for AD was investigated in several case-control studies. A history of previous head trauma was significantly associated with the disease in 3 studies [9,12,13]. In other studies, head trauma was more frequent in cases than in controls, but the difference did not reach statistical significance [10,11,14,15]. On the other hand, other studies were not able to find any association between head trauma and AD [13,24].

A meta-analysis of several case-control studies performed by Mortimer [25] by using the Mantel-Haenszel method demonstrated a highly significant summary odds ratio (2.77, 95% C.I. = 1.77 – 4.33, $P < 0.001$), despite the fact that the majority of studies failed to find significant associations for this risk factor.

A hypothetical mechanism has been proposed to explain the possible role of head trauma as risk factor for dementia: the direct neuronal damage following head trauma may reduce the safety factor provided by redundancy of the brain tissue [23]. It is also possible that large neuronal membrane destruction may lead to the production of a large amount of amyloid compounds [26].

Depression

It has been postulated that previous psychiatric disorder could be a risk factor for AD. Case-control studies have investigated anxiety and depression as possible risk factors for AD [9,11,14,17]. In some studies a history of depression was significantly more frequent in cases than in controls [13,17] and in one a trend towards previous psychiatric morbidity was noted [9]. Moreover, the association between underactivity as a behavioural trait and AD has been pointed out in two case-control studies [3,14].

Environmental exposure

A wide-ranging search has been made in several studies into environmental exposure as risk factor for dementia, including malnutrition, analgesic abuse, organic solvent exposure, aluminum intake and other occupational exposure. No significant association was found in case-control studies, the only exception being that of smoking [11] and the use of aluminum-containing antiperspirants [12].

The interpretation of these data remains uncertain and further studies are needed.

Conclusion

A few of the proposed risk factors for dementias have been established with certainty, such as age and gender; moreover, Down's syndrome in the subject and a history of dementia in first-degree relatives can be considered risk factors for AD.

Among environmental factors, the role of head trauma as a risk factor for AD, although not well defined, is supported by a number of studies.

Finally, low education as a possible risk factor for dementias is an intriguing finding which deserves further investigation.

In general it is possible to speculate that genetic, chromosomal and environmental factors may be non specific and that the common mechanism involved could be the production of β-amyloid which has been documented as toxic for the neuronal cells [27].

References

1. Rocca WA and Amaducci L (1991) In: Anderson DW (ed.) Neuroepidemiology: A Tribute to Bruce Schoenberg. Boston CRL Press, Boca Raton, Ann Arbor, pp. 55–96.
2. Gruenberg EM (1977) Milkbank Mem. Fund. Q. (Winter) 55: 3–24.
3. Kondo K and Yamashita I (1990) In: Hasegawa K and Homma A (eds.) Psychogeriatrics, Biomedical and Social Advances. Excerpta Medica, Amsterdam, pp. 49–53.
4. Zhang M, Katzman R, Salmon D et al. (1990) Ann. Neurol. 27: 428–437.
5. Bonaiuto S, Rocca WA, Lippi A, Luciani P, Turtù I, Cavarzeran F and Amaducci L (1990) Neurology 40 (Suppl. 1): 346.
6. Lua M (1920) Zschr. F.D. Ges. Neurol. Psychiatry 55: 60.
7. Heston LL, Mastri AR, Anderson VE and White J (1981) Arch. Gen. Psychiatry 38: 1085–1090.
8. Breitner JCS, Silverman JM, Mohs RC and Davis KL (1988) Neurology 38: 207–212.
9. Heyman A, Wilkinson WE, Stafford JA, Helms MJ, Sigmon AH and Weinberg T (1984) Ann. Neurol. 15: 335–341.
10. Amaducci LA, Fratiglioni L, Rocca WA et al. (1986) Neurology 36: 922–931.
11. Shalat SL, Seltzer B, Pidcock C and Baker EL (1987) Neurology 37: 1630–1603.
12. Graves AB, White E, Koepsell T, Reifler BV, van Belle G, Larson EB and Raskind M (1990) Ann. Neurol. 28: 140–148.
13. Ferini-Strambi L, Smirne S, Garancini P, Pinto P and Franceschi M (1990) Neuroepidemiology 9: 39–49.
14. Broe GA, Henderson AS, Creasey H et al. (1990) Neurology 40: 1698–1707.
15. Chandra V, Philipose V, Bell PA, Lazaroff A and Schoenberg BS (1987) Neurology 37: 1295–1300.
16. St. George-Hyslop PH, Tanzi, Re, Polinsky RJ et al. (1987) Science 235: 885–890.
17. Schellenberg GD, Bird TD, Wijsman EM et al. (1988) Science 241: 1507–1510.
18. St George-Hyslop PH, Haines JL, Farrer LA et al. (1990) Nature 347: 194–197.
19. Wisniewski KE, Wisniewski HM and Wen GY (1985) Ann. Neurol. 17: 278–282.
20. Cohen D, Eisdorfer C and Leverenz J (1982) J. Am. Geriatr. Soc. 30: 656–659.
21. Urakami K, Adachi Y and Takahashi K (1989) Arch. Neurol. 46: 38–39.
22. Schoenberg BS, Rocca WA, Fratiglioni L et al. (1988) Neurology 38 (Suppl. 1): 311.
23. Mortimer JA, French LR, Hutton JT and Schuman LM (1985) Neurology 35: 264–267.
24. Chandra V, Kokmen E and Schoenberg BS (1987) Neurology 37 (Suppl. 1): 152.
25. Mortimer JA (1990) In: Wurtman RJ, Corkin S, Growdon JH and Ritter-Walker E (eds.) Advances in Neurology, Vol. 51: Alzheimer's Disease. Raven Press, New York, pp. 27–33.
26. Roberts GW, Allsop D and Bruton C (1990) J. Neurol. Neurosurg. Psychiatry 53: 373–378.
27. Yanker BA, Duffy LR and Kirschner DJ (1990) Science 250: 279–282.

© 1991 Elsevier Science Publishers B.V. All rights reserved.
Biological Psychiatry, Volume 2. G. Racagni et al., editors.

Is "probable Alzheimer's disease" a homogeneous disease entity?

Kaj Blennow, Anders Wallin and Carl-Gerhard Gottfries
Department of Psychiatry and Neurochemistry, University of Göteborg, St. Jörgen Hospital, S-422 03 Hisings Backa, Sweden

Introduction

The term Alzheimer's disease (AD) was originally reserved for dementia in patients with presenile (before 65 years of age) onset, while the expression senile dementia was used when the onset was after 65 years of age. Since the 1960s, largely based on the histopathological observations that NFTs and SPs are found in the brains of both AD and senile dementia patients, these disorders have been held to represent a single, homogeneous entity. However, the scientific basis for combining the disorders has been questioned [1]. The purpose of this study was to further analyse the possible heterogeneity of AD.

Materials and Methods

Forty-one consecutive patients were included, 17 men and 24 women, mean age (±S.D.) 71.2 ± 9.1 years, all fulfilling the criteria for "probable AD" [2], except that mildly demented patients were not included on the grounds that brain-regional symptoms may not have developed in these patients [3,4]. The CSF control material consisted of 50 individuals, 28 men and 22 women, mean age (±S.D.) 71.5 ± 10.8 years, without psychiatric or neurological disease. In the AD group, parietal and confusional symptoms were recorded [4,5]. The albumin ratio (CSF-albumin (mg/l)/serum-albumin (g/l)) was used as a measure of blood-brain barrier (BBB) function. In 26 of the AD patients, the CT scans were reviewed for leuko-araiosis (CT-LA) [6,7]. The Wilcoxon 2-sample test was used for quantitative parameters and the χ^2 test for qualitative parameters. The study was approved by the Ethics Committee, University of Göteborg.

Results

On the basis of the clinical symptomatology, "probable AD" was divided into AD type I (n = 23), with marked parietal symptoms and AD type II (n = 18), with absence of or only mild parietal symptoms. The characteristics of AD type I and AD type II are given in Table 1.

Table 1. Characteristics of AD type I and type II

	AD type I		AD type II	
Parietal symptoms	Marked		Absent/mild	
Severity of dementia		Equal (matched)		
Age at onset (years)	60.3 ± 8.6		72.4 ± 7.2	$P < 0.0001$
Duration (years)	5.7 ± 2.5		5.5 ± 2.8	n.s.
Confusion	5/23 (22%)		17/18 (94%)	$P < 0.0001$
CT-leuko-araiosis	5/15 (33%)		10/11 (91%)	$P < 0.005$
CSF/S albumin ratio	119% of controls		147% of controls	n.s.; $P < 0.0001$

Values are given as mean ± S.D. or number (percentage) of patients.

Discussion

The results suggest heterogeneity of "probable AD", i.e. that, on the basis of clinical symptomatology, two subgroups of patients can be delineated.

AD type I is characterized by memory disturbances and marked parietal symptoms, relatively low age at onset, normal BBB function, and low frequency of CT-LA. These characteristics match the classical description of Alzheimer's disease. Therefore, AD type I is suggested to constitute a "classical" or "pure" AD group. AD type II is characterized by memory disturbances and general cognitive impairment, but absence of or only mild parietal symptoms, high frequency of confusional symptoms, relatively high age at onset, mildly impaired BBB function, and high frequency of CT-LA.

The pathogenetic basis of CT-LA in patients with AD has been suggested to be a small vessel disease, a fibrohyaline non-amyloid arteriolosclerosis in the small penetrating vessels supplying the white matter [8]. Small vessel disease may be a plausible explanation for the BBB dysfunction found in the AD type II group, with high frequency of WMLs.

If leuko-araiosis (LA) in AD patients were age-related changes without clinical relevance, AD patients with and without LA would have a similar symptomatology. In this study, however, AD patients with CT-LA were found to have more general cognitive impairment than AD patients without CT-LA, suggesting that CT-LA in AD patients has clinical significance. Thus, age-related and/or vascular changes with CT-LA may be part of the pathogenesis of AD type II.

Acknowledgements

These studies were made possible through grants from Bohuslandstingets FOU Grupp; Medicinska Fakulteten, University of Göteborg; Svenska Läkaresällskapet;

the Swedish Medical Research Council (03X-627) (21X-05002-14C); Stiftelsen för Gamla Tjänarinnor; Stiftelsen Handlanden Hjalmar Svenssons Forskningsfond; Stiftelsen Professor Bror Gadelius' Minnesfond; Stiftelsen Söderström-Königska Sjukhemmet; Gun and Bertil Stohnes Stiftelse; and Torsten och Ragnar Söderbergs Stiftelser.

References

1. Roth M (1986) Br. Med. Bull. 42: 42–50.
2. McKann G, Drachman D, Folstein M et al. (1984) Neurology 34: 939–944.
3. Lishman WA (1987) Organic Psychiatry, the Psychological Consequences of Cerebral Disorder, 2nd Edn. Blackwell Scientific Publications, Oxford.
4. Blennow K, Wallin A and Gottfries CG (1991) Int. J. Geriatr. Psychiatry (in press).
5. Blennow K, Wallin A and Gottfries CG (1990) Aging 2: 395–401.
6. Steingart A, Hachinski VC, Lau C et al. (1987) Arch. Neurol. 44: 36–39.
7. Wallin A, Blennow K, Uhlemann C et al. (1989) Acta Neurol. Scand. 80: 518–523.
8. Bryn A and Englund E (1986) Ann. Neurol. 19: 253–262.

© 1991 Elsevier Science Publishers B.V. All rights reserved.
Biological Psychiatry, Volume 2. G. Racagni et al., editors.

Alzheimer's disease: A vascular disorder?

Anders Wallin, Kaj Blennow and Carl-Gerhard Gottfries
Department of Psychiatry and Neurochemistry, University of Göteborg, St. Jörgen Hospital, 5-422 03 Hisings-Backa, Sweden

Introduction

Today, multi-infarct dementia (MID), a disorder characterized by multiple infarcts of 50–100 ml [1], is considered to be the main vascular dementia (VAD) entity. This position has been questioned, however, since, using brain imaging techniques, widespread white matter lesions (WMLs) without prominent infarcts have been found in VAD [2]. WMLs have also been found in Alzheimer's disease (AD) [3], particularly in patients with dementia onset after 65 years of age (AD type II) [4]. The aim of this investigation was to compare VAD with AD type II, especially with regard to symptomatology and WMLs.

Materials and Methods

All subjects met the criteria for the symptom complex of dementia according to DSM III-R. A vascular origin of the dementia was considered when transitory ischemic attacks (TIA)/stroke episodes and/or pronounced vascular diseases, such as arterial hypertension or diabetes mellitus with complications, were found. When, in addition, non-vascular secondary causes of dementia had been excluded and if the subjects did not fulfil the NINCDS-ADRDA criteria for "probable Alzheimer's disease" [5], a VAD diagnosis was chosen (n = 31; mean age ± (S.D.) 73 ± 8 years). When the subjects fulfilled the NINCDS-ADRDA criteria for "probable Alzheimer's disease" [5] but prominent parietal-lobe symptoms were absent, they were classified as AD type II patients [4] (n = 44; mean age ± (S.D.) 77 ± 5 years).

Frontal and subcortical symptoms and symptoms of confusion were recorded [6,7]. WMLs, also called leuko-araiosis [8] and defined as hypodensities around the ventricles, were evaluated on computed tomography (CT-LA). The albumin ratio [cerebrospinal fluid (CSF)-albumin (mg/l)/serum-albumin (g/l)] was used as a measure of the blood-brain barrier (BBB) function. CSF-sulphatide was determined using a microimmunoaffinity technique [9]. Postmortem sulphatide determinations [10] were performed on 7 VAD patients (mean age ± (S.D.) 81 ± 5 years) and 11 AD type II patients (mean age ± (S.D.) 82 ± 6 years). The severity of dementia was of the same magnitude in VAD as in AD type II.

Table 1. Characteristics of VAD and AD type II patients

	VAD	AD type II	Significance
Frontal symptoms	24/31 (77%)	23/44 (52%)	$P < 0.05$
Subcortical symptoms	21/31 (68%)	16/44 (36%)	$P < 0.01$
Confusion	13/30 (43%)	26/44 (59%)	N.S.
Leuko-araiosis (CT)	17/20 (85%)	24/30 (80%) 26/34 (76%)	N.S.
CSF-sulphatide (nmol/l)	307 ± 118 (212% of controls)	197 ± 84 (136% of controls)	$P < 0.001$
Postmortem sulphatide (pmol/g, ww)	8.3 ± 2.8 (55% of controls)	9.9 ± 2.8 (66% of controls)	N.S.
CSF/serum albumin ratio	8.5 ± 3.8 (149% of controls)	7.1 ± 3.1 (125% of controls)	$P < 0.05$

Values are given as frequencies and percentage of patients or as mean ± S.D. Significances of group differences refer to VAD vs. AD type II.

Results

The results are given in Table 1.

Discussion

In our studies on VAD, frontosubcortical symptomatology, high frequency of CT-LA, BBB dysfunction, increase in CSF-sulphatide and postmortem reduction in sulphatide indicate that the subcortical white-matter region is disturbed in this disorder. The pathogenetic basis of WMLs in VAD is unclear, but appears to be associated with vessel wall damage (hyalinosis) of the small vessels [11]. The pathogenetic importance of the WMLs in VAD is also unclear, but the high frequency of frontosubcortical symptomatology indicates that the symptomatology is white-matter-induced. Thus, VAD appears to be not only a question of MID but also of "subcortical white matter dementia" [2].

In our studies on AD type II, high frequency of CT-LA, BBB dysfunction and postmortem reduction in sulphatide suggest that the subcortical white-matter region is disturbed in AD type II, too. As in VAD, the pathogenetic basis of WMLs in AD type II is unclear, but the similarities between WMLs in VAD and AD (CT-LA, postmortem sulphatide) argue in favour of a vascular origin of WMLs in AD. The less prominent BBB dysfunction and the CSF-sulphatide increase in AD type II compared with VAD suggest less pronounced vascular involvement in AD type II than in VAD. Regarding the pathogenetic importance of WMLs in AD type II, it has been suggested that WMLs in AD type II contribute to the dementia together with the Alzheimer encephalopathy [12]. Thus, AD type II appears to be a question not only of Alzheimer encephalopathy, but also of vascular lesions.

References

1. Tomlinson BE, Blessed G and Roth M (1970) J. Neurol. Sci. 11: 205–242.
2. Wallin A and Blennow K (1991) ADAD-IJ (accepted).
3. Brun A and Englund E (1986) Ann. Neurol. 19: 253–262.
4. Blennow K, Wallin A and Gottfries CG (1991) This volume.
5. McKhann G, Drachman D, Folstein M et al. (1984) Neurology 34: 939–944.
6. Wallin A, Blennow K, Gottfries CG (1991) Int Geriatr. Psychiatry (in press).
7. Blennow K, Wallin A and Gottfries CG (1991) Int. Geriatr. Psychiatry (in press).
8. Hachinski VC, Potter P and Merskey H (1987) Arch. Neurol. 44: 21–23.
9. Davidsson P, Fredman P, Månsson JE et al. (1991) Clin. Chim. Acta (in press).
10. Fewster ME, Burns BJ and Mead JE (1969) 43: 120–126.
11. Ferszt R and Cervos-Navarro J (1983) In: Cervos-Navarro I and Sarkander HI (eds.) Brain Aging: Neuropathology and Neuropharmacology, Aging Vol. 21. Raven Press, New York, pp. 133–151.
12. Blennow K and Wallin A (1991) (submitted).

© 1991 Elsevier Science Publishers B.V. All rights reserved.
Biological Psychiatry, Volume 2. G. Racagni et al., editors.

Co-dergocrine type drugs in the pharmacotherapy of mental and cognitive disorders in aging

Bernd Saletu

Department of Psychiatry, School of Medicine, University of Vienna, Währinger Gürtel 18–20, A-1090 Vienna, Austria

Introduction

The chemical history of co-dergocrine mesylate (CDM), the prototype of the class, dates back to 1906 when Barger and Carr in England and Kraft in Switzerland almost simultaneously isolated the pure active principle of rye ergot. Investigating the pharmacology of the latter, Barger and Dale observed antagonistic effects to adrenaline and sympathetic functions, a uterotonic action and also a high toxicity leading to the name "ergotoxine". In 1943 the Sandoz chemists, Stoll and Hofmann, discovered that ergotoxine consists of three alkaloids (ergocristine, ergocornine and ergokryptine), the dihydro-derivatives of which constitute hydergine®. This combination of dihydroergocornine, dihydroergocristine, dihydro-α-ergokryptine and dihydro-β-ergokryptine in the proportion 3:3:2:1 showed as compared with ergotoxine reduced toxicity, loss of uterotonic action and an enhanced adreno-sympathicolytic effect. The resultant main effects (peripheral vasodilatation and lowering of blood pressure) led in 1949 to indications such as peripheral vascular disorders, hypertension and angina pectoris. Nicergoline (NIC), a 5-bromo-nicotinic acid ester of 1-methyl-10-α-methoxy-dihydrolysergol was selected from a series of nicotinic acid esters because of its potent α blockade and was tested clinically as a peripheral and cerebrovascular vasodilator. Further co-dergocrine-type compounds include terguride – a dopaminergic D_2 agonist designed for Parkinson patients but also tried in Alzheimer's disease (AD) – CBM 36733 – a 2 methyl-α-ergocriptine with dopaminergic and serotoninergic properties – and RU-41656.

As in the fifties and sixties, senile dementia was believed to be due to cerebrovascular insufficiency of arteriosclerotic origin, early clinical pharmacological studies tried to find a possible effect of co-dergocrine type drugs on cerebral blood flow. Disappointment about negative results in this regard was alleviated by the increasing body of evidence that senile-mental impairment was only due in a minority of patients to cerebral ischemia while CDM-related drugs produced more positive effects on metabolic processes.

Pharmacology

The multiplicity of the mode of action of hydergine such as on cerebral circulation (improvement of micro-circulation, inhibition of platelet aggregation), brain metabolism (increase of oxygen uptake, glucose uptake, normalization of glucose metabolism and of glycolysis, increased neuronal ATP content), cerebral neurotransmission (increase of acetylcholine synthesis and the number of ACH receptors, adreno-sympathicolytic properties, affinity for d-dopamine receptors and serotonin receptors resulting in agonistic effects) and synaptic plasticity (increase in number of total compact surface of synaptic junctions) is obviously instrumental for therapeutic effectiveness. Moreover, in human pharmacological trials we demonstrated improvement of vigilance as characterized by a decrease of δ/θ and increase of α and α adjacent β activity both after CDM and NIC. The latter changes were opposite to age-related alterations in brain function. The acute pharmaco-EEG changes could be replicated by sub-acute trials showing also an improvement in noopsychic and thymopsychic functions of elderly volunteers. These single lead results were impressively confirmed by modern brain mapping techniques. Investigating event-related potentials we found an augmentation of P300 amplitudes in elderly subjects, an indicator of improved central cognitive processing. Pharmacokinetic and bioavailability studies showed after oral dosing a T_{max} between 0.5–2.3 h and elimination half-lives of 1.5–4.1 h. Hepatic first pass effects and biotransformations are important, there is a rapid and large tissue diffusion while plasma levels remain low and excretion occurs mainly through the bile. Pharmacokinetics of CDM in the aged are modified considerably as renal clearance is reduced by 50% and the AUC is one third higher in the aged than in young adults. By a facilitated absorption system (FAS), peak concentrations were delayed by 1–2.5 h, with elimination half-lives running around 14–6 h (vs. 12.9 with normal tablets). NIC, because of fast metabolism, reaches the system circulation in the form of 2 metabolites: the ester-linkage hydrolysate 1-methyl-10-methoxydihydrolysergol (1-MMDL) and its demethylated derivative 10-methoxydihydrolysergol (MDL). Peak plasma levels of these 2 metabolites are reached at about 1 and 3 h (in the elderly 3 and 4 h) and their plasma half-lives are about 2 and 11 h respectively (in the elderly between 3–5 and 15–16 h). Seventy percent of the dose is excreted in urine, mostly as the demethylated derivative of the ester linkage hydrolysite. The remainder is probably excreted via the bile and is recovered in the faeces.

Clinical studies

With CDM 52 double-blind controlled trials were performed between 1969 and 1989, some of them probably not meeting today's high methodological standards. Thirty-nine of them were placebo-controlled; in 3 studies treatment duration was up to 6 weeks, in 36 studies 7–12 weeks, in 9 studies 13–26 weeks and in 4 more than 6 months. Twenty-two out of 31 studies showed CDM superior in global assessment, 34 of 35 in symptom changes, 6 out of 6 in performance, 5 out of 5 in neurophysiological measures. Thirty studies showed improvement in depressed mood and emotional instability, 27 in cognitive dysfunction, 20 in social withdrawal and lack of initiative, 17 in somatic symptoms and complaints and 9 in impaired activities of daily life. Thus CDM was effective on both affective and cognitive symptoms of age-related mental decline. With NIC there exist at least 10 double-blind, placebo-controlled trials, mostly with doses of 20 mg t.i.d. and 30 mg b.i.d. In a large study in 315 patients with mild to moderate dementia, the therapeutic effect of NIC was significantly greater than that of placebo but also more sustained, steadily increasing with time. Tolerability of ergotalkaloids is quite good with only 2 out of 315 patients treated with 3 mg/day CDM or 1 of 30 patients taking 6 mg/day or 2 of 27 taking 12 mg/day complaining of side-effects. Likewise, only 75 out of 1351 NIC patients reported adverse reactions (mostly involving the digestive tract, CNS and cardiovascular system). In open field studies, several authors observed a decrease in frequency of virtually all categories of complaints with time (13% in the 4th week vs. 4.3% in the 24th week).

New approaches

In recent years, doses higher than 3–6 mg CDM/day have been tried. While the tolerance was generally very good even after doses up to 30–45 mg/day, the therapeutic benefit of such dosage augmentations is still discussed. In order to elucidate this question, we have employed the hypoxia model in which normal volunteers inhale a hypoxic gas mixture of 9.8–8.6% O_2 which results in a transient hypoxic hypoxidosis [1,2]. The latter is measured at the neurophysiological and behavioural level by EEG brain mapping and psychometry, respectively. Single doses of 5 mg CDM significantly attenuated brain dysfunction and reduced the hypoxia-induced deterioration of performance from 49–26%. However, further augmentation of hypoxia in another study resulted in a loss of brain protection even when CDM was given daily over 2 weeks. In a most recent study we investigated central of effects of higher doses (6 mg and 9 mg CDM) under 6,000 m and 7,000 m altitude conditions. While 6 mg CDM showed significant antihypoxidotic properties in moderate hypoxia and less so in marked hypoxia, an increase of the dosage to 9 mg CDM resulted in less protective effects.

References

1. Saletu B, Grünberger J and Anderer P (1990) Int. J. Clin. Pharmacol. Ther. Toxicol. 28: 510–524.
2. Saletu B, Grünberger J, Linzmayer L and Anderer P (1990) J. Neural Transm. P-D Sect. 2: 305–325.

© 1991 Elsevier Science Publishers B.V. All rights reserved.
Biological Psychiatry, Volume 2. G. Racagni et al., editors.

Neuropeptides: Current status in treatment of dementia

Per Kragh-Sørensen
Odense University Hospital, Department of Psychiatry, DK 5000 Odense C, Denmark

Introduction

Neuropeptides have been the focus of interest for at least 20 years and more than 50 have been identified in the central nervous system. Peptides are compounds consisting of 2 or more (up to 100) amino acid residues that are connected via amide (peptide) bonds. Several neuropeptides have been identified in the post-mortem human brain and spinal cord [1]. The function of most of them is unknown. Many are present in peptidergic neuronal networks in the brain, indicating that they act as "neurotransmitters", "neuromodulators" or "neurohormones". In many cases they coexist with classical transmitters such as dopamine, noradrenaline, serotonin, acetylcholine and amino acid transmitters [2]. During the last few years, several exciting developments have taken place which more firmly underline a messenger role for peptides in the nervous system. Most importantly, it is now clear that peptides have their own receptors in the nervous system.

Available experimental findings show that all neuropeptides studied so far are involved in a large number of biochemical, physiological, autonomic and behavioural functions [3]. This observation combined with reported neuropeptide alterations in CSF and/or postmortem brain tissue in various psychiatric disorders, inclusive dementia, implies the fundamental role of neuropeptides in the balance between normal and disturbed brain function.

Neuropeptides and dementia

Especially two classes of neuropeptides have been investigated and are used in the treatment of demented patients, those related to the adrenocorticotropic hormone (ACTH) and to vasopressin (VP) [4].

The literature reviewed (subchronic administration) on ACTH-like peptides (Table 1) and VP peptides (Table 2) is confusing. The results in the clinic have so far been less dramatic than the developments in the laboratory. Severe design problems in trials published to date make conclusions on therapy efficacy and the place of neuropeptides in the future treatment of dementia very difficult. One of the problems may be the mode of administration of neuropeptides and the penetration of sufficient amounts through the blood-brain barrier.

The need to define homogeneous diagnostic groups with mildly demented cases

Table 1. ACTH peptides[a]: placebo-controlled clinical studies (AD/SDAT)[b]

Authors (cf. [4])	No. of patients	Treatment period	Dosage (mg/day)	Results
Branconnier and Cole (1977)	40	1	5–20	No effect
Bravermann et al. (1981)	35	4	40	Anxiety ↓; Motivation ↑; Initiative ↑; Sociability ↑
Ferris et al. (1981)	50	2	10–20	Depression ↓; Anxiety ↓; Social Competence ↑
Willner (1981)	43	1	10–20	Ward behaviour ↑; Sociability ↑
Martin et al. (1983)	34	4	40	No effect
Soininen et al. (1985)	77	6	40	No effect
Kragh-Sørensen et al. (1987)	156	6	5–80	Significant effect[c] (SCAG total)

[a]Subchronic administration: only drug investigated: Org. 2766;
[b]Several other studies inconclusive [4];
[c]Clinically "significant" for 25% of the patients [4].

is evident [5]. No valid procedure whereby severity of dementia can be graded or operational response criteria defined is in general use [6]. Due to these problems, reports that indicate improvement by a particular drug are often not confirmed by subsequent investigations. At present it is fair to conclude that the effect of ACTH- and VP-peptide agonists on dementia syndromes is not very promising.

Table 2. VP peptides: placebo-controlled studies

Authors (cf. [7])	Patients (no.)	Drug	Dose/day	Treatment period (days)	Efficacy
Ferris et al. (1981)	20[a]	LVP	20 IU	7	Questionable
Weingartner et al. (1981)	7[b]	DDAVP	30–60 μg	10	Yes
Tinklenberg et al. (1981)	3[a]	DDAVP	30–60 μg	3	No
Durso et al. (1982)	17[a]	LVP	16 IU	10	Questionable
Franceschi et al. (1982)	10[a]	LVP	15 IU	7	No
Jenkins et al. (1985)	3[b]	DDAVP	160 μg	7	No
Jennekens-Schinkel et al. (1985)	4[b]	DGAVP	1 mg	5	No
Peabody et al. (1985)	9[a]	DGAVP	202 μg	5	No
Wolters et al. (1990)	115	DGAVP	0.5 or 2 mg	84	No

[a] Between subject comparison; [b] Within subject comparison.

Future perspectives

More recently, several non-peptide antagonists of peptides that can cross the blood-brain barrier have been developed. This development is providing tools that are needed to establish the physiological role of peptides in the nervous system and forms a rational basis for development of new drug therapies for dementia. It can be expected that the drugs presently used in treatment will be replaced by neuropeptides, neuropeptide analogues and eventually their more rigid imitations with more specific effects and fewer side-effects than the drugs in use today.

References

1. Høkfeldt T, Johansson O, Ljungdahl A, Lundberg JM and Schultzberg M (1980) Nature 284: 515–521.
2. Høkfeldt T, Johansson O and Godstein M (1984) Science 225: 1325–1334.
3. De Wied D and Van Ree JM (1989) Eur. Arch. Psychiatr. Neurol. Sci. 238: 323–331.
4. Kragh-Sørensen P and Lolk A (1987) Progr. Brain Res. 72: 269–277.
5. Nielsen H, Lolk A, Pedersen I, Autzen M, Sennef C and Kragh-Sørensen P (1991) Acta Psychiatr. Scand. (accepted for publication).
6. Lolk A, Nielsen H and Kragh-Sørensen P (1988) Acta Psychiatr. Scand. 78: 592–598.
7. Wolters EC, Riekkinen P, Lowenthal A, Van Der Plaats JJ, Zwart JMT and Sennef C (1990) Neurology 40: 1099–1101.

© 1991 Elsevier Science Publishers B.V. All rights reserved.
Biological Psychiatry, Volume 2. G. Racagni et al., editors.

On cognition-enhancing properties of antidepressants (including selegiline)

Peter Gaszner
National Institute for Nervous and Mental Diseases, Budapest, Hungary

A number of antidepressant drugs have been developed for the treatment of mental disorders not necessarily related to cognitive and memory disturbances in elderly patients.

Indeloxazine is a mixed inhibitor of noradrenaline and serotonin reuptake, showing an enhancing effect on learning behaviour and antiamnestic activity and protection against anoxia. Teniloxazine is another mixed inhibitor of amine reuptake, eliciting anti-amnestic effects. Mimaprine is not an inhibitor of amine uptake, but it seems to be active in patients with senile dementia of the Alzheimer type or in multi-infarct dementia [1]. First indications of positive effects of fluvoxamine on memory performance in chronic alcoholic organic brain syndrome have been presented [2]. Increased monoaminergic deficits and increased MAO-B activity in aged and demented patients are well known (Strolin et al., 1989; and [3]).

Selegiline (L-deprenyl) is well known selective MAO-B inhibitor and anti-Parkinsonian agent [4], but has antidepressant activity [5] and has an effect on cognitive functions in Alzheimer type demented patients (Campi et al., 1990; and [6–9]).

It has been established that the monoamine neurotransmitter system, along with the cholinergic system, have important roles in cognition and are disrupted in patients with dementia of the Alzheimer type. This suggests that monoamine-enhancing drugs might ameliorate cognitive symptoms in patients with Alzheimer type dementia [6].

Table 1. Mean (± S.D.) scores on Blessed's Dementia Scale (BDS) in 20 patients treated with selegiline and placebo

BDS	Baseline	One month	Two months	Three months
Part I (autonomy in daily living)				
Selegiline	8.11 ± 1.21	7.41 ± 1.01	6.12 ± 1.09[a,b]	5.4 ± 1.11[a,b]
Placebo	8.19 ± 1.31	8.15 ± 1.23	8.01 ± 1.12	8.11 ± 1.1
Part II (information, memory and concentration)				
Selegiline	16 ± 2.12	20 ± 1.29[a]	25 ± 3.16[a,b]	26 ± 2.91[a,b]
Placebo	17 ± 3.01	21 ± 2.14	18 ± 2.19	17 ± 1.89

[a] $P < 0.01$ vs. baseline; [b] $P < 0.01$ vs. placebo.

Table 2. Mean (± S.D.) scores on Hamilton Depression Rating Scale (HAMD) in 20 patients (selegiline and placebo)

HAMD	Baseline	One month	Three months
Selegiline	30 ± 7.41	22 ± 9.12[a,b]	21 ± 8.96[a,b]
Placebo	29 ± 8.12	30 ± 8.02	31 ± 8.73

[a]$P < 0.01$ vs. baseline; [b]$P < 0.01$ vs. placebo.

A study was conducted on 20 patients with primary degenerative dementia (according to DSM III) and probable Alzheimer type dementia (according to Mc Khann et al.); the score was between 15 and 25 on the Mini-Mental State Examination. Patients scored highly on the Hamilton Depression Rating Scale. The clinical trial's duration was two 3-month periods with single-blind L-deprenyl treatment or placebo as randomly designed crossover study. The patients had given their informed consent before the 7-day washout period. Half of the patients were randomly assigned to treatment with selegiline, 10 mg each morning for 90 days; the other half received placebo. After 90 days the patients had 7 days washout period and then switched treatment.

Efficacy of treatment was evaluated by means of the following battery of tests, administered at baseline and after 1, 2 and 3 months of treatment: Hamilton Depression Rating Scale, Blessed's Dementia Scale (part I and II), five items and short story subtests of the Randt memory test and the digit span forward test from the Wechsel Memory Scale. Adverse effects were measured and blood chemistry was analyzed.

Results

The evaluation of the patients either in the selegiline or in the placebo group is summarized in Tables 1 and 2. The analysis of the data showed the greater efficacy of selegiline compared to placebo. No adverse events were found; tolerance and safety were good.

The results indicate that in patients with Alzheimer type dementia selegiline reduced the signs and symptoms of mental deterioration including depression. In most of the tests, selegiline (10 mg/day) was much more effective than placebo in improving higher cognitive functions and reducing impairment in daily living. In particular short and long-term memory, concentration, attention and cognitive functions as well as depression were positively affected by selegiline.

References

1. Fröstl W and Maitre L (1989) Pharmacopsychiatry 22 (Suppl.): 54-100.

2. Martin PR, Adinoff B, Bone GAH, Stapleton JM, Eckardt MJ and Linnoila (1987) Clin. Pharmacol. Ther. 41: 211 (Abstr. IIC-3).
3. Oreland L and Gottfries CG (1986) Progr. Neuro-Psychopharmacol. Biol. Psychiatry 10: 533–540.
4. Knoll J (1989) Acta Neurol. Scand. 126: 83–91.
5. Mann JJ, Aarons SF and Wilner PJ (1989) Arch. Gen. Psychiatry 46: 45–50.
6. Tariot PN, Sunderland T, Cohen RM, Newhouse PA, Mueller EA and Murphy DL (1988) J. Clin. Psychopharmacol. 8: 23–27.
7. Falsaperla A, Preti PAM and Olini C (1990) Clin. Ther. 12: 376–384.
8. Monteverde A, Gnemmi P, Rossi F and Finali GC (1990) Clin. Ther. 12: 315–322.
9. Piccinin GL, Finali C and Piccirilli M (1990) Clin. Neuropharmacol. 13: 147–163.

Anticonvulsants, epilepsy and organic mental disorders

© 1991 Elsevier Science Publishers B.V. All rights reserved.
Biological Psychiatry, Volume 2. G. Racagni et al., editors.

Animal models of chemically induced lesions of the central cholinergic system

Israel Hanin

Department of Pharmacology and Experimental Therapeutics, Loyola University Chicago Stritch School of Medicine, 2160 S., First Avenue, Maywood, IL 60153, U.S.A.

At first glance it might seem unusual that a presentation on the subject of animal models of chemically-induced *lesions* is included in a symposium dealing with the *pharmacotherapy* of brain lesions. However, there is an excellent rationale for such an arrangement, since a reliable animal model would be invaluable for the purpose of developing appropriate treatment strategies for the disease being modeled. It is, of course, impossible to mimic in an animal model all aspects of a particular disease state caused by brain lesions. One could, nevertheless, at least strive to achieve as good a match as possible for the neurochemical, behavioral and neuropathological features of the disease that is to be modeled. Always keeping the limitations of the specific model in mind, one should then be able to develop some rational approaches to the development of suitable drugs and experimental strategies for the treatment of such lesions, or for the alleviation of some of the symptoms causes by these lesions.

The chemically-induced lesion of the central cholinergic system has been the focus of considerable investigation over almost the past two decades. Emphasis in this arena was particularly stimulated following a variety of observations, initiated in 1976, linking Alzheimer's disease with a central cholinergic hypofunction [1–16]. A number of approaches have been attempted. These range from the electrolytic or surgical lesion [17–18], to the employment of various types of pharmacological agents which have the ability to more selectively affect cholinergic function in vivo.

One of these agents is AF64A (ethylcholine aziridinium), which is structurally related to choline and is targeted toward the active uptake sites of choline at the level of the cholinergic nerve terminal. Its aziridinium moiety renders it cytotoxic, and hence, it serves as a selective cholinotoxin at the cholinergic nerve terminal in vivo [19–21].

Another family of agents are the "excitotoxins" (e.g. kainic, ibotenic, quinolinic, quisqualic, or N-methyl-D-aspartic acids), which can selectively destroy perikarya without affecting axons of passage. Their accurate placement in the brain at a site with a concentrated population of cholinergic cell bodies (e.g. in the nucleus basalis of Meynert) will result in the lesion of these cell bodies, and hence the degeneration of their cholinergic projections [22–35].

Other potential agents for lesioning the cholinergic nerve terminal include fimbria fornix resulted in a decreased performance in a spatial learning task and in retention of a passive avoidance response. Peptide treatment improved the performance in the spatial learning task but not that in the passive avoidance test. This differential effect underscores the notion that the enhancement of post-lesion functional recovery depends not only on the nature of the lesion but also on the behavioral paradigm used [7]. In none of these studies was an attempt made to study possible peptide effects on the post-lesion plasticity in the affected neuronal circuits. In fact, the relatively short period between lesion and recovery of function suggests that the recovery is not related to possible primary sprouting of afflicted neuronal processes. However, in a series of studies on the effect of neuropeptide treatment on recovery of function following a lesion in the n. accumbens, the issue of neural plasticity was addressed in more detail [8].

Destruction of dopamine terminals in the nucleus accumbens by local application of the neurotoxin 6-hydroxydopamine (6-OHDA) resulted in a temporary reduction in motor activity 1–2 weeks following the lesion. Spontaneous functional recovery from the lesion occurred within 3–4 weeks. This functional recovery was accompanied by a development of postsynaptic receptor supersensitivity which may compensate for the reduced levels of dopamine. In addition, denervation supersensitivity was followed by reinnervation of the lesioned area by dopaminergic fibres, although the origin of these DA fibres has still not been elucidated (Vos et al., in preparation). Daily treatment with an $ACTH_{4-9}$ analogue during the first week following the lesion shortened the functional recovery period to 7 days and facilitated the development of the supersensitivity. Peptide treatment was effective after local subcutaneous and oral administration. Local treatment with antibodies raised against α-MSH or the $ACTH_{4-9}$ analogue during the first week after the lesion caused a delay in the spontaneous functional recovery, suggesting that endogenous ACTH/MSH-like factors are involved in the patho-

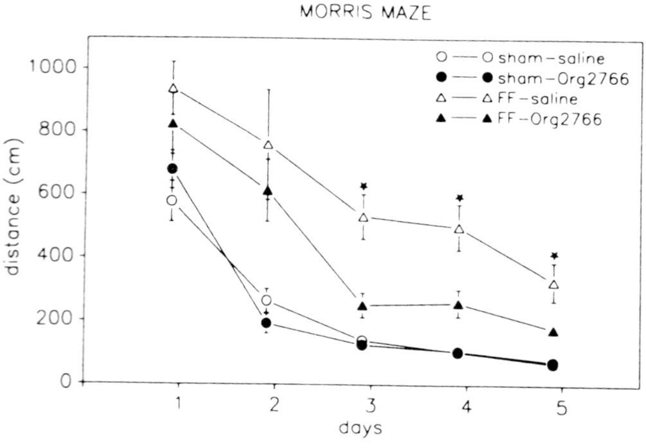

Fig. 1. The distance (cm) swum to find the platform in a Morris maze mean ± S.E.M.). FF = fimbria fornix lesion; Org 2766 = $ACTH_{4-9}$ analogue (from Spruijt et al., 1990)

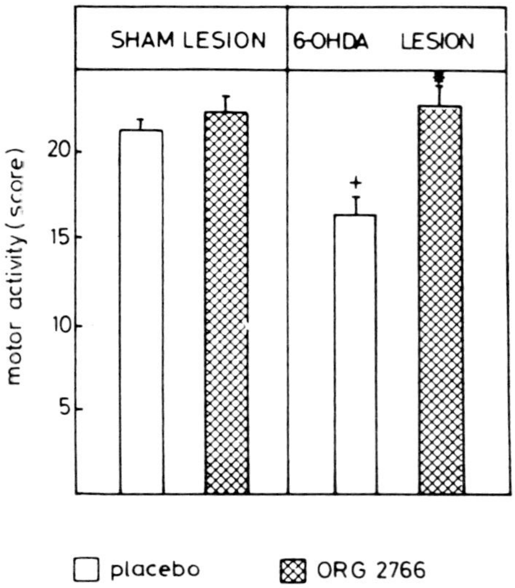

Fig. 2. Motor activity of rats (n = 12–15/group, 7 days after the induction of bilateral sham or 6-OHDA lesions in the nucleus accumbens. Influence of treatment with an $ACTH_{4-9}$ analogue (Wolterink et al., 1990); + different from sham-lesion ($P < 0.05$); * different from placebo treatment ($P < 0.05$).

physiological processes which follow nerve tissue damage and which serve to restore function.

Whether the mechanism of action of the peptides in the CNS lesions is similar to that in PNS lesions is still a subject of study. Differences between the effectiveness of the peptide treatment in the two models concern the effective route of administration (see above) and the amino acid sequence in the primary peptide structure in which the information is encoded (PNS: amino acids $ACTH_{5-7}$; CNS: amino acids $ACTH_{7-10}$). Nonetheless, it has been suggested that both in the PNS and the CNS the peptide treatment is effective in the early phase of the post-lesion repair process by mimicking or amplifying an endogenous signal.

References

1. Bär PR, Schrama LH and Gispen WH (1990) In: Wied D (ed.) Neuropeptides, Basics and Perspectives. Elsevier Science Publishers, Amsterdam, pp. 175–211.
2. Gerritsen van der Hoop R, Vecht CJ, Van den Burg MEL, Elderson A, Haanstra W, Boogerd W, Heijmans JJ, Vries EP, Van Houwelingen JC, Jennekens FGI and Gispen WH (1990) N. Engl. J. Med. 322: 89–94.
3. Flohr H (ed.) (1988) Post-Lesion Neural Plasticity. Springer-Verlag, Berlin.
4. Isaacson RL and Polawsky A (1983) Behav. Neural. Biol. 39: 52–59.
5. Nyakas C, Veldhuis HD and De Wied D (1985) Brain Res. Bull. 15: 257–265.
6. Landfield PW, Baskin RU and Pitler TA (1981) Science 214: 581–584.
7. Spruijt B, Pitsikas N, Algeri S and Gispen WH (1990) Brain Res. 527: 192–197.
8. Wolterink G, Van Zanten E, Kamsteeg H, Radhakishun FS and Van Ree JM (1990) Brain Res. 507: 92–120.

© 1991 Elsevier Science Publishers B.V. All rights reserved.
Biological Psychiatry, Volume 2. G. Racagni et al., editors.

Neuropeptides in the treatment of nervous system lesions

W.H. Gispen, I.M. van Ree, B.M. Spruijt, G. Wolterink and D. de Wied
Department of Pharmacology, Rudolf Magnus Institute, Vondellaan 6, 3521 GD, Utrecht, The Netherlands

Peptides related to ACTH and MSH but without endocrine activity were shown to stimulate differentiation and maturation of neurons from the central or peripheral nervous system in culture. To date it is not yet clear whether such trophic effects are brought about via a direct (neuronal) or indirect (non-neuronal cells) mechanism of action [1]. In the last decade or so, various research groups have investigated whether the trophic feature of these peptides is of benefit to post-lesion repair in the peripheral or central nervous system.

Several authors have demonstrated that ACTH and MSH-like peptide facilitate recovery of function following mechanical damage to the sciatic nerve in rats [1]. Peptide treatment was effective following subcutaneous (repeated injections, mini-pump, degradable capsules) or local administration at the site of the lesion, but not following oral administration. The treatment should commence immediately following surgery, last during the first week or so thereafter and consist of doses in the range of 7.5–75 µg/kg s.c. Their mechanism of action is unclear, albeit that the peptides do not increase elongation rate of newly-formed axons, but increase the number of sprouts that are crossing the distal lesion border. Interestingly, when the peripheral nerve is compromised by means other than mechanical trauma, f.i. by intoxication or metabolic disturbance, these peptides were shown to exert marked neuroprotection from such noxious influence. Thus, in animal models of diabetic or chemotherapy-related neuropathies treatment with an $ACTH_{4-9}$ analogue markedly improved nerve conduction velocities which were otherwise depressed [1]. In fact, women being treated with a cisplatin-based chemotherapy directed against ovarian cancer and receiving the $ACTH_{4-9}$ analogue do not develop signs and symptoms of a cisplatin-related neurotoxicity [2].

In various but not all experimental conditions of brain damage, peptide treatment was effective in facilitating post-lesion recovery of function. In frogs and monkeys, $ACTH_{1-10}$ enhances balance compensation following labyrinthectomy, presumably by affecting adaptive responses in the neuronal network involved [3]. Peptide treatment improved impoverished Y maze performance of rats bearing a lesion in the n. paraventricularis or reduced hyperemotionality of rats bearing a lesion in the septal complex [4,5]. Lesions in limbic structures are of special interest to the study of brain aging and behaviour as aging rodents, primates and humans show age-related pathology in their hippocampus. In aging rats, chronic treatment with an $ACTH_{4-9}$ analogue counteracts the hippocampal damage and improves the corresponding deficit in cognition [6]. Unilateral transection of the several chemical analogs of choline which might act as false neurotransmitters in vivo [36–44], inhibitors of acetylcholine transport into vesicles at the cholinergic nerve terminal in vivo [45–48], and other aziridinium analogs of agents known to interact with the cholinergic nervous system in vivo [49–52].

Of the above, each type of pharmacological agent has its own particular strengths, as well as weaknesses as a specific cholinotoxin. AF64A exerts its neurotoxic action directly at the cholinergic nerve terminal, and thus it is cholino-selective. AF64A's window of selectivity is narrow, however, and is dependent on the dose administered, as well as the site of its administration in vivo [19–20]. The excitotoxins, while shown to lesion cholinergic pathways projecting to the cerebral cortex, rely for their activity on the presence of different subtypes of glutamate receptors for their neurotoxic effects and do not discriminate between cholinergic perikarya and those of other neurotransmitter systems [53–59]. Hence their precise placement in the brain is crucial, otherwise their effect may not be cholinospecific. The other mentioned agents have not been studied as extensively as yet, as have AF64A and the excitotoxins. Thus, an evaluation of their potential use as cholino-toxins in vivo awaits further documentation.

The remarkable natural resilience of the cholinergic nerve terminal makes it highly resistant to perturbation and modification. Therefore it has been difficult to develop a selective cholinotoxin which is able to induce a long-lasting cholinergic deficiency in vivo. It is, nevertheless, encouraging to note that several promising approaches, described above, have been applied to date with considerable success.

References

1. Davies P and Maloney AJF (1976) Lancet ii: 403.
2. Bowen D, Smith CB, White P and Davison AN (1976) Brain 99: 459–496.
3. Boyd WD, Graham-White J, Blackwood G, Glen I and McQueen J (1977) Lancet ii: 711.
4. Perry EK, Perry RH, Blessed G and Tomlinson BE (1977) Lancet i: 189–191.
5. Perry EK, Tomlinson BE, Blessed G, Bergman K, Gibson PH and Perry RH (1978) Br. Med. J. 2: 1447–1459.
6. Davis KL and Yamamura HI (1978) Life Sci. 23: 1729–1734.
7. Sims NR, Smith CCT, Davison AM, Bowen DM, Flack RHA, Snowden JS and Neary D (1980) Lancet i: 333–336.
8. Corkin S (1981) Trends Neurosci. 287–290.
9. Whitehouse PJ, Price DL, Clark AW, Coyle JT and DeLong MR (1981) Ann. Neurol. 10: 122–126.
10. McKinney M, Hedreen L and Coyle JT (1982) In: Corkin S, Davis KL, Growdon JH, Usdin E and Wurtman RJ (eds.) Aging Vol. 19., Raven Press, New York, pp. 259–265.
11. Bartus RT, Dean RL, Beer B and Lippa AS (1982) Science 217: 408–417.
12. Bowen D, Francis PT and Palmer AM (1986) In: Fisher A, Hanin I and Lachman H (eds.) Alzheimer's and Parkinson's Diseases: Strategies for Research and Development. Plenum Press, New York, pp. 53–61.
13. Drachman DA and Leavitt J (1974) Arch. Neurol. 30: 113.
14. Peters BH and Levin HS (1977) Arch. Neurol. 34: 215.
15. Davis KL, Mohs R, Tinklenberg JR, Pfefferbaum A, Hollister LE and Kopell BS (1978) Science 201: 272.
16. Sitaram N, Weingartner H and Gillin JC (1978) Science 201: 274.
17. Pedata F, Lo Conte G, Sorbi S, Marconcini-Pepeu I and Pepeu G (1982) Brain Res. 233: 359–367.

18. Hohmann CF and Coyle JT (1988) Brain Res. Bull. 21: 13–20.
19. Hanin I, Fisher A, Hortnagl H, Leventer SM, Potter PE and Walsh TJ (1987) In: Meltzer HY (ed.) Psychopharmacology: The Third Generation of Progress. Raven Press, New York, pp. 341–349.
20. Hanin I (1990) In: Aquilonius S-M and Gillberg P-G (eds.) Progress in Brain Research Vol. 84. Elsevier, Amsterdam, pp. 289–299.
21. Smith G (1988) Brain Res. Rev. 13: 103–118.
22. Coyle JT (1987) In: Meltzer H (ed.) Psychopharmacology: The Third Generation of Progress. Raven Press, New York, pp. 333–340.
23. Lerer B, Warner J and Friedman E (1985) Behav. Neurosci. 99: 661–677.
24. El-Defrawy SR, Coloma J, Jhamandas K, Boegman RJ, Beninger RJ and Wirsching BA (1985) Aging 6: 325–330.
25. Sato H, Hata Y and Tsumoto T (1987) J. Neurophysiol. 58: 781–794.
26. Robbins TW, Everitt BJ, Ryan CN, Marston HM, Jones GH and Page KJ (1989) Neuroscience 28: 337–352.
27. Dunnett SB, Rogers DC and Jones GH (1989) Eur. J. Neurosci. 1: 395–406.
28. Watson M, Vickroy TW, Fibiger HC, Roeske W and Yamamura HI (1985) Brain Res. 346: 387–391.
29. Cross AJ and Deakin JFW (1985) Neurosci. Lett. 60: 261–265.
30. Hepler DJ, Olton DS, Wenk GL and Coyle JT (1985) J. Neurosci. 5: 866–873.
31. Kesner RP, Crutcher CA and Measom MO (1986) Neurobiol. Aging 7: 287–295.
32. Thal LJ, Dokla CPJ and Armstrong DM (1988) Behav. Neurosci. 102: 852–860.
33. Metcalf RH, Boegman RJ, Quirion R, Riopelle RJ and Ludwin SK (1987) J. Neurochem. 49: 639–644.
34. Scarth BJ, Jhamandas K, Boegman RJ, Beninger RJ and Reynolds JN (1989) Exp. Neurol. 103: 158–164.
35. Stewart GR, Price M, Olney JM, Hartman BK and Cozzari C (1986) Brain Res. 369: 377–382.
36. Collier B, Boksa P and Lovat S (1979) In: Tucek S (ed.) Progress in Brain Research Vol. 49. Elsevier, Amsterdam, pp. 107-121.
37. Kilbinger H, Wanger A and Zerban R (1976) Naunyn-Schmiedeberg's Arch. Pharmacol. 295: 81–87.
38. Large WA and Rang HP (1979) In: Tucek S (ed.) Progress in Brain Research Vol. 49. Elsevier, Amsterdam, pp. 267–275.
39. Von Schwarzenfeld I and Whittaker VP (1977) Br. J. Pharmacol. 59: 69–74.
40. Zimmerman H and Dowdall MJ (1977) Neuroscience 2: 731–739.
41. Hemsworth BA, Shreeve SM and Veitch GBA (1984) Br. J. Pharmacol. 82: 477–484.
42. Newton MW and Jenden DJ (1986) Trends Pharmacol. Sci. 7: 316–320.
43. Aronstam RS, Marshall DC and Buccafusco JJ (1988) Neuropharmacology 27: 217–225.
44. Jenden DJ, Russell RW, Booth RA, Knusel BJ, Lauretz SD, Rice KM and Roch M (1989) In: Frotscher M and Misgeld U (eds.) Central Cholinergic Synaptic Transmission. Birkhauser, Germany, pp. 229.
45. Marshall IG (1970) Br. J. Pharmacol. 38: 503–516.
46. Marshall IG and Parsons SM (1987) Trends Neurosci. 10: 174–177.
47. Gandry-Talarmain YM, Diebler M-F and O'Regan S (1989) J. Neurochem. 52: 822–829.
48. Rogers GA and Parsons SM (1989) Mol. Pharmacol. 36: 333–341.
49. Smart L (1981) Neuroscience 6: 1765–1770.
50. Tagari PC, Maysinger D and Cuello AC (1986) Neurochem. Res. 11: 1091–1102.
51. Russell RW, Crocker AD, Booth RA and Jenden DJ (1986) Psychopharmacology 88: 24–32.
52. Ehlert FJ and Jenden DJ (1986) In: Hanin I (ed.) Dynamics of Cholinergic Function. Plenum Press, New York, pp. 1177–1185.
53. Jones BE and Webster HH (1988) Brain Res. 451: 13–32.
54. Schwarcz R, Whetsel Jr WO and Mangano RM (1983) Science 219: 316–318.
55. Everitt BJ, Robbins TW, Evenden JL, Marston HM, Jones GH and Sirkia TE (1987) Neuroscience 22: 441–469.
56. Dunnett SB, Whishaw IQ, Jones GH and Bunch ST (1987) Neuroscience 20: 653–669.
57. Arbogast RE and Kozlowski MR (1988) Neurotoxicology 9: 39–46.
58. Wenk GL, Markowska AL and Olton DS (1989) Behav. Neurosci. 103: 765–769.
59. Markowska AL, Wenk GL and Olton DS (1990) Behav. Neural Biol. 54: 13–26.

© 1991 Elsevier Science Publishers B.V. All rights reserved.
Biological Psychiatry, Volume 2. G. Racagni et al., editors.

Trimethyltin produces cognitive dysfunction and glucocorticoid receptor changes in rat hippocampus similar to the aging process: A model for senescence?

S.B. Sparber
Department of Pharmacology, University of Minnesota, Minneapolis, MN 55455, U.S.A.

One of the major obstacles which must be overcome in order to search for efficacious treatments of cognitive impairment associated with senescence is the lack of suitable animal models for preclinical experimentation. Numerous approaches have been undertaken to develop such animal models, including the use of aged subjects, the use of surgical lesioning of mature subjects, the search for genetically determined appropriate inborn errors of metabolism and the use of various neurotoxin-induced lesions.

Reports of the consequences of excessive exposure to trimethyltin (TMT) via occupational exposure or industrial accidents during the last 10–15 years have led to a host of studies into the neuropathological, neurophysiological, neurochemical and behavioral effects of exposure of laboratory animals to various doses of this, and other, organoheavy metal compounds [1]. During the past several years, we have attempted to characterize the effects of low doses of trimethyltin, given orally to mature male Long-Evans rats, with the goal of inducing a specific learning impairment of an unambiguous nature. By unambiguous, I mean to say that the possibility of a sensorimotor, memory storage and/or retrieval deficit could be ruled out as being responsible for deficits in performance which we may ultimately attribute to one of consolidation of a specific type of working to one of so-called reference memory.

I will summarize a series of experiments which I believe satisfy this criterion and which have led to the conclusion that impairment caused by a single, low oral dose of TMT given to rats may be of utility as a model for the early stages of senescence-related cognitive impairment in humans.

Although a long list of nuclei and pathways in the CNS show evidence of a lesioning effect after moderate to high doses of TMT (e.g. ≥8 mg/kg), lower doses (e.g. 3–6 mg/kg) in this species may cause more selective limbic system lesions which include mainly pyramidal cells of one or more CA regions of the hippocampus, as well as damage to cells of the pyriform and entorhinal cortices [2,3]. The absence of a monotonic dose-dependent dysfunctional outcome of treatment of rats with a range of relatively low doses of TMT has been described by Cohen et al. [4]. We observed that rats treated with TMT showed little or no apparent effect upon food-reinforced autoshaped learning if a food pellet was automatically delivered to the subject shortly after retraction of a lever manipulandum in an operant behavioral chamber. However, when the pellet was delivered at least 6 s after the lever was retracted, rats treated with 3 or 6 mg TMT/kg (1 dose, p.o.) showed what appeared to be a learning impairment, although a storage or retrieval impairment of this delayed-reinforcement version of the task could not yet be ruled out. Interestingly, a higher oral dose (i.e. 7.5 mg TMT/kg) seemed to produce less of a deficit in performance of this autoshaped behavior, although subsequent experimentation indicated that a latent inhibition variation of the task unmasked a cognitive impairment of a different type. Indeed, when rats administered the highest dose of TMT were compared with rats administered the lower doses, our supposition that qualitatively different lesions, leading to qualitatively different behavioral and neurochemical outcomes was supported when we subjected a different cohort to another behavioral analysis which probed the ability to adapt to daily-changing operant response requirements and analyzed their hippocampi for the concentration of receptors which bound radiolabeled corticosterone (Type I plus Type II). Rats given the highest dose of TMT showed increased progressive fixed ratio responding, relative to controls, when the number of lever presses required to earn a food pellet was doubled every day, while the rats given only 6 mg TMT/kg showed significantly less responding, relative to controls, as the ratio requirements increased. Initial (i.e. FR_1, FR_2) response rates were unaffected by any of the doses of TMT. Interestingly, hippocampal corticosterone receptors, which have been shown to decrease with aging [5] were reduced most after the median dose of TMT (i.e. 6 mg/kg); significantly less so in the group given the high dose (i.e. 7.5 mg/kg). This experiment also demonstrated a significant correlation between corticosterone-binding capacity of "receptors" from hippocampal cytosol and progressive FR_{32} responding, indicating a possible causal relationship between the ability to behaviorally adapt to a daily-changing schedule of reinforcement and the extent of the loss of (pyramidal?) cells in the hippocampus, reflected by the magnitude of the decrease in steroid binding sites [6].

Having established the median dose (i.e. 6 mg/kg) as one which appeared to consistently convey the desired effect upon delayed reinforcement autoshaped behavior, we carried out experiments to determine if we could differentiate between an acquisition (i.e. consolidation) deficit and a deficit in storage or retrieval of information, even though learning may have occurred but was somehow unavailable; similar perhaps to a form of retrograde amnesia. To this end, we first allowed rats to autoshape, again with the 6-s delay of reinforcement interposed between automatic retraction of the lever and automatic delivery of the food pellet, unless the rat touched the lever prior to the 15 s that the lever was extended into the operant chamber. Upon touching the lever, the lever was immediately retracted, but the food pellet was still delivered 6 s after retraction. Thus, the rats could not earn any more pellets than the number of trials they were exposed to daily, but they could receive them sooner if they touched the extended lever before it retracted automatically. After learning to associate the retraction of the lever with delivery of the food pellet 6 s later, performing near or at asymptotic levels, the rats were dosed with 6 mg TMT/kg and allowed to remain undisturbed in their home cages for 3+ weeks, the usual time between dosing and exposing them to acquisition trials had they been behaviorally naive rats. We hypothesized that no performance deficit would emerge if TMT caused a consolidation, rather than a storage, retrieval, or some other non-specific performance deficit. The assumption was that the lesioned structures were involved primarily in maintaining biologically significant information during the temporal gap so that it could be used to form the association between lever retraction and the delivery of the food pellet 6 s later. This capacity may or may not be part of the same (i.e. a single) process which is responsible for the conversion of working memory to reference memory, but the experiment would enable us to determine if the deficit was on the input (i.e. learning), rather than the storage (i.e. memory), or output (i.e. performance) component of the autoshaped behavior. Interestingly, the data were unambiguous. Four weeks after TMT treatment, these rats performed as though they had mastered the association during the previous few days and did not demonstrate evidence of a deficit in remembering what they had learnt before dosing with TMT, which would have prevented them from learning the association, had they been naive.

Another group of rats was first treated with TMT (6 mg/kg) and the worst performers of the cohort, which essentially were touching the extended lever no more during the 10th session than they did during the 1st session, were randomly assigned to either a control group or a group which was to receive the vasopressin analog desglycinamide-8-arginine vasopressin (DGAVP) prior to subsequent acquisition sessions. When it became apparent that the peptide was enhancing learning in these TMT-treated non-learners, we discontinued treatment after 3 days to determine if the reversal of the deficit were transient and/or showed state-dependency. Upon discontinuing DGAVP treatment, the peptide-treated group continued to show enhanced autoshaped behavior, indicating that at least one dose level (i.e. 7.5 mg/kg s.c.) could reverse the deficit induced by the TMT [7].

We [8] and others [9] have been unsuccessful in demonstrating a learning-enhancing effect of DGAVP when young, non-lesioned rats were subjected to autoshaping sessions after peptide treatment. Our previous successful attempts at demonstrating a positive cognitive-enhancing property of DGAVP in non-lesioned rats were carried out with much older rats [10,11], which we feel were not learning optimally to begin with, thereby allowing us the latitude to observe an enhancing effect of the peptide upon learning. Aged rats that show declines in performance of another behavior which requires effective bridging of temporal gaps (i.e. effective working memory) also have dramatic reductions in hippocampal corticosterone receptors [12]. Moreover, rats with diabetes insipidus due to a lack of vasopressin have reduced hippocampal corticosterone receptors that are increased by treatment with vasopressin-related peptides [13]. The relationship between senescence and vasopressinergic pathways (hypothalamic and extrahypothalamic), corticosterone and its CNS receptors, and various aminergic neurotransmitter pathways, especially those which innervate the forebrain and appear to be important in attentional processes (e.g. noradrenergic) should be an interesting area for future investigations.

References

1. Tilson HA and Sparber SB (eds.) (1987) Neurotoxicants and Neurobiological Function: Effects of Organoheavy Metals, Wiley, New York.
2. Chang LW. Fundam. Appl. Toxicol. 6: 217–232.
3. Balaban CD, O'Callaghan JP and Billingsley ML (1988) Neuroscience 26: 337–361.
4. Cohen CA, Messing RB and Sparber SB (1987) Psychopharmacology 93: 301–307.
5. Sapolsky RM, Krey LC and McEwen BS (1983) Brain Res. 289: 235–240.
6. Gerbec EN, Messing RB and Sparber SB (1988) Brain Res. 460: 346–351.
7. Sparber SB, Cohen CA and Messing RB (1988) Life Sci. 42: 171–177.
8. Sparber SB, Bollweg GL and Messing RB (1991) Behav. Process. 23: 59–74.
9. Mundy WR and Iwamoto ET (1987) Pharmacol. Biochem. Behav. 27: 307–315.
10. Messing RB and Sparber SB (1983) Eur. J. Pharmacol. 89: 43–51.
11. Messing RB and Sparber SB (1985) Behav. Neurosci. 99: 1114–1119.
12. Meaney MJ, Aitken DH, van Berkel C, Bhatnagar S and Sapolsky RM (1988) Science 239: 766–768.
13. Veldhuis HD and DeKloet ER (1982) Endocrinology 110: 153–157.

© 1991 Elsevier Science Publishers B.V. All rights reserved.
Biolcgical Psychiatry, Volume 2. G. Racagni et al., editors.

Neuroprotective effects of dihydropyridine Ca^{2+}-antagonists in brain lesions and age-related deficits

J. Traber

Tropon-Bayer Institute for Neurobiology, Tropon Pharmaceuticals, Berliner Str. 156, D-5000 Cologne 80, Germany

Ca^{2+} ions play an important role in the regulation of physiological processes. Minute local changes in intracellular Ca^{2+} can lead to a multiplicity of distinct changes in the functional state of cells [1,2]. In this way, important key enzymes such as protein kinases, phosphodiesterases and proteases are regulated. In nerve cells, Ca^{2+} ions participate in a number of specialized functions such as regulation of neurotransmitter release, excitability, axonal transport and outgrowth of processes [1,2]. In view of the key role, which Ca^{2+} ions play in such complex and distinct physiological events, intracellular Ca^{2+} gradients have to be precisely regulated and finely tuned. In order to maintain this as well as the enormous Ca^{2+} concentration gradient between the extra- (10^{-3} M) and the intracellular (10^{-7} M) milieu of a factor 10,000, nature had to build up a number of very efficient mechanisms. Among these are ion pumps, receptor and voltage-operated Ca^{2+} channels, Ca^{2+} binding and storage proteins [3].

During an acute pathological lesion such as ischemia after stroke, this Ca^{2+} ion gradient may collapse due to the lack of energy supply. The massive Ca^{2+} influx cannot be buffered by the brain cells and finally leads to neuronal cell death [4].

There is increasing evidence for a dysregulation of Ca^{2+} homeostasis not only under acute (ischemic) but also under chronic conditions during aging. According to the calcium hypothesis of brain aging [2], the Ca^{2+} homeostasis may be slightly dysregulated over time. A slight increase in intracellular Ca^{2+} concentration for an extended period of time (months, years) may induce similar pathological changes including cell death as acute massive increases (minutes, hours).

These facts are part of the rationale for the use of Ca^{2+} channel blockers such as nimodipine under the conditions of ischemia and aging. The dihydropyridine nimodipine blocks voltage-dependent Ca^{2+} channels of the L-subtype [5,6]. A few examples of its pharmacology under acute and chromic conditions will be given below.

In a passive avoidance paradigm, nimodipine antagonized the disruptive effects of hypoxia on memory function in the rat [7]. In our hands, the antiamnestic effect followed a bell-shaped dose-response curve with a nearly 100% protection at a dose of 1 mg/kg p.o. and no significant effect at 0.1 and 10 mg/kg p.o. nimodipine.

After a transient middle cerebral artery occlusion in the cat, a massive accumulation of intracellular Ca^{2+} was measured in vivo directly from the cortex using the fluorescent dye indo-1 [4]. The elevation of cytosolic free Ca^{2+} was significantly attenuated by nimodipine during occlusion and reperfusion. The substance was administered by intravenous infusion starting 5 min after occlusion at a dose of 5 μg/kg/min for the first 3 min followed by 1 μg/kg/min for the remainder of the experiment (reopening 60 min after occlusion; 30 min reperfusion time). Histological examination of the cortical gyrus indicated a significant protective effect of nimodipine against ischemic damage [4].

Three-month-old male stroke-prone spontaneously hypertensive rats (SHR-SP) with already established hypertension were given a high salt diet (8% NaCl), which has been shown to accelerate the occurrence of cerebrovascular lesions and stroke [8]. Simultaneous treatment with nimodipine (300 ppm in the food) did not affect the high blood pressure of SHR-SP but dramatically increased survival and completely prevented cerebrovascular lesions [8].

After a crush lesion of the sciatic nerve in rats, recovery of function could be accelerated by nimodipine [9].

The AIDS virus coat protein (gp120) in the picomolar range increased intracellular Ca^{2+} in rat retinal ganglion cells and hippocampal neurons [10]. This effect leads to cell death. Nimodipine (100 nM – 1 μM) prevented the increase in Ca^{2+} and cell death [10].

Rats display an age-related deficit in water maze learning. Nimodipine improved cognitive functions in the paradigm [11].

In the eye-blink-response test, young rabbits learned to avoid an air puff paired with a tone by closing their eyes after the tone (classical conditioning) [12]. Old rabbits learned this task much more slowly. Nimodipine improved this learning deficit [12].

Old rats (24–30 months old) have impaired motor functions. Chronic treatment (up to 6 months) with nimodipine on the food (860 ppm) improved this motor deficit [13,14]. The compound was active under prophylactic as well as under therapeutic conditions. This effect on motor function could be visualized and quantified by a walking pattern analysis. The rat's hindpaws were dipped into photographic developer solution. By walking over photographic paper, the footprints appeared and the respective deficits could be quantified [13,14].

To study the pathology of the abnormal footprints, nerve conduction velocities in sciatic nerves of the old rats were examined. Nerve conduction velocities of untreated 27-month-old rats (50 m/s) were significantly lower than in 3-month-old rats (80 m/s). The mean conduction velocity of the nimodipine-treated old rats (66 m/s) was significantly higher than that of the control animals of the same age and barely lower than that of the young ones [14].

The findings summarized in this short review are just a few examples of the protective effect of the dihydropyridine Ca^{2+}-antagonist nimodipine under a variety of conditions. The exact molecular mechanisms remain to be evaluated.

References

1. Gibson GE and Peterson C (1987) Neurobiol. Aging 8: 319–343.
2. Khachaturian ZS (1989) Aging 1: 17–34.
3. Pansu D and Bronner F (1990) Calcium Transport and Intracellular Calcium Homeostasis. NATO ASI Series H: Cell Biology, Vol. 48. Springer, Berlin.
4. Greenberg JH, Vematsu D, Araki N and Reivich M (1991) In: Scriabine A, Teasdale GM, Tettenborn D and Young W (eds.) Nimodipine, Pharmacological and Clinical Results in Cerebral Ischemia. Springer, Berlin, pp. 9–24.
5. Morad M, Nayler W, Kazda S and Schramm M (1988) The Calcium Channel: Structure, Function and Implications. Springer, Berlin.
6. Traber J and Gispen WH (1989) Nimodipine and Central Nervous System Function: New Vistas. Schattauer, Stuttgart.
7. Hoffmeister F, Bellemann HP, Benz U and van den Kerckhoff W (1985) In: Betz E, Deck K and Hoffmeister F (eds.) Nimodipine, Pharmacological and Clinical Properties. Schattauer, Stuttgart, pp. 77–97.
8. Kazda S, Garthoff G, Luckhaus G and Nash G (1982) In: Godfraind T, Albertini A and Paoletti R (eds.) Calcium Modulators. Elsevier Biomedical Press, Amsterdam, pp. 155–167.
9. van der Zee CEEM, Schuurman T, Traber J and Gispen WH (1987) Neurosci. Lett. 83: 143–148.
10. Dreyer EB, Kaiser PK, Offerman JT and Lipton SA (1990) Science 248: 364–367.
11. Scriabine A, Schuurman T and Traber J (1989) FASEB J. 3: 1799–1806.
12. Deyo RA, Straube KT and Disterhoft JF (1989) Science 243: 809–811.
13. Schuurman T, Klein H, Beneke M and Traber J (1987) Neurosci. Res. Commun. 1: 9–15.
14. van der Zee CEEM, Schuurman T, Gerritsen van der Hoop R, Traber J and Gispen WH (1990) Neurobiol. Aging 11: 451–456.

© 1991 Elsevier Science Publishers B.V. All rights reserved.
Biological Psychiatry, Volume 2. G. Racagni et al., editors.

Prenatally induced brain lesions, cognitive impairment and protein-kinase C-dependent phosphorylation

Monica di Luca[1], Fabio Merazzi[1], Mauro Cimino[2], Willem H. Gispen[3], Pierre N.E. de Graan[3] and Flaminio Cattabeni[1]

[1]Institute of Pharmacological Sciences, University of Milan, Milan; [2]Institute of Pharmacology and Pharmacognosy, University of Urbino, Urbino, Italy; and [3]Rudolf Magnus Institute of and Institute of Molecular Biology, University of Utrecht, The Netherlands

Neuroplasticity is the strategy followed by the brain to attenuate the functional consequences of lesions due to intrinsic (aging, genetically predetermined neurodegenerative disorders) or extrinsic (trauma, ischemia, neurotoxins, viral infections) factors. One of the most relevant consequences of these lesions is the loss of cognitive functions.

The availability of suitable animal models to investigate the molecular mechanisms of neuroplasticity is essential for establishing more appropriate pharmacotherapeutic strategies for the loss of these functions.

We have developed one such model administering a potent alkylating agent, methylazoxymethanol (MAM), to pregnant rats. The toxin exerts its antimitotic effect for no longer than 24 h, so its effects are confined to a limited period of time. Since the neurons forming the different brain areas have a differential time of origin, the gestational day (GD) at which MAM is administered will determine the final outcome of the type of lesion [1].

Since intrinsic cortical neurons are formed mainly around GD 14-15 and since the cortical mass is the major component in total brain weight, Fig. 1 shows that a single administration of MAM (25 mg/kg, i.p.) to pregnant rats at GD 14 or 15 induces a severe microencephaly in all the offspring of treated dams. When administered later in gestation, the effect is less pronounced, since the number of cells affected by the antimitotic is progressively smaller. The offspring treated at day 19 of their embryonic life show only a small reduction of brain weight (10%). Moreover, the effect induced by MAM has been shown to be dose-dependent.

A more detailed examination of the brain areas affected by the treatment at different GDs shows that at days 14 and 15 not only the cortex is reduced in size, but other areas as well, such as the hippocampus and partly, the striatum. Indeed, also the inteneurons of these areas have their birth-date at these times of MAM administration. In the hippocampus, however, the cells affected are only those constituting the CA region, whereas those of the dentate gyrus are not affected, according to the timetable of their origin.

Brains of rats treated at embryonic day 19 do not show any significant reduction of the different brain areas. However, it is expected that a small population of the granule cells of the dentate gyrus in the hippocampus may be killed by the

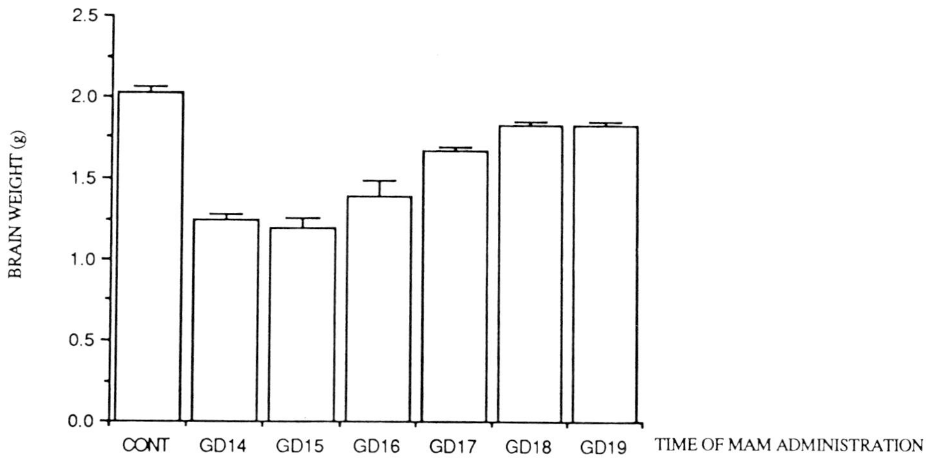

Fig. 1. Brain weights of 60 day-old offspring of dams treated at different gestational days with a single dose of 25 mg/kg i.p. of MAM.

treatment, since these cells enter their final mitotic phase around GD 18 in the rat [2].

The effects induced on brain morphology are paralleled by changes in spontaneous activity, neuromuscular coordination and cognitive functions. Offspring of dams treated at GD 14 are most severely affected in their spontaneous activity and neuromuscular coordination [3]. Offspring of GD 15 MAM-treated rats show nocturnal hyperactivity and some neuromuscular incoordination in the rotarod test, but their major characteristic was that of being severely impaired in several tasks requiring learning and memory. GD 19 MAM-treated rats show no changes in spontaneous activity or in neuromuscular coordination, but show a selective impairment in the active avoidance test (2-way shuttle box) [4]. It is noteworthy that GD 15 MAM-treated rats are similar to controls in the shuttle box avoidance test. Therefore, the choice of the time of MAM administration determines which area of the brain is lesioned and the type of behavioral alterations observed.

We have therefore studied the endogenous phosphorylation of a specific substrate of the Ca^{2+}/phospholipid dependent protein kinase (PKC), the kinase mainly involved in neuronal plasticity associated with learning and memory processes [5]. B-50 is a neuron-specific protein phosphorylated by PKC in its serine in position 41 [6]. It is localized in the inner part of the presynaptic plasma membrane and it affects neurotransmitter release [7]. Moreover, B-50 is highly expressed during axon growth and synaptogenesis. In the adult CNS high levels of expression are maintained only in the cortex and hippocampus, the brain areas known to preserve a high degree of plasticity [8].

Endogenous B-50 phosphorylation was assayed in synaptic plasma membranes using radiolabeled ATP as phosphate donor. The incorporation of labeled phos-

Table 1. Endogenous B-50 phosphorylation in synaptic plasma membranes from brain areas of rats treated with MAM at different gestational days

Brain area	GD 15	GD 19
Cortex	58 ± 7^a	100 ± 9
Hippocampus	51 ± 4^a	56 ± 3^a

Data are expressed as % controls; $^aP < 0.01$ vs. respective controls.

phate was determined by densitometric analysis on autoradiograms of one-dimensional electrophoretic gels of the protein band corresponding to B-50 [9].

Table 1 shows that in this post hoc phosphorylation assay a reduction in the incorporation of labeled phosphate can be detected in both cortex and hippocampus in the GD 15 MAM-treated offspring, whereas the reduction is present only in the hippocampus of the GD 19 MAM-treated group. In the GD 15 group, both areas were affected by MAM, whereas in the GD 19 group only a small population of granule cells in the dentate gyrus was killed by the antimitotic. This different effect on endogenous B-50 phosphorylation could have its functional correlate in the different cognitive impairment observed in GD 15 vs. GD 19 MAM-treated rats.

Several explanations are possible for this reduction in B-50 phosphorylation: however, we can exclude the hypothesis that this effect is due to changes in the expression or the amount of the protein or to changes in its structure.

We favour the hypothesis that these changes are due to alterations in endogenous PKC activity as a consequence of the cytoarchitectonic modifications in the lesioned brain areas. Since a post hoc phosphorylation assay was used, a more direct approach like the in situ phosphorylation assay in synaptosomes will probably reflect a more accurate measure of PKC activity in these animals. Preliminary data show that also with this procedure MAM-treated rats show consistent alterations in PKC-dependent B-50 phosphorylation.

We can conclude therefore that MAM treatment of dams at different gestational days provides a useful in vivo model to study the involvement of PKC-dependent phosphorylation processes in synaptic plasticity, associated with selective impairment of cognitive functions. The understanding of the molecular mechanisms responsible for the changes of PKC activity will help us in gaining more insight into the regulation of associative processes in cognitive functions.

References

1. Johnston MV and Coyle JT (1982) Trends Neurosci. 5: 153–156.
2. Rodier PM (1977) Teratology 16: 235–246.
3. Balduini W, Lombardelli G, Peruzzi G and Cattabeni F (1991) Neurotoxicology 12: 179–188.
4. Balduini W, Elsner J, Lombardelli G, Peruzzi G and Cattabeni F (1991) Neurotoxicology (in press).
5. Lovinger DM, Colley PA, Akers RF, Nelson RB and Routtenberg A (1986) Brain Res. 399: 205–211.

6. Nielander HB, Schrama LH, Van Rosen J, Kasperaitis M, Oestreicher AB, Gispen WH and Schotman P (1990) J. Neurochem. 55: 1442–1445.
7. Dekker LV, De Gran PNE, Oestreicher AB, Versteeg DMG and Gispen WH (1989) Nature 342: 74–76.
8. Skene JHP (1989) Ann. Rev. Neurosci. 12: 127–156.
9. Di Luca M, Cimino M, De Graan PNE, Oestreicher AB, Gispen WM and Cattabeni F (1991) Brain Res. 538: 95–101.

© 1991 Elsevier Science Publishers B.V. All rights reserved.
Biological Psychiatry, Volume 2. G. Racagni et al., editors.

Experimental models for the evaluation of drugs active on neuronal plasticity

Alfredo Gorio, Anna Maria di Giulio and Paolo Mantegazza
University of Milan, Via Vanvitelli 32, 20129 Milan, Italy

In the last decade the fast-growing field of neuronal plasticity has spanned significantly from basic to applied science. There are several reasons for such a drastic change in research programs, but a few of them deserve the largest credit. Neurobiologists have shown that there is an intrinsic potential for neurons to regrow, compensate for injuries, and regenerate after damage even in the central nervous system if the appropriate conditions are supplied [1]. It has also been shown in a large number of in vivo or in vitro experimental models that a variety of natural substances like endogenous neuronal growth factors such as nerve growth factor (NGF), fibroblast growth factor, etc., or simple biological molecules like acetyl-l-carnitine, gangliosides and ACTH-fragments, can effectively exert positive pharmacological activities ranging from enhancement of neuronal survival, neuritogenesis, axonal regeneration, recovery of functions after injury etc. Some of them, such as acetyl-l-carnitine, are under international clinical development with promising results. These experimental data have raised hopes that in the near future we might be able to develop new and powerful agents capable of promoting neuronal repair following injury. These encouraging data are accompanied by the dramatically increasing number of older people. In the year 2000, more than 410 million people will be over 65 years of age [2]. The diseases associated with old age will become more and more relevant with the increasingly longer lifespan. The treatment of brain diseases associated with old age has not progressed as in other cases. Among them degenerative neuronal diseases are at present difficult and, at the same time, very stimulating research tasks.

There is no need for development of new experimental models; neurobiology has supplied an almost endless number of laboratory methods utilizing in vitro and in vivo systems which are perfectly adequate for assessing the potential usefulness of new agents in the treatment of neural injuries and neurodegeneration-related diseases. In this brief report we can only indicate a few examples of experiments that should be performed, aiming mainly at outlining an experimental strategy which stems directly from the authors' direct experience.

The early screening test for a new compound active on injured or degenerating neurons should be simple and at the same time very indicative. The use of tissue cultures allows the direct visualization of the biological phenomena and the precise control of the amounts of active substance, that being added to the medium is in direct contact with the neurons without pharmacokinetic problems. In general, the use of an in vitro system is very useful for assessing potential efficacy on enhancing the process of neurite formation or reducing the dependency upon the presence in the culture media of a neurotrophic substance. Cell lines or primary cultures of neurones can be used according to the strategy employed. For instance, a study on neuritogenesis can be easily performed using neuroblastoma or pheochromocytoma PC12 cell lines. The neurotrophic factor dependency or neuronal survival test in vitro could be performed using mouse embryonic dorsal root ganglion cells in culture or PC12; both are dependent upon NGF presence for differentiation. If NGF is subtracted from the culture medium the differentiated cells die. The prevention of such a death is a rapid and optimal test for effects on neuronal survival [3,4].

On the other hand, such a screening approach may not apply if our target is a peripheral neuropathy originated from a metabolic disorder such as diabetes. In such a case even the early pharmacological studies should be performed in vivo. It is well established that diabetic neuropathy is an axonal disease with progressive axonal atrophy correlated by electrophysiological, morphological and biochemical abnormalities. Among the latter changes the reduction in axonal transport is certainly a key phenomenon that may cause the morphological abnormalities and the consequent process of axonal atrophy and degeneration [5,6]. Five weeks after diabetes induction the content of substance P or the accumulation of acetylcholinesterase at a site of ligature on the sciatic nerve is reduced in diabetic animals. Substances potentially active on diabetic peripheral neuropathy should prevent such a change [7]. After such primarily required pharmacological effects, the drug activity should be tested for activity on a battery of typical alterations present in diabetic neuropathy such as on axonal morphology, excitability, retrograde degeneration, autonomic gastroenteric neuropathy, etc.

A further evaluation for a drug effective on neurotogenesis or on reducing neurotrophic factor dependency in vitro could be the evaluation of its activity upon some of the key processes involved in neuronal regeneration in vivo. A typical model would be the evaluation of nerve regeneration and muscle regeneration following crush lesioning. In such a condition one should evaluate the effects of the drug on the following events:

- reactive sprouting at the site of lesion, that can be evaluated histologically by counting the number of axons a couple of millimeters distal to the lesion site, 5–7 days after crush;
- rate of axonal regeneration (elongation): an acceleration of such a process would reduce the time of nerve regeneration and muscle re-innervation and would be of great value for clinical use due to the length of human nerves. An increase of the rate of regrowth from 1 to 2 mm/day would reduce the time of muscle paralysis by months. Evaluation by histological means or by assessing recovery of muscle contraction following nerve stimulation;
- sprouting during muscle re-innervation: a phenomenon that suggests an activity of the compound on re-innervation processes.

The latter phenomenon should be further analyzed after partial muscle denervation looking at the collateral sprouting and muscle re-innervation by the intact axons. A positive effect on these phenomena involved in nerve regeneration would indicate potential activity of the compound on a variety of peripheral neuropathies and might prompt a further evaluation of the drug on CNS regeneration.

A good simple test of neuronal regeneration in CNS is the recovery of the serotoninergic innervation following neonatal lesion with 5,7-hydroxytryptamine. The serotoninergic axons degenerate distally with denervation of the spinal cord and the cerebral cortex. The regenerative process is slow and 75% complete in 8 weeks. The effect of drugs can be tested on the rate of re-innervation of the spinal cord and cerebral cortex by serotoninergic axons. In addition, the reactive pruning effect of the short axons can be evaluated. The extent of the drug effect can be quantified either biochemically by assaying the serotonin content or by immunocytochemistry in the various CNS areas [8]. In case of positive results, there are many CNS experimental paradigms available for further developing the compound under evaluation [1].

References

1. Gorio A, Perez-Polo JR, de Vellis J and Haber B (eds.) (1988) Neural Development and Regeneration. Cellular and Molecular Aspects. Nato Asi Series. Series H: Cell Biology, Vol. 22. Springer-Verlag, Berlin.
2. Torrey BB, Kinsella K and Taeuber CM (1987) Int. Popul. Rep. 78: 1–85.
3. Purves D and Lichtman JW (eds.) (1985) Principles of Neural Development. Sinauer Ass. Publisher, Sunderland, Massachussetts.
4. Shahar A, de Vellis J, Vernadakis A and Haber B (eds.) (1989) A Dissection and Tissue Culture Manual of the Nervous System. A.R. Liss, New York.
5. Vitadello M, Couraud J-Y, Hassig R, Gorio A and Di Giamberardino L (1983) Exp. Neurol. 82: 143–147.
6. Vitadello M, Filliatreau G, Dupont JL, Hassig R, Gorio A and Di Giamberardino L (1985) J. Neurochem. 45: 860–868.
7. Gorio A (1984) In: Zagoren JC and Fedoroff S (eds.) The Node of Ranvier. Academic Press, New York, pp. 353–389.
8. Jonsson G, Gorio A, Hallman H, Janigro D, Kojima H and Zanoni R (1984) Dev. Brain Res. 16: 171–180.

© 1991 Elsevier Science Publishers B.V. All rights reserved.
Biological Psychiatry, Volume 2. G. Racagni et al., editors.

Biology of epilepsy related mental changes: How should we study it?

Ruggero G. Fariello
Farmitalia Carlo Erba R&D, CNS Department, 20014 Nerviano, Milan, Italy

Introduction

Alterations in mental states have been recognized to occur in association with human epileptic syndromes since the dawn of modern epileptology [1]. Actually, mostly based on anecdotes, early clinical observations have fuelled a rather heated controversy in the field. At one end of the spectrum in this debate are those who dismiss the connection "epilepsy-psychiatric problems" as either non-existent or based on an idiosynchratic background, and who stigmatize the negative connotations that have affected patients with epilepsy because of this undue association. On the other hand, there are those who are convinced that the epileptic process, particularly when affecting the limbic system, must alter the mental activities connected with it and result in behavioural abnormalities.

The nature of the problem

To understand how such a wide disparity of opinion is possible, some considerations are in order. First it should be stressed that "epilepsy" is a clinically useful term that allows some operational decisions on the part of the treating physician, but it is far from being a homogenous nosological category. Human epilepsies encompass a huge variety of etiopathogenic and syndromic conditions. A major task and challenge that modern epileptology is tackling is to sort out and categorize specific entities within this "mare magnum". It is reasonable to expect that only a very small fraction of these conditions will be associated with psychiatric disturbances or it may be found that there is an entity with precise features in which epilepsy and psychiatric problems are intimately linked. Second, in most cases it is very difficult, if at all possible, to single out which behavioural alterations may be caused by the epileptic process per se vs. what may be the results of the non-specific structural damage that often accompanies epilepsy. Other factors that complicate the analysis of the problem are the role of the adverse social conditions in which patients find themselves, the role of antiepileptic drugs [2,3] and the huge variety of the associated psychiatric disturbances. In the temporal domain these can be grouped into 2 major categories: those related to the ictal event (no matter whether pre- or postictal) and those that may be sustained or episodic, but unrelated to the actual seizures. In the former group, the existence of clear EEG abnormalities simultaneous with the behavioural changes has reinforced the hypothesis that the EEG could offer a good measure of the relationship between behavioural changes and epilepsy. In fact, in the past and possibly to this day the EEG has been considered the gold standard to assess the epileptogenic nature of a process. Therefore it appeared logical to assume that if the epileptogenic process is linked to psychiatric symptoms, their variation would be reflected in changes of the EEG markers of epilepsy. This assumption was reinforced by the introduction of the concept of "forced normalization" of the EEG [4]. Landolt [4] reported such negative correlation between EEG epileptiform abnormalities (i.e. disappearance of interictal spikes) and psychotic outbursts.

In summary, the evidence pointing to the EEG as the suitable biological marker of epilepsy-related mental changes consists of the following:

1. several acute mental changes occurring in temporal relationship to the ictus and associated with changes in EEG spiking activity [5];
2. most partial complex seizures can be considered as "micropsychosis";
3. active suppression of EEG epileptiform spikes has been associated with dramatic mental and/or behavioural changes [4].

However, as pointed out by Dongier [5] there are numerous cases in which acute psychiatric changes are not associated with any detectable change in the ongoing EEG activity. Nevertheless, epilepsy appears to be the ideal condition to study the biological basis of psychiatry. Epilepsy when present in a brain area is believed to result, similarly to electrical stimulation, in an extreme distortion of function of that particular area in the direction of hyperfunction as opposed to the hypofunction resulting from destructive lesions. Following such an approach, epilepsy has substantially contributed to the understanding of cerebral localization of most known physical and mental functions.

Contributions of experimental data

A further analysis and a deeper understanding of the biological basis of the changes of higher mental and psychological functions in epilepsy should be fostered by the study of suitable animal models. One intrinsic difficulty with this approach is the impossibility of testing the majority of the complex mental activities in animals. Furthermore, modern neuroscience has drifted away from "in vivo" models shifting more and more frequently to "in vitro" surrogate models where most variables can be controlled and analyzed. One of the most elementary and easily detectable emotions in animals and one that is believed to be frequently deranged in the human psychiatric condition is fear/aggression. Griffith et al. [6], injecting kainic acid (KA), a powerful excitotoxin, in the cat hippocampus have observed sustained inappropriate aggressive behaviour together with rage attacks during the actual seizures. KA destroys a substantial part of the hippocampus; thus is difficult to decide whether the abnormal behaviour results from the destructive lesion or from the epileptic activity. However, in rats the injection of tetanus toxin induces an epileptic syndrome without appreciable changes in morphology [7]. In this model, rats showed definite behavioural abnormalities consisting of both hyper-activity with aggression when handled, and hyper-passivity to intruders' threats. These changes appeared to be sustained over several days when electrobehavioural seizure activity was maximal, even though a direct EEG/behavioural correlation was not made.

Reproducing the tetanus-toxin induced epilepsy in cats by injecting the epileptogenic agent in the amygdala, we observed that the EEG abnormalities evolve through different stages. First there is the appearance of very fast (>25 Hz) low voltage activity, then interictal spikes occur, followed by series of 1–3 s duration recruiting afterdischarges triggered by a high voltage spike, culminating in full-blown seizures. Each stage lasts from 2–5 days. The cycle can be repeated spontaneously or by reinjection of the toxin. In a few animals, occurrence of electrobehavioural seizures was heralded by a dramatic change of the animal response to the experimenter's approach and handling which consisted of a furious hissing and growling, pupil dilation, pulling back of the ears, squatting before launching an attack if the extraneous presence persisted. This occurred in previously tame and mild-tempered animals. The animals were much less aggressive if approached on the side ipsilateral to the epileptic amygdala. The first seizure of the bout would occur within 24 h of the behavioural change. The cat's behaviour returned to normal within a day after cessation of the flurry of seizures. Thus the behaviour started changing much earlier than the EEG did, and lasted beyond the EEG changes. Conversely, the EEG progression from larval to sustained seizure did not bring about any alteration in the changed behaviour. Electrobehavioural seizures did not consist of sham rage attacks.

Thus, in this model the EEG did not prove to be a reliable biological marker of epilepsy-related behavioural changes. Rather, it appears that epilepsy may induce phasic and tonic behavioural alterations for which the EEG is not the appropriate measuring or detective investigative tool.

Conclusions

Other approaches must be devised in order to clarify these phenomena. Longitudinal measurements of biochemical variables, particularly neurotransmitter second messengers and hormones, and of the metabolic state should be used in an attempt to elucidate the probably intricate phenomena at the basis of the undoubtedly existing correlation between epileptiform activity and mental changes, when foci are located in the limbic system.

References

1. Clark RA and Lesko JM (1939) Am. J. Psychiatry 96: 595–607.

2. Demers-Desrosiers LA, Nestoros JN and Vaillancourt P (1978) Am. J. Psychiatry 135: 981–982.
3. Duncan JS, Shorvon SD and Trimble MR (1988) J. Neurol. Neurosurg. Psychiatry 51: 924–928.
4. Landolt H (1958) In: Lorenz de Haas AM (ed.) Lectures in Epilepsy. Elsevier, Amsterdam, pp. 91–133.
5. Dongier (1959) Epilepsia 1: 117–142.
6. Griffith N, Engel J Jr and Bandler R (1987) Brain Res. 400: 360–364.
7. Mellanby J, George G, Robinson A and Thompson P (1977) J. Neurol. Neurosurg. Psychiatry 40: 404–414.
8. Mellanby J, Strawbridge P, Collingridge GI, George G, Rands G, Stroud C and Thompson P (1981) J. Neurol. Neurosurg. Psychiatry 44: 1084–1093.

© 1991 Elsevier Science Publishers B.V. All rights reserved.
Biological Psychiatry, Volume 2. G. Racagni et al., editors.

Statistical approach to computerized EEG in epilepsy: Preliminary data

Silvio Scarone, Orsola Gambini, Enzo Leone and Marco Locatelli
Psychiatric Branch, Department of Biomedical and Technological Sciences, University of Milan Medical School, Istituto Scientifico San Raffaele, Milan, Italy

Introduction

Factor analysis (FA) is a generalized procedure for generating dimensional space among many variables and primarily used for data reduction [1]. Recently FA of spatial features has been successfully applied in computerized EEG studies [2–4]. Further, FA has been suggested as a useful EEG data analysis technique describing the entire EEG pattern during 3 experimental conditions by means of 3 extracted factors. The aim of present study is to explore the use of FA in comparing 14 treated epileptic patients to 50 normal subjects.

Materials and Methods

Fourteen epileptic inpatients (5 males, 9 females; mean age = 27.5 years, S.D. = 9.64), with a positive history of generalized seizures entered the study (10 had tonic-clonic seizures, 4 had absence seizures). All patients had been free from epileptic seizures for at least 3 months before the study began and they were being treated with constant dosages of anticonvulsants such as sodium valproate, phenobarbitone, carbamazepine or phenytoin (drug plasma levels within therapeutic ranges). Fifty normal adults (24 males, 26 females; mean age = 35.16 years, S.D. = 12.23) acted as control group.

EEG was recorded during 3 experimental conditions: a) resting, eyes closed; b) resting, eyes open; and c) hyperventilation with eyes closed; each lasting 3 minutes. EEG measurements were taken using a conventional EEG examination consisting of a 16-channel recording with 19 scalp electrodes with reference at the 2 linked mastoids (F3, C3, P3, O1, F7, T3, T5, Fz, Pz, F4, C4, P4, O2, F8, T4, T6).

For each of the 16 derivations relative power in δ_1 (0–2 Hz), δ_2 (2–4 Hz), θ_1 (4–6 Hz), θ_2 (6–8 Hz), α_1 (8–10 Hz), α_2 (10–12 Hz), β_1 (12–18 Hz), β_2 (18–30 Hz) frequency bands was computed and then the relative values were log-transformed according to the following formula: $Y = \log[X/(1-X)]$ [6,7]. Taking control subjects and epileptic patients together, 8 FA were performed separately for each frequency band. Forty-eight variables (log-transformed relative values for each EEG channel in each experimental condition, that is 16 channels × 3 experimental sessions) were subjected to FA: we considered 3 conditions together (eyes closed + eyes open + hyperventilation) because the 3 conditions are mutually related to each other with highly significant correlation coefficients. The resulting factor scores of epileptic patients and healthy subjects were analyzed for each frequency band by means of ANOVA to check significant differences between the 2 groups.

Results

Statistically significant results between control subjects and epileptic patients were found on the third factor in θ_1 (F = 4.9879; P = 0.0291), on the first factor in θ_2 (F= 13.8873; P = 0.0004), on the first (F= 4.7314; P = 0.0334) and the third factor (F= 4.9635; P = 0.0295) in α_1.

Discussion

Epileptic patients with generalized seizures show significant differences in the factor scores means of the first factor in θ_2 and α_1 EEG frequency bands. On the basis of normative data from our laboratory [5], this factor reflects that background electrical activity in 6–10 Hz range is abnormally organized in epileptic patients under resting, eyes closed condition even in the absence of epileptic interictal abnormalities. Further, significant differences between epileptic patients and controls were observed on factor score means of the third factor in θ_1 and α_1 EEG frequency bands; this factor reflects the background electrical activity under hyperventilation condition. Therefore our results suggest that background activity in 4–6 Hz and 8–10 Hz ranges is abnormally organized in epileptic patients with hyperventilation even in the absence of epileptic interictal abnormalities. Although it is not possible to exclude that anticonvulsant therapy can affect these findings, nevertheless this study confirms the possibility that computerized EEG can be described by a statistical procedure which allows construction of factors with a neurofunctional meaning. Further, this statistical method provides reduction of data and the opportunity of comparing different groups by means of few components resulting from FA. Our study suggests the possibility of group comparisons by factor, analyzing not only several electrodes at different times but also in different functional conditions. This method could open up new ways to deal with computerized EEG data.

References

1. Harmon KK (1960) Modern Factor Analysis. University of Chicago Press.
2. Skrandies W and Lehmann D (1982) Electroencephalogr. Clin. Neurophysiol. 54: 662–667.
3. Gasser T, Mocks J and Bacher P (1983) Electroencephalogr. Clin. Neurophysiol. 55: 445–463.

4. Harner RN (1983) In: Samson-Dollfus et al. (eds.) Quantitative EEG. Elsevier, Paris, pp. 49–61.
5. Cambini O, Locatelli M, Colombo C, Macciardi F and Scarone S (1990) In: Proc. Int. Meet. Psychoneurobiol. 25–28 September 1990, Saint Vincent (in press).
6. John ER, Ahn H, Prichep L, Trepetin M, Brown D and Kaye K (1980) Science 210: 1255–1259.
7. Gasser T, Bacher P and Mocks J (1982) Electroencephalogr. Clin. Neurophysiol. 53: 119–124.

© 1991 Elsevier Science Publishers B.V. All rights reserved.
Biological Psychiatry, Volume 2. G. Racagni et al., editors.

Epilepsy and organic mania

David C. Taylor
Royal Manchester Children's Hospital, Manchester, U.K.

The study of organic (secondary) mania helps us to understand the relationship between affective disorder and cerebral disorder; it is more easily specified diagnostically and more likely to be a severe alteration from usual experience. Mania is less likely to be reactive.

Krauthammer and Klerman's 1978 paper on secondary mania provided a stimulus to research. Cohen and Niska (1980) reported a case of recurrent mania associated with a right brain lesion (subarachnoid haemorrhage) and mentioned 4 other reports of mania secondary to localised cerebral lesions, all of which were in the right brain. They mention Dalen's (1965) suggestion that cerebral damage may provide an alternative to hereditary predisposition in the aetiology of mania. More recent reports by Cummings and Mendez (1984) and by Stasisk and Zetin (1985) have provided further cases and increased interest in whether mania withstands the crude dichotomy of lateralisation.

The paper reports 2 further cases which were predominantly manic and 2 which were manic-depressive.

Case 1

Intelligent, left-handed female of normal background, had sudden seizure onset at age 7 years. Behavioural deterioration at puberty, insulting behaviour and fighting, flagrant sexual displays, led to referral to MNI and removal of mass from R mesial temporal and deeper structures. Seizures stopped and behaviour improved. Florid, severe, prolonged and productive psychosis followed subsequent radiotherapy; female eventually recovered. As she settled her father was admitted for depressive illness.

Case 2

A boy with bipolar swings from the age of about 9 years, failed in school and made several suicide attempts from age 12 years onwards. From 11 years he suffered from very rich experiential psychomotor epilepsy. Despite 2 episodes of viral encephalitis at age 5 and 14, his right temporal lesion proved to be a calcifying haemangioma. His recurrent depressions were interspersed with hypomanic episodes. Lobectomy stopped the attacks, but the boy committed suicide.

Case 3

Overactive distractable oppositional infant with "attacks" attributed to breath-holding. Onset of "epilepsy" as "absences" acknowledged at age 7 years. Seen by psychiatrist for frantic hyperkinesis and unmanageable behaviour; psychomotor sequences diagnosed, deep left temporal lesion discovered in this left-handed boy. Seizures and hyperkinesis stopped immediately after surgery.

Case 4

A 31-year old bank clerk had nocturnal episodes since age 2 years, with nocturnal grand mal observed since age 15 years. His wife had left him because of repeated violent assaults and he had been sent to prison for forging cheques. On discharge he had an acute psychotic episode but recovered after 1 electroshock. Whilst awaiting surgery, he developed a religious psychosis, was resistive and unmanageable. EEGs revealed abnormal activity confined to the left temporal area. Resection of the left temporal lobe was undertaken and mesial temporal sclerosis was found. After operation his ugly moods disappeared though he had an episode of slight hypomania 4 years later.

Reference

1. Taylor DC (1989) Behav. Neurol. 2: 49–68.

© 1991 Elsevier Science Publishers B.V. All rights reserved.
Biological Psychiatry, Volume 2. G. Racagni et al., editors.

Neuroanatomical and neurochemical substrates of defensive rage behavior elicited from the midbrain periaqueductal gray in the cat

Allan Siegel, Majid B. Shaikh and Chang-Lin Lu

Department of Neurosciences, New Jersey Medical School, 185 South Orange Avenue, Newark, NJ 07103, U.S.A.

Introduction

In recent years, our laboratory has begun to determine how the midbrain periaqueductal gray (PAG), which constitutes the most caudally situated structure within the brainstem for the integration of defensive rage responses in the cat, is regulated by two major neurochemical systems: the opioid peptides [1] and excitatory amino acids (EAA). The data presented below represents tests of the hypotheses that the opioid peptide system suppresses defensive rage behavior, while EAA facilitates the occurrence of this response at the level of the PAG.

Materials and Methods

Moveable stimulating electrodes were implanted into the medial, lateral and central amygdaloid nuclei (CE) for the modulation of PAG-elicited defensive rage of adult cats of both sexes. Stimulating electrodes were also implanted into the medial hypothalamus and cannulaelectrodes were implanted into the PAG for the purpose of eliciting defensive rage behavior. In addition, the cannulaelectrode permitted later microinjections of putative transmitter agonists and antagonists into PAG defensive rage sites.

Tests of opioid and EAA agonists

The general paradigm for testing the effects of an agonist upon defensive rage behavior was as follows: initially, a defensive rage response was identified from the PAG. Following determination of stable baseline response latencies and/or thresholds, the agonist was injected in various doses into the PAG defensive rage site and the effects of drug infusion upon the response pattern was determined. When examining selective opioid receptor agonists, the appropriate receptor antagonist was also microinjected into the PAG site as a pretreatment condition. Receptor agonists studied included DAME, morphiceptin for μ, DPDPE for δ, U-50,488H for κ and NMDA.

The use of opioid and EAA antagonists to determine the transmitter properties of amygdaloid and hypothalamic modulating systems

Following establishment of stable PAG response thresholds, dual stimulation procedures involving the application of paired trials of stimulation of either the PAG and amygdala or PAG and medial hypothalamus were employed. After it was determined that a site in the amygdala or medial hypothalamus could modulate the PAG response, specific receptor antagonists for opioid peptides or EAA were microinjected into the PAG site and the effects of drug infusion upon modulation were again determined. Antagonists include naloxone, B-FNA for μ, ICI 174,864 for δ, kynurenic acid, AP7 for NMDA and CNQX for kainate and quisqualate receptors.

Results and Conclusions

Opioid peptides

Agonists. Infusion of opioid agonists into PAG defensive rage sites produced dramatic elevations in response thresholds that were both dose and time-dependent. The most potent effects were observed following microinjections of morphiceptin in doses as low as 0.05 nmol. Such effects were blocked with pretreatment with B-FNA. Similarly, administration of DPDPE (0.08 nmol) also elevated response thresholds and this effect was blocked by pretreatment with ICI 174,864. Administration of the κ agonist in as high a dose as 3.0 nmol had no effect upon the defensive rage response.

Antagonists. Stimulation of CE suppressed PAG-elicited defensive rage. Microinjections of either naloxone (18.9 and 27.5 nmol) or B-FNA (0.05 and 0.2 nmol) blocked the suppressive effects of CE stimulation. However, microinjections of ICI 174,864 (0.8 nmol) did not alter amygdaloid suppression of the PAG response.

Further anatomical analysis of the data indicated that cells in the central nucleus of amygdala in proximity to the sites where stimulation produced suppression of defensive rage could be labelled with both fluorogold (following microinjection into the PAG defensive rage site) as well as with metenkephalin. Collectively, these data are interpreted to mean that the opioid peptide system plays a powerful inhibitory role in the regulation of defensive rage behavior and it does so by the release, at least in part, of enkephalins onto PAG neurons which arise from cells situated in the CE.

Excitatory amino acids

NMDA. Microinjections of NMDA into PAG defensive rage sites facilitated the occurrence of the rage response elicited from those sites in a dose and time-dependent manner. Facilitation, which occurred following administration of 0.5 and 1.0 nmol but not with 0.1 nmol, was relatively short-acting. The effects were seen within 5–15 min of drug infusion and responses returned to baseline levels by 30 min postinjection.

Antagonists. Microinjections of the non-selective antagonist, kynurenic acid (0.1–2.0 nmol) or the selective NMDA antagonist, AP7 (2.0–0.1 nmol), produced dose and time-dependent blockades of the facilitatory effects of medial hypothalamic stimulation upon PAG-elicited defensive rage behavior. In contrast, microinjections of the non-NMDA antagonist for kainate and quisqualate receptors, CNQX (4.0 nmol), had no effect upon medial hypothalamic facilitation. These findings provide evidence that the pathway from the medial hypothalamus to the PAG that normally facilitates defensive rage behavior utilizes EAA as a transmitter.

Acknowledgement

This research was supported by MN Grant NS07941-21.

Reference

1. Shaikh MB, Dalsass M and Siegel A (1990) Aggress. Behav. 16: 191–206.

© 1991 Elsevier Science Publishers B.V. All rights reserved.
Biological Psychiatry, Volume 2. G. Racagni et al., editors.

Neurobiological basis of interictal behavioral disturbances

Jerome Engel Jr.
Departments of Neurology and Anatomy and Cell Biology and the Brain Research Institute, UCLA School of Medicine, Los Angeles, CA 90024, U.S.A.

Introduction

Although environmental factors are responsible, to a considerable degree, for the psychosocial problems experienced by many patients with epilepsy, neurobiological factors undoubtedly play an important role as well. Undesirable effects of antiepileptic medications, the underlying neuropathological process and unrecognized ictal events can all contribute to the appearance of cognitive and psychiatric impairment. More relevant to the topic of this symposium, however, is the fact that epileptic seizures themselves may induce enduring changes in cerebral function, and perhaps even structure, that lead to disturbing or disabling interictal behavioral problems. Basic and clinical research in this area is essential if we are to understand this serious cause of disability among persons with epilepsy.

Confounding biological factors

Antiepileptic medications raise the threshold for ictal onset by nonspecific mechanisms that decrease neuronal excitability, increase neuronal inhibition and reduce neuronal synchronization [1]. Since all of these neuronal functions are also important for normal cerebral activity, it is not surprising that antiepileptic drugs should produce disturbances in interictal behavior. In addition, these medications can induce other systemic or neurologic disturbances such as neuroendocrine dysfunction and REM deficits, which in turn could lead to aberrant interictal behavior [2].

It is often difficult to differentiate neurological and mental deficits due to the presence of recurrent epileptic seizures from those resulting from the destructive effects of the underlying neuropathological substrate. Lesions in limbic structures appear to be more often associated with behavioral disturbances than those located elsewhere in the brain [3], but a relationship between hemispheric lateralization of the epileptogenic lesion and specific interictal behavioral symptoms remains controversial [4].

Most simple partial seizures have no electrographic correlate that can be recorded from scalp EEG [5]. Consequently, prolonged ictal affective, autonomic, and psychic symptoms that occur in clear consciousness without recognizable EEG changes could be mistaken for "interictal" behavioral disturbances. This should be suspected when the interictal behavior in question strongly resembles the patient's habitual aura [2].

Effects of epileptogenesis

In acquired epileptic conditions, a specific insult leads to neuronal reorganization that takes time to develop before spontaneous seizures occur. This epileptogenic process is a dynamic one, and it is more reasonable to assume that it is continuous, than to postulate that it stops completely at the time a first seizure appears. Furthermore, epileptic seizures induce protective homeostatic mechanisms that act to terminate ictal events, prevent ictal spread, and maintain the interictal state. These in turn may also disrupt normal interictal function [2]. Finally, epileptic seizures may indirectly influence interictal behavior as a result of their disruptive effects on neuroendocrine function and sleep [2].

The view that epileptic seizures themselves may induce changes in the brain that cause interictal behavioral disturbances is controversial. Although a belief that some epileptic disorders may be progressive could be discomforting, and perhaps add to the stigma of epilepsy, to deny such a relationship might result in failure to identify a preventable or treatable source of considerable disability among patients with epilepsy [2]. Evidence of epileptic seizure-induced behavioral disturbances is difficult to obtain from clinical investigations because of the confounding factors of antiepileptic drugs, underlying lesions, and unrecognized ictal events. Considerable support for a deleterious effect of secondary epileptogenesis, protective homeostatic mechanisms, and epilepsy-induced disturbances in development can be obtained, however, from studies with experimental animal models.

Kindling in cats induces enduring dopamine receptor supersensitivity [6]. Since schizophrenia is believed to result, at least in part, from excessive dopaminergic influences, this observation suggests a possible mechanism for the development of schizophrenia in patients with epilepsy [2].

Endogenous opioids are known to be released during stimulation-induced epileptic seizures in rats and mediate some postictal behavior [7]. These opioid peptides may act as endogenous mood elevators and account for the beneficial effect of electroconvulsive shock treatment on depression [2]. It is conceivable that some patients may become physiologically dependent on high levels of endogenous opioids when they are experiencing frequent seizures and that interictal depression could occur as a withdrawal symptom when seizure frequency is reduced or seizures no longer occur [2]. This could explain the observation that interictal depression is commonly encountered in patients with epilepsy and may be exacerbated by effective treatment [2].

Postictal hyperreactivity in kindled rats may also reflect endogenous opioid withdrawal phenomena [7]. This behavior resembles the combativeness sometimes encountered in epileptic patients after complex partial seizures and is a form of non-directed aggression [2]. More directed aggressive behavior is better modeled by predatory attack and defensive rage produced in cats by electrical stimulation of specific areas of the hypothalamus and periaqueductal gray [9]. These behavioral and anatomically well defined aggressive feline behaviors can be modulated by stimulation of limbic structures and administration of endogenous opioids and GABA [9]. Interictal defensive rage can also be exacerbated in cats by epileptogenic hippocampal lesions [10], indicating that epileptic limbic hyperexcitability can modulate affective tone. Similar emotional changes in patients with temporal lobe epilepsy would come under cortical control, resulting in more subtle and variable disturbances, such as impulsivity, depression, and insecurity, that are often associated with temporal lobe epilepsy [2].

The results of studies that imply a causative role for epileptic seizures in the appearance of unwanted interictal behavior must be interpreted with extreme caution and reported in a responsible manner, in order to avoid misinterpretations that would be detrimental to those who suffer from epilepsy. However, it is most appropriate to pursue both clinical and basic investigations into possible epileptogenic mechanisms of enduring disturbances in interictal behavior, if these disabilities are to be prevented or actively treated in the future.

Acknowledgments

The author's original work cited here was supported by Grants NS-02808, NS-15654, and MS-20867 from the National Institutes of Health, Grant MH-37916 from the National Institute of Mental Health, Contract DE-AC03-76-SF00012 from the Department of Energy, and a Guggenheim Fellowship.

References

1. Levy RH, Dreifuss FE, Mattson RH, Meldrum BS and Penry JK (eds.) (1989) Antiepileptic Drugs. Raven Press, New York.
2. Engel J Jr, Bandler R, Griffith NC and Caldecott-Hazard S (1991) In: Smith D, Treiman D and Trimble M (eds.) Advances in Neurology, Vol. 55. Raven Press, New York, pp. 97–111.
3. Nielsen H and Kristensen O (1981) Acta. Neurol. Scand. 64: 289–300.
4. Mendius JR and Engel J Jr (1985) In: Benson DF and Zaidel E (eds.) The Dual Brain. The Guilford Press, New York, pp. 263–276.
5. Devinsky O, Kelly K, Porter RJ and Theodore WH (1988) Neurology 38: 1347–1352.
6. Sato M and Ogawa T (1984) In: Fariello RG, Morselli PL, Lloyd KG, Quesney LF and Engel J Jr (eds.) Neurotransmitters, Seizures and Epilepsy, II. Raven Press, New York, pp. 1–9.
7. Caldecott-Hazard S and Engel J Jr (1987) Prog. Neuropsychopharmacol. Biol. Psychiatry 11: 389–418.
8. Kline NS, Li CH, Lehmann HE, Lajtha A, Laski E and Cooper T (1977) Arch. Gen. Psychiatry 34: 1111–1113.
9. Bandler R (1988) In: Epstein A and Morrison A (eds.) Progress in Psychobiology and Physiological Psychology, Vol. 13. Academic Press, New York, pp. 67–153.
10. Griffith N, Engel J Jr and Bandler R (1987) Brain. Res. 400: 360–364.

© 1991 Elsevier Science Publishers B.V. All rights reserved.
Biological Psychiatry, Volume 2. G. Racagni et al., editors.

Evolving anatomy and pharmacology of kindling

R.M. Post, S.R.B. Weiss, M. Clark and J. Rosen
Biological Psychiatry Branch, National Institute of Mental Health, 9000 Rockville Pike, Bethesda MD 20892, U.S.A.

Kindling is not only a model for the development of epileptogenesis, but also provides a conceptual approach to a variety of neuropsychiatric syndromes that undergo progressive evolution and a transition to spontaneity. As such, understanding the evolving biochemical and neuroanatomical changes that occur during kindling may provide insights into a variety of clinical syndromes and their therapeutics. Amygdala kindling undergoes three general phases:

1. The early *developmental* phase where there is a lowering of the threshold for afterdischarges and spread of afterdischarges throughout the brain associated with incremental development of minor to major behavioral seizure phenomena (stages 1–5);
2. The mid or *completed* phase when full-blown seizures are reliably elicited by each stimulation;
3. The late *spontaneous* phase when exogenous stimulation is no longer necessary in order for seizures to be observed.

Similar phases of kindling evolution occur with repeated application of certain drugs, including the local anesthetics lidocaine and cocaine. We have postulated that in animals and in some people, repeated cocaine administration can also be associated with the kindling-like development of seizures, or on a subconvulsant basis, panic attacks [1]. That is, a person may use cocaine for prolonged periods of time without experiencing cocaine-related panic attacks, then enter into a phase where panic attacks occur discretely in response to cocaine administration, and then, finally, emerge into a spontaneous phase where panic attacks occur in an unprecipitated fashion and continue even following discontinuation of cocaine use. In a similar fashion, repeated bouts of alcohol *withdrawal* may be associated with increasing severity of withdrawal symptoms including panic attacks, and ultimately delirium tremens and alcohol withdrawal seizures.

While patients with affective illness do not typically experience seizures or demonstrate evidence of a convulsive disorder either clinically or upon brain imaging, they do experience a variety of paroxysmal psychosensory events and undergo a course of illness that bears some resemblance to kindling evolution. The modal course of unipolar and bipolar affective illness shows cycle acceleration (shorter well intervals) with each successive episode. Older clinical observations and newer systematic evidence indicate that first episodes of major affective disorders are much more likely to be precipitated by psychosocial stressors than subsequent episodes (i.e. later episodes occur more autonomously, perhaps analogous to the process of spontaneity in kindling).

Pharmacological studies have implicated different biochemical and anatomical processes in the development vs. completed phases of kindling. For example, atropine and clonidine inhibit the development but not completed phases of kindling and the glutamate antagonist MK-801 shows the same general pattern, but with modest effectiveness on the completed stage. Thus, like long-term potentiation, glutamate neurotransmission appears critical to the development but not expression of the process. In contrast, carbamazepine is ineffective in the development but highly effective on the completed phase of amygdala-kindled seizures. Yet, carbamazepine shows the opposite profile on local-anesthetic kindling where it is highly effective in the development phase, but is ineffective once full-blown seizures have occurred [2]. Another remarkable double-dissociation has been demonstrated by Pinel [3]; diazepam blocks the development and completed, but not the spontaneous phase of amygdala-kindled seizures, and phenytoin shows the opposite pattern. Thus, we conclude that different phases in the evolution of different types of kindling demonstrate remarkable dysjunctions in pharmacological responsivity, implying that different biochemical and/or anatomical substrates are underlying these phenomena.

This inference can now be studied with new mapping techniques involving in situ hybridization with the proto-oncogene c-fos. Clark and associates [4] have found c-fos is initially induced unilaterally, either in piriform cortex (if afterdischarge duration is short) or dentate gyrus of the hippocampus (if afterdischarge duration is long). With seizure stage progression, induction of c-fos becomes bilateral in these structures and involves other areas of brain. Different seizure pathways can also be progressively activated by different seizure-inducing stimuli [5]. For example, caffeine-induced seizures are almost entirely confined to the striatum in the mouse, while ECT seizures are predominantly limbic in distribution and cocaine-induced seizures show a combination of the 2 patterns.

In addition to its mapping function, the immediate early gene c-fos and related oncogenes including c-jun, jun-B and fos-related antigens (Fras), etc., may be the first steps in a cascade of events that encode the long-term "memory" of the kindled stimulation and provide the biochemical and neural substrates for the lasting if not permanent alterations in responsivity. Briefly, following the receptor or second messenger alterations associated with cell firing, the mRNA for c-fos is induced, translocated to the ribosomes where the c-fos protein is made, dimerizes with c-jun in a leucine zipper motif, is transported to the nucleus where it binds to AP-1 sites on DNA, resulting in transcription of mRNAs for a variety of new substances in promotor regions including enzymes, neurotransmitters, receptors, and nerve growth factors. This process has a spatio-temporal evolution such that repeated kindling stimulation evokes longer-lasting and potentially more widespread increases in CRH, TRH, enkephalin and somatostatin and decreases in dynorphin. The early oncogene inductions may also lead to new synapse formation and dendritic sprouting in hippocampal granule cells which have recently been documented.

Involvement of the piriform cortex appears to occur at an early stage of seizure kindling induced by a variety of agents, including electrical stimulation of the amygdala, cocaine, lidocaine, CRH and the stress associated with sham ECT. The fact that stressors and stress hormones such as CRH can induce the oncogene c-fos initially in piriform cortex and later in hippocampus, raises the possibility that environmental and psychosocial stressors could also activate different aspects of the c-fos-immediate early oncogene cascade and leave behind biochemical and anatomical residues that could carry lasting "memory" traces, as has been elucidated in the kindling paradigm. This model provides an important paradigm for considering the transition to spontaneity in affective illness and emphasizes the importance of early intervention, long-term prophylaxis and differential psychopharmacological interventions as a function of stage of evolution of the syndrome. In addition, the kindling perspective suggests the biochemistry and underlying neurobiology of evolving syndromes such as the affective disorders, alcohol withdrawal syndromes, or cocaine-induced panic attacks may change remarkably over time. Thus clinical studies aimed at elucidating pathophysiology need to adequately define the stage of the illness in their patients as another important variable. We suggest that the progression of many neuropsychiatric disorders, like the evolution of carcinogenesis, may involve multiple and sequential oncogenes and biochemical pathways resulting not only in the potential for malignant transformation, but multiple targets for intervention and new drug development.

References

1. Post RM, Weiss SRB, Uhde TW, Clark M and Rosen JB (1991) Preclinical neuroscience advances pertinent to panic disorder: implications of cocaine kindling, induction of the proto-oncogene c-fos, and contingent tolerance. In: Hoehn-Saric R (ed.) Biology of Anxiety Disorders: Recent Developments. APA Press, Washington D.C. (in press).
2. Weiss SRB, Post RM, Szele F, Woodward R and Nierenberg J (1989) Brain Res. 497: 72–79.
3. Pinel JPJ (1983) Pharmacol. Biochem. Behav. 18: 61–63.
4. Clark M, Post RM, Weiss SRB, Cain CJ and Nakajima T (1991) Regional expression of c-fos mRNA in rat brain during the evolution of amygdala kindled seizures. Mol. Brain Res. (in press).
5. Nakajima T, Post RM, Weiss SRB, Pert A and Ketter T (1989) Convulsive Ther. 5: 274–295.

© 1991 Elsevier Science Publishers B.V. All rights reserved.
Biological Psychiatry, Volume 2. G. Racagni et al., editors.

Experimental models of limbic seizures

Giovambattista De Sarro and Giuseppe Nistico'
Institute of Pharmacology, School of Medicine, Catanzaro, Italy

Limbic seizures can be induced in animal models by a number of chemoconvulsants acting on different neurotransmitter systems. Thus, cholinergic and excitatory amino acid agonists evoke limbic convulsions following systemic or central routes of administration. The importance of cholinergic pathways in epilepsy was realized following reports of seizures resulting from intracerebral or systemic injection of acetylcholine (ACh) analogues in rodents. Iontophoretically applied ACh or carbachol results in excitation of dentate gyrus and hippocampal neurons which can be blocked by the cholinergic antagonist atropine [1,2]. Focal infusions of high doses of carbachol into the dentate gyrus results in behavioural alterations such as seizure activity and "wet dog shaking", and this response can be attenuated by atropine [3]. Injection of cholinergic agonists in the amygdala consistently shows recurrent seizures and a kindled state [4]. One animal model of temporal lobe epilepsy evoked by cholinergic receptor stimulation which has been extensively studied is the pilocarpine model in rodents. Pilocarpine is a potent muscarinic receptor agonist and when injected systemically in large doses results in seizures [5–7]. EEG recordings reveal paroxysmal spiking activity in the hippocampus, amygdala, cortex and striatum. The behavioural manifestations of seizure activity and the seizure-related neuropathological damage following a high dose of pilocarpine (380 mg/kg, i.p.) have been well documented [5,6]. The involvement of excitatory amino acids in epilepsy was first demonstrated by Hayashi, who reported that topical application of sodium glutamate and aspartate onto the cortex of primates and dogs results in clonic convulsions [8]. It has been documented that glutamate, aspartate and their synthetic analogues acting as agonists are all epileptogenic when injected in high doses either systemically or directly into the brain [9]. In particular, the convulsant properties of kainic acid (KA) have received a great deal of attention [10]. Different routes of KA administration all result in limbic seizures; the pattern of hippocampal neuronal damage, however, varies following central or systemic injections of KA. Low doses of KA injected intracerebroventricularly cause preferential damage to the CA3 region of the hippocampus. Following systemic injection of KA, the CA1, subiculum, and the medial portion of CA3 and CA4 are preferentially damaged [11–13]. This latter pattern of neuronal damage in hippocampus closely resembles the damage observed in human temporal lobe epilepsy and suggests that systemically applied KA may be more appropriate as a model for temporal lobe epilepsy [14]. Both pilocarpine- and KA-induced convulsions are referred to as animal models of temporal lobe epilepsy. The models were initially developed with the aim to provide an easy, reproducible seizure syndrome for studying therapeutic approaches to temporal lobe epilepsy. Both models are relatively resistant to conventional antiepileptic treatment. This is also the case in the clinic, where complex partial limbic seizures are resistant to medication [15,16]. Intraperitoneal injection of relatively high doses of pilocarpine in rodents evokes a dose-dependent seizure syndrome [5]. Immediately after pilocarpine (380 mg/kg) injection the animals remain still, crouched and exhibit gustatory automatisms. There is rapid progression into motor limbic seizures characterized by rearing, forelimb clonus and falling. Once limbic status epilepticus is achieved the animals show spontaneous seizure episodes lasting at least 24 h. KA injected systemically in rats results in limbic seizures which have a dose-dependent and time-action relationship [11,12]. Within 30 min after KA injection the rats display staring spells, head-nodding and wet dog shakes. If this stage is accompanied by brief myoclonus of head and forelimbs without rearing, recurrent motor limbic seizures characterized by rearing, forelimb clonus and falling (termed "severe limbic convulsions") become apparent within 1 h [11,12]. The last phase of KA-induced seizures is status epilepticus (i.e. continuous convulsions recur every 5 min and last up to 3 h). These models have also proved useful in the study of the basic mechanisms of epilepsy and of the anatomical pathways involved in the initiation and spread of seizures.

References

1. Bird SJ and Aghajanian GK (1976) Neuropharmacology 15: 273–282.
2. Bernado LS and Prince DA (1982) Brain Res. 249: 315–331.
3. Flicker C and Geyer MA (1982) Brain Res. 4: 137–147.
4. Olney JW, De Gubereff T and Labruyere J (1983) Nature 301: 520–522.
5. Turski WA, Cavalheiro EA, Schwarz M, Czuczwar SJ, Kleinrok Z and Turski L (1983) Behav. Brain Res. 9: 315–336.
6. De Sarro GB, Patel S and Meldrum BS (1987) Eur. J. Pharmacol. 132: 229–236.
7. Patel S, De Sarro GB and Meldrum BS (1988) Neuroscience 23: 837–850.
8. Hayashi T (1952) Jpn. J. Physiol. 3: 46–64.
9. Stone WE and Javid MJ (1983) Brain Res. 264: 165–167.
10. De Sarro G, Rotiroti D, Calo' M, Puja A, Anfosso R and Nistico' G (1982) Res. Commun. Chem. Pathol. Pharmacol. 38: 355–365.
11. Ben-Ari Y, Tremblay E, Ottersen OP and Meldrum BS (1980) Brain Res. 191: 79–97.
12. Lothman EW and Collins RC (1981) Brain Res. 218: 299–318.
13. Ben-Ari Y, Tremblay E, Riche D, Ghilini G and Naquet R (1981) Neuroscience 6: 1361–1391.
14. Nadler JV (1981) Life Sci. 29: 2031–2042.
15. Clifford DB, Lothman EW, Dodson WE and Ferendelli JA (1982) Exp. Neurol. 76: 156–167.
16. Turski WA, Cavalheiro EA, Coimbra C, d'Penha Berzaghi M, Ikonomidou-Turski C and Turski L (1987) Brain Res. Rev. 12: 281–305.

© 1991 Elsevier Science Publishers B.V. All rights reserved.
Biological Psychiatry, Volume 2. G. Racagni et al., editors.

Depression in epilepsy: Biological links

Howard A. Ring and Raymond Way
Institute of Neurology, Queen's Square, London WC1, U.K.

Depression is a clinically important concomitant of epilepsy. A link between the 2 states was described by Hippocrates: "Melancholics ordinarily become epileptics and epileptics melancholics: of these 2 states what determines the preference is the direction the malady takes; if it bears upon the body, epilepsy, if upon the brain, melancholy" [1].

There have been very few studies investigating the absolute prevalence of psychiatric morbidity in epilepsy in the community. Two studies in England have assessed all the patients with epilepsy registered with a number of primary health care family doctors. In a sample of 218 patients Pond and Bidwell [2] recorded psychological difficulties in 29%. In half of these the difficulties were "neurotic" in nature. Fifteen years later Edeh and Toone [3], in a similar community-based survey of 88 patients, recorded neurotic depression in 22% of their sample. Currie et al. [4], in a survey of 666 patients with temporal lobe epilepsy attending a London hospital for any reason over an 18-year period, described clinically apparent anxiety in 19% and depression in 11%.

The importance of understanding depression in epilepsy is highlighted when the frequency of suicide and parasuicide in this population is reviewed. Barraclough [5], reviewing 11 previous studies, reported a suicide rate of five times that in the general population. Mathews and Barabas [6], reviewed 8 studies and noted a suicide rate in epilepsy of 5% compared to 1.4% in control populations.

Mania is rare in association with epilepsy. Williams [7] described elation in just 3 of 2,000 patients. The few cases reported in the literature are in the form of anecdotal accounts of individual cases [8,9].

In order to gain some insight into the possible mechanisms of depression in epilepsy it is important to examine the psychiatric and seizure characteristics that have been associated with depression in the various published studies that have included such data. Unfortunately, although quite a number of studies have examined affective disturbance in epilepsy, the data from these investigations are not strictly comparable. Patients were selected by various differing criteria for entry, affective disturbance was rated using different measures and population sampled have been drawn from the community [3], neuropsychiatric [10] and neurological [11] hospital outpatient clinics, psychiatric [12] and general [13] inpatient units and from patients awaiting temporal lobe surgery [14]. The information in Table 1, presenting some of the seizure and treatment related and other variables described in association with epilepsy, has been culled largely from

Table 1. The associations of depression in epilepsy

Association	No. of studies; finding association	No association
Seizure characteristics:		
Seizure type	1	4
Temporal focus	3	1
Left focus	3	5
Seizure frequency	1	4
Seizure duration	1	4
Treatment-related:		
Polypharmacy	3	3
Phenobarbitone	3	
Low serum folate	3	
Personal factors:		
Male preponderance	2	3
Loss of control	1	1
Family depression history	1	1

Studies providing data [3,4,7,10–14,21–29].

the above studies. It is far from exhaustive but includes conclusions drawn by the authors of these studies about the nature of some of the associations of depression in epilepsy. Consideration of these observations may suggest possible mechanisms that underlie the association of these two conditions.

Examination of the data suggests that some general observations may be made. It appears that neither seizure type (complex partial with or without secondary generalization or primary generalized seizures), or frequency, or duration of epilepsy are often associated with depression. The situation is more equivocal regarding the co-occurrence of a left-sided focus and interictal depression and it appears that a temporal focus is more often associated with depression than not. It should be noted that many of the studies in the literature could not contribute to the latter observations because their entrance requirements included the diagnosis of temporal lobe epilepsy.

The frequency of temporal lobe foci in those with depression is of interest in the light of animal studies on kindling. Repeated seizure involvement of limbic tissue, regardless of the seizure type, may lead to kindling-like processes which alter limbic function interictally. It is thus suggested that limbic activation during seizures is associated with interictal psychopathology. However, recalling that only a minority of patients with limbic involvement in their epilepsy develop significant psychopathology, Adamec [15] concludes that the proposed change in limbic functioning does not cause depression directly but that rather it increases the individual's vulnerability to psychological and social stresses.

Relationships between epilepsy, anticonvulsants and mood have been reported [10,16]. These authors noted that patients receiving phenobarbital were more depressed, whereas those taking carbamazepine were both less depressed and less anxious. Phenobarbitone is thought to enhance GABA-mediated post-synaptic inhibition as part of its anticonvulsant activity both experimentally and in patients [17]. A new anticonvulsant drug, vigabatrin, also acts to increase activity in GABAergic pathways. A small minority of patients who take vigabatrin become depressed in association with this treatment [18,19]. Thus treatment-related depression in epilepsy may be mediated through increases in GABAergic activity. However, there is no evidence that similar processes operate in those patients with epilepsy who become depressed in the absence of drug effects.

Another biochemical and treatment-related mechanism that has been suggested as contributing to depression in epilepsy is folate depletion [18]. A relationship between mental illness and folate deficiency was reported by Carney [20]. Phenytoin and barbiturates may both lead to falls in serum, red blood cell (RBC) and cerebrospinal fluid. Edeh and Toone [3] examined serum and RBC folate levels in a community sample of epileptic patients on monotherapy or polytherapy. They found that there were significantly lower folate concentrations in those on polytherapy and in those achieving psychiatric "caseness" using the Clinical Interview Schedule. This was true for the depressive neurosis subgroup but not the anxiety subgroup. However, the therapeutic trials of folate have not been effective. With respect to a possible mechanism of action, it has been pointed out that the folate cycle is involved in synthesizing methyl groups which in turn become involved in the action of S-adenosylmethionine, a methyl donor involved in the methylation of, amongst other things, neurotransmitters [18].

References

1. Lewis AJ (1934) J. Ment. Sci. 80: 1–42.
2. Pond DA and Bidwell BH (1959) Epilepsia 1: 285–299.
3. Edeh J and Toone BK (1985) Epilepsia 26: 434–440.
4. Currie S, Heathfield KWG, Henson RA and Scott DF (1971) Brain 94: 173–190.
5. Barraclough B (1981) In: Reynolds EH and Trimble MR (eds.) Epilepsy and Psychiatry. Churchill Livingstone, Edinburgh, pp. 72–76.
6. Mathews WS and Barabas G (1981) Psychosomatics 22: 515–524.
7. Williams D (1956) Brain 79: 29–67.
8. Barczak P, Edmunds E and Betts T (1988) Br. J. Psychiatry 152: 137–139.
9. Hurwitz TA, Wada JA, Koska BD and Strauss EH (1985) Neurology 35: 1335–1337.
10. Robertson MM, Trimble MR and Townsend HRA (1987) Epilepsia 28: 364–372.
11. Kogeorgos J, Fonagy P and Scott DF (1982) Br. J. Psychiatry 140: 236–243.
12. Mendez MF, Cummings JL and Benson F (1986) Arch. Neurol. 43: 766–770.
13. Altshuler LL, Devinsky O, Post RM and Theodore W (1990) Arch. Neurol. 47: 284–288.
14. Hermann BP and Wyler AR (1989) Epilepsia 30: 332–338.
15. Adamec RE (1990) Biol. Psychiatry 27: 249–279.
16. Robertson MM (1989) J. Epilepsy 2: 189–230.
17. Engel J Jr (1989) Seizures and Epilepsy. F.A. Davis Company, Philadelphia.
18. Reynolds EH (1991) In: Smith D, Treiman D and Trimble M (eds.) Advances in Neurology, Vol. 55. Raven Press Ltd., New York, pp. 47–58.
19. Ring HA and Reynolds EH (1991) In: Pedley T and Meldrum BS (eds.) Recent Advances in Epilepsy 5. Churchill Livingstone, London (in press).

20. Carney MWP (1967) Br. Med. J. 4: 512–516.
21. Brent DA, Crumine PK, Varma RR, Allan M and Allman C (1987) Pediatrics 80: 909–917.
22. Kramer LD, Fralin C, Berman NG and Locke GE (1987) Epilepsia 28: 629.
23. Mendez MF, Lanska DJ, Manon-Espaillat R and Burnstine TH (1989) Arch. Neurol. 46: 1065–1068.
24. Moller AA and Froscher W (1990) Schweiz. Arch. Neurol. Psychiatr. 141: 139–148.
25. Perini G and Mendius R (1984) J. Nerv. Ment. Dis. 172: 287–290.
26. Shorvon SD and Reynolds EH (1979) Br. Med. J. 2: 1023–1025.
27. Thompson PJ and Trimble MR (1982) Epilepsia 23: 531–544.
28. Trimble MR, Corbett JA and Donaldson D (1980) J. Neurol. Neurosurg. Psychiatry 43: 1030–1034.
29. Reynolds EH, Chanarin I, Milner G and Mathews DM (1966) Epilepsia 7: 261–270.

© 1991 Elsevier Science Publishers B.V. All rights reserved.
Biological Psychiatry, Volume 2. G. Racagni et al., editors.

Anticonvulsants and mood stabilisation – An update

Trevor Silverstone

Department of Psychological Medicine, Medical College of St. Bartholomew's Hospital, London, U.K.

The majority of patients with bipolar affective disorder relapse at least once during their lifetime, most several times, often with disastrous consequences. Thus, there is great need for effective and acceptable treatments to prevent such relapses.

The introduction of lithium greatly improved the outlook for many patients with bipolar disorder. However, not everybody responds. It is for the 20–40% of patients who are non-responsive to lithium despite good compliance that the anticonvulsants can be particularly recommended.

The anticonvulsants which have been used in bipolar disorder include carbamazepine and its analogue oxcarbazepine, valproic acid and clonazepam.

Carbamazepine

Early studies in Japan and the U.S. showed that carbamazepine was effective in improving acute mania, particularly in patients who had failed to respond to lithium. Recent double-blind controlled trials have confirmed this. Carbamazepine is particularly useful in the prophylaxis of bipolar disorder, proving as least as good as lithium, sometimes superior. Side-effects include dizziness, ataxia and drowsiness. An erythematous rash can prove troublesome in up to 15% of patients. Although serious blood dyscrasias are rare, a transient fall in the neutrophil count is common. This requires regular monitoring, at least in the early stages of treatment. Carbamazepine acts as an enzyme-inducing agent in the liver which can interfere with the pharmacokinetics of other drugs which the patient may be taking.

Oxcarbazepine has far less enzyme-inducing activity and is less likely to give rise to hypersensitivity reactions. It appears to be as effective as haloperidol and lithium in acute mania.

Valproic acid

This anticonvulsant compound was first tried in France, where it was reported to be of benefit. Systematic study was not undertaken until the 1980s; valproic acid has been shown to be better than a placebo in the few double-blind controlled trials thus far undertaken.

Valproic acid has been less studied as a prophylactic agent, but an open trial involving 51 rapid cycling patients was encouraging.

Unwanted effects include gastrointestinal symptoms, particularly nausea, increased appetite and weight gain. A rash may prove troublesome and ataxia and lethargy occur occasionally. Alopecia can occur, which is usually reversible on stopping the drug.

Clonazepam

Clonazepam is a benzodiazepine derivative used in the treatment of epilepsy. The rationale of using it in mania was its combination of 5-HT and GABA-enhancing effects. In the only double-blind trial thus far undertaken, clonazepam appeared to be at least as good as lithium.

Relatively few patients have been given clonazepam as a prophylactic and none under double-blind conditions. Of the three studies reported, one failed to reveal any benefit, one found it to be effective in most of the patients, in the other a proportion improved.

Clonazepam, being a potent benzodiazepine compound, can lead to marked drowsiness and may cause psychomotor impairment.

Discussion

The mode of action of these anticonvulsants in ameliorating the symptoms of mania and in preventing relapse is unknown. They all promote 5-HT neurotransmission, some promote GABA neurotransmission and carbamazepine can act as a glutamate antagonist.

Anticonvulsants have clearly proved useful in the treatment of acute mania and in the prophylaxis of bipolar disorder. Their relative efficacy is as yet untested, as are combinations of anticonvulsants with each other and with lithium.

Understanding how anticonvulsants work in bipolar disorder and identifying which patients respond to which drug is likely to greatly increase our understanding of this serious and distressing illness.

References

1. Goodwin FK and Jamison KR (1990) In: Manic Depressive Illness. Oxford University Press, Oxford.
2. Post RM (1990) Int. Rev. Psychiatry 2: 277–320.
3. Silverstone T and Romans-Clarkson S (1989) Br. J. Psychiatry 154: 321–335.

© 1991 Elsevier Science Publishers B.V. All rights reserved.
Biological Psychiatry, Volume 2. G. Racagni et al., editors.

The past, present and future of limbic surgery in psychiatry

H. Thomas Ballantine Jr.
Harvard Medical School and Massachusetts General Hospital, Boston, MA 02114-2696, U.S.A.

Fifty-five years ago, Egas Moniz from Portugal published the results of lesioning the frontal lobes of 20 hospitalized psychiatric patients. This was the first systematic approach to such a method of treatment; the stimulus for these operations was a result of Moniz' attendance at the 1935 Second World Congress of Neurology in London where he heard John Fulton, professor of physiology at Yale University Medical School describe the effects of bilateral frontal lobectomies on the behavior of 2 chimpanzees.

The results reported by Moniz led Walter Freeman and his neurosurgical colleague, James Watts, to embark in the United States on a series of pre-frontal lobotomies, the so-called "psychosurgical" procedures, and psychosurgery was performed world-wide within a few years. Most published reports from many centers stated that more than 50% of patients were improved by lobotomy, but there was a significant mortality and a number of patients had a post-operative "frontal lobe syndrome" characterized by nonchalance, an inability to carry out tasks and a loss of social control. Thus, there ensued a search for more restricted operations but these efforts were not satisfactory.

In 1947, Fulton, at a meeting of the Society of British Neurological Surgeons, introduced the concept of cingulectomy rather than frontal lobotomy in the neurosurgical treatment of psychiatric illness. Sir Hugh Cairns at Oxford and Jacques LeBeau in Paris were thus stimulated to perform open cingulectomies. It was at this point that limbic system surgery became part of the neurosurgeon's armamentarium.

Another equally important event occurred in 1947: the publication by Spiegel and Wycis of a description of their "stereoencephalotome". This instrument was, arguably, the first such stereotactic device designed for operations deep within the human brain. The instrument was, however, somewhat cumbersome and neurosurgeons, notably Leksell in Sweden and Talairach in France designed their own stereotactic devices. In 1949, Talairach described the stereotactic electrocoagulation of the thalamofrontal fibres of the internal capsule for treatment of disabling anxiety. By 1952 Leksell was also performing this same procedure which is currently used for treatment of obsessive-compulsive disorders and anxieties.

The use of stereotactic approaches to various regions within the limbic system was gradually expanded over the next 20 years. Those most commonly employed for the treatment of psychiatric illness at present are: subcaudate tractotomy, limbic leucotomy, anterior capsulotomy and anterior cingulotomy.

The fact that 4 different centers (2 of which are in London) for the neurosurgical treatment of psychiatric illness utilize 4 different approaches to the limbic system is ample evidence that the term "psychosurgery" (which became a synonym for frontal leucotomy) should be supplanted by "limbic system surgery". But this fact also calls for a consideration of the indications for each of these 4 procedures. In 1981 Bartlett et al. [1] published a statement which said that subcaudate tractotomy should be used for the following:

- Depression;
- Anxiety and tension;
- Obsessional neurosis;
- Schizo-affective illness.

Limbic leucotomy was recommended for the treatment of obsessional neurosis and schizophrenia accompanied by depression, anxiety or obsessional symptoms. In Sweden, Meyerson and Mindus advocate anterior capsulotomy for obsessive-compulsive disorders and anxiety [2]. In the United States, Ballantine and colleagues perform anterior cingulotomy for all of the above [3].

There has been no definitive study which unequivocally demonstrates the efficacy of one surgical procedure over the others. The literature would indicate that both limbic leucotomy and anterior capsulotomy are more effective than cingulotomy in the treatment of obsessive-compulsive disorders but both of these procedures carry a higher risk (although still only slight) of undesirable personality changes. A joint study by the 4 centers would be most helpful.

Despite the enormous numbers of psychotropic drugs that have been developed over the years, none of them are completely free of side-effects and some patients appear to be refractory to all of them. Moreover, in the United States at least, limbic system surgery is grossly under-utilized. This can be attributed to a lack of publication on the part of psychiatrists and neurosurgeons. It seems incontrovertible that there is a need for more surgical intervention and more leadership in this direction from the psychiatric community.

An opportunity currently exists for furthering our knowledge by observations which can be safely made during surgery. It is possible to assay specific neurotransmitters in the ventricular fluid and the tissue selected for ablation can be assayed for the presence or absence of neurotransmitters deemed important in the cause and treatment of psychiatric illness.

It is also possible that ablative procedures may be replaced by the introduction of neurochemicals or even of tissues. Both of these possibilities are being investigated. The use of implantable pumps, if current research is successful, could result in higher central nervous system concentrations of drugs at specific intracerebral sites. The recent attempts to treat Parkinson's disease by tissue transplantation may lead to another type of supplemental rather than ablative limbic system surgery.

In conclusion, it can be unequivocally stated that, in the near future, there is a place for limbic system surgery in psychiatry. It is, however, the responsibility of psychiatrists and neurosurgeons to be certain that it is employed only for the benefit of suffering patients and never for investigative, social or political purposes.

References

1. Bartlett J, Bridges P and Kelly D (1981) Br. J. Psychiatry 138: 508–511.
2. Meyerson B and Mindus P (1988) In: Lunsford L (ed.) Modern Stereotactic Neurosurgery. Martinus Nijhoff, Boston, pp. 353–364.
3. Ballantine HT, Jr (1986) In: Berger PA and Brodie HKH (eds.) American Handbook of Psychiatry, Vol. VIII. Basic Books Inc., pp. 1029-1047.
4. Ballantine HT, Jr, Bouckoms AJ, Thomas EK and Giriunas IE (1987) Biol. Psychiatry 21: 807–819.

The papers listed above contain a comprehensive list of other references for the interested reader.

© 1991 Elsevier Science Publishers B.V. All rights reserved.
Biological Psychiatry, Volume 2. G. Racagni et al., editors.

Selecting patients for psychosurgery

Andrea L. Malizia and Paul K. Bridges
Geoffrey Knight National Unit For Affective Disorders, Brook General Hospital, London SE18 4LW; and Division of Psychiatry, UMDS, Guy's Campus, London SE1 9RT, U.K.

Diagnostic issues

Psychosurgery, like most other treatments in psychiatry, draws it's raison d'être from empiricism. Its role therefore must be understood in terms of its historical context. While at its inception it was the only available effective treatment for the functional psychoses, it should now only be used when the beneficial effects of surgery for a particular illness, resistant to all the other treatments, are established and when the anatomical placement of the lesions is known to be effective [1].

Procedures designed by extension of theoretical constructs or animal experiments either produce intolerable side-effects or have failed to show consistent beneficial results; this is the case of multifocal leuco-coagulation [2] or of surgery for the treatment of obesity [3]. Therefore there is no place today for experimental lesions designed on dubious theoretical grounds. Equally, addressing behaviour control rather than symptomatology of psychiatric illnesses is unacceptable. This is especially so when the subject is in a position where free consent may be doubted, i.e. a prisoner [4].

Principles of patient selection in modern psychosurgery should include:

1. A clear diagnosis of a recognised psychiatric illness which has been shown to respond to surgery when all other available treatments have failed, and an absence of contraindications such as concurrent substance abuse and severe organic cerebral damage.
2. The patient's ability to give informed consent at the time of operation or a record that the patient was willing, when well, to have surgery if he or she fell ill again.

In practice therefore the indications are: affective and schizoaffective disorders, anxiety and tension states, obsessive-compulsive disorder, pathological episodic aggression related to abnormal limbic or temporal lobe function.

For the accepted indications, differences in reported practice between units are sometimes difficult to assess. For instance, do the operations used at present have different effects on different symptom profiles (e.g. stereotactic subcaudate tractotomy (SST) for affective disorders [5] and gamma anterior capsulotomy for anxiety disorders [6])? Is the referring psychiatrists' perception of what the surgery may be appropriate for differ between different countries? Confusion is added by published reports where the diagnostic criteria are not made clear [7].

Table 1. Operations as percentage of resistant affective disorders referrals

	Year			
	1979	1983	1987	1990
No. of referrals	74	64	61	96
No. of operations	47	28	21	20
Operations as % of referrals	64	44	33	21

Practical issues

In the United Kingdom, patients referred for psychosurgery are assessed by a team consisting of a neurosurgeon and a psychiatrist who both specialise in this field. This is because the neurosurgeon must retain the decision to operate, but the psychiatric assessment is best done by a psychiatrist who can decide whether other treatment avenues have indeed been exhausted. Any system of assessment which departs from this scheme is in our view inadequate.

For instance, while over 1200 operations have been carried out in our unit over the past 25 years, the proportion of patients going on to surgery has decreased because of the more resolute pharmacotherapeutic approaches adopted (Table 1).

Referrals for psychosurgery to the Geoffrey Knight Unit 1988–1989

Our outpatient work consists of assessments and reassessments for psychosurgery, assessments for a psychiatric second opinion, surgery follow-up, pharmacotherapy of affective disorders and a small number of liaison referrals. We assess 80–100 new cases per year. Out of these, 100 consecutive cases which were specifically referred for a psychosurgery opinion in 1988–1989 were selected for audit. The outcome of referral is summarised below:

100
Referred

90
Appropriate referrals

53
Psychosurgery recommended

41
Stereotactic subcaudate tractotomy (SST)

Two of the patients had previous non-stereotactic leucotomies. Of the 10 patients considered unsuitable referrals, 6 had personality disorders.

Patients who were suitable referrals, but not accepted for surgery at the time, were considered to have had insufficient medication. Five of these were subsequently successfully treated with pharmacotherapy in our unit, 4 of these as inpatients.

The reasons for which 12 patients were recommended for surgery but did not have SST were as follows:

- Two had diagnoses which required other operations (Gilles de la Tourette and episodic dyscontrol);
- Two were refused by the Mental Health Act Commission;
- Three did not want to take up the offer of surgery;
- One has continued to be too retarded to consent;
- One was lost to the referrers due to a move of home;
- One improved spontaneously while on the waiting list;
- One is still considering whether to take up the offer;
- One responded to an increased dose of tricyclics while on the waiting list, but died of inhalation following an epileptic fit.

Of the 53 which were recommended for surgery, 38 were recommended at their first outpatient visit. Of the 41 operated on, 16 had bipolar affective disorder, 16 had unipolar affective disorder, 1 had schizoaffective disorder, 2 had obsessive compulsive disorder, 2 had generalised anxiety and panic disorder and 4 had a combination of obsessive-compulsive disorder and other affective or anxiety related diagnoses. Eleven out of 36 reassessed to date have had very good outcome, while 9 have experienced significant relief of symptoms.

References

1. Bridges PK and Bartlett JR (1977) Br. J. Psychiatry 131: 249–260.
2. Crow HJ, Cooper R and Phillips DG (1961) J. Neurol. Neurosurg. Psychiatry 24: 353–360.
3. Quaade F (1974) Lancet i: 267.
4. Dieckmann G, Horn HJ and Schneider H (1979) Long-term results of anterior hypothalamotomy in sexual offences. In: Hitchcock ER, Ballantine HT Jr and Meyerson BA (eds.) Modern Concepts in Psychiatric Surgery. Elsevier, North Holland.
5. Bridges PK (1991) Resistant Depression. In: E. Paykel (ed.) Handbook of Affective Disorders, Churchill/Livingstone.
6. Mindus P (1991) Capsulotomy in Anxiety Disorders: A Multidisciplinary Study. Kongl Carolinska Medico Chirurgisk.
7. Van Manen and Van Veelen CW (1988) Acta Neurochir. Suppl. (Wien) 44: 167–169.

© 1991 Elsevier Science Publishers B.V. All rights reserved.
Biological Psychiatry, Volume 2. G. Racagni et al., editors.

Severe, chronic, refractory polysubstance dependence and ventromedial hypothalamotomy

Renzo Zamboni[1], Veronica Larach[1], Ximena Rubio[1], Roberto Gallardo[2], Roberto Mancini[1], Humberto Mancini[1] and Mario Poblete[1]

[1]*Psychiatric Institute, Department of Stereotaxic Neurosurgery P.O. Box 2677, Santiago; and* [2]*Department of Pharmacology, University of Chile, Chile*

Introduction

One of the major reasons of referral to our psychosurgical team is long-standing, violent, uncontrolled autoaggressive or heteroaggressive behavior associated with various diagnoses, when all current methods of treatments have been proved unsuccessful [1]. We found a group of patients in which the aggressive episode was closely linked to severe chronic consumption of drugs and/or alcohol. In this restricted and specific group of patients, behavior maladjustment was directly related with the compulsive need for the substances abused. They were considered refractory to all psychiatric treatments, with multiple hospitalizations, frequent progression into delinquency and other antisocial behavior. Considering the reports of stereotactic target lesion in the ventromedial nucleus of the hypothalamus (VMH) for patients with drug and alcohol addiction [2,3], we decided to use the same target with modifications of the surgical procedure in order to avoid side-effects described by the above authors. The functional activity of the VMH in different drives has been stressed; in sexual and mating behavior [4] and in the mechanism of satiety, food and liquid intake [5]. Experimental evidence of suppression of morphine physical dependence has been described in addicted rats, by specific lesion of the VMH nucleus [6]. The relationships between the opiate and reward system and its association to drug and alcohol abuse has been recently discussed [7]. The aim of this report is to continue to communicate [8] our experience in stereotactic ventromedial hypothalamotomy in 13 patients operated in our department.

Material and Method

A series of 13 patients, 26.1 ± 3.6 years old, with severe long-standing history of drug and alcohol abuse (13 ± 3.6 years), starting early in life (13.38 ± 1.3 years) were classified according to DSM III-R diagnosis, all as severe psychoactive polysubstance dependence disorder, associated with the diagnosis of schizophrenia (3 patients), personality disorder (6 patients), and borderline intellectual functioning

(4 patients). Individual and family informed consent was independently obtained for this surgical procedure. Patients were operated with the Riechert and Mundinger stereotaxic apparatus, using Dieckmann and Schneider [3] parameters for the VMH. Two lesions of 2 mm in diameter were made in each nucleus. Before lesioning stimulation of the VMH was carried out by low-frequency pulses (for 5 to 10 s), obtaining a variety of autonomic responses (increasing blood pressure and heart rate, tachypnea and mydriasis). Emotional responses could be observed in some patients including pleasure sensation. Preoperative and postoperative clinical states were assessed by psychiatric and neurological examination, EEG, CAT scan, BPRS, Hamilton Depression, Hamilton Anxiety, TAT, Rorschach, WAIS, Bender-Bip and Luria Nebraska Neuropsychological Battery (LNNB).

Results

Patients were followed up for 67.3 ± 35.9 months. We present the results on 12 patients, because one patient died 4 months later, due to a heart infarction. Three patients underwent two operations on the same target with a difference between surgical procedures of 3, 6, 31 months respectively. In this series of 12 patients, the transient side-effects observed were: mild neurovegetative symptoms with moderate hyperthermia in 8 cases lasting 2 days (38.1 ± 6°C) and moderate confusion in 4 cases which lasted a period of 15 to 21 days. Long-standing side-effects such as weight gain were observed in 11 patients (91.6%), with a total increase of 33.4% from the basal weight after one year. Polydipsia of variable duration, 4.7 ± 2.71, occurred by day. Decrease in sexual drive was reported by 7 patients (6 without problems with their couples and one complained of sexual impotence).

Psychological evaluation showed the following pre- to postoperative WAIS average I.Q. scores (n = 11). Verbal I.Q.: 85.4 to 89.4 N.S.; Manual I.Q.: 87.2 to 88.9 N.S.; Total I.Q.: 85.8 to 88.9 N.S. Ten patients had LNNB postoperative assessment; 7 had pre- and post-evaluations. In these seven patients, t-test calculation of raw scores, pre- to postoperative changes showed significant improvement in: Rhythm (10.7 to 7.6, $P < 0.05$); Intellectual Processes (33.6 to 25.3, $P < 0.05$); Visual (14.0 to 9.7, $P < 0.01$); Memory (15.7 to 9.1, $P < 0.01$). No deterioration was observed in the other scales. The pre- and postsurgical results of Bender Bip evaluation showed no changes.

Results regarding the consumption and abuse of drugs and alcohol are summarized in Table 1. Actually 8 patients are totally free from drug and alcohol abuse, all ambulatory base, 2 patients abuse of drug and alcohol, are ambulatory: 1 patient with only drug abuse even while hospitalized and 1 patient hospitalized occasionally abused drug on ambulatory bases. Results dealing with quality of life are discussed in [9].

Table 1. VMH hypothalamotomy: postoperative pattern of psychoactive substance dependence

Associated diagnosis	Patient	Drugs	Alcohol	Living situation
Schizophrenia	J.B.	+++	(+)	Hospitalized
	A.G.	(+)	–	Hospitalized[a]
	H.S.	–	–	Ambulatory
Personality disorders	J.T.	–	–	Ambulatory
	C.A.	–	–	Ambulatory
	R.D.	–	–	Ambulatory
	C.H.	–	–	Ambulatory
	W.H.	+++	++	Ambulatory
Borderline intellectual functioning	R.M.	–	–	Ambulatory
	E.C.	–	–	Ambulatory
	P.S.	–	–	Ambulatory
	O.V.	+	+++	Ambulatory

+ Slight; ++ Moderate; +++ Severe; – No abuse; (+) Occasional abuse; [a] Patient occasionally abused drug while ambulatory.

Discussion

In our series 2 patients were reoperated because no signs and symptoms of hypothalamic neurovegetative activity and no changes were observed on the drug and alcohol abuse pattern. The third patient was reoperated 31 months later because alcohol abuse stopped and we wanted to wait for a possible retarded effect on the drug abuse. The modification of our surgical technique deals with a smaller size and number of lesions avoiding the contiguity to the preoptic area. The complete abolition of the substance abuse pattern obtained in 8 patients (66.6%), and the modification obtained in 2 other patients (16.6%) indicates that the VMH has a significant role in the psychoactive dependence mechanism. The reward system in man, with the participation of the medial forebrain bundle and other pathways, with important connections with the limbic system including the hypothalamus and frontal lobes, share a neurochemical substrate that is involved in the activation of this system [7]. We suggest that the lesion on the VMH could be one of the sites related to the reward system whose modification produce the cessation of the underlying mechanism of drug and alcohol abuse. The clinical results obtained suggest that ventromedial hypothalamotomy should be considered as a possible treatment for severe, chronic, refractory psychoactive dependence.

References

1. Zamboni R (1981) Rev. Chil. Neuropsiq. 19: 70–76.
2. Muller D, Roeder F and Orthner H (1976) Neurochirugia 16: 113–126.
3. Dieckmann G and Schneider H (1978) Appl. Neurophysiol. 41: 93–98.
4. Dorner G, Docke F and Moustafa S (1968) J. Reprod. Fertil. 17: 583-586.

5. Shimizu N, Oomura Y, Plata-Salaman CR and Morimoto M (1987) Brain Res. 416: 153–156.
6. Kerr FWL and Pozuelo J (1971) Mayo Clin. Proc. 46: 633–665.
7. Blum K, Briggs AH and Trachtenberg MC (1989) Experientia 45: 444–452.
8. Larach V, Zamboni R, Rubio X and Herreros J (1985) Severe chronic mixed substance abuse disorder treated with psychosurgery: 30 months follow-up. Proc. IV World Congress of Biol. Psychiatry, Sept. 8–13.
9. Larach V, Zamboni R, Rubio X, Gallardo R, Mancini R, Mancini H and Poblete (1991) In: Racagni G (ed.) Proc. V World Congress of Psychiatric, Elsevier, Amsterdam.

© 1991 Elsevier Science Publishers B.V. All rights reserved.
Biological Psychiatry, Volume 2. G. Racagni et al., editors.

Psychosurgical procedures for severe refractory depressive patients

D.A. da Costa[1] and Raul Marino Jr.[2]
[1]*Faculdade de Ciências Médicas de Minas Gerais; and* [2]*Faculdade de Medicina da Universidade de São Paulo, Brazil*

Introduction

Most people see psychiatric illness as a mental disturbance that can be solved by a simple change of environment, which is good both for patient and family.

This erroneous assumption, that appears to guarantee the success of the treatment, ignores both genetic and biological bases of depressive illness, as well as its pharmacological and biological treatment.

When a psychosurgical treatment is considered, that erroneous assumption can create greater barriers. In this study we shall attempt to overcome them.

Materials and Methods

Nineteen patients, after evaluation, underwent surgery. The DSM III criteria included 19 patients suffering from Major Depression, all of them exhibiting chronical evolution of severe refractory depression. Among these were included 12 women and 7 men between 23 and 71 years of age, with more than 10 years' evolution of illness. All patients were away from their normal work. The severity of the depression was estimated by the Hamilton Depression Rate Scale and by the Clinical General Impression (CGI). The same patients showed a 32-point minimum score and a 39-point maximum. According to the Clinical General Impression, all patients were included among the chronically ill.

The concept of severe refractory depression is based on clinical case severity, as well as on chronic evolution lasting more than 2 years and which was non-responsive to a conventional form of antidepressant treatment. Six types of treatment schedule were set up, as follows:

1. At least 2 tricyclic antidepressants (TCA), by oral application in up to 300 mg doses per day within a 2-month period, at adequate blood levels;
2. Intravenous drip infusion of antidepressants (cloromipramine + maprotiline) 150 mg each, in 20 infusions over 20 days;
3. MAOI – tranylcypromine 90 mg per day, phenelzine 60 mg per day for 2 consecutive months;
4. Increased action of antidepressants via lithium carbonate and/or low doses of thyroid hormone;

Table 1. Results

	Name	Sex	Age of onset (years)	Illness duration (years)	Surgery year	Follow-up 1991
1.	M.S.M.	F	12	25	1978	Minimally improved
2.	E.A.	M	19	8	1978	Much improved
3.	R.R.A.	F	6	31	1978	Very much improved
4.	M.R.V.	F	19	28	1980	Much improved
5.	M.A.A.	F	35	8	1981	Very much improved
6.	T.F.	F	16	29	1982	Improved
7.	F.R.F.	M	16	8	1982	Much improved
8.	M.H.F.	F	20	32	1982	Very much improved
9.	M.S.S.	F	32	21	1982	Very much improved until 1988: much worse
10.	H.A.	M	15	22	1982	Much improved
11.	L.F.J.	F	20	12	1982	Improved
12.	O.P.T.	F	20	32	1982	Much improved
13.	A.J.A.C.	M	7	21	1984	Very much improved
14.	C.A.F.	F	32	21	1984	Very much improved
15.	S.M.S.	F	50	21	1985	Improved; died from a heart attack, 1 month after surgery
16.	J.P.M.	M	16	7	1990	Very much improved
17.	M.A.D.	M	12	8	1990	Improved
18.	C.S.S.	F	20	28	1990	Minimally improved
19.	J.L.T.	M	18	9	1990	Much improved

5. ECT – 12 treatments;
6. Association of tricyclic antidepressants (TCA) and MAOI.

It must be pointed out that special care should be taken of the patient who exhibits compliance towards treatment, which does not seem to be frequent among severely depressed patients. On the other hand, one cannot by any means ignore other factors such as drug abuse, as well as some antibiotics, smoking, alcohol etc., for they can reduce antidepressive levels. Only after all treatment possibilities have been exhausted as factors that could interfere with its effectiveness, has psychosurgery been recommended.

Once psychosurgical treatment has been decided upon, the following necessary steps should be taken:

Pre-operative:

1. Basic information on procedures as well as risks to and advantages for both patient and family.
2. Patient's consent. Fundamental item for procedure.
3. General clinical check-up.
4. Neuropsychological check-up.

Postoperative:
1. Clinical and neuropsychological follow-up.
2. HAMD and CGI evaluation.

All patients mentioned in Table 1 are under regular treatment by antidepressants and uninterrupted psychiatric control; from 6 months after surgery until now, these patients have shown a 13-point minimum score and a 18-point maximum by the Hamilton Depression Rating Scale. All 19 patients have been submitted to cingulo-inominatotomy performed by the same neurosurgeon.

Conclusion

The cingulo-inominatotomy consists of a surgical procedure which should not be neglected by psychiatrists either in treating severe refractory or conventional psychiatric depression. In our series, morbidity and mortality caused by surgical intervention were zero and patient improvement may occur within a month to 2 years. All cases presented modifications in progression of illness, and a better response to pharmacological treatment with low doses of antidepressants.

Psychosurgery is an open field for research and will be used until such time as biological and psychopharmacological means are able to relieve human suffering to a greater degree.

References

1. Ballantine HT Jr, Cassidy WL, Flanagan NB and Marino R Jr (1969) Neurosurgery 26: 488–495.
2. Kelly D (1980) Anxiety and Emotion: Physiological Basis and Treatment. Thomas, Baltimore.
3. Kelly D (1985) In: Marcel Dekker (ed.) Psychosurgery – Handbook of Biological Psychiatry, Part VI. IVC, New York, pp. 459–467.
4. Marino R Jr. Biological Psychiatry. Interamerican, Buenos Aires, pp. 174–187.

© 1991 Elsevier Science Publishers B.V. All rights reserved.
Biological Psychiatry, Volume 2. G. Racagni et al., editors.

Intractable obsessive compulsive disorder (OCD) treated by limbic leucotomy

Desmond Kelly
The Priory Hospital, Priory Lane, London SW15 5JJ, U.K.

Introduction

Obsessional compulsive disorder (OCD) can be extremely distressing and treatment-resistant. It can lead to suicide. When all other methods of treatment, including behaviour therapy have failed, and incapacity and distress are marked, limbic leucotomy can be considered.

Method

The patients

Forty-nine patients with severe intractable OCD, who had failed to respond to every form of treatment were examined clinically and psychometrically before, 6 weeks and 20 months after limbic leucotomy. Selection criteria included, amongst others, extreme severity and chronicity of illness and the patients' full agreement (no patients underwent surgery while detained in hospital under a section of The Mental Health Act).

Psychometric ratings

The Leyton Obsessional Inventory which measures obsessional traits, symptoms, resistance (distress) and interference (intrusion), was used as was the Taylor Scale of Manifest Anxiety, Hamilton Anxiety and Depression Scales, Middlesex Hospital Questionnaire (MHQ), Self and Observer Ratings of Anxiety and Depression on a 10-point scale from zero symptoms to 10 (extreme), the Beck Depression and the Maudsley Personality Inventory (MPI). All the psychometric ratings were made by Dr. Nita Mitchell-Heggs.

Clinical ratings

These were carried out by 2 "team" psychiatrists; the least favourable rating was used for statistical purposes. A five-point scale was used:
1. Symptom-free;

2. Much improved (minimal residual symptoms);
3. Improved (definite improvement, but significant residual symptoms);
4. Not improved;
5. Worse (though not necessarily as a result of the operation).

Limbic leucotomy

Lesions are placed using a stereotactic technique, a method of locating a target in three-dimensional space. Lesions are made in the lower medial quadrant of the frontal lobe and in the cingulate bundle. The operation and assessment methods used are described in "Anxiety and Emotions: Physiological Basis and Treatment" [1]. All the operations are carried out at Atkinson Morley's Hospital (part of St. George's Hospital Medical School, London SW17) by Alan Richardson or Henry Marsh.

Results

Clinical ratings

At 20 months, 84% of the 49 patients with OCD were rated as improved (i.e. in category 1, 2 or 3; see above). Seven were symptom-free, 23 much improved, 11 improved, 5 not improved, and 3 were worse. Many of the patients were extremely suicidal prior to surgery and had said "If this fails I will certainly kill myself." Two patients committed suicide during the follow-up period (4%), one as a result of the withdrawal of social support and the other because of no change in the preoperative state. Both patients had made serious suicidal attempts prior to surgery.

Psychometric ratings

There were highly significant reductions postoperatively in mean values of obsessions (as measured on the Leyton Obsessional Inventory):
Symptoms: 32 pre-, 21 post-, difference 11;
Resistance and distress: 48 pre-, 25 post-, difference 23;
Interference (intrusion): 60 pre-, 23 post-, difference 37.

There were also significant decreases in *anxiety* as measured by the Taylor Scale, Hamilton Scale, and resting Self and Observer Ratings, and neuroticism (mean difference 9 points on the MPI).

A case history

A 34-year-old divorced mother of 3 children, who has a degree in psychology and is an accomplished tennis player, was referred with severe OCD. Her boyfriend in April 1990, at the time of her referral, "I pray that I can capture on paper at least

Table 1. Obsessional patients' mean psychometric values before and 20 months after limbic leucotomy; (n = 44)

	Pre-	20 months post-	Mean difference	P^a
Obsessions				
Symptoms	32.3	21.3	10.9	0.001
Traits	12.3	10.0	2.3	0.01
Resistance	48.5	25.5	23.0	0.001
Interference	59.8	23.2	36.6	0.001
MHQ	12.3	8.9	3.4	0.001
Anxiety				
Taylor	30.3	19.7	10.6	0.001
Hamilton	22.9	12.4	10.4	0.001
MHQ Anxiety	11.1	7.2	3.9	0.001
– Phobic	6.3	4.6	1.7	0.01
– Somatic	7.4	4.0	3.4	0.001
Basal Self Rating	5.1	3.8	1.4	0.01
– Observer Rating	4.8	3.4	1.4	0.001
Depression				
Beck	26.5	13.8	12.7	0.001
Hamilton	22.2	11.8	10.4	0.001
MHQ	10.0	5.9	4.0	0.001
Self Rating	5.9	3.5	2.4	0.001
Observer Rating	5.4	2.9	2.5	0.001
Neuroticism				
MPI	33.2	24.1	9.1	0.001
Psychiatric symptoms				
Cornell	22.5	12.6	9.9	0.001

[a]Correlated group's *t*-test; 5 patients out of the total of 49 did not complete all the pre- and postoperative psychometric ratings.

some sense of the magnitude of the havoc and destruction this monstrous disorder has wrought both upon her life and upon her relationships with others. She will eventually choose suicide as preferable to the unending purgatory of OCD. What she is living is not a life worthy of the name. She deserves so much more. She deserves to get up in the morning and rejoice at the dawning of a brand-new day, rather than to lie immobilized by the sheer dread of facing another day of hard labour, to which she is sentenced to by her mind. I pray that this surgery will deliver her from the purgatory to which the ghoulish disorder has condemned her". Following limbic leucotomy, her Leyton *symptom* scores had fallen from 27 to 1; *resistance and distress* from 58 to 1 and *interference* from 58 to 0.

Nine months following limbic leucotomy her referring psychiatrist wrote to The Mental Health Act Commissioners who had seen her before her operation: "Thus, for all practical purposes, she has currently no dysfunction as a result of her illness. On the Yale Brown Obsessive-Compulsive Scale, prior to the surgery she scored

32 out of a total of 40 and currently she scores 10. On the NIMH Global Obsessive Scale, which is a 15-point scale, she was 12 before the surgery which put her in the severe end of the spectrum. Currently she is 5, which is subclinical in intensity of symptoms." Ten months postoperatively her boyfriend wrote "When she first returned from her surgery I was stunned at the change. The extent of her improvement was beyond anything that my mind was prepared to accept as possible. She appeared to me (and to herself) to have left the horrors of OCD far behind. It took several weeks to become apparent that while the OCD had subsided to a remarkable degree, it had not entirely vacated the premises. For the first month or so, she was virtually without symptoms. I believe her history suggests that while she is highly susceptible to reversions to old habits, the surgery has generally removed the element of compulsion. She can now choose whether to give in to the habit, whereas before, there was no choice in the matter".

It is still early days in her postoperative course. She is still seeing a behaviour therapist and is busy bringing up her children and is planning to get a job.

Summary

Stereotactic limbic leucotomy, which has been performed in London over the past 20 years, can produce improvement in 84% of patients with the most severe forms of OCD, who have failed to respond to all available forms of psychotherapy, medication and behaviour therapy. Sixteen percent fail to improve and in those the illness is unchanged and postoperation suicide occurred in 4% of the sample of 49 patients studied.

Reference

1. Kelly D (1980) Anxiety and Emotions: Physiological Basis and Treatment. Charles C. Thomas, Springfield, Illinois.

© 1991 Elsevier Science Publishers B.V. All rights reserved.
Biological Psychiatry, Volume 2. G. Racagni et al., editors.

The role of capsulotomy in the treatment of chronic, severe and otherwise intractable anxiety disorder

Per Mindus

Departments of Psychiatry, Psychology and Neurosurgery, Karolinska Hospital, S-104 01 Stockholm, Sweden

Introduction

Anxiety disorders are among the most common mental illnesses, with 6–12 month prevalence rates of 1–6%, a high incidence of chronicity and high rates of co-morbidity with other anxiety disorders, depression, suicidal behaviour, alcohol and drug dependence, and somatic disorders, such as cardiovascular disease. The sufferers may have reduced quality of life and even reduced life expectancy. Despite great progress in recent years in the treatment of the anxiety disorders, 20% or more of patients do not respond to treatment or relapse soon afterwards. Some of these patients are possible candidates for psychosurgery.

Therefore, psychosurgical intervention is performed, if to a limited extent, both in the United States and in Europe. Cingulotomy, subcaudate tractotomy, limbic leucotomy and capsulotomy are the most commonly reported procedures in cases of anxiety disorder. Interconnections between the frontal lobes and the limbic structures have been described to pass through the anterior limb of the internal capsule, which is the target of capsulotomy.

The present multidisciplinary study was carried out to determine the relative efficacy of capsulotomy in cases of obsessive-compulsive disorder (OCD) and of generalized anxiety disorder, agoraphobia with panic attacks, and social phobia (i.e. non-OCD anxiety disorders), the risks of adverse effects on personality, and the structural and functional image of the patients' brains studied with magnetic resonance imaging (MRI) and positron emission tomographic (PET) techniques.

Materials and Methods

Two cohorts of patients were studied, the first consisting of 24 consecutive patients with chronic, severe OCD (n = 10) and non-OCD (n = 14) anxiety disorders (DSM III). Their mean duration of illness was 14.5 years, and they had all been subjected to numerous intensive treatment trials, with no appreciable effect on their illnesses. Their levels of symptoms and of psychosocial functioning were assessed prospectively by independent raters using, inter al, the Comprehensive Psychopathological Rating Scale (CPRS) and the Axis V of the DSM III. The patients' personality features were studied with both a self-report inventory (the Karolinska Scales of Personality, KSP) and the Rorschach test evaluated under blind conditions using modem scoring systems with established reliability and validity. A subsample of the OCD patients were studied prospectively with PET using ^{11}C as the tracer. The patients in the first cohort underwent capsulotomy by means of the radiofrequency (RF) thermolesion technique, and were followed-up for 1 year.

A second cohort of seven consecutive patients with severe, chronic OCD (n = 2) or non-OCD (n = 5) anxiety disorder unresponsive to conventional treatment underwent gamma capsulotomy by means of a radiosurgical technique. These patients were rated prospectively by two independent evaluators on some of the above scales and followed-up for 7 years.

Results

At the 1-year follow-up, clinically and statistically significant improvements were noted in the first cohort in all assessments of symptomatic and psychosocial functioning; 19 patients (79%) were rated as free of symptoms or much improved, and no patient was rated as worse after RF capsulotomy [1]. The proportion of patients rated as free of symptoms was comparable in the two diagnostic categories (OCD: 5/10; non-OCD: 7/14 = 50%). Postoperatively, there was no evidence of negative personality changes such as disinhibition or psychopathy [2,3]. There were, however, significant changes in the direction of normality in personality features related to anxiety proneness which correlated with reductions of state anxiety symptoms. A subsample of five OCD patients examined with PET displayed abnormal rates of glucose metabolism in their orbital gyri and caudate nuclei [4].

The response to gamma capsulotomy was rated as satisfactory in five of the seven patients. The clinical outcome in this cohort was found to correlate significantly with the neurosurgical precision in placing the lesion in the intended target, as reflected in independent, blind ratings based on the MR images [5].

Discussion

The results of RF or gamma capsulotomy seemed favorable, the majority of these severely incapacitated, chronic, and otherwise intractable cases had no or only minor residual symptoms at 1 year follow-up and 7 years postoperatively. There was no postoperative evidence of disinhibition or of psychopathy. The results are comparable with those published in other studies, the overall figure for patients rated as "symptom free" and "much improved" averaging 70%, and the overall figure of "unchanged" or "worse" averaging 10% of the over 360 capsulotomy cases reported to date (for a review, see [1]).

These salutary results have not, of course, been achieved without risk. Although capsulotomy compares well with other stereotactic procedures inasmuch as it carries little risk of surgical complications, and no death has been reported in conjunction with the intervention, hemorrhage, epileptic seizures, and considerable weight gain have been observed in some cases. Mental complications such as lassitude, increased fatigability, brusqueness and poor memory (not corroborated in tests) have also been reported in occasional patients. As has been pointed out, anxiety disorders themselves carry certain risk: it is the delicate task of the responsible clinician to weigh the risk of non-intervention against that of intervention.

Conclusion

Provided the candidates are carefully and correctly selected, capsulotomy would seem to produce useful results in most cases of chronic, severe and otherwise intractable anxiety disorder, and this at the price of no mortality, little somatic morbidity, and with little risk of negative personality changes. Despite the relatively small lesions made in capsulotomy the results compare favorably with those reported after other procedures in current use.

References

1. Mindus P (1991) Capsulotomy in anxiety disorders. A multidisciplinary study. Thesis, the Karolinska Institute, Stockholm. ISBN 91-628-0190-2. (Copies of the monograph available through the author.)
2. Mindus P and Nyman H (1991) Acta Psychiatr. Scand. 83: 283–291.
3. Mindus P, Nyman H, Rosenquist A, Rydin E and Meyerson B (1988) Acta Neurochir. (Suppl.) 44: 138–144.
4. Mindus P, Nyman H, Mogard J, Meyerson B and Ericson K (1990) Nord. Psykiatr. Tidsskr. 44: 309–312.
5. Mindus P, Bergström K, Levander S, Norén G, Hindmarsh T and Thuomas K-Å (1987) J. Neurol. Neurosurg. Psychiatry 50: 1288–1293.

© 1991 Elsevier Science Publishers B.V. All rights reserved.
Biological Psychiatry, Volume 2. G. Racagni et al., editors.

Stereotactic surgery in severe unresponsive aggressive syndromes

Juan A. Burzaco
Dpto. Neurocirugia, Fundación Jiménez Díaz, Ciudad Universitaria, Madrid 28040, Spain

Introduction

Pathological aggressive behaviour, in some psychiatric disorders, may become at times such a severe symptom that it requires special hospital care, obnubilating-dosage of psychodrugs or the use of physical restraints.

Stereotactic neurosurgical technics allow small lesions to be made on specific brain structures to reduce the inputs to or from the limbic system, and so relieve pathological aggressive behavior with no additional clinical deficit in the patient's condition.

Materials and Methods

Patients

From 1966 to 1990, 116 patients (26 female) underwent surgery. All of them had dangerous aggressive behavior in common. They can be grouped into 4 clinical categories, although there was not always a clear distinction between the different disorders.

Mental retardation (MR)

Fifty-nine patients (13 female) had a low I.Q. as the most important disorder, subdivided into profound (PMR), severe (SMR) and moderate (MMR), each group accounting for about 1/3 of the total. Epilepsy was present in a high percentage of cases: 80% of the MMR and 35% of the SMR and PMR patients.

Organic mental disorders (OMD)

This group consisted of twenty-two patients (7 female). All of them had a well-documented organic pathology, secondary to traumatic head injury, meningo-encephalitis, cerebrovascular pathology, etc., in the PnEG, CT, MR imaging studies and in the EEG. Almost 90% of these patients had a clinical history of epilepsy.

Epilepsy

Eight patients (2 female). Epilepsy was the main symptom in this group with uncontrollable aggressive impulses and a normal I.Q.

Psychotic disorders and schizophrenia

Twenty-seven patients (4 female) presented with very severe auto- and hetero-aggressive symptoms: self-mutilation, suicide attempts, physically attacking people, homicide (one case).

Selection

Specific neurological, psychiatric and psychological protocols were used in the pre- and post-operative studies. The criteria to select the candidates for surgical treatment were that the disorder was *chronic* (more than 4 years), *irreversible*, *invalidating* and *refractory* to other forms of treatment; *informed consent* from the patient or from his tutors, and the written *approval* of 2 independent psychiatrists was required for the operation.

Surgical technique

All patients were operated on by the same surgeon (J.A.B.) using Leksell's stereotactic method. Bipolar radiofrequency heating was used for the thermo-coagulations.

Surgical targets

The fundus stria terminalis [1] was the main target in over 90% of the operated patients (size of thermocoagulation: 6×4 mm). The baso-medial amygdala (8×8 mm) [2]; n. posteromedialis hypothalamus (4×4 mm) [3], anterior internal capsule (16×8 mm) [4] and cingulum (6×8 mm) [5] were combined with s. terminalis as complementary targets.

Results

The effects of surgery could be seen as soon as the patient awoke from the anaesthesia, so that if the lesion had been ineffective a new operation could be performed in the following days or weeks. A second operation was performed in 27% of the patients. In some cases this was done as a result of relapse in aggressive behavior; in other patients the operation had been previously planned in two stages to observe the clinical effects of the stereoencephalotomy before proceeding with the complementary targets or to enlarge the size of the previous ones. The result of the operation was determined as stable 6 months after the operation.

Rating

The rating was as follows: R-1: no aggressive behaviour; R-2: much improvement, still needs medical assistance; R-3: slight improvement; R-4: no change; R-5: worse.

	PMR	*SMR*	*MMR*	*Schizophr.*	*Org. Mental*	*Epilep.*
R-1 + R-2	53%	65%	80%	77%	77%	75%

Mortality and morbidity

There was no operative mortality or neurological deficit in over 140 operations. During the first postoperative week about half of the patients showed episodes of confusion, urinary incontinence, increase of appetite. Epilepsy was rare; many of the patients were already under antiepileptic medication. Frontal lobe symptoms were seen during the following 6–12 weeks, mostly after bilateral capsulotomy, but as a rule, were less evident than in obsessive-compulsive disorders. Two patients committed suicide, 8 and 12 months after the operation; both had attempted it before the operation; one was a schizophrenic, the second was a young man suffering from Bournevill's disease. Their previous hetero-aggressive behaviour had been controlled in both cases by the operation.

Discussion

Stereotactic technic has dramatically reduced the danger of side-effects in functional neurosurgery, even in cases of potentially high-risk structures such as fundus s. terminalis or hypothalamus. Hundreds of operations have been performed with no mortality and very few complications [4,5]. Still there are problems regarding the anatomical variations in brains with organic lesions and in the pathological mechanisms of aggressivity.

Selection of candidates is as important as the choice of the surgical targets. We consider fundus s. terminalis to be very effective target in the treatment of aggressive behaviour and, according to our experience, safer than hypothalamotomy or amygdalotomy. Capsulotomy and cingulotomy may also be effective complementary targets.

The *results* have improved in the last 10 years due to better selection of candidates. It seems that the chances of success in sedative surgery are better than in obsessive-compulsive disorders.

References

1. Burzaco JA (1973) In: Laitinen LV and Livingston KE (eds.) Surgical Approaches in Psychiatry, pp. 135–137.
2. Narabayashi H and Shima F (1973) In: Laitinen LV and Livingston KE (eds.) Surgical Approaches in Psychiatry, pp. 129–134.
3. Sano K (1962) Neurol. Med.-Chir. 4: 112.
4. Mindus P (1991) Capsulotomy in Anxiety Disorders. A Multidisciplinary Study. K. Karolinska Med. Chirur. Institutet, Stockholm.
5. Ballantine HT Jr, Bouckoms AJ, Thomas EK and Giriunas IE (1987) Biol. Psychiatry 22: 807–819.

© 1991 Elsevier Science Publishers B.V. All rights reserved.
Biological Psychiatry, Volume 2. G. Racagni et al., editors.

Quality of life before and after psychosurgery

Veronica Larach[1], Renzo Zamboni[1], Ximena Rubio[1], Roberto Gallardo[2], Roberto Mancini[1], Humberto Mancini[1] and Mario Poblete[1]

[1]Psychiatric Institute, Department of Stereotaxic Neurosurgery P.O. Box 2677, Santiago; and [2]Department of Pharmacology, University of Chile, Chile

Health has been declared by World Health Organization WHO [1] as a fundamental human right, determinant of the degree of social and economical development of countries and therefore of the quality of life of their inhabitants. Three central aspects to the quality of life concept would be accessibility to goods and opportunities, autonomy, and to be in a valued social position or role, which allows personal growth [2]. Illness in general and psychiatric illness in particular will always limit these issues. In chronic, severe, refractory psychiatric conditions, patients are diminished in their rights and stigmatized [3]. Their families show high levels of emotional problems [4] and distortion in family interaction [5]. Health teams and institutions as well as society are usually overloaded and the situation is often denied [6].

We discuss 3 commonly observed passive attitudes, at all levels involving severely disabled psychiatric patients:

1. "fictitious status-quo", that is to say "why do something if things are to remain the same", but pathological processes are always progressive;
2. "wishful thinking", that is to say "why do something if things probably will get better or we will get used to them", which will not be the case, because at least aging will add to the problem;
3. "null offer", that is to say, "why do something if everything has been done".

These assertions are the central aim of this communication because patients are rarely offered solutions outside the theoretical framework of their treating team. There is less prejudice to life-saving procedures than to quality of life-saving procedures.

Active approaches, with their risk and benefits, can be classified in 3 groups:

1. Psychotherapy: changes in the functioning of the central nervous system (CNS) through language and behavior. It has been studied by basic science, through learning and stimulation techniques [7]. Early loss and sensorial deprivation will leave indelible traces in CNS functioning [8]. Risks and benefits of psychotherapy have been reported [9].
2. Pharmacotherapy affects CNS through chemical action. Severe patients usually use heavy dosage of drugs, with the known risk of this procedure. Permanent modifications of molecular substrate of the CNS are not infrequently reported [10].

3. Procedures:
   a) Electroconvulsive therapy modification in CNS functioning through electrical current with subsequent neurochemical changes. Its definite mechanism of action and long-term changes are not fully understood, but it is a life and quality of life saving procedure [11].
   b) Psychosurgery is a neurosurgical procedure with a therapeutic goal that acts upon the CNS through the interruption of pathways, modifying its already altered functioning because of severe, chronic, refractory psychiatric illness [12]. It enables a new level of functional state of the CNS, which could ameliorate the chronicity and severity of the symptoms that significantly disable a patient, allowing him to have access to improved quality of life.

We will illustrate the changes in quality of life in a group of 12 patients, who underwent stereotactic ventromedial hypothalamotomy because of severe refractory, chronic polysubstance dependence [13].

These 12 male patients aged 25.5 ± 3.1 years had 12.5 ± 3.3 years of addiction, starting at age 13.3 ± 1.3 years, with multiple hospitalizations (6.8 ± 2.4), and were followed up for 67.3 ± 35.9 months after surgery.

Remission of the psychoactive polysubstance dependence was obtained in 8 of 12 patients, partial modification in 2 patients and 2 continued with the dependence. Psychiatric evaluation through rating scales is shown in Table 1.

Before surgery 9 patients (75 %) had made (2.4 range 1–7) suicidal attempts. Postsurgery no patients have presented suicidal attempts.

Rorschach pre to postoperative changes show that in 8 of 12 cases, an increase of cognitive and affective control and decrease of impulsive and aggressive responses was observed as well as rational social contact. Four cases remained with the same affective blunting and type of psychotic functioning. There was an overall decrease of anxiety. TAT revealed in 7 of 12 cases an increase of goal-oriented activity and decrease of impulsive responses.

When social, economic and familiar variables, central to quality of life, were assessed, significant changes were observed. Antisocial behavior changes are described in Table 2.

In the preoperative evaluation, all patients had no stable couple (10 were single and 2 divorced). Postoperative follow-up showed 4 patients with stable couple (1 married, 2 living with partner, 1 dating regularly).

Before surgery no patients had held stable jobs. Seven had never worked and 5 were unskilled workers that had seldom worked. In the follow-up period, 5 have

Table 1. Psychiatric rating scales pre- to postsurgical changes (n = 12)

Scale	Preoperative	Postoperative	% Decrement
BPRS	42.0 ± 11.3	28.5 ± 7.5	36.6
Hamilton Depression	20.3 ± 9.9	7.2 ± 4.4	64.2
Hamilton Anxiety	17.8 ± 8.2	6.4 ± 4.2	64.0

Table 2. Ventromedial hypothalamotomy: antisocial behavior changes (n = 12)

Antisocial behavior	Preoperative		Postoperative	
	n	%	n	%
Burglary	11	92	2	17
Robbery	10	83	2	17
Drug traffic	4	33	2	17
Homicidal attempts	2	17	0	0
Homosexual prostitution	4	33	1	8
Promiscuity	3	25	1	8
Hypersexuality	3	25	0	0

stable jobs, 3 have occasional jobs, 2 never work and 2 continue to be hospitalized. Four patients are now skilled workers and 4 unskilled workers. In summary, 8 patients (66.6%) have changed their working status and also 3 (25%) have obtained a professional title, which allows them to accessibility, position and income. When living situation is analyzed, preoperatively 11 patients (91.6%) were hospitalized, on sick pension and supported by their family. At present 7 patients (58.3%) support themselves (5 totally, 2 partially). Family interaction has improved postoperatively in 8 cases (66.6%).

Final comment

In accordance with the reports of other authors regarding psychosurgical treatment, of remarkable improvement in two-thirds or more [14], this series of patients improved not only in symptomatology but also in their accessibility, autonomy and status. The burden and suffering of their families, health institutions and society was lessened. Therefore psychosurgery should be an alternative treatment to be considered for severe, chronic, refractory psychiatric conditions. As the WHO has emphasized, it is the patient's right to be offered a treatment which could alleviate his suffering and allow an improvement in quality of life.

Acknowledgement

We are grateful to Dr. Martin Cordero for his assistance in the discussion of quality of life issues.

References

1. WHO (1980) Health for All by the Year 2000: Strategies. Official Document No. 173.

2. Platt S (1986) In: Bradley and Hirsch (eds.) The Psychopharmacology and Treatment of Schizophrenia. Oxford Medical Publ. pp. 263–285.
3. Goffman E (1968) Stigma: Notes on the Management of Spoiled Identity. Prentice-Hall Inc., Englewood Cliffs, New Jersey.
4. Leff J and Vaughn C (1980) Br. J. Psychiatry 136: 146–153.
5. Falloon JRH (1986) Psychiatr. Clin. North Am. 9: 165–182.
6. Goffman E (1984) In: Amorrortu (ed.) Essays on the Social Situation of Mental Patients and other Inmates. Doubleday and Co. Inc., New York.
7. Seligman MEP (1976) J. Abnorm. Psychol. 85: 11–26.
8. Akiskal M and McKinney W (1973) Science 182: 20–29.
9. Klerman GL (1990) Am. J. Psychiatry 147: 409–418.
10. Rama Krishnan KR, Ellinwood EH and Rayasam K (1988) Wolf and Mosnaim (eds.) Tardive Dyskinesia: Biological Mechanisms and Clinical Aspects. American Psychiatric Press, Washington D.C., pp. 167–177.
11. Grahame-Smith DG (1988) In: Malkin and Brandon (eds.) Current Approaches ECT. Duphar Medical Relations, pp. 43–48.
12. Pahl JJ, Swayze VW and Andreasen NC (1990) In: Kales A, Stefanis CN and Talbott J (eds.) Recent Advances in Schizophrenia. pp. 163–189.
13. Zamboni R, Larach V, Rubio X, Gallardo R, Mancini R, Mancini H and Poblete M (1991) In: Racagni G (ed.) Severe, chronic, refractory polysubstances dependence and ventromedial hypothalamotomy. Proc. 5th World Congr. Biol. Psychiatry. Elsevier.
14. Ballantine HT, Bouckoms AJ, Thomas EK and Giriunas IE (1987) Biol. Psychiatry 22: 807–819.

© 1991 Elsevier Science Publishers B.V. All rights reserved.
Biological Psychiatry, Volume 2. G. Racagni et al., editors.

Carbamazepine and other anticonvulsants in the treatment of psychiatric disorders – An introduction

Teruo Okuma

National Center Hospital for Mental, Nervous and Muscular Disorders, National Center of Neurology and Psychiatry, 4-1-1 Ogawahigashi-cho, Kodaira, Tokyo, 187 Japan

It has been our common experience that the use of anticonvulsants to treat patients with epilepsy can lead not only to the control of seizures but also to an improvement in concomitant psychotic symptoms and personality disorders. In particular, carbamazepine (CBZ), an antiepileptic drug effective for psychomotor and convulsive seizures, has been found to be effective for psychiatric symptoms of epileptic patients. It seems therefore natural that psychiatrists should have tried CBZ for the treatment of psychiatric disorders other than epilepsy. As a result, CBZ has been found to be effective for the treatment of emotional and mood disturbances of various etiology.

Antimanic and prophylactic effects of carbamazepine

In the early 1970s, CBZ was found to be effective for the treatment of manic state. That is, application of CBZ in manic state of bipolar affective disorder was initiated as open trials by Takezaki and Hanaoka (1971) in 20 cases and by Okuma et al. (1973) in 90 cases and it was found that CBZ had antimanic and prophylactic effects for bipolar disorder. The antimanic effect was confirmed in double-blind studies by Okuma et al. (1977, 1979) and by Ballenger and Post (1978, 1980), and the prophylactic effect in a double-blind study of Okuma et al. (1981). Following these observations, antimanic and prophylactic effects of CBZ in bipolar disorder have been confirmed by many researchers in the world. Bipolar disorder with rapid cycling episodes, of early onset, or with atypical symptoms such as alteration of consciousness have been reported to respond well to CBZ treatment.

Carbamazepine and lithium

Several double-blind studies comparing antimanic and prophylactic effects of CBZ and lithium have demonstrated that CBZs effects are comparable to those of lithium (Placidi et al., 1986; Okuma et al., 1990). It was also found that CBZ may exhibit its antimanic effect for some lithium non-responders. It would thus appear that the mechanism of action of CBZ and lithium might be different. It has been observed that cases which showed unfavorable response to either CBZ or lithium sometimes respond favorably to the combination of CBZ and lithium (Kishimoto et al., 1986). Whether the efficacy of combination therapy is due to a synergistic or additive effect has not yet been elucidated.

Antidepressant effect of carbamazepine

The acute antidepressant effects of CBZ have been less well established than its acute or prophylactic antimanic effects. Post (1990) reported that 17 of 54 (31%) patients with bipolar or unipolar depressive episodes showed a moderate to marked improvement, and that the result was compatible with that of Neumann et al. (1984). It was suggested that a sub-group of patients may be acutely responsive during depressive episodes. With regard to the prophylactic effect of CBZ, a case of periodic depression in which the recurrence of episodes was completely suppressed during CBZ treatment has been reported (Kobayashi et al., 1988)

Carbamazepine in excited psychotic state and atypical periodic psychosis

CBZ has also been found to be effective for excited psychotic states of schizophrenic and schizoaffective disorders when it was combined with the previous neuroleptic medication. Following open trials by several researchers (Shibahara et al., 1970; Hakola and Luulumaa, 1982; Neppe, 1984; Okuma et al., 1987, 1989), the effect has been confirmed by double-blind studies (Klein et al., 1984; Dose et al., 1987; Okuma et al., 1989). Remarkable therapeutic and prophylactic effects of CBZ on atypical periodic psychosis which occurred in association with menstrual cycles and which were characterized by bipolar swings between stupor and excitement were reported in 9 cases (Koyama and Yamashita, 1983). These observations suggest that CBZ might act on a switch process which is supposed to be located in the hypothalamus.

Carbamazepine in aggressive and dyscontrol syndromes

The therapeutic effect of CBZ in aggressive and dyscontrol syndromes has also been reported. In several open trials, patients with violent and aggressive behavior of mixed diagnosis (Luchins et al., 1973; Neppe, 1990) were reported to have responded favorably to CBZ treatment. Kagomoto (1983) reported that intrafamilial violence or selective battered parents syndrome in adolescence was controlled successfully with administration of CBZ. Effect of CBZ against dyscontrol syndromes in patients with borderline personality disorders has also been reported (Cowdry et al., 1984).

Oxcarbazepine

Oxcarbazepine, the keto-homologue of carbamazepine, seems to share the therapeutic profile of CBZ, and has been shown to be effective in epilepsy and acute mania and also in the prophylaxis of bipolar disorders (Greist, 1990; Wildgrube, 1990).

Valproate

In a double-blind study, Emrich et al. (1980) observed acute antimanic effects using sodium valproate combined with lithium in bipolar patients. They also reported a prophylactic effect of valproate on manic-depressive and schizoaffective psychoses. Clonazepam (CZP), a benzodiazepine anticonvulsant, has been reported by Chouinard et al. (1983) to have an antimanic effect comparable to that of lithium. Antidepressant effect of CZP has been reported in an open trial on 27 unipolar and bipolar depressive patients (Kishimoto et al., 1988).

Carbamazepine in aggressive and assaultive behavior of patients with dementia

Recently, CBZ has been reported to be effective for the treatment of aggressive and assaultive behavior of patients with dementia due to Alzheimer's disease and other organic brain diseases (Patterson, 1988; Endo et al., 1989; Gleason and Schneider, 1990). Though a previous placebo-controlled crossover trial of CBZ in behaviorally disturbed patients suffering from severe dementia of Alzheimer type showed a negative result (Chambers et al., 1982), recent studies suggest that CBZ may be useful to treat agitated demented patients.

Mechanism of action

The mechanism of the mood-stabilizing action of antiepileptic drugs is not yet clear. Waldmeier (1987) reviewed the literature and indicated that the mechanism most common to CBZ, lithium and other antimanic drugs seemed to be that of an inhibitory effect on the dopaminergic system and, to a lesser degree, also on the GABAergic and cholinergic systems. The effect of CBZ on the adenosine receptor system and its antikindling effect are also proposed as underlying mechanisms of its mood-stabilizing effect. Furthermore, it has recently been demonstrated that inhibition of voltage-sensitive sodium channels is a main primary site of action of CBZ, and that depressant action of CBZ on catecholamine turnover, on glutamate release and on membrane excitability in general could all possibly result from this primary effect (Olpe et al., 1990)

In the present symposium, the most updated problems in each field mentioned above will be discussed.

References

Available from author upon request.

© 1991 Elsevier Science Publishers B.V. All rights reserved.
Biological Psychiatry, Volume 2. G. Racagni et al., editors.

Mechanism of action of antiepileptic drugs with special reference to carbamazepine and valproate

Hans-Rudolf Olpe, Markus Schmutz, Felix Brugger, Urs Wicki, Thomas Ferrat, Mario Pozza and Martin W. Steinmann

Research and Development Department, Pharmaceuticals Division, Ciba-Geigy Ltd., Basle, Switzerland

Carbamazepine and valproate are two antiepileptic drugs which are also used for the treatment of affective disorders. Their modes of action in both clinical indications are not well understood. They exert a wide spectrum of activities, but it is not clear which features contribute to their antiepileptic or antimanic properties respectively. We first discuss two hypotheses which attempt to explain their antimanic actions and then present the other major pharmacological characteristics, which are probably responsible for their antiepileptic effects. However, the "antimanic" features could also contribute to the antiepileptic effects and vice versa.

Emrich et al. (1980) proposed the GABA hypothesis of affective disorders [1]. One of the pillars of this proposal is the observation that carbamazepine and valproate reduce the GABA turnover in rodents [2]. This effect was interpreted to reflect the GABA "facilitating" feature of the drugs which in turn leads to a reduction in transmitter turnover. The molecular basis for these effects is not well understood. In the case of carbamazepine, electrophysiological studies have not demonstrated an acute effect on GABA transmission in the hippocampus [3] and no affinity to the GABA receptor has been reported. It is conceivable that this effect results from the inactivation of Na^+-channels (see below) located on GABA cells leading to limitation of cell firing [4] and thus to a reduction in transmitter turnover. There is, however, some evidence for an action of valproate on GABA transmission. Schmutz et al. [5] originally observed that valproate enhances exogenously applied GABA responses in vivo. Subsequent investigations performed in vitro were controversial and only one study reported a potentiating effect at therapeutic concentrations [6]. We report here for the first time that valproate potentiates GABA transmission in vivo in the CA1 area of the hippocampus. In the chloral hydrate anaesthetized rat intravenously administered valproate (30, 100 mg/kg) potentiated paired-pulse inhibition of the population spike. Diazepam and phenobarbital elicit the same effect as a result of their affinity to the GABA receptor complex.

Recently, it has been speculated that the antimanic properties of valproate and carbamazepine may be linked with their depressant effect on dopamine turnover [7]. Both drugs reduce dopamine synthesis in a dose-dependent manner as measured by the accumulation of DOPA after central decarboxylase inhibition. These findings are in keeping with a modified version of the original catecholamine hypothesis of affective disorders. It states that an increase in central dopamine activity may be linked with mania [8]. The biochemical basis for the drugs' depressant effect on dopamine turnover is unknown. It is conceivable, as in the case of GABA, that the primary action occurs at the level of the use- and voltage-dependent Na^+-channels [4].

The antiepileptic features of these drugs could rely on their action on GABA neurons or the Na^+-channels. It has also been reported that carbamazepine reduces [^{3}H]-L-glutamate release from hippocampal slices [3], but in a recent study the release of endogenous glutamate was not affected by carbamazepine (K. Fagg and K. Thedinga, personal communication). The important role of N-methyl-D-aspartate (NMDA) receptors in mediating epileptiform activity is well documented. Recently it has been shown that carbamazepine blocks NMDA-activated currents in cultured spinal neurons [9]. We have verified this hypothesis but failed to confirm it. In the hemisected neonate rat spinal cord, carbamazepine at 40 μM had only a small depressant effect on responses evoked by NMDA, quisqualate or kainate. Turning behavior induced in mice by subcutaneously administered NMDA was not antagonized by carbamazepine (10, 60 mg/kg p.o.). Furthermore, carbamazepine (30 mg/kg i.p.) had no effect on the excitatory responses of CA1 pyramidal neurons evoked by in vivo ionophoretically applied quisqualate, kainate or NMDA.

Recently, two laboratories have discovered that the action of carbamazepine involves an effect on potassium currents [10,11]. The drug was shown to increase potassium currents in rat cortical neurons at therapeutic concentrations [10]. In hippocampal slices made "epileptic" by the exposure to penicillin the antiepileptic activity of carbamazepine was strongly attenuated by the K^+-channel blockers 4-aminopyridine and $BaCl_2$ [11]. Given the important role of K^+-ions in the control of neuronal activity, these findings point to a possibly important function of K^+-channels in mediating the therapeutic effects of carbamazepine in epilepsy and/or affective disorders. Such an effect was not observed in the case of valproate. The list of pharmacological effects described for these two agents includes additional features that have not been discussed in this paper. The selection made here represents effects that we feel are currently considered to be particularly important. Table 1 summarizes these actions.

Table 1.

Effects on rat brain tissue	Carbamazepine	Valproate
GABA-turnover	↓	↓
Dopamine turnover	↓	↓
K^+-conductance	↑	Ø
Na^+-channel (voltage- and use-dependent)	↓	↓

References

1. Emrich NM, Zerssen DV, Kissling W, Möller HJ and Windorfer A (1980) Arch. Psychiatr. Nervenkr. 229: 1–16.
2. Bernasconi R and Martin P (1979) Arch. Pharmacol. 307: 251–256.
3. Olpe HR, Baudry M and Jones RSG (1985) Eur. J. Pharmacol. 110: 71–80.
4. McLean MJ and MacDonald (1983) Neurology 33: 213–214.
5. Schmutz M, Olpe HR and Koella WP (1979) J. Pharm. Pharmacol. 31: 413–414.
6. Olpe HR, Steinmann MW, Pozza MF, Brugger F and Schmutz M (1988) Naunyn-Schmiedeberg's Arch. Pharmacol. 338: 655–657.
7. Waldmeier PC (1987) Pharmacopsychiatry 20: 37–47.
8. Bunney WE and Garland BL (1982) Pharmacopsychiatry 15: 111–115.
9. Lampe H and Bigalke H (1990) Neuropharmacol. & Neurotoxicol. 1.
10. Zona C, Tancredi V, Palma E, Pirrone GC and Avoli M (1990) Can. J. Physiol. Pharmacol. 68: 545–547.
11. Olpe HR, Kolb CN, Hausdorf A and Haas HL (1991) Experientia (in press).

© 1991 Elsevier Science Publishers B.V. All rights reserved.
Biological Psychiatry, Volume 2. G. Racagni et al., editors.

Carbamazepine, oxcarbazepine, and valproate in psychiatric treatment

Hinderk M. Emrich
Max Planck Institute for Psychiatry, Kraepelinstr. 10, W-8000 Munich 40, Germany

The anticonvulsants carbamazepine and oxcarbazepine were tested clinically in an acute double-blind, placebo-controlled ABA design and an acute antimanic effect of carbamazepine was demonstrated [1]. In the meantime, a larger number of studies have been performed regarding the acute antimanic effect of oxcarbazepine (Trileptal) [2] and an antimanic action, similar to that of carbamazepine, has been demonstrated. In carbamazepine-prophylaxis of affective and schizoaffective psychoses, another sample of 12 patients, poorly responding to lithium prophylaxis, were treated with carbamazepine. In a similar fashion to valproate, carbamazepine long-term treatment resulted in an approximately 4-fold increase of the relapse-free time during treatment [3]. Interestingly, a comparison regarding the psychopharmacological profile of action of carbamazepine in comparison to valproate showed a more pronounced prophylactic therapeutic effect of carbamazepine in schizoaffective psychoses, whereas valproate appears to be more effective in the pure mood disorders without schizophrenic symptomatology.

This finding is plausible, bearing in mind the study by Dose et al. [4] which showed that carbamazepine is an effective adjuvant to neuroleptic therapy of schizophrenic psychoses. Recently, it could be demonstrated [5] that in acute schizophrenic psychoses, under double-blind conditions, carbamazepine revealed a more pronounced adjuvant effect in comparison to the adjuvant treatment with valproate. On the other hand, chronic-defective schizophrenic psychoses, which constitute particularly difficult problems in the pharmacopsychiatry of schizophrenia and in which monotherapy with neuroleptics often induces a deterioration of defective symptoms, showed, in a pilot investigation, some improvement as a result of valproate medication: in these open trials, 8 severely ill patients with chronic-defective psychoses were treated with valproate as an adjuvant. In 2 cases a very pronounced therapeutic effect was observed, and in 4 cases a slight improvement occurred [6]. As a consequence of this, double-blind studies on the possible beneficial effects of valproate in chronic-defective psychoses should be performed.

The interest in the acute therapeutic effect of the GABAergic anticonvulsant valproate resulted from pharmacopsychiatric investigations indicating the possibility that mania results from a dysfunction of inhibitory monotransmitters in the CNS. GABA was an extremely challenging candidate in this regard. It was shown, using a double-blind ABA design, that high dosage propranolol exerts a rather specific antimanic action [7]. Similarly, we treated patients with manic psychosis with valproate, using a double-blind, placebo-controlled variable ABA design (A = placebo, B = active substance). An average reduction of the initial IMPS values by 49.6 ± 36.6% resulted from the valproate therapy (significant at the 5% level, Wilcoxon-test, one-tailed).

References

1. Emrich HM, Altmann H, Dose M and von Zerssen D (1983) Pharmacol. Biochem. Behav. 19: 369–372.
2. Emrich HM (1990) Int. Clin. Psychopharmacol. (Suppl. 1) 5: 83–88.
3. Emrich HM (1990) In: Marneros A and Tsuang MT (eds.) Affective and Schizoaffective Disorders. Springer, Berlin, pp. 83–88.
4. Dose M, Apelt S and Emrich HM (1987) Psychiatr. Res. 22: 303–310.
5. Dose M, Hellweg R, Loycke A, Garcia-Borreguero D, Bremer D-E, Theison M and Emrich HM (1991) Biol. Psychiatry (in press).
6. Emrich HM, Weber MM and Garcia-Borreguero D (1990) In: Möller H-J and Pelzer E (eds.) Neuere Ansätze zur Diagnostik und Therapie schizophrener Minussymptomatik. Springer, Berlin, pp. 91–99.
7. Rackensperger W, Fritsch W, Schwarz D, Stutte KH and von Zerssen D (1976) Arch. Psychiatr. Nervenkr. 222: 223–243.

© 1991 Elsevier Science Publishers B.V. All rights reserved.
Biological Psychiatry, Volume 2. G. Racagni et al., editors.

Antiepileptics and lithium in the treatment of food disorders

Akira Kishimoto

Department of Neuropsychiatry, Tottori University School of Medicine 36-1, Nishimachi, Yonago 683, Japan

Introduction

The introduction of antiepileptic drugs, carbamazepine (CBZ), valproic acid (VA) in the treatment of mood disorders brought a therapeutically new strategy in this area since it seems that the clinical characteristics of CBZ-responders in the acutely manic patients is different from that of lithium-responders [1]. Moreover, the combined use of lithium and these antiepileptic drugs is anticipated to be a strong strategy against drug (lithium or antiepileptics)-resistant patients. From our earlier study on the combination therapy of lithium and CBZ, the synergistic interaction was found in the cases of partial responder to CBZ and lithium [2]. In order to clarify the clinical usefulness of antiepileptic drugs, clinical characteristics of CBZ responder was analysed based on a larger number of cases treated prophylactically with CBZ and the prophylactic efficacy of another antiepileptic drug clonazepam (CNZP), and also the prophylactic interaction of CNZP and lithium was investigated in this study.

Subjects and Methods

Study I

Ninety-two patients with affective disorders who met the following criteria were selected as subjects:

a) Patients who had had 2 or more affective episodes during 2 years before CBZ therapy.
b) Duration of the prophylactic CBZ therapy exceeded 24 months before Feb. 1991.
c) The period of prophylactic CBZ therapy was clearly longer than the mean duration of lucid intervals and the prophylactic effect of CBZ could be assessed.

The prophylactic effect of CBZ was judged according to the following criteria:

a) *Markedly effective*: the affective episode completely disappeared during the prophylactic therapy with CBZ therapy.
b) *Moderately effective*: the duration of affective episodes per year was reduced to 50% or less of that before CBZ therapy but did not disappear by the CBZ therapy.

c) *Unchanged*: the duration of affective episode per year was more than 50% of that before CBZ therapy.

The clinical background, age of onset, type of disorder (BP I or BP II) and the mode of episode occurrence in each patients was investigated based on the clinical record. Patients were divided into the mania-abundant type, that is, the number of manic episodes was 2.5 times or more that of depressive episodes before the prophylaxis with lithium or CBZ was started, or into the other type, that is, the number of manic episodes was less than 2.5 times that of depression. Furthermore, the patients were divided into the following 4 types by the mode of episode occurrence:

1. Continuous type, i.e. manic and depressive episodes appear continuously without interruption by lucid interval;
2. DMI type, i.e. starting with a depression which is followed by a mania;
3. MDI type, i.e. starting with a mania which is followed by a depression; and
4. Independent type, i.e. a manic or a depression occurred independently without a following episode.

The relationship between the prophylactic effect of CBZ and the clinical backgrounds was investigated.

Study II

The subjects were 24 cases treated prophylactically with CNZP for more than 24 months who met almost the same criteria as Study I. In 13 of these cases, CNZP was added to the preceding lithium therapy and the combination therapy of CNZP and lithium was maintained. In order to assess the prophylactic effect of CNZP and the prophylactic interaction of CNZP and lithium, the duration of manic and depressive episodes observed during the CNZP therapy was compared with that during the control period or that during the preceding lithium therapy.

Results

Study I

Table 1 shows the relationship between the mode of episode occurrence and the prophylactic effect of CBZ. As the results show, CBZ was significantly ($P < 0.001$) more effective in the patients of mania-abundant type than in the other type. As for the mode of episode occurrence, CBZ was significantly ($P < 0.001$) more effective in the patients with independent type than in the patients with other types. On the other hand, CBZ was significantly ($P < 0.05$) more effective in the patients in whom the age of onset was under 20 years than in those over 20 years.

Study II

Among 24 cases, CNZP was effective prophylactically in 10 cases (42%) and not

Table 1. The clinical backgrounds and the prophylactic effect of CBZ

Type	Markedly effective	Moderately effective	Unchanged	Markedly effective rate
BP disorder (n = 91)				
BP I (77)	18	40	19	18/77 (23%)
BP II (14)	1	9	4	1/14 (7%)
Mania/depression ratio (n = 92)				
Mania-abundant type (20)	12	5	3	12/20 (60%)[a]
Mania-not abundant type (72)	7	44	21	7/72 (10%)
Mode of episode occurrence (n = 86)				
Continuous (19)	1	13	5	1/19 (5%)
DMI (22)	0	14	8	0/22 (0%)
MDI (13)	3	7	3	3/13 (23%)
Independent (32)	15	12	5	15/32 (47%)[b]
Age of onset (n = 92)				
~ 19 years (26)	8	15	3	8/26 (31%)[c]
20 years ~ (66)	11	34	21	11/66 (17%)

[a] $P < 0.001$; [b] $P < 0.001$ (independent vs. others); [c] $P < 0.05$ (Wilcoxon's Rank Sum Test).

in 14 cases (58%). The duration of manic and depressive episodes per year was compared between the control period, that is, the 2 years just before the CNZP therapy. As results, the duration of manic and depressive episode were significantly ($P < 0.02$, $P < 0.01$, respectively) decreased compared with those during the control period (Fig. 1). In the cases in which CNZP was added to the preceding lithium therapy, the duration of affective episodes per year was compared between

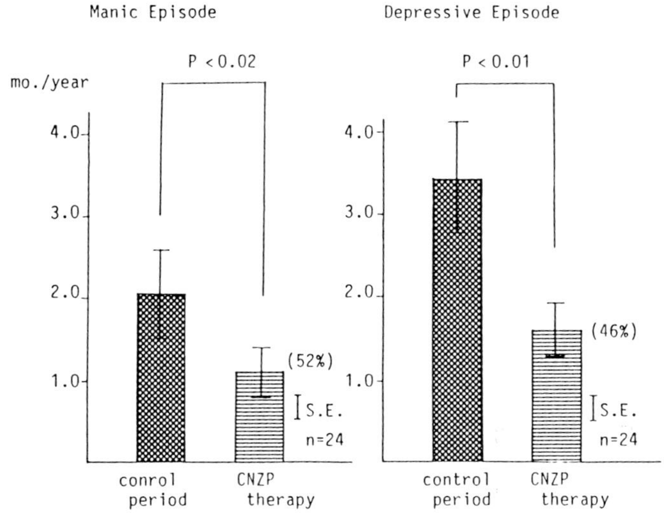

Fig. 1. Duration of affective episode during control period and CNZP therapy.

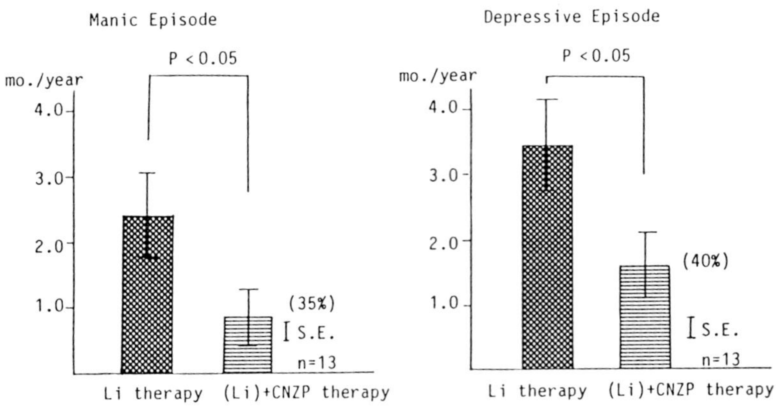

Fig. 2. Duration of affective episode during the preceding period and CNZP therapy.

the CNZP (+ lithium) therapy and the preceding lithium therapy. The manic and the depressive episodes during the CNZP (+ lithium) therapy were decreased significantly ($P < 0.05$) compared with those during the preceding lithium therapy (Fig. 2). The analysis of background characteristics of CNZP responder revealed that patients with BP II disorders responded better than those with BP I disorder. Moreover, the patients who responded to CNZP also responded more to the preceding lithium therapy ($P < 0.05$).

Conclusion

Some clinical characteristics, especially the mode of episode occurrence such as mania-abundant type and episode-independent type were recognized as the predictors of CBZ-responder in this study observing the episode prophylaxis by CBZ. In the episode prophylaxis with lithium, Koukopoulos et al. [3] reported that the patients with MDI course, i.e. starting with a mania which is followed by a depression and then a free interval, were much better responders to lithium than the patients with DMI course; they considered that lithium prevents the depressive episodes by suppressing the manic episodes. The clinical characteristics of CBZ and lithium are more effective in the prophylaxis of mania-dominant phenomena rather than that of depression-dominant phenomena, and coincide with the fact that CBZ and lithium are more useful in the treatment of acutely manic patients than in the treatment of depression.

Through a long-term observation of episode occurrence, CNZP seemed to be an effective agent for episode prophylaxis in this study. Interestingly, the clinical characteristics of this drug seemed to be different from the above-mentioned 2 drugs since CNZP was slightly more effective in the prophylaxis of the depressive episode than in the manic episode and, moreover, was more effective in the cases with BP II disorder, that is, with hypomania and severe depression, rather than in the BP I disorder. These findings parallel to our earlier report [4] indicating a strong antidepressant effect of CNZP in the treatment of acutely depressive patients and also discordant antimanic effects [5,6]. As for the prophylactic interaction between CNZP and lithium, there might be a possibility that these drugs act synergistically, as in the case of lithium and CBZ.

From the above-mentioned results, it is considered that the clinical characteristics of CBZ are similar to lithium, but somewhat different from that of CNZP. However, when used in combination with lithium, these antiepileptics seem similarly to act synergistically with the drug.

References

1. Post RM, Uhde TW and Roy-Byrne PP (1987) Psychiatr. Res. 21: 71–83.
2. Kishimoto A (1990) The treatment of affective disorders with carbamazepine. In: Lithium and Other Mood-Stabilizing Agents. Presented at the 17th CINP Congress, Kyoto.
3. Koukopulous A and Reginaldi D (1980) In: Johnson FN (ed.) Handbook of Lithium Therapy. MTP Press, Lancaster, pp. 109–117.
4. Chouinard G (1985) Psychosomatics 26: 7–12.
5. Bradwejn J, Shriqui C, Koszycki D et al. (1990) J. Clin. Psychopharmacol. 10: 403–408.

© 1991 Elsevier Science Publishers B.V. All rights reserved.
Biological Psychiatry, Volume 2. G. Racagni et al., editors.

Carbamazepine treatment of symptomatic behaviors in primary dementia patients

Lon S. Schneider

Department of Psychiatry, University of Southern California, 1934 Hospital Place, Los Angeles, CA 90033, U.S.A.

Disruptive symptoms such as agitation, outbursts, violence, sleep disturbance, motor restlessness, delusions, hallucinations and misidentifications each occur in approximately one-third of various Alzheimer's disease (AD) patient samples, and remain principal problems in the clinical management of elderly patients with Alzheimer's disease and other dementias [1]. Between 50 and 75% of AD patients show significant disruptive behavior at some time during their illness. The consequences of agitated behaviors in AD and other dementia patients include the inability of families to care for them and possible institutionalization. Even within an institution, symptomatic behaviors may significantly affect patients' care and quality of life. The ideal management of such behaviors in dementia patients involves the search for treatable physical, environmental and psychiatric precipitants before the use of pharmacological treatments [2].

The use of neuroleptics for treating symptomatic behaviors in dementia has been extensively reviewed [3]. At best, they have been modestly effective for controlling agitation in elderly demented patients and no particular neuroleptic seems more effective than another. Because randomized, controlled treatment trials of disruptive behavior in dementia are few, Schneider et al. [4] performed a meta-analytic review to develop a more precise estimate of the clinical efficacy of neuroleptics in dementia. The results of 7 double-blind, parallel-group studies suggested that, overall, neuroleptics were more effective than placebo, but with only a small magnitude of effect, such that only 18 of 100 agitated dementia patients benefited from neuroleptic treatment beyond that obtained with placebo.

Over the last decade there has been an increasing number of clinical reports advocating the use of various non-neuroleptic medications in dementia patients with symptomatic behaviors. This interest may be based on the clinical dissatisfaction and limitations of neuroleptics, and on increased concern about their neurologic effects [5].

Carbamazepine

Carbamazepine is approved by the U.S. FDA for seizures and trigeminal neuralgia, and is used commonly in treating bipolar disorder and chronic pain syndromes. It has been reported to decrease agitation, irritability, aggression and impulsivity in neuropsychiatric syndromes such as bipolar disorder, acute intermittent explosive disorder, schizophrenia, violent interictal behavior and mixed frontal lobe syndromes and it was very effective in reducing affective lability in five inpatients with frontal lobe syndrome – four of whom had schizophrenia [6]. Four case reports and three open pilot studies describe significant improvement of agitation in dementia patients with carbamazepine treatment. One placebo-controlled crossover study was negative.

Anton [7] reported improvement in memory, orientation, agitation, sleep and hallucinations in a 50-year old man with bipolar disorder and multi-infarct dementia. There was initial improvement within 4 weeks (plasma level 4.5 μg/ml), with subsequent relapse; and then improvement again on rechallenge within 3 weeks (plasma level 8.5 μg/ml). (The therapeutic, steady-state plasma levels for the treatment of seizures ranges from 6–12 μg/ml.)

Essa [8] reported a 59-year old AD patient with pacing and restlessness who had first responded to thioridazine, but then became resistant to this, other neuroleptics, benzodiazepines and lithium. His agitation was controlled within one month on 300 mg/d of carbamazepine and he was able to be cared for by his family.

Leibovici and Tariot [9] reported two patients, without prior psychiatric history, who were severely cognitively impaired and had concomitant medical problems. An 81-year old female with multi-infarct dementia had symptoms of paranoia and agitation; had not responded to nortriptyline; had a severe extrapyramidal syndrome on haloperidol, 3 mg/d; and was lethargic on lorazepam. With carbamazepine, 500 mg/d, she was less dysphoric, less confused, and more cooperative with caregivers. An 83-year old man with primary degenerative dementia had outbursts of rage associated with changes in daily routine, and had had a transient response to neuroleptics. After carbamazepine, 300 mg/d (plasma level 6.2 μg/ml), his agitation dramatically improved, allowing him to cooperate with staff, eat in the cafeteria and stay out of restraints. There was transient mild sedation and no improvement in cognition. Both patients responded within two weeks. Behavioral improvement was reported also with carbamazepine in five of six other demented, convalescent hospital patients. A double-blind, placebo-controlled study is in progress.

Eight organically impaired, assaultive male inpatients were treated with carbamazepine, 200 mg q.i.d., until steady state levels between 8 and 12 μg/ml were achieved in about 7 to 10 days [10]. Incidents of violent behavior were decreased in all eight patients from an average of 3.4/wk to 1.5/wk after about a 14 to 24-day treatment period. Three of the patients had primary degenerative dementia (ages 58 to 66 years) and the five others had brain damage due to gunshots, meningioma, hematoma and hemorrhage (ages 37–55 years).

Marin and Greenwald [11] reported 2 female AD inpatients and 1 male alcoholic, multi-infarct dementia inpatient, 70–72 years old, all with combative, agitated and physically violent behavior. Having failed to respond to haloperidol, they were treated with 100 to 300 mg/day of carbamazepine, improving markedly within two weeks. Plasma levels were between 1.5 and 4.4 μg/ml.

Patterson [12] studied the effects of 600–800 mg/d (mean blood level 8.1 μg/ml) of carbamazepine on 13 male primary dementia inpatients (48–69 years) who were belligerent, uncooperative, agitated, rageful and assaultive. Overall, aggressive episodes decreased from an average of 6 to 3 per week and increased again after carbamazepine was discontinued. No patients were excluded because of side-effects; 2 had transient diplopia and ataxia.

Gleason and Schneider [13] treated 9 agitated AD patients who had failed to respond to neuroleptic trials. Five showed clear improvement and 1 had an equivocal response as assessed clinically and by BPRS scores. Improvements were in areas of hostility, agitation, and cooperation. Carbamazepine doses were determined by behavioral improvement, or the emergence of significant side-effects. Ataxia and confusion in two responders resolved with dosage reduction. Mean dose was 480 mg/d (range 200 to 1,000 mg); mean plasma level was 6.5 μg/ml ± 2.7 S.D.

One well-designed double-blind, placebo-controlled crossover study [14], reported no overall benefit from carbamazepine. In this study, 19 female senile dementia diagnosed inpatients, who showed wandering, overactivity, and restlessness, with a minority showing aggression, were randomized to receive either carbamazepine (100 to 300 mg/day) or placebo for 4-week periods and then crossed over for an additional 4 weeks after a 3-week placebo washout period. There was no significant drug-placebo difference in behavior; subjects tended to improve in the placebo condition; cognitive function may have deteriorated with carbamazepine. Plasma levels averaged 3.4 to 3.8 μg/ml (± 0.7 S.D.); 2 patients had prolonged drowsiness which responded to dosage reduction.

This study, comprising a relatively large number of senile dementia patients, stands in contrast to the uncontrolled observations reviewed above. Negative crossover studies are hard to interpret because of period effects, carryover, and the episodic nature of the symptoms. Negative results may have been due to the short treatment period, relatively low plasma levels, only one third of the patients being aggressive, or the actual ineffectiveness of carbamazepine.

Discussion

Carbamazepine may be effective in primary dementia patients with agitation, rage, combativeness, and mood lability. In published reports approximately 48 patients with possible AD have been treated. Clinical improvement occurred within 2 to 4 weeks, and at levels below the therapeutic range for seizure disorders. Side-effects, when they occurred, consisted of sedation, drowsiness and ataxia. Many – but not all – of these patients were previously nonresponsive or intolerant to neuroleptics. Therefore, they may represent a particular subset of patients who do not respond to neuroleptics, and who may be particularly responsive to carbamazepine.

Table 1. Summary of carbamazepine in agitated patients with possible Alzheimer's disease

Author	Dose, mg/d (plasma level, μg/ml)	No./ gender	Age (years)	Behavior	Response	Remarks
Essa, 1986	300	1/M	59	pacing and restlessness, "hyperactive", "catatonic posture"	improved within 1 month	previous improvement with thioridazine but not with other medications
Leibovici & Tariot, 1988	300	1/M	83	rage outbursts	dramatic improvement within 2 weeks	severely impaired inpatient; failed neuroleptic trial
Patterson, 1987	800 (8–12)	3/M	58–60	assaultive, violent	violence decreased by half within 10–24 days	inpatients
Patterson, 1988	600–800 (8.1)	13/M	48–69	aggressive & assaultive	violent incidences decreased by half	inpatients; refractory to prior medication
Marin & Greenwald, 1989	100–300 (1.5–4.4)	2/F	70,72	combative, agitated	improved markedly within 2 weeks	inpatients; failed to respond to haloperidol
Gleason & Schneider, 1990	200–1000 (6.5)	2/M 7/F	60–85	agitated combative	5 of 9 improved within 2–4 weeks	outpatients; non-response to neuroleptics
Chambers, 1982	200–300 (3.6)	19/F	80 ± 7	wandering, overactivity, restlessness	no significant improvement overall	inpatients, 4 week crossover trial

Possible relevant mechanisms of action of carbamazepine in agitated AD patients include an anti-kindling effect on the limbic system, increased locus caeruleus firing rate, other complex noradrenergic actions, increased serum tryptophan levels, possible enhancement of presynaptic dopamine release and enhancement of vasopressin [15]. Locus ceruleus dysfunction, serotonin dysfunction, extensive limbic system pathology and decreased vasopressin are all characteristics of AD.

In summary, while the use of carbamazepine in AD patients with agitation appears promising, controlled studies are needed, paying attention to diagnosis, specific behavioral syndromes, the use of uniform descriptions of symptomatic target behaviors, and the magnitude and latency of therapeutic response, so that behavior changes may be compared across studies. There is little evidence to suggest that carbamazepine is more effective than neuroleptics in treating agitated behavior in dementia patients, but it is quite possible that it may be differentially effective. That is, it may be effective when a neuroleptic is not.

References

1. Reisberg B, Borenstein J, Salob SP et al. (1987) J. Clin. Psychiatry (Suppl.) 48: 9–15.
2. Leibovici A and Tariot PM (1988) Psychopharmacol. Bull. 24: 49–53.
3. Salzman C (1987) In: Meltzer HY (ed.) Psychopharmacology. A Generation of Progress. Raven Press, New York, pp. 1167–1176.
4. Schneider LS, Pollock VE and Lyness SA (1990) J. Am. Geriatr. Soc. 38: 553–563.
5. Jenike MA (1983) J. Am. Geriatr. Soc. 31: 71.
6. McAllister TW (1985) J. Clin. Psychiatry 46: 393–394.
7. Anton RF, Waid LR, Fossey M and AuBuchon P (1986) J. Clin. Psychopharmacol. 6: 232–234.
8. Essa M (1986) J. Clin. Psychopharmacol. 6: 234–236.
9. Leibovici A and Tariot PM (1988) J. Geriatr. Psychiatry Neurol. 1: 110–112.
10. Patterson JF (1987) Psychosomatics 28: 579–581.
11. Marin DB and Greenwald BS (1989) Am. J. Psychiatry 146: 805.
12. Patterson JF (1988) J. Geriatr. Psychiatry Neurol. 1: 21–23.
13. Gleason R and Schneider LS (1990) J. Clin. Psychiatry 51, 115–118.
14. Chambers CA, Bain J, Rosbottom R, Ballinger BR and McLaren S (1982) IRCS Med. Sci. 10: 505–506.
15. Post RM (1987) In: Meltzer HY (ed.) Psychopharmacology. A Generation of Progress. Raven Press, New York, pp. 567–576.

© 1991 Elsevier Science Publishers B.V. All rights reserved.
Biological Psychiatry, Volume 2. G. Racagni et al., editors.

Carbamazepine in recurrent mood disorders: Six years experience

Gian Franco Placidi, Alessandro Lenzi and Liliana Dell'Osso
Institute of Psychiatry, University of Pisa, via Roma 67, Pisa, Italy

Introduction

The existence of some bipolar patients either refractory or intolerant to lithium salts (Li) was one of the reasons for looking for alternative therapies. Many studies have indicated the efficacy of carbamazepine (CBZ) in the treatment of manic episode and in the prophylaxis of bipolar disorder [1–3].

In order to compare the efficacy and the safety of Li and CBZ, we planned two double-blind studies: one in 30 acute psychotic patients and one lasting three years in 83 subjects. All patients showed an affective component and were categorized according to whether they had "classical" affective features (i.e. major recurrent depression, bipolar disorder, or bipolar psychosis with mood-congruent features) or schizophrenic features (i.e. bipolar psychosis with mood-incongruent features, or schizophreniform disorder).

By further analysis of these data an attempt was made to answer some questions of clinical importance, such as compliance to medication and the predictors of response.

Additional data were obtained from a naturalistic three-year follow-up after the end of the prospective study.

Material and Methods

The characteristics of patients, designs, outcome measures and statistical analysis have been previously reported [4,5].

Results and Discussion

In the acute psychosis study, in which CBZ and Li were administered in combination with chlorpromazine, the two drugs showed a similar efficacy. CBZ appeared to possess a greater sedative effect than Li, especially at the beginning of treatment; thus lower doses of chlorpromazine to control the acute symptomatology were used. Furthermore, CBZ showed greater efficacy on psychotic mood-incongruent features.

In the long-term double-blind study, during the first two months, a statistically significant higher number of dropouts occurred in the Li-treated subgroup with schizophrenic features. During a 36-month period at least two-thirds of the patients in each drug group were very much or moderately improved; there were no statistically significant differences in rates of improvement. The two drugs appeared equally effective in alleviating most psychopathological dimensions but equally ineffective in anxiety-depression symptomatology. Twelve relapses were observed in 8 patients in the CBZ group and 9 relapses in 7 patients in the Li group; the incidence of side-effects for both drugs was similar, although it appeared that Li was somewhat less well tolerated, that is, more Li-treated patients reported diarrhea, weight gain, and tremor. In contrast, the rate of abnormal findings in laboratory indices (hematologic, liver and urinary) were higher in CBZ-treated patients.

In this study the compliance to medication was also analyzed by regular plasma check. The analysis of the anamnestic data showed that patients living alone or with collateral relatives defaulted more often than those living with their spouses, parents or children. The higher score of the BPRS item "somatic concern" in the Li-defaulters group suggests that patients overconcerned about their health overestimated side-effects and hence stopped treatment. Unpleasant psychotic experiences, especially mood-incongruent features, tended to favour compliance. During a depressive episode, patients seem to accept the treatment and follow it carefully to avoid unpleasant relapses while pharmacological suppression of mood during a manic episode is not well accepted by patients who, more or less deliberately, refuse treatment which removes their feelings of "well-being". The emerging profile of patients who are negligent in taking Li or CBZ and who prematurely interrupt treatment is characterized by manic and hypochondriac symptomatology, and by their not having social supervision. This would suggest that in recurrent mood disorders compliance with prophylactic therapy would be more successful if started after a depressive – or after an unpleasant psychotic – rather than after an euphoric manic episode. Thus, every patient is a potential drug-defaulter, depending on when in the course of illness prophylactic treatment is begun.

The clinical features of the patients enrolled in the long-term study were then examined further, to identify possible response predictors to CBZ. Three (family history, schizophrenic features and Li refractoriness) out of the five criteria identified by Kishimoto [6] were confirmed, whereas regarding the age at onset, our findings were similar to those reported by Post [3]. The previous "good response to ECT" that we found as a possible CBZ response predictor, may be linked to antikindling activity of both treatments.

At the end of the three-year double-blind study, 20 patients (11 of Li and 9 of CBZ group) were followed up in a three-year naturalistic study.

In the CBZ group 3 "pure" bipolar patients continued to receive the drug for 3 years without relapsing. Six patients discontinued the treatment: 2 (bipolar disorder with mood congruent psychotic features) did not relapse; 2 (schizoaffective disorder) showed relapses precipitated by life events and 2 discontinued the CBZ treatment for pregnancy and relapsed in the post-partum period. In the Li group 7 patients continued treatment: 3 (1 "pure" bipolar disorder, 2 bipolar disorder with mood-congruent psychotic features) did not relapse; 2 had several relapses; 2 (bipolar disorder with mood-incongruent psychotic features) showed hypomanic or mild depressive episodes without a marked impairment in social or occupational functioning. Four patients discontinued the treatment: 3 (1 "pure" bipolar disorder, 1 schizophreniform disorder, 1 major depressive episode) did not relapse, while 1 patient relapsed.

The most striking observation emerging from this research was the significantly higher dropout rate during the acute phase in Li-treated patients with prevalent schizophrenic symptoms. On all other outcome measures (i.e. relapses, survival analysis, or symptomatic improvement) both drugs appeared essentially similar.

CBZ and Li showed comparable efficacy and safety in prophylactic treatment of recurrent psychotic disorders with strong affective colouring. Both medications seem to exert their main therapeutic action against excited rather than depressive states, yet Li salts may be more efficacious in classical affective disorders, whereas CBZ may be more effective in the treatment of mood disorders with schizo-affective or schizophreniform features. This suggests the possibility that the therapeutic action of CBZ may be exerted on all forms of "atypical psychoses" falling outside the classical boundaries of the affective and schizophrenic disorders which generally respond poorly to Li; the hypothesized pathogenetic linkage to temporal lobe epilepsy of these forms may be confirmed by good response to CBZ. Since CBZ also appeared to exert an acute and prophylactic effect comparable to Li on the more "classical" mood groups, it might be that CBZ is a less specific compound than Li, possessing a broader spectrum of activity in several overlapping classes of recurrent psychoses. Furthermore, the polarity of episode and personality profile may predict compliance to treatment.

The naturalistic follow-up data showed no relapses in patients who continued the CBZ, and raises the problem of discontinuation of prophylactic treatment.

References

1. Ballenger JC and Post RM (1980) Am. J. Psychiatry 137: 782–790.
2. Okuma T, Kishimoto A, Otsuki S et al. (1979) Psychopharmacology 55: 211–217.
3. Post RM and Uhde TW (1983) In: Ayd FJ, Taylor IJ and Taylor BT (eds.) Affective Disorders Reassessed. Add Medical Communications, Baltimore.
4. Placidi GF, Lenzi A, Lazzerini F, Cassano GB and Akiskal HS (1986) J. Clin. Psychiatry 47: 490–494.
5. Lenzi A, Lazzerini F, Grassi E, Massimetti G and Placidi GF (1986) J. Int. Med. Res. 14: 78–84.
6. Kishimoto A, Ogura G, Hazama H and Inone K (1983) Br. J. Psychiatry 143: 327–331.

Eating disorders: Basic and clinical research

© 1991 Elsevier Science Publishers B.V. All rights reserved.
Biological Psychiatry, Volume 2. G. Racagni et al., editors.

Hypothalamic neurotransmitters controlling food intake

Sarah F. Leibowitz and Meena Jhanwar-Uniyal
The Rockefeller University, 1230 York Avenue, NY 10021, U.S.A.

Hypothalamic neurotransmitters, which appear to be involved in coordinating the ingestion and metabolism of nutrients, include the monoamines, norepinephrine (NE) and serotonin (5-HT), and the peptides, neuropeptide Y (NPY) and galanin (GAL). Evidence from recent pharmacological, biochemical and endocrine studies have shown that the activity of these neurochemical systems vary as a function of the circadian cycle and also in relation to circulating levels of specific hormones, such as the adrenal steroids, corticosterone (CORT) and aldosterone (ALDO).

Norepinephrine

Studies conducted with NE [1] suggest that this catecholamine in the hypothalamus may control the first meal of the active feeding cycle (dark period for the rat), which is characteristically rich in carbohydrate. At this time, when blood glucose and liver glycogen levels are relatively low and glucagon and CORT levels are high, immediate energy requirements dictate the need for robust eating, specifically of carbohydrate. In support of this hypothesis, injection of NE into the hypothalamus, in particular, the paraventricular nucleus (PVN), stimulates feeding behavior via the activation of α_2-noradrenergic receptors and this phenomenon, as well as circadian patterns of nutrient intake, are disturbed by lesions of the PVN. The main behavioral effect of NE in the PVN is to stimulate selectively an increase in the animal's appetite for carbohydrate, at the expense of protein. This action is associated with a decrease in energy expenditure and an increase in circulating levels of glucose, CORT and vasopressin, hormones which act synergistically with NE to potentiate feeding and carbohydrate intake. Biochemical studies demonstrate that the activity of this α_2-noradrenergic system in the PVN peaks at the beginning of the natural feeding cycle and is positively correlated with blood levels of CORT and glucose, as well as with total daily food intake and body weight in both Sprague-Dawley and genetically obese Zucker rats.

Serotonin

Brain 5-HT has an inhibitory effect on feeding behavior. Recent pharmacological and biochemical studies indicate that this action of 5-HT is mediated by nuclei in the medial hypothalamus, specifically the PVN and ventromedial nuclei, which are involved in controlling energy balance. In these nuclei, 5-HT injection, or drugs which potentiate endogenous 5-HT, preferentially reduce carbohydrate intake in naturally feeding animals, possibly through activation of satiety mechanisms involved in the termination of feeding [2]. This action of 5-HT, which is mediated by 5-HT_{1B} receptors, exhibits a circadian rhythm possibly controlled by the suprachiasmatic nucleus. The evidence indicates that 5-HT is most active at the start of the nocturnal feeding cycle, when it is required to terminate the carbohydrate-rich meals that naturally predominate at that time. Biochemical studies have revealed that the density of 5-HT_{1B} receptors in the medial hypothalamic nuclei is responsive to the light/dark cycle as well as to alterations in nutritional state and it is more active and responsive in female rats (relative to males) which show a strong preference for carbohydrate [3].

Neuropeptide Y

Neuropeptide Y acts in the PVN in a similar fashion to NE, specifically to enhance carbohydrate intake at the start of active (dark) cycle and to stimulate the release of hormones, e.g. CORT, ALDO, and vasopressin, which modulate energy metabolism as well as feeding behavior. Relative to NE, this anabolic peptide is more potent and long-term in its action and is released by more intense stimulation, suggesting that it is physiologically activated under specific conditions where requirements for energy intake and replenishment of energy stores are particularly strong [4]. Consistent with this proposal is the evidence that NPY, in contrast to NE which reduces energy expenditure, modulates energy metabolism through an effect on substrate utilization and lipogenesis, and produces obesity after chronic administration. Biochemical studies demonstrate a sharp rise in NPY-like immunoreactivity in the PVN at the onset of the active feeding cycle, after food deprivation and in genetically obese animals, and a significant decline in NPY occurs shortly after the first meal of the natural feeding cycle [5]. These findings strongly suggest that hypothalamic NPY may contribute to the development of eating disorders and obesity.

Galanin

Galanin, which coexists with NE in the PVN, appears to have a dual function in the restoration of energy balance [6]. Specifically, an initial glucoregulatory function of GAL is suggested by the evidence that:

1. GAL, like NE, produces a short-duration carbohydrate feeding response primarily at the start of the active feeding period;
2. GAL's site of action is also localized to the PVN, which controls CORT release;

3. This GAL induced feeding response is blocked by α_2-receptor antagonists, NE synthesis inhibitors and PVN lesions, and it is dependent upon circulating levels of CORT;
4. GAL stimulates glucagon secretion, which naturally rises to induce gluconeogenesis at the dark onset.

The second function of GAL in energy homeostasis is to produce a more potent and long-term stimulatory effect on fat ingestion. A single injection of GAL at the start of the feeding cycle potentiates fat intake over the next 24 h. This potent effect is inversely correlated with GAL's impact on carbohydrate intake at dark onset, suggesting different underlying neurochemical and neuroendocrine mechanisms. Moreover, the stimulation of fat intake by GAL occurs independently of NE and CORT, and it is most potent in the later hours of the active cycle when GAL may be physiologically active in mediating the rise in fat consumption that rats normally exhibit in the latter half of the active period. Recent studies examining GAL gene expression in the hypothalamus of genetically controlled Zucker obese rats [7] reveal disturbances in GAL mRNA, at puberty and maturity, which may be linked with the physiological and endocrine changes seen in these obese rats.

References

1. Leibowitz SF (1988) Neurosci. Biobehav. Rev. 12: 101–109.
2. Leibowitz SF (1990) Drugs 39: 33–48.
3. Leibowitz SF and Jhanwar-Uniyal M (1990) Soc. Neurosci. Abstr. 16: 294.
4. Leibowitz SF (1991) Brain Res. Bull. (in press).
5. Jhanwar-Uniyal M, Beck B, Burlet C and Leibowitz SF (1990) Brain Res. 536: 331–334.
6. Leibowitz SF (1991) In: T Hokfelt and T Bartfai (eds.) Galanin: A New Multifunctional Peptide in the Neuro-Endocrine System. Macmillan Press, New York. (in press).
7. Jhanwar-Uniyal M, Chua Jr. SC and Leibowitz SF (1991) FASEB J. 5: A1320.

© 1991 Elsevier Science Publishers B.V. All rights reserved.
Biological Psychiatry, Volume 2. G. Racagni et al., editors.

Mechanism of action of serotoninergic anorectic agents

Silvio Gabattini
Istituto di Ricerche Farmacologiche "Mario Negri" via Eritrea 62, 20157 Milan, Italy

d-Fenfluramine (dF) has proved an important tool for investigating the role of serotonin (5-HT) in the central and peripheral control of food intake. dF has no amphetamine-like activity and has a broad spectrum of activities in a wide range of experimentally induced hyperphagias [1].

When administered orally, parenterally [2] or intracerebrally [3] at appropriate doses dF reduces the levels of 5-HT and its principal metabolite 5-hydroxyindolacetic acid (5-HIAA) in various brain areas. Depending on the dose and animal species this depletion of brain 5-HT and 5-HIAA may be long-lasting although fully reversible [2,4]. This effect in vivo is relatively specific because there is no effect – at least at minimal anorectic doses – on the brain levels of catecholamines. The 5-HT depleting activity of dF is currently interpreted through its in vitro capacity to block the uptake of 5-HT and to enhance the release of 5-HT by synaptosomes [5,6]; this effect in vitro has been observed with several animal species including rats, mice, guinea pigs [7] and marmosets (Mennini, unpublished results).

That the effect of dF on the serotoninergic system may help explain its anorectic effect is shown by the observation that a non-specific 5-HT antagonist such as metergoline completely antagonizes the decrease in food intake induced by dF [8]. A number of other antagonists for noradrenaline and dopamine are ineffective in antagonizing the anorexia induced by dF in food-deprived rats [9].

Controlled clinical trials have established that dF reduces appetite in man [10–12] and during prolonged administration lowers body weight significantly more than placebo. The possibility of using dF as an adjuvant in controlling body weight has aroused considerable interest in developing direct or indirect 5-HT agonists. Several compounds have proved active experimentally in animals and some of them have reached the clinical investigation stage.

Two of these, namely fluoxetine and sertraline, appear to be effective in man [13,14]. It was therefore of interest to investigate their mechanism of action on the serotonergic system. Both compounds are very strong inhibitors of 5-HT uptake and in this respect they are much more effective than dF (see Table 1). However, this effect is probably not relevant for their anorectic activity because at the ED_{50} for that activity [15] the brain levels are 2 or 3 orders of magnitude higher than the IC_{50} for inhibition of 5-HT uptake. These levels are, however, compatible with those inducing enhancement of ^{3}H overflow from synaptosomes previously loaded with [^{3}H]-5-HT, suggesting that the decrease of food intake in deprived rats requires both inhibition of 5-HT uptake and enhancement of 5-HT release.

Table 1. Biochemical effects of anorectic agents

Biochemical parameter	dF	Fluoxetine	Sertraline
Inhibition of synaptosomes [^{3}H]-5-HT uptake (IC_{50} μM)	0.4	0.07	0.01
Enhancement of synaptosomes [^{3}H]-5-HT release (SC_{20} μM)	2.4	6.3	2.3
% of true [^{3}H]-5-HT release/total ^{3}H	62 ± 8	18 ± 6	17 ± 5
Inhibition of vesicle [^{3}H]-5-HT uptake (IC_{50} μM)	4.2	4.1	–
Inhibition of vesicle [^{3}H]-DH-tetrabenazine binding (IC_{50} μM)	127.6	1.6	–
Inhibition of membrane [^{3}H]-dF binding (IC_{50} μM)	0.04	0.03	0.01
Inhibition of synaptosomes [^{3}H]-dF uptake (IC_{50} μM)	0.27	2.75	0.15
Anorectic activity (ED_{50} mg/kg i.p.)[a]	1.3	12.0	16.7
95% fiducial limits	(0.9–2.0)	(8.8–17.2)	(7.9–23.4)
Brain level 30 min after ED_{50} (μM)	8.8 ± 0.5	32.0 ± 9.8	72.8 ± 11.4

[a] In rats kept without food during the night and trained for 15 days to eat their food during 5 h in the daytime (10:00 a.m. – 3:00 p.m.).

However, the question is much more complicated because the mechanism of release may be not the same for the 3 agents considered. A careful analysis of the release of ^{3}H from [^{3}H]-5-HT preloaded synaptosomes indicates that, at equal releasing activity, dF releases much more true [^{3}H]-5-HT than fluoxetine or sertraline. In addition, a comparison of dF and fluoxetine shows that 5-HT-induced release by low concentrations of dF, but not fluoxetine, is calcium-dependent; furthermore the effect of dF, but not that of fluoxetine, is inhibited by a 5-HT uptake inhibitor such as indalpine, probably because dF at low concentrations is actively transported into the synaptosomes [15]. Other differences emerge between the mechanism of action of dF and fluoxetine when vesicles rather than intact synaptosomes are considered. The effect of both drugs on [^{3}H]-5-HT uptake is similar, but fluoxetine is more effective than dF in inhibiting the binding of [^{3}H]-DH tetrabenazine, considered to be representative of 5-HT retention in the vesicles. Despite the different mechanisms involved, repeated treatment with anorectic doses of fluoxetine, like dF, reduces both 5-HT and 5-HIAA in the brain [16].

The mechanism of action of fluoxetine's anorectic activity is far from being elucidated; in fact, differently from dF, its anorectic effect is not inhibited by metergoline, suggesting that at least in food-deprived rats 5-HT is not the chemical mediator involved. It should be recalled in this respect that at low μM concentrations fluoxetine inhibits dopamine uptake and enhances dopamine release [16]. The classification as a serotonergic anorectic agent may therefore not be altogether accurate for fluoxetine.

References

1. Samanin R and Garattini S (1990) In: Nutrition and the Brain, Vol. 8. Raven Press, New York, pp. 163–192.
2. Garattini S, Mennini T, Bendotti C, Invernizzi R and Samanin R (1986) Appetite 7 (Suppl.): 15–38.
3. Invernizzi R, Fracasso C, Caccia S, Garattini S and Samanin R (1991) Neuropharmacology 30: 119–123.
4. Zaczek R, Battaglia G, Culp S, Appel NM, Contrera JF and De Sousa EB (1990) J. Pharmacol. Exp. Ther. 253: 104–112.
5. Mennini T, Borroni E, Samanin R and Garattini S (1981) Neurochem. Int. 3: 289–294.
6. Borroni E, Ceci A, Garattini S and Mennini T (1983) J. Neurochem. 40: 891–893.
7. Mennini T, Bizzi A, Caccia S, Codegoni AM, Fracasso C, Frittoli E, Guiso G, Martin Padura I, Taddei C, Uslenghi A and Garattini S (1991) Naunyn Schmiedebergs Arch. Pharmacol. 343: 483–490.
8. Garattini S and Samanin R (1976) In: Silverstone T (ed.) Dahlem Workshop on Appetite and Food Intake. pp. 83–108.
9. Garattini S (1985) In: Hirsch J and Van Itallie T (eds.) Recent Advances in Obesity Research, IV. John Libbey, London, pp. 208–216.
10. Silverstone T and Goodall E (1986) Adv. Biosci. 60: 361–366.
11. Guy-Grand B, Apfelbaum M, Crepaldi G, Gries A, Lefebvre P and Turner P (1989) Lancet ii: 1142–1145.
12. Wurtman JJ and Wurtman RJ (1977) Science 198: 1178–1180.
13. Lucki I, Kreider MS and Simansky KJ (1988) Psychopharmacology (Berlin) 96: 289–295.
14. Heym J and Koe BK (1988) J. Clin. Psychiatry 49 (Suppl.): 40–45
15. Gobbi M, Frittoli E, Mennini T and Garattini S (1991) Naunyn Schmiedebergs Arch. Pharmacol. (in press).
16. Caccia S, Bizzi A, Coltro G, Fracasso C, Frittoli E, Mennini T and Garattini S (1991) J. Pharm. Pharmacol. (in press).

© 1991 Elsevier Science Publishers B.V. All rights reserved.
Biological Psychiatry, Volume 2. G. Racagni et al., editors.

Central and peripheral dopamine receptors involved in the regulation of feeding behavior and energy expenditure

E. Nisoli, M. Memo, C. Tonello, M. Pizzi, P.F. Spano and M.O. Carruba
Department of Biomedical Sciences and Biotechnology University of Brescia, Via Valsabbina, 19-25124 Brescia, Italy

Body weight of mammals is regulated by a complex array of interrelated influences originating both from central nervous system and peripheral tissues. Indeed, numerous experimental studies have indicated that various monoamines, amino acids and peptide neurohormones, within anatomically connected hypothalamic nuclei, modulate feeding behavior [1]. Furthermore, it has been established that in normal rats, hyperphagia, induced by feeding a highly palatable cafeteria diet, is often accompanied by a large increase in heat production – i.e. diet-induced thermogenesis – by brown adipose tissue (BAT) which tends to prevent excessive weight gain and obesity [2]. Finally, it was found that the hypothalamic nuclei involved in modulation of feeding behavior regulate the heat production in BAT through the sympathetic nerve fibres innervating this tissue [3]. Dopamine (DA) and DA drugs have been reported to modulate food intake and energy balance acting directly in the hypothalamic nuclei and indirectly through the hypothalamic nerve fibres innervating BAT. To biochemically, pharmacologically and functionally characterize the DA receptor subtypes involved in these phenomena, we performed a series of experiments on the two main hypothalamic nuclei implicated in food intake, namely the lateral perifornical hypothalamus (PFH) and paraventricular nucleus (PVN) and the brown fat adipocytes.

DA receptors in discrete hypothalamic areas of rat

Previous results have shown that DA agonists, injected into the PFH, reduce food intake [4]. We performed measurements of adenylate cyclase (AC) activity as a biochemical index of DA receptors. We found that DA and more selective D_2 agonists, such as quinpirole and lisuride, strongly reduced AC activity in homogenates from the PFH, whereas the selective D_1 agonist SKF 82526 was completely inactive in modifying the basal enzyme function. Moreover DA, quinpirole and SKF 82526 were unable to affect AC activity in homogenates from rat PVN, consistent with previous pharmacological evidence showing DA in this hypothalamic area to have no effect on feeding [4]. In a previous report, Carruba et al. [5] showed that systemic administration to hungry rats of dopaminergic drugs acting on D_2 receptors such as lisuride strikingly decreased food consumption, whereas D_1 agonists were ineffective. The present results demonstrate that systemic administration of selective D_2 but not D_1 receptor antagonists specifically blocked the inhibitory effect of lisuride on food intake. The hypothesis that lisuride affected feeding behavior through the D_2 receptors present in PFH was verified by studying the anorectic effect of lisuride in rats after selective blockade of PFH D_2 receptors, achieved by local injection of specific antagonists. We report here that (–)sulpiride, but not SCH 23390, infused intra-PFH, was able to completely counteract the anorexia caused by lisuride [6] (Fig. 1).

Furthermore, our results indicate that DA, through D_2 receptors, physiologically exerts an inhibitory tone on the feeding controlling neuronal circuits in normal rats. Indeed, the D_2 antagonists, sultopride and (–)sulpiride, administered systemically or intranuclearly respectively, counteract the lisuride effect and enhance food consumption "per se" (see Fig. 1). It may be inferred that the suppression of the dopaminergic tone shifts the regulatory set point of feeding behavior towards enhanced food consumption. In summary, our data indicated that D_2 receptors are present in the PFH but not in the PVN of the rat hypothalamus, and that they are functionally and pharmacologically relevant in modulating feeding behavior in rats.

DA receptors in brown adipose tissue of rat

Measurements of radioligand binding sites, AC activity and lipid metabolites

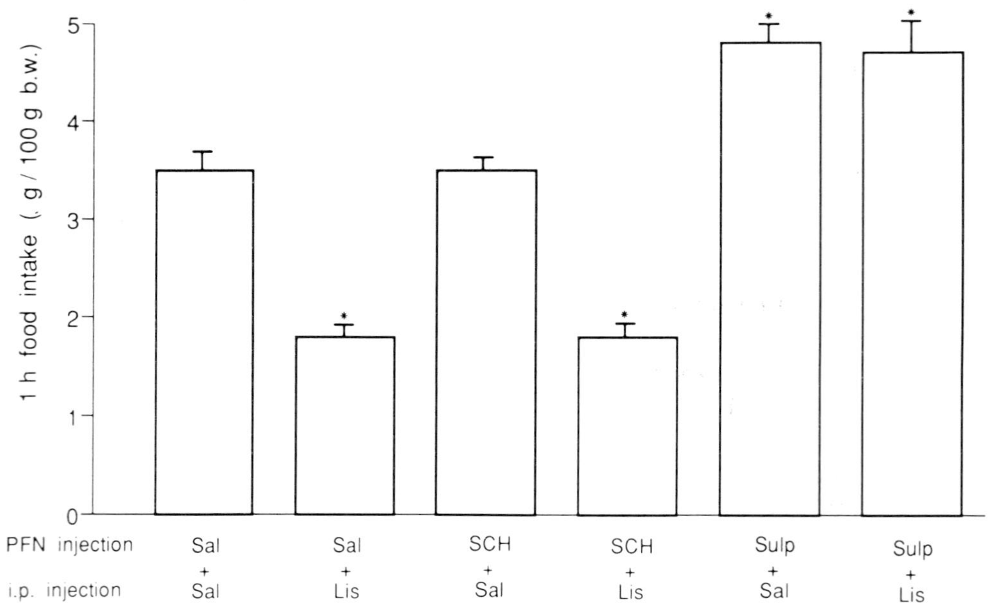

Fig. 1. Specific inhibition of lisuride-induced anorexia by intra-perifornical area injection of (–)sulpiride. SCH 23390 and (–)sulpiride were injected into the PFH 30 min before food presentation. $*P < 0.01$ vs. saline + saline group.

release were performed to characterize the DA receptor subtypes controlling thermogenesis in rat BAT. D_2 but not D_1 receptor binding sites were found in membrane preparations from BAT. The selective stimulation of these receptors lowered the cyclic AMP (cAMP) levels, in homogenates, and also in dispersed brown adipocytes, strongly suggesting that the D_2 receptors are mainly localized on the fat cell membranes and not on nerve terminals or vessels. Moreover, it was found that DA or more selective D_2 agonist drugs lowered the AC activity enhanced by forskolin or the β-adrenoceptor agonist, (−)isoproterenol, in BAT homogenate, suggesting the notion that the D_2 receptors are functionally linked to β-adrenoceptors, the main trigger of BAT metabolism. This was further confirmed by the finding that selective D_2 agonists induced a significant decrease of β-adrenoceptor-stimulated glycerol and non-esterified fatty acids release from brown adipocytes. These results show that D_2 but not D_1 receptors are present in rat BAT and that the reduction of intracellular cAMP induced by D_2 receptor stimulation can play a functional role in modulating thermogenesis induced by sympathetic activity in rats.

Taken together, these data suggest that DA and DA drugs can coordinately affect body weight acting in PFH and in BAT.

References

1. Leibowitz SF (1980) In: Morgane PJ and Panksepp J (eds.) Handbook of the Hypothalamus, Vol. 3A. Marcel Dekker, New York, pp. 299–437.
2. Rothwell NJ, Stock MJ and Wyllie MG (1982) Eur. J. Pharmacol. 77: 45.
3. Cottle WH (1970) In: Lindberg O (ed.) Brown Adipose Tissue. Elsevier, New York, pp. 155–178.
4. Leibowitz SF and Rossakis C (1979) Brain Res. 172: 101.
5. Caaruba MO, Ricciardi S, Muller EE and Mantegazza P (1980) Eur. J. Pharmacol. 64: 133.
6. Carruba MO, Nisoli E, Garosi V, Pizzi M, Memo M and Spano PF (1991) J. Pharmacol. Exp. Ther. (in press).

© 1991 Elsevier Science Publishers B.V. All rights reserved.
Biological Psychiatry, Volume 2. G. Racagni et al., editors.

Benzodiazepine receptor ligands, appetite and taste preferences

Steven J. Cooper

Laboratory of Psychopharmacology, School of Psychology, University of Birmingham, Birmingham B15 2TT, U.K.

Introduction

The major hypothesis presented here is that benzodiazepine receptors (BZR) located in the brain play an important role in determining sweet taste preference [1], and that this function contributes to the hyperphagic response elicited by benzodiazepine treatments [2]. A further aspect of the hypothesis is that BZR-mediated control of sweet taste preference and of food (or fluid) intake is bi-directional in nature [1].

Benzodiazepine receptor pharmacology

Benzodiazepine receptors

High-affinity, specific and saturable binding sites for benzodiazepines were discovered in the brain [3,4]. BZRs form part of a receptor complex, and are closely associated with $GABA_A$ receptors, which in turn are involved in the regulation of Cl^- ion movement across neural membranes through a chloride ion channel [5]. Classical BZR agonists, like diazepam, enhance the $GABA_A$ receptor-mediated opening of chloride channels. On pharmacological grounds, two types of BZR have been distinguished: Type 1 (or cerebellar type) and Type 2 (or hippocampal type). Certain drugs are more selective for one than the other, whereas diazepam and others do not distinguish between the two.

Benzodiazepine receptor ligands

The range of BZR ligands is critical to an understanding of BZR functions. They can be grouped according to three main categories: agonists, antagonists, and inverse agonists.

Agonists include the familiar benzodiazepines, like diazepam, oxazepam, chlordiazepoxide and midazolam. They also include other drugs which do not share the benzodiazepine chemical structure, but which nevertheless are capable of producing typical benzodiazepine effects. Within the agonists, one can distinguish between full agonists (like diazepam) which elicit the complete range of benzodiazepine effects, and partial agonists (like Ro16-6028 and Ro17-1812) which produce a more restricted set of effects. Antagonists, by definition, block agonist effects, and good examples of BZR antagonists are flumazenil and the β-carboline ZK93426. Inverse agonists are an unusual category, which bind with high affinity to BZR but generally produce effects that are opposite to those produced by classical benzodiazepines [8]. Their effects are also blocked by BZR antagonists, and they can be differentiated into full and partial inverse agonists.

Benzodiazepines and food intake

It has been known for a long time that benzodiazepines (more correctly, BZR full agonists) increase food consumption in many animal species, and that this hyperphagic effect can be divorced, on behavioural grounds, from their anxiolytic effect [1].

More recently, work in my laboratory has demonstrated that partial agonists (e.g. Ro16-6028, Ro17-1812) produce large increases in food intake, in the relative absence of sedative effects [9]. Furthermore, we have demonstrated that BZR inverse agonists (e.g. FG 7142, Ro15-3505, Ro15-4513, CGS 8216) constitute a new class of anorectic agents [10–12].

Benzodiazepines and taste

Taste reactivity

In rats, certain species-typical reactions to taste stimuli provide a reliable measure of palatability. Berridge and Treit found that chlordiazepodixe selectively increased the number of ingestive responses elicited by a variety of tastes, but had little effect on the number of aversive responses elicited by the same tastes [13]. They concluded that drugs acting at BZR enhance the positive palatability of taste stimuli.

Sweet taste preferences

This issue was addressed using preference tests involving choices between saccharin solutions and water. Our hypotheses were: first, that BZR agonists would selectively increase the choice of sodium saccharin solution in a preference test; second, that BZR inverse agonists would selectively decrease the choice of the saccharin solution in a preference test.

The first hypothesis was upheld in a study with the potent BZR agonist, clonazepam [14]. It stimulated the consumption of saccharin solution without affecting intake of water. The same result has been obtained with the BZR partial agonists, Ro16-6028 and Ro17-1812 (Cooper and Green, submitted for publication). The second hypothesis was upheld in several studies with BZR inverse agonists. In the cases of FG7142, CGS8216 and Ro15-4513, there were selective reductions in saccharin intake in two-choice tests [15,16].

References

1. Cooper SJ (1989) Ann. N.Y. Acad. Sci. 575: 321–336.
2. Cooper SJ (1980) Appetite 1: 7–19.
3. Squires RG and Braestrup C (1977) Nature (London) 266: 732–734.
4. Mohler H and Okada T (1977) Science 198: 849–851.
5. Richards G, Schoch P and Jenck F (1991) In: Rodgers RJ and Cooper SJ (eds.) 5-HT_{1A} Agonists, 5-HT_3 Antagonists and Benzodiazepines: Their Comparative Behavioural Pharmacology. John Wiley, Chichester (in press).
6. Hunkeler W, Mohler H, Pieri L, Polc P, Bonetti EP, Cumin R, Schaffner R and Haefely W (1981) Nature (London) 290: 514–516.
7. Jensen LH, Petersen EN, Braestrup C, Honore T, Kehr W, Stephens DN, Schneider H, Seidelmann D and Schmiechen R (1984) Psychoparmacology 83: 249–256.
8. Braestrup C, Nielsen M, Honore T, Jensen LH and Petersen EN (1983) Neurpharmacology 22: 1451–1457.
9. Yerbury RE and Cooper SJ (1987) Pharmacol. Biochem. Behav. 28: 427–431.
10. Cooper SJ (1985) Brain Res. 346: 190–194.
11. Cooper SJ, Barber DJ, Gilbert DB and Moores WR (1985) Psychopharmacology 86: 348–355.
12. Cooper SJ, van der Hoek G and Kirkham TC (1988) Physiol. Behav. 42: 211–216.
13. Berridge KC and Treit D (I986) Pharmacol. Biochem. Behav. 24: 217–221.
14. Cooper SJ and Yerbury RE (1988) Brain Res. 456: 173–176.
15. Cooper SJ (1986) Neuropharmacology 25: 213–216.
16. Kirkham TC and Cooper SJ (1986) Pharmacol. Biochem. Behav. 26: 145–151.
17. Cooper SJ, Bowyer DM and van der Hoek GA (1989) Brain Res. 494: 172–176.

© 1991 Elsevier Science Publishers B.V. All rights reserved.
Biological Psychiatry, Volume 2. G. Racagni et al., editors.

CRF and glucocorticoids: Central regulation of appetite and peripheral metabolism

David A. York

Pennington Biomedical Research Center, 6400 Perkins Road, Baton Rouge, LA 70808, U.S.A.

Glucocorticoids and CRF have major effects on the regulation of food intake and energy expenditure. Indeed, abnormalities in the hypothalamic and pituitary-adrenal system may be implicated in the development of obesity [1,2].

CRF has a number of major behavioral and metabolic effects independent of its role in control of the pituitary-adrenal axis [3]. CRF, injected into the third ventricle of rats produces a dose-dependent reduction in food intake which lasts for up to 3 h in overnight starved animals [4]. CRF may indeed mediate the reduction in food intake associated with stress [5] and with interleukin-induced fever [6].

The mechanism of action of CRF in regulation of food intake is unclear. Krahn et al. [6,7] have suggested that the PVN is the site of action, although only a limited number of areas were tested. From studies of the effects of CRF on monoamine levels in the lateral hypothalamus, Bray and colleagues [8] have suggested that CRF depresses feeding by altering the monoamine pattern in the LH to one of a fed rat, that is to reduce NE, MHPG and DOPAC of fasted rats to the levels seen in the fed rats. Oxytocin receptors may also mediate the CRF anorectic response as evidenced by its prevention by the oxytocin antagonist [d(CH_2)$_5$, Tyr(Me)^2, Orn^8-vasotocin] [9], by the similarity of oxytocin and CRF responses in inhibiting food intake [10] and by the recognized action of CRF to stimulate oxytocin secretion [11].

CRF also regulates the activity of the autonomic nervous system, enhancing sympathetic adrenal secretions and hepatic glucose production [12], enhancing thermogenesis through its central stimulation of the activity of sympathetic nerves innervating brown adipose tissue (BAT) [13] and reducing parasympathetic drive to the stomach and endocrine pancreas [14]. The relationship of these autonomic changes to the control of food intake is unclear. A consistent reciprocal relationship between sympathetic activity and food intake has been identified for responses to numerous across a range of peptides, transmitters, diets, hypothalamic lesions and animal species [1,2]. The relationship between the CRF stimulation of sympathetic activity and its reduction of food intake is not clear; different hypothalamic sites may be involved, the PVN for food intake [7] and the preoptic area for sympathetic activity [15]. However, adrenal demedulation reduced the inhibitory effect of CRF on food intake [16] as does ganglionic blockade with chlorisondamine, suggesting a role for autonomic activity in the CRF control of feeding.

We have recently demonstrated that CRF impairs and corticosterone enhances atropine-blockable insulin secretion in obese fa/fa rats [13], indicative that the glucocorticoid-CRF system might also modulate parasympathetic drive to the endocrine pancreas. We have also investigated the effects of chronic CRF (5 μg/day i.c.v. for 7 days) on the metabolic clearance rate of intravenously infused glucose in the obese fa/fa rat using the non-steady state technique of Steele [18]. These data (Fig. 1) showed that CRF improved the insulin stimulated clearance of glucose. It is not yet clear if this improvement is secondary to the reduction in insulin secretion or independent of this effect.

The glucocorticoid-CRF system may be a major control system modulating energy balance. Extensive studies on animal models has shown that adrenalectomy prevents all forms of animal obesity associated with a reduction in food intake, an increase in sympathetic activity (and thermogenesis) and a decrease in parasympathetically mediated insulin secretion [1,2]. CRF infused chronically into the third ventricle of genetically and hypothalamic obese rats has the same effects [12,19]. Blockade of type II glucocorticoid receptors with RU-486, which enhances CRF production, reverses both genetic [20] and dietary obesity [21]. Taken with our recent observations that the number of type II receptors is increased in the hypothalamus and hippocampus of obese rats [22], we have hypothesized that overactivity of glucocorticoids within the CNS may be a fundamental cause of obesity. However, the apparent hyperactivity of the CRF-pituitary-adrenal axis in

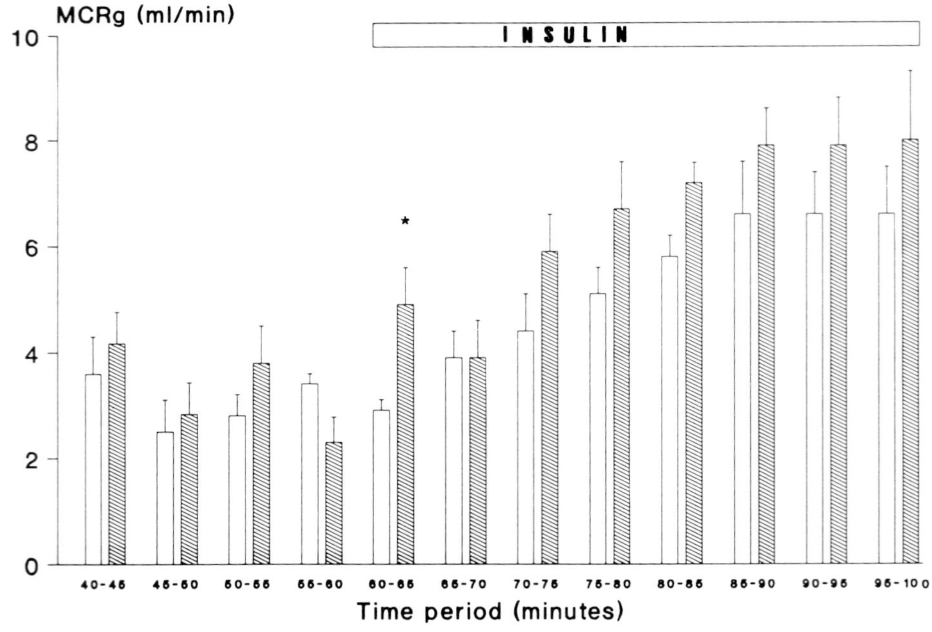

Fig. 1. Metabolic clearance rates of glucose prior to and during insulin infusion (0.5 U/h/kg) in obese fa/fa rats infused i.c.v. with either saline (open bars) or CRF (5 μg/day for 7 days) (hatched bars). The insulin response was significantly greater ($P < 0.05$) in CRF compared to saline group.

the obese fa/fa rat [23] has been difficult to integrate with suggestions that the hyperphagia and autonomis imbalances were secondary to a lack of CRF activity. The recent observation that an oxytocinergic pathway is involved in the anorectic, but not ACTH-response [11] allows us to hypothesize that a glucocorticoid inhibition of oxytocinergic pathways controlling food intake and possibly autonomic responses to CRF might underlie obesity.

References

1. Bray G and York D (1990) Prog. Neuroendocrinol. 11: 128–181.
2. Bray G, York D and Fisler J (1989) Vitam. Horm. 45: 1–124.
3. Britton D, Varela M, Garcia A and Rosenthal M (1986) Life Sci. 38: 211–216.
4. Arase K, York D, Shimizu M, Shargill N and Bray G (1988) Am. J. Physiol. 255: E255–E259.
5. Krahn D, Gosnell B, Grace M and Levine A (1986) Brain Res. Bull. 17: 285–289.
6. Uehera A, Sekiya C, Yakasugi Y, Namiki M and Arimura A (1989) Am. J. Physiol. 257: R613–R617.
7. Krahn D, Gosnell B, Levine A and Morley J (1988) Brain Res. 433: 63–69.
8. Shimizu H and Bray GA (1989) Neurosci. Lett. 103: 74–80.
9. Olson B, Drutarosky M, Stricker E and Verbalis J (1991) Am. J. Physiol. 260: R448–R452.
10. Arletti R, Bennelli A and Bertolini A (1989) Peptides 10: 89–93.
11. Bruhn T, Sutton S, Plotsky P and Vale W (1986) Endocrinology 119: 1558–1563.
12. Brown M, Fisler L and Speiss J (1982) Endocrinology 111: 928–931.
13. Holt S and York D (1989) Physiol. Behav. 500: 384–388.
14. Stubbs M and York D. (1991) Int. J. Obesity (in press).
15. Egawa M, Yoshimatsu H and Bray G (1990) Am. J. Physiol. 259: R799–R806.
16. Gosnell B, Morley J and Levine A (1983) Peptides 4: 807–812.
17. Britton D and Indyk E (1989) Brain Res. 478: 205–210.
18. Steele R (1980) Ann. N.Y. Acad. Sci. 82: 420–430.
19. Arase K, Shargill N and Bray G (1989) Am. J. Physiol. 256: R751–R756.
20. Langley S and York D (1990) Am. J. Physiol. 259: R539–R544.
21. Okada S, York D and Bray G (1990) Int. J. Obesity (Suppl. 2) 14: 91.
22. Langley S and York D (1990) Brain Res. 533: 268–274.
23. Bestetti G, Abramo F, Guillame-Gentil C, Rohmer-Jeanrenaud F, Jeanrenaud B and Rossi G (1990) Endocrinology 126: 1880–1887.

© 1991 Elsevier Science Publishers B.V. All rights reserved.
Biological Psychiatry, Volume 2. G. Racagni et al., editors.

Clinical overview of bulimia nervosa

David B. Herzog, Martin B. Keller, Philip W. Lavori and Christine Yeh

Bulimia nervosa has been the subject of intense scientific and clinical inquiry ever since its classification as a psychiatric disorder in 1980 with the publication of the DSM III. A recent review of epidemiologic studies reported the prevalence of bulimia nervosa in high school and college age females to be 1–2% [1]. However, the frequency of bulimic symptomatology may be as high as 5–15% [2].

Bulimia nervosa is commonly considered a multifactorial disorder requiring multimodal treatment. Risk factors are sociocultural, cognitive, behavioral, developmental, neurochemical, familial and genetic. Depression and trauma may also have etiologic roles. Based on studies using a structured diagnostic interview, 47–73% [3,4] of bulimics were found to have a lifetime history of major depressive disorder, 23% have substance use disorder [5] and 22–69% have a personality disorder [6,7].

Results from a survey distributed at the 1990 International Conference on Eating Disorders in New York support the notion that a variety of therapies are often necessary to treat bulimia nervosa [8]. Conference participants were questioned about which treatments they endorsed for their last outpatient with bulimia nervosa; they recommended psychotherapy (96%), pharmacotherapy (53%), nutritional counseling (71%) and regular medical management (86%). The orientation of the clinicians who endorsed psychotherapy was also determined. The majority (65%) used a combination of cognitive behavioral and psychodynamic approaches, 27% used a cognitive behavioral approach alone and 6% used a psychodynamic approach alone.

Published studies on the course and outcome of bulimia nervosa suggest that the disorder is often chronic with frequent relapses [9]. These studies were predominantly retrospective and cross-sectional. In an effort to control for some of these problems, we are currently conducting a prospective, naturalistic longitudinal study of anorexia nervosa and bulimia nervosa designed to collect comprehensive information about the course and outcome of these disorders.

We have recently analyzed data on 229 treatment-seeking women who met DSM III-R criteria for bulimia nervosa (n = 98), anorexia nervosa (n = 41) or mixed disorder (n = 90) i.e., bulimia nervosa and anorexia nervosa, during the episode prior to entering into our study. We compared the mixed disorder group and the bulimia nervosa group on measures of psychiatric comorbidity, course and outcome. In the mixed disorder group, subjects were older than the bulimics (mean = 24.8 ± 6.1 years) at intake. The mean duration of the intake eating disorder episode was 110 months (9 years) for mixed disorder subjects as compared to only 57.7

months (5 years) for the bulimics. In terms of psychiatric comorbidity, 82% of the mixed disorder subjects had a concurrent comorbid Axis I disorder while only 60% of the bulimics had concurrent Axis I disorder. Fifty-three percent of the mixed disorder subjects were diagnosed with major depressive disorder compared to 32% of the bulimics, and 39% of the mixed disorder group were diagnosed with an Axis II disorder as compared to 22% of the bulimics. Borderline personality disorder was the most common Axis II diagnosis in mixed disorder subjects.

The clinical course of the mixed disorder group appears to be quite distinct from that of bulimia nervosa. The retrospective course of the 90 mixed disorder subjects indicated that nearly as many of the subjects started their episode with bulimia nervosa (n = 29) as with anorexia nervosa (n = 39). In contrast, the course of the bulimic subjects prior to intake was quite stable. The prospective course for the mixed disorder group seems more severe, with a slower rate of recovery, than that of bulimia nervosa alone. When we define recovery as loss of full criteria sustained for eight weeks, at 13 weeks 46% of the bulimics had recovered in contrast to only 16% of the mixed group and at 26 weeks, 64% of the bulimics had recovered as compared to 28% of the mixed group.

Our data suggest that subjects with mixed disorders have more comorbid psychopathology and a more severe course than the subjects with pure bulimia nervosa. Future research should address the pathophysiology, nosology and treatment of this mixed disorder population.

References

1. Fairburn CG and Beglin SJ (1991) Am. J. Psychiatry 147: 401–408.
2. Schotte DE and Stunkard AJ (1987) J. Am. Med. Assoc. 258: 1213–1215.
3. Walsh BT, Roose SP, Glassman AH et al. (1985) Psychosom. Med. 47: 123–131.
4. Hudson JI, Pope HG, Yurgelun-Todd D et al. (1987) Am. J. Psychiatry 144: 1283–1287.
5. Mitchell JE, Hatsukami D, Eckert ED et al. (1985) Am. J. Psychiatry 142: 482–485.
6. Frankel JS, Sadik C, Dantzic S et al. (1988) The systematic study of personality disorders in bulimic patients. Presented at the Third International Conference on Eating Disorders (April 1988), New York.
7. Wonderlich SA, Swift WJ, Slotnick HB and Goodman S (1990) Int. J. Eating Disord. 9(6): 607–616.
8. Herzog DB, Keller MB, Strober M, Yeh C and Pai S (1991) The current status of treatment for anorexia nervosa and bulimia nervosa. Int. J. Eating Disord. (in press).
9. Keller MB, Herzog DB, Lavori PW, Bradburn IS and Mahoney EM (1991) The naturalistic history of bulimia nervosa: Extraordinarily high rates of chronicity, relapse, recurrence and psychosocial morbidity. Int. J. Eating Disord. (in press).

© 1991 Elsevier Science Publishers B.V. All rights reserved.
Biological Psychiatry, Volume 2. G. Racagni et al., editors.

Biochemical parameters of bulimia nervosa

Walter H. Kaye

Department of Psychiatry, University of Pittsburgh School of Medicine and Western Psychiatric Institute and Clinic, 3811 O'Hara Street, Pittsburgh, PA 15213, U.S.A.

Bulimia nervosa (BN) [1] is a disorder of unknown etiology which is characterized by pathological feeding behavior and often associated with dysphoric mood. It has been postulated that disturbances of one or more brain neurotransmitter systems [2,3] may contribute to the symptom complex. In fact, disturbances have been found in the following systems:

Serotonin (5-HT)

In animals and man, interventions which increase intrasynaptic 5-HT or directly activate 5-HT receptors tend to produce satiety [4–6] while interventions which diminish serotonergic neurotransmissions or 5-HT receptor activation reportedly increase food consumption and promote weight gain. In addition, medial hypothalamic 5-HT administration to rats has been reported to decrease the size and duration of meals and rate of eating [3]. Theoretically, hyposerotonergic function in BN patients could contribute to reduced satiety, increased meal size, meal duration, rate of eating and increased grams of carbohydrate ingested. Some but not all studies suggest that bulimics are hyposerotonergic. Brewerton et al. [7] found that BN patients given m-chlorophenylpiperazine (m-CPP), a 5-HT agonist, had a blunted prolactin response as compared to controls. However, only BN patients with major depression had a blunted prolactin response to tryptophan administration. Goldbloom et al. [8] found BN patients had an increase in platelet 5-HT uptake. BN patients as a group have normal concentrations of CSF 5-HIAA, the major 5-HT metabolite in the brain [9]. CSF 5-HIAA levels, however, are reduced in more symptomatic BN patients [10] and in weight-recovered bulimic anorexics after probenecid administration [11]. In addition, preliminary data supports the possibility that bingeing behavior may constitute an attempt to increase 5-HT-mediated neurotransmission [12].

Norepinephrine (NE)

NE, at near physiological doses, produces eating in satiated animals and potentiates eating in hungry animals [13] when administered into medial hypothalamus areas known to modulate feeding. Such effects are thought to act through α_2 noradrenergic receptors. Studies have consistently found [9,14–18] reduced plasma and CSF NE levels in normal weight bulimic patients. In addition, ill BN patients have been shown to have increased β-adrenoreceptor activity in two studies [15,16], but not in another [17]. BN patients have been shown to have increased α_2-adrenoreceptor activity in platelets [19] but not after clonidine administration [20]. Theoretically [13], bingeing behavior is consistent with increased activity of medial hypothalamic α_2 noradrenergic receptors. While such a hypothesis is consistent with most available data, no studies have directly proved this.

Opioids

Opioid agonists increase and opioid antagonists decrease food intake in animals and man [21]. Moreover, opioid administration seems to preferentially affect fat and protein consumption in animals and man [22,23]. Patients with BN have stereotypic patterns of food consumption, such as bingeing on sweet, high fat foods, that could reflect alterations in endogenous opioid activity [23]. In fact, there is evidence of opioid disturbances in ill BN. *CSF* β-endorphin levels were reduced in two studies (W. Kaye, unpublished data) [24], whereas CSF dynorphin levels were normal [24,25]. *Plasma* β-endorphins have been reported to be both increased [26] and decreased [27]. Initial studies found that brief trials of opioid antagonists decrease bingeing [28,29], but this was not confirmed by a recent study [30].

Peptide YY (PYY)

PYY and neuropeptide Y (NPY) are members of the same neuropeptide family. Administration of these peptides stimulates feeding in animals to a greater degree than that produced by *any* other neurochemical-specific manipulations examined to date [31,32]. Both peptides are selective for carbohydrate-rich foods. These two peptides have neuroanatomically separate systems and presumably have different roles. PYY is 3 times as potent as NPY in stimulating feeding. Morley et al. [30] found that PYY, injected ICV into rats, caused massive food ingestion to which tolerance did not develop and postulated that increased activity of PYY may contribute to bulimia. Two studies (M. Lesem, personal communication) [33] have found that CSF PW values were elevated in ill BN patients when compared to healthy female volunteers. In comparison, BN patients had normal CSF NPY levels [32].

Cholecystokinin (CCK)

Peripheral CCK activity has been implicated in satiety since exogenously administered CCK reduces food intake in animals and humans [34,35]. Geracioti and Liddle [36] found that ill BN patients, as compared to controls, had a reduced plasma CCK response to a liquid meal and reduced ratings of postprandial satiety. Thus impaired satiety in BN may be related to an impaired secretion of CCK in response to a meal.

Summary

Theoretically, bingeing behavior is consistent with reduced brain 5-HT or peripheral CCK activity, increased brain NE or PPY activity, altered opioid modulation, or some combination of these disturbances. Studies of neurotransmitters have only been performed in patients who were actively bingeing and purging or when abstinent from bingeing and purging for short periods of time (up to 4 weeks). Since a month of abstinence may not be a long enough period of time for neurobiological systems to fully recover, it is possible that neurotransmitter disturbances in ill bulimic patients are a consequence of extremes of dietary intake, such as are found in anorexia nervosa. Even if this is the case, bulimia nervosa patients may enter a vicious cycle where pathological feeding sustains and provokes pathological behavior. Persistent disturbances of neurotransmitter function after abstinence from bingeing and purging could contribute to their high rate of recidivism. Alternatively, we cannot rule out the possibility that bulimic patients have a trait-related disturbance of neurotransmitter activity that contributes to their appetitive disregulation.

References

1. DSM III-R (1987) Diagnostic and Statistical Manual of Mental Disorders. American Psychiatric Association, Washington, D.C.
2. Morley JE and Blundell JE (1988) Biol. Psychiatry 23: 53–78.
3. Leibowitz SF (1990) Drugs 39: 33–48.
4. Fernstrom JE and Wurtman RG (1971) Science 174: 1023–1025.
5. Wurtman JJ and Wurtman RJ (1979) Life Sci. 24: 895–903.
6. Blundell JE (1984) Neuropharmacology 23: 1537–1551.
7. Brewerton TD et al. (1991) In: EF Cocan and DL Murphy (eds.) Serotonin in Major Psychiatric Disorders. American Psychiatric Press, Washington D.C. (in press).
8. Goldbloom DS, Hicks L and Garfinkel PE (1990) Biol. Psychiatry 28: 644–647.
9. Kaye WH, Ballenger JC, Lydiard RB, Stuart GW, Laraia MT, O'Neil P, Fossey MD, Stevens V, Lesser S and Hsu LKG (1990) Am. J. Psychiatry 147: 225–229.
10. Jimerson DC, Lesem MD, Kaye WH and Brewerton TD (1988) Psychopharmacology 96: S124.
11. Kaye WH, Ebert MN, Gwirtsman HE and Weiss SR (1984) Am. J. Psychiatry 141: 512–516.
12. Kaye WH, Gwirtsman HE, George DT and Wurtman RG (1988) Psychiatr. Res. 23: 31–43.
13. Leibowitz SF (1988) Neurosci. Biobehav. Rev. 12: 101–109.
14. Pirke KM, Pahl J, Schweiger U and Warnhoff M (1985) Psychiatr. Res. 15: 33–39.
15. Buckholtz N, George DT, Davies AO, Jimerson DC and Potter WZ (1988) Arch. Gen. Psychiatry 45: 479–482.
16. George DT, Kaye WH, Goldstein DS, Brewerton TD and Jimerson DC (1990) Psychiatr. Res. 33: 1–10.
17. Lonati-Galligani M and Pirke EM (1986) Psychiatry Res. 19: 189–198.
18. Kaye WH, Gwirtsman HE, George DT, Jimerson DC, Ebert MN and Lake CR (1990) Biol. Psychiatry 27: 4–21.
19. Heufelder A, Warnoff M and Pirke KM (1985) J. Clin. Endocrinol. Metab. 61: 1053–1060.
20. Kaplan AS, Garfinkel PE, Warsh JJ and Brown GM (1989) Int. J. Eating Disord. 8: 425–435.
21. Morley JE, Levine AS, Plotka ED and Seal US (1983) Physiol. Behav. 30: 331.
22. Bhakthavatsalam P and Leibowitz SF (1986) Pharmacol. Biochem. Behav. 24: 911.

23. Drewnowski A et al. (1989) NR 396, New Research Abstracta from the American Psychiatric Association Annual Meeting, San Francisco, CA, May 1989.
24. Brewerton TD et al. (1990) Abstr. 205, 4th International Conference on Eating Disorders.
25. Lesem MD, Berrettinni WH, Kaye WH and Jimerson DC (1991) Biol. Psychiatry 29: 244–252.
26. Fullerton DT, Swift WJ, Getto CJ and Carlson IH (1986) Psychol. Med. 16: 59–63.
27. Waller DA, Kiser RS, Hardy BW, Fuchs I, Feigenbaum LP and Uauy R (1986) Am. J. Clin. Nutr. 44: 20.
28. Mitchell JE, Laine DE, Morley JE and Levine AS (1986) Biol. Psychiatry 21: 1399–1406.
29. Jonas JM and Gold MS (1987) Psychiatr. Res. 24: 195–199.
30. Mitchell JE et al. (1989) J. Clin. Psychopharmacol. 9: 291–293.
31. Morley JE, Levine AS, Grace M and Kneip J (1985) Brain Res. 341: 200–203.
32. Stanley BG, Kyrkouli SE, Lampert S and Liebowitz SF (1986) Peptides 7: 1189–1192.
33. Kaye WH, Berrettinni W, Gwirtsman H and George D (1990) Arch. Gen. Psychiatry 47: 548–556.
34. Smith GP and Gibbs J (1985) Ann. N.Y. Acad. Sci. 417: 23.
35. Kissileff HR, Pi-Sunyer FX, Thornton J and Smith GP (1981) Am. J. Clin. Nutr. 34: 154–160.
36. Geracioti TD and Liddle RA (1988) N. Engl. J. Med. 319: 683–688.

© 1991 Elsevier Science Publishers B.V. All rights reserved.
Biological Psychiatry, Volume 2. G. Racagni et al., editors.

The research on the treatment of bulimia nervosa

Christopher Fairburn
University Department of Psychiatry, Warneford Hospital, Oxford, OX3 7JX, U.K.

Introduction

Given that bulimia nervosa has only recently been described, it is remarkable how much has been learned about its treatment. More than 25 controlled trials have been completed and more are in progress [1]. The aim of this brief synthesis of the work to date is to review the research findings and consider their implications for clinical practice.

Pharmacological treatment studies

Most of the studies of pharmacological treatments have focussed on the effects of antidepressant drugs. Other drugs have been studied, including appetite suppressants, opiate antagonists, antiepileptic drugs and lithium. None seems promising and their use is not recommended. In contrast, it is clear that antidepressant drugs benefit most patients with bulimia nervosa, at least in the short-term. Three groups of findings have emerged. First, these drugs are superior to placebo at reducing many of the features of the disorder. There is a marked reduction in the frequency of overeating and self-induced vomiting and this is accompanied by an enhanced sense of control over eating. At the same time the degree of general psychiatric disturbance lessens substantially. However, the high level of dietary restraint seen in patients with bulimia nervosa appears not to be affected. The effect of these drugs on these patients' overvalued ideas concerning shape and weight has yet to be established. The second group of findings concern the rapidity of the antidepressant drug effect and the dose needed to achieve it. It seems that the time course resembles that seen in the treatment of depression. It has been suggested that the dose required is also similar, but systematic dose-response studies have yet to be conducted. In the case of fluoxetine, it has been reported that a 60-mg dose is more effective than the 20-mg dose conventionally used to treat depression [2]. The third finding is that no consistent predictors of response can be identified. The level of depressive symptoms prior to treatment does not seem to predict outcome.

Maintenance of change following treatment with antidepressant drugs has received remarkably little attention. This is a serious gap in our knowledge, since experience suggests that amongst clinical cases bulimia nervosa tends to run a chronic course. Unless the beneficial effects are sustained, this form of treatment is likely to be of little value. The findings of 2 recent studies suggest that maintenance is poor, whether or not the patient stays on the drug. The rapid return of symptoms may be in part due to the continuing high level of dietary restraint.

Psychological treatment studies

The main focus of the psychological treatment studies has been on the cognitive behavioural approach. This has been compared with being on a waiting list, antidepressant drug treatment, supportive psychotherapy, focal psychotherapy, a purely behavioural version of the treatment and exposure with response prevention. With one exception, it has been shown to be superior in its effects. It is as least as effective as antidepressant drug treatment at reducing the frequency of overeating and vomiting and it appears to have a much greater effect on the level of dietary restraint. Perhaps because of this, maintenance of change seems good.

With the possible exception of interpersonal psychotherapy [3], too little research attention has been paid to other treatment approaches to evaluate their effectiveness relative to cognitive behaviour therapy or antidepressant drugs.

Implications for clinical practice

The research on treatment indicates that the overall approach of choice is the cognitive behavioural one. If clinicians are to use one single form of treatment, this is the one to adopt. However, the cognitive behavioural approach is neither necessary nor sufficient for all patients with bulimia nervosa. For some patients it probably constitutes overtreatment. For these patients simpler and briefer interventions are likely to be as effective. For others, cognitive behaviour therapy is not sufficient. There is therefore a need to develop and evaluate treatments for those who do not respond.

No single treatment is going to be the answer to bulimia nervosa. Clinicians should aim to provide patients with a variety of treatment options according to their needs. These should range from simple education and advice, probably administered in a group format, through to inpatient treatment. At present too little is known about the factors that predict response to particular forms of treatment to allow the matching of patients with treatments. For this reason a "stepped care" approach seems sensible in which treatments are provided sequentially according to need. Patients receive a simple intervention initially and only move on to more complex ones if they fail to respond. Comprehensive treatment programmes of this type have yet to be evaluated.

Acknowledgements

I am grateful to the Wellcome Trust for their support and to Eli Lilly for inviting me to contribute to the Congress. This paper was prepared whilst I was a Fellow at the Center for Advanced Study in the Behavioral Sciences at Stanford. Support for this Fellowship was provided by the Foundation Fund for Research in Psychiatry and the MacArthur Foundation.

References

1. Fairburn CG, Agras WS and Wilson GT (1992) In: Anderson GH and Kennedy SH (eds.) The Biology of Feast and Famine: Relevance to Eating Disorders. Academic Press, New York.
2. Enas GG, Pope HG and Levine LR (1989) Paper presented at 142nd Annual Meeting of the American Psychiatric Association, San Francisco, California.
3. Fairburn CG, Jones R, Peveler RC, Carr SJ, Solomon RA, O'Connor ME, Burton J and Hope RA (1991) Arch. Gen. Psychiatry (in press).

© 1991 Elsevier Science Publishers B.V. All rights reserved.
Biological Psychiatry, Volume 2. G. Racagni et al., editors.

Inpatient treatment of bulimia nervosa

Sidney H. Kennedy, Randy Katz and Paul E. Garfinkel
Department of Psychiatry, University of Toronto, Toronto, Ontario, Canada

Introduction

The vast majority of studies evaluating treatment for bulimia nervosa (BN) have involved outpatients. These include the various psychotherapies [1] and in all but one instance [2] pharmacotherapies [3]. As described in antecedent chapters, most BN patients in the Toronto Programme for Eating Disorders receive either outpatient or intensive day hospital treatment. Of those patients requiring inpatient treatment, less than 20% have BN, while the remainder suffer from anorexia nervosa (AN) alone or AN in association with bingeing and purging activity (AN+BN).

Comparison between inpatients and outpatients

In an earlier publication [4], inpatients from the three diagnostic subgroups were compared to outpatients who were evaluated at the same centre. The two groups demonstrated equivalent eating disorder psychopathology based on the Eating Attitude Test [5] and the Eating Disorder Inventory [6], although BN subjects had a higher premorbid weight and a longer duration of illness than their outpatient counterparts. The BN inpatients also suffered more from concurrent medical disorders.

Current treatment approaches

Since 1987, those BN patients who require admission to hospital have been given a time-limited programme (between 6–8 weeks). The aims of admission are to break the binge-purge cycle and to re-establish a regular eating pattern, since BN patients not only consume large quantities of food during binges, but also eat less than controls during non-binge meals [7]. Maximum emphasis is placed on exposure to situations most likely to precipitate binge eating and on linking hospital treatment to suitable outpatient follow-up. Patients with AN+BN also require a structured approach to refeeding and weight gain during a longer period of hospitalization.

Eating attitudes and perceptions

Measures of eating attitudes and perceptions, including the urge to binge, sense of fatness and anxiety associated with eating, were all evaluated before and after meals for each patient.

During the first 6 weeks of treatment, AN patients displayed a reduction in the "urge to binge" after meals, associated with a significant increase in the perception of fatness; while AN + BN patients reported no change in their "urge to binge" before and after meals but decreased their "urge to vomit" before meals.

Exposure to binge foods

The BN patients have, in addition, been treated with "Exposure to binge foods with prevention of binge eating" [8]. During sessions each patient was individually presented with specific binge food and instructed to sample but not complete the serving. As shown in Fig. 1, there was a significant reduction in "meal anxiety" at the end of the exposure between the first and last trial and a decrease in the "urge to binge" at the end of the last trial compared to the end of the first trial. So far, the effects of this adjunctive treatment on outcome have not been evaluated.

In certain instances concomitant pharmacotherapy may also be indicated, particularly during the transition from impatient to outpatient treatment.

Conclusions

Although hospital-based treatment for BN is required for only a minority of people, such treatment is an important and under-evaluated component of any comprehensive program for the treatment of eating disorders.

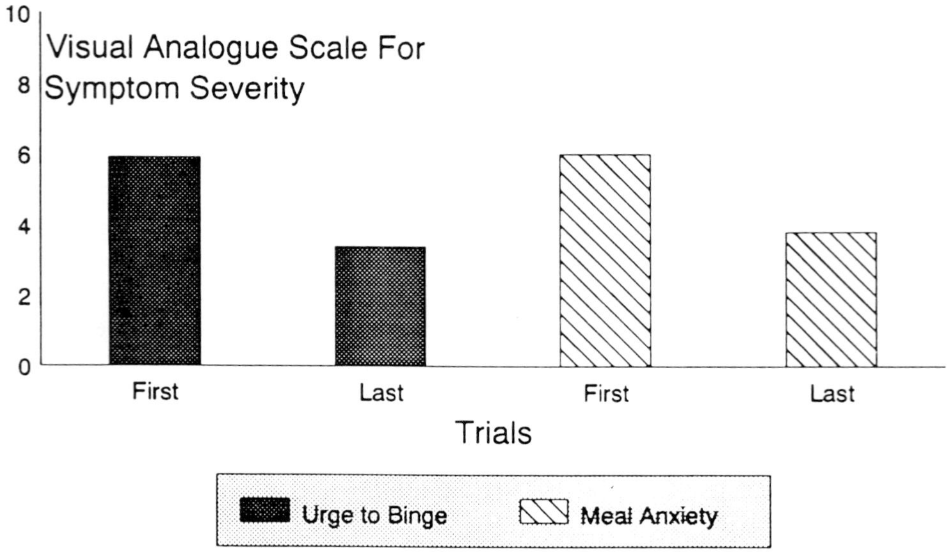

Fig. 1. Differences at the end of exposure between first and last trials ($P < 0.05$ for both comparisons).

References

1. Agras WS, Schneider JA, Arrow B et al. (1989) J. Consul. Clin. Psychol. 57: 215–221.
2. Fichter MM, Leibl K, Rief W et al. (1991) Pharmacopsychiatry (in press).
3. Kennedy SH and Goldbloom DS (1991) Drugs 41: 367–377.
4. Kennedy SH and Garfinkel PE (1989) Int. J. Eating Disord. 8: 181–190.
5. Garner DM, Olmsted MP, Bohry and Garfinkel PE (1) Psychol. Med. 12: 871–878.
6. Garner DM, Olmsted MP and Polivy J (1983) Int. J. Eating Disord. 2: 15–34.
7. Walsh BT, Hadigan CM, Kissileff HR et al. (1991) In: Anderson GH and Kennedy SH (eds.) Biology of Feast and Famine. New York Academic Press (in press).
8. Schmidt U and Marks IM (1989) J. Nerv. Ment. Dis. 177: 259–266.

© 1991 Elsevier Science Publishers B.V. All rights reserved.
Biological Psychiatry, Volume 2. G. Racagni et al., editors.

Day hospital treatment of anorexia and bulimia nervosa

A.S. Kaplan, M.P. Olmsted, S. Maddocks and B. Woodside
Toronto General Hospital, 101 College St., CW 1-311, Toronto, Ontario, M5G 2C4, Canada

Rationale

The outpatient treatment of emaciated patients with anorexia nervosa is a difficult process for both professionals and patients. These patients are often unable to utilize psychological therapies because of the detrimental effects of starvation and emaciation on cognition and mood. Without external controls, nutritional rehabilitation rarely occurs in such patients. Similarly, in a group of seriously ill patients with bulimia nervosa, outpatient, individual and group psychotherapies as well as pharmacotherapies, have been utilized with only limited success. Both these groups of patients have traditionally been treated in a behaviourally-oriented inhospital unit. Such an approach has often been successful in producing weight gain or control over eating behaviours in the short-term, but is associated with a disturbingly high rate of relapse and post-discharge recidivism over time. This process whilst in hospital care is often difficult for both patients and staff, with regression, psychological fragmentation and acting out behaviours not uncommon accompaniments of inpatient treatment. Such treatment also requires a high staff-patient ratio of specially trained highly vigilant professionals. This often results in expensive and inefficient utilization of resources.

Description of the program at Toronto General Hospital

These above considerations have led to the need to provide intensive treatments in a controlled setting for this group of seriously ill eating disorder patients. The intensive Day Hospital Group Treatment Program (DHP) at Toronto General Hospital incorporates a balance between the controlling structured environment of an inpatient setting and the flexibility of outpatient treatment. It provides a structured program that delivers nutritional and psychological treatments through the cumulative effects of group therapy. The goals of the program are weight gain and the normalization of disturbed eating behaviours along with the identification of underlying disturbed psychological and familial processes. The multidisciplinary staff include a psychiatrist-director, psychologist, psychometrist, two nurses, occupational therapist, nutritionist and social worker. The treatment program incorporates biological, psychological and sociocultural interventions, 8 h per day, 5 days per week for a maximum of 12 patients over a 2 to 4-month period.

The primary indication for admission to the Day Hospital Program is the presence of a severe eating disorder that has failed to respond to outpatient treatment. Patients who are at imminent risk for suicide or who are acutely medically ill, or have comorbid severe substance abuse and dependence are inappropriate for such a treatment program.

Advantages of the program

Clinical

The group format of the intensive treatment program provides specific advantages. Group treatment increases the power of therapeutic intervention through group confrontation and pressure while also providing mutual support in the process. Regression and dependency are to some extent controlled by the presence of group interaction which diffuses the intensity of the psychotherapeutic experience. The mutual sharing of what has previously been felt to be humiliating and degrading behaviours provides a sense of universality and helps to counteract the isolating effects of the disturbed eating behaviours. The group treatment helps to diffuse the power struggle that so often develops in an individual context around weight gain and eating.

The outpatient nature of the program limits regression and dependency as patients have to maintain themselves in a functioning state outside of hospital during the intensive treatment. As part of this process autonomy is promoted and the generalization of newly acquired tools to regulate eating behaviour is facilitated through the difficult yet crucial process of internalization of external controls. Because patients are not totally externally controlled they are less likely to feel compelled to oppose treatment, are more likely to feel an active partner in it and are more likely to experience it empathically rather than punitively.

Financial

There are clear financial advantages to providing intensive treatment in a day hospital group format. The outpatient component of the treatment alleviates the need for any hospital beds and is thus cost-effective in that resources are specifically directed at providing treatment rather than housing patients. The group format allows greater flexibility of patient numbers and greater availability of treatment resources.

Disadvantages of the program

Patient difficulties

For some patients who require complete physical containment, either because of psychological or medical instability, the DHP does not provide enough of a sense of containment as might be found in an inpatient unit. Such patients are best treated in an inpatient setting.

Staff difficulties

For staff, the outpatient nature of the program requires continual monitoring of mental status, as patients can become emotionally unstable with increasing weight and changes in eating behaviour. The intense and continuous patient contact required to provide an empathically controlling environment can lead to staff feeling at times like they are attempting to fill a bottomless pit and this can contribute to a sense of therapeutic nihilism and eventually burnout.

Response to treatment

Two hundred and forty-six female first admissions (AN = 29, ANBN = 43, BN = 154, NOS = 20) who completed at least 4 weeks of treatment were assessed at pre- and post-treatment on variables related to eating behaviour, attitudes towards weight and shape, mood, and family functioning. The mean age for all three groups was 25 years, with duration of illness for AN, ANBN and BN patients being 8.7, 11.4 and 11.7 years respectively. As expected, bulimics were heavier at admission and at maximum and minimum ever weight. They were also younger at age of onset of illness. Weeks spent in the program were similar for all diagnostic groups (AN = 10.0, ANBN = 11.3 BN = 10.3).

There were significant reductions in binge eating ($P < 0.0001$), vomiting ($P < 0.0001$) for bulimics and significant weight gain for AN patients (77% MPMW to 87% MPMW; $P < 0.0001$). Over 50% of the BN group were free of all bingeing and purging for the last 4 weeks of treatment. Patients were significantly less depressed (BDI, 24 to 13, $P < 0.001$) and had less disturbed eating attitudes and beliefs, as measured by the EAT and EDI, at discharge. Assessment of family functioning using the Family Assessment Measure demonstrated improved ratings by patients ($P < 0.01$, General and Self-Rating scales) from pre- to post-treatment.

This data suggests that seriously ill patients with AN and BN can be effectively treated in an intensive group therapy outpatient setting. Outcome at 2 and 5-year follow-up will determine whether this treatment has long-lasting effects.

© 1991 Elsevier Science Publishers B.V. All rights reserved.
Biological Psychiatry, Volume 2. G. Racagni et al., editors.

Drug therapies in bulimia nervosa

David S. Goldbloom

Department of Psychiatry, Toronto Hospital and University of Toronto, Eaton 8N-219, 200 Elizabeth St., Toronto, Ontario, M5G 2C4, Canada

The first decade of research on bulimia nervosa (BN) has included not only elucidation of the clinical, psychological and biological aspects of this disorder but also application of a range of therapeutic approaches. The first generation of drug therapy studies in bulimia nervosa has passed and its results are reviewed here, along with its implications for future research.

The rationale for the use of antidepressant drugs in bulimia nervosa stems from two sources: the complex relationship between bulimia nervosa and mood disorders [1] and the role of monoamines in the hypothalamic regulation of appetitive behaviour [2].

Since 1983, more than a dozen double-blind, placebo-controlled trials of antidepressants in BN have been described. These include: heterocyclic agents such as amitriptyline, imipramine, desipramine and mianserin; monoamine oxidase inhibitors such as phenelzine, isocarboxazid and brofaromine; and second-generation antidepressants such as nomifensine, bupropion, trazodone and fluoxetine. All but two of these studies have demonstrated a short-term antibulimic effect of these drugs compared to placebo with regard to the behavioural variables of binge-eating and purging. It is evident that this effect is not contingent on the presence of depression, although the mechanism of action of antidepressants in this disorder is unknown; a unitary model of action is weakened by the fact that these drugs act on multiple neurotransmitter systems.

Methodological limitations of the first generation of studies include: small and inadequately described samples, lack of control for concurrent treatments, brief duration of treatment and absence of follow-up data, lack of comparison with other established forms of treatment, and limited assessment of non-behavioural variables such as disturbed attitudes to weight and shape that are central to the disorder. To date, only one published study has compared a drug directly with a psychological intervention [3]. The antibulimic efficacy of fluoxetine has been studied in the greatest number of subjects [4–7] thus far. Its results are comparable to other antidepressants and its success in producing remission at the end of acute treatment is comparable to results in cognitive behavioural psychotherapy [8]. Further, it is associated with clinically significant change in disturbed attitudes toward weight and shape [9], a variable ignored not only in many drug studies but also in a number of psychotherapy studies of bulimia nervosa.

The second generation of drug therapy research in bulimia nervosa will both address the methodological shortcomings of previous studies and provide a model for optimal sequencing and integration of disparate treatments for this multi-determined and challenging disorder.

References

1. Keck PE, Pope HG, Hudson JI, McElroy SL, Yurgelun-Todd D and Hundert EM (1990) Compr. Psychiatry 31: 275–283.
2. Leibowitz SF and Shor-Posner G (1986) In: Carruba MO and Blundell JE (eds.) Pharmacology of Eating Disorders: Theoretical and Clinical Developments. Raven Press, New York, pp. 29–49.
3. Mitchell JE, Pyle RL, Eckert ED, Hatsukami D, Pomeroy C and Zimmerman R (1990) Arch. Gen. Psychiatry 47: 149–157.
4. Fluoxetine Bulimia Nervosa Collaborative Study Group (1991) Arch. Gen. Psychiatry (in press).
5. Freeman CPL, Davies F, Morris J, Cheshire K and Hampson N (1991) Br. J. Psychiatry (in press).
6. Foss I and Trygstad O (1990) Abstract No. 240, Fourth International Conference on Eating Disorders, New York City, U.S.A.
7. Fichter MM, Leibl K, Rief W, Brunner E, Schmidt-Auberger S and Engel RR (1991) Pharmacopsychiatry (in press).
8. Garner DM, Fairburn CG and Davis R (1987) Behav. Modif. 11: 398–431.
9. Goldbloom D and Olmsted M (1991) New Research Abstract 144th Annual Meeting, American Psychiatric Association, New Orleans, U.S.A.

© 1991 Elsevier Science Publishers B.V. All rights reserved.
Biological Psychiatry, Volume 2. G. Racagni et al., editors.

FSH and LH responses to GnRH in anorexia nervosa patients at a ten-year follow-up

Katherine A. Halmi, Peter Stokes, Elke Eckert and Suzanne Sunday
Eating Disorders Unit, Cornell Medical Center-Westchester, 21 Bloomingdale Rd., White Plains, NY 10605, U.S.A.

Introduction

Amenorrhea is an essential feature of anorexia nervosa (AN). Measurements of the circadian pattern of pituitary gonadotropin secretion in adult women with AN have shown a regression to pre- and mid-puberty patterns. Weight restoration did not produce normal adult patterns of luteinizing hormone (LH) secretion in all patients and degree of immaturity of LH secretion did not correlate with duration of illness or degree of weight loss [1]. A diminished or absent response of LH to gonadotropin-releasing hormone (GnRH) has been a fairly consistent finding in AN patients [2–4]. In order to study the robustness of the hypothalamic-pituitary-ovarian axis after an insult of AN and over time, we measured the follicular stimulating hormone (FSH) and LH responses to GnRH in 35 women 10 years after they had participated in a collaborative treatment study for AN.

Materials and Methods

Procedure

All participants were admitted to the Clinical Research Units of the Cornell Medical Center or the University of Minnesota where they received a battery of psychological and behavioral assessments in addition to an endocrinological investigation over the course of 1 week. For this study following an overnight fast, patients were injected at 8 a.m. with 500 g GnRH and FSH and LH were measured at baseline, 15, 30, 60, 90, 120, 180, 240 and 360 min. FSH and LH were determined by radioimmunoassay.*

Patients

At the time of the 10-year follow-up endocrine testing, the patients were divided among 4 DSM III-R diagnostic eating disorder groups. Those groups with ages

*Sucrosep kits for LH and FSH produced by Celltech Diagnostic Ltd.

and % ideal body weights (%IBW) given as means ± S.D. are as follows:
- Eating disorder N.O.S. (n = 17), age 29.53 ± 6.16, %IBW 96.3 ± 15.6;
- Bulimia nervosa (n = 11), age 27.82 ± 4.02, %IBW 92.2 ± 9.9;
- Anorexia nervosa (n = 5), age 34 ± 6.4, %IBW 64.9 ± 5.9;
- *No* eating disorder diagnoses (n = 2), age 26.5 ± 4.9, %IBW 108.2 ± 7.3.

ANOVAS and Pearson correlates were used for statistical analyses.

Results

Table 1 shows FSH and LH responses to GnRH in patients categorized by menstrual stage.

Six patients were on birth control pills. Their FSH and LH responses to GnRH (means ± S.D.) were as follows: FSH baseline 8.33 ± 5.69, LH baseline 24.2 ± 39.55; area FSH 9,535.75 ± 7,711.26, area LH 10,937.13 ± 9,092.83, area FSH/area LH 1.8 ± 1.82; FSH peak/baseline 3.95 ± 2.53, LH peak/baseline 4.6 ± 2.24. Two patients had extremely sparse menstrual flow. Their responses were: FSH baseline 5.95 ± 1.06, LH baseline 4.15 ± 1.49; area FSH 6,788 ± 191.45, area LH 18,128.25 ± 16,824.14, area FSH/area LH 0.649 ± 0.592; FSH peak/baseline 5.3 ± 2.26, LH peak/baseline 17.25 ± 7.99. These eight patients were excluded from the analyses.

There were no significant differences in persons with normal menstrual cycling in the follicular phase (n = 5) and those in the luteal phase (n = 9) for FSH area and peak, and LH baseline, area and peak. However, cyclers in the follicular phase had higher *baseline* levels of FSH than cyclers in the luteal phase ($F(1,12) = 7.48$, $P = 0.018$). Persons with normal cycles showed significant correlations between cycle

Table 1. FSH and LH responses to GnRH[a]

	Amenorrheic (n = 9)	Follicular (n = 5)	Luteal (n = 9)
FSH baseline (IU/ml)	9.30 (± 5.37)	12.94 (± 3.15)	7.80 (± 3.48)
LH baseline (IU/ml)	6.40 (± 7.06)	14.16 (± 14.24)	7.94 (± 2.15)
Area FSH	7,496.48 (± 4,665.05)	10,370.10 (± 8,035.56)	5,189.50 (± 4,482.77)
Area LH	14,810.00 (± 19,184.62)	14,430.15 (± 10,492.06)	11,951.08 (± 6,033.58)
Area FSH/area LH	1.37 (± 1.58)	0.94 (± 0.62)	0.64 (± 0.86)
FSH peak/baseline	3.54 (± 2.26)	2.64 (± 1.64)	2.09 (± 0.91)
LH peak/baseline	54.27 (± 130.29)	7.80 (± 6.99)	13.82 (± 12.68)

[a]Mean ± S.D.

day and FSH baseline (r = –0.72, P = 0.004), FSH peak (r = –0.53, P =0.05) and FSH area under the curve (r = –0.53, P = 0.05). Analogous correlations between cycle day and LH were all non-significant.

There were no significant differences between amenorrheics and self-reported normal cyclers on any measures listed in Table 1.

There were no significant differences between the ED diagnostic groups on LH and FSH measures, nor were there significant relationships on these measures to %IBW.

The Diagnostic Interview Schedule was used to determine DSM III Affective Disorder Diagnoses in these patients. Twenty-eight of the 35 patients had a lifetime and 15 had a current diagnosis of Affective Disorder. There were no significant differences among persons with and without current or lifetime Affective Disorder on FSH and LH responses in GnRH.

The hypothalamic-pituitary-ovarian axis remained surprisingly resilient 10 years after treatment for anorexia nervosa even in those patients who currently had eating disorder symptomatology.

Acknowledgements

This study was supported by NIMH Grants MH-38054 and MH-26409 and CRC Grant RR-00047.

References

1. Katz JL, Boyar R and Roffwarg H (1978) Psychosom. Med. 49: 549–561.
2. Sherman BM, Halmi KA and Zamudo R (1975) J. Clin. Endocrinol. Metab. 41: 135–141.
3. Marshall JC and Kelch RP (1979) J. Clin. Endocrinol. Metab. 49: 712–719.
4. Warren MP, Jewelewicz R and Dyrenfuth I (1975) J. Clin. Endocrinol. Metab. 40: 601–608.

© 1991 Elsevier Science Publishers B.V. All rights reserved.
Biological Psychiatry, Volume 2. G. Racagni et al., editors.

State and trait related abnormalities in anorexia nervosa

Walter H. Kaye

Department of Psychiatry, University of Pittsburgh School of Medicine and Western Psychiatric Institute and Clinic, 3811 O'Hara Street. Pittsburgh, PA 15213, U.S.A.

Anorexia nervosa [1] is a disorder characterized by pathological feeding behavior, distortions of body image, dysphoric mood, and various forms of hypothalamic-pituitary dysfunction. While the etiology of anorexia nervosa is unknown, it has been postulated [2] that intrinsic biological alterations, dieting, psychosocial influences and stress are among the factors contributing to the onset of this illness. Whatever the cause, once weight loss and malnutrition occur, anorexic patients appear to enter a downward spiraling circle with malnutrition sustaining and perpetuating the desire for more weight loss and dieting. Disturbances of brain neurotransmitter systems could contribute to both a trait to develop anorexia nervosa as well as to be altered by malnutrition. Such cause and effect relationship can be teased apart by studying anorexics at various stages in their illness; while underweight and at intervals after weight restoration.

State-related neurotransmitter alterations

Underweight anorexics have been found to have elevations of cerebrospinal fluid (CSF) concentrations of coricotropin-releasing-hormone (CRH) [3,4] neuropeptide Y (NPY), [5] and vasopressin (AVP) [6] and reductions of beta-endorphin [7,8] and oxytocin [9] (Fig. 1). The correction of these neuropeptide disturbances by weight-restoration implies that such disturbances are secondary to malnutrition and/or weight loss and not the cause. However, it is important to note that some neuropeptide alterations persist in anorexics after short-term recovery (at goal weight for 2 months or less), suggesting these disturbances are strongly entrenched and are not easily corrected by improved nutrition. Most neuropeptide disturbances normalize after long-term weight recovery (goal weight for more than 1 year).

Alterations of neuropeptide activity (Table 1) are likely to contribute to several characteristic psychophysiological disturbances in acutely ill anorexics. For example, starvation-induced alterations of CRH contribute to hypercortisolemia [10]. Alterations of CRH, NPY, and opioids may contribute to hypothalamic amenorrhea [11,12] and decreased sexual activity [13]. Elevated CRH and reduced beta-endorphin may contribute to dysphoric symptoms [7,10]. Importantly, alterations of β-endophin [14], CRH [15], and NPY [16] could contribute to the dissociation anorexics often display between reduced caloric intake and obsessive thoughts about food. Demitrack et al. [9] hypothesized that elevated brain oxytocin

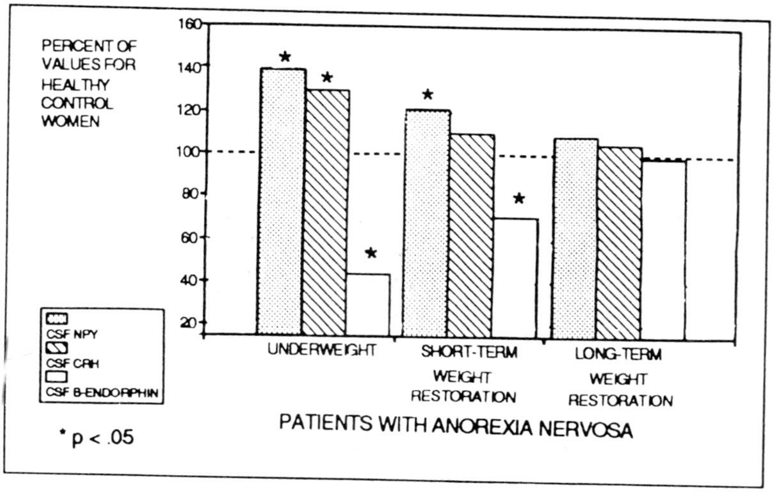

Fig. 1. CSF concentrations of NPY, CRH and β-endorphin in patients with anorexia nervosa at 3 stages of treatment expressed as a percent of the values found in matched healthy volunteer. *($P < 0.05$).

acting in concert with reduced brain vasopressin could impair the extinction of aversely-conditioned learning in underweight anorexics; in other words, exacerbate the tendency for restricting anorexics to have persevering preoccupation with the adverse consequences of food intake.

Serotonin – a possible trait-related neurotransmitter disturbance

Our group has found [17] that long-term weight-restored anorexics have elevated CSF 5-HIAA levels, the major metabolite of brain serotonin. These data are of

Table 1. Hypothetical relation between symptoms in underweight anorexics and neurotransmitter disturbances

	Underweight anorexics	↑ NPY	↑ CRH	↓ β-Endorphin	↑ AVP	↓ Oxytocin
Feeding	↓	↑	↓	↓		
Motor activity	↑		↑			
Blood pressure	↓	↓				
Sexual interest	↓	↓	↓			
Gonadal axis	↓	↓	↓	↑		
Cortisol secretion	↑	↑	↑	↑	↑	↑
Depression	↑		↑	↑		
Cognitive distortions	↑				↑	↑

↑ Indicates increased; ↓ indicates decreased.

interest because most anorexics have ingrained traits of psychopathology that are consistent with a possible intrinsic disturbance of serotoninergic activity. Considerable evidence shows that brain serotoninergic pathways are inhibitory of appetite [18,19]. Thus an alteration in serotonin activity could be a trait which contributes to pathological feeding behavior and weight loss. It is well recognized that anorexia nervosa patients are rigid, ritualistic, perfectionistic and preoccupied with details and that such behaviors persist after weight restoration [20,21]. Considerable studies have found that low levels of CSF 5-HIAA are associated with impulsive, suicidal and aggressive behavior [22–25]. Thus higher levels of CSF 6-HIAA in long-term weight-restored anorexics are of interest, since these patients tend to be the opposite of impulsive and aggressive patients. Importantly, patients with anorexia nervosa have a high prevalence of obsessive-compulsive symptoms or disorders [20,26,27]. Several lines of evidence support the possibility of an abnormality of serotonin activity in obsessive-compulsive disorder (OCD) [28–31]. In fact, medications with serotonin properties have been shown to have some efficacy in anorexia nervosa [32–35]. Finally, it has been noted [36] that adult women with OCD have an increased incidence of prior anorexia nervosa. We hypothesize that increased serotonin activity is associated with certain characteristics, such as rigid, anxious, inhibited, or obsessional behaviors, that cut across the boundaries of diagnostic categories.

Conclusions

Anorexia nervosa is a disorder of considerable morbidity and mortality, with a high rate of relapse and with no known treatment. Our ability to treat this illness has been limited, to a great extent, by a lack of understanding of its psychobiology. It is possible that the core characteristics of anorexia nervosa, such as obsessionality and pathological feeding, are related to increased serotonin activity. Once weight loss and malnutrition begin, anorexics may enter a vicious cycle in which the consequences of malnutrition perpetuate pathological behavior. Thus, starvation-induced alterations of CRH, β-endorphin, NPY, vasopressin and oxytocin activity may contribute to neuroendocrine disturbances and may play a role in subsequent and more extreme behavioral and appetitive abnormalities.

References

1. DSM III-R (1987) Diagnostic and Statistical Manual of Mental Disorders. American Psychiatric Association, Washington, DC.
2. Ploog D and Pirke KM (1984). The Psychobiology of Anorexia Nervosa. Springer-Verlag, Berlin, pp. 35–45.
3. Hotta M, Shibasaki T, Masuda A, Imaki T, Demura H, Ling N and Shizume K (1986) J. Clin. Endocrinol. Metab. 62: 319–324.

4. Kaye WH, Gwirtsman HE, George DT, Ebert MH, Jimerson DC, Tomai TP, Chrousos GP and Gold PW, (1987) J. Clin. Endocrinol. Metab. 64: 203–208.
5. Kaye WH, Berrettini W, Gwirtsman H and George D (1990) Arch. Gen. Psychiatry 47: 548–556.
6. Gold PW, Kaye W, Robertson GL and Ebert M (1983) N. Engl. J. Med. 308: 1117–1123.
7. Kaye WH, Berrettini WH, Gwirtsman HE, Chretien M, Gold PW, George DT, Jimerson DC and Ebert MH (1987) Life Sci. 41: 2147–2155.
8. Brewerton TD (1990) Abstr. 205, 4th Int. Conf. Eating Disorders, New York, April.
9. Demitrack MA, Lesem MD, Listwak SJ, Brandt HA, Jimerson DC and Gold PW (1990) Am. J. Psychiatry 147: 882–886.
10. Gold PW, Gwirtsman H, Avgerinos PC, Nieman LK, Gallucci WT, Kaye WH, Jimerson D, Ebert M, Rittmaster R, Loriaux DL and Chrousos GP (1986) N. Engl. J. Med., 314: 1335.
11. Kalra SP, Allen LG, Clark JT, Crowley WR and Kalra PS (1986) In: Moody TW (ed.) Neural and Endocrine Peptides and Receptors. Plenum Press, New York, pp. 353–366.
12. Rivier C and Vale W (1984) Endocrinology 114: 914–921.
13. Sirinathsinghji DJ, Rees LH, Rivier J and Vale W (1983) Nature 305: 232–235.
14. Leibowitz SF and Hor L (1982) Peptides 3: 421–428.
15. Britton DR, Koob GR, Rivier J and Vale W (1982) Life Sci. 31: 363–367.
16. Stanley BC and Leibowitz SF (1984) Life Sci. 35: 2635–2642.
17. Kaye WH, Gwirtsman HE, George DT and Ebert MH (1991) Arch. Gen. Psychiatry (in press).
18. Blundell JE (1984) Neuropharmacology 23: 1537–1551.
19. Leibowitz SF and Shor-Posner G (1986) Appetite 7: 1–14.
20. Strober M (1980) J. Psychosom. Res. 24: 353–359.
21. Casper RC (1990) Psychosom. Med. 52: 156–170.
22. Asbert M, Traskman L and Thoren P (1976) Arch. Gen. Psychiatry 33: 1193–1197.
23. van Praag HM (1983) Lancet ii: 977–978.
24. Brown GL, Goodwin FK, Ballenger JC, Goyer PF and Major LF (1979) Psychiatr. Res. 1: 131–139.
25. Linnoila M, Virkkunen M, Scheinin M, Nuutila A, Rimon R and Goodwin FK (1983) Life Sci. 33: 2609–2614.
26. Hudson JI, Pope HG, Jonas JM and Yurgelun-Todd D (1983) Psychiatr. Res. 9: 345–354.
27. Rothenberg A (1988) Comp. Psychol. 29: 427–432.
28. Thoren P, Asberg M, Cronholm B, Jornestedt L and Traskman L (1980) Arch. Gen. Psychiatry 37: 1281–1285.
29. Perse TL, Greist JH, Jefferson JW, Rosenfeld R and Dar R (1987) Am. J. Psychiatry 144: 1543–1548.
30. Goodman WK, Price LH, Rasmussen SA, Delgado PL, Heninger GR and Charney DS (1989) Arch. Gen. Psychiatry 46: 36–44.
31. Zohar J, Insel TR, Zohar-Kadouch RC, Hill JL and Murphy DL (1988) Arch. Gen. Psychiatry 45: 167–172.
32. Crisp AN, Lacey JH and Crutchfield M (1987) Br. J. Psychiatry 150: 355–358.
33. Halmi KA, Eckert ED, LaDu TJ et al. (1986) Arch. Gen. Psychiatry 43: 177–181.
34. Weltzin TE, Kaye WH, Hsu LKG and Sobkiewicz T (1990) American Psychiatric Association, New Research Program and Abstracts, 237.
35. Gwirtsman HE, Guze BH, Yager J and Gainsley B (1990) J. Clin. Psychiatry 51: 378–382.
36. Kasvikis YG, Tsakiris F, Marks IM, Basoglu M and Noshirvani HF (1986) Int. J. Eating Disord. 5: 1069–1075.

© 1991 Elsevier Science Publishers B.V. All rights reserved.
Biological Psychiatry, Volume 2. G. Racagni et al., editors.

Immunoendocrine regulation in eating disorders

F. Brambilla[1], E. Ferrari[2], F. Petraglia[3], P. Sacerdote[4] and A. Panerai[4]
[1]Osp. Psichiat., Pini, Milan; [2]Dip. Medicina Int., Terapia Med. Univ., Pavia; [3]Clin. Ostretica, Ginecol. Univ., Modena; and [4]Dip. Farmacologica Univ., Milan, Italy

Introduction

Global nutritional deficiency and reduced protein intake are well known causes of increased susceptibility to infections, possibly due to depressed cell-mediated immunity [1–2]. Data on anorexia nervosa (AN), an eating disorder specifically characterized by reduced food intake with or without protein deficiency, is scarce and controversial. A decreased incidence of infectious disease, normal T-lymphocyte population and normal or even elevated responses to mitogenic stimulations with concanavalin A and phytohaemagglutinin (PHA) have been reported. Spontaneous in vitro production of tumor necrosis factor (TNF) by peripheral blood mononuclear cells is increased in AN, but PHA-stimulated TNF is normal and lipopolysaccharide-stimulated TNF is decreased or increased. Interferon activity is normal, but cell-mediated cytotoxicity is defective [3–5].

We recently had the opportunity to investigate cell-mediated immunity of a group of restricted anorectics and anorectic-bulimic patients, by measuring T-lymphocyte proliferative response to PHA. Since the hypothalamo-pituitary-adrenal (HPA) hormones are known to inhibit the immune function [6], we investigated whether in our patients the alterations of the HPA which are present in the course of the disease interfered with the immune response to PHA stimulation. For this purpose, we measured in parallel basal and corticotropin-releasing hormone (CRH)-stimulated HPA hormone secretion and lymphocyte proliferative response to PHA. We also examined basal and CRH treated T-lymphocyte beta-endorphin (β-EP) secretion, which is known to modulate the immune function in a sort of paracrine-autocrine mechanism [7]. The dexamethasone suppression test (DST) was part of the investigation.

Materials and Methods

Eleven female patients with AN according to the DSM III-R diagnostic criteria and 11 psychophysically healthy controls, matched for sex and age, entered the study. Six patients were anorectic-restricted type and 5 suffered from anorexia-bulimia. They had been drug-free since at least 1 month and had never received psychotropic therapy before our study. Duration of the disease was 2–18 years; body mass index was 12–18 and reduction from ideal body weight 16.5–37.8%. The CRH test

(1 mcg/kg b.w. i.v.) was administered at 9:00 a.m. to both patients and controls. ACTH and cortisol plasma concentrations were measured at 15–30-min intervals for 2 h by RIA using commercial kits. In parallel, we measured the T-lymphocyte mitogenic response to PHA (0.3, 1.2, 5 μg/ml) and lymphocyte β-EP concentrations before and 30 min after the CRH administrations (methods of Barcellini et al., Panerai et al. and Sacerdote et al., respectively [8–10]).

The DST was performed by administering 1 mg of dexamethasone at 11:00 p.m. p.o. and by measuring cortisol plasma concentrations at 4:00 p.m. the following day.

Data were analyzed statistically by the Mann-Whitney test and by MANOVA for repeated measures.

Results

Basal ACTH and cortisol plasma concentrations were significantly higher in patients than in controls (M ± SD: ACTH = 26.1 ± 17.6 vs 12.2 ± 6.8 pg/ml, P = 0.03; cortisol = 20.3 ± 8.9 vs 11.4 ± 2.3 mcg/dl; P = 0.04). CRH stimulation induced ACTH and cortisol rises which were not significantly different in patients and controls when measured as area under the curve (AUC). The ratio between ACTH-AUC and cortisol-AUC was also not significantly different in patients and controls. DST was blunted in 55% of patients. T-lymphocyte responses to PHA stimulation were not significantly different in the two groups of subjects, either in basal conditions or 30 min after CRH administration, which also did not significantly modify the mitogenic response. T-lymphocyte β-EP concentrations were higher in patients than in controls both in basal conditions and 30 min after CRH administration, but due to the large scattering of values the difference was not statistically significant.

Discussion and Conclusions

Cell-mediated immunity seems to be well preserved in AN patients, at least in regard to T-lymphocyte mitogenic response to PHA stimulation. Our data are in keeping with those of Golla et al. [3] and in contrast with those of Emeric-Sauval et al. [5], who found hyperresponsiveness to PHA in 2 anorectics. The higher than normal ACTH and cortisol basal concentrations of our patients, their HPA axis incapacity to be inhibited by dexamethasone and the CRH-induced increased levels of ACTH and cortisol in both anorectics and controls did not seem to significantly influence the immune response, in contrast with the inhibitory effect of the HPA hormones observed in preclinical investigations [6]. It may be that the normal-high levels of T-lymphocyte β-EP concentrations have counteracted the inhibitory effects of HPA hormones, since it is well known that opioids tend to stimulate the immune system [7].

Our data are obviously preliminary and must be confirmed in a larger group of patients, and by a wider spectrum of immunological and neuroendocrine tests before advancing definite statements on the functional state of the immunoendocrine unit in anorexia nervosa.

References

1. Chandra RK (1983) Clin. Exp. Immunol. 51: 126–132.
2. Cason J, Ainley CC, Wolstencroft RA, Norton KRW and Thompson RPH (1986) Clin. Exp. Immunol. 64: 370–375.
3. Golla JA, Larson WR, Anderson CF, Lucas AR, Wilson WR and Tomasi TB (1981) Am. J. Clin. Nutr. 34: 2756–2762.
4. Schatter A, Steinbock M, Tepper R, Schonfeld A, Vaisman N and Hahn T (1990) Clin. Exp. Immunol. 79: 62–66.
5. Emeric-Sauval E, Polack E, Bello E, Bello M, Guitelman A, Finkielman S, Nahmod V and Arzt E (1989) Neuroendocrinol. Lett. 11: 270.
6. Irwin M, Daniels M, Risch SC, Bloom E, Weiner H (1988) Biol. Psychiatry 24: 173–178.
7. Stefano GB (1989) Prog. Neurobiol. 33: 149–159.
8. Barcellini W, Borghi MO, Sguotti C, Palmieri R, Frasca D, Meroni PL and Zanussi C (1988) Clin. Immunol. Immunopathol. 47: 142–151.
9. Panerai AE, Martini A, Di Giulio AM, Fraioli F, Vegni C, Pardi G, Marini A and Mantegazza P (1983) J. Clin. Endocrinol. Metab. 57: 537–544.
10. Sacerdote P, Rubboli F, Locatelli L, Ciciliato I, Mantegazza P and Panerai AE (1991) J. Neuroimmunol. (in press).

© 1991 Elsevier Science Publishers B.V. All rights reserved.
Biological Psychiatry, Volume 2. G. Racagni et al., editors.

Hormonal responses to glucose load in anorexia nervosa and bulimia nervosa compared to healthy controls

Regina C. Casper, Arthur Rubenstein, Ghanshyam Pandey and Jonathan Jaspan
The University of Chicago and Michael Reese Hospital, Department of Psychiatry, Lake Shore Drive at 31st Street, Chicago, IL 60616, U.S.A.

Anorexia nervosa (AN) and bulimia nervosa (BN) as disorders produce profound behavioral, cognitive and neuroendocrine changes. The distinction between the restricting and bulimic forms of AN is important in conducting metabolic and endocrine studies. Restricted food intake induces a physiological state of undernutrition combined with malnutrition and nutritional deficiencies. Malnutrition is usually not as pronounced in the bulimic form of AN or in BN due to episodic eating binges, but vomiting may lead to undetermined loss of electrolytes, enzymes and gastrointestinal hormones.

Starvation or restriction of carbohydrates have been observed to result in a marked decrease in the ability to utilize carbohydrates. Either a flat glucose uptake curve or more commonly hyperglycemic and hyperinsulinemic curves (the so-called starvation diabetes) are observed.

Studies in anorexia nervosa

Similar findings have been reported in AN ([1,2]; Sheldon, 1938; Vanderlaan, 1970; Garfinkel et al., 1975; and Kalucy et al., 1976)

Variably nourished yet severely underweight, hospitalized AN patients regularly show abnormal glucose absorption and tissue uptake of glucose. Fasting serum glucose levels are normal or slightly decreased, as are insulin and GH levels. Most often, glucose ingestion results in prolonged hyperglycemia, due to delayed insulin release, excess HGH secretion and high FFA levels. Interestingly, Kalucy et al. (1976) observed nocturnal hyperinsulinism, perhaps as a result of increased cortisol and GH levels.

Differences in results may be a function of meal composition (% protein, fat, carbohydrate), its caloric content, liquid or solid, variability in the patient population, age, chronicity, degree of weight loss, severity of illness, eating habits and stage of refeeding of the patient population studied, or differences in assay procedures.

Gut hormone studies in anorexia nervosa

Gut hormones have been studied by several investigators ([3,4]; Dixon et al., 1985, 1987; Nelson and Solymon, 1986). Fasting gut hormone levels were found to be normal. Considerable variation in the release of gastrointestinal inhibitory peptides (GIP) following meal stimulation in AN has been observed with decreased GIP plasma levels ([4]; and Nelson and Solymon, 1986) normal GIP and pancreatic polypeptide (PP) levels and increased GIP levels (Dixon et al., 1985, 1987).

Studies in bulimia nervosa

Studies in BN ([5]; Mitchell and Bantle, 1983; Hohlstein et al., 1986; Schweiger et al., 1987; and Geracioti et al., 1989) have reported plasma levels of glucose, insulin, glucagon, cortisol, PP and cholecystokinin (CCK) in the fasting state to be in the normal range. In the studies in which binge-eating/vomiting was encouraged to continue, slight deviations in glucose and insulin release and lower CCK levels following a meal or glucose load were observed, suggesting that intermittent nutritional deficit may be responsible for metabolite abnormalities.

The present study was undertaken to test the hypothesis suggested by Crisp et al. [1] that glucose intolerance and insulin resistance constitute a trait in AN and persist in women recovered from AN, and that BN patients as a result of excess carbohydrate intake show disturbed glucose utilization.

Sample

Nineteen women who met good outcome criteria for AN according to Morgan and Russell (1975), at a prospective 8-year follow-up, meaning they were of average weight for height, sex and age and had regular cyclical menstruation had a mean ideal body (IBW) weight of 101.3 ± 7.6% (age 23.5 years). Seven women with intermediate and poor outcome were called non-recovered (IBW 81.0 ± 5.9%; age 26.9 years). They were compared to 14 patients with BN (IBW: 104.4 ± 2.8%; age 23.7 years) and 14 female control subjects (IBW: 102.1 ± 5.6%; age 25.3 ± 2.9 years). All subjects participated in a 4-h glucose (100 g orally) tolerance test.

Methods

Criteria for defining an abnormal GTT were based on recommendations of the World Health Organization (1980). Plasma glucose (Young et al., 1975) and FFA (Bergman et al., 1980) were assayed immediately. Samples for estimating plasma GH (Odell et al., 1967), cortisol (RIA), serum insulin (Morgan and Lazarus, 1963), glucagon (Kuku et al., 1976) and PP (Hagopian et al., 1983) were stored at –200°C before being assayed.

Results

Glucose

Fasting glucose levels were within normal limits in all 4 groups. Glucose peak and glucose utilization levels were normal in recovered AN and BN patients, but non-recovered AN subjects had higher ($P < 0.05$) glucose levels with delayed clearance.

Insulin

Rises in plasma insulin levels and rates of descent were similar to normals in recovered AN and BN patients, whereas non-recovered AN subjects showed a delay in time to peak insulin levels ($P < 0.02$) at 90 min instead of 60 min.

FFA

Fasting and declining FFA plasma levels were normal in BN patients, but AN subjects regardless of recovery state, had fasting FFA levels twice the normal values ($P < 0.01$). By 60 min FFA levels were not different from controls.

Cortisol

Cortisol plasma levels throughout were similar in all 4 groups.

GH

Fasting GH levels were within normal limits. Non-recovered AN patients showed a paradoxical ($P < 0.02$) GH rise following glucose ingestion, while recovered AN and BN subjects showed rates of GH decline similar to normals. Glucagon and PP plasma levels in BN subjects showed similar secretion pattern to normal controls.

Discussion

The study was designed to test patients under near-optimal nutritional conditions after 5 days of a standard carbohydrate diet and in BN patients to eliminate vomiting episodes as much as possible. Under these conditions, recovered AN or BN patients displayed normal glucose tolerance curves, normal insulin and glucagon release and normal cortisol and PP secretion. The only abnormality was high baseline FFA levels in recovered AN subjects. By contrast, non-recovered underweight AN patients showed glucose intolerance, delayed insulin release and high GH and FFA secretion. The data are consistent with published reports (see Refs.). The high resting FFA plasma levels which suggest a propensity towards lipid mobilization in restricting AN represent new observations which deserve further investigation.

References

1. Crisp AH, Ellis J and Lowy C (1967) Br. Med. J. 43: 97–102.
2. Casper RC, Davis JM and Pandey GN (1977) In: Vigersky RA (ed.) Anorexia Nervosa, Raven Press, New York.
3. Besterman HS, Sarson DL, Hsu G, Crisp AH and Bloom SR (1979) Gut Hormones in Thyrotoxicosis and Anorexia Nervosa. Proc. Soc. Endocrinol., 143 pp.
4. Alderdice JT, Dinsmore WW, Buchanan KD and Adams C (1985) J. Psychiatr. Res. 19: 207–213.
5. Casper RC, Pandy GN, Jaspan JB and Rubenstein AH (1988) Biol. Psychiatry 24: 663–674.

Remaining references available upon request.

© 1991 Elsevier Science Publishers B.V. All rights reserved.
Biological Psychiatry, Volume 2. G. Racagni et al., editors.

Neuroendocrine effects of starvation in eating disorders

Manfred M. Fichter[1] and Karl-Martin Pirke[2]
[1]Department of Psychiatry, University of Munich, Munich; and Klinik Roseneck, Prien; and [2]Max-Planck-Institute for Psychiatry, Munich, Germany

Introduction

Numerous endocrine changes have been described for anorexia nervosa and more recently for bulimia nervosa. A relevant and major issue is whether some or all of these endocrine changes are the expression of an underlying biological disturbance specific for these eating disorders, or whether they are the result of a temporarily reduced caloric intake. During the evolution of mankind, the biological adaptation to times of famine has been of great importance. According to our "nutritional hypothesis", endocrine changes in anorexia and bulimia nervosa are the result of a temporarily reduced caloric intake. In order to test this hypothesis, we conducted a series of studies with healthy subjects before, during and after a 3-week period of total food abstinence and patients with anorexia or bulimia nervosa.

Method

Starvation study with healthy subjects: The Munich University Starvation Experiment (MUSE)

Five healthy female subjects (average age = 23.2 years; average weight = 58 kg) were assessed during several weeks of an initial baseline phase (A) with stable (ideal) body weight (IBW), during a 3-week fasting phase (B) resulting in a weight loss of about 8 kg, a weight restoration phase (C) of several weeks and a final baseline phase (D) with stable (ideal) body weight over 6 weeks. Neuroendocrine assessments of several hormonal axes were performed several times in each phase [1].

Patients with anorexia nervosa

Sixteen patients with anorexia nervosa according to DSM III criteria neuroendocrine assessments were determined over the course of weight gain 1 week after admission, after 10% initial weight gain and before discharge (average weight increased from 63% to 88% of IBW) [2].

Patients with bulimia nervosa

Two separate samples of patients with bulimia (nervosa) were studied. The first sample consisted of 27 patients with bulimia according to DSM III criteria with an average age of 26.7 years, duration of illness 4.9 years and average body weight at 98% of matched population mean weight. The second sample consisted of 30 patients with bulimia nervosa according to DSM III-R criteria [3]. In both bulimia (nervosa) samples, food intake was protocolled and biological measures of reduced food intake (T_3, β-hydroxy-butyric acid, free fatty acids) were assessed in addition to neuroendocrine analyses concerning hypothalamic-pituitary adrenal, thyroid and gonadal axes as well as growth hormone. The following tests of endocrine functioning were performed: dexamethasone suppression test with 1.5 mg fortecortin taken orally at 11 p.m. on the preceding evening; the TRH-test was performed with injection of 1.0 ml TRH (= 0.2 mg relefact-TRH intravenously); the clonidine test was performed with perfusion of 150 μg clonidine in 10 ml NaCl-solution for 10 min and the HGH response to clonidine was measured. Additional healthy controls of the same sex and age were assessed (n = 15 for DST; n = 15 for nocturnal cortisol secretion; n = 11 for nocturnal gonadotropine, prolactin and growth hormone secretion; n = 12 for TRH test). The method of laboratory assessment has been described elsewhere [1].

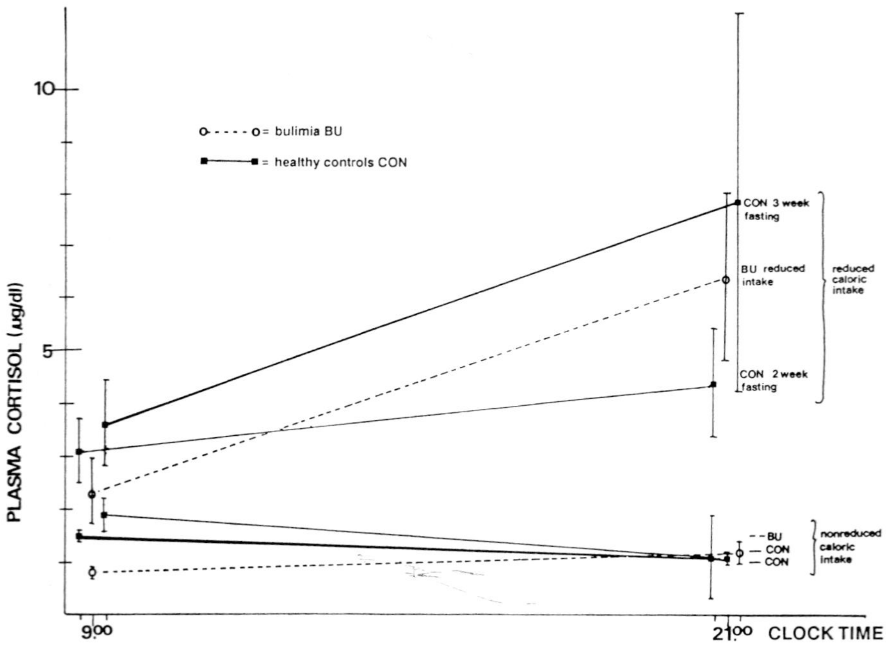

Fig. 1. Plasma cortisol levels following ingestion of dexamethasone in healthy controls (CON) before and after experimental starvation and in bulimic patients (BU) with higher or lower caloric intake (mean and S.E.).

Results

Results concerning the hypothalamo-pituitary adrenal axis are shown in Fig. 1. Healthy subjects showed a dramatic elevation of plasma cortisol level after 3 weeks of total food abstinence; this normalized with weight restoration. Patients with anorexia nervosa showed elevated plasma cortisol levels on admission; cortisol secretion patterns normalized already with an initial 10% weight gain and remained normal with further weight gain until discharge. Half of all dexamethasone tests in healthy subjects during total food abstinence were abnormal (below 5 µg/dl). Plasma cortisol levels in bulimia nervosa were normal in our study irrespective of recent caloric intake, but other researchers have reported increased cortisol levels in bulimia nervosa. Plasma cortisol levels following DST were insufficiently suppressed in those bulimics, who showed signs of reduced caloric intake in the preceding weeks.

The growth hormone response to the α_2-adrenergic receptor agonist clonidine in bulimia nervosa and healthy controls is shown in Fig. 2. During the luteal phase the growth hormone response in bulimics was blunted when compared to the healthy controls. A blunted growth hormone response to clonidine was seen mainly in bulimics with restricted caloric intake. Healthy controls under conditions of total food abstinence also showed a blunted HGH-response to clonidine which, however, occurred not during or after fasting but after subsequent weight restoration.

The hypothalamic-pituitary gonadal axis was assessed in patients with anorexia

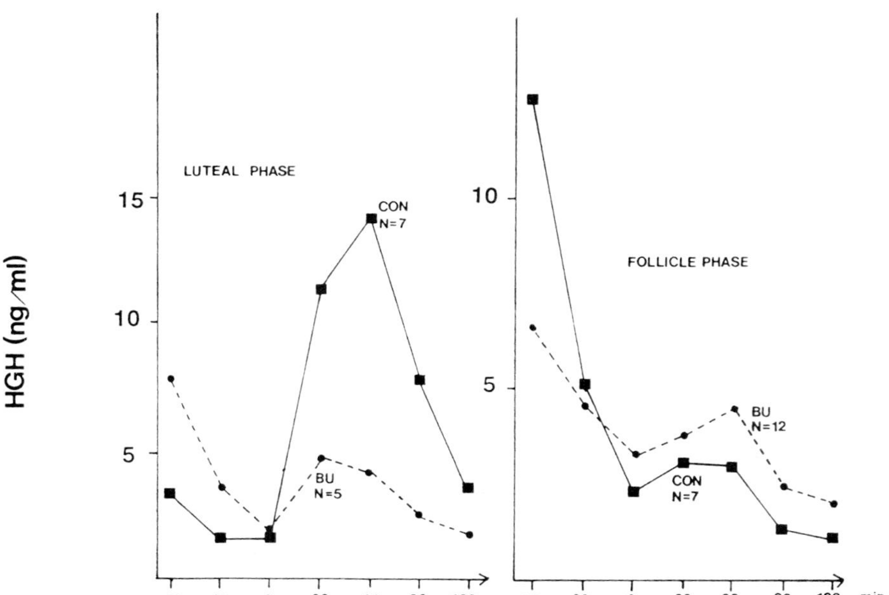

Fig. 2. Response of growth hormone (HGH) to clonidine in bulimia nervosa (BU) and healthy controls (CON).

nervosa, bulimia nervosa and healthy controls. Fourteen of 16 patients with anorexia nervosa had an infantile plasma-LH secretion pattern on admission. The LH-secretion pattern progressed to a more mature pattern during the course of weight gain. An important finding concerning gonadal regulation is shown in Fig. 3. Only 3 out of 30 normal-weight bulimics (10 %) showed a normal pattern of secretion of estradiol, progesterone and LH over one complete cycle. Forty percent showed a luteal phase defect with low estradiol peaks (> 200 pg/nl) and a lack of progesterone secretion in the luteal phase. Fifty percent of the normal weight bulimic patients showed continuously low estradiol and progesterone plasma levels, indicating lack of growth of a dominant follicle. This finding is of importance concerning reproductive functions and fertility and concerning the develop-

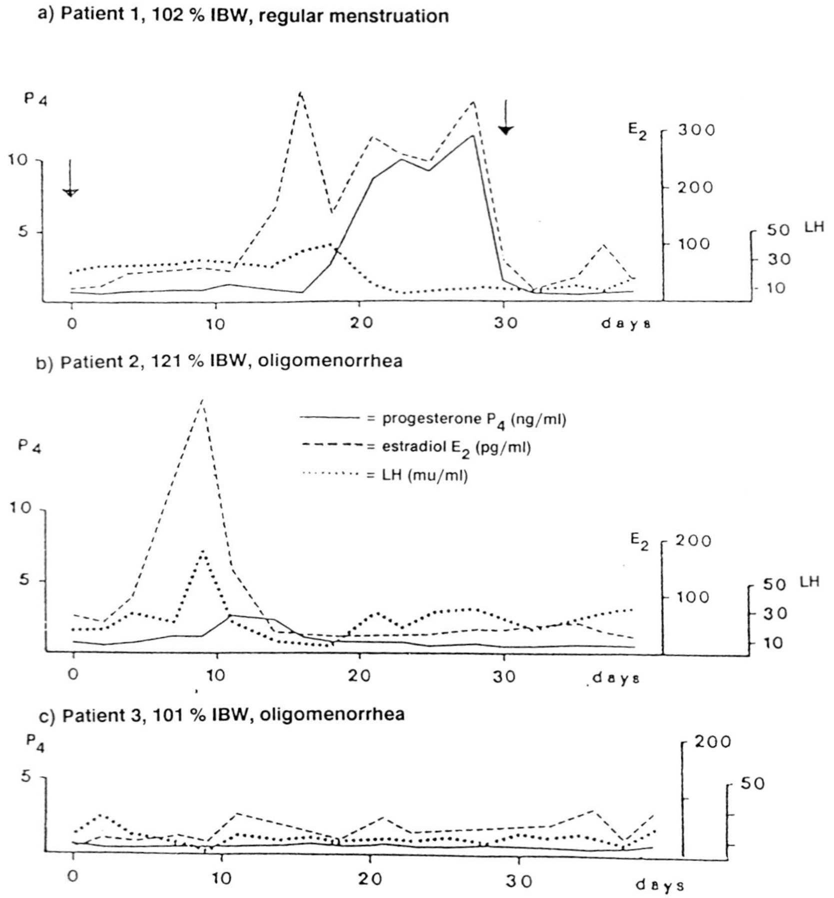

Fig. 3. Plasma levels of estradiol (E_2), progesterone (P_4) and luteinizing hormone (LH) in bulimia nervosa over a complete menstrual cycle. a) Example of a bulimic patient with normal menstrual cycle; b) example of a bulimic patient with luteal phase defect (LPD) and normal follicular development; and c) example of a bulimic patient with a disturbance in follicular development. IBW = ideal body weight according the tables of the Metropolitan Life Insurance (1959).

ment of osteoporosis in normal weight bulimia with periods of reduced caloric intake [3].

Conclusion

Neuroendocrine and neurotransmitter changes in anorexia and bulimia nervosa appear to be adaptations to a temporary state of starvation. Our finding in a series of studies with healthy subjects under conditions of total food abstinence (starvation), anorexia nervosa and bulimia nervosa support this “nutritional hypothesis”.

References

1. Fichter MM, Pirke KM and Holsboer F (1988) Psychiatr. Res. 17: 61–72.
2. Doerr P, Fichter MM, Pirke KM and Lund R (1980) J. Steroid Biochem. 13: 529–537.
3. Fichter MM and Pirke KM (1989) In: Pirke KM, Wuttke W and Schweiger U (eds.) The Menstrual Cycle and Its Disorders. Springer-Verlag, Berlin, pp. 179–188.
4. Fichter MM, Pirke KM, Poellinger J, Wolfram G and Brunner E (1990) Biol. Psychiatry 27: 1021–1037.

© 1991 Elsevier Science Publishers B.V. All rights reserved.
Biological Psychiatry, Volume 2. G. Racagni et al., editors.

Bone mineral content and calcium metabolism regulating hormones in anorexia nervosa

N. Kiriike, S. Nakanishi, T. Nagata, T. Iketani, K. Inoue and Y. Kawakita
Department of Neuropsychiatry, Osaka City University Medical School, Osaka 545, Japan

Introduction

Several investigators have reported that the patients with anorexia nervosa (AN) often exhibit reduced bone density and develop osteoporosis which may result in pathological fractures [1–4]. The mechanism of osteoporosis in AN is not fully established, but estrogen deficiency, cortisol excess, malnutrition and low calcium intake have all been proposed as contributory factors [1–10]. The purpose of this study was to determine the relationships of the major hormones regulating calcium metabolism to bone density in patients with anorexia nervosa. In addition, we examined the roles of body weight, physical activity, duration of amenorrhea and binging-purging behavior in reducing the bone density.

Subjects and Methods

The subjects were 17 hospitalized female patients who met the DSM III-R criteria for anorexia nervosa. Twelve of them had binge eating more than twice a week for at least 3 months and were also diagnosed as having bulimia nervosa. Ten age-matched healthy females were studied as controls. All subjects gave informed consent to participate in this study. Bone mineral density for the lumbar vertebrae (L2-4) and for the whole body were measured by dual photon absorptiometry using a Norland 2600 dichromatic bone densitometer (Norland Corporation, Wisconsin). On the same day, blood samples were drawn from each patient for the determinations of serum calcium (Ca), inorganic phosphate (P), total protein (TP), albumin (Alb), electrolytes, alkaline phosphatase, triiodothyronine (T_3), thyroxine (T_4), cortisol (Cor), estrogen (E_2, E_3), parathyroid hormone (PTH), calcitonin (Cal), 25-hydroxyvitamin D (25-OH-D), 1,25-dihydroxyvitamin D (1,25-$(OH)_2$D) and 24, 25-dihydroxyvitamin D (24,25-$(OH)_2$D). Statistical analysis was done with Student's t-test and Pearson's (or Spearman's) correlation coefficient.

Results

Clinical characteristics and bone mineral densities of patients and controls are

Table 1. Clinical characteristics and mean bone mineral densities (BMD)

	Age (years)	Body weight (kg)	BMI[a]	Duration of amenorrhea (years)	BMD (g/cm^2)		
					L_3	$L_{2\text{-}4}$	Whole body
Anorexia nervosa (n = 17)	20.9 ± 3.9	34.8 ± 4.0[b]	13.8 ± 1.2[b]	2.6 ± 3.0	0.92 ± 1.14[b]	0.91 ± 1.13[b]	1.02 ± 2.24
Control (n = 10)	22.4 ± 1.0	48.9 ± 3.8	19.5 ± 0.8	–	1.05 ± 0.11	1.02 ± 0.10	0.94 ± 0.05

Values were expressed as mean ± S.D.; [a]BMI: body mass index; [b]$P < 0.05$.

shown in Table 1. The patients had significantly ($P < 0.05$) lower body weight, BMI and BMD in L_3 and $L_{2\text{-}4}$ than did controls. Four of the anorectics had BMD in L_3 more than 2 S.D. below the mean for controls.

Table 2 shows mean serum levels of major hormones regulating calcium metabolism for the patients. Mean serum total protein was low, but mean serum Ca and Alb levels were normal. Mean serum T_3, T_4, Cor, PTH, Cal, 25-OH-D, 1,25-$(OH)_2D$ and 24,25-$(OH)_2D$ levels for the patients were normal. Half of the patients showed abnormally low T_3 levels, and a few patients showed abnormally high (Cor) or low (PTH, 1,25$(OH)_2D$) levels. Serum E_2 level was abnormally low in all patients. To determine the factors contributing to bone loss, the relationship of L_3 BMD to clinical variables and levels of major calcium metabolism regulating hormone was analysed. L_3 BMD was negatively correlated with serum levels of Alb ($P < 0.01$) and with the duration of amenorrhea ($P < 0.05$) and was positively correlated with body weight ($P < 0.07$). However, no significant correlation of L_3 BMD to the presence of binging-purging behavior or to level of any major calcium metabolism regulating hormone was found.

Discussion

The anorectic patients in this study had significantly lower BMD in L_3 and $L_{2\text{-}4}$

Table 2. Mean serum levels of major calcium metabolism regulating hormones

	T_3 (ng/ml)	T_4 (μg/dl)	Cor (μg/dl)	E_2 (pg/ml)	PTH (pg/ml)	Cal (pg/ml)	1,25-$(OH)_2D$ (pg/ml)
Mean ± SD	0.75 ± 0.2	7.3 ± 1.3	14.7 ± 4.8	<10	276 ± 115	44.7 ± 24.7	31.4 ± 14.7
Abnormal[a]							
Low	46	0	18[b]	100	20	0	20

[a]% of the patients; [b] abnormally high.

than did controls. This finding is consistent with those in earlier reports [1–8]. However, we found no significant correlation of L_3 BMD with serum level of thyroid hormone, parathyroid hormone, calcitonin or vitamin D. Therefore, it seems unlikely that changes in the level of any of these major calcium metabolism regulating hormones is the main factor contributing to reduced bone density in the anorectic patients. Because we did not measure 24-h urinary cortisol output which has been reported to be negatively correlated with bone density [5,6], it is premature to conclude that hypercortisolemia did not contribute to bone loss in AN on the basis of only lack of association between L_3 BMD and serum cortisol level in our patients.

In this study, all patients had abnormally low serum E_2 level, and L_3 BMD was strongly negatively correlated with duration of amenorrhea. This findings are compatible with previous findings [8]. We also found that L_3 BMD was positively correlated with body weight. It is therefore suggested that severe weight loss, longer duration of amenorrhea and deficiency of estrogen contribute to reduction of bone density in patients with anorexia nervosa.

References

1. Rigotti NA, Nussbaum SR, Herzog DB et al. (1984) N. Engl. J. Med. 311: 1601–1606.
2. Ayers JWT, Gidwani GP, Schmidt IMV et al. (1984) Fertil. Steril. 41: 224–228.
3. Szmukler GI, Brown SW, Parsons V et al. (1985) Br. Med. J. 290: 26–27.
4. Brotman AW and Stern TA (1985) Am. J. Psychiatry 142: 495–496.
5. Bachrach LK, Guido D and Katzman D (1990) Pediatrics 86: 440–447.
6. Newman MM and Halmi KA (1989) Psychiatr. Res. 29: 105–112.
7. Biller BMK, Saxe V and Herzog DB (1989) J. Clin. Endocrinol. Metab. 68: 548–554.
8. Crosby L0, Kaplan FS, Pertschuk MJ et al. (1985) Clin. Orthopaed. Relat. Res. 201: 271–277.
9. Treasure JL, Russell GF, Fogelman I et al. (1987) Br. Med. J. 295: 474-475.
10. Davies KM, Pearson PH, Huseman CA et al. (1990) Bone 11: 143–147.

Biological markers, brain imaging, evoked potentials and EEG mapping

© 1991 Elsevier Science Publishers B.V. All rights reserved.
Biological Psychiatry, Volume 2. G. Racagni et al., editors.

The coupling of neurotransmitter release to precursor supply: Some recent microdialysis studies

Ian N. Acworth
ESA Inc., 45 Wiggins Avenue, Bedford, MA 01730, U.S.A.

Introduction

The relationship between circulating levels of precursor amino acids and central monoamine metabolism has been studied extensively over the past decade. Using both in vitro and in vivo techniques, scientists have explored this relationship in an attempt to understand normal physiology, the consequences of pharmacological intervention and the effects of disease.

Indirect in vitro experiments showed that the rate of monoamine synthesis and turnover may be directly affected by precursor availability to the brain. This was particularly true for serotonin, where a wide variety of physiological and pharmacological treatments were used to increase plasma tryptophan levels. This in turn, was found to increase the levels of tryptophan in the brain and ultimately lead to increased serotonin synthesis and turnover. The relationship between plasma tyrosine levels and central catecholamine metabolism was found to be much more complex. Although increases in circulating tyrosine levels did, in some instances, result in increased catecholamine synthesis, the magnitude of the change was relatively small. Only when catecholaminergic neurons had been rendered especially active (e.g. after drug treatment, lesioning or stress) did exposure to elevated levels of tyrosine promote catecholamine synthesis and turnover [1].

But what of release? Because of the nature of many of the in vitro experiments, researchers were unable to directly measure extracellular events. Many equated turnover with release, often ignoring the fact that the former may be due to both intra- and inter-neuronal events. Several perfusion and electrochemical techniques were then developed, aimed at overcoming the inherent problems associated with the interpretation of in vitro measurements. One such technique – microdialysis perfusion (when coupled to highly sensitive HPLC-EC) enables researchers to *directly* and routinely estimate levels of neurotransmitters within the extracellular space in vivo. Several reports have now shown that the peripheral administration of amino acids *may* affect the temporal release of monoamines in brain tissue in both anesthetized and freely-moving, conscious animals (Table 1).

The tripeptide, thyrotropin releasing hormone (TRH), is one of several small peptides present in the brain which participates in the physiological regulation of anterior pituitary hormone secretion (stimulates TSH release). A variety of studies have revealed that the administration of TRH to experimental animals can also

Table 1. Effects of amino acids on monoamine release

Amino acid	Route	Monoamine	Area	Dose (mg/kg)	Effect (%)	Ref.
Tryptophan	i.p.	5-HT	Hypothal.	200	130	3
Tyrosine ME	i.v.	DA	Striatum	20	190	4
Tyrosine	i.p.	DA	Striatum	200	45	5
			N. Acc.	200	104	5
Phenylalanine	i.p.	DA	Striatum	200	59	6
		DA	Striatum	1000	–25	6
Valine	i.p.	DA	Striatum	200	No effect	7
TRF and imipramine	i.p.	5-HT	Striatum	100	50	8
Tyrosine ME	i.p.	DA	Striatum	250	No effect	8
Phenylananine	i.p.	DA	Striatum	250	No effect	8

result in intriguing and potentially important clinical actions secondary to its pituitary function. Depending on the species dose and route of administration, TRH appears to have analeptic action; can alter cardiovascular response and gastro-intestinal tract motility; alter spinocerebellar function; but probably most interestingly, possesses antidepressive action [2]. Previous data have shown that the administration of TRH can affect several aspects of monoamine metabolism. However, its effects on monoamine *release* have not been fully examined.

We have studied the effects of peripheral TRH and/or tyrosine administration on striatal dopamine (DA) release in anesthetized animals, using microdialysis perfusion.

Materials and Methods

Briefly, male Sprague-Dawley rats (250–400 g) were anesthetized with chloralose-urethane (50: 500 mg/kg i.p.) and had a heparinized catheter sutured into their right jugular vein. After being secured in a stereotaxic frame, a hole was drilled through the cranium and a previously calibrated 4-mm dialysis probe placed in the left striatum (AP +0.5, ML +2.7, DV –7.0). The probe was continuously perfused with artificial CSF (containing 1.0 mM calcium, pH 7.4) at a flow rate of 1.5 μl/min. (Under these conditions, in vitro probes showed dopamine recoveries of 12–15%.) After 2 h (injury release), samples were analyzed using HPLC-EC (ESA Inc., Bedford, MA). When dopamine release fluctuated by less than 12%, 0.25 ml of blood was withdrawn and the drug slowly (0.2 ml/min) infused through the catheter. Animals received either saline (control), or TRH (10 μg), or L-tyrosine (methyl ester – TME) (20 mg/kg), or TRH (10 μg) and TME (20 mg/kg) together. Samples of blood (0.25 ml) and microdialysates (23 μl into 5 μl 0.5 M perchloric acid) were collected every 15 min. Donor blood (2 × 1.0 ml) was infused after 45 and 105 min. In additional experiments, some animals received higher doses of

TRH (50 μg i.v.) 1 h after intrathecal administration of active or denatured prolactin antibody (10 μl). Statistical significance was determined by MANOVA, calculating a 2 factorial design with repeated measurements (1 dependent factor), followed by a MANOVA and Duncan's multiple range *t*-test.

The effects of the above drug treatments were also determined in vitro (striatal homogenates) after equivalent in vitro doses of the above drugs. Statistical significance was calculated by an ANOVA followed by Dunnet's multiple comparison of treatments against a single control.

Results

Basal levels of DA and its metabolites in dialysate samples were comparable between treatments (DA ~3 nM; n = 38). Saline administration had little effect on any measured parameter. TRH (10 μg) significantly increased DA release to 240% above baseline at 150 min. TME caused a similar but more attenuated response, DA only rising to 190% above baseline at 150 min. The co-administration of TRH and TME together caused a synergistic increase in ECF DA levels (640% above baseline). TRH given alone or together with TME tended to decrease the dialysate levels of DOPAC and HVA throughout the time course of the experiment. The higher dose of TRH (50 μg) caused a marked increase in DA release (1150% above baseline) regardless of whether the animals received active or denatured prolactin antiserum. The in vivo administration of TRH and/or TME had little effect on DA or its metabolites when measured in homogenates.

Discussion

These data show that the peripheral administration of tyrosine can increase striatal release of DA; that TRH is a very potent DA releaser in vivo, its action appears not be mediated by prolactin; and that microdialysis can show altered monoamine release even if homogenate data show no change. These results support previous in vitro data showing the TRH can effect dopamine metabolism.

The slow response to TRH administration may be due to its slow passage through the blood-brain barrier. More recently, however, we have had data suggesting that TRH's effects may be, in part, due to the formation of one of its metabolites – cyclo-histidyl-proline, which is also capable of promoting dopamine release in vivo.

By co-administering tyrosine and TRH, it is hoped that this may be an effective treatment for disorders associated with monoamine dysfunctions such as depression and in diseases involving degeneration of the DA tracts.

Acknowledgements

This research was completed in conjunction with Michael R. Kreutz (Department of Molecular Neuroendocrinology, Max-Plank-Institute for Experimental Medicine, Gottingen, Germany), Hendrik Lehnert (Department of Endocrinology and Metabolism, III Med. Clinic, University Hospital Mainz, Mainz, Germany) and Richard J. Wurtman (Laboratory of Neuroendocrine Regulation, Dept. of Brain and Cognitive Sciences, MIT, Cambridge, MA 02139, USA). The research was partly supported by The United States Air Force. At the time Dr. Kreutz was supported by a fellowship from The Center For Brain Sciences and Metabolism Charitable Trust. We thank Dr. A. Parlow (NIADDK) for providing the prolactin antiserum.

References

1. Acworth IN and Wurtman RJ (1990) In: Richardson MA (ed.) Amino Acids in Psychiatric Disease. Progress in Psychiatry. American Psychiatric Press Inc., Washington, DC, pp. 3–29.
2. Horita A, Carino MA and Lai H (1986) Ann. Rev. Pharmacol. Toxicol. 26: 311–332.
3. Carboni E, Cadoni C, Tanda GL and Di Chiara G (1989) J. Neurochem. 53: 976–978.
4. Kreutz MK, Acworth IN, Lehnert H and Wurtman RI (1990) Brain Res. 536: 347–352.
5. During MJ, Acworth IN and Wurtman RJ (1989) Brain Res. 452: 378–380.
6. During MJ, Acworth IN and Wurtman RJ (1988) Neurosci. Lett. 93: 91–95.
7. During MJ, Acworth IN and Wurtman RJ (1989) J. Neurochem. 52: 1449–1454.
8. Westerink BHC and De Vries JB (1991) J. Neurochem. 56: 228–233.

© 1991 Elsevier Science Publishers B.V. All rights reserved.
Biological Psychiatry, Volume 2. G. Racagni et al., editors.

Some effects of altered tryptophan availability on mood, aggression, food selection and pain perception

Simon N. Young
Department of Psychiatry, McGill University, 1033 Pine Avenue West, Montreal, Quebec, H3A 1A1, Canada

Introduction

Low serotonin levels have been implicated in the etiology of several different types of psychopathology. However, although low serotonin levels are found in a variety of disorders, it remains unclear to what extent low serotonin causes the disorder, or is merely an associated feature with no etiological role. One approach to this problem is to lower brain serotonin in normal humans and look at the symptoms that are elicited. We have now done this using a tryptophan deficient amino acid mixture (T-mixture). When human subjects ingested a T-mixture of amino acids, their plasma tryptophan showed a dramatic decline, reaching its lowest value after 5 h [1,2]. At this time the decline in plasma tryptophan was between 70 and 80%. The decline in tryptophan levels occurred because the T-mixture induced protein synthesis, and tryptophan in the blood and tissues was incorporated into protein. A decline in plasma tryptophan levels of this magnitude is accompanied by a substantial decline in brain serotonin synthesis in experimental animals [2] and should have the same effect in humans. In studies using a T-amino acid mixture, the control treatment is an amino acid mixture identical to the T-mixture, except that it contains the appropriate amount of tryptophan for a balanced protein (balanced or B mixture).

Effect of tryptophan depletion on mood

In the first study on the effect of tryptophan depletion on mood [1], normal males were given T-mixtures and mood was measured before the treatment and 5 h later, when plasma tryptophan was at its lowest. The T-mixture, but not the control balanced (B) mixture, produced a significant lowering of mood. Since research supports the involvement of environmental setting and cognition in the production and experience of emotion, a second study looked at how these factors might influence the mood-lowering effect of tryptophan depletion [3]. The second study confirmed the mood-lowering effect of tryptophan depletion, and also demonstrated that this effect occurs directly rather than via cognitive processes. Furthermore, the mood-lowering effect was reasonably robust to environmental manipulation.

In the studies on the effect of tryptophan depletion on mood, the baseline depression scores of the subjects were in the normal range, but were at the high end of normal. The decline in mood produced a state that was not in a range that could be considered full clinical depression, but could be classified as mild depression [3]. However, recently the effect of tryptophan depletion, using the same amino acid mixtures, has been studied in recovered depressed patients who were still receiving antidepressant treatment [4]. Fourteen of the 21 remitted depressed patients experienced a full depressive relapse after ingestion of the T-mixture, but not the B mixture, with gradual return to the remitted state over 24 to 48 h on return to regular food intake.

If susceptibility to depression enhances the response to tryptophan depletion, then an obvious question is whether very low baseline depression scores would protect against this effect. This was answered in a recent study which was designed primarily to study the effect of tryptophan depletion on the analgesic effect of morphine [5]. As some of the subjects in this study received morphine, there was careful screening of all potential subjects. This resulted in a group of subjects with abnormally low baseline depression scale scores. In the group which received an injection of saline placebo instead of morphine and a T-mixture, there was no decline in depression scale scores as a result of tryptophan depletion.

The data on tryptophan depletion and mood support the idea, which is gaining increasing acceptance, that depression is, from a neurochemical point of view, heterogeneous and multifactorial. Serotonin does seem to have a direct effect on mood in many subjects, but low serotonin will result in depression only if there is a susceptibility to depression. Thus, the data indicate that low serotonin is one of the factors involved in the etiology of depression in some patients.

Effect of tryptophan depletion on aggression

Initial attempts to demonstrate that altering tryptophan availability in normal humans could influence aggressive responding were not successful [6]. In this study the laboratory measure of aggression was one in which subjects were asked to deliver shocks to a (non-existent) partner in response to tones over earphones, delivered by their "partner" in another room. The measures of aggression were the intensity and duration of the shock supposedly delivered. Elevated arousal can increase the firing rate of serotonin neurons [7] and altered serotonin levels should have a greater effect on serotonin release when serotonin neurons are firing at a higher rate. Thus, the effect of altering tryptophan levels may be greatest when experimental subjects are at a high level of arousal. Partial confirmation of the hypothesis was obtained from an experiment in which vervet monkeys in social groups were given T or B amino acid mixtures and their aggression was measured at low and high levels of arousal [8]. A second event looking at the effect of amino acid mixtures on aggressive responding in humans has been performed recently (R.O. Pihl and S.N. Young, unpublished data). The design was the same as in the study described above [6], except that the stimulus for the subjects to administer a shock to their "partner" was an electric shock, supposedly delivered by their partner, instead of an auditory tone. A shock was used as the stimulus in the expectation that it would be more arousing than a tone. In this situation, altered tryptophan levels did result in significant changes in the intensity of shock that the subjects delivered in response to the stimulus. As expected, low tryptophan was associated with increased aggressive responding. If elevated arousal is important in the response to altered tryptophan, then pathologically aggressive patients, who exhibit impulsive aggression and therefore high levels of arousal, might be expected to respond to tryptophan administration. Preliminary evidence that this may be so comes from two separate studies [9,10].

Effect of tryptophan depletion on food selection

The effect of tryptophan depletion on macronutrient selection in humans has been the subject of a single study [11]. In a double-blind cross-over study, normal adult males were given T and B amino acid mixtures on two occasions one week apart. Five hours after the mixtures the subjects were allowed to eat alone from a buffet which provided ten different foods of widely varying macronutrient composition. Unknown to the subjects, the foods were weighed before and after the subjects ate. Tryptophan depletion resulted in no significant alteration in selection of total calories, fat or carbohydrate. However, there was a small but significant decline in protein selection. These data are not consistent with the hypothesis [12] that carbohydrate craving in a variety of disorders is due to low serotonin levels.

Effect of tryptophan depletion on pain

Animal studies implicate serotonin in the inhibition of nociceptive afferents, and as one of the neurotransmitters involved in the analgesic effect of morphine [13]. A recent report deals with the effect of B and T-mixtures on response in the cold pressor test, in subjects who received injections of morphine or saline [5]. In the cold pressor test, subjects immersed their arms in 0°C water. They said when their arm started to hurt (pain threshold) and took it out of the water when they could not stand the pain any more (pain tolerance). Although tryptophan depletion had no effect on the measures in subjects who received saline injections, it abolished the analgesic effect of morphine, as far as pain tolerance was concerned. This supports a role for serotonin in the analgesic effect of morphine in humans.

References

1. Young SN, Smith SE, Pihl RO and Ervin FR (1985) Psychopharmacology 87: 173–177.

2. Young SN, Ervin FR, Pihl RO and Finn P (1989) Psychopharmacology 91: 508–511.
3. Smith SE, Pihl RO, Young SN and Ervin FR (1987) Psychopharmacology 91: 451–457.
4. Delgado PL, Charney DS, Price LH, Aghajanian GK, Landis H and Heninger GR (1990) Arch. Gen. Psychiatry 47: 411–418.
5. Abbott FV, Etienne P, Franklin KBJ, Morgan MJ, Sewitch MJ and Young SN (1991). Psychopharmacology (in press).
6. Smith SE, Pihl RO, Young SN and Ervin FR (1986) Aggress. Behav. 12: 393–407.
7. Trulson ME and Jacobs BL (1979) Brain Res. 169: 135–150.
8. Chamberlain B, Ervin FR, Pihl RO and Young SN (1987) Pharmacol. Biochem. Behav. 28: 503–510.
9. Morand C, Young SN and Ervin FE (1983) Biol. Psychiatry 18: 575–578.
10. Volavka J, Crowner M, Brizer D, Convit A, van Praag HM and Suckow RF (1990) Biol. Psychiatry 28: 728–732.
11. Young SN, Tourjman SV, Teff KL, Pihl RO and Anderson GH (1988) Pharmacol. Biochem. Behav. 31: 149–152.
12. Wurtman JJ and Wurtman RJ (1986) Appetite (Suppl.) 7: 99–103.
13. Yaksh TL (1979) Brain Res. 160: 180–185.

© 1991 Elsevier Science Publishers B.V. All rights reserved.
Biological Psychiatry, Volume 2. G. Racagni et al., editors.

Altered transport of tyrosine across the blood-brain barrier in patients with schizophrenia

Frits-Axel Wiesel[1], Gunnar Blomqvist[2] Nicolaus Venizelos[3], Lars Bjerkenstedt[4], Christer Halldin[4], Lars Hagenfeldt[3] and Irene Sjögren[4]
[1]Department of Psychiatry, University of Uppsala, Ulleråker, S-750 17 Uppsala; and [2]Clinical Neurophysiology; [3]Clinical Chemistry; and [4]Psychiatry and Psychology, Karolinska Institute, Sweden

Introduction

Tyrosine is the precursor amino acid in dopamine synthesis and has therefore attracted interest in schizophrenia research. The importance of tyrosine turnover was evident when we obtained results indicating a reduced availability of tyrosine for dopamine synthesis in patients with schizophrenia [1]. Several of the amino acids sharing the L-transport system with tyrosine were found to be elevated in the patients (n = 33) in comparison with the controls (n = 65). HVA levels in CSF were decreased and the plasma levels of the amino acids competing with tyrosine for transport into the brain were all negatively correlated to HVA. These findings could be explained by a change in the affinity of the L-system or by a decrease in its overall capacity in schizophrenia limiting the brain uptake of tyrosine. This motivated us to study tyrosine transport in vitro and in vivo in patients with schizophrenia.

Materials and Methods

In vitro studies

Skin biopsies were obtained from 10 male patients with schizophrenia (DSM III) and in 7 healthy controls [2]. In a second study a further 5 male patients and controls were studied in whom tyrosine transport was also determined by positron emission tomography (PET). Fibroblasts were cultured from the skin biopsies. Uptake into the cells was measured using a ^{14}C- or ^{3}H-labelled amino acid and varying concentrations of the unlabelled amino acid. In the determination of the kinetic parameters of transport, amino acid uptake was measured at 12 different concentrations in duplicate in the same incubation. From Lineweaver-Burke plots values of K_m (μmol/l) and V_{max} (μmol/min/mg protein) were determined.

In vivo studies

Five healthy male volunteers and 5 male patients with schizophrenia (DSM III-R) were selected for the study. The patients were in an acute phase of their disease and without medication for at least 6 months. The subjects fasted for 15 h before the PET experiment. L-[1-^{11}C] tyrosine was injected i.v. as a bolus and radioactivity was measured in arterial blood. The radioactivity in the brain was measured with a four-ring positron camera (PC-384-7B, FWHM = 7.6 mm) for 25 min. Kinetics for tyrosine transport were determined according to a two-compartment model using radioactivity data of arterial blood and brain tissue between 1 and 3.5 min (20 scans) after the tracer injection. For data sampled between 5 and 25 min (11 scans), the net accumulation rate of tyrosine into the brain was determined according to Patlak et al. [3]. It should be pointed out that the fractional extraction of amino acids is low and their clearance through the brain is diffusion-limited and flow-independent at normal rates of cerebral blood flow.

Results

The transport capacity for tyrosine (V_{max}) was significantly lower in the patients (4.5 ± 0.9 (S.D.) μmol/min/mg protein, $P < 0.01$) than in the controls (7.8 ± 2.1 (S.D.) μmol/min/mg protein) [2]. The K_m values did not differ between patients (22 ± 8 (S.D.) μmol/l) and controls (27 ± 13 (S.D.) μmol/l). For the other amino acids studied, L-phenylalanine, L-tryptophan and L-leucine, no differences were observed in either of the kinetic parameters. Tyrosine transport was inhibited by 96 to 99% by the addition of the other amino acids in both the patients and the controls. There was no sodium-dependent component of the tyrosine transport in cells from either group. Intracellular amino acids levels were the same in the two groups. In the second study results in the first study were replicated. Thus V_{max} for tyrosine was significantly lower in the patients (7.2 ± 0.5 (S.D.) μmol/min/mg protein) than in the controls (12.3 ± 3.4 (S.D.) μmol/min/mg protein). The K_m values did not differ between the patients (15 ± 3 (S.D.) μmol/l) and the controls (21 ± 8 (S.D.) μmol/l).

In the PET studies the intransport rate constant was calculated from data obtained between 1 and 3.5 min after the tracer injection. The rate constant of tyrosine intransport did not differ between the groups (controls K_1 0.052 ± 0.018 (S.D.) ml/g/min, patients K_1 0.045 ± 0.011 (S.D.) ml/g/min). The tyrosine concentration was lower in the patients (43 ± 1.5 (S.D.) nmol/ml, $P < 0.05$) than in the controls (60 ± 12 (S.D.) nmol/ml). The influx rate of tyrosine was also lower in the patients (1.95 ± 0.50 (S.D.) nmol/g/min, $P < 0.05$) than in the controls (2.97 ± 0.59 (S.D.) nmol/g/min). The net accumulation rate of radioactivity did not differ between the controls (0.0148 ± 0.0007 (S.D.) ml/g/min) and the patients (0.0156 ± 0.0017 (S.D.) ml/g/min). The apparent volume of distribution was lower in the controls (0.369 ± 0.044 (S.D.) ml/g) than in the patients (0.419 ± 0.014 (S.D.) ml/g,

$P < 0.05$). The brain net utilization of tyrosine was different between the groups (controls 0.883 ± 0.176 (S.D.) nmol/g/min), patients 0.672 ± 0.066 (S.D.) nmol/g/min, $P < 0.05$). The estimated brain tissue concentration of tyrosine did not differ between controls and patients.

Comments

In two independent studies we have found an isolated decrease in the capacity for tyrosine transport in cultured skin fibroblasts in patients with schizophrenia. The K_m for tyrosine and the other amino acids transported by the L-system did not differ between the groups. Thus the overall capacity of the L-system was not changed in the patients. The decreased capacity for tyrosine uptake in cells from patients with schizophrenia could not be explained in terms of known amino acid transport mechanisms. The in vitro findings indicate a more general alteration in plasma membrane function in schizophrenia.

The in vivo results demonstrated a lower influx of tyrosine in the patients which are in accordance with the in vitro findings demonstrating a lower V_{max} for tyrosine in the same patients. The intransport rate constant was similar in the two groups but was expected to be larger in the patients (increased efficiency of the transport) due to their lower tyrosine concentrations. This was not case, which might be explained by an enhanced concentration of the other amino acids, sharing the transport system with tyrosine. If the summed concentrations of the competing amino acids are the same in the groups, then the intransport rate constant should be determined by the total concentration and the patients and the controls should have similar rate constants. However, this does not explain that the brain net utilization rate of tyrosine was lower in the patients than in the controls despite similar tissue concentrations of tyrosine in the two groups.

Taken together, the in vitro and the in vivo results give strong indications of an altered tyrosine transport in patients with schizophrenia. The results may be interpreted as an indication of a disturbed membrane function involving not only the brain but also the periphery. Membrane abnormalities have been reported in schizophrenia; and in another study we found morphological changes in skeletal muscle biopsies from patients with schizophrenia [4]. We propose that patients with schizophrenia suffer from a general membrane dysfunction which will involve different functional consequences depending on the cell type.

Acknowledgements

Ms. Anita Liberg is gratefully acknowledged for preparing the manuscript. This work was supported by grants from the Swedish Medical Research Council.

References

1. Bjerkenstedt L, Edman G, Hagenfeldt L, Sedvall G and Wiesel F-A (1985) Br. J. Psychiatry 147: 276–282.
2. Hagenfeldt L, Venizelos N, Bjerkenstedt L and Wiesel F-A (1987) Life Sci. 41: 2749–2757.
3. Patlak CS, Blasberg RG and Fenstermacher JD (1983) J. Cereb. Blood Flow Metab. 3: 1–7.
4. Borg J, Edström L, Bjerkenstedt L, Wiesel F-A, Farde L and Hagenfeldt L (1987) J. Neurol. Neurosurg. Psychiatry 50: 1655–1664.

© 1991 Elsevier Science Publishers B.V. All rights reserved.
Biological Psychiatry, Volume 2. G. Racagni et al., editors.

Amino acid metabolism and tardive dyskinesia vulnerability in schizophrenics

Mary Ann Richardson, Raymond Suckow, Howard Kushner, Istvan Sziraki and William Boggiano
Nathan S. Kline Institute for Psychiatric Research, Orangeburg, NY 10962, U.S.A.

Introduction

Tardive dyskinesia (TD) is an abnormal movement disorder seen secondary to neuroleptic treatment. It afflicts large numbers of chronically ill psychiatric patients, primarily schizophrenics, for whom these drugs are the prime treatment medium. The pathogenesis and pathophysiology of the disorder have resisted definition despite the fact that it has received much research attention.

A large-scale epidemiological study (n = 211) conducted by the first author defined a risk factor for TD which offered a clue to a possible mechanism of its development. That investigation was conducted among mentally retarded inpatients; the risk factor defined was the disease of phenylketonuria (PKU).

PKU is a profound hyperphenylalaninemia caused (in its classical form) by a deficiency of phenylalanine-4-hydroxylase. Symptoms of the disorder include mental retardation, seizures, spasticity and EEG irregularities. The excessive accumulation of phenylalanine (Phe) in plasma and tissues leads to high levels of brain Phe. Also, because of the competition among the large neutral amino acids (LNAA) for brain entrance, higher plasma Phe leads to correspondingly lower brain levels of tyrosine and tryptophan. Precursor availability for catecholamine and indolamine synthesis is thus reduced. PKU patients, therefore, have been shown to have low CSF and brain levels (on autopsy) of dopamine, norepinephrine and serotonin.

PKU having been found to be a risk factor for TD in the mentally retarded, and the known impact of the disorder on neurotransmitter metabolism led to the question of whether a PKU-like phenylalanine metabolism (though less severe) was a risk factor for TD in psychiatric patients. The following study was thus undertaken to test for a relationship between phenylalanine metabolism and TD in male schizophrenics.

Methods and Procedures

All male inpatients of a state psychiatric center between December 1984 and March 1986 who satisfied DSM III or RDC criteria for schizophrenia were screened for study inclusion. The final study population consisted of 53 consenting male schizophrenics.

All subjects fasted from 10 p.m. the evening prior to the experimental session. Fasting blood samples were collected at 6:30 a.m. All subjects were served the same breakfast as a protein loading. Blood samples were also drawn 2 h subsequent to meal completion for postloading assays. Analysis of amino acids in plasma was accomplished by a technique involving high performance liquid chromatography preceded by precolumn derivatization of the samples by phenylisothiocyanate [1]. Ratios of plasma levels of Phe to the other large neutral amino acids were calculated to estimate the rates at which Phe entered the brain [2].

Patients were evaluated at the experimental session and at subsequent rating sessions for neuroleptic side-effects and psychiatric status. The TD criterion measure [3] was based on a mild-severe global rating of a subset of the Simpson Abbreviated Dyskinesia Scale (ADS) [4]. Psychiatric status was evaluated by use of the BPRS. Several other variables were also quantified for study; among these were age at first neuroleptic treatment, neuroleptic dosage at the experimental session, and average neuroleptic dosage for the two weeks prior to the session.

The independent variables were analyzed both successively and simultaneously. The successive analyses consisted of *t*-tests testing differences between TD Yes/No groups. The simultaneous approach used was a logistic regression analysis [5] with TD status as the dependent variable.

Results

Patients were classified by TD status: Yes ($n = 34$) and No ($n = 19$). The postloading (PL) plasma Phe and both the fasting (F) and PL Phe/LNAA ratios were significantly higher for the TD Yes patients (PL Phe, $P \leq 0.05$; F Phe/LNAA, $P \leq 0.05$; PL Phe/LNAA, $P \leq 0.01$). Age at first neuroleptic treatment and BPRS total score also both showed significantly higher values for the TD Yes patients ($P \leq 0.05$ and $P \leq 0.01$, respectively).

Two logistic regression models (fasting and postloading) both showed the Phe/LNAA ($P \leq 0.05$), the age at first neuroleptic treatment ($P \leq 0.05$) and the BPRS total score ($P \leq 0.05$) to be significant risk factors for TD status, thus showing these three variables to be independent risk factors for TD presence.

Discussion

The present study based on a PKU model of Phe metabolism is the first investigation of a relationship between TD and amino acid metabolism. The results imply a major role for the balance of plasma amino acids in the pathogenesis and pathophysiology of TD. Looking again to our PKU model, as we stated in the introduction, the hyperphenylalanemia of that disease has been demonstrated to directly cause low plasma, urine, CSF and brain levels of 5-HIAA, HVA, MHPG, DA, NE and 5-HT [6–11]. These data incorporating our study results would lead us to postulate a hyponeurotransmitter model of TD etiology. The question remains, however: would the more subtle differences in Phe metabolism as those seen between TD Yes/No groups in this study be sufficient to be the sole cause of a neurotransmitter imbalance that could lead to increased TD vulnerability? Some other work on schizophrenic patients lends support to this notion [12]. The latter study reported for schizophrenics but not for normals that high plasma Phe was associated with decreased CSF levels of HVA and 5-HIAA.

References

1. Bidlingmeyer BA, Cohen SA and Farvin TL (1984) J. Chromatogr. 336: 93–104.
2 Pardridge WM and Choi TB (1986) Fed. Proc. 45: 2073–2078.
3. Richardson MA and Craig TJ (1982) Am. J. Psychiatry 139: 341–343.
4. Simpson GM, Lee JH, Zoubok B et al. (1979) Psychopharmacology (Berlin) 64: 171–179.
5. Harrell FE, Lee KL, Califf RM et al. (1984) Stat. Med. 3: 143–152.
6. Butler IJ, O'Flynn ME, Seifert WE Jr et al. (1981) J. Pediatr. 98: 729–733.
7. Cession-Forsion A, Vandermeulen R, Dodinval P et al. (1966) Pathol. Biol. 14: 1157–1159.
8 Curtius H-Ch, Niederwieser A, Viscontini M et al. (1981) Adv. Exp. Med. Biol. 133: 277–287.
9. Nadler HL and Hsia DY (1961) Proc. Soc. Exp. Biol. Med. 107: 721–723.
10. Pare CMB, Sandler M and Stacey RS (1975) Lancet i: 551–553.
11. Weil-Malherve H (1955) J. Ment. Sci. 101: 733–775.
12. Bjerkenstedt L, Edman G, Hagenfeldt L et al. (1985) Br. J. Psychiatry 147: 276–282.

© 1991 Elsevier Science Publishers B.V. All rights reserved.
Biological Psychiatry, Volume 2. G. Racagni et al., editors.

The importance of the plasma dexamethasone window: A dose response study in depressed patients and controls

G.F. Johnson[1], G.E. Hunt[1], B.T. O'Sullivan[1] and I. Caterson[2]

[1] Department of Psychiatry, University of Sydney; and [2] Department of Endocrinology, Royal Prince Alfred Hospital, Sydney, N.S.W., Australia

Introduction

There is wide variability in plasma dexamethasone (DEX) levels following a standard 1-mg dexamethasone suppression test (DST), and this has been shown to significantly affect cortisol response [1]. Cortisol escape following DEX may reflect central disinhibition of the hypothalamic pituitary adrenal (HPA axis) or it may result from inappropriately low levels of plasma DEX. Conversely, in some patients, high plasma DEX levels result in cortisol suppression regardless of HPA axis function [2,3]. To accurately define the range or "window" with minimum and maximum circulating DEX for a DST result to be considered valid, dose-response studies were undertaken in depressed patients, non-depressed psychiatric controls and normal subjects.

Material and Methods

Subjects

The subjects included 71 inpatients (54 major depression and 17 psychiatric controls) and 19 healthy controls. Inpatients underwent a baseline observation and washout period of 3–7 days. Diagnoses were made using research diagnostic criteria following interview with The Schedule for Affective Disorders and Schizophrenia (SADS). Standard DST exclusion criteria were used.

Procedure

In a randomised crossover design, 35 subjects received 0.5 mg and 1.0 mg DEX and 55 subjects 0.5 mg and 1.5 mg. Blood for pre-DST cortisol was obtained at 4 p.m. on day 1. At 11 p.m. the first dose of DEX was given orally. On day 2 blood was collected at 8 a.m. and 4 p.m. for cortisol and DEX determination. On days 3 and 4 the procedures were repeated with the alternate dose. Plasma cortisol and DEX were measured by radioimmunoassay as previously described [4]. All samples from each subject were assayed in the same batch. The co-efficients of variation between assays of DEX were less than 10% and the variations within each assay were less than 5%. The detection limit for plasma DEX was 0.3 nmol/l. The standard criterion for defining cortisol suppression was a plasma cortisol concentration of greater than 139 nmol/l at either 8 a.m. or 4 p.m. following DEX administration. Receiver operating characteristic (ROC) curves were generated for each DEX dose while calculating the sensitivity (% of true positives) and 1-specificity (% false positives) at each sampling time over a wide range of cortisol criterion values (55–330 nmol/l). In addition, ROC curves were generated for various ranges of 4 p.m. plasma DEX concentrations. For each plotted value on the ROC curve, there were at least 10 subjects with a positive or negative DST result [5].

Results

There were no significant differences between the pre-DST cortisol levels before the 0.5 mg or the 1 or 1.5 mg DST. There were significant differences in the 4 p.m. post-DST cortisol levels between diagnostic groups after all doses. These were due to lower cortisol levels in healthy controls compared to the non-depressed psychiatric controls and depressed patients. There were no significant differences in plasma DEX and diagnostic groups at 8 a.m. or 4 p.m. There were, however, significant differences in plasma DEX between suppressors and non-suppressors after the 0.5 mg and the 1 or 1.5 mg.

Using the 4 p.m. cortisol level, reliable suppression was obtained in control subjects at DEX levels of 2 nmol/l or above, ensuring high specificity. The DST performance comparing the 3 doses 0.5, 1 and 1.5 mg and 3 plasma dexamethasone ranges 1–4 nmol/l, 1.5–4 nmol/l and 2–4 nmol/l are compared using ROC analysis (Fig. 1). The ROC curve for the plasma DEX range of 2–4 nmol/l was superior to the other DEX ranges or compared to the DEX doses. Both specificity and sensitivity remained high over a broad range of cortisol criterion 83–220 nmol/l when 4 p.m. plasma DEX fell within 2 and 4 nmol/l.

Nine out of the 10 control subjects who were non-suppressors with low DEX levels following the 0.5-mg dose switched to suppression after 1 or 1.5 mg, while 11 out of 21 depressed patients remained non-suppressors. All of these subjects had DEX levels greater than 2.0 nmol/l. DST status remained uncertain in 10 patients, 5 depressed and 5 controls, with elevated cortisol levels but DEX levels below 2 nmol/l following the 1- or 1.5-mg dose.

A total of 19 subjects who were suppressors had plasma DEX levels above 4 nmol/l. After testing with the lower dose, all of the controls remained suppressors. In contrast, 8 out of 10 depressed patients who were suppressors with plasma DEX levels greater than 4.0 nmol/l at 4 p.m. became non-suppressors with DEX levels between 2–4 nmol/l.

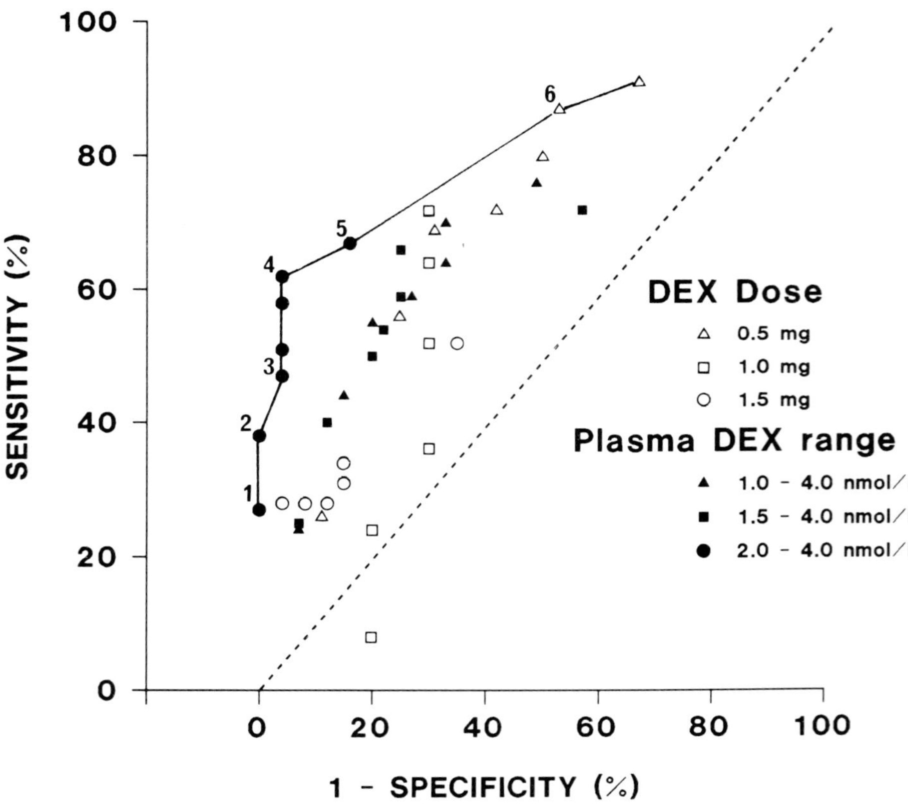

Fig. 1. ROC analysis for 4 p.m. cortisol after each dose of DEX and after 3 plasma DEX ranges. The solid line indicates the upper convex hull of the ROC analysis, showing the superiority of the plasma DEX range (2–4 nmol/l). The diagonal dotted line indicates the line of no information. The numerals indicate the following combinations of cortisol (nmol/l) and DEX dose or plasma DEX range (nmol/l): 1) cortisol 330 and DEX 2–4; 2) cortisol 220 and DEX 2–4; 3) cortisol 166 and DEX 2–4; 4) cortisol 83 and DEX 24; 5) cortisol 55 and DEX 2–4; 6) cortisol 83 and DEX 0.5 mg.

Conclusion

Accurate interpretation of HPA axis activity requires simultaneous measurement of plasma cortisol and DEX. The use of plasma dexamethasone window enhances test performance. Using the standard 1 mg DST 70% of patients will be correctly typed, 17% will fall below the window and 13% will have DEX levels above the window and will require retesting at a higher dose of 2 mg or lower dose of 0.5 mg respectively to confirm DST status.

References

1. Johnson GF, Hunt G, Ken K and Caterson I (1984) Psychiatr. Res. 13: 305–313.
2. O'Sullivan BT, Hunt GE, Johnson GF and Caterson ID (1989) Biol. Psychiatry 25: 739–754.
3. Hunt GE, O'Sullivan BT, Johnson GF and Caterson ID (1991) Psychiatr. Res. 36: 209–222.
4. Johnson GF, Hunt G and Caterson I. (1988) J. Affective Disord. 15: 93–100.
5. Kraemer HC (1987) Psychoneuroendocrinology 12: 411–427.

© 1991 Elsevier Science Publishers B.V. All rights reserved.
Biological Psychiatry, Volume 2. G. Racagni et al., editors.

A pharmacokinetic study of dexamethasone and the pharmacodynamic response of cortisol, ACTH and β-endorphin in normal control subjects, depressed patients and non-depressed psychiatric controls

B.T. O'Sullivan[1], G.F. Johnson[1], G.E. Hunt[1], D. Cutler[2] and I. Caterson[3]

[1]*Department of Psychiatry, University of Sydney;* [2]*Department of Pharmacy, University of Sydney; and* [3]*Department of Endocrinology, Royal Prince Alfred Hospital, Sydney, Australia*

Introduction

The Dexamethasone Suppression Test (DST) has been widely studied as a dynamic test of hypothalamic-pituitary-adrenal (HPA) axis function in patients with major depression. Recent research has clearly identified plasma dexamethasone (DEX) as an important intervening variable in determining the DST response with wide inter-individual differences in plasma DEX levels achieved following the standard 1-mg oral dose of DEX administered at 11 p.m. [1]. A formal pharmacokinetic study was undertaken in order to detail the pharmacokinetic parameters of DEX as well as the pharmacodynamic changes which occur in cortisol, ACTH and β-endorphin.

Methods

The study involved 3 nights of multiple serial blood sampling via an intravenous catheter in each subject. Subjects were fasted throughout each procedure. The first night was a "placebo" run to define the normal cortisol, ACTH and β-endorphin secretory profile for that individual. On the second and third nights (separated by at least 48 h), 1 mg oral DEX and 1 mg intravenous DEX was administered at 11 p.m. in a randomized cross-over design. Plasma DEX, cortisol, ACTH and β-endorphin were then measured throughout the course of the night. Pharmacokinetic parameters of DEX were calculated including C_{max}, T_{max}, volume of distribution (V_d), clearance (CL), half-life, area under the curve (AUC), and percent bioavailability (F%) (oral AUC/i.v. AUC).

Results

A total of 25 subjects were studied consisting of 10 normal controls (a male and a female from each of the decades 20s, 30s, 40s, 50s and 60s), 9 depressed inpatients with DSM III "melancholia", and a further 6 non-depressed psychiatric control patients. There were 4 males and 5 females in the depressed group and 2 males and 4 females in the psychiatric control group. There was no significant difference in the mean age of normal subjects, 47.7 (14.4) years; and depressed inpatients, 41.0 (14.9) years; however, the psychiatric control group was significantly younger, consisting mainly of young schizophrenics with a mean age of 24.0 (3.7) years. Both the oral and the i.v. doses of DEX suppressed cortisol in all normal controls. All of the depressed patients suppressed initially; however 4 of the 9 depressed patients escaped from suppression by 4 p.m., as did 1 of the non-depressed psychiatric controls.

There was considerable interindividual variation in pharmacokinetic parameters between subjects from all 3 diagnostic groups. No statistically significant differences were found in C_{max}, T_{max}, V_d, half-life, clearance or bioavailability between the 3 diagnostic groups, or between suppressors and non-suppressors. However, a trend was observed in which psychiatric patients (depressed and non-depressed) had a lower AUC (oral and i.v.), a faster clearance and shorter half-life compared with normal control subjects. Following the i.v. dose of DEX, depressed patients and non-depressed control patients had a mean AUC ($\pm$ standard deviation) of 15900 (2850) and 15100 (3040) respectively, compared with normal controls 20200 (5880) nmol.l/min. The clearance was 141 (25) and 146 (29) ml/min compared with 115 (34) ml/min in normal controls and half-lives of 314 (63) and 324 (60) min compared with 364 (75) min for the normal controls. After the oral dose of DEX, the half-lives were very similar to those from the i.v. data: 325 (82) and 321 (45) min for the depressed and psychiatric control patients respectively, compared with 355 (78) min for normal controls. The C_{max} was 20.1 (7.8) and 24.0 (9.9) nmol/l for the depressed and psychiatric control patients respectively and was not sigificantly different from the C_{max} for the normal controls, 22.4 (6.5) nmol/l. There was wide interindividual variation in the T_{max} following the oral dose with a mean of 160 (196) and 70 (29) min in the depressed and psychiatric control subjects and 124 (80) min in the normal controls. The bioavailability of DEX (oral AUC/i.v. AUC) did not differ significantly between groups: 58.2 (16.2) and 67.2 (19.0) % in depressed and psychiatric controls respectively, compared with 62.8 (11.6) % in the normal control subjects. Males had a significantly longer half-life compared with females after the i.v. dose: 373 (73) min vs. 308 (51) min, although this may have been the result of males also having a significantly greater weight and a larger volume of distribution: 48.5 (16.2) l compared with 36.4 (9.7) l. There was no significant difference in the plasma clearance rates of DEX between males and females: 137 (32) vs. 128 (33) ml/min. Suppressors and non-suppressors did not differ significantly on any pharmacokinetic parameter although the numbers of non-suppressors was small; only 5 following the oral dose of DEX out of the total of 25 subjects in the study.

The wide interindividual variation in all pharmacokinetic parameters in subjects from all diagnostic groups emphasizes the importance of actually measuring plasma DEX levels in order to interpret DST results in each individual, since very high or very low plasma DEX levels may result in both false negative and false positive DST results, respectively [2,3].

ACTH and β-endorphin levels were suppressed together following DEX administration. There was no clear connection between cortisol escape and ACTH levels, although sampling times were relatively infrequent. β-endorphin levels were not particularly useful in view of limitations in the assay procedure.

An unexpected finding which emerged in 5 of the depressed patients was a transient large increase in cortisol (and ACTH) release immediately following DEX administration at 11 p.m., more marked following i.v. DEX dose compared with the oral dose. This response was not present in any of the normal controls. A similar early response has been previously reported in several depressed patients [4] as well as Cushing's patients, and may represent an abnormality in the fast feedback arm of corticosteroid inhibition, distinct from abnormalities in the longer intermediate feedback control of the HPA axis which the standard DST procedure normally assesses [5]. The early transient release of ACTH was not clearly associated with DST non-suppression and may represent a separate phenomenon which requires further explanation.

Acknowledgements

Dr. O'Sullivan was supported by a research fellowship from the N.S.W. Institute of Psychiatry and a travel award from the World Federation of Societies of Biological Psychiatry.

References

1. Lowy MT and Meltzer HY (1987) Biol. Psychiatry 22: 373–385.
2. Johnson GF, Hunt G, Ken K and Caterson I (1987) Biol. Psychiatry 22: 1035–1039.
3. O'Sullivan BT, Hunt GE, Johnson GF and Caterson ID (1989) Biol. Psychiatry 25: 739–754.
4. Carr DB, Wool C, Lydiard B et al. (1984) Am. J. Psychiatry 141: 590–592.
5. Young EA, Watson SJ and Akil H (1986) In: van Ree JM and Matthysse S (eds.) Progress in Brain Research, Vol. 65. Elsevier, Amsterdam, pp. 153–166.

© 1991 Elsevier Science Publishers B.V. All rights reserved.
Biolcgical Psychiatry, Volume 2. G. Racagni et al., editors.

Towards a pharmacokinetic-pharmacodynamic model of plasma dexamethasone concentration during the DST

J.C. Ritchie[1], S.K. Gupta[2], D. Knight[1], B.J. Carroll[1] and K.R.R. Krishnan[1]
[1]Department of Psychiatry, Duke University, Durham, North Carolina; and [2]Abbbott Laboratories, Abbott Park, Illinois, U.S.A.

Introduction

Patients with endogenous depression or "melancholia" have been described as having an abnormal hypothalamic-pituitary-adrenal (HPA) axis. Findings in such patients often include hypersecretion of cortisol, inappropriate nocturnal cortisol secretion, and escape from suppression during the dexamethasone suppression test (DST). Among properly screened psychiatric patients, non-suppression during the standardized DST has been suggested to be a specific marker of melancholia [1]. The precise relationship between the pharmacokinetics and pharmacodynamics of dexamethasone (DEX) has never been fully elucidated. Recently several research reports have appeared in which "normal" or altered (decreased $t_{1/2}\beta$) DEX pharmacokinetics have been demonstrated [2–5]. Since it is not known to what extent plasma DEX concentrations during the early biophase and/or elimination phase reflect the dynamic actions of DEX on the fast or delayed glucocorticoid feedback systems, the significance of plasma DEX concentrations during the DST have raised much debate. Previously [6] we developed a combined pharmacokinetic-pharmacodynamic (PK-PD) model for dexamethasone after intravenous (i.v.) dosing. We now report on our recent attempts to extend this model to the oral dosing paradigm most commonly used in the standard DST.

Methods

This study protocol was reviewed by the Duke University Institutional Review board prior to its initiation. All subjects gave written informed consent before the protocol was begun. An intravenous catheter was inserted into the forearm of each subject at 21:00 h. Baseline blood samples were drawn at 22:30 and 23:00 h. One mg of dexamethasone was administered orally at 23:00 h. Serial blood samples were collected every 30 min until 01:00 and thereafter every 15 min until 08:00. Subjects were fasted and kept recumbent throughout the evening. Subjects resumed normal activities at 08:00 and returned at 15:00 and 23:00 h to have blood samples drawn by venipuncture in accordance with the standard DST protocol.

Plasma cortisol (FPIA, Abbott TD_x), ACTH (extracted RIA) and dexamethasone (RIA-IgG Corp.) were measured in all samples. Pharmacokinetic parameters were analyzed on both individual and mean data using the non-linear least squares fitting program, NONLIN [7]. A two-compartment model (with elimination assumed to occur from the central compartment only) was used to describe the DEX pharmacokinetics for all groups. A parametric model approach was used to simultaneously characterize the pharmacokinetics and pharmacodynamics of DEX.

Results

Three groups of subjects were studied in this protocol: normal controls ($n = 6$), "suppressing" depressed patients ($n = 9$), and "non-suppressing" depressed patients ($n = 6$). There were no significant differences in age or sex between the three groups although the depressed patients tended to be older than the normal controls. All normal controls were DST suppressors. There was considerable interindividual variation in plasma DEX concentrations amongst all three groups. Depressed "suppressors" exhibited a somewhat higher distribution rate constant (K_a) than did either the controls or the DST non-suppressors (2.39 h vs. 0.91 and 0.95 h, respectively). DST non-suppressors had a significantly higher C_{max} (19.58 mN/l) than the two other groups (normals = 8.85, DST suppressors = 10.06) and a higher terminal elimination rate constant ($t_{1/2}\beta$). This is in contrast to previous studies. DST non-suppressors also had a shorter t_{max} than the other two groups (controls = 3.03 h, suppressors = 3.15 h, non-suppressors = 1.61 h). Volume (area) and clearance rates were similar in all three groups. The interpretation of these results may be confounded by the unique composition of each group and the small number of individuals involved in this study.

The dynamic model demonstrated that non-suppressing patients had a faster rate of DEX elimination from the effect site ($t_{1/2}k_{eo}$) and a 50% effect site concentration (EC_{50}) at least 5 times higher than that of the normals or the suppressing patients (normals = 0.52, DST suppressors = 0.78, DST non-suppressors = 8.6 nM/l). This data may be interpreted as showing that for the non-suppressing group the onset and termination of the effect of DEX is at least 5 times faster than for the other two groups. It should be noted that the above data is generated from mean concentrations. Similar parameters calculated from individual control or patient data exhibited a high degree of variability indicating the need for further studies. Additionally, no attempt has been made to include the "ACTH link" in the above calculations. This work is currently in progress along with the inclusion of baseline cortisol concentrations as a dynamic variable.

In summary, we have developed a PK-PD model to establish the quantitative relationship between plasma DEX and plasma cortisol after a 1.0 mg or dose of DEX at 23:00 h. Refinement and extension of this construct to a larger population may allow the development of a population-based model which potentially could be used to "tailor" the DST cortisol cut-off criterion to each patient's individual DEX kinetics and dynamics.

Acknowledgements

We wish to thank Ms. Andrea Laws for her help in preparing this manuscript. This work was supported in part by NIMH Grants No. MH 39593 and MH 42510.

References

1. Carroll BJ, Feinberg M, Greden JF, Tarika J, Albala AA, Haskett RF, McI James N, Kronfol Z, Lohr N, Steiner M, de Vigne JP and Young E (1981) Arch. Gen. Psychiatry 38: 15–22.
2. Carroll BJ, Schroeder K, Mukhopadhyay S, Greden JR, Feinberg M, Ritchie JC and Tarika J (1980) J. Clin. Endocrinol. Metab. 52: 433–437.
3. Holsboer F (1983) Pharmacopsychiatria 15: 186–191.
4. Johnson GF, Hunt G, Kerr K and Caterson I (1984) Psychiatr. Res. 13: 305–313.
5. Arana GW, Workman RJ and Baldessarini RJ (1984) Am. J. Psychiatry 141: 1619–1620.
6. Gupta SK, Ritchie JC, Wiedemann K and Holsboer F (1991) Modeling the pharmacokinetics and pharmacodynamics of dexamethasone in depressed patients. Eur. J. Clin. Pharmacol. (in press).
7. Metzler CM, Elfrins GL and McEween AJ (1974) Biometrics 30: 562–563.

© 1991 Elsevier Science Publishers B.V. All rights reserved.
Biological Psychiatry, Volume 2. G. Racagni et al., editors.

Platelets as peripheral models for neuropsychiatry: A brief review

Alfred Pletscher
Swiss Academy of Medical Sciences, CH-4051 Basel, Switzerland

The neurotransmitter system of blood platelets

Figure 1 shows some main elements of this system. The plasma membrane exhibits *receptors*, similar to those involved in neurotransmission in the central nervous system (CNS), and specific binding sites whose functional role remains to be clarified. The *morphological* changes of the platelets which are induced by receptor stimulation, e.g. the shape change and release reactions and aggregation, are mediated by various *intracellular messengers*. In addition the plasma membrane exhibits a specific Na^+-dependent, carrier-mediated *5-HT-uptake* and a less well-investigated DA-uptake. Psychotropic drugs, especially tricyclic antidepressants which show specific, high affinity binding to the 5-HT-carrier, are potent inhibitors of 5-HT-uptake. Platelets contain various types of organelles, for instance *dense bodies*, α-granules, lysosomes. The dense bodies accumulate biogenic amines, using a granular membrane carrier, along an intra extragranular proton gradient generated by an ATP/ATPase dependent mechanism. This carrier is sensitive to reserpine-type drugs. Intragranularly the amines are retained by formation of reversible complexes with nucleotides such as ATP and ADP. Furthermore, platelets contain mitochondrial enzymes, especially *monoaminoxydase* (MAO), which in man is of type B [1,2].

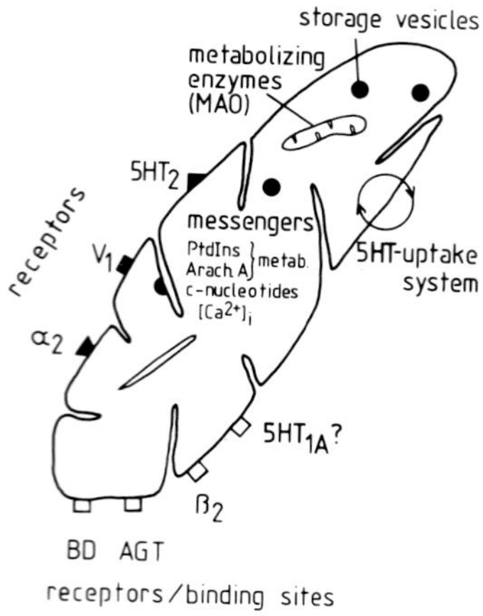

Fig. 1.

Table 1. Similarities between platelets-neurons

5-HT_2 receptor	+	Amine storage	+
α_2-adrenergic receptor	+	Release mechanisms	+
β_2-adrenergic receptor	+	MAO-B	+
V_1-vasopressin receptor	+	Amine biosynthesis	–
Intracellular messengers	+	Intrasynaptic regulation	–
		Electric response	–
		Neuron-specific enolase	+
Membrane uptake 5-HT	+	5-HT-binding protein	–
DA	(+)	Synaptophysin (rabbit)	+
NA	–	Neuropeptide Y (rabbit)	+
Aantidepressant binding	+		

Many tools used in neurons are also available for investigations of the transmitter system in platelets e.g. receptor ligands, amine uptake inhibitors, drugs interfering with amine storage and enzyme inhibitors.

Use of platelets in neuropsychiatry

Some similarities (+) and dissimilarities (–) between platelets and neurons regarding the properties of their neurotransmitters are shown in Table 1 [1,2]. These data indicate that platelets can be considered as limited models for neurons. Thereby, it has to be kept in mind that even the similarities are not absolute.

A wealth of studies using platelets as models in neuropsychiatry has been published in the last decades. These investigations are full of controversies. Table 2 gives a summary of some of them indicating (by thick arrows) where a limited consensus seems to be emerging. Many of the controversies are likely to be due to methodological reasons, e.g. differences in incubation media, platelet size populations, nature of radioactive ligands and competitors and time and temperature parameters. Further progress depends on the application of standardized, well established methods and the choice of patients from clearly-defined diagnostic categories.

New findings

Recently, the occurrence of *brain-derived neurotrophic factor* (BDNF) in human platelets has been reported [3]. Its biological activity is very similar to that of pig brain BDNF but is 50–100 times higher in platelets. Molecular cloning and DNA-sequencing revealed striking homologies between the two factors. Also, the molecular weights were similar (13,000 D). Furthermore, BDNF mRNA derived from the cytoplasm of megakaryocytes was shown by reverse transcriptase polymerase chain reaction to be present in human platelets. The functional role of

Table 2. Neuropsychiatric disorders and platelet changes

Mental depression	5-HT-uptake ⇓; imipramine binding ⇓n; α_2 binding ⇑; LSD binding ↑; MAO-B ↑n↓; PI, cAMP responses disturbed
Panic disorders	5-HT-uptake ↑; α_2 binding ↑↓; LSD binding ↓
Anxiety	Benzodiazepine binding ↓
Alcoholism	5-HT-uptake ↑; 5-HT-content ↓ (withdrawal)
Schizophrenia	Antidepress. binding ↓n; α_2 binding ↑; MAO-B ↓n; cAMP response disturbed
Migraine	5-HT-uptake ↓; 5-HT-content ⇓; 5-HT-release ⇑; α_2 binding ↓
Down's syndrome	5-HT-uptake ⇓; 5-HT-content ⇓
Parkinson	α_2-Binding ↓; MAO-B↑↓
Stress	Benzodiazepine binding ↑↓
Alzheimer's disease	Antidepress. binding n↑; 5-HT receptor binding n↓; MAO-B ↑; membrane fluidity ↑

↑ = increased; ↓ = decreased; n = no change.

platelet BDNF is not yet clear. It is possible that this factor, like that of brain, might provide trophic support for regenerating sensory nerves.

Human platelets were also found to contain large amounts of protease nexin-II (PN-II) which is identical to the secreted form of *amyloid precursor protein* (APP) exhibiting the Kunitz protease inhibitor domain (PN-II/KPI-APP). The whole molecule occurs in the platelets as indicated by the presence of the carboxy-terminal epitope. The protein is abundant in the α-granules from where it can be secreted on platelet activation. In addition, human platelets contain an APP lacking the Kunitz domain. Platelets seem to be the major circulatory source for APPs.

PN-II/KPI-APP and β-A_4 (a proteolytic cleavage product of APP) occur in neuritic plaques and cerebrovascular deposits in Alzheimer's disease and it has been suggested that such deposits originate in part from the circulation [4,5]. It appears worthwhile to investigate whether pathological changes in the kinetics and metabolism of platelet PN-II/KPI-APP (possibly as expression of a systemic process) might be indicative for the disease process in the brain of patients with Alzheimer's disease or Down's syndrome. It has also been suggested that membrane abnormalities of platelets present in Alzheimer's disease (Table 2) might affect APP release and induce formation of amyloidogenic fragments [5].

References

1. Pletscher A (1988) Experientia 44: 152–155.
2. Da Prada M, Cesura AM, Launay JM and Richards JG (1988) Experientia 44: 115–126.
3. Yamamoto H and Gurney ME (1990) J. Neurosci. 10: 3469–3478.
4. Van Norstrand WE, Schmaier AH, Farrow JS, Cines DB and Cunningham DD (1991) Biochem. Biophys. Res Commun. 175: 15–21.
5. Bush AI, Martins RN, Rumble B, Moir R, Fuller S, Milward E, Currie J, Ames D, Weidemann A, Fischer P, Multhaup G, Beyreuther K and Masters CL (1990) J. Biol. Chem. 265: 15977–15983.

© 1991 Elsevier Science Publishers B.V. All rights reserved.
Biological Psychiatry, Volume 2. G. Racagni et al., editors.

Inhibition of platelet MAO-B in the rabbit by Ro 19-6327 as peripheral marker for monitoring brain MAO-B blockade

R. Kettler and M. da Prada
F. Hoffmann-La Roche Ltd, Pharma Division, Preclinical Research, CH-4002 Basel, Switzerland

Introduction

In several clinical studies with irreversible monoamine oxidase type B (MAO-B) inhibitors, the degree of MAO-B inhibition in the CNS has been evaluated indirectly by measuring the extent of MAO-B inhibition in circulating blood platelets [1]. In the present study in rabbits we confirm and extend previous results [2] demonstrating that the time-course of MAO-B inhibition in platelets and liver parallels that occurring in brain tissue (frontal cortex and striatum).

The present investigations with Ro 19-6327 (N-(2-aminoethyl-5-chloro-2-pyridine carboxamide HCI) were aimed at demonstrating that Ro 19-6327, a novel mechanism-based inhibitor [3] even at high doses, behaves as a highly selective and reversible inhibitor of MAO-B. They also provide additional evidence that platelets are a reliable peripheral model for monitoring central MAO-B inhibition.

Materials and Methods

After oral administration of Ro 19-6327 to rabbits, blood was collected and tissue samples (liver, frontal cortex and striatum) were prepared. Blood platelets were isolated by centrifugation and tissue MAO-B activity was measured radiochemically [2].

Results

As shown in Table 1, Ro 19-6327 (10 mg/kg p.o.) markedly inhibited MAO-B activity in all central and peripheral tissues investigated (>90%) already 30 min after dosing; MAO-B inhibition lasted about 48 h. At this time, a slight MAO-B inhibition was still present in platelets (23%) and frontal cortex (16%).

At a lower dose (1 mg/kg p.o.) complete MAO-B inhibition was measured 30 min after dosing only in the liver. One hour post-dosing, marked inhibition was measured in platelets and brain (frontal cortex and striatum), and in all tissues MAO-B activity recovered 16 h after drug administration.

Table 1. Time-course of the effects on brain and peripheral MAO-B activity of Ro 19-6327 administered p.o. to rabbits

Tissue	(mg/kg, p.o.)	Postinjection time: h								
		0.5	1	2	6	12	16	24	32	48
Platelets	(1)	17.7	9.4	9.5	11.1	41.7	90.9	–	–	–
Liver	(1)	4.9	2.7	2.1	5.5	69.3	94.2	–	–	–
Striatum	(1)	97.1	7.2	7.7	6.6	65.3	98.2	–	–	–
Frontal cortex	(1)	79.3	5.2	6.7	4.1	64.4	100.5	–	–	–
Platelets	(10)	9.0	–	–	7.7	–	7.9	23.4	33.3	77.0
Liver	(10)	1.1	–	–	1.7	–	5.4	75.0	75.9	97.6
Striatum	(10)	4.2	–	–	2.9	–	10.8	63.4	75.4	110.5
Frontal cortex	(10)	2.6	–	–	2.5	–	8.1	61.2	78.1	94.7

Ro 19-6327 was given p.o. to rabbits at 1 and 10 mg/kg. MAO-B activity was measured using phenethylamine ($2 \cdot 10^{-5}$ M) as the substrate [2]. Values are expressed in percent of control (untreated) rabbits and are means of at least 3 animals. S.E.M. (not given) was ≥10%. Absolute MAO-B activities of untreated controls (n = 6, mean values) were: platelets, 1.6 nmol/h/mg protein; liver, striatum and cerebral cortex: 44.5, 4.8 and 4.1 nmol/h/mg wet tissue, respectively.

Discussion

The main finding of the present study in rabbits is that a high dose of Ro 19-6327 (10 mg/kg p.o.) produces MAO-B inhibition with virtually the same time-course in both central (frontal cortex and striatum) and peripheral tissue (liver and platelets). At lower doses (1 mg/kg p.o.), Ro 19-6327 inhibited more rapidly and efficiently MAO-B activity in peripheral than in brain tissue, possibly due to its polarity. The relatively rapid recovery of MAO-B activity, which after 10 mg/kg p.o. attained control values within 48 h both centrally and peripherally, demonstrates that Ro 19-6327 behaves as a short-lasting and reversible MAO-B inhibitor also in rabbits.

In contrast to the irreversible inhibitors selegiline [4] and MDL 72,974 [5], high doses of Ro 19-6327 produced a highly selective MAO-B inhibition in rats [4] and also in rabbits, since no MAO-A inhibition was produced by 10 mg/kg Ro 19-6327 in rabbit platelets, kidney and lung.

In recent positron emission tomography (PET) investigations in healthy subjects, Ro 19-6327 was administered p.o. and (^{11}C) selegiline injected i.v. as a tracer, and platelet MAO-B inhibition was measured concomitantly. These experiments clearly showed that also in man the degree and time-course of platelet MAO-B inhibition virtually paralleled the inhibitory effect of Ro 19-6327 on the brain enzyme [6]. Clinical trials have already demonstrated a good tolerability of Ro 19-6327 in single or in repeated doses of up to 200 mg.

In conclusion, MAO-B inhibition in rabbit platelets reflects accurately the time-course of central MAO-B inhibition induced by the reversible inhibitor Ro 19-6327.

Ro 19-6327 represents an attractive and safe new adjuvant in the long-term therapy of Parkinson's and Alzheimer's diseases.

References

1. Kabins D and Gersohn S (1990) Dementia 1: 323–348.
2. Kettler R, Cesura AM, Dingemanse J and Da Prada M (1990) J. Neural Transm. (Suppl.) 32: 211–214.
3. Cesura AM, Muggli-Maniglio D, Lang G, Imhof R and Da Prada M (1990) J. Neural Transm. (Suppl.) 32: 165–170.
4. Haefely W, Kettler R, Keller HH and Da Prada M (1990) Adv. Neurol. 53: 505–512.
5. Zreika M, Fozard JR, Duddley MW, Bey Ph, McDonald IA and Palfreyman MG (1989) J. Neural Transm. (Sect. P-D) 1: 243–254.
6. Bench CJ, Price GW, Lammertsma AA, Cremer JC, Luthra SK, Turton D, Dolan RJ, Kettler R, Dingemanse J, Da Prada M, Bizière K, McClelland GR, Jamieson VL, Wood ND and Frackowiak RSJ (1991) Eur. J. Clin. Pharmacol. 40: 169–173.

© 1991 Elsevier Science Publishers B.V. All rights reserved.
Biological Psychiatry, Volume 2. G. Racagni et al., editors.

Phosphoinositide turnover in platelets of depressed patients and the effect of antidepressants

Moshe Rehavi, Alex Aviv, Eduardo Podliszewski, Nathaniel Laor, Sara Shavit and Ronit Weizman

Department of Physiology and Pharmacology, Sackler Faculty of Medicine, Tel-Aviv University, Tel Aviv 69978, Israel

Introduction

Mood disorders are among the most frequent disorders in psychiatry. Tricyclic antidepressants (TCAs) are effective in the treatment of major depression, however, the exact mode of action of these agent is still unclear. Most biological theories of affective disorders have suggested dysfunction in neurotransmission of one or more neurochemical pathways. Despite the intensive efforts to identify specific alterations in monoamine metabolism or their receptors in major affective disorders, no coherent model for mood disorders has emerged. It is yet possible that depression is associated with dysregulation of transduction mechanisms that mediate the activity of a variety of neurotransmitters. The possible involvement of phosphoinositide (PI) system, a major second messenger system in the brain, in the pathophysiology of depression is indicated by the interaction between TCAs and PI turnover [1,2]. Platelets have been utilized extensively as peripheral model for presynaptic neurons in research of neuropsychiatric disorders. Receptor-linked PI transduction systems were demonstrated in platelets [3]. The present study was designed to investigate the in vitro effect of antidepressants on the serotonin- and thrombin-induced formation of IP in [^{3}H]-myoinositol prelabeled human platelets. In addition, we studied the responsiveness of the PI system in platelets of depressed patients in comparison to normal controls.

Materials and Methods

Human venous blood was collected in 16 mM citrate buffer and 1 mM EDTA. Platelet-rich plasma was separated as described previously [4]. Platelet pellet was sedimented by centrifugation, the resultant platelet pellet was washed and resuspended in buffer and used to assess the formation of [^{3}H]-inositol phosphates, according to the method described by De Chaffoy de Courcelles et al. [5]. [^{3}H] Myoinositol (15 Ci/mmol) was purchased from New England Nuclear (Boston, MA).

Results

Serotonin up to 1,000 μM for 10 min failed to stimulate [^{3}H]-inositol phosphates (IPs) formation in platelets prelabeled for 3 h with [^{3}H]-myoinositol. The addition of 10 μM pargyline or 20 mg/ml ascorbic acid (to prevent serotonin metabolism by monoamine oxidase or serotonin oxidation) did not enhance IP accumulation in response to serotonin stimulation. In contrast, thrombin 5 units/0.5 ml induced a robust increase in IP formation (100–200%).

Similar results were obtained when the serotonin stimulation time was shortened to 5 and 1 min or extended to 15 and 45 min. Changes in [^{3}H]-myoinositol incubation time (1–3 h) did not result in any positive response of IP formation to serotonin stimulation in contrast to a 1–2-fold increase following thrombin stimulation.

Thus, serotonin under these conditions is devoid of any stimulatory effect on platelet PI turnover. This finding is in accordance with recent observation of De Chaffoy de Courcelles [6] who demonstrated only slight serotonin activation of the PI system in platelets. It seems that the role of phospholipase C (PLC) in serotonin transduction in platelets is unclear.

In order to further examine the possible interaction of antidepressants with the PI signalling system, we examined the in vitro effects of antidepressants on thrombin-stimulated formation of IPs. Thrombin-induced increase in IPs formation in platelets was inhibited in a dose-dependent manner by a variety of heterocyclic antidepressants, but not by the monoamine oxidase inhibitor phenelzine (Table 1).

Clomipramine and desipramine were the most potent inhibitors (IC_{50} = 40 μM) while the non-tricyclic antidepressants fluvoxamine and mianserine were weaker (IC_{50} > 100 μM). The MAO inhibitor phenelzine was devoid of any inhibitory activity (IC_{50} > 500 μM) at this signal transduction system. Similar results have been recently reported by Pandey et al. [7].

We are currently investigating the thrombin stimulated IPs formation in platelets of depressed patients maintained (6 months) on clomipramine treatment (75–125 mg/day). Preliminary results from 9 depressed patients (5 females and 4 males,

Table 1. Effects of antidepressants on thrombin stimulated [^{3}H]-inositol phosphate formation in human platelets

Drug	IC_{50} (μM)
Clomipramine	40 ± 10
Desipramine	40 ± 10
Amitriptyline	66 ± 15
Imipramine	81 ± 15
Nortriptyline	85 ± 17
Fluvoxamine	100 ± 12
Mianserine	170 ± 15
Phenelzine	>500

aged 20–54 years) showed no difference in the responsiveness of the inositol phospholipid signalling system when compared to 6 controls (3 males and 3 females) of similar ages. In the depressed patients thrombin increased the mean IP formation by 286% while the mean increase in the control group was 325%.

We intend to further evaluate the PI signaling system in platelets of untreated major depressed patients as well as the effect of treatment with various heterocyclic antidepressants on this system.

References

1. Kendall DA and Nahorski SR (1985) J. Pharmacol. Exp. Ther. 233: 473–479.
2. Osborne NN (1988) Neurochem. Res. 13: 105–111.
3. Daniel JL, Dangelmaiez CA and Smith JB (1987) Biochem. J. 246: 109–114.
4. Weizman A, Carmi M, Hermesh H, Shahar A, Apter A, Tyano S and Rehavi M (1986) Am. J. Psychiatry 143: 335–339.
5. De Chaffoy de Courcelles D, Roevens P, Wynants J and Van Belle H (1987) Biochem. Biophys. Acta 927: 291–302.
6. De Chaffoy de Courcelles D and Clerck F (1990) In: Saxena PR, Wallis DI, Wouters W and Bevan P (eds.) Cardiovascular Pharmacology of 5-Hydroxytryptamine. Kluwer Academic Publishers, Dordrecht, pp. 445–457.
7. Pandey SC, Davis JM, Schwertz DW and Pandey GN (1991) J. Pharmacol. Exp. Ther. 256: 1010–1018.

© 1991 Elsevier Science Publishers B.V. All rights reserved.
Biological Psychiatry, Volume 2. G. Racagni et al., editors.

Changes in platelet membrane-connected functions of demented patients

Maria Hasitz, A. Nagy, Z. Rácz and A. Lipcsey
Department of Neuropsychiatry, St. John Hospital, P.O.Box 243, 1536 Budapest, Hungary

Introduction

The similarity between platelets and presynaptic ending of the central nervous system has been compared characterizing the neurotransmitter related abnormalities. Platelets are also altered in the patients with Alzheimer's disease; platelet membrane fluidity is increased [1] and it is significantly correlated with lowered cholesterol/phospholipid ratio of platelets [2]. The platelet membrane fluidity may be controlled by a single genetic locus with two alleles that have additive effects [3] and the early-onset form of dementia is more common in the family of patients with Alzheimer's disease having abnormal platelet membrane fluidity [4]. The platelet monoamine oxidase activity increases with age and it is further increased in patients with Alzheimer-type dementias [5]. The vitamin B_{12} level reduced is associated with mental disturbances [6] without any haematological complications [7]. The high activity of platelet monoamine oxidase in demented patients may be due to the macrocytosis caused by vitamin B_{12} deficiency [8].

Patients and Methods

Patients with Alzheimer's disease (AD), senile dementia of Alzheimer-type (SD-AT), probable vascular dementia (PVD) and multi-infarct dementia (MID) were clinically diagnosed generally according to DSM III and some criteria of Erkinjuntti [9] as we detailed earlier [10]. All the patients were routinely investigated using basic Boehringer tests. The preparation of platelet-rich plasma (PRP), washed discoid and spherical platelets; in vitro digestion of platelets with different drugs; the detection of circulating platelet-aggregates and measuring the aggregation induced by adenosine diphosphate (ADP) or thrombin have been detailed elsewhere [11]. The characteristics of aggregation were calculated according to Frojmovic [12] and evaluated by Student's *t*-test. The parameter of platelet shape is independent of platelet concentration and the initial rate of aggregation varied linearly between 185 10^9/l to 380 10^9/l [12].

Results and Discussion

Platelets of patients with Alzheimer dementias are more spherical and the 50-μM ADP-induced aggregation faster than platelets of normal and other demented aged patients.

The initial rate of 50 μM ADP caused aggregation measured in PRP and did not depend on the shape of platelets either in the cases of PVD and MID patients or in the cases of AD and SDAT patients.

The platelet shape and velocity of aggregation measured in PRP change independently. In vitro treatment of platelets with pentoxifyllinum (Trental) resulted in the discoid shape of control platelets being changed markedly to spherical but the initial rate of 50 μM ADP-caused aggregation was unchanged while in the AD platelets both parameters were unchanged.

Our data revealed that in the case of AD, the examined spherical platelets which were aggregated fast were not hypersensitive ones. The acetylsalicylic acid-treatment in vitro and in vivo did not result in typical effects [13]. The initial rate of 50 μM ADP-caused aggregation was affected at the same rate in the platelets of AD as in control platelets. There were no abnormal amount of circulating platelet aggregates and no thrombotic problems in AD were noted.

There were no correlations between platelet shape and initial rate of 50 μM ADP-caused aggregation measured in PRP with level of vitamin B_{12}.

There was a significant negative correlation between the initial rate of 50 μM ADP-induced aggregation measured in PRP and serum iron-level only in platelets of patients with PVD and MID but in the platelets of AD and SDAT patients this correlation was not found.

Our findings that the initial rate of ADP caused aggregation determined in PRP were fast in the case of AD patients having decreased amount of cholesterol [2] was in contrast to the fact that the in vitro cholesterol-enriched platelets and platelets of type II A hyperlipidaemia showed increased sensitivity to ADP [14,15].

Preparing washed discoid and spherical platelets the aggregation was detected with different agonists (including ADP thrombin etc.). There were not any differences in the aggregation of discoid platelets in the case of control and AD platelets. The thrombin-induced aggregation of spherical platelets showed a marked difference in the case of AD patients compared to either healthy normal or non-AD demented patients. Washed spherical platelets of AD patients needed more thrombin for the same extent of aggregation than control platelets. We would like to emphasize that the behaviour of AD platelets was different from that of other spherical platelets.

It has been proposed that the first step in platelet activation by thrombin is the binding of thrombin to a surface structure and the second step is the interaction of thrombin with the effector, leading to the platelet aggregation and release [16]. The thrombin binding affinity of in vitro cholesterol-depleted platelets is increased while the thrombin binding capacity is decreased [17].

Our results lead us to conclude that the platelet function in AD was influenced by two effects: 1. plasma effects/fast aggregation in PRP and normal after wash; 2. change in the structure of platelet itself/shape change, thrombin caused aggregation of spherical AD platelets.

It is known that the platelet protease nexin plays a definite role in the interaction of thrombin with platelets [18]. The protease nexin II, the amyloid beta-protein precursor, is localized in the alpha-granules of human platelets and is secreted upon platelet activation [19].

The Alzheimer platelet is not only useful tool supporting the diagnosis of Alzheimer's disease but it may play an important role in the pathogenesis circulating the precursor of the amyloid beta-protein.

References

1. Zubenko GS, Cohen BM, Growdon J and Corkin S (1984) Lancet ii: 235.
2. Cohen BM, Zubenko GS and Babb SM (1987) Life Sci. 40: 2445–2451.
3. Chakravati A, Slaugenhaupt SA and Zubenko GS (1989) Am. J. Hum. Genet. 44: 799–805.
4. Zubenko GS, Huff FJ, Beyer J, Auerbach J and Teply I (1988) Arch. Gen. Psychiatry 45: 889–893.
5. Adolfsson R, Gottfries CG, Oreland L, Wibwrg A and Winblad B (1980) Life Sci. 27: 1029–1034.
6. Holmes JM (1956) Br. J. Med. 2: 1394–1398.
7. Strachan RW and Hendersen JG (1965) J. Med. 34: 303–317.
8. Regland B, Gottfries CG, Oreland L and Svennerholm L (1988) Acta Psychiatr. Scand. 78: 451–457.
9. Erkinjuntti T (1987) Acta Neurol. Scand. 76: 439–442.
10. Hasitz M, Nagy A and Lipcsey A (1989) Excerpta Medica Int. Congr. Ser. 899: 736.
11. Hasitz M, Rácz Z and Lipcsey A (1991) Vinazzer H (ed.) Proc. 7th Meeting Danubian League (in press).
12. Frojmovic MM (1973) J. Lab. Clin. Med. 82: 137–153.
13. Packham MA (1978) Thromb. Haemostasis 40: 175–195.
14. Shattil SJ, Anaya-Galindo R, Bennett J, Colman RW and Cooper RA (1975) J. Clin. Invest. 55: 636–643.
15. Shattil SJ, Bennett J, Colman RW and Cooper RA (1977) J. Lab. Clin. Med. 89: 341–353.
16. Okumura T, Hasitz M and Jamieson GA (1978) J. Biol. Chem. 253: 3435–3443.
17. Tandon N, Harmon JT, Rodbard D and Jamieson GA (1983) J. Biol. Chem. 258: 11840–11845.
18. Gronke RS, Bergman BL and Baker JB (1987) J. Biol. Chem. 262: 3030–3036.
19. Van Nostrand WE, Schmaier AH, Farrow JS and Cunningham DD (1990) Science 248: 745–748.

© 1991 Elsevier Science Publishers B.V. All rights reserved.
Biological Psychiatry, Volume 2. G. Racagni et al., editors.

Neuropathology and MRI of limbic system in schizophrenia

Bernhard Bogerts[1,2], Jeffrey A. Lieberman[2], Manzar Ashtari[2], Gail Lerner[2] and Peter Falkai[1]

[1]*Department of Psychiatry, University of Düsseldorf, Postfach 120510, W-4000 Düsseldorf, Germany; and* [2]*Hillside Hospital, Division of Long Island Jewish Medical Center, Albert Einstein College of Medicine, Glen Oaks, New York, U.S.A.*

Introduction

In recent years, a new era of pathomorphological interest in schizophrenia began receiving strong impetus from the modern neuroimagimg technics. Contrary to the mainly qualitative investigations performed during the first half of the century, most of the new neuropathological studies applied quantitative statistical methods and focussed on limbic stuctures [1–12], the physiology of which became known relatively late and which are now regarded by many authors to be crucial for the pathophysiology of the disease [1,2].

In addition to the postmortem studies, there is an increasing number of magnetic resonance imaging (MRI) studies which found reduced volumes or cross-sectional areas of the limbic mesiotemporal lobe structures [13–19] or reduced whole temporal lobe volumes [20,21] in schizophrenics.

The postmortem and MRI studies that determined volumes or cross-sectional areas by applying planimetric methods are summarized in Table 1. Of the 18 planimetric studies of mesiotemporal volumes in schizophrenia published so far (post-mortem plus MRI), only one group reported entirely negative results [22,23]. The reasons for the differences between the results obtained by these authors and the other planimetric studies have been discussed recently [24].

Some authors have reported anatomical changes in other than limbic structures e.g. in the basal ganglia, corpus callosum, thalamus and frontal cortex (for review see [1]). These findings were, however, less often reported than the limbic system abnormalities and await further confirmation.

Clinical correlates of reduced temporolimbic structure size

To investigate whether reduced temporolimbic structure size correlates with the typical clinical symptoms of the disease, volumes of the mesiotemporal structures (hippocampus-amygdala complex) were measured in 19 male chronic multi-episode schizophrenics from the Hillside Hospital, Long Island Jewish Medical Center, New York and 18 age-matched healthy controls using T1 weighted contiguous coronal magnetic resonance images of 3.1 mm width. Using the level of

Table 1. Planimetric postmortem and MRI studies in medial temporal lobe structures of schizophrenics

Positive results	
Bogerts et al. 1984/85 [3,4] (Vogt collection)	Smaller volumes of left hippocampus, parahippocampal gyrus and amygdala
Brown et al. 1986 [5] (Runwell collection)	Reduced cross-sectional area of left parahippocampal gyrus gray matter
Falkai and Bogerts 1986 [6] (Vogt collection)	Smaller volumes of whole left hippocampus and hippocampal CA-segments
Colter et al. 1987 [7] (Runwell collection)	Reduced cross-sectional area of parahippocampal white matter
Falkai et al. 1988 [8] (Vogt collection)	Reduced left entorhinal cortex volume
Jeste and Lohr 1989 [9] (Yakovlev collection)	Smaller volumes of left anterior hippocampus and hippocampal CA4 segment
Crow et al. 1989 [10] (Runwell collection)	Left temporal horn enlargement
Altshuler et al. 1990 [11] (NIMH collection)	Reduced parahippocampal but not hippocampal cross-sectional area
Bogerts et al. 1990a [12] (new D'dorf collection)	Reduced volumes of total right and left hippocampus
DeLisi et al. 1988 [13] (MRI)	Reduced hippocampus and parahippocampal cross-sectional areas
Suddath et al. 1989a [14] (MRI)	Reduced temporal lobe gray matter at hippocampus-amygdala levels
Suddath et al. 1989b [15] (MRI)	Smaller anterior hippocampus in discordant monozygotic schizophrenic twins
Bogerts et al. 1990b [16] (MRI)	Reduced left hippocampus in male first-episode schizophrenics
Barta et al. 1990 [17] (MRI)	Reduced volume of left amygdala and left superior temporal gyrus
Becker et al. 1990 [18] (MRI)	Reduced hippocampal and enlarged temporal horn volumes
Dauphinais et al. 1990 [19] (MRI)	Reduced temporal lobe size and medial temporal structures cross-sectional areas
Negative results	
Heckers et al. 1990a [22] (Würzburg collection)	No difference in parahippocampal gyrus volume
Heckers et al. 1990b [23] (Würzburg collection)	No difference in hippocampus and amygdala volumes

the mammillary bodies as an anatomical landmark, the whole hippocampus-amygdala complex was divided into an anterior section (mainly containing amygdala tissue) and a posterior section (mainly containing the hippocampal formation). Further details of patients and controls, anatomical delineation criteria, MRI and mensuration system have been reported previously [16]. The psychopathology of the patients was rated using the BPRS and the SANS.

The left (–20%) and the right (–15%) posterior section and the total limbic (right + left) tissue (–11%) of the patient group were significantly reduced compared to the control sample. There were significant negative correlations between the severity of the psychopathology and structure volumes; i.e. the smaller the structure, the higher the clinical symptom scores. Negative correlations were found for positive psychotic symptoms reflected by the BPRS psychosis factor and right and left whole mesiotemporal volumes ($r = -0.65$ and -0.62, $P < 0.01$), right and left anterior section volumes ($r = -0.46$ and -0.50, $P < 0.05$) and left hippocampal volume ($r = -0.39$, $P = 0.06$). Negative symptom scores (BPRS anergia factor and SANS global items) were not significantly correlated with mesiotemporal structure volumes.

The data confirm and extend previous findings of temporolimbic structure volume reductions in schizophrenia and demonstrate that the positive psychotic symptoms of schizophrenic psychopathology are associated with anatomical anomalies in mesiotemporal structures.

Discussion

It is a general principle of all brain diseases that reduced structure volumes reflect a reduced functional capacity and/or a disturbed function of the affected brain regions. If this principle can be applied to schizophrenia, the present postmortem and MRI data confirm that there is limbic system pathology in schizophrenia. Moreover, the significant inverse correlations between temporolimbic structure volumes and the severity of positive psychotic symptoms in chronic treatment of refractory schizophrenics provide direct evidence that limbic system pathology can be directly related to the characteristic clinical symptoms.

The pathomorphological changes in schizophrenia are subtle and not comparable in magnitude to the brain tissue loss seen in the well-known degenerative brain disorders. The changes cannot be seen in all schizophrenic patients and morphometrically, only a minority (some 10–30%) have values below the range of matched healthy control cases. Another difference from the neurodegenerative disorders is that, at least in most patients, the structural changes are not progressive and probably were acquired very early in life [25,26].

The limbic parts of the temporal lobe are anatomically and functionally interposed between the neocortical supramodal sensory association and integration areas and the septum-hypothalamus complex. All sensory informations finally converge in the entorhinal cortex, hippocampus and amygdala. These key limbic structures play an important role in the so-called sensory gating, i.e. the filtering out of irrelevant sensory stimuli by the neuronal comparison of present with past experience. Furthermore, amygdala and hippocampus link by several fibre bundles neocortical cognitive activities to the phylogenetically old basic drives and emotions which are generated in neuronal networks of the septum-hypothalamus complex. Thus, in addition to the disturbed sensory information processing, limbic pathology could also explain the dissociation between cognitive activities and emotional reactions to these activities as well as the dyscontrol syndrome of basic emotions which is frequently seen in schizophrenia.

References

1. Bogerts B (1990) In: Häfner and Gattaz WF (eds.) Search for the Causes of Schizophrenia II. Springer, Berlin, pp. 229–241.
2. Bogerts B (1989) In: Mednick SA, Cannon TD and Barr CE (eds.) Fetal Neural Development and Adult Schizophrenia. Cambridge University Press, pp. 153–173.
3. Bogerts B (1984) Fortschr. Neurol. Psychiatr. 52: 428–437.
4. Bogerts B, Meertz E and Schönfeld-Bausch R (1985) Arch. Gen. Psychiatry 42: 784–791.
5. Brown R, Colter N, Corsellis JAN, Crow TJ, Frith CD, Jagoe R, Johnstone EC and Marsh L (1986) Arch. Gen. Psychiatry 43: 36–42.
6. Falkai P and Bogerts B (1986) Eur. Arch. Psychiatry Neurol. Sci. 236: 154–161.
7. Colter N, Battal S, Crow TJ, Johnstone EC, Brown R and Bruton C (1987) Arch. Gen. Psychiatry 44: 1023.
8. Falkai P, Bogerts B and Rozumek M (1988) Biol. Psychiatry 24: 515–521.
9. Jeste DV and Lohr JB (1989) Arch. Gen. Psychiatry 46: 1019–1024.
10. Crow TJ, Ball J, Bloom SR, Brown R, Bruton CJ, Colter N, Frith CD, Johnstone EC, Owens DGC and Roberts GW (1989) Arch. Gen. Psychiatry 46: 1145–1150.
11. Altshuler L, Conrad A, Kovelman JA and Scheibel A (1987) Arch. Gen. Psychiatry 44: 1094–1098.
12. Bogerts B, Falkai P, Haupts M, Greve B, Ernst S, Tapernon-Franz U and Heinzmann U (1990) Schizophr. Res. 3: 295–301.
13. DeLisi LE, Dauphinais ID and Gershon E (1988) Schizophr. Bull. 14: 185–191.
14. Suddath RL, Casanova MF, Goldberg TE, Daniel DG, Kelsoe J and Weinberger DR (1989a) Am. J. Psychiatry 146: 464–472.
15. Suddath RL, Christison GW, Torrey EF, Casanova MF and Weinberger DR (1989b) N. Engl. J. Med. 322(12): 62–67.
16. Bogerts B, Ashtari M, Degreef G, Alvir JMJ, Bilder RM and Lieberman JA (1990) Psychiatr. Res. Neuroimaging 35: 1–13.
17. Barta PE, Pearlson GD, Powers RE, Richards SS and Tune LE (1990) Am. J. Psychiatry 1457–1462.
18. Becker T, Elmer K, Mechela B, Schneider F, Taubert S, Schroth G, Grodd W, Bartels M and Beckmann H (1990) Eur. Neuropsychopharmacol. 1: 83–86.
19. Dauphinais D, DeLisi LE, Crow TJ, Alexandropoulos K, Colter N, Tuma I and Gershon ES (1990) Psychiatr. Res. 35: 137–147.
20. Rossi A, Stratta P, D'Albenzio L, Tartaro A, Schiazza G, di Michele V, Bolino F and Casacchia M (1990) Biol. Psychiatry 27: 61–68.
21. Johnstone EC, Owens DGC, Crow TJ, Frith CD, Alexandropolis K, Bydder G and Colter N (1989) J. Neurol. Neurosurg. Psychiatry 52: 736–741.
22. Heckers S, Heinsen H, Heinsen YC and Beckmann H (1990a) J. Neural Transm. 80: 151–155.
23. Heckers S, Heinsen H, Heinsen YC and Beckmann H (1990b) Arch. Gen. Psychiatry 47: 1016–1022.
24. Bogerts B, Falkai P and Greve B (1991) Arch. Gen. Psychiatry (letter) (in press).
25. Weinberger DR (1987) Arch. Gen. Psychiatry 44: 660–669.
26. Bogerts B (1989) In: Schulz SC and Tamminga CA (eds.) Schizophrenia: Scientific Progress. Oxford University Press, pp. 216–227.

© 1991 Elsevier Science Publishers B.V. All rights reserved.
Biological Psychiatry, Volume 2. G. Racagni et al., editors.

Abnormalities of hemisphere asymmetries and interhemispheric integration in schizophrenia

S. Galderisi, A. Mucci, M. Maj and D. Kemali
Department of Psychiatry, First Medical School, University of Naples, Naples,Italy

An abnormal hemispheric lateralization of brain function in schizophrenia has been rather consistently reported, although the interpretation of the experimental findings is controversial. As a matter of fact, it is still debated whether the observed abnormalities reflect a dysfunction of either the left or the right hemisphere, or a disturbed interhemispheric transmission.

A left hemisphere dysfunction is apparently supported by a rather large body of evidence, including structural [1], neurochemical [2], metabolic [3], neuropsychological [4] and neurophysiological [5] findings. The hypothesis of an impaired interhemispheric integration has been substantiated by data concerning callosal structural abnormalities in schizophrenic patients [6], by an association between schizophrenia-like symptoms and callosal tumors and by evidence of a partial brain disconnection syndrome in schizophrenia [7]. A few experimental results have been reported in favour of the hypothesis of a selective right hemisphere impairment, involving autonomic and neuropsychological indices [8].

Discrepancies in experimental results can be partially explained by the heterogeneity of subjects with respect to sex, handedness and medication status. Moreover, most of the research findings are compatible with more than one interpretation [9]; in fact, theoretically, the presence of structural abnormalities in one hemisphere might produce defective interhemispheric communication and/or, via disinhibition mechanisms, a pathological overactivation of the contralateral hemisphere.

In the present paper, we summarize the results of some recent studies carried out by our group, relevant to the question at issue.

Anatomical brain asymmetries were investigated by computed tomography in a group of 20 schizophrenics and 16 normal controls in relationship with sex and diagnosis. Irrespectively of diagnosis, a main effect of sex on frontal asymmetry was observed, since asymmetry was reversed in control females (left > right) and reduced in patient females. Sex-related asymmetry was observed in the control group also for the occipital lobes, with left > right only in males. Female schizophrenics did not differ from female controls, while male patients presented a significantly reduced occipital asymmetry as compared with healthy males. These results are in line with Crow's findings of a reduced rather than reversed occipital asymmetry in schizophrenia [10]. Developmental abnormalities of the left hemisphere may play a crucial role in the pathogenesis of schizophrenia in males, who present a higher degree of structural and functional hemispheric lateralization.

The influence of sex and medication status on functional indices of hemispheric lateralization was explored in a neuropsychophysiological study. Event-related potentials (ERPs) and performance indices were recorded during a visual target detection task in which consonant pairs were tachistoscopically presented to the right visual field/left hemisphere (RVF/LH) or to the left visual field/right hemisphere (LVF/RH). Male controls showed larger ERP late components and shorter reaction time (RT) for RVF than for LVF stimuli. The RVF advantage was neither observed in female controls nor in a group of right-handed male schizophrenics. Moreover, patients showed reduced ERP late components and slower RT for RVF stimuli as compared with matched healthy controls. These ERP abnormalities almost disappeared after 1 month of neuroleptic treatment, demonstrating that functional asymmetry is strongly influenced by medication, as also documented by some behavioural studies [11]. On the whole, these results suggest a left hemisphere impairment, probably involving a disturbed interhemispheric integration and seem to exclude the presence of a right hemisphere overactivation (slow reaction time for both hemifields, ERP amplitude comparable with normal controls for LVF stimuli). Early et al. [12] proposed that a lateralized dysfunction of systems for language processing and visuospatial attention is fundamental in the pathogenesis of schizophrenia. Their model assumes a dopaminergic imbalance in the left cortico-striato-pallido-thalamic circuit, that can be reversed by neuroleptics. A loss of the normal dominance of the left over the right circuit would be responsible for the disinhibition of homologous regions of the right hemisphere. The activity of the disinhibited regions would be perceived as "alien", explaining Schneiderian symptoms of schizophrenia, as previously proposed by other authors [13,14].

In conclusion, although a large amount of structural and functional data suggest a lateralized dysfunction in schizophrenia, mechanisms underlying the process are still speculative. Hypotheses and models of schizophrenia as a disorder of hemispheric asymmetry can be tested by studies focusing on reciprocal interactions between functional and structural abnormalities.

Acknowledgements

The authors gratefully acknowledge the valuable technical assistance of Anna Grimaldi and Eugenio Fontanella. A special note of thanks is due to Fulvio Magara for his contribution in setting up the method for brain asymmetry measurement on CT scans.

References

1. Crow TJ (1990) Schizophr. Bull. 16: 433–443.
2. Reynolds GP (1983) Nature 305: 527–529.

3. Early TS, Reiman EM, Raichle ME and Spitznagel EL (1986) Proc. Natl. Acad. Sci. U.S.A. 84: 561–562.
4. Gur RE, Gur RC, Saykin AJ (1990) Schizophr. Bull. 16: 445–451.
5. Galderisi S, Maj M, Mucci A, Monteleone P and Kemali D (1988) Int. J. Psychophysiol. 6: 167–176.
6. Rossi P, Stratta P, D'Albenzio L, Tartaro A, Schiazza G, Di Michele V, Bolino F and Casacchia M (1990) Biol. Psychiatry 27: 61–68.
7. Doty RW (1989) Behav. Brain Res. 34: 1–33.
8. Venables PH (1984) In: Spaulding WD and Cole JK (eds.) Nebraska Symposium on Motivation, 1983: Theories of Schizophrenia and Psychosis. University of Nebraska Press, Lincoln, pp. 47–91.
9. Posner MI, Early TS (1990) Arch. Gen. Psychiatry 47: 394–395.
10. Crow TJ, Ball J, Bloom SR, Brown R, Bruton CJ, Colter N, Frith CD, Johnstone EC, Owens DG and Roberts GW (1989) Arch. Gen. Psychiatry 46: 1145–1150.
11. Tomer R and Flor-Henry P (1989) Biol. Psychiatry 25: 852–860.
12. Early TS, Posner MI, Reiman E and Raichle ME (1989) Psychiatr. Dev. 2: 85–108.
13. Nasrallah HA (1985) Compr. Psychiatry 26: 273–282.
14. Kemali D, Maj M, Galderisi S and Mucci A (1991) Ital. J. Psychiatry (in press).

© 1991 Elsevier Science Publishers B.V. All rights reserved.
Biological Psychiatry, Volume 2. G. Racagni et al., editors.

A quantitative morphometric study of the corpus callosum and cingulate cortex in schizophrenia: An MRI study

Manuel Casanova, Dennis Atkinson, Terry Goldberg, Mark Zito, E. Fuller Torrey, Llewelyn Bigelow and Daniel Weinberger

Clinical Brain Disorders Branch, Intramural Research Program, National Institute of Mental Health, Neurosciences Center at St Elizabeths, 2700 Martin Luther King Jr. Ave., Washington, D.C., U.S.A.

Introduction

Recent morphometric studies by our group have shown that the corpus callosum (CC) of schizophrenic (SC) patients is distorted due to an upwards bowing of its middlemost segment [1]. Since the corpus callosum forms the roof of the lateral ventricles, the authors suggested that the observed conformational abnormality was the result of ventriculomegaly. Distortion of the CC during gestation (e.g. hydrocephalus) is often associated with major developmental abnormalities of the closely adjacent gyri (e.g. cingulate). Since cortical growth rate and therefore the ratio of exposed to intrasulcal cortex is fixed in adults, hydrocephalic processes in postnatal individuals may produce secondary atrophy or thinning of the cerebral cortex but no major change in the overall gyrational pattern. In this study the authors presumed that significant shape distortion of the cingulate gyrus of SC patients would be most consistent with a hydrocephalic process having its onset during development. In addition to the quantitative shape and area analysis of the cingulate cortex, the study explores several different linear and angular measurements of the CC to determine which one is the best predictor of schizophrenia.

Materials and Methods

Patients were selected from the project "Biological Markers in Discordant Twins" directed by Dr. Fuller Torrey. The groups consisted of 15 pairs of monozygotic twins discordant for schizophrenia, 5 pairs concordant for the illness and 5 normal monozygotic twins. Characteristics of the patient population and MRI scanner have been published elsewhere [1]. Two coronal sections (anterior and middle) were used for the morphometric analysis of the cingulate gyrus. The midsagittal section was used to calculate various morphometric parameters of the corpus callosum. MRI scans were digitized and analyzed for shape using a Loats computerized image analysis system [1]. Four different measurements were made:

1. the "mean curvature" is measured as the ratio of the angle subtended at the intersection of the tangents drawn at either end of the linear structure to the length of the intervening segment [2];

2. the "major callosal angle" was determined according to the method described by Oppenheim et al. [3];
3. the third angle studied was formed by drawing lines from the 2 maximally distant points of the genu and splenium to the highest point of the corpus callosum;
4. a fourth angle was determined by drawing lines from the 2 closest points of the genu and splenium to the highest point of the corpus callosum.

All of the linear segments used in determining the above angular measurements were also considered in the statistical analysis.

Results

Areas of the right and left anterior and midcingulate cortex were compared between groups by matched pair *t*-test. No differences emerged at the $P = 0.05$ level. Shape analysis using the Fourier expansion series yielded significant differences only in the monozygotic twins discordant for schizophrenia for the first harmonic amplitude of the left anterior cingulate cortex ($t = 2.429$, $P = 0.02$).

Shape analysis of the corpus callosum showed significant differences for all diagnostic groups. In the monozygotic twins discordant for schizophrenia a trend towards significance was found for harmonic amplitude 2 (the predominant determinant of shape for the corpus callosum) in the anterior ($t = -1.82$, $P = 0.09$) and middle ($t = 1.80$, $P = 0.09$) segment. The concordant schizophrenic twins exhibited shape differences for the anterior harmonic amplitude 4 ($t = -4.45$, $P = 0.0113$) and the middle segment harmonic 2 ($t = 8.86$, $P = 0.0009$). In the control monozygotic twin group a trend towards significance was found in the middle segment harmonic 2 ($t = -2.53$, $P = 0.06$) and in harmonic 2 at the posterior level ($t = 2.52$, $P = 0.07$).

Of the linear and angular measurements performed only the mean curvature and the major callosal angle proved significant in differentiating between the groups. The mean curvature distinguished between the monozygotic twins discordant for schizophrenia (affected vs. normal cotwin) by a *t*-test procedure ($t = 2.02$, $P < 0.05$). The major callosal angle was able to detect differences only between the monozygotic twins discordant for schizophrenia ($t = 2.02$, $P = <0.05$).

Discussion

In a recent postmortem study, Brown et al. [4] examined the area of the cingulate cortex in a population of SC and affective patients. The result of the study showed no significant differences between groups. At present we expand on this observation by describing no abnormalities in cingulate cortex area or shape in a population of monozygotic twins discordant for schizophrenia. However, the results of our study indicate significant differences in the shape descriptors of the CC between patients of each particular group. Since our twin pairs shared the same genetic constitution, the differences observed in CC morphology may have been primarily determined by environmental factors. Linear and angular measurements proved less effective at detecting any morphological differences of the corpus callosum. Only the mean curvature and major callosal angle proved significant in distinguishing between any of our monozygotic twin groups, viz. those discordant for schizophrenia. Given the fact that the mean curvature reflects the amount of bending of a linear structure, our findings indicate that the middle portion of the CC of SC patients is "bowed upwards" as compared to their normal cotwins.

In summary, based on the morphometric analysis of the cingulate cortex, our study failed to elucidate the time of onset of ventriculomegaly in SC patients. Differences in CC shape were evident in all of our monozygotic twin groups. In some of our SC patients the mean curvature and major callosal angle indicated that distortions of the CC reflected an upwards bowing of this structure. Previous studies suggest that this conformational abnormality is secondary to ventricular enlargement and not the result of intrinsic CC pathology. Since both patients and controls shared the same genetic constitution, variations in the shape of the CC between monozygotic twins appears to be dictated, in part, by environmental influences.

References

1. Casanova MF, Sanders RD, Goldberg TE, Bigelow LB, Christison G, Torrey EF and Weinberger DR (1990) J. Neurol. Neurosurg. Psychiatry 53: 416–421.
2. Casanova MF, Zito M, Goldberg TE, Suddath RL, Fuller Torrey E, Bigelow LB and Sanders RD (1990) Biol. Psychiatry 27(1): 83–84.
3. Oppenheim JS, Skerry JE, Tramo MJ and Gazzinaga MS (1989) Ann. Neurol. 26: 100–104.
4. Brown R, Colter N, Corsellis JAN et al. (1986) Arch. Gen. Psychiatry 43: 36–42.

© 1991 Elsevier Science Publishers B.V. All rights reserved.
Biological Psychiatry, Volume 2. G. Racagni et al., editors.

Functional aspects of schizophrenia: Preliminary PET data

Cristina Colombo[1], Anna Bonfanti[1], Daniela Perani[2], Ferruccio Fazio[2], Enrico Smeraldi[1] and Silvio Scarone[1]

[1]Psychiatric Branch, Department of Biological and Technological Sciences, University of Milan Medical School, Istituto Scientifico San Raffaele, via Prinetti 29, 20127 Milano; and [2]Department of Nuclear Medicine, University of Milan, Istituto Scientifico San Raffaele, Milan, Italy

Introduction

Beginning from the first study with positron-emission tomography (PET) in schizophrenic patients [1], interest was focused on frontal regions. Several groups of researchers replicated studies involving frontal regions which, initially, provided relatively reduced metabolic rates in the frontal cortex.

More recently lower frontal/occipital ratio in schizophrenic patients compared to controls, higher frontal/parietal ratio or no reduction of frontal lobe low activity in schizophrenics compared to controls has been reported [2–4].

If drug treatment is taken into the account, frontal hypometabolism secondary to prolonged neuroleptic treatment has been reported [5].

The purpose of this study is to evaluate the glucose metabolic rates in four cerebral regions of both hemispheres in five never-treated young male schizophrenics with positive symptomatology at the onset of their disease.

Subjects and Method

Five schizophrenic patients, 4 males, 1 female (mean age 21.8 ± 3.4 years, mean educational level 10.0 ± 2.0), at their first episode of disease, drug-naive, and 10 control subjects, 6 males, 4 females (mean age 23.6 ± 7.9 years, mean educational level 14.7 ± 7.1), underwent PET studies. The diagnosis was made by two senior psychiatrist, according to DSM III-R Diagnostic Criteria; out of the 5 patients, 4 were undifferentiated and 1 was paranoid subtype. The duration of illness was less than 2 years for all the patients.

PET method

(18F)FDG PET studies were performed in resting state using a four ring whole-body positron emission tomograph (Siemens/CPS, 931-04/12). The scanner allows the simultaneous acquisition of data from 7 transaxial planes, 4 direct and 3 cross-planes, equally spaced, slice thickness 6.75 mm, covering an axial field of view of 5.4 cm. The image spatial resolution for a line source in air, positioned in the centre of the field of view, was 6.1 mm (transaxial) full-width at half maximum (FWHM). A transmission scan was taken, using a ring source of 68Ge, to measure attenuation in the scanned cross-sections for later use in attenuation correction. Fourteen transaxial slices, parallel to the orbitomeatal line, were obtained by two consecutive emission scans, between 40 and 60 min after the (18F)FDG administration. For the calculation of the rCMRglu the 3-rate constants operational equation of Sokoloff was used [6] and the kinetic constants, K_1-K_2-K_3 and lumped constant, reported by Reivich [7].

Results

As a whole, schizophrenics showed higher glucose metabolism in frontal and temporal regions compared to controls: left frontal = 7.75 (1.28) vs. 6.28 (0.31) P = 0.004; right frontal = 7.74 (1.33) vs. 6.25 (0.36) P = 0.005; left temporal = 6.76 (1.20) vs. 5.49 (0.69) P = 0.02; right temporal = 6.74 (1.22) vs. 5.55 (0.73); left parietal = 7.47 (0.96) vs. 6.74 (0.67) P = N.S.; right parietal = 7.51 (0.90) vs. 6.82 (0.64) P = N.S.; left occipital = 7.21 (1.27) vs. 6.81 (0.64) P = N.S.; right occipital = 7.21 (1.24) vs. 6.84 (0.47) P = N.S.

As far as the single case data was concerned, three patients showed hypermetabolism in frontal and temporal regions in both hemisphere, one showed low glucose metabolism rates in both hemisphere, one showed low glucose metabolism rates in frontal regions and one was normal. Further, no significant interhemispheric differences were observed either in schizophrenics or in controls.

Discussion

Up to now PET studies have shown alterations in glucose metabolism in frontal areas of schizophrenic patients. In contrast with evidence of hypofrontality [2] the data of this study do not evidentiate a reduction of metabolism in schizophrenia. On the contrary schizophrenics showed an increased metabolism in frontal and temporal regions compared to controls. These results are consistent with the Cleghorn results [3], but not consistent with the majority of data published in the recent literature. It should be emphasized, nevertheless, that the patient's sample of the present investigation is not comparable with the samples of previous studies in terms of chronicity, duration and amount of neuroleptic treatment, heterogeneity of symptomatological picture. It is reasonable to suppose a strong effect of each one of these variables on brain metabolism.

Further, there are other variables like psychologic state, anxiety, drowsiness, environmental influences during the PET study, measurement errors in scanning and glucose quantification, incorrected evaluation of clinical variables such as previous head injury. But it is necessary to stress again that the first cause of variability is the disease heterogeneity.

The lack of consistence in metabolic studies reproposes the variability in biological studies applied to the schizophrenia syndrome and calls for caution in the interpretation of the results.

References

1. Ingvar DH and Franzen G (1974) Acta Psychiatr. Scand. 50: 425–462.
2. Wolkin A, Angrist B, Wolf A, Brodie JD, Wolkin B, Jaeger J, Cancro R and Rotrosen J (1988) Am. J. Psychiatry 145: 251–253.
3. Cleghorn JM, Garnett ES, Nahmias C, Firnau G, Brown GM, Kaplan R, Szechtman H and Szechtman B (1989) Psychiatr. Res. 28: 119–133.
4. Gur RE, Resnick SM and Gur RC (1989) Psychiatr. Res. 27: 325–334.
5. Szechtman H, Nahmias C, Garnett ES, Firnau G, Brown GM, Kaplan R and Cleghorn JM (1988) Arch. Gen. Psychiatry 45: 523–532.
6. Sokoloff L (1976) In: Siegel GJ, Albers RW, Katzman R and Agranoff BW (eds.) Basic Neurochemistry. Little Brown, Boston, pp. 388–413.
7. Reivich M, Kuhl D, Wolf A, Greenberg J, Phelps M, Ido T, Casella V, Fowler J, Hoffman E, Alavi A, Som P and Sokoloff L (1979) Circ. Res. 44: 127–137.

© 1991 Elsevier Science Publishers B.V. All rights reserved.
Biological Psychiatry, Volume 2. G. Racagni et al., editors.

Temporal lobe morphometry and cerebral asymmetries by magnetic resonance in schizophrenia

A. Rossi, P. Stratta and M. Casacchia
Department of Psychiatry, University of L'Aquila, L'Aquila, Italy

Over the past 15 years there has been a renewed interest in neuroanatomical studies of schizophrenia. However the initial observation of anomalies in gross indexes of brain damage, such as ventricular brain ratio (VBR), sulcal widening or cerebellar atrophy, only led to the indication that a pathological process might have occurred somewhere in the brain, but the location, the specificity and the meaning of the structural changes remained obscure.

The latest technological advances in brain imaging devices, and particularly magnetic resonance, have enabled researchers to obtain reliable assessments of a number of cerebral structures possibly involved in the pathophysiology of schizophrenia.

Several magnetic resonance imaging (MRI) studies of schizophrenic patients by independent groups have reported various changes within the temporal lobe [1–4]. These reports have added more refined information to the findings of a smaller size of temporal lobe structure in previous postmortem studies [5] the interpretation of which was complicated by possible artifacts due to various confounding variables, such as agonal events, postmortem preparation, ageing and incidental findings that may have obscured the essential pathology.

We hypothesize that the study of temporal lobe anatomy may add further clues to the pathophysiological meaning and specificity of eventual brain abnormalities in schizophrenia. Therefore three MRI studies were designed to further explore our hypothesis, evaluating temporal lobe structure in schizophrenic and bipolar disorders and healthy control subjects.

In a first multiplanar controlled study [3] we found a bilateral reduction in the temporal lobe areas in schizophrenics compared to healthy controls matched for age, educational level and gender. A strong hemisphere factor, with the left temporal lobe areas smaller than the right in both patients and controls was shown. Moreover, the left temporal lobe areas evaluated on the more anterior slice, usually showing the hippocampal structure, was the best discriminator variable between schizophrenics and controls.

In a second independent study [6] on bipolar and schizophrenic patients, schizophrenics showed a reduction of temporal lobe areas in those sections corresponding to the hippocampal region. This finding was more pronounced for the left side, although no diagnosis by side interaction was present. Temporal lobe volume was also markedly reduced among schizophrenics. When a side factor was present, both patient groups showed a right temporal lobe which was larger than the left.

Our MRI reports, as well as being in agreement with the above-mentioned postmortem findings of abnormal growth or atrophy of temporal lobes, seem to suggest that a most marked abnormality of this structure is present in the left hemisphere.

With regard to the left-right temporal lobe asymmetry, these data confirm the observation of Jack et al. [7] who found the non-dominant temporal lobe to be larger than the dominant one, but in our samples this finding was more marked for the left side in schizophrenics, particularly in the architecture of the anteromedial temporal lobe containing structures such as the hippocampus and the parahippocampal gyrus. The left side seems to show a major role in such a reduction, although we have been unable to find a side by status interaction in the statistical analysis.

The study of human brain asymmetries is an interesting issue which deserves more research in order to obtain useful information on cerebral lateralization in normal subjects and in psychiatric patients [8].

Since the major foci of cerebral asymmetries still cannot be ascertained, several researchers point out the importance of the study of asymmetry in the temporal lobe in its posterior regions [9], with particular attention given to the planum temporale (PT).

Given the importance of this region in language processing and intelligence, deviation in its normal asymmetry may provide an interesting correlate of human higher cerebral malfunction in schizophrenia.

MRI technology seems to provide reliable information on PT asymmetry [10], which until now was only available by direct observation after brain dissection, and which made postmortems necessary and thus correlative studies administratively difficult.

To further verify this hypothesis, we undertook an MRI controlled study to explore the morphometry of the PT in 17 schizophrenic patients (mean age 31.76 ± 6.25 years) and 10 healthy controls strictly matched for age, sex and educational level.

A 2-way ANOVA with side as within-subjects and status as between-subjects factors showed a statistically significant factor interaction (d.f. 1,25, $F = 5.11$, $P < 0.05$) with no significant side- and status-effects. Control subjects showed the physiologically reported larger left vs. right PT while patients showed the reverse.

The data from this ongoing MRI study could permit us to better analyse the role of laterality in the pathophysiology of schizophrenia.

Acknowledgement

Supported in part by a Grant from Consiglio Nazionale delle Ricerche (No. 91.00111.PF41).

References

1. Suddath RL, Casanova MF, Goldberg TE et al. (1989): Am. J. Psychiatry 146: 464.
2. Johnstone EC, Cowens DG, Crow TJ et al. (1989): J. Neurol. Neurosurg. Psychiatry 52, 736–741.
3. Rossi A, Stratta P, D'Albenzio L et al. (1990): Biol. Psychiatry 27: 61.
4. Suddath RL, Christison GW, Torrey EF et al. (1990): N. Engl. J. Med. 322: 789–794.
5. Roberts GW (1991): Br. J. Psychiatry 158: 8–17.
6. Rossi A, Stratta P, Di Michele V et al. (1991): J. Affective Disord. 21: 19–22.
7. Jack CR, Gehring DG and Sharbrough FW (1988): J. Comput. Assisted Tomogr. 12: 21.
8. Stratta P, Rossi A, Gallucci M et al. (1989): Biol. Psychiatry 25: 275–284.
9. Crow TJ, Frith CD, Johnstone EC et al. (1991): Arch. Gen. Psychiatry 48: 86–87 (letter).
10. Larsen JP, Odeagaard H, Grude TH et al. (1989): Acta Neurol. Scand. 80: 438–443.

© 1991 Elsevier Science Publishers B.V. All rights reserved.
Biological Psychiatry, Volume 2. G. Racagni et al., editors.

Magnetic resonance spectroscopy of the human brain in neuropsychiatric disorders

Raymond F. Deicken, Giovanna Calabrese, Dieter J. Meyerhoff, Dominique Sappey-Marinier, George Fein and Michael W. Weiner

Magnetic Resonance Unit and Psychiatry Service, VA Medical Center, 4150 Clement St., San Francisco; and Departments of Medicine, Radiology and Psychiatry, University of California, San Francisco, California, U.S.A.

Introduction

With the advent of high-resolution magnetic resonance spectroscopy (MRS) and magnetic resonance spectroscopic imaging (MRSI), it is now possible to directly and non-invasively study intermediary metabolism of brain tissue in vivo in humans. The magnetic resonance unit at the San Francisco Veterans Affairs Medical Center has been utilizing in vivo MRS to study the brain in various neuropsychiatric disorders. Specifically, we have been investigating the brain in HIV disease; the effects of chronic alcohol abuse on the central nervous system (CNS) morbidity of HIV infection; white matter signal hyperintensities (WMSH) in demented and non-demented elderly; and schizophrenia. More recently, we have also been successful in developing and implementing magnetic resonance spectroscopic imaging (MRSI) [1,2] to study diseases of the CNS.

Hypotheses and Methods

All MRS and MRSI studies were conducted at the San Francisco VA Medical Center Magnetic Resonance Unit on a Philips Gyroscan 2.0 T MRI/MRS system.

1. *HIV disease*. Studies were initially conducted on 17 HIV patients and 6 controls to determine if there were alterations in brain phosphate compounds in patients with HIV disease, and, if so, to determine whether the MRS alterations were correlated with the severity of neuropsychiatric impairments. 31-Phosphorous (^{31}P) MRS was performed using a single volume ISIS procedure [3] on a 125-ml centrally located VOI. We subsequently used a 100-ml primarily white matter VOI and a 90-ml primarily subcortical gray matter VOI, and studied 3 HIV patients and 11 HIV seronegative controls using the ISIS procedure. Spectra were processed using NMR1 software. Molar concentrations were calculated according to a quantitative method [4] and pH determined from the chemical shift of Pi referenced to PCr [5]. All HIV patients underwent neuropsychological, neurological,

and psychiatric examinations and were given a composite neuropsychiatric impairment score.

We also used ^{1}H MRSI to test the hypothesis that changes of N-acetylaspartate (NAA) and other metabolites are a sensitive index of brain impairment in HIV infection. For ^{1}H MRSI, a double-spin echo sequence (PRESS) [6] was used to preselect a $100 \times 100 \times 20$ cm volume (which encompassed mainly white matter above the ventricles) in 4 HIV+ patients with moderate neuropsychiatric impairment and 6 controls. Spectra were extracted from left and right parieto-occipital white matter, parietal white matter, and frontal white matter regions.

2. *Alcohol effects on the CNS morbidity of HIV.* We used ^{31}P MRS to test the hypothesis that HIV infection in combination with chronic alcoholism produces a greater change in brain metabolism that HIV infection alone. We studied 57 subjects divided into 3 groups: Group 1 consisted of 14 HIV+ chronic alcoholics; Group 2 consisted of 33 HIV+ non-alcoholics; and Group 3 consisted of 10 HIV− chronic alcoholics. ^{31}P MRS was performed using the ISIS sequence on the same two subcortical gray and white matter VOIs described in 1 above. Spectral processing and calculation of molar concentrations and pH were as described in 1.

3. *White matter signal hyperintensities.* We utilized ^{31}P MRS to test both the hypothesis that WMSH have an ischemic basis, resulting in reductions in energy phosphates, and the hypothesis that they are associated with changes in white matter phospholipid metabolism. ^{31}P MRS was performed on 30 elderly subjects with varying degrees of WMSH using a single volume ISIS procedure on a standard 100 ml VOI in the hemispheric white matter. In cases of extensive WMSH, the VOI was placed in the hemisphere with the most severe WMSH. Spectral processing and calculation of molar concentrations and pH were as described in 1.

4. *Schizophrenia.* A pilot study was conducted to test the hypothesis of metabolic asymmetry of the temporal lobes in schizophrenia, and to determine whether there was an association between phosphorous MRS measures and the severity of psychiatric symptomatology as measured by the Brief Psychiatric Rating Scale (BPRS). ^{31}P MRS was performed on 9 schizophrenic patients and 9 controls using the ISIS procedure on an 87-ml VOI in the right and left temporal lobes. Spectral processing and quantitation were as described in 1.

Results and Discussion

1. *HIV disease.* Patients with HIV disease demonstrated significantly lower ATP/Pi than controls (1.45 ± 0.45 vs. 2.07 ± 0.5, $P = 0.03$) for the 125-ml VOI and significantly decreased ATP and PCr concentrations ($P = 0.036$ for both) in the white matter VOI. In addition, the ATP/Pi and PCr/Pi ratios were both significantly

negatively correlated (r = –0.63, P = 0.002 and r = –0.45, P = 0.03, respectively) with overall severity of neuropsychiatric impairment. These results suggest that HIV infection of the brain may impair brain cellular oxidative metabolism and that the degree of metabolic compromise may be related to the severity of neuropsychiatric impairment. For the ^{1}H MRSI, we noted a 30% overall decrease of NAA/creatine as well as a 30% decrease in the NAA/choline and a 50% increase in choline/creatine in frontal and parietal white matter regions in HIV patients compared to controls. The observed reduction of NAA in brain is widely considered to reflect neuronal damage or viability. Therefore, the ^{1}H MRSI results support the hypothesis that diminished NAA may be a highly sensitive marker of neuronal damage.

2. *Alcohol effects on the CNS morbidity of HIV*. In the white matter VOI, we noted: 1) reduced ATP (2.7 to 2.2 mM, P = 0.05), decreased ATP/Pi (2.1 to 1.6, P = 0.04), and increased PCr/ATP (1.3 to 1.5, P = 0.06) in HIV+ alcoholics relative to HIV+ non-alcoholics; 2) very similar metabolite concentrations and ratios in HIV– alcoholics and HIV+ non-alcoholics; 3) relative to HIV– alcoholics, HIV+ alcoholics had significantly increased PCr/ATP (1.3 to 1.5, P = 0.04), which was due to decreased ATP (2.5 to 2.2 mM, P = 0.08); and 4) detectable metabolic changes in the absence of changes on MRI. The subcortical gray matter VOI did not reveal any statistical differences between metabolite concentrations or ratios of the 3 groups. These findings suggest that HIV infection in combination with chronic alcohol abuse is associated with a greater deterioration in brain energy metabolism than HIV infection alone.

3. *White matter signal hyperintensities*. The major finding was a 25% decrease in ATP/Pi of the hemispheric white matter VOI in subjects with extensive WMSH compared to those with no WMSH (P = 0.04). No statistical differences or trends were observed for phosphomonoester (PME) and phosphodiester (PDE) metabolites in either VOI to be associated with the extent of WMSHs. These findings suggest that extensive WMSHs are associated with changes in cellular white matter energy phosphate metabolism but not with changes in phospholipid metabolism. Because ischemia and infarction are associated with decreased ATP/Pi, these findings are consistent with the hypothesis that WMSHs are caused by vascular disease.

4. *Schizophrenia*. The major finding was that the PCr/ATP was significantly increased (P = 0.03) in the right (3.14 ± 0.92) compared to the left (2.43 ± 0.46) temporal lobe in schizophrenic patients. No such asymmetry was observed in the controls. A second finding was a significant negative correlation between PCr/ATP and the total BPRS scores for both the right (r = –0.84) and left (r = –0.73) temporal lobes. Assuming that an increase of PCr/ATP is probably due to a decrease of ATP, since PCr and pH were unchanged, these results suggest lower metabolic activity in the right compared to the left temporal lobe. The correlations

of PCr/ATP with the BPRS suggest that higher metabolic activity in the temporal lobes is associated with more severe psychiatric symptomatology.

References

1. Twieg DB, Meyerhoff DJ, Hubesch B et al. (1989) Magn. Reson. Med. 12: 291–305.
2. Maudsley AA, Twieg DB, Sappey-Marinier D et al. (1990) Magn. Reson. Med. 14: 415–422.
3. Matson GB, Twieg DB, Karczmar GS et al. (1988) Radiology 169: 541–547.
4. Roth K, Hubesch B, Meyerhoff DJ et al. (1989) J. Magn. Reson. 81: 299–311.
5. Petroff OAC, Prichard JW, Behar KL et al. (1985) Neurology 35: 781–788.
6. Segebarth CM et al. (1990) Magn. Reson. Med. 13: 62.

© 1991 Elsevier Science Publishers B.V. All rights reserved.
Biological Psychiatry, Volume 2. G. Racagni et al., editors.

Striatal dopamine D_2 receptor density in neuroleptic-naive schizophrenics studied with positron emission tomography

J. Hietala[1,2], E. Syvälahti[1,2], K. Vuorio[3], K. Någren[2], P. Lehikoinen[2], U. Ruotsalainen[2], V. Räkköläinen[3], V. Lehtinen[4] and U. Wegelius[2]

[1]Department of Pharmacology, University of Turku; [2]Turku Medical Cyclotron/PET Project; [3]Psychiatric Clinic, Turku City Hospital; and [4]Psychiatric Clinic, Turku University Hospital, Turku, Finland

Introduction

One of the basic assumptions in the dopamine hypothesis of schizophrenia is an abnormally high D_2 dopamine receptor density in the brains of schizophrenic patients. Most data supporting this concept derives from post-mortem studies [1], whereas in vivo studies with positron emission tomography (PET) concerning striatal D_2 receptor number and neuroleptic-naive schizophrenia are extremely controversial. Previous PET-experiments with [^{11}C]N-methylspiperone or [^{11}C]raclopride as radioligands have reported increased [2] or equal [3] D_2 receptor densities in the striata of neuroleptic-naive schizophrenics compared to healthy volunteers. In addition, two PET studies using [^{76}Br]bromospiperone and [^{76}Br]bromolisuride have reported unchanged striatal D_2 binding [4,5] (expressed as striatum/cerebellum ratios) in schizophrenics, or marginally but significantly elevated D_2 binding in a small subgroup of acute schizophrenics [4]. In order to clarify these discrepancies, we tested the D_2 dopamine receptor excess hypothesis in newly admitted neuroleptic-naive schizophrenic patients and healthy volunteers using PET and [^{11}C]raclopride.

Method

PET technique

The measurement of striatal D_2 receptor density and affinity was done by using [^{11}C]raclopride as a radioligand. The experiments were performed using a whole-body PET scanner (ECAT 931/08-12) with a spatial resolution of 6.1 mm on the plane and an axial resolution of 6.7 mm (measured values). Two experiments (injected dose 104 Mbq) were performed on each patient/volunteer using two specific activities (high and low) of [^{11}C]raclopride [6]. Striatal regions-of-interest were drawn on integrated images from 10–49 min using two middlemost planes cutting the caudate-putamen. Data was analyzed in terms of an equilibrium model using the cerebellum as a D_2 receptor-free reference region [6].

Patients

Eleven patients and 10 healthy volunteers were studied. The patients met the DSM III-R criteria for schizophrenia (n = 8), schizophreniform disorder (n = 2) or schizoaffective disorder (n = 1). Ten patients were completely neuroleptic-naive and one patient had received a single 50 mg dose of chlorpromazine orally one month before the PET scan. The ages were 25.2 ± 6.8 years and 26.8 ± 7.3 years (mean ± S.D.) for patients and controls, respectively.

Results

There were no statistically significant differences in D_2 receptor densities (B_{max}) between the whole patient population and normal controls. The B_{max} values were 39.8 ± 16.0 and 34.6 ± 7.5 pmol/ml (mean ± S.D.) for patients and controls, respectively. However, 4 patients (2 schizophrenia patients, 1 schizophreniform and 1 schizoaffective patient) appeared to have increased D_2 receptor B_{max} values not overlapping with the control group. Especially 2 of them had an almost 2-fold-elevated density of striatal D_2 receptors. No consistent D_2 receptor laterality was observed in patients or controls. Additionally, the apparent affinity of D_2 receptors was not statistically different in patients and controls (12.5 ± 4.8 and 10.4 ± 2.9 nM, respectively, mean ± S.D.).

Conclusion

Our results suggest that there is not a generally elevated D_2 receptor number in the striata of schizophrenic patients. However, in accordance with postmortem studies [1] there may be a subpopulation of schizophrenic patients with a markedly increased striatal D_2 receptor level.

Acknowledgements

This work was financially supported by the Jalmari and Rauha Ahokas Foundation and the Medical Research Council, Academy of Finland.

References

1. Seeman P et al. (1987) Neuropsychopharmacology 1: 5–15.
2. Wong D et al. (1986) Science 234: 1558–1563.
3. Farde L et al. (1990) Arch. Gen. Psychiatry 47: 213–219.
4. Martinot JL et al. (1990) Am. J. Psychiatry 147: 44–50.
5. Martinot JL et al. (1991) Br. J. Psychiatry 158: 346–350.
6. Farde L et al. (1990) J. Cereb. Blood Flow Metab. 9: 696–708.

© 1991 Elsevier Science Publishers B.V. All rights reserved.
Biological Psychiatry, Volume 2. G. Racagni et al., editors.

D_2 Dopamine receptors: In vivo investigations in schizophrenia

J.L. Martinot
Service Hospitalier Frédéric Joliot, C.E.A., Hopital d'Orsay, 91406, Orsay, France

Introduction

Among the reasons for studying the D_2 dopamine receptors in schizophrenic patients, important ones are that the neuroleptics seem to exert their therapeutic action by decreasing the dopaminergic activity mediated by this class of receptors and that the density of the D_2 receptors has consistently been found to be elevated in the striata and nuclei accumbens of schizophrenic patients studied postmortem [1]. However, a critical question is to determine whether the elevated density of dopamine D_2 receptors reported postmortem is associated with schizophrenia or whether it is simply induced by the neuroleptic medication.

Ligands and Methods

Positron emission tomography (PET) allows the in vivo study of the striatal D_2 receptor density (and affinity). In 1986, Wong et al. [2] reported a 2.5-fold elevation of the striatal uptake of ^{11}C-N-methylspiperone in patients that they interpreted as an elevation of the D_2 striatal receptor density. But one year later, Farde et al. found no significant difference between patients and controls with the ^{11}C-raclopride, a ligand highly selective for D_2 receptors [3,4]. Both studies used a sophisticated mathematic model to quantify the D_2 receptor density.

In a first PET study, we used the spiperone labelled with bromine 76; this ligand has a good affinity for the D_2 receptors but an incomplete selectivity due to its affinity for the serotonin 5-HT_2 receptors, which are mostly located in the cortical regions. In a second study, we used the lisuride labelled with bromine 76, a ligand highly selective for D_2 receptors.

In order to estimate in vivo the striatal D_2 receptor density, we used the striatum to cerebellum ratio (S/C) method in our studies, which is based on the assumption that, as the cerebellum is almost devoid of D_2 receptors, the radioactivity concentration measured in the cerebellum at the so-called equilibrium state is an estimate of the free ligand in the brain, while the radioactivity measured at the striata level represents both the ligand bound to the D_2 receptors and the free ligand. This index represents a measure of the density/affinity of the D_2 receptors.

Results

In our study with [^{76}Br]bromospiperone, 12 untreated schizophrenics were studied. There was no difference for S/C when the whole schizophrenic group was compared to 12 sex- and age-matched controls and no relationship between the estimated D_2 receptor density and the DSM III clinical types of the illness. However, slight but significant differences were found when the patients whose symptoms had recently appeared or worsened were compared to the chronic patients whose symptoms were stable, suggesting variations in the D_2 receptor densities with the course of the illness [5]. Also, unlike in the controls, the S/C was not correlated with age in schizophrenics.

We tried to replicate these results in a subsequent study using [^{76}Br]bromolisuride. Nineteen untreated schizophrenics were compared to 14 age-matched normal controls. Again, there was neither significant difference between patients and controls in the S/C mean values (4.04 ± 0.46 in patients and 3.86 ± 0.38 in controls, N.S.) nor any relationship between the DSM III clinical types of the illness and the S/C values. The differences in striatum-cerebellum ratio depending on the course of the illness were not confirmed [5], but as in the first study, the S/C was not related to age in the patients, whereas a negative correlation was present in controls.

Conclusion

Over 4 PET studies, three did not report D_2 receptor increase, with 3 different ligands, suggesting that there is no marked increase in the D_2 striatal dopamine receptors associated with the schizophrenia. However, we recently studied 10 highly screened young (20 ± 2 years) drug-free negative schizophrenic inpatients [7]. In these patients, the mean S/C ratio did not differ from that of age-matched controls. But factor analysis of the Scale for the Assessment of Negative Symptoms (SANS) scores in a large group of schizophrenics (n = 104) isolated a "psychomotor expressiveness" factor including most items of the "affective flattening" and "alogia" subscales [8]; both this factor and the SANS total score were clearly negatively correlated ($r = -0.80$ and $r = -0.79$ respectively, Spearman rank correlation) to the S/C values in the 10 negative patients investigated with PET. Hence, the estimated D_2 receptor density does not appears to be a marker of the diagnosis of schizophrenia, but our recent findings suggest that some aspects of the negative symptoms are linked to the central D_2 receptor density and to the dopaminergic transmission.

References

1. Seeman P (1987) Synapse 1: 133–152.

2. Wong DF, Wagner HN, Tune LE et al. (1986) Science 234: 1558–1563.
3. Farde L, Wiesel FA, Hall H et al. (1987) Arch. Gen. Psychiatry 44: 671–672.
4. Farde L, Wiesel FA, Stone-Elander S et al. (1990) Arch. Gen. Psychiatry 47: 213–219.
5. Martinot JL, Peron-Magnan P, Huret JD et al. (1990) Am. J. Psychiatry 147: 44–50.
6. Martinot JL, Paillère-Martinot ML, Loc'h C et al. (1991) Br. J. Psychiatry 158: 346–350.
7. Martinot JL, Paillère-Martinot ML, Loc'h C et al. (1991) (in preparation).
8. Aubin F, Lecrubier Y, Boyer P et al. (1991) (in preparation).

© 1991 Elsevier Science Publishers B.V. All rights reserved.
Biological Psychiatry, Volume 2. G. Racagni et al., editors.

Brain electric field mapping and map analysis in psychiatry: The "atoms of thought"

D. Lehmann
EEG-EP Mapping Laboratory, Department of Neurology, University Hospital, CH-8091 Zurich, Switzerland

Brain electric activity permits non-invasive, harmless and continuous monitoring of brain functional conditions with very high sensitivity for changes of condition such as psychopathology [1–3], medication [4–6], even type of spontaneous thought [7], mental task execution [8] or induced percept. These major advantageous characteristics had recommended the EEG as successful tool for the assessment of normal and pathological brain conditions in mentation and emotion, analyzing the traditional "wave patterns" of EEG traces, using time and frequency domain tools (e.g., power spectra). Such trace-oriented EEG studies could deal with EEG states in the range of minutes to seconds, lately approaching about a second as minimal unit in adaptive segmentation of EEG traces. Much shorter basic units are required to examine the brain mechanisms of individual thoughts and emotions. Event-related potential studies and reaction time studies suggested that the duration of steps in thought processes might well be in the sub-second range, probably around 100 ms [9]. Libet's [10] work has suggested 500 ms as sufficient presence time of information to qualify for access to consciousness.

Techniques to assess the continuously changing brain electric field as a whole are now available, resulting not in traces, but in a series of momentary maps of the field distributions that can be viewed similarly to changing geographic landscapes or facial expressions. This approach permits a very high time resolution down to the millisecond range.

A particular type of brain function is expected to consist of the activity of a certain number of neuronal elements that have a certain three-dimensional geometry and accordingly, produce an electric field of a certain spatial configuration recordable from the scalp as a certain electric landscape. We proposed to call such a condition a global functional microstate. A sequence of landscape-defined microstates is expected to constitute a macro-state as defined by the trace patterns discussed above. If this scalp-recorded landscape of a microstate changes, a set of neuronal elements, at least partially different, must have become active. It is reasonable to assume that a different set of active elements will execute a different function. Thus, in order to identify different momentary functional states of the brain, it is theoretically expected that the decision "same or different functional state" can be made using the map of the instantaneous momentary brain electric field (without any extension in time). In practice, the EEG momentary maps are amply sampled at a rate of about 256 maps per s. Considering the hypothesized time structure of conscious thoughts and percepts, this time resolution still is very high, and certainly qualifies brain electric field mapping as a tool to assess conscious processes.

When there is interest in brain mechanisms of thought and emotions as such, parts of thoughts and emotions (lower level components) cannot suffice for explanations, even though there need to be very many correctly functioning parallel local subprocesses at the same moment in time in order to give rise to a complete thought. However, only the complete description of all relationships between the subprocesses would provide a complete correspondence to the thought; none of its parts, and no listing of all parts will suffice (the parts of a radio receiver form a radio receiver only if they are assembled properly). Hence, in the study of brain mechanisms of thought, emotion and percept, even though steps within thoughts (decisions) might be identifiable, the sequence of private thoughts can be adequately described in physical terms only as a sequence of brain states of which each represents a thought, as a whole. The brain's electromagnetic field is a promising candidate for this role, as it constitutes a homogeneous whole even though it is produced by very many simultaneously active neural generators, reminiscent of the normally indivisible subjective consciousness that emerges from the proper functioning of a very large number of brain processes.

We observed map-defined brain microstates with a mean duration (across normal subjects) of 210 ms for the alpha EEG band; however, 50% of the recording time was covered by states lasting 323 ms or longer [11]. We tested these microstates for behavioral correlates: selective reaction time differed significantly, depending on the class (landscape) of the microstate which existed at the moment of stimulus arrival; the effects were similar across eight subjects [11]. We have suggested that psychopathological conditions might be associated with aberrant durations, frequency of occurrence, or sequence of the classes of these microstates. In fact, Merrin et al. [12] reported that significantly more classes ("types") of microstates ("segments") in the θ frequency band occurred in schizophrenics than in normals, and, in addition, that medication reduced the number of classes of microstates ("segments").

We also studied the hypothesized representation of whole thoughts and their emotional signature by the brain electric microstates. In order to avoid brain mechanisms of task execution we worked with spontaneous subjective experiences that the subjects agreed to report ("what just went through your mind") upon having been presented with a prompt tone; for the assessment of the experiences, we considered the complementary aspects of thought and emotion [13]. In a recent study with B. Henggeler, 13 male volunteers were prompted 30 times in 3 recording sessions each; the reports were classed by two independent raters (agreement required) into the following classes in three categories: a) visual imagery vs. abstract thought; b) content being related to past experience, present lab situation, or future planning; c) distinct emotions involved vs. relaxed emotional condition. In each category, less than 30% of the reports were rated as "no classification possible". For each classified report, the momentary EEG map of maximal relief prominence preceding the prompt (this occurred within the last 50 ms) was used for further analysis as classifier of the microstate. This map's landscape was described by the locations of its most positive and most negative potential values (the two extremes). For each subject, the locations of the extremes of all maps associated with each class of thought and emotion were collected. The median location of all extremes was computed for each class of thought and emotion, for each subject. Finally, the grand median locations of the extremes across subjects were computed for each class of thought and emotion, and the differences in location between classes of the same category were statistically compared using paired tests.

Significant differences of the grand median locations of the map extremes values on the scalp were observed between microstate maps associated with thoughts related to the past (more posterior) vs. thoughts related to the present (more anterior), and thoughts related to the past (more posterior) vs. thoughts related to the future (more anterior), and reports rated as associated with positive or negative emotions (more posterior) vs. reports associated with a relaxed emotional state (more anterior).

These results mean that the momentary brain functional microstate that existed immediately before a verbal report of a private experience reflects the type of this experience: past- or present- or future-related, and emotion-associated or emotion-neutral, following rules that are common across subjects. Different momentary brain electric landscapes must have been generated by different neural components: hence, the different types of subjective experiences are associated with a different brain geometry of the generating neuronal elements. We suggest that brain functional microstates as defined by the momentary landscape of the brain electric field constitute the functional building blocks of mentation and emotion, the "atoms of thought". Knowledge about the types (repertoire), the concatenations (syntax), and the frequencies of occurrence of these building blocks are expected to contribute to the elucidation and biological classification of psychopathological conditions.

References

1. John ER, Prichep LS, Fridman J and Easton P (1989) Science 239: 162–169.
2. Koukkou M and Manske W (1986) In: Shagass C, Josiassen RC and Roemer RA (eds.) Brain Electric Potentials and Psychopathology. Elsevier, Amsterdam, pp. 91–114.
3. Maurer K (ed.) (1989) Topographic Brain Mapping of EEG and Evoked Potentials. Springer, Berlin.
4. Itil T and Itil KZ (1986) In: Shagass C, Josiassen RC and Roemer RA (eds.) Brain Electric Potentials and Psychopathology. Elsevier, Amsterdam, pp. 345–358.
5. Saito M, Kita S, Kagono Y, Suitsu N and Honda Y (1982) Electroencephalogr. Clin. Neurophysiol. (Suppl.) 36: 524–537.
6. Saletu B (1989) In: Maurer K (ed.) Topographic Brain Mapping of EEG and Evoked Potentials. Springer, Berlin, pp. 482–506.
7. Lehmann D, Koukkou M and Andreae A (1981) Sleep Res. 10: 152.

8. Makino A, Horie S, Ebisutani D and Matsumoto K (1989) In: Tsutsui J (ed.) EEG Topography 1987. Neuron Publishers, Shinagawa-Tokyo, pp. 47–56.
9. Brandeis D and Lehmann D (1989) Electroencephalogr. Clin. Neurophysiol. 73: 507–519.
10. Libet B (1982) Human Neurobiol. 1: 235–242.
11. Lehmann D, Ozaki H and Pal I (1987) Electroencephalogr. Clin. Neurophysiol. 67: 271–288.
12. Merrin EL, Meek P, Floyd TC and Callaway E (1990) Int. J. Psychophysiol. 9: 231–236.
13. Ciompi L (1991) Affects as central organizing and integrating factors. Br. J. Psychiatry 159 (in press).

© 1991 Elsevier Science Publishers B.V. All rights reserved.
Biological Psychiatry, Volume 2. G. Racagni et al., editors.

EEG mapping in clinical treatment of depressive disorders

Masami Saito, Yoshiki Ohashi, Yoshiyasu Okajima, Naomi Saito, Masato Fukushima and Kenji Nobuhara

Department of Neuropsychiatry, Kansai Medical University, Fumizono-cho 1, Moriguchi, Osaka 570, Japan

Introduction

The main aims of the EEG studies on depressive disorders were as follows: first, whether there is any basic difference in EEG from depressive patients and from normal subjects or not; second, whether there is any difference in EEG responses to antidepressant drugs between depressive patients and healthy subjects; and third, whether there is any difference between therapy responsive patients and refractory patients to antidepressant drug treatment.

The authors have attempted several times to clarify the issue with computer-assisted EEG technique over the last 20 years and have not yet been able to reach this goal, due to the limitations of the system. EEG functional mapping appears to provide much more information than previously expected. Thus, the authors have studied EEG of patients with major depression in comparison to those of selected normal subjects.

Material and Methods

Subject

Depressive patients. Sixteen drug-free inpatients with typical depression of major affective disorders were selected for the present study. Their ages ranged from 22–68 years and they consisted of 6 males and 8 females.

They were treated with amitriptyline 25 mg t.i.d. for the first week as a fixed dose and thereafter dosages were varied according to the doctor's choice. On the first day, EEGs were recorded before and after the first drug treatment, in order to compare them with those of normal controls; EEGs were then recorded weekly. Severity of depressive symptoms were regularly assessed using the Hamilton Depression Scale and the daily observations of the doctors in charge.

Normal controls. Eighteen healthy young male volunteers, whose ages ranged from 23–26 years, were selected for study after all the necessary procedures. They were given one single oral dose of the same drug and EEGs were recorded 1 h, 3 h and 6 h after drug administration. Since the screening standards were so extremely strict, both mentally and physically, they should be regarded not as "normal" subjects but as "NORMAL normal" subjects.

EEG processing and statistical treatment. All the EEGs were processed by quantitative analysis and mapping techniques using HZI BFMS and our KMU system. The results were examined in reference to individual evolution of clinical features, particularly those of the Hamilton Depression scores.

Results

In the comparison of baseline EEG measurements of depressive patients with those of normal controls, there were statistically significant differences such as less δ to θ activity and more α activity of higher frequency and more β activity above 20 Hz in depressives than in normal controls. Not taking into account the possible bias due to the age difference between groups, none of the patients' EEGs was outside the limit of normal variations.

As to the EEG responses to the single dose of amitriptyline 25 mg in the normal controls, a marked increase of lower θ activity was seen in the posterior half from parietal to occipital regions and a significant decrease of α activity all over the brain, more or less markedly in the left hemisphere.

EEG changes induced by the first single dose of amitriptyline in the depressive patients, showed a marked increase of δ and lower θ activities in central to occipital areas, a significant decrease of α activity common to all the derivations, more markedly in the left hemisphere and an increase of fast activity in the frontal and left occipital regions.

In the comparison of the EEG responses between the 2 groups, it should be noted that there were common changes in the left hemisphere but less in the right hemisphere in the patient group than in the normal group and more in δ and β activities in the patient group than in the normal group.

The patient groups were divided into 2 subgroups based on the changes in HAM-D scores; one was therapy-responsive, the other therapy-refractory. EEG changes in the former group were summarized as increases in δ, lower θ and β activities and decreases of α, higher θ and average amplitude, while in the latter group they were summarized as increases in θ activity and amplitude and decreases in α activity. The EEG changes in the latter group appear more like those of normal subjects.

Discussion and Conclusion

As the EEG traits of depressive disorders, an increase of α activity and a lower shift of α frequency were noted out from visual observations, but these differences from control subjects are only statistical ones, and there have never been any specific signs which could be applicable to clinical diagnostics.

In the present study, some statistically significant differences were found but there seems to be nothing particular of specific or diagnostic value. However, the localized or hemispherical differences may suggest a certain biological difference of the right hemisphere in patients with major depression. The increase of slow activity may be interpreted as due to the sedative or inhibitory effects of amitriptyline.

The difference between responsive and refractory patients was seen in higher θ activity, β activity and average amplitude. In case of early prediction, however, it seems important to take notice of the increases of δ and β activities and decreases in higher θ and corresponding decrease in average amplitude, because it would seem that the more significant the initial δ increase due to amitriptyline is, the earlier the antidepressant effects appear. It can be concluded that the induced EEG changes in responsive patients are exactly the same as the thymoleptic reaction type which may correspond to sedative and tranquilizing effects without mood elevation.

Summary

1. In the comparison of EEG between normal subjects and patients with major depression, there were only minor differences within the normal range, such as less slow activity and more higher frequency α and more β activity above 20 Hz. The slow wave decrease was generally seen in all the derivations, while the rapid activity increase was more predominant in the left hemisphere, particularly in the central to parietal region of the brain than in the right hemisphere.
2. In the comparison of EEG responses to the first oral administration of amitriptyline 25 mg in normal subjects and depressive patients, there was an increase of slow activity associated with a decrease of α activity in the normal subjects, and an increase of slow activity accompanied by a decrease in α and an increase of rapid activity, in the 3-h postdrug EEG.
3. Regarding to 3-h postdrug EEG with the first amitriptyline 25 mg, there was an increase of rapid activity in the patients who were responsive to further medication, while there was a decrease of the same in those who were refractory to the treatment. In addition, the initial increase of δ activity was more significant in the responsive group than in the other group of depressive patients. Based on these results, it appears possible to predict the clinical outcome of the patient with drug treatment solely based on the 3-h postdrug EEG changes.

References

1. Tsuda T (1979) J. Kansai Med. Univ. 31: 548–578.
2. Ohashi Y, Yagyu T, Nobuhara K and Saito M (1991) Neurosciences 17: 35–38.

© 1991 Elsevier Science Publishers B.V. All rights reserved.
Biological Psychiatry, Volume 2. G. Racagni et al., editors.

On diagnosis, differential diagnosis and pharmacotherapy of dementia; mapping of EEG and its correlations to clinical variables

Bernd Saletu, Peter Anderer, Josef Grünberger, Eveline Paulus, Kurt Peter Fischhof, Lothar Wicke and Andreas Neuhold
Department of Psychiatry, School of Medicine, University of Vienna, Währinger Gürtel 18–20, A-1090 Vienna, Austria

Introduction

Previous brain mapping studies demonstrated that SDAT and MID patients exhibited more δ and θ and less α and β activities as well as a slowed centroid suggesting a deterioration of vigilance [1]. While these findings differed topographically in the two subtypes of dementia, the most discriminating measures concerned differences between maximum and minimum power and asymmetry indices. Brain maps of correlation coefficients between CT and EEG variables demonstrated: the more brain atrophy, the more δ/θ and the less α and β activity in the EEG, which in turn was correlated with higher SCAG scores and worse psychometric performance [2]. The aim of the present study was to replicate these findings utilizing both confirmatory and descriptive statistics.

Materials and Methods

CT, EEG, clinical and psychometric data were obtained in 96 mildly to moderately demented patients in old people's/nursing homes (72 females, 24 males), aged between 61–96 years (mean 82 years), diagnosed according to DSM III criteria. Patients had to score on the SCAG between 45 and 90 and on the mini-mental status (MMS) between 10 and 24, and had to be able to perform the labyrinth test. They had to be off psychopharmaceutical agents for at least 14 days and were sub-diagnosed according to the modified Marshall Hachinski's Ischemic Score (<4 = SDAT; >7 = MID) and CT in 45 SDAT and 51 MID patients. The groups did not differ in regard to sex, or age. CT measures included 10 CSF space variables, as well as 17 cortical density measures underneath the EEG electrodes. EEG recordings, clinical and psychometric evaluations were carried out before as well as 12 weeks after treatment with either 100 mg denbufylline b.i.d. or placebo b.i.d. Three minute-vigilance controlled EEGs (V-EEG) were recorded by means of Nihon-Kohden 4317F and 4321F polygraphs. Topographic brain mapping was carried out based on a method described in detail elsewhere [3]. Clinical and psychometric investigations included the SCAG score/factors, the clinical global impression (CGI), the digit-symbol substitution test (DSST), the trail-making test (TMT) and the digit-span test (DS). Statistical analysis was based on the concept of descriptive data analysis as proposed by Abt [4] including confirmatory statements concerning differences between SDAT, MID and normals in the absolute δ/θ power as well as regarding the correlations of the latter to a CT variable (greatest distance between lateral ventricles) the SCAG score and the DSST. α Adjustment was carried out according to Bonferroni. An informed written consent was obtained.

Results

EEG maps of SDAT and MID patients as compared with controls

Confirmatory statistics were carried out regarding differences between SDAT, MID and normals in absolute δ/θ power. The preselected maximal error probability $\alpha = 0.05$ was corrected for multiple comparisons (2×17 electrode positions) by the procedure of Bonferroni-Holme ($P < 0.05/34 = 0.0015$). The null hypothesis that there is no difference in absolute δ/θ power between controls and SDAT and MID patients respectively was rejected. δ/θ Power was increased in SDAT over all brain regions except the occipital occipitally, while in MID cases this exception was seen left frontally, bioccipitally and right occipito-temporally. Descriptive analysis showed no differences in absolute α and β power, while relative δ/θ power was enhanced and relative α and β power reduced in patients as compared with controls. Total power was augmented bitemporally and fronto-polarly, the centroid slowed down over many brain regions. The increase of δ/θ power in SDAT was 3.9 standard deviations from controls, that of MID patients 4.9 in the left temporal region (highest P values).

On differences between SDAT and MID patients

Descriptive data analysis on differences in 36 EEG variables demonstrated only few significant findings (β power being lower right parietally and occipitally in MID than SDAT patients, with the former also showing a slower centroid left frontally and centrally and a faster β centroid bifrontally than the latter. A better discrimination between the two subtypes of dementia was obtained by means of power asymmetry indices, which revealed more asymmetry in MID than SDAT patients concerning δ/θ power frontally, α power parietally and β power fronto-polarly, frontally and centrally.

Correlations between CT, EEG clinical and psychometric measures

Confirmatory statistics failed to find significant correlations between the chosen CT-variable and δ/θ power, while significant correlations were found between the latter and the SCAG score and the DSST: the more δ/θ power, the higher was the SCAG score rated by the psychiatrist and the worse the performance in the DSST.

Descriptive data analysis utilizing Spearman's rank correlations between 11 CT and 36 EEG variables demonstrated: the greater the distance between the anterior horns and the caudate nuclei and the lower the cortical density, the higher the δ power. Cortical density was generally correlated negatively with power in all frequency bands. The larger the distance between the choroid plexus, the less β power and the slower the centroid of the total activity.

More significant and higher correlations were found between EEG measures and clinical variables such as the MMS, SCAG and CGI. The more δ/θ and the less α and β activity, and the slower the centroid of the total activity, the lower was the MMS, the higher the SCAG and the CGI. Many significant correlations were also found between EEG and psychometric performance measures: the higher the δ/θ and the less the α and β activity and the slower the centroid of the total activity, the worse the performance in the DSST, the TMT and the DS.

Clinical findings and EEG mapping during denbufylline treatment

Clinical evaluations based on the CGI, MMS, SCAG, DSST, TMT and the DS demonstrated after denbufylline a significant improvement in both SDAT and MID patients as compared with baseline, while after placebo this was not the case in CGI, TMT and DS. Interdrug comparison revealed a significant superiority of denbufylline over placebo in all psychopathological and psychometric variables except for the TMT in the MID group. EEG brain mapping exhibited in denbufylline-treated SDAT patients a decrease of δ activity and acceleration of the slow activity as compared with placebo-treated SDAT patients, denbufylline-treated MID cases showed mostly an increase of fast α and α adjacent β activity as well as a decrease of slow α and fast β activity as compared with placebo-treated MID cases. Thus both the degenerative and vascular type of dementia exhibited a therapeutic benefit, assessed objectively by rating scales and psychometric tests, which was obviously due to an improvement in vigilance at the neurophysiological level.

References

1. Saletu B, Anderer P, Paulus E, Grünberger J, Wicke L, Neuhold A, Fischhof PK, Litschauer G, Wagner G, Hatzinger R and Dittrich R (1988) In: Samson-Dollfus D, Guieu JD, Gotman J and Etevenon P (eds.) Statistics and Topography in Quantitative EEG. Elsevier, Paris, France, pp. 251–275.
2. Saletu B, Paulus E, Anderer P, Fischhof PK and Wicke L (1990) Clin. Neuropharmacol. 13: 166–167.
3. Anderer P, Saletu B, Kinsperger K and Semlitsch H (1987) Meth. Find. Exp. Clin. Pharmacol. 9: 371–384.
4. Abt K (1988) In: Samson-Dollfus D (ed.) Statistics and Topography in Quantitative EEG. Elsevier, Paris, France, pp. 150–160.

© 1991 Elsevier Science Publishers B.V. All rights reserved.
Biological Psychiatry, Volume 2. G. Racagni et al., editors.

Toward a quantitative electrophysiological classification system for psychiatry

E. Roy John[1,2], L.S. Prichep[1,2] and M. Almas[1]

[1]*Department of Psychiatry, NYU Medical Center, New York; and* [2]*Nathan S. Kline Psychiatric Research Institute, Orangeburg, New York, U.S.A.*

Neurometrics is a method for quantitative analysis of the electroencephalogram (QEEG) which involves 3 basic steps [1]:

1. objective computerized measurements are made of the absolute power, relative power, coherence and symmetry in the δ, θ, α and β frequency bands, derived by spectral analysis of 1–2 min of artifact-free EEG (edited with the use of a computer algorithm with visual concordance);
2. transformation of the data to achieve a Gaussian distribution;
3. Z-transformation of the data relative to normative age-regression equations.

The result of these operations is an abnormality matrix, in which columns represent brain regions, rows represent electrophysiological aspects of various brain function and an entry represents the probability of abnormality. Currently, a great deal of interest is directed toward the clinical utility of interpolated topographic brain maps, in which the data from **one row** of this matrix are graphically displayed using a colour scale proportional to probability of abnormality. While such maps are attractive and often informative, they are of limited diagnostic utility because patients with the same disease may show markedly different maps and patients displaying similar maps may have different diseases. We believe that the greatest utility of the neurometric method will come from the application of multivariate pattern recognition to neurometric data matrices as an adjunct to diagnosis and a major aid in subtyping to predict response to treatment.

The entry in every cell of the neurometric abnormality matrix represents the **probability** that the corresponding electrophysiological feature is abnormal in that brain region. The matrix is a representation of the patient in a "probabilistic signal space". With appropriate corrections for intercorrelations, the patient can be represented by an "abnormality vector" or "brain state vector" in a multidimensional signal space. The length of the vector reflects the **severity** or quantity of abnormality, the orientation of the vector reflects the **disease nature** or quality of abnormality. In previous reports, we have provided evidence of the high correlation between multivariate abnormality (length) and degree of cognitive impairment [2,3] and of differences in orientation of the abnormality vector with different diseases [3].

Abnormality vectors from a large number of patients can be considered to define a "swarm" of points in abnormal signal space. Theoretically, patients with a given disease would be expected to group primarily within one region of this hyperspace, while patients with another disease are expected to group in a different region.

Multivariate statistical methods are available to cleave such point swarms into sectors of signal space which contain mostly members of one category but minimally members of another. **Multivariate discriminant** functions do so by constructing a pattern recognition template on a previously labelled *training group*; the recognition rule is then validated by independent replication in a *test group*. Classification procedures using such methods can be described as informed, in the sense that the procedure is based upon the availability of a criterion group presumed to epitomize a *true* category.

We have reported the use of discriminant analysis to categorize psychiatric patients with different disorders, achieving high sensitivity and specificity [4–6]. We continue to extend our library of discriminant functions as our database of psychiatric patients increases in size and diversity. Table 1a and 1b summarize the present status of these discriminant functions, many of which have received confirmation from other clinical workers [7,8].

Table 1. Summary of discriminant results for 2 group (a) an multiple group (b) neurometric QEEG discriminant functions

1a. Neurometric QEEG discriminants

Groups			n		Mean discriminant accuracy (%) (Initial discrim./independent replication)	
I	vs.	II	I	II	I	II
N	vs.	Dep	95	111	88/86	83/93
Uni	vs.	Bip	65	32	84/87	88/94
N	vs.	MHI	150	52	91/84	89/92
N	vs.	Sz	149	57	96/99	90/82
Dep	vs.	Sz	103	46	84/88	84/85[b]
N	vs.	Alc	120	30	95/95	75/90
Abn	vs.	Alc	32–97	30	91/88	96/93
N	vs.	LD	158	175	89/79	72/71
RitResp	vs.	Non-Resp	16	12	81/81[a]	83/83[a]

1b. Neurometric QEEG discriminants – multiple groups

Groups	n	Mean discriminant accuracy (%) (Initial discrim./independent replication)			
N vs. Dep vs. Dem	85/87/125	84/85	84/80	84/71	–
Vasc Dem vs. Non-Vasc	93/13	94/82	92/85[a]	–	–
N vs. Dep vs. Alc vs. Dem	120/103/30/125	77/75	72/85	80/80	79/77

[a]Jack-knifed replication; [b]Med. group used for replication; Group codes are as follows: N = normal; Dep = major affective disorder, depression; Uni = unipolar depression; Bip = bipolar depression; MHI = mild head injury; Sz = chronic schizophrenia; Abn = abnormal groups combined; Alc = alcoholic; LD = learning disabled; RitResp = responders to ritalin; Non-Resp = non-responders to ritalin.

Recently, we have sought ways to depart from dependence upon the current nosology of psychiatry, which restricts neurometric pattern recognition methods to the confirmation of DSM III-R categorization of clinical symptoms. We regard such informed discriminant classification as confirming that clinical symptoms have a correlate in recognizable pathophysiological indices. This reveals little about different categories of pathophysiological process which may underlie similar psychiatric manifestations in behaviour.

Accordingly, we have subjected diagnostically homogeneous groups of patients to **cluster analysis**. The difference between discriminant analysis and cluster analysis is illustrated in Fig. 1.

Discriminant analysis seeks a rule to separate previously identified patients in 2 or more categories (X's and O's in Fig. 1) from each other, such that, using this rule, previously unidentified mixtures of patients in those categories can subsequently be accurately separated. Cluster analysis restricts itself to an uninformed evaluation of the data, examining its structure in a purely mathematical sense with no prior identification (cluster 1, 2 and 3 in Fig. 1). It is, therefore, more independent of a priori beliefs than discriminant analysis.

We have previously reported the use of cluster analysis to explore the natural

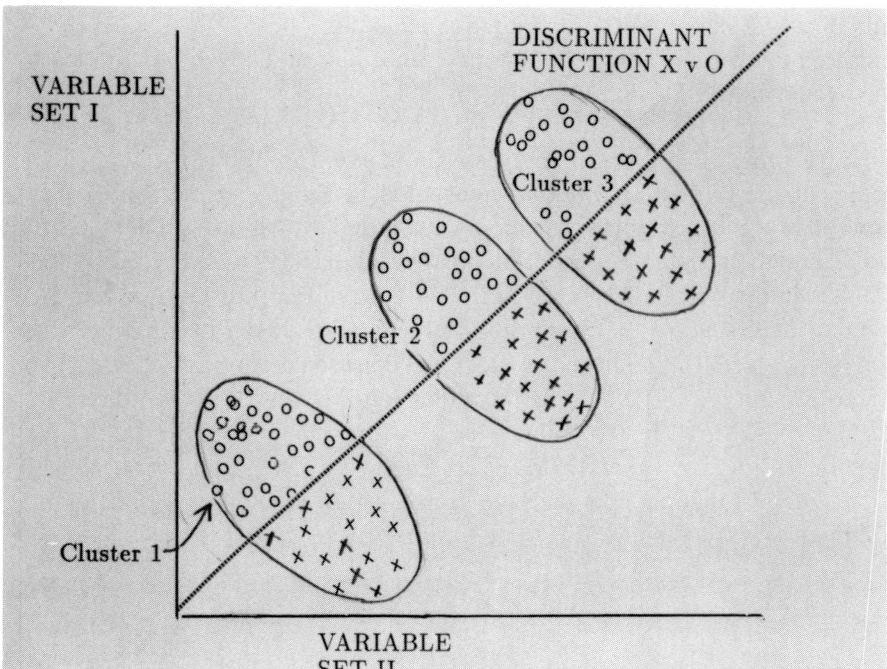

Fig. 1. Schematic representation of idealized discriminant analysis and cluster analysis. Given a training set of X's and O's a discriminant function (diagonal line) can be constructed which can be used subsequently to separate X's and O's cluster analysis, basing itself upon analysis of variance of a distance matrix between all elements in the space (X's and O's), will group the X's and O's into 3 neighborhoods (subtypes), cluster 1, 2 and 3 in this figure.

structure of neurometric data sets. Applying this method to a large group of schizophrenic patients, we reported that 5 clusters of non-medicated patients were obtained, one of which contained most of the haloperidol responders [9]. Applying this method to patients with obsessive-compulsive disorder, we reported that 2 clusters of non-medicated patients were obtained, one of which contained most of the patients responsive to OCD specific medications [10].

The present study sample contained 140 "normally" functioning adults and 624 psychiatric patients, all of whom were multiple rater DSM III or DSM III-R diagnosed and drug-free for at least 7 days at the time of the neurometric evaluation (with the exception of a group of 99 chronic schizophrenic patients tested while receiving halperidol). The diagnoses includes the following: 84 unipolar depressions, 38 bipolar depressions, 25 chronic schizophrenics, 12 first-break schizophrenics, 99 medicated schizophrenics, 30 alcoholics, 197 dementias (SDAT), 103 mild cognitively impaired elderly and 31 obsessive-compulsive disorders*. Each category was randomly divided into 2 split half samples (see [1,4] for details of inclusion and exclusion criteria of these groups).

Twenty minutes of eyes closed resting EEG data was recorded from the 19 channels of the International 10/20 system, referenced to linked ears. Transorbital electrodes were used to record eye movement. From this EEG record, 1–2 min of artifact-free data was submitted to quantitative analysis.

We submitted this entire sample of 764 mixed normals and psychiatric patients to a cluster analysis (BMDP K means), using a 12-cluster solution. A set of 26 variables was selected for this analysis, including those variables found most useful in the informed discriminant analyses summarized in Table 1.

The results of the cluster analysis are presented in Fig. 2. Inspection of this figure shows that each category of patients classified by rigorous DSM III-R criteria, represented on separate rows of the histogram display, was divided by the cluster analysis into several subtypes. These subtypes did not differ significantly with respect to age, severity of morbidity or medication history. Although the cluster analysis yielded 108 cells (12 clusters × 9 disease categories), 62% of the cases fell into 22 subtypes. The split half samples replicated well in their distribution across subtypes. Most clusters, represented by separate columns in the figure, contained patients in 2 or more DSM III-R diagnostic categories. Preliminary followup data suggest that patients with the same diagnosis belonging to different clusters (subtypes) may display different long-term prognosis or responses to treatment.

*The depressed population was studied in collaboration with Dr A. Lieber, Dept. Neuroscience, St. Francis Hosp. FL; the schizophrenic in collaboration with K. Alper, M.D., Dept. Psychiatry, New York University Medical Center and Bellevue Hospital Center, N.Y., N.Y.; the demented in collaboration with S. Ferris and B. Reisberg, Millhauser Laboratories, Dept. Psychiatry, New York University Medical Center. Supported in part by NIH Grant #AG03051 and #MH32577; the OCD in collaboration with E. Hollander and M. Liebowitz, New York State Psychiatric Institute, N.Y., N.Y.; the alcoholic in collaboration with Dr. C. Rohrs, Manhattan Veterans Admin. Hospital, N.Y., N.Y.

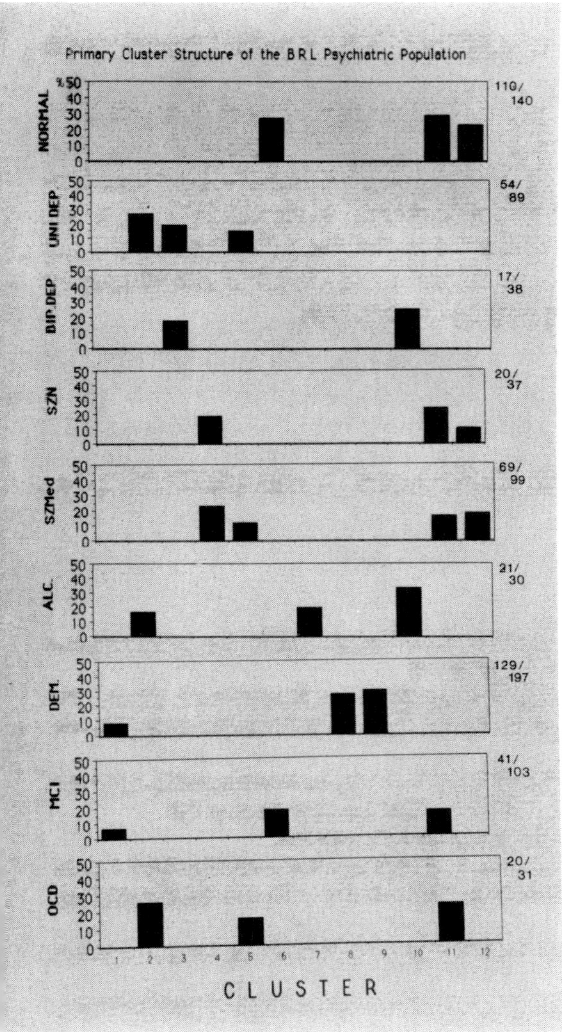

Fig. 2. Results of cluster analysis constructing 12 clusters from a mixed sample of 140 normal subjects and 624 psychiatric patients in 8 DSM III diagnostic categories (see text). Each now represents the major subtypes into which each diagnostic category was divided. The column on the right gives the size of the total sample in each category and the number of cases included in the indicated subtypes. Note that most clusters contain patients from multiple categories. In this figure first-break schizophrenic patients are combined with the unmedicated schizophrenic sample.

These findings can only be regarded as of the most preliminary sort, in that marked differences in the putative structure of the **psychopathology space** may appear as different variable sets are selected and different numbers of clusters sought. The basic algorithm is severely constrained by the requirement that one specify the number of clusters to be found, since no method yet exists which identifies the *true structure* of the signal space with no instruction from the user as to the numerosity of subtypes; results yielded by the algorithm will also depend upon judicious selection of appropriate variables which span the relevant signal space.

Nonetheless, with all of these caveats and cautions, we propose that a method like the one here described, based upon a set of objectively measured biological variables (whether or not restricted to electrophysiological measures) subjected to uninformed mathematical definition of the true structure of the abnormality space, will eventually prove to be a more useful basis for the selection of optimal treatments for psychiatric patients than criteria based only on evaluation of clinical symptoms. This paper may be an early step upon that path.

Acknowledgement

This work was supported in part by Cadwell Laboratories, Kennewick, Washington.

References

1. John E, Prichep L, Friedman J and Essig-Peppard T (1988b) In: Samson-Dollfus D (ed.) Statistics and Topography in Quantitative EEG. Elsevier, Paris, pp. 88–95.
2. John E and Prichep L (1990) In: Uylings H, Eden CV, Bruin JD, Corner M and Feenstra M (eds.) The Prefrontal Cortex, Its Structure, Function and Pathology. Progress in Brain Research, Elsevier, Amsterdam, pp. 545–555.
3. Prichep L, John E, Ferris S, Reisberg B, Alper K and Cancro R (1990b) In: New Research Program and Abstracts: American Psychiatric Association 143rd Annual Meeting, New York, p. 301.
4. John E, Prichep L, Fridman J and Easton P (1988a) Science 293: 162–169.
5. Prichep L, Lieber A, John E, Alper K, Gomez-Mont F, Essig-Peppard T and Flitter M (1986) In: Shagass C, Josiassen R and Roemer R (eds.) Brain Electrical Potentials and Psychopathology. Elsevier, Amsterdam, pp. 223–244.
6. Prichep L, John E, Mas F and Essig-Peppard T (1990c) In: Machinery of the Mind. Birkhauser, Cambridge, pp. 460–470.
7. Suffin S, Hamlin E and Cantor D (1991) Brain Topography, Proc. 2nd Int. Congr. Brain Electromagnet. Topogr. (in press).
8. Morré H (1991) Brain Topography, Proc. 2nd Int. Congr. Brain Electromagnet. Topogr. (in press).
9. Prichep L, John E, Essig-Peppard T and Alper K (1990a) In: Cazzullo C, Invernizzi G, Sacchetti E and Vita A (eds.) Plasticity and Morphology of the Central Nervous System. M.T.P. Press, London.
10. Prichep L, Mas F, John E and Levine R (1991) In: Stefanis C, Rabavilas A and Soldatos C (eds.) Psychiatry: A World Perspective – Vol. 1. Elsevier, Amsterdam, pp. 557–562.

© 1991 Elsevier Science Publishers B.V. All rights reserved.
Biological Psychiatry, Volume 2. G. Racagni et al., editors.

Evoked potential topography in schizophrenia and major depression

Charles Shagass and Richard A. Roemer
Temple University and Philadelphia Psychiatric Center, Ford Road and Monument Ave, Philadelphia, PA 19131, U.S.A.

We present here our main findings concerning evoked potential (EP) topography in schizophrenia and major depression (MD). EP topographic comparisons offer the possibility of relating psychopathology to loci of deviant brain electrical activity. Our data base contains EPs to 4 kinds of stimuli, recorded from 15 electrodes, in 195 nonpatient controls and 644 psychiatric patients.

Earlier topographic analyses on part of the data indicated differences from normal in both schizophrenia and MD [1,2]. Present results were obtained with different data analysis methods, selected to facilitate group comparisons of EP topography [3]. These included:

a) mapping by interpolation;
b) principal component factor analysis (PCA) of EP waveforms to reduce large numbers of values to a limited set of variables (factors);
c) normalization (Z-transform across leads) to avoid confounding group differences in mean level with spatial distribution differences.

Material and Method

Present results come from age and gender matched groups of unmedicated patients (72 schizophrenics, 69 MD) and controls. Details of recording and data analysis were as described previously [3]. Stimuli were: electrical pulses (0.1 ms duration, intensity 10 mA above sensory threshold) to right and left median nerves for somatosensory EP (left nerve, LSEP; right nerve, RSEP); pattern flash for visual EP (VEP); binaural clicks for auditory EP (AEP). Leads were: F3x, C3x, T3, T5, 03, 01, Oz, 02, 04, T6, T4, C4x, F4x, Cz and an eye monitor lead below Fpz. EPs were averages of 192 EEG sweeps with 448 poststimulus data values. Microvolt values were reduced by ninthering (medians of medians of three consecutive original data values). PCA of ninthers, across leads and subjects, yielded 6 LSEP, 6 RSEP, 4 VEP and 4 AEP factors. Separate PCAs, for alternate values from 10 to 81 ms poststimulus, yielded 4 factors each for LSEP, RSEP and AEP. Scores of the 32 factors (untransformed and Z-transformed) were compared between groups by ANOVA. Group × lead interactions on Z-transformed scores indicated topographic differences.

Results

Schizophrenics vs. controls (n = 72 each)

Topographic differences were obtained for scores of 11 factors. These differences converged at left temporo-parietal and right fronto-central-temporal areas; left hemisphere values were higher (hyperactivity) and right hemisphere values were lower (hypoactivity) in schizophrenics.

MD vs. controls (n = 69 each)

Scores of 8 factors differed topographically. Regional convergence of differences was found only for 2 AEP factors (MD values lower posteriorly).

MD vs. schizophrenics (n = 52 each)

Five factors differed topographically (2 RSEP factors and one LSEP, VEP and AEP factor). All could be interpreted as long latency activities (P300 or slow wave). Differences were antero-posterior (AP), with higher posterior and lower anterior values in MD. An AP gradient score, reflecting composite differences between posterior and anterior leads for the 5 factors, differed ($P < 0.003$) between matched MD, schizophrenic and control groups; control and schizophrenic gradient scores were alike and both differed from MD, with higher posterior scores for MD. Fig. 1 shows the mean topographies of the 5 factors for schizophrenics and MDs, and a map of the differences between means.

Discussion

Present findings of left posterior quadrant hyperactivity in schizophrenics seem consistent with the evidence marshalled by Morihisa and Duffy [4] that schizophrenics show "focal cortical arousal" in this region. It should be noted that such convergence of EP topographic differences from normal was observed only in unmedicated schizophrenics, not being found in medicated patients [3]. We did not find here similarly convergent topographic differences from normal in unmedicated MDs. However, differences between MDs and schizophrenics did converge antero-posteriorly, with higher posterior and lower anterior values in MD. These AP gradient differences appear relatively specific to MD, as AP gradients of schizophrenics and controls were alike.

Mean values of the 5 factors giving AP gradient differences between MDs and schizophrenics did not differ significantly between the groups, so that EPs in the two disorders differed primarily in topography. These 5 factors reflect long latency EP events, like P300, usually considered to be related to cognition. Although our recording situation involved no task beyond eye fixation, the random order of

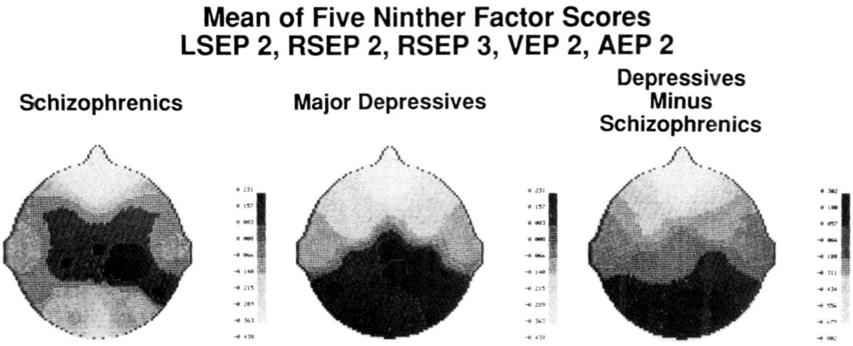

Fig. 1. Spatial distributions of means of five factor scores differing topographically between age and gender matched groups of 52 schizophrenics and 52 major depressives. Right, distribution of mean differences between maps.

stimuli probably accounts for regular elicitation of a small P300. The results suggest that the two disorders differed with respect to the pattern of brain regions that were activated in relation to these cognition-related events.

The fact that some degree of systematic activation was taking place may be responsible for differences between present EP findings and results with other methods that have shown functional topography differences between MDs and controls. Both regional cerebral blood flow (RCBF) [5] and glucose utilization (PET scan) [6], measurements have been found globally and regionally (mainly frontal and anterior) reduced in MD. However, these measurements were made at "rest," under which condition MDs seem to be generally underactivated (less overall cerebral blood flow, lower glucose metabolism, more EEG α). When activated, MDs tend to show greater than normal EEG and RCBF changes [7,8]. Schizophrenics, by contrast, seem more than normally activated "at rest"; also, they respond less to activating stimuli, [9] perhaps because already activated. The concept of activation may help to integrate various kinds of observations bearing on differences in regional brain physiology between MD and schizophrenia.

Acknowledgement

Supported (in part) by USPHS Grant MH12507.

References

1. Shagass C, Roemer RA, Straumanis JJ and Amadeo M (1979) In: Gruzelier J and Flor-Henry P (eds.) Hemisphere Asymmetries of Function in Psychopathology. Elsevier, Amsterdam, pp. 293–316.
2. Shagass C, Roemer RA, Straumanis JJ and Amadeo M (1980) Biol. Psychiatry 15: 183–207.

3. Shagass C and Roemer R (1991) Int. J. Psychophysiol. 10: 213–224.
4. Morihisa JM and Duffy FH (1986) In: Duffy H (ed.) Topographic Mapping of Brain Electrical Activity. Butterworth/Stoneham MD, pp. 371–379.
5. Sackeim HA, Prohovnik I, Moeller JR, Brown RP, Apter S, Prudic J, Devanand DP and Mukherjee S (1990) Arch. Gen. Psychiatry 47: 60–70.
6. Martinot JL, Hardy P, Feline A, Huret JD, Mazoyer B, Attar-Levy D, Pappata S and Syrota A (1990) Am. J. Psychiatry 147: 1313–1317.
7. Shagass C, Roemer RA and Josiassen RC (1988) Neuropsychobiology 19: 169–175.
8. Gur RE, Skolnick BE, Gur RC, Caroff S, Rieger W, Obrist WD, Younkin D and Reivich M (1984) Arch. Gen. Psychiatry 41: 695–699.
9. Shagass C, Roemer RA, Josiassen RC and Straumanis JJ (1986) In: Shagass C, Josiassen RC, Bridger WH, Weiss K, Stoff D and Simpson GM (eds.) Biological Psychiatry 1985. Elsevier, New York, pp. 424–426.

© 1991 Elsevier Science Publishers B.V. All rights reserved.
Biological Psychiatry, Volume 2. G. Racagni et al., editors.

Subclassification of schizophrenics and prediction of tardive dyskinesia by P300

U. Hegerl, G. Juckel, W. Gaebel and W.M. Herrmann
Laboratory of Clinical Psychophysiology, Department of Psychiatry, Freie Universität Berlin, Germany

Introduction

The unsatisfactory predictive validity of psychiatric diagnoses has led to various attempts to classify psychiatric patients according to biological variables. In line with this strategy are studies which suggest a subclassification of schizophrenic patients in those with a genetic vulnerability for psychiatric illness and those with a vulnerability due to exogenous factors like perinatal complications. The latter are supposed to exhibit more signs of structural cerebral abnormalities [1–4]. This subclassification is of clinical importance, because there is some evidence that tardive dyskinesia under neuroleptic treatment is more frequent in patients with structural cerebral abnormalities [1,5,6] and less frequent in patients with a positive family history [7].

In this context the P_3-amplitude (P300) of auditory event related potentials is of interest, because a reduction of this component can be found in many, but not in all schizophrenic patients. Since structural abnormalities due to degenerative processes or acute lesions can lead to reduced P_3-amplitudes, this characteristic may be found in those schizophrenics with exogenous vulnerability.

Within a follow-up study 89 stabilized schizophrenic outpatients were investigated in order to answer the following questions:

- Is a reduced P_3-amplitude an indicator of an enhanced risk for tardive dyskinesia?
- Do schizophrenics with reduced P_3-amplitudes differ from those with higher amplitudes concerning other clinically relevant aspects?

Methods

Subjects and design

Eighty-nine stabilized schizophrenic outpatients (age: 33.9 ± 9.5 years; BPRS score: 25.4 ± 6.5; Global Assessment Scale (GAS): 62.9 ± 10.2; chlorpromazine equivalents (CPZ): 192.7 ± 135.9), diagnosed according to ICD 9 and RDC criteria, were studied within a follow-up study on long-term neuroleptic treatment [8].

AEP-method

Binaural tones (80%, 800 Hz; 20%, 1600 Hz; ISI 1.1 s; 65 db SPL) were presented in randomized order by headphones. The patients were asked to close their eyes and to count silently the rare tones. In every run the responses to 240 frequent and 60 rare tones were averaged. In the first run we recorded from Cz to linked mastoids, in the second and third run bilaterally from C3 and C4 to linked mastoids. Bandpass filters were set to 1 and 30 Hz. Trials with voltages exceeded ± 50 μV were excluded. Sampling was done at a rate of 683 Hz from 150 ms prestimulus to 600 ms poststimulus. For the rare tones, P_3-amplitude was determined as the most positive value within a latency window from 240–390 ms.

Since systematic effects of ocular artifacts cannot be excluded, single sweep analysis was performed in 38 healthy subjects and in an additional group of 15 schizophrenics. The responses were averaged, firstly, without excluding trials with ocular artifacts and secondly, after excluding trials with amplitudes greater ± 50 μV in the ocular channel. Excluding these trials had no systematic effect on P_3-amplitude in both groups.

Results and Discussion

Tardive dyskinesia

The relationship between P_3-amplitude and tardive dyskinesia was studied after excluding those patients with incomplete longitudinal data and those with signs of

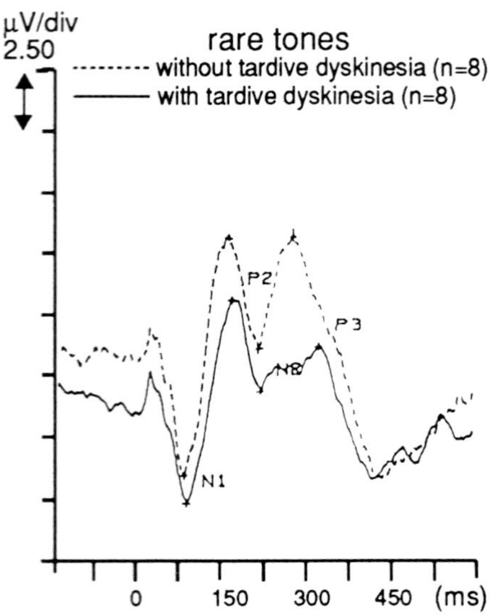

Fig. 1.

Table 1. Clinical description of the patients who developed tardive dyskinesia and of the matched control group

	Patients with tardive dyskinesia (n = 8)	Patients without tardive dyskinesia (n = 8)	*t*-test (two-tailed)
Age	33.7 ± 10.7	33.2 ± 6.4	
Gender	4 males, 4 females	4 males, 4 females	
BPRS-score	28.1 ± 4.8	27.7 ± 4.5	
GAS-score	59.9 ± 8.6	62.9 ± 8.2	
CPZ(mg/day)	222.6 ± 148.9	198.7 ± 164.6	
P_3-amplitude (Cz)	3.8 ± 1.3	7.0 ± 3.4	$P < 0.05$

tardive dyskinesia or acute extrapyramidal side-effects already at the time of recording. Eight of the resulting 51 patients developed tardive dyskinesia during the 2-year follow-up. The severity of tardive dyskinesia, as rated with AIMS (Abnormal Involuntary Movement Scale) was minimal or light in all patients. Patients, who developed tardive dyskinesia had significantly smaller P_3-amplitudes. Since influence of covariables has to taken into account, we compared the 8 patients who developed tardive dyskinesia with a control group, matched according to sex, age, neuroleptic medication and BPRS-score. As can be seen in the grand average curves (Fig. 1) and in Table 1, those patients who developed tardive dyskinesia again showed significantly smaller P_3-amplitudes.

These results suggest that P_3-amplitude might be useful as an indicator of vulnerability to tardive dyskinesia. Further indirect support stems from findings, that cognitive impairment, which is related to small P_3, indicates a higher risk for tardive dyskinesia [9-12].

Subclassification

Taking the median of the P_3-amplitude (Cz) we compared patients with high to those with low P_3-amplitudes. All 5 patients with perinatal complications were in the group with small P_3-amplitudes. However, positive family history was equally distributed in both groups and no differences between patients with low and high P_3-amplitudes can be found in the number of prior hospitalizations and the present psychopathological state (BPRS-score, GAS).

Some further evidence for a relationship between low P_3 and higher risk for tardive dyskinesia is given, when those patients, who had tardive dyskinesia already before or at the time of the ERP recording, are considered. Twelve of these 16 patients can be found in the group with small P_3-amplitudes.

References

1. Bartels M and Themelis J (1983) Arch. Psychiatr. Nervenkr. 233: 371.
2. Reveley AM et al. (1984) Br. J. Psychiatry 144: 89–93.
3. Schulsinger F et al. (1984) Arch. Gen. Psychiatry 41: 602–606.
4. Romani A et al. (1987) Br. J. Psychiatry 151: 506–513.
5. Edwards H (1970) Br. J. Psychiatry 116: 271–275.
6. Stuckstedte H et al. (1984) Nervenarzt 55: 483–487.
7. Bartels M, Mann K and Friedrich W (1985) Biol. Psychiatry 20: 101–103.
8. Pietzcker A (1985) Pharmacopsychiatry 18: 333–338.
9. Struve FA and Willner AE (1983) Br. J. Psychiatry 143: 597–600.
10. Karson CN et al. (1990) Am. J. Psychiatry 147: 1646–1649.
11. Waddington JL and Youssef HA (1988) Am. J. Psychiatry 145: 613–616.
12. Wegener JT et al. (1985) Arch. Gen. Psychiatry 42: 860–865.

© 1991 Elsevier Science Publishers B.V. All rights reserved.
Biological Psychiatry, Volume 2. G. Racagni et al., editors.

Effects of drugs upon the brain, estimated by computation of equivalent dipoles for spontaneous EEG and for P300

T. Dierks[1], K. Maurer[1], W.K. Strik[1] and W. Engelhardt[2]
[1]Department of Psychiatry and [2]Department of Anesthesiology, University of Würzburg, Füchslein 15, D-W-8700 Würzburg, Germany

Introduction

The in vivo investigations of effects of drugs on the brain have mostly been accomplished by measuring brain electrical activity as pharmaco-EEG or pharmaco-EP. Until recently, however, these measurements were relative vague descriptors of intracerebral physiological processes.

When Berger discovered the EEG, brain activity was represented as a single trace from one point on the scalp: it was more or less a 1-dimensional display. However, in 1942 Motokawa realized a 2-dimensional map of brain electrical activity, yet it took a long time before a 2-dimensional representation of brain activity was used in a wider sense. It was Duffy who in 1979 with the aid of advances in computer technology introduced the 2-dimensional BEAM (brain electrical activity) into clinical practice.

Numerous topographical pharmaco-EEG and EP studies have been performed; however, they still suffer from the fact that description of the electrical fields on the scalp only partly allows conclusions regarding the activity of the true intracerebral generators of the measured activity. Already in the 1970s there were advances in the computation of intracranial sources of electrical brain activity in the time domain, mainly for the EEG [1] and later for the EPs [2,3]. Recently Lehmann and Michel [4] developed the FFT-approximation which allows the computation of 3-dimensional intracerebral sources of activity in different frequency bands of spontaneous or activated EEG. In the present paper we used the experimental application of a short-acting benzodiazepine to demonstrate that by calculation of intracerebral generators of EEG and EPs drug effects on electrical brain activity can be shown in an unambiguous and physiological way.

Methods

We investigated the effect of midazolam (dormicum) on 10 young healthy subjects. Midazolam was applied in a dosage of 0.2 mg/kg b.w. The electrical brain activity was recorded before application, after half the dosage of midazolam and after full dosage of midazolam. All electrodes were placed according to the international 10–20 system. EEG was recorded with 19 channels, a bandpass of 1.0–30 Hz was used and the signals were amplified 1:20000. The signals were stored on magnetic disc for further offline analysis. The first 10 s, after 20 s eye closure were used for FFT approximation [4].

For elicitation of P300 we used an acoustically oddball paradigm: non-target; 1000 Hz, target; 2000 Hz [5]. The brain response of non-target and target tones were averaged separately and on the target tone in a time-window between 270–470 ms equivalent dipoles were calculated using the spatio-temporal dipole model (STDM) [2]. Furthermore, different psychometric tests were performed. For safety reasons blood pressure, heart rate and O_2-saturation were monitored during the whole experiment.

Results

The FFT-approximation showed a typical occipitally directed α-activity and also the β-activity was more occipital than frontal (Fig. 1a). After application of 0.2 mg/kg b.w. midazolam the α- and β-activity were located significantly ($P < 0.001$) more frontally and superficially (Fig. 1b).

The activity of the equivalent dipole representing the P300 was significantly ($P < 0.05$) reduced from 20.7 ± 4.4 μVeff before midazolam application to 8.6 ± 5.3 μVeff after application of half dosage. The latency (strongest activity) of the equivalent dipole standing for the P300 was clearly and significantly ($P < 0.05$) prolonged from 375 ± 31 ms before to 402 ± 54 ms after application of 0.1 mg/kg b.w. midazolam. The calculation of the equivalent dipole depicting the generator of P300 showed a parietal direction before application and a significantly more occipital direction after application of 0.1 mg/kg b.w. midazolam (Fig. 2). It was not possible to measure any P300 after application of 0.2 mg/kg b.w. midazolam. The psychometric tests showed a clear-cut dose-dependent decline in performance application of 0.1 mg and 0.2 mg/kg b.w. midazolam. No significant changes could

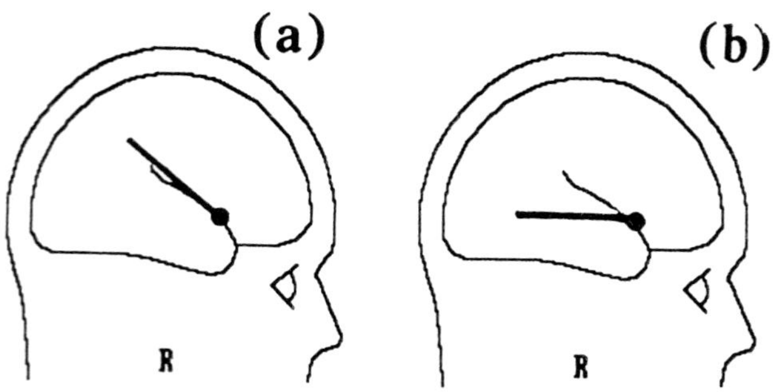

Fig. 1. View from the side into the brain with mean location and S.E.M. (square or circle area) for conventional frequency bands in frontal-occipital and superficial-depth direction: (a) before application; and (b) after application of 0.2 mg/kg b.w. midazolam.

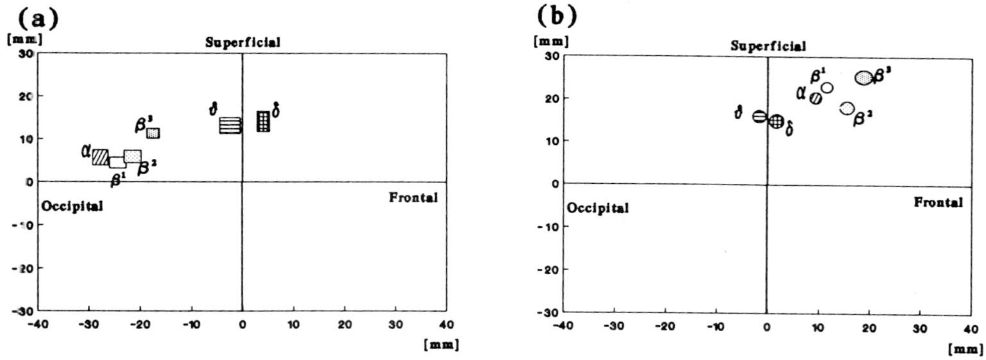

Fig. 2. Mean location and direction of equivalent dipole responsible for the P300 surface field distribution: (a) before application; and (b) after application of 0.1 mg/kg b.w. midazolam.

be observed regarding the safety parameters of blood pressure, heart rate and O_2-saturation before and after application of midazolam.

Discussion

In this study we have shown that drug effects can be well measured and objectivized by computation of 3-D-descriptors of intracerebral electrical activity. With regard to P300 we could observe alterations which correlated well with the psychometeric measurements. These results support the view that endogenous evoked potentials are objective parameters of cognitive function [6] and that it may be useful in the evaluation of altered information processing due to drug effects [7].

The results of the FFT-approximation showed that topographical changes after application of drugs may be quantified in a physiological way. Frontal movement especially of the β-activity may be seen in connection with varying distribution of benzodiazepine receptors in different brain areas.

Both the calculation of equivalent dipoles of P300 responsible for the electrical field distribution on the scalp and the calculation of "generators" of spontaneous EEG-activity by FFT-approximation demonstrates that by using appropriate methods, the activity of intracerebral neuronal processes can be described in an unambiguous and physiological way. Furthermore, these methods significantly reduce the amount of data needed and thus decrease the problems related to the statistical analysis of multichannel EEG and EP [8].

References

1. Kavanagh RN, Darcey TM, Lehmann D and Fender DH (1978) IEEE Trans. Biomed. Eng. 25: 421–429.

2. Scherg M and Von Cramon D (1985) Electroencephalogr. Clin. Neurophysiol. 62: 290–299.
3. Gutowitz H, Zemon V and Knight BW (1986) Electroencephalogr. Clin. Neurophysiol. 64: 308–327.
4. Lehmann D and Michel CM (1990) Electroencephalogr. Clin. Neurophysiol. 76: 271–276.
5. Maurer K and Dierks T (1987) EEG-EMG 18: 21–23.
6. Morstyn R, Duffy FH and McCarley RW (1983) Arch. Gen. Psychiatry 40: 729–734.
7. Maurer K, Dierks T and Ihl R (1989) Psychiatr. Res. 29: 413–415.
8. Oken BS and Chiappa KH (1986) Ann. Neurol. 19(5): 493–497.

© 1991 Elsevier Science Publishers B.V. All rights reserved.
Biological Psychiatry, Volume 2. G. Racagni et al., editors.

Bit-mapped cognitive potentials in patients with deafferentation or destruction of multimodal prefrontal cortical areas

R. Zappoli, A. Versari, G. Arnetoli, P.F. Gangemi, M. Mascalchi, M.G. Arneodo, M. Bartelli and S. Pallanti

Department of Neuro-Psychiatry University of Florence, Viale Morgagni 85, 50134 Florence, Italy

Introduction

The main components of the contingent negative variation (CNV) complex [1] and reaction time (RT) to imperative signals (S2) have been proved to be sensitive to changes in behavioural alertness, attention, concentration, distraction, memory function, motivation and personality. The present investigation was conducted to study the neural substrate of some CNV components and the functional connections between uni- and multimodal eulaminate cortical association areas in man.

Materials and Methods

With a topographic bit-mapped colour imaging method of analysis [2,3], the best known CNV components were examined in 7 patients (3 M and 4 F; age range 34–64 years) with no appreciable functional disorders in the sensorimotor system:

1. One patient with Pick's disease showing progressive bifrontal white matter degeneration, deafferentation of frontal cortex and convolutional atrophy;
2. Three patients with very extensive right and 1 with left prefrontal cortex ablation for severe post-traumatic lesions, in some cases with epileptic seizures;
3. One patient with right prefrontal extensive lobectomy for a diffuse frontopolar abscess and 1 with a diffuse ischemic right frontal cortical lesion and severe prefrontal cortical atrophy.

All patients underwent thorough medical, neuropsychological and laboratory assessments, including CT and MRI examinations.

The standard CNV paradigm was: S1 (0.2 ms, 70 dB SL binaural clicks)– 2 s ISI– S2 (visual signals)– MR (button press). Bit-mapped CNV complex (post-S1 N100 a-b-c, P200, P300; four CNV 200 ms window areas (uV.s) at 500–700 ("0-wave"), 1100–1300, 1800–2000 ("P-wave") ms post-S1 and 400–600 ms after S2 interruption variable relative to RT were recorded, together with electro-oculogram (EOG), RT, S1 and S2 using 2 sets of 19 and 15 scalp electrodes (CNV activity and post-S1 N100, P200 and P300 components respectively; 10–20 system) and bimastoid reference. Sampling rates were 100 and 400 Hz for the 19 and 15 channels, respectively. Colour-voltage values were assigned with a 4-NN interpolating method (Shepard's algorithm) and the amplitude colour-coding scale had 32 levels 1 uV apart, blue for positive and dark red for negative.

Results

All the CNV components were abnormally reduced or practically absent over the

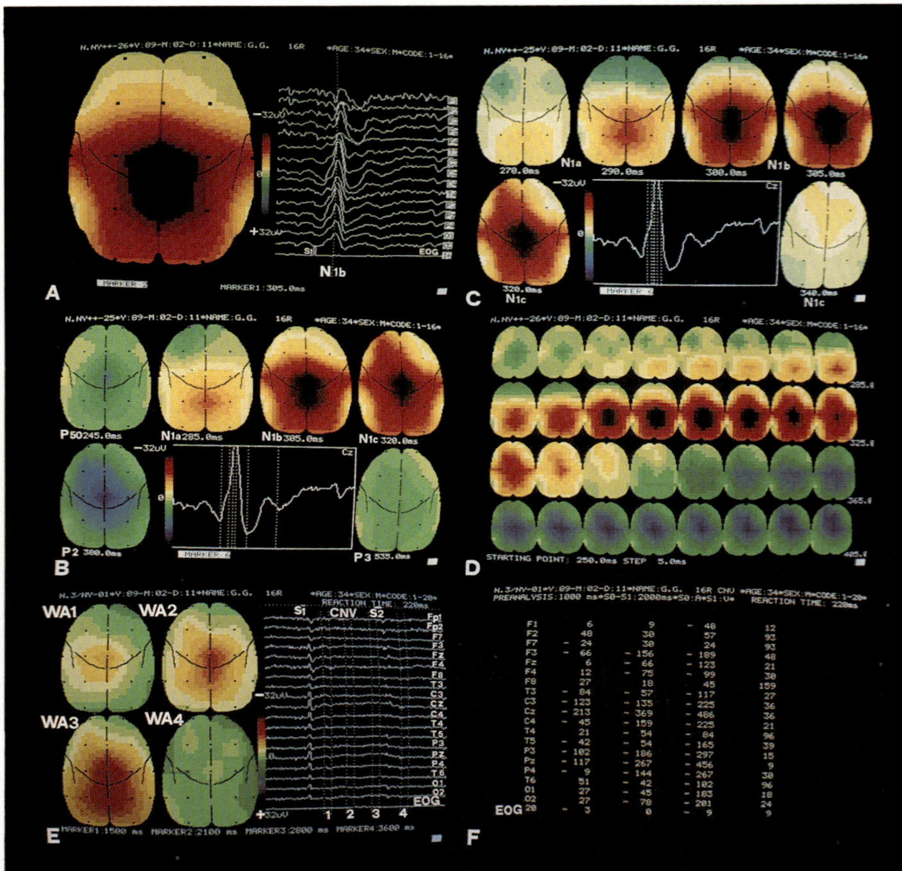

Fig. 1. Male aged 34 years with extensive right prefrontal post-traumatic cortical atrophic lesion, epileptic seizures and surgical ablation of part of cortical areas 9, 10. A–D: 15 EEG electrodes and EOG; E: 19 electrodes and EOG; bimastoid reference. A: N100 b (vertex auditory potential 105 ms post-binaural warning clicks); average of 16 responses to S1. B: post-S1 P50 (45 ms); N100 a (85 ms); N100 b (105 ms); N100 c (120 ms); P200 (180 ms); P300 (335 ms). C: N100 a between about 70–90 ms; N100 b between 95–105; N100 c between 120–140 (frontal exhaustion of N100 c) respectively. D: "Cartooning" with steps of 5 ms. E: CNV activity analysis with 4 window areas (WA) of 200 ms. Average of 16 S1-S2 responses with mean reaction time (RT) to S2 of 220 ms. F: Values of the 4 WAs (uV.ms); positive values without any sign (for more technical details see [2,3]). All CNV complex components practically absent on right prefrontal region.

prefrontal cortical areas with severe atrophy, also when this was associated with diffuse deafferentation due to bifrontal white matter degeneration (Pick's patient). A lack of all components of CNV activity, including post-warning auditory N100 complex, P200 and P300, was observed on the scalp over the ablated fronto-cortical areas. One example is depicted in Fig. 1.

Previous research has shown almost normal bihemispheric CNV activity and RT to S2 in most patients undergoing either commissurotomy (split brain; [4]) or multifocal selective frontal leucotomy [1], extensive bilateral prefrontal lobotomy with the classic Freeman-Watts "radical" plane of sectioning [5] or bimedial prefrontal leukotomy [6]. None of these irreversible psychosurgical lesions in the frontal white matter (especially transection of anterior bidirectional thalamo-frontal connections) actually provoked any substantial modifications of bifrontal CNV complex development, thus suggesting that transcortical mechanisms (cortico-cortical longitudinal connections), play an essential role in generating and regulating CNV complexes in fronto-cortical anterior regions [5].

The lack of CNV complex components over the ablated or severely-damaged fronto-cortical areas in this new series of investigations seems to bear out the hypothesis of the important role played in the genesis of many CNV components by the bidirectional homohemispheric long- and short-distance pathways which connect konio-parakonio and eulaminate association parieto-temporo-occipital cortical areas to the multimodal prefrontal regions, in particular the superior and inferior occipito-frontal and longitudinal fasciculi. Differences in latency of 8.5–12.8 ms were measured between the post-warning auditory temporo-parieto-central N100 a-b and the more frontal components (N100 b and c). This time-lapse, roughly measured along the scalp, is probably accounted for by the transcortical conduction time of about 0.5–1 ms/cm. The longitudinal fasciculi which occur also in the VI/V layers of the cerebral cortex, running along all its sulci and fissures are very long; hence the real conduction velocity along these pathways is certainly greater.

Acknowledgement

This work has been supported by the National Research Council (C.N.R. Grant No. 91.00457.40).

References

1. Walter WG (1966) In: Masserman JH (ed.) Current Psychiatric Therapies, VI. Grune Stratton, New York, pp. 13–55.
2. Zappoli R and Versari A (1990) Ital. J. Neurol. Sci. 11: 339–344.
3. Zappoli R, Versari A, Arnetoli G et al. (1990) In: Brunia CHM, Gaillard AWK and Kok A (eds.) Psychophysiological Brain Research. Tilburg University Press, Le Tilburg, pp. 248–254.

4. Hillyard S (1973) In: McCallum WC and Knott JR (eds.) Event-Related Slow Potentials of the Brain: Their Relations to Behaviour. Electroencephalogr. Clin. Neurophysiol. (Suppl. 33): 161–171.
5. Zappoli R, Papini M, Denoth F et al. (1978) In: Otto DA (ed.) Multidisciplinary Perspectives in Event-Related Brain Potentials Research. U.S. Government Printing Office, Washington D.C. pp. 376–382, 625.
6. Tecce JJ, Orzack MH and Mirsky AF (1978) In: Otto DA (ed.) Multidisciplinary Perspectives in Event-Related Brain Potentials Research. U.S. Government Printing Office, Washington D.C. pp. 383–386.

© 1991 Elsevier Science Publishers B.V. All rights reserved.
Biological Psychiatry, Volume 2. G. Racagni et al., editors.

Mapping of evoked potentials in psychiatry and psychopharmacology

Werner Konrad Strik, Thomas Dierks and Konrad Maurer
Psychiatrische Klinik der Universitaet Würzburg, Fuechsleinstr. 15, 8700 Würzburg, Germany

Introduction

Endogenous components of evoked potentials appear after more than 100 ms up to 1 s after stimulus presentation with a stable scalp distribution independent of stimulus modality. Their parameters change with psychological factors and they are thought to reflect cerebral activities related to cognitive processes. Among the endogenous waves there are the late positive complex (P300 and slow wave), the processing negativity, the mismatch-negativity and the N450. Evoked potentials like the CNV and the Bereitschaftspotential which appear before an expected event can also be classified among the endogenous components. Alterations of the endogenous components are found in several psychiatric disorders. A great body of research has been dedicated to the P300 wave, and this component is of particular interest in psychotic disorders because it is supposed to reflect cognitive disturbances based on impaired information processing. Psychopharmacological studies support this hypothesis.

Amplitude of P300 as well as the cognitive performance of demented patients is enhanced by the cholinergic drug physostigmine with a peak about 1 h after application, whereas after administration of the anticholinergic substance biperidene P300-amplitude decreases significantly [1]. In schizophrenic patients amplitude reduction of the P300 has been described since 1972 and in most reports reliably discriminates groups of schizophrenics from controls [2–4]. Neuroleptic medication does not contribute to this phenomenon and rather tends to enhance P300-amplitude [5,6]. P300-amplitude reduction is found during acute psychoses but also in remitted patients. Pritchard [6] has therefore proposed this feature as a trait marker of schizophrenia.

A state-dependent variability, however, is suggested by the fact that during neuroleptic treatment improvement of the clinical state correlates positively with enhancement of P300-amplitude [7]. In recent studies correlations of the amplitude reduction and clinical features of schizophrenic patients are reported. Shenton et al. [8] found the P300 amplitude reduction in 11 schizophrenics using the Goodin paradigm, but also reported a significant correlation within the schizophrenic group, positive symptoms being associated with high P300-amplitudes over left temporal areas. The authors tried to explain these results by the presence of 2 factors, one responsible for the overall schizophrenic-normal difference and another operating within the schizophrenic group and reflecting secondary and compensatory processes. Pfefferbaum et al. [5] found an inverse correlation between auditory and visual P300 amplitude and negative symptoms measured with the BPRS in a group of 13 medicated and 18 drug-free schizophrenics, Eikmeier et al. [9] reported on significant correlations between amplitude reductions and negative symptoms from the SANS (scale for the assessment of negative symptoms), and similar results were found by our group [10]. P300-amplitude reduction seems to be a rather sensible feature of schizophrenia, but unfortunately there is a lack of specificity as similar reductions are found in depression and dementia [11]. There are preliminary results which indicate that brain mapping techniques can help to distinguish specific features in different patient groups. Maurer et al. [12] showed that there were differences in the topographical distribution of P300 in schizophrenia and dementia, where the maxima were dislocated into frontal areas in the demented group. In samples of schizophrenic patients, asymmetries in P300 have been described, but results are still contradictory. Morstyn et al. [13] reported that the topographical distribution of the P300 maxima of schizophrenics was displaced anteriorly and to the right with respect to the control group which only had a small asymmetry with the maxima on the left. Faux et al. [14] replicated the findings of asymmetries in the form of left temporal amplitude reductions. Pfefferbaum et al. [5], however, could not confirm the asymmetries of the P300-maxima in schizophrenics. In conclusion, the well-documented alterations especially of the P300-wave in psychiatric disorders need further investigation to define specific features. The results of the cited studies indicate that in future the techniques of topographical brain mapping will be able to characterize patterns of alterations in electric scalp fields with diagnostic and/or prognostic utility in the major psychoses.

References

1. Maurer K, Dierks T, Ihl R and Laux G (1989) Mapping of evoked potentials in normals and patients with psychiatric diseases. In: Maurer K (ed.) Topographic Brain Mapping of EEG and Evoked Potentials. Springer, Berlin.
2. Roth WT and Cannon EH (1972) Arch. Gen. Psychiatry 27: 466–471.
3. Levit RA, Sutton S and Zubin J (1973) Psychol. Med. 3: 487–494.
4. Roth WT, Pfefferbaum A, Kelly AF, Berger PA and Kopell BS (1981) Psychiatr. Res. 4: 199–212.
5. Pfefferbaum A, Ford JM, White PM and Roth WT (1989) Arch. Gen. Psychiatry 46: 1035–1044.
6. Pritchard WS (1986) Psychol. Bull. 1: 43–66.
7. Duncan CC, Morihisa JM, Fawcet RW and Kirch DG (1987) Psychopharmacol. Bull. 23: 497–501.
8. Shenton ME, Faux SF, McCarley RW, Ballinger R, Coleman M, Torello and Duffy FH (1989) Biol. Psychiatry 25: 710–716.
9. Eikmeier G, Lodemann E, Olbrich HM, Zerbin D and Gastpar M (1991) Changes and clinical correlations of P300 in schizophrenia. In: Maurer K (ed.) Imaging of the Brain in Psychiatry and Related Fields. Springer, Berlin (in press).
10. Strik WK, Dierks T, Müller T and Maurer K (1991) Cognitive components of auditory evoked potentials in schizophrenic disorders: Topography and clinical correlations. In: Maurer K (ed.) Imaging of the Brain in Psychiatry and Related Fields. Springer, Berlin (in press).

11. Blackwood DH, Whalley LJ, Christie JE, Blackburn IM, St Clair DM and McInnes A (1987) Br. J. Psychiatry 150: 154–160.
12. Maurer K, Ihl R, Frölich L and Dierks T (1989) Pharmakologische beeinflußbarkeit der informationsverarbeitung. In: Saletu B (ed.) Biologische Psychiatrie. 2.Drei-Länder-Symposium für biologische Psychiatrie,Innsbruck, September 1988. Thieme, Stuttgart, New York.
13. Morstyn R, Duffy FH and McCarley RW (1983) Altered P300 Topography in schizophrenia. Arch. Gen. Psychiatry 40: 729–734.
14. Faux SF, Shenton ME, McCarley RW, Nestor PG, Marcy B and Ludwig A (1990) Electroencephalogr. Clin. Neurophysiol. 75: 378–391.

© 1991 Elsevier Science Publishers B.V. All rights reserved.
Biological Psychiatry, Volume 2. G. Racagni et al., editors.

Brain mapping in the development of nootropics

Masami Saito, Naomi Saito, Masato Fukushima, Yoshiki Ohashi, Kenji Nobuhara, Yoshiyasu Okajima and Toshihiko Kinoshita

Department of Neuropsychiatry, Kansai Medical University, Fumizono-cho 1, Moriguchi, Osaka 570, Japan

Introduction

The authors have been studying nootropic substances using pharmaco-EEG methods for the last 5 years. EEG mapping is quite a useful technique to find local differences in EEG changes in clinical issues. The present authors have presented the results of several EEG studies on nootropic substances and discussed several problems arising in these studies.

Materials and Method

Substances used

In the present article, normal volunteer studies were carried out with possible nootropic substances, such as meclofenoxate, amantadine, piracetam, teniloxazine, nebracetam, idebenone, bifemelane, the last four of which were studied in demented patients.

EEG recording and processing

EEG was recorded before, 1 h, 3 h and 6 h after the single dose administrations of each substance in normal subjects, while it was recorded before and 3 h after the first single dose administration, and after every 8 weeks of the treatment with one of the substances. All the EEG were analyzed with HZI BFM system and the results were statistically examined and converted into various types of mapping.

Clinical evaluation

In the patient study, clinical features were rated with GBS, MMS and HDS (Hasegawa's Dementia Scale) for examination in comparison to EEG measurements.

Results

EEG responses in normal subjects

EEG changes common to all the normal subjects who received a single dose of the substances were a decrease in slow waves and an increase in α activity associated with a decrease in fast activity and they were quite identical to those many investigators. Nevertheless, when compared in detail, there were certain differences which seem to represent the individual characteristics of the substances used. For instance, meclofenoxate induced long-lasting but milder changes than the others, teniloxazine produced fast but relatively short-lasting changes. Amantadine, piracetam and nebracetam provoked relatively massive and long-lasting changes. Idebenone caused a decrease in slow waves, an increase in high frequency α waves and an increase in fast waves, while bifemelane produced an increase in slow activity, a decrease in α waves and an increase in fast activity.

Comparison of bifemelane and idebenone

The comparative trial with bifemelane 50 mg and idebenone 30 mg t.i.d. was made in 8 patients with cerebral vascular dementia (CVD) in a single-blind cross-over design. The total treatment period was 16 weeks. At the end of first 8 weeks of bifemelane treatment, there was a decrease in slow activity, an increase in low and medium α, a decrease in high α, and an increase in fast activity. In the same of idebenone treatment, there was a decrease in slow activity and an increase in low and medium α in the same way as that observed in bifemelane treatment, but there was an increase in high α and low β activities. Differences between the two drugs varied by the locations of electrodes on the scalp, and the most important differences were seen in the right frontal pole. Both drugs improved generally and significantly the initiative or the spontaneity disorders in patient behaviors as well as emotional functions in GBS scores.

Comparison between types of dementia

In the clinical trial with nebracetam, we have studied the differences of drug effects between dementia of Alzheimer type (DAT) and CVD. In either type of dementia, it is an undeniable fact that intellectual functions are hardly improved by drug treatment; it may be not unusual that clinical responses appear most markedly in GBS scores. This may be because the improvements are seen mainly in emotional functions and behavioral disturbances in some items and also certain differences of pretreatment scores in some items. In other words, there seem to be no essential differences in drug response between two different types of dementia as far as clinical evolution is concerned. The actual differences appear to be caused by the differences in disorders at the pretreatment stage.

Correlation between EEG and dementia rating scores

Correlation analysis was applied to examine the relationship of EEG measurements to each of the three rating scales. In the correlation matrix between GBS and EEG, significantly high correlations were found mainly in α to fast activity, a little more predominant in the left hemisphere than in the right. Next, the relationship between MMS scores and EEG measurements was examined. Between MMS and EEG, high correlations were mostly seen in slower EEG frequencies and posterior part of the brain than in GBS. Between HDS and EEG, high coefficients were seen in all the frequency bands and not predominantly in any particular location.

Discussion

For the time being, the difference in EEG responses of bifemelane and idebenone are attributed to the differences in clinical efficacy and in mechanism of action in the brain. By the way, bifemelane does not act as nootropic agent in a narrow sense but probably as antidepressant or emotional regulator from the EEG viewpoint.

In the nebracetam trial, there were differences in EEG changes between left and right hemispheres of the brain; the former was clearly marked and more significant than the latter, particularly in the anterior brain. Changes in higher α and β activities were seen only in the left fronto-central area while those of lower α and β activities were in the right hemisphere. The most important changes were those in the left central area which were basic changes of δ, θ and high α activities, which have been pointed out by Kinoshita as characteristic EEG signs of nootropic substances and just the opposite of the EEG signs of senile dementia. Itil called it a *miller pattern*, but Kinoshita considered it an *antagonistic pattern*.

Conclusion

It is quite difficult to determine the specific signs of aging and senescence in EEG, mainly because of difficulty in preparing *normal among the normal* aged subjects for the baseline control of the psychogeriatric EEG study.

The second big problem is a lack of appropriate scale or parameters to measure the dementia syndrome. The authors used three different scales to assess the dementia patients, namely GBS, MMS and HDS. However, the correlation coefficients highly related to EEG measurements were respectively different from each other. This means that each of the three scales evaluated different aspects of the dementia patients. It is necessary to have more psychobiological parameters than the three scales in order to determine the decisive correlations to neurophysiological parameters like the EEG.

References

1. Itil TM (1983) Biol. Psychiatry 5: 521–523.
2. Kinoshita T (1990) Psychiatr. Neurol. Jpn. 92: 255–276.
3. Saito M (1990) In: Hasegawa K and Homma H (eds.) Psychogeriatrics: Biomedical and Social Advances. Excerpta Medica, Tokyo, pp. 380–383.
4. Saito M, Kinoshita T, Yamamoto Y, Okajima Y, Saito A and Nobuhara K (1989) Clin. EEG 31: 392–396.
5. Saito M (1989) Clin. Neurosci. 7: 1202–1204.

© 1991 Elsevier Science Publishers B.V. All rights reserved.
Biological Psychiatry, Volume 2. G. Racagni et al., editors.

Brain mapping and neuroleptic treatment in schizophrenia

S. Galderisi, A. Mucci, M.L. Mignone, M. Maj and D. Kemali
Department of Psychiatry, First Medical School, University of Nàples, Naples, Italy

Introduction

In order to improve pharmacological treatment of schizophrenic patients, several clinical, biological and pharmacological variables have been studied as possible predictors of response to antipsychotic drugs. None of them has consistently been assigned a reliable predictive value [1].

The very few studies which examined QEEG variables as predictors of neuroleptic responsiveness reported different baseline characteristics in association with a favourable or poor clinical response to drug treatment [2]. In the present paper baseline QEEG parameters and their modifications after a single dose of haloperidol are discussed as promising tools in the identification of haloperidol responsive schizophrenics.

Methods

The study has been carried out in 20 DSM III-R schizophrenics, 7 females and 13 males, with an age range 19–37 years (mean ± S.D., 25.65 ± 4.84), a duration of illness ranging from 6–17 years (mean ± S.D., 6.1 ± 4.8), an age at onset from 16–26 years (mean ± S.D., 20.9 ± 2.8). Patients completed a wash-out period of at least 15 days (45 days for long-acting neuroleptics) before entering the study. The control group included 21 healthy subjects, matched with patients for age, sex and handedness.

A baseline (day 0) resting EEG was recorded from all subjects. Patients were then administered a single oral dose of haloperidol and EEGs were recorded after 1, 3, 6, and 8 h. Treatment with haloperidol was continued for 4 weeks (with dosage increased weekly up to 7 mg/day) and further EEG recordings were obtained weekly.

EEG was recorded from 16 unipolar leads of the 10-20 system; the HZI BFM system [3] was used for A/D conversion and Fast Fourier Transform of the EEG signal. Eight frequency bands were considered (δ, 1.3–3.5 Hz; θ_1, 3.75–5.5 Hz; θ_2, 5.75–7.5 Hz; α_1, 7.75–9.5 Hz; α_2, 9.75–12.5 Hz; β_1, 12.75–15.0 Hz; β_2, 15.25–26.0 Hz; β_3, 26.25–35.0 Hz). Further methodological details can be found elsewhere [4].

Clinical evaluation was done on the basis of psychiatric interviews, at day 0 and then weekly. Andreasen's scales for positive (SAPS) and negative (SANS) symptoms were used for symptom ratings.

Baseline CEEG characteristics and changes induced by acute and chronic haloperidol administration were studied in relationship with patients' responsiveness to treatment. Patients were considered "responders" when a 50% reduction of the global score on SAPS + SANS was observed after 28 days of treatment.

For comparisons between groups the Mann-Whitney U-test was used; changes induced by treatment were assessed by the Wilcoxon-Wilcox test.

Results

Twelve patients (6 males and 6 females) were responders (R) and 8 (7 males and 1 female) were non-responders (NR). R and NR did not differ for age, education and duration of illness, but NR showed a significantly younger age at onset than R ($P <$ 0.01).

As to clinical evaluation, no significant baseline difference was observed between responders and non-responders on psychopathological ratings.

When baseline CEEGs of the 2 subgroups were compared, R vs. NR showed significantly higher α_2, β_1, and β_2 amplitude (mainly over posterior regions) and less θ_2 and α_1, as well as more α_2 and β_1 relative power (over most of the explored leads).

R and NR had different patterns of QEEG changes following the acute haloperidol administration. Both subgroups presented a significant decrease of δ and an increase of β (in terms of both amplitude and relative power), but while R showed a significant increase of θ_2 and α_1, NR had unchanged θ_2 and significantly decreased α_1. After 28 days of haloperidol monotherapy, QEEG modifications (consisting of a significant and diffused θ_2 and α_1 increase as well as a reduction of the fast β, significant over the right hemisphere leads) could be observed only in patients with a favourable clinical response, whereas almost no change was observed in non-responders.

Discussion

According to our findings, significant neurophysiological differences exist between R and NR.

Demographic and clinical variables assessed in the present study did not differentiate between R and NR, excepting the age of onset, that was significantly earlier for NR.

Baseline QEEG parameters were different in R and NR. The former group showed a predominance of fast α and β activity, the latter more θ_2 and slow α.

Slow and hyperstable alpha activity has already been reported in treatment resistant schizophrenics [1], as well as in schizophrenics with enlarged lateral ventricles [5,6]. Since the thalamus represents a portion of the lower margin of the cerebral ventricle and seems to play an important role in α rhythm generation, Karson et al. [5] have speculated that neuropathological processes involving the thalamus might be responsible for the low-frequency α observed in some schizophrenics. Interestingly a reduction of the neuron number has recently been reported in the mediodorsal nucleus of the thalamus [7]. Giannitrapani and Kayton [8] suggested that slow α in some schizophrenics might be the result of an arrested development or regression of this activity. An arrested development of α frequency suggests a parallel with an arrested maturation process of the brain. Such a process should be completed by the adolescence, that is the age of onset of early schizophrenic syndromes, generally associated with a poor prognosis.

The baseline QEEG pattern observed in R has also been previously reported [9]. The prevalence of fast activities would be the neurophysiological expression of the presence in these patients of an abnormal cortical stimulation exerted by subcortical mechanisms [10]. Such a hyperafferentation condition would be modified by neuroleptics in responders; as a matter of fact, after 28 days of haloperidol treatment these patients show a significant reduction of β activity.

Results from our study show that CEEG differences between R and NR were not confined to their baseline profiles, but involved their respective patterns of drug-induced changes. They support the predictive value of QEEG parameters (in particular the opposite reactivity of the slow α to a single dose of haloperidol) in schizophrenic patients.

Acknowledgements

The authors gratefully acknowledge the valuable technical assistance of Anna Grimaldi and Eugenio Fontanella.

References

1. Lydiard RB and Laird LK (1988) J. Clin. Psychopharmacol. 8: 3–13.
2. Itil TM, Shapiro DM, Schneider SJ and Francis IB (1981) J. Nerv. Ment. Dis. 169.
3. Itil TM, Shapiro DM, Eralp E, Akman A, Itil KZ and Garbizu C (1985) New Trends Exp. Clin. Psychiatry 1: 107–177.
4. Galderisi S, Mucci A, Mignone ML, Maj M and Kemali D (1991) Schizophr. Res. (in press).
5. Karson CN, Coppola R and Daniel DG (1988) Am. J. Psychiatry 145: 861–864.
6. Kemali D, Galderisi S and Maj M (1988) In: Giannitrapani D and Murri L (eds.) The EEG of Mental Activities. Karger, Basel, pp. 169–181.
7. Pakkenberg B (1990) Arch. Gen. Psychiatry 47: 1023–1028.
8. Giannitrapani D and Kayton L (1974) Electroencephalogr. Clin. Neurophysiol. 36: 377–386.
9. Itil TM, Marasa MS, Saletu B, Davis S and Mucciardi N (1975) J. Nerv. Ment. Dis. 160: 188–203.
10. Hill D (1956) Electroencephalography. MacDonald, London.

© 1991 Elsevier Science Publishers B.V. All rights reserved.
Biological Psychiatry, Volume 2. G. Racagni et al., editors.

Deterioration of brain functioning in relapsing heroin addicts

A. El Azayem[1], A. Abdeen[2], M. Amin[2] and A. Gunaidy[3]
[1]Aboul Azayem Research Center and Hospital, P.O. Box 8180, Cairo; [2]Ain Shams University; and [3]Aboul Azayem Hospitals, Cairo, Egypt

Using quantitative EEG and an Arabic adaptation of the MMPI, the authors have studied a group of 37 relapsing heroin addicts. The aim was to search for an explanation for psychotic decompensation occurring in this borderline narcissistic vulnerable group: a neurophysiological mediating process in the form of substance-induced generalized cerebral dysfunction with a significant left/right difference. The implications of these findings in terms of follow-up and management are discussed.

Introduction

The aim of the present study is to delineate the role of cerebral dysfunction in the pathogenesis of relapsing heroin addicts. Previous studies have considered that BEAM evidence of cerebral dysfunction is, either non-specific, related to the temporary cognitive dysfunction improving following detoxification [1], or that it represents a maturational lag, related to the MMPI evidence of borderline narcissistic psychopathic personality disorder [2,3]. However, studies attempting to correlate CEEG evidence of cerebral dysfunction to the psychotic disorganisation of these patients are notoriously lacking.

Importance of the present study

Our main hypotheses is that CEEG parameters of cerebral dysfunction show a steadily progressive deterioration from one relapse to the next in heroin addicts; and that this neurophysiological dysfunction acts as a mediating process, precipitating the psychotic schizophrenic decompensation, affecting those vulnerable, personality disordered, relapsing heroin addicts. We studied the personality profile of a group of 37 male heroin addicts, aged from 20–40. Then, we studied its pattern of change and that of their quantitative EEG parameters, from their first to their last relapse.

Tests and Instruments

The Minnesota Multiphasic Personality Inventory: an Arabic adaptation of the

MMPI has been applied, and the results analyzed statistically according to Egyptian norms [4].

Quantitative EEG brain mapping: we have employed the HZI system of brain mapping [5], examining each patient following detoxification. EEG's were recorded with a time constant of 5 s in the unipolar montage according to the 10–20 montage system.

Statistical analysis

We first estimated the means for the 10 subtests of the MMPI and that of the Goldberg Index of Psychoticism and Psychoticism Subscale of the Wiggins Content Scale (Table 1).

Then, we used the moving average option of time series analysis to inspect the pattern of change of quantitative EEG variables, from their first to their last relapse (Table 2).

Results

The MMPI results denote clearly the presence of a psychotic pattern of personality disorganization, as shown by:

- The clinically significant score (above 70), on the Schizophrenia, Paranoia and Psychasthenia Scale, representing the psychotic triangle;
- The clinically significant scores on the Psychoticism Index of the Wiggins Content Scale and the Goldberg Index of Psychoticism;
- The very low ego strength (less than 40).

Moreover, there is a steadily progressive increase, from one relapse to the next, on the Scales of Psychoticism and Narcissism.

Table 1. MMPI profile of relapsed addicts

Name	Mean
HS	76.4615
D	77.5385
HY	67.8462
PD	76.9231
MF	61.2308
PA	78.0000
SC	88.6154
MA	68.3077
SI	64.4615

Table 2. Quantitative EEG-2 term moving AVG

Relapse No.	TF3	TF4	DT3	DT4	AO1	AO2
1						
2	29.80	28.90	5.45	3.65	47.05	48.50
3	35.55	35.50	7.20	6.70	37.55	38.30
4	37.40	36.50	6.9	8.60	35.25	33.30
5	37.15	37.95	6.85	9.10	37.65	34.70
6	39.15	40.15	10.85	12.30	34.10	29.00
7	40.25	39.00	13.00	18.15	27.10	21.90

The quantitative EEG results denote clearly the presence of a cerebral dysfunction, having the following characteristics: a progressive increase in % of θ-activity in frontal leads and of Δ-activity in temporal leads, with a significant left/right difference and a progressive decrease in α-activity in both occipital leads.

Discussion of results

This MMPI psychotic profile most probably represents an organic schizophrenic disorder, produced by the long-term use of heroin. This is evidenced by the CT scan findings of atrophy and enlarged ventricles, [6] and the steadily progressing generalized cerebral dysfunction shown by quantitative EEG. However, to accept or refute such a hypothesis, we have to demonstrate whether CT changes are temporary, stationary, or steadily progressive. A second diagnostic possibility that cannot be ruled out is that of substance-induced residual or late onset psychotic disorder, related to the left/right significant difference in Δ-activity in temporal lobe leads, raising the hypothesis of a neuropsychological disconnection syndrome.

Conclusion

The most plausible explanation for the MMPI profile is that the neurophysiological dysfunction produced by the long-term use of heroin acts as a mediating process that precipitates the schizophrenic decompensation.

Recommendations

In planning the follow-up programmes for relapsing heroin addicts, the following investigations are mandatory:

- Serial MMPI to detect the earliest possible evidence of this mixed borderline narcissistic personality disorganization before psychotic decompensation occurs. This should be dealt with through a confrontation milieu therapy program.

– Serial quantitative EEG-BEAM to detect the earliest possible evidence of generalized cerebral dysfunction, before it produces psychotic decompensation. This can be done easily for each patient, using the pre-post mapping option of the HZI computerized EEG system.

References

1. Okasha A and Raafat M (1988) Egypt. J. Psychiatry 13: 37–43.
2. Fishbein D et al. (1989) Biol. Psychiatry 26: 595–611.
3. Blackburn R (1979) Psychophysiology 16: 143–150.
4. Louis Melika (1978) Minnesota Multiphasic Personality Inventory. Nahda Bookshop, Cairo.
5. Itil TM, Shapiro DM and Itil K (1986) Psychopharm. Bull. 22 (1): 237–300.
6. Wolf SG and Michael MA (1979) Am. J. Psychiatry 136 (43).

© 1991 Elsevier Science Publishers B.V. All rights reserved.
Biological Psychiatry, Volume 2. G. Racagni et al., editors.

CEEG modifications during cold water pressor test

Stefano Ferracuti[1], Stefano Seri[2], Donatella Mattia[3] and Giorgio Cruccu[3]
[1]Institute of Psychology, School of Medicine; [2]Institute of Child Neuropsychiatry and [3]Department of Neurosciences, University degli Studi "La Sapienza", P.le A. Moro 5, Rome 00185, Italy

Introduction

The immersion of the hand in cold water is a standardized experimental model of tonic pain, also known as the Cold Water Pressor Test (CWPT). With water at about 1°C, the sensation of pain is immediate and no adaptation occurs. The pain induced in this test is probably secondary to activation of C nociceptors by ischemia [1]. We studied the EEG power spectra modification occurring in subjects undergoing the CWPT without and with previous administration of a standard benzodiazepine, diazepam. Our aim was to identify possible EEG changes and determine whether they were stress- or pain-related.

Material and Methods

Fifteen right-handed healthy male volunteers, aged 23–34 years, were recruited for the study. Informed consent was obtained from all subjects.

Recording technique and data processing

The subjects sat comfortably, with eyes closed, on an EEG chair. Surface electrodes were placed on the scalp according to the 10-20 system at F3, F4, C3, C4, P3, P4, O1, O2, with linked earlobes as a reference. EEG signals were amplified, filtered (1–35 Hz), A/D converted (128 samples/s), divided into 2-s epochs, and stored for off-line analysis by means of a brain surveyor analyzer. Raw EEG data were examined by 2 independent observers and only the artifact-free epochs were further processed. By means of a fast Fourier transform, the absolute and relative power spectra were calculated for the frequency bands delta-2 (2–4 Hz), theta (4–8 Hz), alpha (8–12 Hz), beta (12–16 Hz) and total (2–16 Hz).

Experimental procedure

Each subject participated in 3 sessions: "cold water", "warm water", and "diazepam", on different days. To minimize circadian variations the sessions were always held at the same time of the day. At the beginning of each session, at least 3 min of base-line artifact-free EEG were recorded. The subject was then instructed to immerse his right hand in iced water (±1°C) and to leave it there as long as he could stand the painful sensation. At least 6 epochs (12 s) were examined for the first 30, 60, 90, and over 90 s. At the end of the test the subject quantified the pain sensation by means of a Visual Analogue Scale (VAS). After a 30-min rest period, a further control EEG was recorded. In the "warm water" session, an identical procedure was repeated with the water maintained at 25°C. In the "diazepam" session, after IV administration of 10 mg of diazepam, the subject was submitted to baseline EEG recording and recording during immersion of the right hand in cold water.

Statistical analysis

Data for each lead and each frequency were examined and showed a normal distribution. Intra-individual differences within a session were evaluated by Student's *t*-test for paired data and differences between sessions by analysis of variance (F-test).

Results

Cold water

During the first 30 s of immersion a widespread reduction in alpha activity (by 12% in the posterior regions) was observed over the scalp during the first 30 s of immersion. EEG activity was similar in the 2 hemispheres, with no difference between leads. The alpha power reduction vanished promptly and at 60 s was no longer significant. Unlike alpha activity, delta and theta power increased during the first 30 s. The increase in delta power lasted throughout the period of stimulation (over 90 s). This change was diffuse, but more evident in the frontal areas, where delta activity increased by 9%. Again activity was similar in the right and left hemispheres. The control recording at the end of the session showed that the EEG data had returned to pretest values. All subjects reported that the CWPT was painful (mean VAS score 5.8).

Warm water

No EEG change was observed except for a slight transient reduction in alpha activity, so short-lasting that it did not reach significance even in the 30-s period.

Diazepam

Baseline recordings showed the classic benzodiazepine-induced changes, namely a marked increase in beta activity. The CWPT did not modify this pattern, and in particular delta power was equal to the pretest values. Nevertheless, the subjects not only still felt pain, but even gave it a higher score (mean VAS score 7.1).

Discussion

During the CWPT two main changes characterized the EEG: 1) a sudden widespread reduction in the first 30 s, which probably represents an arrest reaction; and 2) a long-lasting increase in delta activity, diffuse, but more pronounced in the frontal areas. These findings are consistent with previous reports [2–3]. The mechanism responsible for the heightened delta activity has not been clarified. Since C-fiber input projects mainly to the medial thalamic nuclei and activates the paleothalamic cortical system, it is expected to influence the activity of the limbic forebrain-frontal cortex bilaterally [4,5]. We believe, however, that rather than reflecting the arrival of nociceptive impulses, the increase of delta activity is the result of cortical inhibition in reaction to pain, or stress. Some kinds of acute stress are known to produce a diffuse delta increase [6]. The view that delta activity reflects a stress-induced cortical inhibition is further supported by the attenuation of these EEG changes in subjects pretreated with diazepam, which might possibly explain why they consistently reported an intense pain sensation.

References

1. Wolf S and Hardy JD (1941) J. Clin. Invest. 20: 521–533.
2. Chen ACN, Dworking SF, Haug J and Gehrig J (1989) Pain 37: 129–141.
3. Gotliebsen K and Arendt-Nielsen L. (1990) Pain (Suppl.) 5: S421.
4. Willis WD (1989) In: Wall PD and Melzack R (eds.) Textbook of Pain. Churchill-Livingstone, Edinburgh, pp. 112–127.
5. Pribam KM (1981) In: NP Bechtereva (ed.) Psychophysiology. Pergamon Press, Oxford, pp. 155–170.
6. Low MD (1987) In: Niedermeyer E and Lopes da Silva F (eds.) Electroencephalography. Urban and Schwarzenberg, Baltimore, pp. 531–548.

Genetics in psychiatry: Basic and clinical aspects

© 1991 Elsevier Science Publishers B.V. All rights reserved.
Biological Psychiatry, Volume 2. G. Racagni et al., editors.

Progressive neurodegenerative changes in transgenic mice overexpressing Mos oncogenes in the brain

Friedrich Propst[1], Linda C. Cork[2], Robert M. Kovatch[3], George F. Vande Woude[4] and Michael P. Rosenberg[5]

[1]Ludwig Institute for Cancer Research, Norfolk Place, London W2 6QE, U.K.; [2]Division of Comparative Medicine, The Johns Hopkins University School of Medicine, 720 Rutland Avenue, Baltimore, MD 21205; [3]Pathology Associates, Inc., Worman's Mill Court, Frederick, MD 21701; [4]ABL-Basic Research Program, NCI-Frederick Cancer Research and Development Center, P.O.Box B, Frederick, MD 21702; and [5]Department of Molecular Biology, Bristol-Myers Squibb Pharmaceutical Research Institute, P.O. Box 4000, Princeton, NJ 08543, U.S.A.

Introduction

The c-Mos protooncogene is the cellular homolog of the transforming gene of the Moloney murine sarcoma virus [1]. The c-Mos gene of several species including human, mouse, chicken and Xenopus has been cloned and sequenced and found to be conserved throughout vertebrate evolution. In humans Mos maps to chromosome 8q11 and in mouse the gene is located on chromosome 4 close to the centromere [2]. The gene codes for a 39 kDa protein-serine/threonine kinase which can phosphorylate itself, tubulin, vimentin and the cell cycle regulatory protein cyclin B_2. Both genes, mouse c-Mos as well as the viral v-Mos, have high transforming activity in mouse fibroblasts.

The expression of the c-Mos gene is tightly regulated. For example, in the mouse expression of Mos RNA can be detected only at very low levels in few adult somatic tissues including the brain, kidney and epididymis [2]. During fetal development Mos is expressed at slightly higher levels. Remarkably, Mos expression can be readily detected in fetal and newborn mouse brain but thereafter expression drops to very low levels [3]. The highest levels of Mos expression have been detected in male and female germ cells of vertebrates [2]. Subsequent work on mouse and Xenopus oocytes has identified a function of the gene in oocyte maturation where Mos is necessary to induce and regulate crucial events in meiotic cell division.

The tight regulation of Mos expression during mouse development, in adult mouse tissues and during oocyte maturation suggests that overexpression or expression of the gene in the wrong cell types might have deleterious effects on the organism. Indeed, induction of expression of the normal c-Mos protooncogene in NIH3T3 fibroblasts leads to tumorigenic transformation of these cells [1]. We have therefore analyzed the effect of c-Mos overexpression using the transgenic mouse approach. To this purpose we have linked the mouse c-Mos gene to the transcriptional control region of the Moloney murine sarcoma virus. This strong promoter can drive expression of adjacent genes in many adult mouse tissues, in particular in the central nervous system [4,5] and has enabled us to study the effect of Mos overexpression in the brain where normal Mos expression is developmentally regulated and very low in the adult.

Results and Discussion

Using the recombinant DNA construct pTS74 in which the c-Mos gene is linked to the transcriptional control sequences of the long terminal repeat of the Moloney murine sarcoma virus we obtained several independent founder animals from which we established 7 independent transgenic lines [3,4]. In lines TG5A, TG5B and TG6 expression of the transgene in the brain was low or undetectable and no phenotypes were observed in these lines. Transgenic mice of the remaining 4 lines TG1-4 were examined in detail and consistently displayed a variety of behavioural and pathological phenotypes concomitant with high transgene expression [3,4].

The behavioural abnormalities in c-Mos transgenic mice included rapid pivoting in the center of the cage, repeated somersaults, hyperactivity, head bobbing, ataxia and tilting of the head or the entire body in repose and in motion. The severity of these abnormalities was most pronounced in line TG4 where each mouse carrying the transgene was affected.

Histological examination of the brain revealed extensive neuronal and axonal degeneration in all transgenic mice of lines TG1-4 that were analyzed irrespective of whether they showed the behavioral abnormalities [3]. These neuropathological changes increased in severity with age between 1–5 months after birth. Swollen and degenerating axons were present in several areas of the brain including the granule cell layer of the cerebellum, motor nuclei of the fifth and seventh cranial nerves, the habenular nucleus, ventral and posterior nuclei of the thalamus, brain stem, striatum and deep cortical layers. Axonal degeneration was accompanied by astrocytosis and infiltration of the neuropil and meninges by inflammatory cells including mast cells which were frequently associated with apparently normal neurons in the thalamus. In addition we observed abnormal neurons with large, eccentric nuclei that stained positive for phosphorylated epitopes of the neurofilaments in the cytoplasm and abnormal astrocytes with large, atypical nuclei. Moreover, the mice displayed intense inflammation of the choroid plexus within the lateral ventricle with massive infiltration of lymphocytes, plasma cells, neutrophils, eosinophils and mast cells.

The progressive ataxia observed in c-Mos transgenic mice can be attributed to cerebellar degeneration detected in the histological analysis. On the other hand, the circling phenotype is reminiscent of spontaneous mouse mutations affecting the inner ear. Indeed, examination of the inner ear of c-Mos transgenics revealed absence of hair cells and degeneration of the spiral ganglia [3]. Other pathological alterations in c-Mos transgenic mice included opacity of the eye lens which is due to a defect in the postnatal differentiation of ocular lens fiber cells [4]. Whereas at birth the lens of transgenic animals is indistinguishable from the lens of their normal littermates, lens fiber cells in transgenic mice fail to enucleate, are not oriented properly and fail to complete the posterior part of the lens. As a consequence the incomplete lens capsule bursts and fiber cells fill the entire chamber of the eye.

In all transgenic lines that display the described phenotypes we observed high levels of transgene expression in brain and eye lens as well as in other tissues [3,4]. A detailed analysis of transgene expression in the brain by in situ hybridization revealed high levels of Mos RNA in neurons and astrocytes in areas where the pathological lesions are observed [3]. In particular, Mos expression was detected in posterior thalamic nuclei, habenula, pineal body, the motor nuclei of the fifth cranial nerve, brain stem and in the Purkinje cells and Bergmann glia in the cerebellum. These results strongly suggest that the overexpression of c-Mos in these cells in the central nervous system and in the ocular lens fiber cells causes degeneration and/or defects in differentiation and function.

Conclusions

The results obtained with transgenic mice overexpressing the c-Mos protooncogene and similar results obtained with v-Mos transgenics (not shown) suggest that the Mos protein-serine/threonine kinase has the potential to regulate or interfere with a number of processes involved in cellular growth, differentiation and function perhaps by phosphorylating tubulin or intermediate filament proteins. Transgenic mice overexpressing Mos in the central nervous system display progressive neuropathological alterations, could help to study the possible function of Mos in the brain and might serve as a model system to study progressive neurodegenerative disease.

References

1. Seth A and Vande Woude GF (1988) In: Curran T, Reddy EP and Skalka A (eds.) The Oncogene Handbook. Elsevier, The Netherlands, Vol. 1, pp. 213–253.
2. Propst F, Storm SM and Rapp UR (1991) In: Kumar R (ed.) The Molecular Basis of Human Cancer. Futura Scientific Publishers, New York (in press).
3. Propst F, Rosenberg MP, Cork LC, Kovatch RM, Rauch S, Westphal H, Khillan J, Schulz NT, Vande Woude GF and Newmann PE (1990) Proc. Natl. Acad. Sci. U.S.A., 87: 9703–9707.
4. Khillan JS, Oskarsson MK, Propst F, Kuwabara T, Vande Woude GF and Westphal H (1987) Genes Dev. 1: 1327–1335.
5. Theuring F, Gotz W, Balling R, Korf HW, Schulze F, Herken R and Gruss P (1990) Oncogene 5: 225–232.

© 1991 Elsevier Science Publishers B.V. All rights reserved.
Biological Psychiatry, Volume 2. G. Racagni et al., editors.

Association and linkage studies of affective disorders

Maria del Zompo[1], Mariangela Pedditzi[1], Stefania Ruiu[1], Lynn R. Goldin[2], Wade H. Berrettini[3] and Alberto Boccheta[1]

[1]Department of Neurosciences "B.B. Brodie", University of Cagliari, Cagliari, Italy; [2]Clinical Neurogenetics Branch, NIMH, Bethesda, Maryland; and [3]Department of Psychiatry, Jefferson Medical College, Philadelphia, Pennsylvania, U.S.A.

Introduction

Numerous reports have been published concerning linkage of Xq28-chromosome markers to manic-depressive illness (MDI) with evidence of heterogeneity [1–9]. Positive reports indicate that the disease locus is within 5 centimorgans of the color blindness (CB) or glucose-6-phosphate dehydrogenase (G6PD) loci. Xq28-linked inheritance of MDI may be more pronounced among non-Ashkenazi Jews and other Mediterranean communities [8]. We already reported 2 Sardinian pedigrees suggestive of linkage with CB or G6PD [7]. Subsequently, we found an association between G6PD deficiency and bipolar (BP) illness in Sardinia, suggesting linkage disequilibrium [10]. To help clarify the status of Xq28 linkage, we studied polymorphic DNA loci, tightly linked to the CB and the G6PD markers, in three multigenerational Sardinian pedigrees with no male-to-male transmission of MDI.

Subjects and Methods

Diagrams for the 3 pedigrees are presented in Fig. 1. Diagnosis was established by review of interview, medical records and information from relatives, using modified Research Diagnostic Criteria. DNA polymorphisms at loci DXS52 and DXS15 were identified with probes St-14-1 and DX13 after digestion with restriction endonucleases TaqI or Bgl II. Genotypic assignment was performed blindly. The computer program LINKAGE [11] (version 5.03) was used to calculate lod scores, assuming a dominant disease locus with a gene frequency of 1% and maximum penetrance of 90%. Subjects with schizoaffective, BP-1, BP-2 and unipolar illness were included as affected.

Results and Discussion

Table 1 shows the lod scores for linkage of MDI to the 2 DNA markers. Data on family 1 had already been published in 1984 [7], being informative for CB. Maximum lod score was 0.50 at a recombination fraction (θ) of 0. Data on DXS52

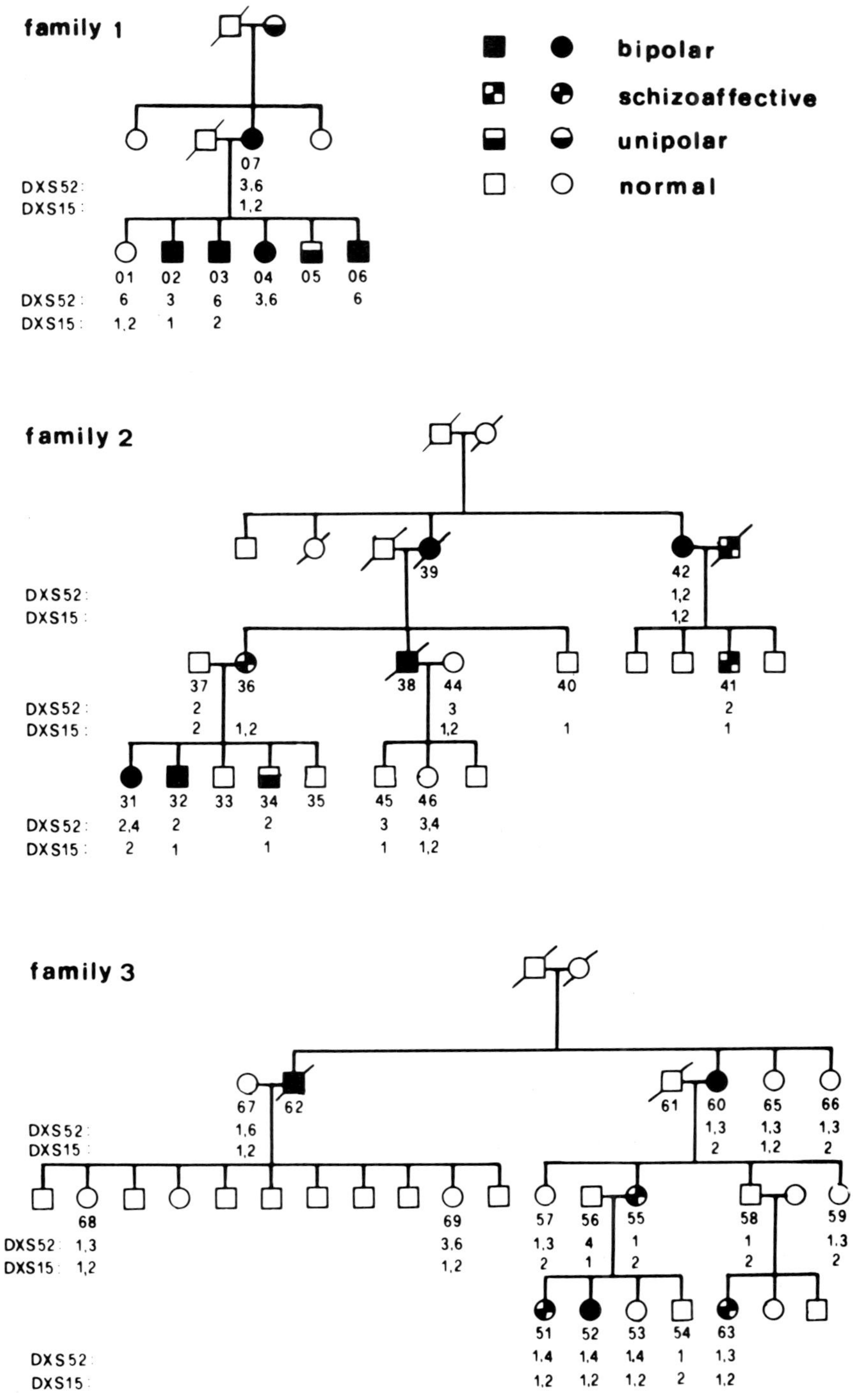

Fig. 1. Pedigrees studied at the DNA loci DXS52 and/or DXS15. Genotypes are given beneath the symbols and the identification numbers for each individual. Squares represent male subjects; circles, female subjects.

Table 1. Lod scores for linkage of DXS15 and DXS52 to manic-depressive illness

Locus		θ = 0	θ = 0.05	θ = 0.10	θ = 0.20	θ = 0.30
DXS15:	Family 1	–0.79	–0.49	–0.33	–0.16	–0.06
	Family 2	–0.89	–0.36	–0.20	–0.07	–0.03
	Family 3	–0.34	–0.25	–0.19	–0.09	–0.04
	Total	–2.02	–1.10	–0.72	–0.32	–0.13
DXS52:	Family 1	–0.81	–0.72	–0.57	–0.30	–0.12
	Family 2	–2.01	–1.14	–0.81	–0.42	–0.24
	Family 3	–1.63	–0.84	–0.65	–0.50	–0.36
	Total	–4.45	–2.71	–2.04	–1.22	–0.73

and DXS15 confirm the most probable Xq28 phase of 02 (normal vision) and 03 (CB); phase has also been identified in 01 and 04. The lowering of lod score is mostly due to the fact that diagnostic follow-up has revealed new BP illness onset in 03 and 06 in the absence of the putative marker of predisposition (normal vision).

In family 3, subject 62 appears as a recombinant in the linkage analysis. Alternatively, he may represent a non-genetic case (phenocopy), which is consistent with the absence of illness in his 11 children, who have already passed most of the risk period for MDI (current age, 36–59 years).

In conclusion, at the present stage, our study does not support linkage of Xq28 markers to MDI in these 3 Sardinian pedigrees. Nevertheless, the extension of pedigree and the use of additional Xq28 markers to make subject 55 heterozygous may lead to different conclusions, at least in family 3.

References

1. WinoKur G, Clayton PJ and Reich T (1969) Manic-Depressive Illness. CV Mosby Co., St. Louis.
2. Mendlewicz J and Fleiss JL (1974) Biol. Psychiatry 9: 261–294.
3. Baron M (1977) Arch. Gen. Psychiatry 34: 721–725.
4. Mendlewicz J, Linkowski P, Guroff JJ and Van Praag HM (1979) Arch. Gen. Psychiatry 36: 1442–1447.
5. Gershon ES, Targum SD, Matthysse S and Bunney WE Jr (1979) Arch. Gen. Psychiatry 36: 1423–1430.
6. Mendlewicz J, Linkowsy P and Wilmotte J (1980) Br. J. Psychiatry 137: 337–342.
7. Del Zompo M, Bocchetta A, Goldin LR and Corsini GU (1984) Acta Psychiatr. Scand. 70: 282–287.
8. Baron M, Risch N, Hamburger R, Mandel B, Kushner S, Newman M, Drumer D and Belmaker RH (1987) Nature 326: 289–292.
9. Berrettini WH, Goldin LR, Gelernter J, Gejman PV, Gershon ES and Detera-Wadleigh S (1990) Arch. Gen. Psychiatry 47: 366–373.
10. Bocchetta A, Del Zompo M, Martis G and Corsini GU (1985) IV Biological World Congress of Biological Psychiatry, Abstr. 231.1.
11. Lathrop G, Lalouel JJ, Julier C and Ott J (1985) Am. J. Hum. Genet. 37: 482–490.

© 1991 Elsevier Science Publishers B.V. All rights reserved.
Biological Psychiatry, Volume 2. G. Racagni et al., editors.

Genomic screening for genes predisposing to bipolar disease: Results for one third of the genome

Wade H. Berrettini[1], Sevilla D. Detera-Wadleigh[2], Lynn R. Goldin[2], Maria Martinez[2], Wang-Ting Hsieh[2], Margaret Hoehe[2], Henry Choi[2], David Muniec[2], Diane Coffman[2], Denise Y. Rollins[2], Denise Wiesch[2], Julie Guroff[2] and Elliot S. Gershon[2]

[1]*Department of Psychiatry and Human Behavior, Jefferson Medical College, Thomas Jefferson University, 1025 Walnut Street, 312 College, Philadelphia, PA 19107; and* [2]*Clinical Neurogenetics Branch, National Institute of Mental Health, 9000 Rockville Pike, Building 10, Room 3N218, Bethesda, MD 20892, U.S.A.*

Introduction

The development of molecular genetic techniques and of relatively complete DNA marker maps of the human genome have led to the chromosomal localization of vulnerability genes for many Mendelian diseases, even though the biochemical defects causing these illnesses remain unknown. We have conducted a linkage study of 20 multiplex bipolar (BP) pedigrees, including 350 informative persons (whose genotypes can be determined from available DNA samples), of whom 145 have BP, schizoaffective (SA) or recurrent unipolar (UP) diagnoses. The power of this pedigree series to detect linkage has been estimated through simulations [1], indicating that this series has greater than 50% power to detect linkage when only 25% of the families are linked (1% recombination) to a locus (70% heterozygosity) under study. No pedigrees in our BP families support linkage to either Xq28 or 11p15 [2–4].

Methods

The 125 probes used in this study were selected from published linkage maps of chromosomes 2 [5], 5 [6], 10 [7], 11 [8,9], 13 [10], 15 [9,11] and 17 [11]. Most probes were obtained as gifts from Ray White's laboratory or were purchased from the American Type Culture Collection (Rockville, MD), or Collaborative Research, Inc. (Bedford, MA). DNA probes were labelled with ^{32}P-deoxycytosine triphosphate (3000 Ci/mmol) as described [4]. DNA, extracted from lymphoblastoid cell lines or from whole blood, was digested with restriction endonucleases according to the manufacturer's recommendations, using five units per µg of DNA. Agarose gel electrophoresis (10 µg of digested DNA per lane), transfer to nylon membranes, hybridization, washing and autoradiography were carried out as described previously [4].

Autoradiograms were read by 2 blind independent readers (familiar with the polymorphism in question) whose results were compared by computer matching to detect discrepancies. Any discrepancies were resolved by reference to a third reader. Inconsistencies with pedigree structure were resolved by reinspection of the autoradiogram and reference to a pedigree structure without diagnoses. If the inconsistencies could not be resolved, the person(s) were considered as genotype unknown.

Linkage analysis was conducted with LINKAGE package (version 5.03). A variable age of onset (15–50 years) was assumed with a maximal penetrance of 90% (at 50 years) in an autosomal dominant model. A disease gene frequency of 1.5% was assumed. Penetrance of the normal genotype was set at 0.001%. Two affection status models were used. Model 1 included SA, BPI, and BPII with major depression; model 2 added recurrent UP to the model 1 diagnoses. Two- and 3-point analyses were calculated for each interval along the chromosomal maps. To address the issue of heterogeneity, 2-point lod scores for individual families were examined at each locus. Lod scores were calculated, assuming heterogeneity, using the admixture test. A modified version of LINKMAP was used to estimate the fraction of families linked.

Results

These analyses did not reveal any evidence of linkage. Admixture analysis and visual inspection of the 2-point scores for individual families did not reveal a subset of linked families, where the fraction of linked families was at least 25%.

Discussion

These results suggest that a common heritable form of BP disease does not arise from the chromosomal regions studied. However, there are limitations of this pedigree series concerning power to detect linkage under assumptions of heterogeneity [1]. This pedigree series has 50% power to detect linkage (at 1% recombination to a marker with 70% heterozygosity, under affection status model two) when only 25% of the families are linked to that marker. Thus a linkage involving a small fraction of these families may have been missed.

References

1. Berrettini WH, Goldin LR, Martinez MM, Maxwell E, Smith AL, Guroff JJ, Kazuba DM, Nurnberger Jr JI, Hamovit J, Simmons-Alling S, Robb AS and Gershon ES (1991) J. Psychiatr. Genet. (in press).
2. Berrettini WH, Goldin LR, Gelernter J, Gejman PV, Gershon ES and Detera-Wadleigh SD (1990) Arch. Gen. Psychiatry 47: 336.

3. Berrettini WH, Detera-Wadleigh SD, Goldin LR, Martinez MM, Hsieh W-T, Hoehe MR and Gershon ES (1990a) Neuropsychopharmacology.
4. Detera-Wadleigh SD, Berrettini WH, Goldin LR, Martinez M and Hsieh W-T (1987) Nature 325: 806.
5. O'Connell P, Lathrop GM, Nakamura Y, Leppert ML, Lalouel J-M and White R (1989) Genomics 6: 738.
6. Weiffenbach B, Falls K, Bricker A, Hall L, McMahon J, Wasmuth J, Funanage V and Donis-Keller H (1991) Genomics 10: 173.
7. White R, Lalouel M-M, Nakamura Y, Donis-Keller H, Green P, Bowden DL, Mathew CGP, Easton DB, Robson EE, Morton NE, Gusella JF, Haines JL, Retief AE, Kidd KK, Murray JC, Lathrop GM and Cann HM (1990) Genomics 6: 393.
8. Julier C, Nakamura Y, Lathrop M, O'Connell P, Leppert M, Litt M, Mohandas T, Lalouel J-M and White R (1990) Genomics 7: 335.
9. Keats BJ (1989) Cytogenet. Cell Genet. 51: 501.
10. Bowcock AM, Farrer LA, Hebert JM, Agger M, Bale AE, Buys CH, Donis-Keller H and Cavalli-Sforza LL (1990) Cytogenet. Cell Genet. 51: 966.
11. Nakamura Y, Lathrop M, O'Connell P, Leppert M, Barker D, Wright E, Skolnick M, Kondolean S, Litt M and Lalouel J-M (1988) Genomics 3: 342.

© 1991 Elsevier Science Publishers B.V. All rights reserved.
Biological Psychiatry, Volume 2. G. Racagni et al., editors.

Molecular genetic analysis in bipolar illness

Christine van Broeckhoven[1], An de Bruyn[1], Peter Raeymaekers[1], Lodewijk Sandkuijl[2], Karine Mendelbaum[3], Veronique Delvenne[3] and Julien Mendlewicz[3]

[1]*Department of Biochemistry, Laboratory of Neurogenetics, Born Bunge Foundation, University of Antwerp (UIA), B-2610 Antwerp;* [2]*Department of Clinical Genetics, Dijkzigt University Hospital, 3000 DR, Rotterdam, The Netherlands; and* [3]*Department of Psychiatry, Erasme Hospital, University of Brussels (ULB), B-1070 Brussels, Belgium*

Introduction

The involvement of genetic factors in the etiology of affective disorders has been suggested by twin, adoption and family studies [1]. The identification of genes involved in the genetic susceptibility to mental illness has largely been stimulated by the application of molecular genetic strategies [2]. Evidence in favour of X linkage of manic depressive illness (MDI) has been provided using genetic markers located in Xq27-q28: F9, coagulation factor IX; CB, colour blindness; G6PD, glucose-6-phosphate dehydrogenase. Linkage has also been claimed in an Old Order Amish pedigree with two chromosome 11 markers located in 11p15: INS, insulin and HRAS, c-Harvey-ras oncogene. However, families unlinked to either set of markers have been described. In addition, reanalysis and extension of the initial chromosome 11 data led to exclusion of linkage to the chromosome 11p15 region. These inconsistent findings may be attributed to genetic heterogeneity. However, it has been recognized that phenotypic misclassifications may lead to spurious linkage findings and to biased estimates of genetic parameters [3].

Materials and Methods

Subjects

Fifteen informative families of bipolar patients admitted between November 1988 and 1990 to the Erasme Hospital (Brussels, Belgium) were included in the linkage analysis. After obtaining informed consent, all probands and available relatives were personally interviewed using the Schedule for Affective Disorders and Schizophrenia [4]. Information from close relatives and hospital records were also used when available. The diagnoses were based on the Research Diagnostic Criteria [5]. The pedigrees contain 224 adult individuals (14 years or older) with a known diagnostic status, 48 of whom have diagnoses of bipolar illness (BP I and BP II) or schizoaffective-mainly affective (Szaf), while 52 have a diagnosis of unipolar depression (UP). In addition the pedigrees contained 12 individuals with cyclothymia (CY), a milder affective condition.

DNA analysis

Of a total of 206 individuals, blood samples were collected for molecular genetic analysis. The DNA was extracted from total blood, digested with the appropriate restriction enzyme, separated by agarose gel electrophoresis, transferred to a nylon membrane and hybridized with the radiolabelled probe according to standard DNA procedures [6]. The probes and restriction enzymes used are : F9, P1 on TaqI; DXS52, St14-1 on TaqI; TH, pJ4.7 on TaqI and pHGTH4 on PstI; INS, phins310 on PvuII and HRAS, pUCEJ6.6 [7].

Linkage analysis

Linkage analysis was performed using the LINKAGE computer program [8], assuming a dominant disease locus with an allele frequency of 0.01 and a maximum penetrance of 99% at age 60 years or older. Twelve liability classes were used for the age-dependent penetrance with, for each liability class, a phenocopy rate of 0.0001 [9].

Results

We examined 15 multiply affected MDI families ascertained through BP probands for linkage with chromosome X and 11. The mean age at onset including all phenotypes was 26.14 ± 10.42 years with an overall disease penetrance of 96.4%. In each family the inheritance of MDI is consistent with segregation of a single dominant gene. In 10 out of 15 families no male-to-male transmission was observed suggesting X linkage of the disease. The 10 families were analyzed with DNA markers on the X-chromosome: F9 and DXS52, the latter located within a distance of 5% recombination of CB and G6PD. All 15 families were analyzed with DNA markers on chromosome 11: HRAS, INS and tyrosine hydroxylase

Table 1. Two-point lod scores for linkage of MDI with chromosome X and 11 DNA markers

	Recombination fraction					
	0.00	0.05	0.10	0.20	0.30	0.40
F9	− 5.53	− 2.20	−1.19	−0.35	−0.11	−0.09
DXS52	−11.24	− 4.11	−2.63	−1.45	−0.82	−0.36
TH	−15.66	− 5.81	−3.38	−1.08	−0.22	0.02
INS	−13.06	− 4.68	−2.91	−1.33	−0.50	−0.13
HRAS	−23.88	−10.77	−6.98	−2.95	−1.02	−0.24

(TH), the rate limiting enzyme for the synthesis of catecholamines. In Table 1, the results of the pairwise linkage analyses of MDI (comprising BP + Szaf + UP + CY patients) and each of the DNA markers are shown as lod scores (logarithm of the likelihood ratios for linkage calculated at different recombination fractions). The lod scores are significantly negative, excluding tight linkage of MDI with the chromosome regions Xq27-q28 and 11p15 in the families analyzed. Negative results were also obtained if more conservative diagnostic definitions of the MDI phenotype were used.

References

1. Mendlewicz J (1988) Br. J. Psychiatry 153: 16–25.
2. Owen MJ and Mullan MJ (1990) Trends Neurosci. 13: 29–31.
3. Baron M, Hamburger R, Sandkuijl LA, Risch N, Mandel B, Endicott, Belmaker RH and Ott J (1990) Acta Psychiatr. Scand. 82: 196–203.
4. Spitzer RL and Endicott J (1970) Schedule for Affective Disorders and Schizophrenia. State Psychiatric Institute, New York.
5. Spitzer RL, Endicott J and Robins E (1978) Arch Gen. Psychiatry 35: 773–782.
6. Sambrook J, Fritsch EF and Maniatis T (1989) Molecular Cloning. A Laboratory Manual. Cold Spring Harbor Laboratory Press, New York.
7. Human Gene Mapping 10 (1989) Cytogenetics and Cell Genetics. Karger, Basel.
8. Lathrop GM and Lalouel JM (1984) Am. J. Hum. Genet. 36: 460–465.
9. Baron M, Risch N and Mendlewicz J (1983) J. Psychiatr. Res. 17: 5–18.

© 1991 Elsevier Science Publishers B.V. All rights reserved.
Biological Psychiatry, Volume 2. G. Racagni et al., editors.

Genetic mapping of affective disorder: Opportunities and pitfalls

Miron Baron

New York State Psychiatric Institute and Columbia University, 722 West 168th Street, Box 58, New York, NY 10032, U.S.A.

Introduction

Progress in molecular and quantitative genetics (particularly the identification of polymorphic DNA markers and the development of statistical methods for linkage analysis) has led to new insights into the genetic mechanisms for some single-gene disorders. Of special note is the cloning of several disease genes, including those for Duchenne muscular dystrophy, cystic fibrosis and neurofibromatosis. By contrast, similar approaches to diseases of more complex inheritance have been marred by conflicting findings. This has heightened concerns over potential methodological faults and spurious linkage results. A discussion of these issues, with a view to linkage studies in affective disorders, is presented.

Background

Linkage studies in complex diseases (i.e. disorders with unknown mode of inheritance and unclear phenotype) are of great current interest. These diseases have assumed a special place in human genetics owing to their complex etiologies and high prevalence in the population.

The application of linkage strategies to rare, Mendelian disorders is relatively straightforward. A successful outcome can usually be predicted. The complex diseases have endured a different fate, as evidenced by conflicting linkage findings, especially in neuropsychiatric disorders such as affective illness [1]. This has led several investigators to advise caution in interpreting linkage findings in these disorders [1–5].

Discussions concerning spurious linkage results in complex disorders have largely centered on type I errors (false claims that linkage exists). Understandably, this is an immediate source of concern when reported linkages cannot be reproduced. By contrast, much less attention has been focused on type II errors (false conclusion that linkage is not present). However, this issue, too, is of primary importance. First, owing to the genotypic and phenotypic complexities of these disorders, linkage can be more easily missed than detected. Second, type II errors which go undetected undermine confidence in genuine linkage findings and may lead to the erroneous exclusion of genomic segments which may contain disease genes.

Problems and pitfalls

False linkage can be encountered under the following scenarios:
a) Maximization of the lod score (the statistical test criterion for linkage) over a wide range of genetic parameters (e.g. penetrance, allele frequency and disease definition);
b) a statistical artifact resulting from the testing of multiple marker systems;
c) preferential presentation of families with positive lod scores;
d) borderline lod scores representing a chance finding;
e) non-blind procedures leading to biased assignment of genotypes and/or clinical status.

To be sure, opportunities abound for false negative linkage. These include:
a) Etiologic heterogeneity, i.e. if the proportion of linked cases is small, linkage can be missed under "realistic" sampling schemes;
b) mis-specified genetic parameters, including the assumption of single gene inheritance when the true genetic model calls for interaction between alleles at different loci (i.e. epistasis);
c) phenocopies (i.e. cases erroneously considered affected), especially among the milder clinical variants (e.g. bipolar II and unipolar depressive disorders, as opposed to the "core" bipolar I phenotype);
d) assortative mating or bilineal transmission leading to enhanced genetic heterogeneity within the pedigree;
e) laboratory errors in reading marker alleles;
f) non-blind procedures coupled with a bias against a particular hypothesis;
g) inclusion of pedigrees which are a priori inconsistent with the hypothesis under study (e.g. families with male-to-male transmission when X-linkage is evaluated).

As will be shown, most of the studies hitherto published did not fully account for these potential pitfalls.

Recommendations

Various corrective measures and potential remedies can be considered in order to overcome or minimize the problems leading to spurious linkage results. These include fully documented research procedures (to enable independent review and to facilitate exchange of information among investigators); blind and systematic procedures for data collection and analysis (to avert biased conclusions); narrowly defined phenotypes, high illness density and unilineal transmission (to increase diagnostic certainty and to reduce the occurrence of phenocopies); corrections for multiple test effects, such as placing limits on the number of diagnostic and analytic schemes and "adjusting" the lod score (to avoid inflated lod values); "penetrance-free" models (both in pedigrees and in sib-pair analysis) focusing on affected individuals only (to obviate the question of variable penetrance and cases erroneously considered unaffected); extension of phenotypic and genotypic information in pedigrees with reported linkages (to examine the credibility of the original findings); large enough samples (to detect or exclude linkage with confidence in the face of etiologic heterogeneity); rigorous diagnostic procedures (i.e. well-trained diagnosticians, high interrater reliability); careful laboratory work (to minimize typing errors and cases of non-paternity); and lod scores higher than the conventional "cutoff" value of 3 (to offset some of the methodological uncertainties that might lead to false conclusion of linkage). Last but not least, replication, with due attention to potential methodological faults, is the ultimate litmus test for linkage findings.

Conclusion

Caution is required in accepting the linkage results hitherto published. This also pertains to the negative linkage findings, with the possible exception of the purported chromosome 11p linkage in the Old Order Amish which, in effect, has been retracted. Improved methodology along the lines proposed herein, while enhancing the prospects of linkage studies in this field, may still fall short of an optimal approach to the genetics of psychiatric disorders. A fuller appreciation of the phenotypic and genotypic complexities of these disorders may require new paradigms such as methods incorporating behavioral dimensions (as opposed to all-or-none disease states) and other quantitative traits (i.e. biological covariates) in the phenotypic expression of the illness, as well as models for various forms of epistasis (interacting genes that account for small amounts of phenotypic variation).

Acknowledgements

This work was supported by Research Scientist Development Award MH00176, by Grants MH42535, MH44115 and MH43979 from the NIMH and a grant from the W.M. Keck Foundation.

References

1. Baron M, Endicott J and Ott J (1990a) Br. J. Psychiatry 157: 645–655.
2. Baron M, Hamburger R, Sandkuyl LA et al. (1990b) Acta Psychiatr. Scand. 82: 196–203.
3. Risch N (1990) Genet. Epidemiol. 7: 13–16.
4. Clerget-Darpoux F, Babron MC and Bonaiti-Pellie C (1990) Genet. Epidemiol. 7: 245–253.
5. Weeks DE, Lehner T, Squires-Wheeler E et al. (1990) Genet. Epidemiol. 7: 237–244.

© 1991 Elsevier Science Publishers B.V. All rights reserved.
Biological Psychiatry, Volume 2. G. Racagni et al., editors.

New molecular techniques for genetic linkage studies

Cathy L. Barr and Kenneth K. Kidd
Department of Genetics, Yale University School of Medicine, New Haven, CT 06510, U.S.A.

Over the last decade the number of identified DNA polymorphism loci has risen from about 2 dozen in 1981 to well over 2,500 today [1]; most of these loci are defined as restriction fragment length polymorphisms (RFLP). With this large number of polymorphic loci available, there have been many linkage studies of psychiatric disorders but, so far, these studies have been largely unsuccessful. One of the reasons is that the RFLP markers generally are not very informative. This general lack of informativeness necessitates the use of new types of more informative markers.

Genetic linkage between a disease and a marker locus is detected by finding a concordance when comparing: a) the inferred pattern of transmission of the hypothetical disease susceptibility allele with b) the inferred pattern of transmission of a known marker. The statistical methods for measuring this concordance usually involve comparing probabilities of the observed data based on different hypotheses about the linkage relationship between the hypothetical disease locus and the marker locus. Only when these probabilities differ greatly for the different hypotheses can any conclusions be drawn. Uncertainty arises when different hypotheses are equally good (or bad) at predicting the observed data. Whenever no pattern of transmission can be inferred for either of the loci, all hypotheses about their linkage relationship give the same result and no conclusions can be drawn. In linkage studies of psychiatric disorders such uncertainty often arises from the inability to infer any clear pattern of transmission of the hypothetical disease susceptibility allele. Factors which contribute to this uncertainty are the complexity of pedigree structure, the absence of clear Mendelian inheritance of the disease and the complexity of diagnosis coupled with nosologic uncertainty. In an ideal genetic study we would work with a pedigree in which there are DNA samples available on all members of a multigenerational family with large sibships. In such families linkage phase could be established. Ideally, the disease would show complete penetrance, being inherited in a Mendelian fashion through grandparent, parent, and children. Unfortunately, the pedigrees which are available for study and the expression of the psychiatric diseases are much more complex. DNA samples are not available from all individuals either because they are deceased or the individuals are unwilling to participate. Additionally, the relationship of the affected members is not always direct, that is, the disease is not always distributed among relatives in an apparent Mendelian fashion.

We are currently studying 3 psychiatric diseases, Gilles de la Tourette syndrome, bipolar affective disorder and schizophrenia. The differences in the relative complexity of the pedigrees and the expression of the diseases are evident in the different percentages of the genome which we have been able to exclude for these diseases. For example, we have searched for linkage in 4 Tourette syndrome kindreds with DNA samples on over 300 individuals. The pedigree structures of these families are relatively simple with DNA samples available on a large number of the individuals in the pedigree. The expression of the disease is relatively direct with the disease being expressed in some branches through 4 generations. In a collaborative effort of several groups we have typed 267 markers on these families, and have been able to exclude 77% of the genome for the disease ([2]; and Pakstis et al., subsequent unpublished results). In comparison, in the search for linkage in schizophrenia we have studied a large Swedish kindred in which DNA has been collected on 80 individuals, 29 of which have been diagnosed for schizophrenia. The transmission of the disease in this family is not always direct. For example in one particular branch the disease is expressed in an uncle and his nephews but not in the connecting parent. In collaboration with 2 other groups [3], we have analyzed the typings of 99 markers, yet have only been able to exclude 5% of the genome. Therefore, with over 1/3 of the number of markers typed for schizophrenia as has been typed in the Tourette families, we have been able to exclude about 1/15 of the amount of the genome excluded for Tourette syndrome. Of intermediate complexity between the kindreds used to study schizophrenia and Tourette syndrome is the Old Order Amish kindred used for linkage analysis of bipolar affective disorder. The Old Order Amish extended pedigree structure contains 99 individuals with diagnoses available on 90 of the persons. We have now screened 189 segregating loci for linkage and have excluded 25% of the genome for the disease [4].

To compensate for the uncertainty in the transmission of the hypothetical disease allele, we must make the transmission of the known marker more informative. One possible source of more informative markers is the use of variable number of tandem repeats (VNTRs). The advantage of the VNTR systems is that they are highly informative systems, with some VNTR loci having more than 10 alleles. One disadvantage is that VNTRs can be difficult to score on a Southern blot experiment, especially in complex kindreds in which it is often difficult to determine identity by descent when many alleles have similar sizes. Another disadvantage of the VNTR systems is that they seem to have a non-random distribution in the genome. VNTRs are more often found near the ends of chromosomes and on some chromosomes VNTRs are particularly scarce, for example chromosome 10 [5].

An abundant source of polymorphic markers in the genome are the short tandem repeats (STR) or microsatellites [6]. These repeats are blocks of repeating di-, tri-, or tetra-nucleotide repeats, with the most common being repeating dinucleotides such as CA repeats. The number of repeat units is often polymorphic and is inherited in a Mendelian fashion. To utilize one of these polymorphic sequences as a marker, appropriate DNA fragments are produced by the polymerase chain reaction (PCR) using primers designed to anneal to the single copy DNA that flanks a specific block of repeats. Amplified DNA is visualized by incorporating radiolabeled nucleotides into the PCR reaction and the alleles are then separated on a denaturing sequencing gel. Estimates of the number of the STR loci in human DNA range from about 35,000–130,000 [7], making STRs one of the most abundant sources of polymorphisms. With over 200 of these repeats having already been identified as being polymorphic, it is rapidly becoming possible to efficiently scan the genome using these markers [6].

A second, relatively new technique, single-stranded conformational polymorphism (SSCP), can identify as little as a single base pair substitution in a given DNA sequence [8]. To detect sequence polymorphism the region of interest is amplified using PCR in the presence of labeled nucleotide. An aliquot of the PCR reaction is then diluted sufficiently to prevent the 2 strands from reannealing to each other, denatured by heat and then run on a non-denaturing polyacrylamide gel. Under non-denaturing conditions, the DNA assumes a folded conformation that is stabilized by intrastrand interaction. These conformations affect the mobility of the DNA on the gel and therefore the position of the band on the autoradiogram. A single base pair difference can result in a change in the intrastrand interactions and therefore the mobility of the DNA. This technique, although sensitive enough to detect a single base pair change, is only sensitive to mutations which interfere with intrastrand interactions, and therefore many base pair changes can go undetected.

Denaturing gradient gel electrophoresis (DGGE) is analogous to SSCP in that it is able to detect single base pair differences. DGGE is more sensitive than SSCP but is also technically more demanding. The separation of DNA molecules by DGGE is based on the fact that DNA molecules differing by a single base change have slightly different melting properties. These base pair differences cause them to migrate differently in a polyacrylamide gel containing a linear gradient of DNA denaturants. As electrophoresis moves the DNA through the gradient, the DNA is exposed to progressively higher concentrations of denaturants and shifts to a partially single-stranded, partially-double stranded molecule. In this partially denatured state the mobility of the DNA is retarded relative to the completely double or single-stranded forms. The retardation is such that the molecules are essentially trapped in the gel and migrate no further. The base pair sequence of the molecule determines the position at which the molecule stops along the gel and in some cases it is possible to scan most of the possible single base pair sequence changes in a given fragment.

In summary, the ability to find polymorphisms in any region of the genome using SSCP and DGGE and the use of more informative markers, such as STRs, will enable us to search the 23% of the genome which has not been searched for Tourette syndrome. For affective disorder and schizophrenia, traditional RFLP markers give only a small amount of information. We hope that the use of the more informative markers will allow us to scan more conclusively the genome for linkage to complex psychiatric diseases.

References

1. Kidd (1991) Progress towards completing the human linkage map. Curr. Opin. Genet. Dev. (in press).
2. Pakstis AJ, Heutink P, Pauls DL, Kurlan R, van de Wetering BJM, Leckman JF, Sandkuyl LA, Kidd JR, Breedveld GJ, Castiglione CM, Weber J, Sparkes RS, Cohen DJ, Kidd KK and Oostra BA (1991a) Am. J. Hum. Genet. 48: 281–294.
3. Barr CL, Kennedy JL, Pakstis AJ, Wetterberg L, Sjogren B, Gelernter J, Hallmayer J, Moises H, Cavalli-Sforza LL and Kidd KK (1991). Progress in Genome Scan for Linkage in Schizophrenia. Abstr. 8th International Congress of Human Genetics.
4. Pakstis AJ, Kidd JR, Castiglione CM and Kidd KK (1991b). Status of the search for a major genetic locus for affective disorder in the Old Order Amish. Hum. Genet. (in press).
5. White R, Lalouel JM, Nakamura Y, Donis-Keller H, Green P, Bowden C, Mathew C, Easton D, Robson E, Morton N, Gusella J, Haines J, Retief A, Kidd K, Murray J, Lathrop M and Cann H (1990) Genomics 6: 393–412.
6. Weber JL (1990) Curr. Opin. Biotechnol. 1: 166–171.
7. Weber JL and May PE (1989) Am. J. Hum. Genet. 44: 388–396.
8. Orita M, Suzuki Y, Sekiya T and Hayashi K (1989) Genomics 5: 874–879.

© 1991 Elsevier Science Publishers B.V. All rights reserved.
Biological Psychiatry, Volume 2. G. Racagni et al., editors.

Modular biology of the human D_4 and D_5 dopamine receptors

David K. Grandy, Hubert H.M. van Tol and Olivier Civelli
Vollum Institute for Advanced Biomedical Research, Oregon Health Sciences University, Portland, OR 97201, U.S.A.

Introduction

Dopamine (DA) is an important transmitter molecule at the synapses of neurons in the mesocortico-mesolimbic, nigrostriatal and tuberoinfundibular pathways. To a lesser extent DA is also thought to be involved in the signaling between some hippocampal neurons. The central dopaminergic tracts have been of considerable medical interest due to their association with several psychiatric and neurological disorders including psychosis, compulsive behavior, drug abuse and Parkinson's disease. Originally DA was thought to evoke its physiological responses through the stimulation of two receptor subtypes, D_1 and D_2. These receptors were differentiated on the basis of their pharmacology, physiology and anatomical distribution. Although the two-receptor view was generally accepted prior to 1990, it is worth noting that there was a sound pharmacological basis for believing that this was an oversimplification [1]. With the cloning of the D_1 [2] and D_2 DA receptors [3], the actual complexity of the dopaminergic system could be addressed at the molecular level. In an effort to identify new DA receptors we developed a strategy based on homology screening which has resulted in the cloning of the D_4 [4] and D_5 [5] DA receptor genes.

Material and Methods

For the cloning of D_4 a fragment of the rat D_2 DA receptor cDNA, containing transmembrane domains VI and VII, was used to probe RNA from several cell lines and rat tissues. Under reduced hybridization (25% formamide, 0.2% polyvinypyrolidone, 0.2% Ficoll, 0.2% BSA, 50 mM Tris pH 7.5, 1 M NaCl, 1% SDS and 100 $\mu g\ ml^{-1}$ salmon sperm DNA at 37°C) and washing (0.1% SDS; 2 × SSC: 300 mM NaCl, 30 mM Na_3 citrate, pH 7.0; 55°C) conditions RNA from human pituitary tissue and the human cell line SK-N-MC gave signals with the D_2 probe. cDNA libraries from both human pituitary tissue and the SK-N-MC cell line were prepared and screened by standard techniques. Partial cDNAs were obtained from both libraries. In order to obtain a full-length coding region a human genomic library (Clontech) was screened.

For the cloning of D_5 the complete coding region of the human D_1 gene was used to probe a Southern blot of EcoRI-digested human genomic DNA as described above, with the exception that 50% formamide was used. A signal corresponding to a fragment of 5-kb was observed and based on this information a genomic library enriched in 5-kb EcoRI fragments was constructed in λ GT10. The library was screened and several positives were isolated and characterized by standard procedures [6].

All transient expression, binding and cAMP studies were performed as previously described [2–4].

Results and Discussion

Characterization of the human D_4 dopamine receptor

The D_4 mRNA is very rare and several attempts to obtain a full-length cDNA were unsuccessful. The cloning of the human gene revealed that the coding region is interrupted by four introns and that one of the splice junctions is unusual. The composite open reading frame predicts seven putative transmembrane domains (TMDs) which are from 36% (TMD I) to 78% (VII) identical to D_2. In lieu of a full-length cDNA the pharmacological evaluation of D_4 was performed using a construction composed of cDNA and genomic sequences. This construct was transiently expressed in COS-7 cells and directed the synthesis of receptors which stereospecifically bound [^{3}H]spiperone [4]. The pharmacological profile of the D_4 receptor revealed that it has a drug profile similar to the D_2 [7] and D_3 [8] receptors with one important exception. The D_4 receptor shows a higher affinity for the antipsychotic clozapine with a dissociation constant of 9 nM which is in the range of therapeutic dosage levels. Some of the current work on this interesting and potentially clinically important receptor is focused on linkage studies and human disease.

Characterization of the human D_5 dopamine receptor

The screening of the 5-kb enriched human genomic library yielded several positive phage which upon restriction analysis looked very similar. One of these clones, HGRI-6, was further characterized by sequencing and was found be 65% identical to the human D_1 receptor gene. However, this gene contained a stop codon in-frame instead of residue 152. The presence of an in-frame stop codon and the lack of typical splice site consensus sequences suggested that this clone was a pseudogene. In an effort to establish if the human genome contains a functional homologue of this gene the sequences of several other positive phage were analyzed. Two additional clones were identified: HGRI-8 which is 98% identical and the other, HGRI-4 which is 95% identical to HGRI-6. Although HGRI-8 was also found to contain a stop codon in place of residue 152, and so is most likely a pseudogene, HGRI-4 had an uninterrupted open reading frame. The deduced amino acid sequence of HGRI-4 consists of 477 residues which are organized into seven putative TMDs that are from 56% (TMD I) to 96% (TMD V) identical to the corresponding human D_1 TMDs. Overall the receptor's amino acid sequence is 49% identical to the human D_1 receptor. The extensive sequence conservation between the D_1 and D_5 TMDs is further reflected in their pharmacological profiles. Both bind [^{3}H]SCH23390 with high affinity ($K_d = 0.35$ nM) and basically share the same rank order of ligand potency with two notable differences: the human D_5 receptor shows a 5-fold lower affinity for the antagonist (+) butaclamol and a 10-fold higher affinity for DA. Furthermore, the two receptors are distinguishable at the second messenger level: the D_5 receptor is able to stimulate adenylyl cyclase at dopamine concentrations which are 30-fold lower than required by the D_1 receptor in the same A293 cell line. Attempts to determine the distribution of mRNA corresponding to HGRI-4 by in situ hybridization have been difficult due to its very low abundance.

When HGRI-6 and 8 were transiently expressed in either COS-7 or A293 cells there was no detectable [^{3}H]SCH23390 binding or coupling to cAMP, further supporting the conclusion that they are D_5 pseudogenes. The existence of two nearly identical genes that contain in-frame stop codons raises the question of their origin. In order to begin an evolutionary study of this small gene family, we performed Southern blotting experiments on human and rat genomic DNA. Our results indicate that the duplication of the human D_5 gene was a fairly recent event because the rat genome contains only one copy. Current studies are focusing on the possible role of this gene in human disease.

Acknowledgements

We would like to thank Yuan Zhang, Claudia Bouvier, Qun-Yong Zhou, Robert A. Johnson, Lee Allen, James R. Bunzow and John Salon for excellent technical assistance and advice. This research was supported by grants from the Scottish Rite Foundation and NIH Grant MH45614.

References

1. Andersen PH et al. (1990) Trends Physiol. Sci. 11: 231.
2. Zhou Q-Y et al. (1990) Nature 347: 76.
3. Bunzow JR et al. (1989) Nature 336: 783.
4. Van Tol HHM et al. (1991) Nature 350: 610.
5. Grandy DK et al. (1991) (submitted).
6. Sambrook J, Fritsch EF and Maniatis T (1989) Molecular Cloning: A Laboratory Manual. Cold Spring Harbor Laboratory, Cold Spring Harbor, New York.
7. Grandy DK et al. (1989) Proc. Natl. Acad. Sci. U.S.A. 86: 9762.
8. Sokoloff P et al. (1990) Nature 347: 146.

© 1991 Elsevier Science Publishers B.V. All rights reserved.
Biological Psychiatry, Volume 2. G. Racagni et al., editors.

The "candidate gene" approach to the genetics of schizophrenia and other psychoses

Enrico Smeraldi and Fabio Macciardi
Istituto Scientifico H. San Raffaele, Department of Neurosciences, University of Milan, School of Medicine, via L. Prinetti 29, 20127 Milan, Italy

The past decade has been witness to technical developments in molecular biology which have greatly increased our understanding of the genetic bases for many human diseases. Unfortunately, complex disorders such as psychiatric diseases are still in a sort of "limbo". Even though it is now generally acknowledged that genetics plays a major role in the development of most psychiatric disorders, no specific gene defect has been identified for any disease; with the possible exception of Alzheimer's [1] and Huntington's diseases [2], which are characterized by a Mendelian pattern of transmission.

Complex disorders, such as schizophrenia, are plagued by a large number of factors that affect the successful application of a simple genetic approach, i.e. from the definition of a true phenotype to the detection of a reliable mode of transmission. Therefore, it seems that in psychiatry we are still one step away from applying the tools that molecular biology offers; and the main task for most disorders, and especially for the group of schizophrenic psychoses, is still to identify the putative locus (or loci) responsible for those forms of the disease representing an inherited condition. In simplified terms, this requires the use of a traditional approach, that is demonstrating a linkage for a major locus controlling for the disease to a marker locus (or to some marker loci) on a defined chromosomal location.

Linkage analysis in psychiatry today can be facilitated by the use of DNA probes which increase the number of polymorphic loci which can be studied. However, several pitfalls should be noted [3].

The hypothesis

Compared to a random scan of the genome in searching for a gene(s) causing schizophrenia, a more appealing strategy is to examine a disease candidate gene. Focusing on a candidate gene has several advantages [4]; however, given the large number of genes expressed in the brain, it also requires a strong a priori hypothesis for a particular gene to be considered as a good candidate. In regard to schizophrenia, it has been known for a long time that the dopaminergic (DA) system is probably involved in the pathophysiology of the disease, in particular, the DRD_2

gene [5] is of great interest since its protein derivative, the D_2 receptor, binds neuroleptics. At present, the DA hypothesis for schizophrenia is even more complex, since recently other DA receptor genes have been cloned in addition to the classic D_1 [6] and D_2 [5] subtypes. The D_3 [7], D_4 [8] and D_5 [9] genes share a high degree of similarity with D_2 and D_1, but nonetheless are different genes with different chromosomal locations as well as different biochemical and pharmacological profiles.

Our aim is to test the DA hypothesis for schizophrenia, controlling for a linkage between a hypothesized susceptibility locus for schizophrenia and any DA receptor gene for which genetic information is available, i.e. D_1, D_2 and D_4.

To minimize sources of uncontrolled bias as a result of pooling together data derived from different origins, we have chosen to investigate only one extended pedigree (herein referred to as F05), which is large enough to accept or refuse the linkage hypothesis in simulation studies. The family consists of more than 150 living subjects and we have complete information and medical records for about 300 additional subjects dating back to the mid-19th century. Family F05 derives from a well defined region in northern Italy and at the present state of the investigation, schizophrenia is the only mental disorder segregating in such a way as to suggest a genetic pattern. A few other psychiatric diagnoses are present in some distant relatives of the original proband, but their frequency is very close to the general population estimates for those diseases (alcoholism and major depression, recurrent) suggesting that they represent a chance finding in this family. Following the suggestions recently proposed for linkage investigation in psychiatric disorders [10], we considered only patients diagnosed as schizophrenic according to DSM III-R criteria [11]. Only a few members of the family have been typed to date and consequently the present data must be considered as preliminary.

SEGREGATION ANALYSIS

Results

MODEL	d	t	q	H	Z	2lnLik
NO TRANSM.	(0)	(0)	(0)	(0)	(0)	-106.35
SML:						
RECESSIVE	(0)	7.5	.02	(0)	(0)	- 0.75
DOMINANT	(1)	4.9	.002	(0)	(0)	- 10.53
ADDITIVE	(0.5)	10.3	.01	(0)	(0)	- 10.75
MENDELIAN	0.781	5.4	.002	(0)	(0)	- 10.53
POLIGENIC	(0)	(0)	(0)	1	.002	- 12.71
UNRESTRICTED	0.25	3.6	.02	(0)	(0)	- 18.78
MIXED	0.59	9.2	.098	.76	(0.4)	- 4.21

Family F05

Fig. 1. Segregation analysis.

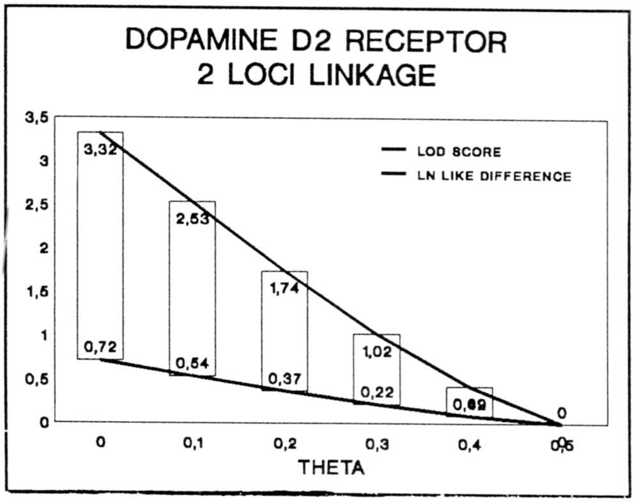

Fig. 2. 2-Locus linkage model.

Results and Conclusion

The segregation analysis of the family generated a best fit for 2 alternative models: a single major locus (SML) recessive (model 1) and a mixed model (model 2 – Fig. 1). Testing for the presence of linkage between the D_1, D_2 and D_4 receptor genes in turn, under conventional linkage analysis (i.e. using model 1 or a slightly modified version of model 2) with a Mendelian SML for the affection locus, yielded negative (for D_4 and D_1) or inconclusive results (for D_2), either when we used a pairwise or a multipoint strategy. The point has been made, however, that simple genetic models, even including incomplete penetrance and sporadic cases, generally do not fit the family data for psychiatric disorders and it has also been suggested that a likely model for schizophrenia is a 2- or 3-locus system acting epistatically [12].

When we repeated the analysis using an oligogenic 2-locus model [13] to describe susceptibility for schizophrenia, we did not find any significant deviation from the lod score values generated by conventional analysis. We were about to improve the fit for all the markers tested.

References

1. St George-Hyslop P et al. (1990) Nature 347: 194–196.
2. Gilliam TC et al. (1987) Science 238: 950–952.
3. Giuffra LA and Kidd KK (1990) Int. Rev. Psychiatry 1: 231–242.
4. Kennedy JL and Giuffra LA (1991) In: Tamminga CA and Schulz SC (eds.) Schizophrenia Research, Vol. 1. Raven Press, New York, pp. 21–29.

5. Grandy DK, Marchionni MA, Makam A, Stofko RE, Alfano M, Frothingham L, Fisher JB, Burke-Howie KJ, Bunzow JB, Server AC and Civelli O (1989) Proc. Natl. Acad. Sci. U.S.A. 86: 9762–9766.
6. Zhou QY, Grandy DK, Thambi L, Kushner JA, Van Tol HHM, Cone R, Pribnow D, Salon J, Bunzow J and Civelli O (1990) Nature 347: 76–80.
7. Sokoloff O, Giros B, Martres MP, Bouthenet ML and Schwartz JC (1990) Nature 347: 146–151.
8. Van Tol HHM, Bunzow JR, Guan HC, Sunahara RK, Seeman P, Niznik HB and Civelli O (1991) Nature 350: 610–614.
9. Sunahara RK, Guan HC, O'Dowd BF, Seeman P, Laurier LG, Ng G, George SR, Torchia J, Van Tol HHM and Niznik HB (1991) Nature 350: 614–619.
10. Grandy DK, Zhang Y, Bouvier C, Zhou QY, Johnson RA, Allen LA, Buck K, Bunzow JR, Salon J and Civelli O (1991) Proc. Natl. Acad. Sci. U.S.A. (in press).
11. Weeks DE, Brzustowicz L, Squires-Wheeler E, Cornblatt B, Lehner T, Stefanovich M, Bassett A, Gilliam TC, Ott J and Erlenmeyer-Kimling L (1990) Schizophr. Bull. 16: 673–686.
12. American Psychiatric Association: Diagnostic and Statistical Manual for Mental Disorders, 3rd Edition, Revised (1987) A.P.A., Washington.
13. Risch N (1990) Am. J. Hum. Genet. 46: 222–228.
14. Lathrop GM and Ott J (1990) Am. J. Hum. Genet. 47: A188 (Abstr.).

© 1991 Elsevier Science Publishers B.V. All rights reserved.
Biological Psychiatry, Volume 2. G. Racagni et al., editors.

Use of PCR and DGGE to detect possible genetic variations in dopamine D_2 receptor gene: A preliminary report

Marco Catalano, Maria Nobile, Emanuela Novelli, Cecilia Marino and Enrico Smeraldi

Istituto Scientifico H. San Raffaele, Dipartimento di Scienze Neuropsichiche, Universita' degli Studi di Milano, Cattedra di Clinica Psichiatrica III, Via Prinetti 29, I-20127, Milan, Italy

Introduction

The role of dopamine in the pathophysiology of schizophrenia is one of the most investigated topics in psychobiology. In particular, a dysfunction in D_2 receptor-mediated signaling from midbrain to limbic and/or cortical regions was supposed to contribute to this psychiatric disorder, even if there are data against this and other hypotheses [1].

The D_2 receptor is 443 amino acid residues long and contains seven transmembrane spanning regions (TM1–TM7) which have come to be recognized as hallmarks of all G-protein coupled receptors [2]. The D_2 transcript undergoes alternative splicing of an exon (exon X) to produce two mRNAs whose translation products differ in 29 amino acids (called D_{2A} and D_{2B}) [3,4]. The additional amino acids may be functionally important, because they are inserted in the third cytoplasmic loop which is believed to be involved in G-protein coupling [5,6]. It displays the highest sequence variability between different receptors and their subtypes [7,8]. Intracellular signalling mediated by D_2 includes inhibition of adenylate cyclase activity [9], inhibition of phosphatidylinositol turnover [10], increase in K^+ channel activity [11] and inhibition of $[Ca^{2+}]i$ mobilization [12]. To account for such diverse effects the evidence from biochemical studies suggests that signal transduction of D_2 receptors is mediated by at least 2 different G proteins, G_i and G_o [13–15] with the possible involvement of receptor heterogeneity; so there is the possibility that the 2 molecular forms of the D_2 receptor interact with different signal transduction pathways mediated by the G-protein. These findings give rise to the intriguing possibility that an imbalance between the two receptor forms caused by inappropriate splicing of the primary D_2 receptor gene transcript may contribute to the pathogenesis of schizophrenia.

So we set up a study on D_2 receptor gene looking for mutations in the 3 exons coding for the third cytoplasmic loop in 3 groups of subjects.

Materials and Methods

Sample

Thirty one psychiatric out- and inpatients (14 men and 17 women) aged 20–63 years, fulfilling the DSM III-R [16] criteria for schizophrenia and 33 patients (12 men and 21 women) aged 22–66 years, fulfilling the criteria for delusional disorder were included in this study with the aim to gain more information, because of the well-known differences, also in neuroleptic response, between these 2 pathologies which, however, have some symptoms in common [17]. As a control group we used 26 healthy subjects (15 men and 11 women) aged 24–46 years. All subjects were unrelated.

Procedure

DNA was extracted according to the method proposed by M.B. Johns and J.E. Paulus-Thomas [18]. The first exon considered in our study (exon 5) was amplified in a Violet Biostar thermal cycler in 50 μl reaction containing 500 ng DNA and using a GeneAmp kit (Perkin-Elmer-Cetus). The primers used for PCR were 5'-GGTCCTGGAAGGACATGAAT-3' and 5'-CTCTTGGTAATGGTTAGGTG-3'. After an initial incubation at 95°C for 5 min, 35 cycles were carried out at 94°C for 60 s, 56°C for 30 s, 72°C for 30 s, followed by an incubation at 72°C for 10 min and at 25°C for a further 10 min, then 10 μl of amplified samples were electrophoresed on a 1.4 % agarose gel to test the correct amplification. Another 10 μl of amplified samples were electrophoresed on a 7% denaturing gradient polyacrylamide gel according to standard methods [19–21]. One amplified fragment was initially screened on a perpendicular gradient gel with a concentration of denaturant ranging from 0–80%. Subsequently, a narrower range of denaturant concentration (i.e. 30–60%) was determined for parallel gels on the basis of the melting point as determined from the perpendicular gel (44% approx.).

Results and Discussion*

This initial screening revealed no mutation either in patients or in healthy controls. Although these data are preliminary and limited to a single exon, we consider this approach useful all the same in the complex field of biological psychiatry, as we are of the opinion that even negative results may be informative in this context. Although DGGE has been reported to detect only 50–95% of all base substitutions [19], it makes a rapid screening of large samples easily feasible. Moreover, DGGE proves extremely powerful when combined with PCR [22,23] thus allowing more careful further investigations (for example, direct sequencing of PCR products in case of detection of mutations to characterize them).

*Note: Due to space problems, photographs of gels are not included. They are available upon request.

Acknowledgements

We gratefully acknowledge Prof. Francesca Andronico and her coworkers for their friendly and invaluable suggestions and help.

References

1. Brunello N, Lucca A, Catalano M and Racagni G (1990) In: Racagni G and Smeraldi E (eds.) Farmaci Nella Terapia Antipsicotica. Edi Ermes, Milan, Italy, pp. 51–64.
2. Dohlman HG, Caron MG and Lefkovitz RJ (1987) Biochemistry 26: 2657–2664.
3. Dal Toso R, Sommer B, Ewert M, Herb A, Pritchett DB, Bach A, Shivers BD and Seeburg PH (1989) EMBO J. 8: 4025–4034.
4. Grandy DK, Marchionni MA, Makam H, Stofko ME, Alfano M, Frotingham L, Fischer JB, Burke-Howie KJ, Bunzow JR, Server AC and Civelli O (1989) Proc. Natl. Acad. Sci. U.S.A. 86: 9762–9766.
5. Kobilka BK, Kobilka TS, Daniel K, Regan JW, Caron MG and Lefkowitz RJ (1988) Science 240: 1310–1316.
6. O'Dowd BF, Hantowich M, Regan JW, Leader WM, Caron MG and Lefkowitz RJ (1988) J. Biol. Chem. 263: 15985–15992.
7. Kubo T, Maeda A, Sugimoto K, Akiba I, Mikami A, Takahashi H, Haga T, Haga K, Ichiyama A, Kangawa K, Matsuo H, Hirose T and Numa S (1986) FEBS Lett. 209: 367–372.
8. Peralta EG, Ashkenazy A, Winslow JW, Smith DH, Ramachandran J and Capon DJ (1987) EMBO J. 6: 3923–3928.
9. Creese I, Sibley DR, Hamblin MW and Leff SE (1983) Rev. Neurosci. 6: 43–71.
10. Vallar I and Meldolesi J (1989) Trends Pharmacol. Sci. 10: 74–77.
11. Lacey MG, Mercury MB and North RA (1987) J. Physiol. 392: 397–416.
12. Bigornia L, Suozzo M, Ryan KA, Napp D and Schneider AS (1988) J. Neurochem. 51: 999–1006.
13. Senagles SE, Benovic JL, Amlaiky N, Unson C, Milligan G, Vinitsky R, Spiegel AM and Caron MG (1987) J. Biol. Chem. 262: 4860–4867.
14. Ohara K, Haga K, Bernstein G, Haga T, Ichiyama A and Ohara K (1988) Mol. Pharmacol. 33: 290–296.
15. Elazar Z, Siegel G and Fuchs S (1989) EMBO J. 8: 2353–2357.
16. DSM III-R: Diagnostic and Statistical Manual of Mental Disorders, Third Edn., Revised (1987) The American Psychiatric Association, Washington D.C.
17. Kendler KS (1980) Arch. Gen. Psychiatry 37: 699–706.
18. Johns MB Jr and Paulus-Thomas JE (1989) Anal. Biochem. 180: 276–278.
19. Myers RM, Fischer SG, Maniatis T and Lerman LS (1985) Nucleic Acid Res. 13: 3111–3129.
20. Myers RM, Sheffield VC and Cox DR (1988) In: Davies K (ed.) Genome Analysis: A Practical Approach. IRL Press, Oxford, pp. 95–139.
21. Sheffield VC, Cox DR and Myers RM (1990) In: Innis MA, Gelfand DH, Sninsky JJ and Thomas JW (eds.) PCR Protocols: A Guide to Methods and Applications. Academic Press, San Diego, pp. 206–218.
22. Fodde R (1983) In: Gasperini P and Pignatti F (eds.) Oltre la PCR: Nuove Metodologie di Analisi Genetica nella Ricerca Biomedica. University of Verona, Verona, Italy pp. 16–18.
23. Sheffield VC, Cox DR, Lerman LS and Myers RM (1989) Proc. Natl. Acad. Sci. U.S.A. 86: 232–236.

© 1991 Elsevier Science Publishers B.V. All rights reserved.
Biological Psychiatry, Volume 2. G. Racagni et al., editors.

Chromosome 5q11-q13 and pseudo-autosomal region in schizophrenia

T. d'Amato, D. Campion, G. Waksman, O. Sabate, M. Jay, P. Gorwood, M. Leboyer, F. Clerget-Darpoux and J. Mallet

Département de Génétique Moléculaire, Laboratoire de Neurobiologie Cellulaire et Moléculaire, CNRS UPR 0023, 1 Av. de la Terrasse, 91198 Gif sur Yvette, France

Introduction

Twin and adoption studies support the assumption that genetic factors contribute to the etiology of schizophrenia, but analyses of segregation have failed to demonstrate a clear mode of inheritance of the disease. We report here two linkage studies on chromosome 5q11-q13, and on the pseudo-autosomal region of sex chromosomes.

Chromosome 5q11-q13

The report of a chromosomal abnormality in a man and his nephew both suffering from schizophrenia first implicated a short region of the long arm of chromosome 5: 5q11-q13 [1]. This observation was followed by linkage studies using RFLP markers. Sherrington et al. [2] reported a linkage between the DOMSSF phenotype (schizophrenia, schizophrenia spectrum disorders, and other psychiatric diagnoses) and the two loci D5S76 and D5S39. The DOMSS phenotype (schizophrenia and schizophrenia spectrum disorders) also provided linkage, but to a lesser degree. However, all subsequent reports have failed to replicate this study [3–6].

Method

We have identified 28 multiplex families of schizophrenics. Subjects provided informed consent and blood sample for establishment of lymphoblastoid cell lines and DNA extraction. Paternity was confirmed by histocompatibility antigens analysis. Subjects were evaluated by trained clinicians using the French translation of the SADS-LA. Phenotype was defined by the DOMSSF and the DOMSS models previously described. We studied the inheritance of 3 RFLP markers. Locus D5S76 was defined by TaqI polymorphisms detected by Southern hybridization by the probe 599Ha. Loci D5S39 and D5S78 were defined by MspI polymorphisms respectively detected by probes 153Ra and 798Rb.

Table 1. Two-point lod scores between DOMSSF and markers 5q11-q13

Probes	Recombination fraction				
	0.00	0.10	0.20	0.30	0.40
599Ha	–9.38	–1.75	–0.32	0.06	0.06
153Ra	–7.64	–1.80	–0.53	–0.07	–0.02
798Rb	–1.56	0.33	0.46	0.29	0.07

Results

Table 1 presents the results obtained with the DOMSSF phenotype, under the parameters utilized by Sherrington et al. [2]. They exclude a locus of susceptibility for schizophrenia up to about 10 centiMorgans from loci D5S76 and D5S39. Under the DOMSS model, the lod score values are even lower.

Our results thus provide no evidence for a linkage between schizophrenia and markers from 5q11-q13. These results are in agreement with those of previous reports. Taken together, all the data suggest that if a locus exists within the long arm of chromosome 5, it concerns only a small sample of cases. However, another possibility remains, that the first result may have occurred by pure chance.

Pseudo-autosomal region of sex chromosomes

On the basis of association studies between sexual aneuploidies and schizophrenia, sex chromosomes are candidates for a locus of susceptibility for schizophrenia. According to the observation that schizophrenic siblings are more often of the same sex than of the opposite sex, it has been suggested that this locus could lie within the pseudo-autosomal region of sex chromosomes [7]. A recent sibpair analysis plainly supports this hypothesis [8]. We present here a preliminary replication study.

Method

Thirty-eight multiplex families of schizophrenic have been identified as previously described. A subsample of 33 sibships has been analysed. Criteria for inclusion of sibships in the present study implied at least two members were affected with a DSM III-R diagnosis of schizophrenia, schizoaffective disorder, schizophreniform disorder, or schizotypal personality. The sibships included 18 pairs, 13 trios and 2 quartets of affected siblings. We have studied the DXYS14 locus defined by the probe 29C1. The statistical analysis was performed using the affected sibpairs method [9]. By contrast to the lod score analysis, this method does not imply the specification of unknown epidemiologic parameters such as penetrance, age of

Table 2. Sex composition and IBD scores of affected sibships

	No. of sibships	Sex composition	Possible IBD scores	No. of times each score was observed
Pairs	18	5 MM	0	4
		4 FF	1	6
		9 MF	2	8
Trios	13	4 MMM	2	5
		4 MMF	3	7
		5 MFF	4	1
Quartets	2	1 FFFF	4	1
		1 MMFF	5	1
			6	0

onset or mode of inheritance of the disease. If a gene of susceptibility for the disease is linked to the marker, affected siblings are more likely to be of the same genotype at this locus than is to be expected by pure chance (null hypothesis).

Results

Table 2 presents IBD scores. The t statistic is 1.718 and rejects the null hypothesis at $P < 0.05$. When our data are pooled with those of Collinge et al. [8], $t = 2.554$ ($P < 0.01$). These results are consistent with the pseudo-autosomal hypothesis.

The recombination rate between the DXYS14 locus and the sex locus has been estimated to be 50% in male meiosis [10]. It is thus theoretically not linked to the sex. However, a weak linkage between these loci could not be excluded. This notion is of importance, because even if a weak linkage exists, the above results could be interpreted as a bias related to an excess of same-sex affected sibships. Indeed, in a clinical survey of 38 multiplex families, we found an excess of same-sex over opposite-sex affected sibships (Gorwood et al., in preparation). However, in the present subsample we failed to observe such an excess. In order to minimize the possibility of a bias, we have analysed 21 same-sex pairs discordant for the disease. The distribution is very close to the expected random one for a locus not linked to the sex, and the application of the sib-pair method provides the expected non-significant result for a locus not linked to the sex. When these 21 pairs are pooled with the 49 from Collinge et al. [8], the global result remains non-significant.

This first replication of a linkage between DXYS14 and schizophrenia increases the validity of the pseudoautosomal hypothesis. We are currently testing this hypothesis in extensive pedigrees with other probes linked to 29C1.

Acknowledgements

We are grateful to J. Weissenbach and C. Petit for providing probes and advice, and to the Fondation pour la Recherche Medicale for financial support.

References

1. Basset AS, McGillivray BC, Jones BD et al. (1988) Lancet i (8589): 799–801.
2. Sherrington R, Brynjolfsson J, Petursson H et al. (1988) Nature 336: 164–167.
3. Kennedy JL, Giuffra LA, Moises HW et al. (1988) Nature 336: 167–170.
4. St.Clair D, Blackwood D, Muir W et al. (1989) Nature 339: 305–309.
5. Detera-Wadleigh S, Goldin LR, Sherrington R et al. (1989) Nature 340: 391–393.
6. McGuffin P, Sargeant M, Hetti G et al. (1990) Am. J. Psychiatry 47: 524–535.
7. Crow TJ (1988) Br. J. Psychiatry 153: 675–683.
8. Collinge J, Delisi LE, Boccio A et al. (1991) Br. J. Psychiatry 158: 624–629.
9. Green JR and Woodrow JC (1977) Tissue Antigens 9: 31–35.
10. Brown WRA (1988) EMBO J. 7: 2377–2385.

© 1991 Elsevier Science Publishers B.V. All rights reserved.
Biological Psychiatry, Volume 2. G. Racagni et al., editors.

X-Linked mental retardation: Update 1991

Giovanni Neri and Fiorella Gurrieri
Istituto di Genetica Umana, Facoltà di Medicina "A. Gemelli", Università Cattolica, Rome, Italy

Introduction

There is an approximately 25% excess of males among mentally retarded individuals [1], due to the existence of several X-linked mental retardation (XLMR) syndromes, caused by X-linked mutant genes and manifesting almost exclusively in males [2].

By far, the best known and most prevalent of these XLMR syndromes is the fragile X (fra(X)) syndrome, also known as the Martin-Bell syndrome [3]. Its phenotype is characterized by long, narrow face with prominent forehead and mandible, large ears, macro-orchidism, connective tissue dysplasia, congenital hypotonia and mental retardation. Cytogenetically the syndrome is characterized by the presence of the fragile site FRAXA at band Xq27.3 in a variable proportion of peripheral lymphocytes cultivated in folic acid-free culture media [4]. The prevalence of affected males in the general population has been estimated at about 1/1,300 [5] and that in the population of mentally retarded individuals at about 1/20 [6].

It has been calculated that the fra(X) syndrome accounts for about half of the cases of XLMR. The other half is represented by a host of different conditions, each one caused by a distinct mutant gene, resulting in a characteristic phenotype. This report deals with these letter syndromes from a clinical and genetic standpoint.

Heterogeneity of non-fra(X) XLMR syndromes

We have recently reviewed this subject [7], and listed 38 XLMR syndromes, excluding the fra(X) syndrome and other conditions in which: a) mental retardation is the consequence of an inborn error of metabolism; b) mental retardation appears to be accessory with respect to the prevailing disorder, such as in Duchenne muscular distrophy and in several forms of X-linked spastic paraplegia; c) mental retardation is a component manifestation of syndromes caused by X-linked dominant mutant genes, lethal in the hemizygote.

The 38 conditions, in which mental retardation seems to be the primary element, have been subdivided into "syndromal" and "non-syndromal", depending on the existence of a recognizable pattern of minor anomalies and/or malformations or lack thereof. Their number has now increased to 41, following the report of 3 additional families, segregating multiple congenital anomalies/mental retardation syndromes, 2 in which the X-linkage is certain [8,9] the other in which it is possible [10]. Most likely this list is far from complete, as testified by the ever-increasing number of new syndromes reported in the literature.

Computer programs such as that recently described by Arena and Lubs [11] can be of great practical value for the correct diagnosis of known and for the definition of new syndromes.

XLMR genes

Of the 40 or so XLMR syndromes defined above, 17 including the fra(X) syndrome are caused by mutant genes whose loci have been regionally mapped onto the X chromosome [7]. Most of these assignments should be considered as tentatively based as they are in single-family studies, with lod scores of less than 3. More data are needed, and therefore the report of new families should be encouraged.

Although the map of the XLMR genes should still be considered incomplete and provisional, an interesting trend is already visible, i.e. a tendency of the assigned loci to map in the pericentromeric area and around the 2 telomeres of the X chromosome. If this is due to chance or to a real clustering of mental retardation genes in discrete areas of the chromosome is too early to tell. Progress is needed in this direction, and also towards the cloning of these genes. Cloning is the first step in a process leading, by reverse genetics, to the identification of the gene product and eventually to the understanding of the pathogenetic mechanisms involved in mental retardation.

Acknowledgement

This work was supported in part by the National Research Council of Italy, Contract No. 89.04207.04 to G.N.

References

1. Penrose LS (1938) Special Report Series No. 229. London Medical Research Council, London.
2. Lehrke RG (1972) Am. J. Ment. Defic. 76: 611–619.
3. Martin JP and Bell J (1943) J. Neurol. Psychiatry 6: 154–157.
4. Lubs HA (1969) Am. J. Hum. Genet. 21: 231–244.
5. Webb T, Bundey SE, Thake AI and Todd J (1986) Am. J. Med. Genet. 23: 573–580.
6. Sutherland GR (1985) Ann. Hum. Genet. 49: 153–161.
7. Neri G, Gurrieri F, Gal A and Lubs HA (1991) Am. J. Med. Genet. 38: 186–189.
8. Otto EB, Carpenter NJ and Proud VK (1990) Am. J. Hum. Genet. 47: A69.
9. de Cassia Stocco dos Santos R, de O Barreto OC, Nonoyama K, Castro NHC, Moura JW, Ferraz OP, Silva Veschio CC and Becak W (1991) Am. J. Med. Genet. 39: 133–136.
10. Sommer A (1990) Am. J. Med. Genet. 47: A78.
11. Arena JF and Lubs HA (1991) Am. J. Med. Genet. 38: 190–199.

© 1991 Elsevier Science Publishers B.V. All rights reserved.
Biological Psychiatry, Volume 2. G. Racagni et al., editors.

Psychiatric aspects in the fragile (X) form of mental retardation

U.G. Froster-Iskenius
Klinik für Frauenheilkunde und Geburtshilfe der Medizinischen Universitat zu Lubeck, Ratzeburger Allee 160, W-2400 Lubeck, Germany

The fragile X form of mental retardation can be distinguished from other forms of mental impairment by a fragile site at the long arm of the X chromosome at Xq27.3. This phenomenon was first described by Lubs [1] in 2 mentally retarded brothers. Sutherland [2] demonstrated that the expression of this cytogenetic marker depended on the composition of the culture medium in which the cells for cytogenetic analysis are grown. Low folate culture media or dihydrofolate reductase inhibitors (aminopterine or trimethoprim) are required and even then the fragile X can only be expressed in a proportion of cells [3].

The fragile X form of mental retardation is presently recognized as one of the most common forms of inherited mental retardation. Large epidemiological studies found a frequency of 1 in 1000 males and 0.6 in 1000 females [4,5]. The disorder segregates as an X-linked condition, but it shows marked distortion from classical X-linked recessive inheritance [6]. In classical X-linked recessive inheritance it can be expected that a heterozygous carrier mother randomly passes on her two X chromosomes. On average 1 in 2 of her sons could be expected to inherit the fragile X and 1 in 2 of her daughters could be a carrier. In fragile X families transmission of the trait through intellectually normal males has been described in many instances [6]. These normal male hemizygotes do not express the fragile site in cytogenetic testing and are of normal intelligence. In a large study [7] analyzing the segregation pattern, a reduced penetrance of the disorder of 80% was found for males. Furthermore, about 30% of heterozygous females are mentally impaired and express the fragile X [8]. Daughters of normal transmitting males, who are obligate heterozygotes, are almost never mentally retarded and only express the fragile site at very low levels in 1–2% of their cells. This distortion of inheritance is commonly known as the Sherman paradox and numerous hypotheses had been proposed to explain the situation. One recent hypothesis by Laird [9] postulates that the mutation results in an alteration of reactivation of this particular stretch of the X chromosome during oogenesis. If the imprinted X is passed on by a female, the defect will show in the male offspring who inherited the imprinted X, while the mutation could be passed on to the sons of this heterozygous carrier without clinical effect if the fragile X is not imprinted.

The use of DNA markers first focused on the factor IX gene (F9) which is localized proximal to the fragile site at Xq27.1. Further clusters of polymorphic DNA markers proximal and distal to the fragile X locus had been applied in studying families with fragile X [10]. Further DNA markers detect differences between affected and non-expressing hemizygotes [11].

The clinical phenotype in patients with fragile X syndrome undergoes age-specific changes: in the newborn no significant physical anomalies are obvious; however, a tendency towards increased birth-weight, length and head-circumference was noted. In infancy, mental retardation and behavioural anomalies become obvious. The major anomalies include generalized muscle hypotonia, hyperactivity, delayed speech with abnormal speech pattern. During adolescence in 50–60% of males macro-orchidism can be noted. The phenotype changes of the face become more apparent. In the adult patient the face is found to be somewhat oblong, with a prominent chin, and large, sometimes protruding ears [12].

While physical features had been studied intensively, the behavioural and psychological aspects of the disorder are less well understood. Autism was recognized in about 15% of children with fragile X [13]. Gillberg [14] found in a study of 66 autistic patients 25% with fragile X. In a clinico-neurological investigation among 39 hemizygous patients with fra(X) we recognized hyperactivity in 50%, short attention span in 59% and autism in 34% of the patients. Other behavioural anomalies in this group included bizarre behaviour, such as hand biting or odd attachment to objects and stereotypic mannerism [15].

If autism is part of the clinical spectrum of the syndrome features in fragile X syndrome in more severely affected individuals, the less affected heterozygotes could show other signs of psychiatric disturbances. Reiss [16] observed schizoid pattern in heterozytoges with fragile X. This is in agreement with other observations [17]. In an evaluation of psychiatric features and behavioural anomalies among 24 females from fragile X families using the SADS/LS, preliminary results show psychiatric anomalies in 50% of the fragile X heterozygotes, while no anomalies were noted in the controls. Behavioural abnormalities such as poor eye contact which are associated with the schizophrenia spectrum diagnosis were recognized in the heterozygotes with an IQ between 70 to 100, while in 1 family with above average IQ psychoses were found in 2 out of 3 heterozygotes. Mendlewicz et al. [18] found linkage with a polymorphic DNA marker at Xq28 and manic depressive illness, but father to son transmission occurred and thus ruled out X-linked inheritance. The observations in fragile X families at present show that there are families in which the fragile X mutation and psychiatric anomalies appear to be more than just coincidental. Further studies in heterozygotes with fragile X are necessary to clarify the relationship between fragile X and psychiatric anomalies.

References

1. Lubs HA (1969) Am. J. Hum. Genet. 21: 231–244.
2. Sutherland GR (1977) Science 197: 265–266.

3. Jacky PB, Ahuja YR, Anyane-Yeboa I, Breg WR, Carpenter NJ, Froster-Iskenius UG, Fryns JP, Glover TW, Gustavson KH, Hoegerman SF, Holmgren G, Howard-Peebles PN, Jenkins EC, Krawczun MS, Neri G, Pettigrew A, Schaap T, Schonberg SA, Shapiro LR, Spinner N, Steinbach P, Vianna-Morgante AM, Watson MS and Wilmot PL (1991) Am. J. Med. Genet. 38: 400–403.
4. Froster-Iskenius U, Felsch G, Schirren C and Schwinger E (1983) Hum. Genet. 63: 153–157.
5. Webb TP, Bundey SE, Thake AI and Todd J (1986) Am. J. Med. Genet. 23: 573–580.
6. Froster-Iskenius UG, McGillivray BC, Dill FJ, Hall JG and Herbst DS (1986) Am. J. Med. Genet. 23: 619–631.
7. Sherman SL, Jacobs PA, Morton NE, Froster-Iskenius UG, Howard-Peebles PN, Nielsen KB, Partington MW, Sutherland GR, Turner G and Watson M (1985) Hum. Genet. 69: 289–299.
8. Paul J, Froster-Iskenius U, Moje W and Schwinger E (1984) Hum. Genet. 66: 344–347.
9. Laird CD (1987) Genetics 117: 587–599.
10. Froster-Iskenius U, Patterson MN, Bell MV, Bloomfield J and Davies KE (1988) Quart. J. Med. New Ser. 69: 755–763.
11. Vincent A, Heitz D, Petit C, Kretz C, Oberlé J and Mandel JL (1991) Nature 349: 624–626.
12. Froster-Iskenius UG (1988) Focus MHL 5: 239–244.
13. Brown WT, Jenkins EC, Friedman E, Brooks J, Wiesniewski K, Raguthen S and French J (1982) J. Autism. Dev. Dis. 12: 303–308.
14. Gillberg C (1983) Br. J. Psychiatry 143: 256–260.
15. Vieregge P and Froster-Iskenius U (1989) J. Neurol. 236: 85–92.
16. Reiss AL, Feinstein C, Toomey KE, Goldsmith B, Rosenbaum K and Caruso MA (1986) Am. J. Med. Genet. 23: 393–401.
17. Froster-Iskenius U, Schwinger E, Weigert M and Fonatsch C (1982) Hum. Genet. 60: 278–280.
18. Mendlewicz J, Sevy S, Brocas H, Simon PN, Charon F, Legros S and Vassart G (1987) Lancet i: 1230–1232.

© 1991 Elsevier Science Publishers B.V. All rights reserved.
Biological Psychiatry, Volume 2. G. Racagni et al., editors.

Evidence that distinct regions on the X chromosome have a high concentration of genes causing mental retardation

C.E. Schwartz[1], H.A. Lubs[2], J.F. Arena[2] and R.E. Stevenson[1]

[1]Greenwood Genetic Center, 1 Gregor Mendel Circle, Greenwood, SC 29616; and [2]Department of Pediatrics, Genetics Division, The Mailman Center for Child Development, University of Miami School of Medicine, Box 016820, Miami, FL 33101, U.S.A.

The concept of X-linked mental retardation has continuously evolved over the last 50 years. Penrose [1], in 1938, first suggested that the more frequent occurrence of mental retardation in males was not due to the number of X-linked genes but to social factors. However, since the mid 1910s there have been many families described which clearly exhibit an X-linked pattern of inheritance of mental retardation. The best known of these are the families of Martin and Bell [2] and Allan et al. [3]. The former is now known to be representative of the fragile X syndrome [4]. Over the last two decades there has come the realization of the existence of a rather large number of different forms of X-linked mental retardation. It now appears that about a third of severe mental retardation in males may be caused by X-linked genes and X-linked mental retardation (XLMR) is presently considered the second most frequent cause of mental retardation in males, after Down Syndrome. Recent developments in molecular genetics and cytogenetics have assisted the mapping of more than 20 of these entities. This, in turn, has allowed us to develop a map of mental retardation genes on the X chromosome.

A survey of both the literature and McKusick's catalogue [5] reveals at least 41 X-linked disorders in which mental retardation appears as a primary characteristic. In most cases the retardation is of unknown pathogenesis. However, some of the entities have occurred in rather large families, facilitating the use of informative DNA markers spaced along the X chromosome to be used in standard linkage studies. Using this approach, our group, as well as others worldwide, have generated a substantial body of knowledge from which it is possible to draw some tentative conclusions.

Of the potential 41 entities 21 have been mapped with a degree of good certainty and their locations are visually represented on the X chromosome in Fig. 1. In order for the syndrome to be given a location, a lod score greater than 2 had to have been established for a DNA marker or more than one DNA marker in the same region gave lod scores greater than 1.5. This was done to insure that the localization is at least "highly suggested".

A review of Fig. 1 indicates that the mapped XLMR conditions are concentrated in 3 major regions of the X chromosome: Xp22-pter, Xcen-q21 and Xq27-qter. This may represent a bias of ascertainment. However, this would appear to be unlikely as the families have been chosen at random by various research groups.

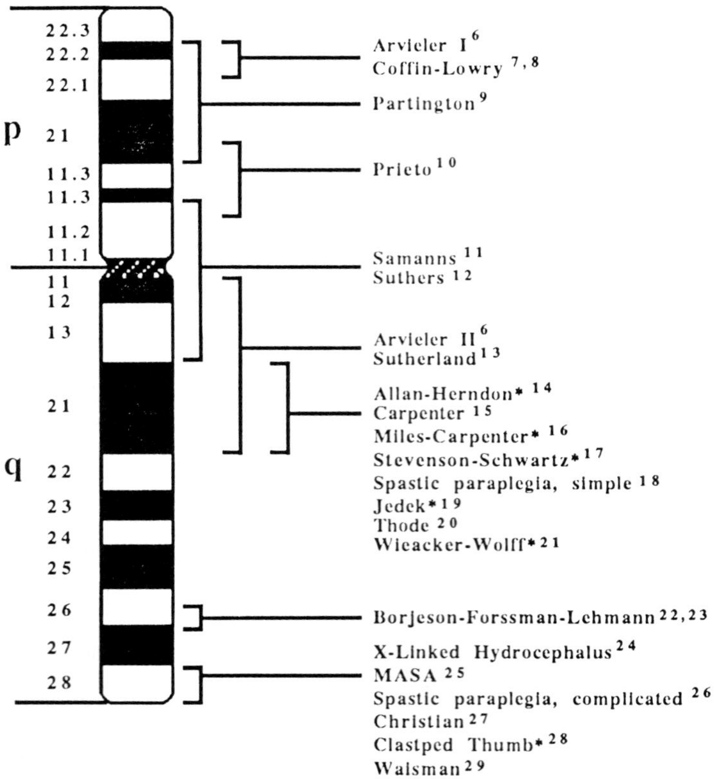

Fig. 1. Chromosomal location of mapped XLMR syndromes. *Entities presently being studied at the Greenwood Genetic Center.

Furthermore, the families are from different locations throughout the world. Explanations which cannot be ruled out are that some of the conditions may represent allelic forms of one gene defect (i.e. like Duchenne and Becker muscular dystrophy) or variations of a "contiguous gene syndrome". There is evidence for either of these possibilities when one examines the XLMR disorders linked to DXS52 in Xq28. MASA, X-linked hydrocephalus, clasped thumb and spastic paraplegia (complicated) share MR and clasped thumb as part of their phenotypes. The same possibility could exist for other entities exhibiting linkage to DNA markers in the same region (e.g. Samanns and Arvieler II in the X pericentric or Wieacker-Wolff and Allan-Herndon in Xq2l).

One approach which our group is taking to address these possibilities is to construct a high density linkage map of the Xq13-q21 region. Once the map is made, it will be possible to position the various entities along the map based on recombination between the disorders and the markers. This will allow us to see if some conditions fall within the same interval. Those that do will be explored further to determine if the conditions indeed represent phenotypic variants with the same mutation, allelic mutations or are components of a shared contiguous gene complex.

Acknowledgements

This work was supported by NIH Grant RO1HD26208 and the South Carolina Department of Mental Retardation.

References

1. Penrose LS (1938) Special Rep. Ser. No. 229, Med. Res. Council, London.
2. Marti JP and Bell J (1943) J. Neurol. Psychiatry 6: 154–157.
3. Allan W, Herndon CN and Dudley FC (1944) Am. J. Ment. Defic. 48: 325–334.
4. Richards BW (1981) J. Ment. Defic. Res. 25: 253–256.
5. McKusick VA (1990) Mendelian Inheritance in Man. Johns Hopkins University Press, Baltimore.
6. Arveiler B, Alembik Y, Hanauer A, Jacobs P, Tranebjaerg L, Mikkelsen M, Puissant L, Larget Piet L and Mandel JL (1988) Am. J. Med. Genet. 30: 473–484.
7. Partington MW, Mulley JC, Sutherland GR, Thode A and Turner G (1988) Am. J. Med. Genet. 30: 509–521.
8. Hanuer A, Alembik Y, Gilgenkrantz S, Mujica P, Nivelon-Chevallier A, Pembrey ME, Young ID and Mandel JL (1988) Am. J. Med. Genet. 30: 523–530.
9. Partington MW, Mulley JC, Sutherland GR, Hockey A, Thodes A and Turner G (1988) Am. J. Med. Genet. 30: 251–262.
10. Watty A, Prieto F, Beneyto M, Neugebauer M and Gel A (1991) Am. J. Med. Genet. 38: 234–239.
11. Samanns C, Albrecht R, Neugebauer M, Neri G and Gal A (1991) Am. J. Med. Genet. 38: 224–227.
12. Suthers GK, Turner G and Mulley JC (1988) Am. J. Med. Genet. 30: 485–491.
13. Sutherland GR, Gedeon AK, Haan EA, Woodroffe P and Mulley JC (1988) Am. J. Med. Genet. 30: 493–508.
14. Schwartz CE, Ulmer J, Brown A, Pancoast I, Goodman HO and Stevenson RE (1990) Am. J. Hum. Genet. 47: 446–453.
15. Carpenter NJ, Wajiri M, Leston J and Patil SR (1989) Am. J. Hum. Genet. 43: A139.
16. Miles JK and Carpenter NJ (1991) Am. J. Med. Genet. 38: 215–223.
17. Stevenson R, May M, Arena F, Lubs H and Schwartz C (1991) Am. J. Hum. Genet. (in press).
18. Goldblatt J, Ballo R, Sachs B and Moosa A (1989) Clin. Genet. 35: 116–120.
19. Jedele KB, Michels VV, Wagner KV, Schaid DJ and Thibodeau SN (1990) Am. J. Hum. Genet. 47: A62.
20. Thode A, Partington MW, Yip M-Y, Chapman C, Richardson VF and Turner G (1988) Am. J. Med. Genet. 30: 239–250.
21. Wieacker P, Wolff G and Wienker TF (1987) Am. J. Med. Genet. 28: 245–253.
22. Turner G, Gedeon A, Mulley J, Sutheriand G, Rae J, Power K and Arthur I (1989) Am. J. Med. Genet. 34: 463–469.
23. Mathews KD, Ardinger HH, Nishimura DY, Buetow KH, Murray JC and Bartley JA (1989) J. Med. Genet. 34: 470–474.
24. Willems PJ, Kijkstra I, Van der Auwera BJ, Vits L, Coucke P, Raeymaekers P et al. (1900) Genomics 8: 367–370.
25. Winter RM, Davies RE, Bell MV, Huson SM and Patterson MN (1989) Hum. Genet. 82: 367–370.

26. Kenwrick S, Ionasescu V, Ionasescu G, Searby C, King A, Dubowitz M and Davies KE (1986) Hum. Genet. 73: 264–266.
27. Dlouhy SR, Christian JC, Haines JL, Couneally PM and Nodes ME (1987) Hum. Genet. 75: 136–139.
28. Willems PJ, Dijkstra I, Van der Auwers BJ, Vits L, Coucke PJ, Raejmaekers P, Van Broeckhoven C and Dumon JE (1990) Am. J. Hum. Genet. 45: A167.
29. Gregg RG, Metzenberg AB, Hogan K, Seghou G and Laxova R (1991) Genomics 9: 701–706.

© 1991 Elsevier Science Publishers B.V. All rights reserved.
Biological Psychiatry, Volume 2. G. Racagni et al., editors.

XX Males and psychosis

Shinichiro Nanko
Department of Psychiatry, Teikyo University School of Medicine, 2-11-1, Kaga, Itabashi, Tokyo, Japan

Introduction

XX-males are characterized by a male phenotype with a female karyotype 46,XX. Since the first reports in 1964 of males with the karyotype 46,XX [1,2], more than 150 cases have been described.

The incidence of 46,XX males among newborn boys has been estimated to be 1 per 220,000 [3,4] or 1 per 250,000 (Emery and Rimon, 1983), while the prevalence of 46,XX males has been estimated at about 1 in 450,000 males [5].

In 1981, Nanko reported the first case of XX males with psychosis. This case was found during an X chromatin survey among 4,543 male inpatients in Japanese mental hospitals [6]. After this report, 2 XX male cases with psychosis were described, one by Müller and Endres [7] and another by Ichikawa et al. [8]. Here we investigate the psychiatric features of the three cases reported and discuss the etiological relationship between XX male and psychosis.

Psychiatric features

Tables 1 and 2 show the psychiatric findings of these 3 cases. All cases were diagnosed as suffering from schizophrenia or schizophrenia-like psychosis. Two of the authors [7,8] found that the physical and psychiatric features of XX males were indistinguishable from those of XYY males.

Table 1. Psychiatric findings in 3 XX males

Case No.	Age (years)	Age of onset (years)	Total I.Q.	Verbal I.Q.	Perform. I.Q.	Diagnosis	Author
1	67	34	72	68	75	Schizophrenia-like psychosis	Nanko, 1981
2	27	27	84	72	95	Schizophrenia-paranoid type (DSM III)	Müller and Endres, 1987
3	52	28	–	–	–	Schizophrenia-like psychosis	Ichikawa et al., 1989

Table 2. Psychiatric findings in 3 XX males

Case No.	Psychiatric findings
1	Delusion of persecution, delusion of reference, auditory hallucination, loosening of association
2	Delusion of persecution, auditory hallucination, influenced act, formal thought disorder
3	Delusion of persecution, delusion of reference, auditory hallucination, monologue

Discussion and Conclusion

Psychoses have frequently been reported in patients with abnormal sex chromosome constitutions, for example, schizophrenia or schizophrenia-like psychosis in XYY males, XXX females or XYY males, or paranoid psychosis in XYY males. Based on an X and Y chromatin survey among 7,974 inpatients in mental hospitals, Yanko insisted on an association of mental disorders with supernumerary X chromosomes but not with supernumerary Y chromosomes [6].

Regarding psychiatric conditions in 46,XX males, Sørensen et al. [4] reported the psychiatric features of 8 XX males found among the general population. All cases showed no psychopathological traits, except for one who had neurotic symptoms. According to de la Chapelle [9], an X chromatin screening revealed no XX males among 21,252 males who were mentally retarded or in mental hospitals. The prevalence rate (1/4,543) determined by Nanko [10] is 5 times higher than the expected rate (1/22,000) according to Sørensen et al. [4], but the difference is far from significant. Hence, the coincidence of XX male constitution and psychosis could be merely a chance phenomenon, and it has not been established whether the risk of psychosis increased or decreased in XX males, as a whole.

Recently, Crow [11] proposed a pseudoautosomal hypothesis on functional psychosis. XX males with psychosis are quite interesting with special reference to this hypothesis.

In XX males, the testis determining factor (TDF) on the Y chromosome has been transferred to the X chromosome. TDF is considered to be located to the border of pseudoautosomal region (PAR), where in male meiosis, a single obligatory crossing over takes place. If the point of crossing over on Yp happens to occur proximal to TDF, there would be an X chromosome with TDF. On Xp, crossing over can occur either proximal to MIC2 or distal to MIC2 in PAR. In the former case, both the paternal X and paternal Y copies of this region are inherited and hence there is partial trisomy of PAR.

There are 2 types of XX males phenotypically. One is XX males with psychosis as reported here, and the other is XX males without psychosis as reported by Sørensen et al [4]. If all XX males with psychosis show the former case, while all XX males without psychosis show the latter case, it is evident that trisomy of these regions is involved in the development of psychosis. This notion also explains the finding that the psychiatric features of XX males were indistinguishable from those of XXY males, who also have trisomy of PAR.

Therefore, it is worth trying to find the point of crossing over of XX males with psychosis and without psychosis.

References

1. Chapelle A de la, Hortling H, Niemi M and Wennstrom J (1964) Acta Med. Scand. (Suppl. 412) 175: 25–38.
2. Court Brown WM, Harnden DG, Jacobs PA, Maclean N and Mantle DJ (1964) Spec. Rep. Ser. MRC (London) No 305.
3. Therkelsen AJ (1964) Cytogenetics 3: 207–218.
4. Sørensen K, Nielsen J, Froland A and Johnsen SG (1979) Acta Psychiatr. Scand. 59: 153–163.
5. Polani PE (1972) In: Ounsted C and Taylor DC (eds.) Gender Differences. Churchill Livingstone, Edinburgh, London.
6. Nanko S (1985) In: Sakai T and Tsuboi T (eds.) Genetic Aspects of Human Behavior. Igaku-Shoin, Tokyo, pp. 209–214.
7. Müller N and Endres M (1987) J. Clin. Psychiatry 48: 379–380.
8. Ichikawa H, Uchiyama M and Kishi K (1989) Seishinigaku 31: 519–525.
9. Chapelle A de la (1972) Am. J. Hum. Genet. 24: 71–105.
10. Nanko S (1981) Folia Psychiatr. Neurol. Jpn. 35: 461–464.
11. Crow TJ (1988) Br. J. Psychiatry 153: 675–683.

© 1991 Elsevier Science Publishers B.V. All rights reserved.
Biological Psychiatry, Volume 2. G. Racagni et al., editors.

Rett syndrome: A genetic disorder in females?

Ingegerd Witt Engerström
Pediatric Habilitation Center, Tallåsliden, Tallåsvägen 4, 5-83142 Östersund, Sweden

Introduction

Ever since Rett syndrome (RS) was first described in the medical literature by Andreas Rett in 1966 [1], it has been reported in females only, with single exceptions [2]. Its occurrence in both monozygotic twin pairs, as opposed to dizygotic, has led to the assumption that the basis is genetic. The clinical diversity observed even in sisters and half-sisters suggests that the Rett genotype may express itself with great variability, and may appear also as "formes frustes" [3]. The aim of this paper was to describe clinical characteristics and variability of the syndrome, and to discuss genetic information received.

Material and Methods

In Sweden a search program was used for RS [4], by March 1990 producing a number of 105 girls and women, 97 conforming to the Classic Criteria [5,6], and 8 to those for "formes frustes" (FF) [7]. All the girls had been diagnosed and examined by the author or coworker (B. Hagberg). They were born between 1945–1988, covered an age range of 19 months to 44 years, with a median age of 17.5 years, and were followed up for 30 years or less [4].

The clinical examination program applied included neuropediatric examination and observation, compilation of developmental data from pediatric records and child health charts; and from parents, family notes, photos and films for the purpose of reconstructing symptomatology and natural history [4].

For characterising the clusters of symptoms and signs, the clinical staging system, dividing the course of RS into four stages [7], was applied. For early detection, and for a closer study of the period of regression, symptomatology was systematically studied in more detail [8,9].

Results

The course of the disorder was characterised by a sequential development of neurological signs producing a severe and puzzling mental and motor disorder. At birth no abnormal signs revealed the severe future disability, but already during infancy a characteristic – although not diagnostic – pattern of developmental deviation occurred (stage I) [8]. Loss of acquired skills and withdrawal reversed development at a crucial stage (stage II), while the course later, surprisingly, turned into the pseudostationary stage with characteristic involuntary and stereotyped movements and severe mental retardation (stage III).

In adulthood, the long-term follow-up revealed three phenotypes among the women conforming to the Classic Criteria [10]:

- those still walking (stage III);
- those previously walking (stage IV:A);
- those who were never able to walk (stage IV:B).

Common clinical features for the three phenotypes were: sequential development of ataxia, apraxia, distal spastic reflex signs, increasing weakness and wasting, dystonia and a final complex state of rigidity. The severity of each component, however, varied considerably, creating a personal composition for each woman and a wide range of disability all together.

Characteristic of the stage III-phenotype was apraxia, for the stage IV:A-phenotype a preponderance of dystonic features and for the stage IV:B-phenotype dominating weakness, wasting and rigidity [10].

Contrasting to a progressive loss of gross motor ability was the increasing use of staring, to indicate things wanted and also to express emotions and desire for contact. Involuntary and stereotyped movements, seizures, bruxism, breathing irregularities with breath-holding and hyperventilation and bloating, were more age-related than phenotype-related [11].

Among the four adults conforming to FF, three showed the stage III-phenotype and one the stage IV-phenotype.

Two of the girls in the Swedish series (S8 and S9) [12] were half-sisters, with their mother in common. Their symptomatology differed considerably: S8, the older sister at 29 years of age, was still walking and showed the stage III-phenotype with much dystonia and apraxia, while her younger sister was severely hypotonic, wheelchair bound from age 12 years and had an early severe scoliosis. Another of the girls (S68) conforming to the classic criteria, had a maternal aunt with a variant of the FF [13]. S64 in 1989 gave birth to a daughter, who has now developed RS.

Discussion

RS emerged as subtle variation of normality already in infancy, gradually to disclose itself as loss of development and coordination of motor and mental functions, and with concomitant appearance of involuntary and stereotyped movements (hand-mouthing, hand stereotypies in the midline, grimacing, bruxism, breathing irregularities). For the majority in the Swedish series, seizures were added within a few years. Detailed studies of the period of regression in classic RS has revealed that development invariably comes to a definite break at a crucial level of maturation, at the decisive step from the somatosensory into the symbolic period [9]. A prenatal etiologic factor, uniformly restricting the capacity of development among the girls, may therefore be suspected.

The occurrence of RS in both monozygotic twin pairs, as opposed to dizygotic, has led to the assumption that its origin is genetic. This was supported by the recent genealogic study in Sweden, reporting common origins and consanguineous marriages in a significantly high percentage in the ancestry of 77 investigated females with RS [14].

The challenging finding that only females seem to be affected has led to a search for an X-linked gene defect; the puzzling observation that RS rarely occurs among sisters or other family members has hampered molecular as well as cytogenetic studies. As long as no biologic marker has been identified, neither the genotypic expression nor the phenotypic variation of RS can be delineated, although the clinical diversity observed in sisters and half-sisters does give some advice.

The appearance of RS in the daughter of one of our females with classic RS may favour the genetic hypothesis, as the daughter was perfectly well sized, well shaped, well nourished and well breathing at her birth and for her first 6–8 months, in spite of her mother's severe disability (unreported).

As for the X chromosome, a significantly raised frequency of fragile X(p22) in 13 of the Swedish girls with RS as compared to a control group was recently reported by Wahlström et al. [15]. However, only the X chromosome was studied.

Acknowledgements

This study was supported by all the participating girls and their families, and by grants from the Sigurd and Elsa Golje Memorial Foundation, the Swedish Society for Medical Research, and the Marcus and Amalia Wallenberg Memorial Foundation.

References

1. Rett A (1960) Über ein cerebral-atrophisches Syndrom bei Hyperammonämie. Brüder Hollinek, Vienna.
2. Coleman M (1990) Brain Dev. 12: 31–32.
3. Hagberg B and Rasmussen P (1986) Am. J. Med. Genet. 24: 175–181.
4. Witt Engerström I (1990) Acta Paediatr. Scand. (Suppl.): 369.
5. Hagberg B, Goutieres F, Hanefeld F, Rett A and Wilson I (1985) Brain Dev. 7: 372–373.
6. The Rett Syndrome Diagnostic Criteria Work Group (1988) Ann. Neurol. 23: 425–428.
7. Hagberg B and Witt Engerström I (1986) Am. J. Med. Genet. 24: 47–59.
8. Witt Engerström I (1987) Brain Dev. 9: 481–486.
9. Witt Engerström I (1991) Rett Syndrome: The late infantile regression period. Acta Paediatr. Scand. (in press).
10. Witt Engerström I and Hagberg B (1990) Brain Dev. 12: 23–26.
11. Witt Engerström I (1991) Age-related occurrence of signs and symptoms in Rett syndrome. Brain Dev. (submitted).

12. Hagberg B and Witt Engerström I (1990) Acta Paediatr. Scand. (Suppl.): 369.
13. Hagberg B and Anvret M (1990) Brain Dev. 12: 47–48.
14. Åkesson HO, Hagberg B, Wahlström I and Witt Engerström I (1991) Rett Syndrome: A search for gene sources. Am. J. Med. Genet.
15. Wahlström I, Witt Engerström I, Mellquist L, Anvret M and Oden A (1990) Brain Dev. 12: 128–130.

© 1991 Elsevier Science Publishers B.V. All rights reserved.
Biological Psychiatry, Volume 2. G. Racagni et al., editors.

Formal genetic evidence for X-linked dominant inheritance of bipolar illness is lacking

Johannes Hebebrand

Klinik für Kinder- und Jugendpsychiatrie der Universität Marburg, Hans-Sachs-Str. 6, 3550 Marburg, Germany

Introduction

Positive lod scores have been obtained in several (but not all) X-linkage studies of bipolar illness. The major underlying assumption has been that a subgroup of manic-depressive illness follows an X-linked dominant mode of inheritance. A warranted assumption of this mode of inheritance critically depends on the segregation ratios observed among the offspring of affected males: all their sons should be free of the trait whereas almost all daughters should be affected if the penetrance rate is high. We have evaluated the segregation patterns in all bipolar pedigrees that have been analyzed for X-linkage over the past 20 years. We conclude that not a single pedigree is suggestive of the assumed mode of inheritance. This is due to the fact that in these pedigrees males have either not reproduced, or their offspring were not considered informative by the respective investigators. Thus, the positive lod scores obtained by some groups need to be viewed critically in the light of the complete lack of evidence for the assumed X-linked dominant mode of inheritance.

Results and Discussion

Linkage of a subgroup of bipolar illness to the general region of Xq27 seems an almost established fact [1–4], even though some investigators were not able to replicate these results [5,6].

Not a single bipolar pedigree has been ascertained in which the segregation patterns are suggestive of the assumed X-linked dominant mode of inheritance [7]. Almost all pedigrees – whether small or large – have in common that males apparently have not reproduced [1,4]. Alternatively, the investigators did not consider the offspring of male pedigree members, as indeed in X-linkage studies only female meioses are informative. As an exception Baron et al. [2] provide information on the offspring of 4 males. However, their children have not or have just reached the manifestation age so that segregation ratios cannot be evaluated.

Since penetrance rates were found to be high [2,4], most daughters of affected males should also be ill. The occurrence of a single male-to-male transmission would preclude the respective pedigree from analysis for X-linkage.

Apparently, the X-linkage studies have been carried out using pedigrees that due to the absence of segregation patterns characteristic of X-linked dominant inheritance do not substantiate the assumed mode of inheritance. A priori, the pedigrees are more suggestive of autosomal or multifactorial inheritance. The mere fact that a bipolar pedigree in which segregation patterns are suggestive of X-linked dominant inheritance has not been ascertained raises questions as to the existence of X-linked bipolar illness.

In linkage analysis the posterior odds ratio equals the prior odds ratio multiplied by the observed odds ratio. If the assumed mode of inheritance has not been proven, the prior odds ratio needs to be adjusted (J. Ott, personal communication). At present, the prior odds ratio in the bipolar X-linkage studies appears very small because:

1. Bipolar pedigrees suggestive of X-linked dominant inheritance have not been ascertained;
2. Assumed hemizygous males have not been found to be more severely affected than heterozygous females;
3. Dominant disorders as a whole are under-represented on the X-chromosome.

In conclusion, in the light of the lack of evidence for X-linked dominant inheritance of bipolar illness, the validity of positive lod scores that have been obtained previously must be questioned. A large pedigree suggestive of X-linked dominant inheritance must be ascertained in the future in order to warrant the major assumption in the X-linkage studies. The statistical problems concerning the validity of lod scores in linkage studies of complex disorders, in which the mode of inheritance is uncertain, need to be addressed.

References

1. Baron M (1977) Arch. Gen. Psychiatry 34, 721–725.
2. Baron M, Risch N, Hamburger R, Mandel B, Kushner S, Newman M, Drumer D and Belmaker RH (1987) Nature 326: 289–293.
3. Mendlewicz J, Linkowski P and Wilmotte J (1980) Br. J. Psychiatry 137: 337–342.
4. Mendlewicz J, Sevy S, Brocas H, Simon P, Charon F, Legros S and Vassart G (1987) Lancet i: 1230–1232.
5. Gershon ES, Targum SD, Matthysse S and Bunney WE (1979) Arch. Gen. Psychiatry 36: 1423–1430.
6. Berettini WH, Goldin LR, Gelernter J, Gejman PV, Gershon ES and Detera-Wadleigh S (1990) Arch. Gen. Psychiatry 47: 366–373.
7. Heberbrand J (1991) A critical appraisal of X-linked bipolar illness: Evidence for the assumed mode of inheritance is lacking. Br. J. Psychiatry (in press).

© 1991 Elsevier Science Publishers B.V. All rights reserved.
Biological Psychiatry, Volume 2. G. Racagni et al., editors.

Chromosome aberrations in different populations of psychiatric patients

Jan Wahlström and Hans Olof Åkesson
Department of Clinical Genetics, East Hospital, S-416 85 Gothenburg, Sweden

Introduction

Mental illness is probably caused by a variety of mechanisms among which hereditary factors are significant. In diagnosing an individual it is of great importance to know whether a particular disorder is hereditary. Chromosome analysis is one of many different techniques that have been used to study the correlation between mental illness and hereditary factors.

Methods

We have used chromosome analysis over the past 10 years; the banding of chromosomes was done according to the method described by Borsgård et al. [1]. When fragile X was analysed, we used the culture method described by Wahlström et al. [2].

Materials

Forty-six cases of infantile autism. These comprised of: firstly 25 cases (20 boys, 5 girls) identified in a population-based study of all cases diagnosed as childhood psychosis in the Gothenburg area between 1962 and 1976; and secondly 21 cases (20 boys, 1 girl) were identified consecutively by the Department of Child and Youth, Psychiatric University Clinic of Gothenburg [3].

Twenty cases of childhood psychosis. These comprised of: firstly 13 cases (9 boys, 4 girls) identified in a population-based study of all cases diagnosed as childhood psychosis in the Gothenburg area between 1962 and 1976 and secondly 7 (6 boys, 1 girl) consecutively identified cases from the Department of Child and Youth, Psychiatric University of Gothenburg [3].

Fifty-three cases of schizophrenia. These comprised of: 39 women and 15 men treated at a psychiatric hospital (Säter Hospital) who, in fulfilling the RDC criteria for schizophrenia, were considered for inclusion in the study [4].

Seventy-six cases of affective disorder. These comprised of: the 57 women and 19 men who attended the outpatient clinic at the Department of Psychiatry III, Lillhagen Hospital, in April–May 1980 for treatment of major depression, manic depression, or cycloid psychosis [5]. The women were 37–86 years old (mean age 62 years), and the men were 42–78 years old (mean age 61 years).

Fifty-three cases of Alzheimer's dementia. These comprised of: a subsample of patients with Alzheimer's dementia selected from a longitudinal study of 70-year old people in Gothenburg [6,7].

Three hundred and twenty-one cases of psychosis. These cases comprised of: 321 male inpatients, aged 15–77 years, consecutively admitted to the Department of Psychiatry III (University of Gothenburg, Sweden) for treatment of various psychotic disorders.

Results

Altogether we found 5 cases of sex chromosome aberrations in these populations: one case of 47,XYY; 1 case of 47,XXX; and 3 cases with Klinefelter syndrome 47,XXY. Of the latter, two were Klinefelter's syndrome mosaicism with about 50% abnormal 47,XXY cells and 50% normal 46,XY cells.

The five balanced structural aberrations among the psychotic patients included three translocations and two inversions, the karyotypes being:

46,XY,inv(10)(p12;q21) in one case;
46,XY,inv(16)(p11;q12) in one case;
46,XY,t(14;20)(p13;q21) in one case;
46,XY,t(3;20)(p14;p12) in one case;
46,XY,t(5;6)(q13;q15) in one case.

Fragile X predominated among the cases of infantile autism, 4 boys having more and 4 less than 4% fragile X positive cells, giving a total of 8 such cases.

Table 1. Chromosome aberrations in 6 different populations

Population studied	n	Male	Female	Sex chromosome	Structural aberration	Fragile-X
Infantile autism	46	40	6	1	0	8
Childhood psychosis	20	15	5	0	0	0
Schizophrenia	53	15	38	1	0	–
Affective disorder	76	19	57	0	0	–
Alzheimer's dementia	53	13	40	0	0	–
Psychosis	321	321	0	3	5	1
Total	569	423	146	5	5	9

Furthermore, the one psychotic patient with fragile X fulfilled the criteria for Martin Bell's syndrome: large testicles, mental retardation and prominent ears. But he also had a paranoid psychosis.

Discussion

If a structural chromosome aberration such as a duplication or is co-segregated in a family with a history of psychotic disease, it may be postulated that a gene for the disease is situated in the trisomic part of the chromosome. Pursuing this postulation, Basset et al. [8] first found an indication for a gene for schizophrenia on chromosome 5 and described a duplication on the long arm of this chromosome.

Other structural chromosome aberrations such as translocations co-segregating in a family with a history of psychiatric disease can also be used to locate a possible gene for the disorder. Both of the two breakpoints in translocations can be of interest in locating a potential gene for psychiatric disease.

If two or more patients with the same psychiatric disease have structural chromosome aberration with the same breakpoint, there is reason to believe that this is the point at which a gene can be located.

The possibility of using common breakpoints in psychotic patients to discover such locations is of the utmost interest in suggesting where to apply molecular genetic techniques to reveal the susceptibility genes responsible for psychiatric diseases.

References

1. Borsgård JI, Sabel KG and Wahlström J (1974) Hereditas 77: 159–161.
2. Wahlström J, K:son Blomqvist H, Bohman M, Edvinsson SO, Gillberg C, Gustavson KH and Holmgren G (1985) Clin. Genet. 27: 113–117.
3. Gillberg C and Wahlström J (1985) Dev. Med. Child Neurol. 27: 293–304.
4. Eklund K and Forsman A (1991) Personal communication.
5. Nilsson A (1989) Thesis: From the Department of Psychiatry III, Univeristy of Gothenborg, Sweden.
6. Rinder L, Roupe S, Steen B and Svanborg A (1975) Acta Med. Scand. 198: 397–407.
7. Svanborg A (1977) Acta Med. Scand. (Suppl.) 611: 3–37.
8. Basset AS, McGillivray, BC, Jones BD and Pantzar JT (1988) Lancet i: 799–800.
9. Landahl S, Wahlström J, Skoog I, Holmqvist D and Johannesson T (1991) Personal communication.
10. Wahlström J, Nilsson A and Axelsson R (1991) Personal communication.

© 1991 Elsevier Science Publishers B.V. All rights reserved.
Biological Psychiatry, Volume 2. G. Racagni et al., editors.

Autosomal abnormalities and schizophrenia

Anne S. Bassett

Department of Psychiatry, University of Toronto, Queen Street Mental Health Centre, 1001 Queen Street West, Toronto, Ontario M6J 1H4, Canada

Introduction

Chromosomal abnormalities associated with various genetic disorders have proved valuable for localizing and isolating causative genes. The fortuitous observation of these events has suggested candidate regions for linkage studies. For example, researchers found significant linkage of tuberous sclerosis (TS) to markers from 11q22-11q23 [1] following a report of an unbalanced translocation associated with TS. Associations of specific diseases with chromosomal aberrations in rare individuals have also substantially aided in the physical mapping and subsequent cloning of causative genes, e.g. neurofibromatosis (NF-1) [2]. Many similar examples for other disorders suggest that chromosomal abnormalities associated with major psychoses may play an important role in isolating genes for schizophrenia.

Methods for literature review

A broad search strategy was used to identify pertinent references for autosomal (chromosomes 1–22) anomalies associated with schizophrenia and related disorders (associated sex chromosome anomalies had recently been reviewed [3]). This included a Medline search (1966–1990) and examination of catalogues of chromosomal aberrations [4–6] and previous reviews [3,7,8]. A critical review of the reported associations of autosomal abnormalities and adult psychiatric illness was undertaken using standardized criteria developed for specificity, diagnosis, family history and overall weight of evidence [9].

Results

Most of the 26 reports of psychiatric illness or symptoms found to be associated with autosomal abnormalities have been identified since 1976, when cytogenetic techniques improved. Nine of these reports came from 4 cytogenetic surveys of psychiatric patient populations and the remaining 17 were case reports. Using the relevancy rating system [9] developed for the review, there were 3 reports [10–12] (13%) with modest relevance and 5 [13–17] with possible relevance (Table 1). The

Table 1. Potentially relevant autosomal abnormalities

Site	Study		Caution	Relevance
9p22;11q22.3 b/t[a]	Family case report	[12]	11q22.3 common break-point	Modest
13;14 b/t	Cytogenetic survey	[10]	Common translocation	Modest
13;14 b/t	Cytogenetic survey	[11]	Common translocation	Modest
5q11.2-q13.3 p/t	Family case report	[13]		Possible
1q43;11q21-22 b/t[a]	Family case report	[17]		Possible
6q14.2;11q25 b/t[a]	Family case report	[16]		Possible
2q21;18q23 b/t[b]	Case report	[15]		Possible
19p13 fra	Family case report	[14]		Possible

b/t = balanced translocation; p/t = partial trisomy; fra = fragile site;
[a] 11q22-q23 is the location of the D_2 dopamine receptor [18];
[b] 18q23 is a ring chromosome break point; ring 18 associated with psychosis [7].

remaining 18 (69%) of the reported associations appeared to have no or low relevance to localizing genes for schizophrenia.

Potential significance of chromosomal associations

From this literature review, the proximal 5q, distal 11q, distal 18q and distal 19p regions appear reasonable candidates for linkage studies of schizophrenia and related disorders. Alternatively, other break-point regions from the more promising reports (e.g. 1q43;6q14.2) may be considered, although less overall evidence points to these areas. However, researchers must use caution when drawing inferences about associations of psychiatric disorders with chromosomal aberrations because major psychiatric illnesses are common, increasing the possibility of chance findings. Also, some cytogenetic abnormalities (e.g. 13;14 translocation) are common in the general population.

If true associations exist, however, they may be of two main types: linkage and causal. A chromosomal abnormality linked to schizophrenia is one that is so close to a schizophrenia susceptibility gene that the two may co-segregate in a particular family. These may include fragile sites, e.g. 19p13, and translocation breakpoints, e.g. 11q22.3, 11q25, 18q23. A causal association implies that the chromosomal abnormality itself somehow involves a faulty gene or genetic mechanism that directly or indirectly leads to a schizophrenic illness; partial trisomy 5q11.2-q13.3 is a possible example.

Future directions

Overall, there have been few reported autosomal abnormalities associated with psychiatric illness. This number may be increased by improved methodology in several areas. First, cytogenetic surveys of dysmorphic or mentally handicapped patients with psychotic disorders may increase the yield of positive results. Second, consistently used diagnostic criteria and reporting of segregation patterns of both psychiatric illness and chromosomal abnormality would help determine the potential relevance of case reports. Third, expensive techniques such as high resolution cytogenetics and fragile site analysis should be utilized in consultation with medical geneticists, and when warranted should maximize the likelihood of identifying significant chromosomal abnormalities. Identification of many more truly associated chromosomal aberrations may well be essential to the successful localization and subsequent isolation of the likely several major genes underlying the complex psychiatric syndrome of schizophrenia.

References

1. Smith M, Smalley S, Cantor R et al. (1990) Genomics 6: 105–114.
2. Wallace MR, Marchuk DA, Andersen LB et al. (1990) Science 249: 181–186.
3. DeLisi LE and Lovett M (1990) In: Kales A, Stefanis CN and Talbott J (eds.) Recent Advances in Schizophrenia. Springer-Verlag, New York, pp. 131–161.
4. Borgaonkar DS (1989) Chromosomal Variation in Man. Alan R. Liss Inc., New York.
5. McKusick VA (1990) Mendelian Inheritance in Man. The Johns Hopkins University Press, Baltimore.
6. Schinzel A (1984) Catalogue of Unbalanced Chromosome Aberrations in Man. De Gruyter & Co., Berlin.
7. Propping P (1983) Hum. Genet. 65: 1–10.
8. Schmid W and Nielsen J (eds.) (1981) Human Behavior and Genetics. Elsevier/North Holland Biomedical Press, Amsterdam.
9. Bassett AS (1991) Chromosomal Aberrations and Schizophrenia (submitted).
10. Escobar JI (1976) Compr. Psychiatry 17: 309–313.
11. Nielsen J, Astradur B, Hreidarsson B et al. (1973) Hereditas 75: 131–135.
12. Smith M, Wasmuth J, McPherson JD et al. (1989) Am. J. Hum. Genet. 45: A178.
13. Bassett AS, McGillivray BC, Jones BD et al. (1988) Lancet i: 799–801.
14. Chodirker BN, Chudley AE, Ray M et al. (1987) Clin. Genet. 31: 1–6.
15. Genest P, Dumas L and Genest FB (1976) Union Méd. Canada 105: 1676–1681.
16. Holland T and Gosden C (1990) Psychiatry Res. 32: 1–8.
17. St. Clair DM, Blackwood D, Muir W et al. (1990) Lancet 336: 13–16.
18. Grandy DK et al. (1989) Am. J. Hum. Genet. 45: 778–785.

© 1991 Elsevier Science Publishers B.V. All rights reserved.
Biological Psychiatry, Volume 2. G. Racagni et al., editors.

Y-to-X translocation and schizophrenia: A case report

Shinichiro Nanko
Department of Psychiatry, Teikyo University School of Medicine, 2-11-1, Kaga, Itabashi, Tokyo, Japan

Introduction

During an X and Y chromatin survey among 7,974 inpatients in Japanese mental hospitals, 6 males with double Y chromatin were found [1]. Chromosomal analyses of these 6 males revealed that 5 males were 47,XYY and the other one was Y-to-X translocation, 46,Y,der(X)t(X;Y)(p22;q11) [2] (Fig. 1). The male with Y-to-X translocation was diagnosed as schizophrenic. The case of a psychotic male with Y-to-X translocation has not been reported in the literature.

Case report

The patient is a 35-year-old unmarried unemployed male. The karyotype 46,Y, der(X)t(X;Y)(p22;q11) was established at the age of 25 years when he was an inpatient in a mental hospital. He was the last born of 3 siblings. His birth and early childhood were fairly normal. His school results were always below the average of his classmates. After leaving school at the age of 15, he was trained as a restaurant cook's helper, but soon afterwards began to change jobs frequently without any particular reason. He was first examined by a psychiatrist at the age of 21 years because of insomnia, continuous auditory hallucination and a feeling of passivity. Several months before visiting the psychiatric clinic, he gradually developed a delusional idea of being persecuted and referred to. He spoke to himself and walked around his room, complaining that someone was speaking ill of him, commenting on his thought and behavior. He also felt himself to be influenced by the voice.

Six months later, he was referred to a mental hospital where he was diagnosed as having schizophrenia. He appeared to have dull normal intelligence, although his I.Q. of 90 (WAIS) was within the normal range. He was 155 cm in height (short stature) and showed disproportion of extremities. Neither ichthyosis nor hyperterolism was found, but he had hypogonadism. After a stay of 6 months the patient was discharged, showing little improvement. He continued to give rude answers, could not reply immediately and gave the impression of being stupid.

Two years later he suffered from insomnia, developed delusional ideas again, became dysphoric and hot-tempered. He was readmitted to the mental hospital where he stayed for 5 months. During his stay he was found to have a Y-to-X translocation. His mother and his brother are also carriers of a Y-to-X translocation

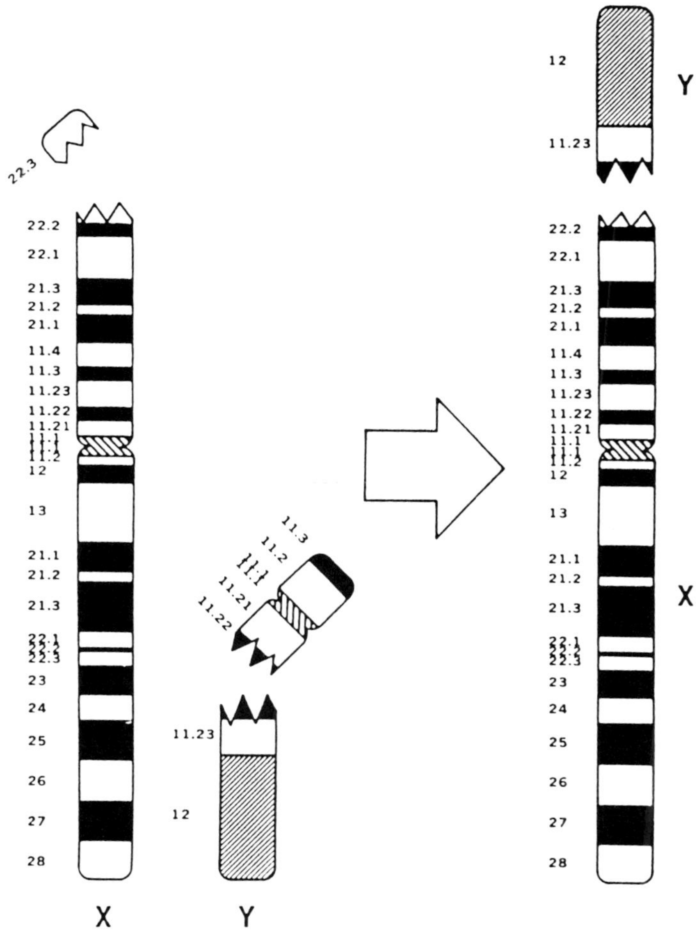

Fig. 1. Y-to-X translocation.

(Fig. 2). After 10 years' follow-up, he was admitted a total of 5 times to mental hospitals, staying several months each time. Presently, he is an outpatient at a mental hospital and is diagnosed as a schizophrenic, residual type, according to the DSM III-R criteria.

Comment

Y-to-X translocation is a rare structural chromosome aberration, over which 10 sporadic cases and 8 familial cases have been reported [3]. Symptoms commonly noted are short stature, hyperterolism, ichthyosis, developmental and mental retardation [4].

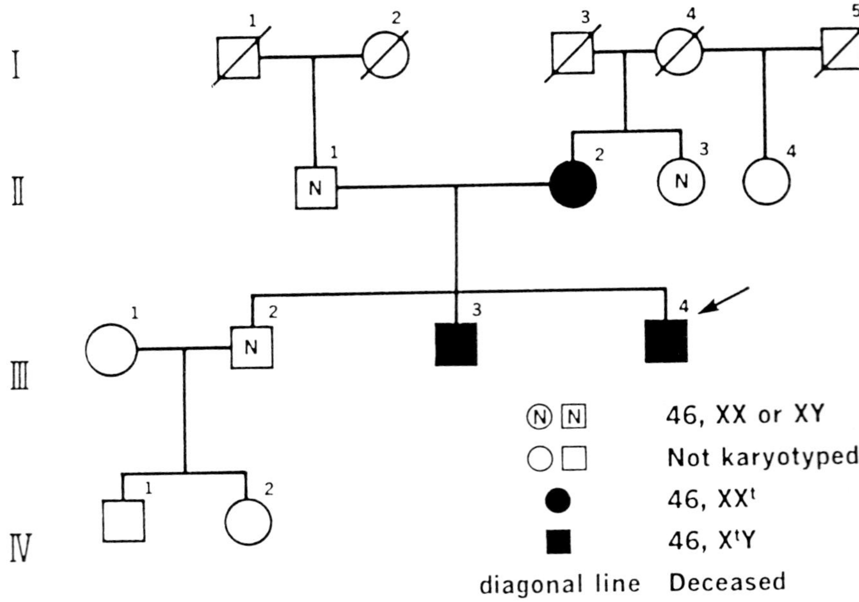

Fig. 2. Pedigree of the family with t(X;Y) translocation X^t = der(X)t(X;Y) (p22;q11).

The case of a psychotic male with Y-to-X translocation has not been reported in the literature. Thus the etiological relation between the 2 conditions was unknown. As Y-to-X translocation causes monosomy of the pseudoautosomal region of the sex chromosome or partial nullisomy for the distal portion of Xp22 to Xpter in males, this case would be interesting with regard to pseudoautosomal hypothesis on functional psychosis after Crow (1988).

According to Ballabio et al. [5], a gene related to mental retardation is located on the Xp, distal to the steroid sulfatase gene locus – Xp22,32 band – (STS). This suggests that the break-point of the present case might be distal to the STS gene. In view of the mildness of the symptoms, we also assume in the present case the range of nullisomy of the Xp22 to pter region is smaller than that of reported cases in the literature.

References

1. Nanko S (1985) In: Sakai T and Tsuboi T (eds.) Genetic Aspects of Human Behavior. Igaku-Shoin, Tokyo, pp. 209–214.
2. Yamada K, Nanko S, Hattori S and Isurugi K (1982) Hum. Genet. 60: 85–90.
3. Agematsu K, Koike K, Morosawa H, Nakahori Y and Akabane T (1988) Hum. Genet. 80: 105–107.
4. Ohdo S, Yamada K, Madokoro H, Sonoda T, Kawaguchi K and Ohba K (1988) Jpn. J. Hum. Genet. 33: 377–384.
5. Ballabio A, Parenti G, Carrozzo R, Coppa G, Felici L, Migliori V, Silengo M, Franceschini P and Andria G (1988) Clin. Genet. 34: 31–37.

© 1991 Elsevier Science Publishers B.V. All rights reserved.
Biological Psychiatry, Volume 2. G. Racagni et al., editors.

The interrelationship of major psychotic disorders as evidenced by patterns of familial transmission: The Mainz family studies

W. Maier and D. Lichtermann
Department of Psychiatry, University of Mainz, Untere Zahlbacher Straße 8, D-6500 Mainz, Germany

Introduction

The question of whether there is interdependence among the major psychoses or not has already been forwarded by the ancestors of psychiatry, but has given rise to much controversy ever since. It was Kraepelin's merit to deduce the postulation of two completely separate disease entities – dementia praecox and manic depressive insanity – from the observation of quite different long-term outcome. This position has been contradicted by Griesinger's hypothesis of unitary psychosis as the common underlying disorder, a concept that has recently been re-formulated by Crow [1] as a continuum of psychosis, steadily ranging with increasing severity from unipolar affective through bipolar affective and schizoaffective disorders to schizophrenia.

Besides differences or similarities of outcome and treatment response, patterns of familial transmission of these four disorders as evidenced by family studies may contribute substantially to the clarification of that historical issue: the Kraepelinean position will be supported if each of the nosological entities (such as schizophrenia, bipolar disorder, unipolar disorder and – in modern versions of nosological classifications – schizoaffective disorder) "breeds true", i.e. if an increase in the familial morbid risk of every disorder is exclusively found in patients of the same type ("homotypicity" of transmission). On the other hand, a partly or complete overlap of morbid risk figures among these four major syndromes might, moreover, speak in favour of the continuum model of psychoses.

However, family studies matching current methodological standards [2] such as diagnostic assessments of patients and relatives by structured interview schedules according to recently developed diagnostic criteria and with the interviewer kept blind to the index subject's diagnostic status are rare.

Materials and Methods

In a controlled family study of major psychotic disorders 525 consecutive psychiatric hospital admissions of unipolar and bipolar affective, schizoaffective, and schizophrenic psychoses and nearly 80% of their living first-degree relatives have been personally interviewed with the Schedule for Affective Disorders and Schizophrenia (SADS-LA) blindly to the index subjects' diagnoses. Psychiatric lifetime diagnoses according to the Research Diagnostic Criteria (RDC) have been assigned as "best estimate" [3] of the interview and every other diagnostic information available. A total of 109 randomly-selected control subjects out of the general population living in the same district and their families underwent an identical procedure. A subsample of index patients' families was matched by sex, age and educational status.

Familial morbid risks of these four disorders were calculated by applying the Strömgen-Weinberg method for age at onset correction [4].

Results

Table 1 shows the age-corrected lifetime prevalence rates (morbid risks) of the four major disorders in first-degree relatives as they were found in each of the four subsamples of patients' diagnoses and in healthy control subjects.

It is noteworthy to mention that bipolar affective disorder was not found among the relatives of index subjects with *unipolar* schizoaffective disorder by contrast with the relatives of index cases suffering from *bipolar* schizoaffective disorder. Furthermore, unipolar depression was more common in families of schizophrenic probands as compared with the control subjects' relatives, even if those probands who had reported affective or schizoaffective episodes in addition to the schizophrenic episode(s) were excluded from the analysis.

Discussion

The diagonal of the table indicates that each of the four major disorders segregates in the families of patients with the same disorder as compared with the morbid risks among the families of healthy controls, a finding that has been replicated by a large number of earlier family studies.

Table 1.

	First-degree relatives' lifetime morbid risk of:			
	Schizophrenia (%)	Schizoaffective disorder (%)	Bipolar affective disorder (%)	Unipolar affective disorder (%)
Patients' disorders				
Schizophrenia	5.1	3.3	1.9	19.6
Schizoaffective	4.1	5.3	5.4	20.4
Bipolar affective	1.2	1.0	8.8	23.6
Unipolar affective	0.8	0.9	1.6	21.6
Healthy controls	0.4	0.3	1.2	9.9

None of the disorders revealed strict "homotypicity". However, two homotypical clusters of disorders were found:

1. The familial morbid risk of schizophrenia (5.1%) was not only enhanced in schizophrenic, but also in schizoaffective patients (4.1%) in comparison with affective disorder patients and healthy controls. The same finding emerged with respect to the risk of schizoaffective disorder in families of both schizoaffective and schizophrenic patients: schizophrenia and schizoaffective disorder are transmitted as a common disease entity.
2. Bipolar disorder showed the highest familial risk figures among patients with bipolar affective and bipolar schizoaffective disorder, thus forming a second diagnostic entity of a separate mode of familial transmission independent of schizophrenia or unipolar depression.

These observations are in agreement with Kraepelin if probands with schizoaffective disorder are ignored. However, another finding is in strict contradiction with Kraepelin: the risk of unipolar depression was found to be increased not only among the relatives of unipolar affective probands, but also in the families of schizophrenic subjects.

As to the criterion of familial transmission, the final conclusion can be drawn that none of the competing hypotheses modelling the interrelationship of major psychoses is able to describe their morbid risk patterns in a consistent manner.

References

1. Crow TJ (1986) Br. J. Psychiatry 149: 419–429.
2. Weissman MM, Merikangas KR, John K, Wickramaratne P, Prusoff BA and Kidd KK (1986) Arch. Gen. Psychiatry 43: 1104–1116.
3. Leckman JF, Sholomskas D, Thompson WD, Belanger A and Weissman MM (1982) Arch. Gen. Psychiatry 39: 879–883.
4. Gershon ES, DeLisi LE, Hamovit J, Nurnberger JI, Maxwell ME, Schreiber J, Dauphinais D, Dingman CW II and Guroff JJ (1988) Arch. Gen. Psychiatry 45: 328–336.

© 1991 Elsevier Science Publishers B.V. All rights reserved.
Biological Psychiatry, Volume 2. G. Racagni et al., editors.

A case for discontinuity in the psychotic illnesses

George Winokur and William Coryell
University of Iowa College of Medicine, 500 Newton Road, Iowa City, IA 52242, U.S.A.

Introduction

If continuity exists in psychotic illnesses, the mixed form (schizoaffective) should differ from the pure forms of affective disorders in epidemiology, family history, course and outcome, laboratory findings, and response to treatment. These variables essentially define a disease and provide evidence of the validity of diagnosis.

Relevant findings

Schizoaffective disorder shares clinical characteristics of schizophrenia and the affective disorders. Typically, a schizoaffective patient has mood incongruent psychotic symptoms, and meets a full set of symptoms for either mania or depression. Assuming that affective disorder and schizoaffective disorder and schizophrenia are on a continuum, schizoaffective disorder should differ substantially from the two polar illnesses on a variety of variables. Of 28 acute schizophrenic patients, 26 had four or more affective symptoms, which suggests the diagnosis of schizoaffective disorder [1]. If acute schizoaffective disorder were like affective disorder, it should show the same sex ratio. Table 1 shows the sex ratio in acute schizophrenia. It is similar to that of the affective disorders (predominantly female) and dissimilar to the sex ratio in schizophrenia. These data come from a very large group of hospital patients that were consecutively admitted [2].

The course of the illness in both schizoaffective depressive patients and schizo-

Table 1. Sex ratios; hospitalized patients

	No. of males	No. of females	F to M ratio
Schizophrenia	461	343	0.74
Acute schizophrenia alone	103	136	1.21
Acute schizophrenia and psychotic depression	161	195	1.32
All affective disorders	729	1174	1.61

Schizophrenia vs. acute schizophrenia and psychotic depression $Y^2 = 14.6$ $P < 0.0005$; acute schizophrenia alone vs. all affective disorders P = N.S.

Table 2. A comparison of non-psychotic unipolar depression vs. depression with congruent and incongruent symptoms

	Non-psychotic unipolar (%) 604	Congruent psychotic unipolar (%) 76	Acute SA depressive (%) 60
Duration of illness at admission			
≤ to 4 weeks	9	9	12
Marked improvement at discharge	61	68	57
Marked improvement with ECT	59	56	70
Follow-up two-plus years	42	45	41
No relapse in follow-up	50	31	52
No significant difference	–	–	–

SA = Schizoaffective.

affective manic patients is similar to the course in non-psychotic unipolar and non-psychotic manic patients [3]. The duration of illness is defined as the time between onset and hospitalization.

In Tables 2 and 3, the schizoaffective patients had mood incongruent psychotic symptoms whereas those that had congruent affective episodes were delusional but the delusions were congruent with the affective state. Notably, 78% of the schizoaffective depressives had been ill less than 6 months prior to hospitalization and in the non-psychotic depressives, 61% were similarly acute. For manic with no psychotic symptoms, admission occurred within 42 days of onset in 84%; for schizoaffective manics, 78%.

In data from the same study, the family history between the three groups of depressives was quite similar. There were no significant differences in the proportion of probands with a family history of depression only and no difference in the proportion of probands with a family history of mania.

Table 3. A comparison of non-psychotic manias vs. manias with congruent and incongruent psychotic symptoms

	Non-psychotic mania (%) 188	Congruent mania (%) 113	Acute SA mania (%) 88
Duration of illness at admission			
≤ 4 weeks	37	46	51
Outcome marked improvement	61	64	58
Improvement with ECT	69	65	78
Follow-up 2-plus years	40	40	42
No relapse in follow-up	46	45	45
No significant difference	–	–	–

SA = Schizoaffective.

Table 4. Family history of non-psychotic depression vs. depression with mood congruent and incongruent psychotic symptoms

	Non-psychotic depression (%) 561	Congruent depression (%) 72	SA depression (%) 28
Proportion of probands with family history of depression only	26.0	25.0	32.0
Proportion of probands with family history of mania	1.2	2.7	1.9

SA = Schizoaffective.

For the family history of schizoaffective bipolars (first rank and/or catatonic symptoms) vs. other bipolars, Table 5 gives the information. Notably, there is no difference in morbid risk for affective illness in primary relatives. That is also true for morbid risk for schizophrenia in primary relatives. However, there is an increase in schizophrenia in the parents, grandparents, and third-degree relatives of the schizoaffective bipolars. Both the schizoaffective bipolars and the other bipolars have small amounts of schizophrenia in the relatives, 2.1% vs. 0.7%. To arrive at these numbers, family history was evaluated for 660 parents, grandparents and third-degree relatives of the schizoaffective bipolars and 1,640 similar relatives of the other bipolars. This finding, though not large, is significant and would be quite consistent with some diagnostic impurity in the groups. Thus some of the patients who had schizoaffective bipolar illness with rather typical schizophrenic symptoms may simply have been misdiagnosed. The two groups of patients, schizoaffective manics and other manics were similar on age at onset, age at admission, the number of manic and depressive episodes at follow-up, being asymptomatic at follow-up, suicide rates and hospital admissions, but the schizoaffective group was significantly less acute ($P < 0.05$), they had been ill less than one month prior to admission in 46% of the cases as compared to 62% in the other bipolars.

Finally, as regards chronic hospitalization, we might evaluate a group of manic, depressive, schizophrenic and schizophreniform patients admitted to the hospital

Table 5. Family history of schizoaffective bipolars vs. other bipolars

	Schizoaffective bipolars (%) n = 66	Other bipolars (%) n = 164
Morbid risk for affective illness in primary relatives	12.0	11.0
Morbid risk for schizophrenia in parents, grandparents and third-degree relatives	2.1	0.7[a]

[a] $\chi^2 = 6.93$; $P < 0.01$.

Table 6. Continuous hospitalization of bipolars, unipolars, schizophrenics and schizophreniform patients

1–6	Months	=	157/785	=	20%
1	Year	=	136/634	=	21%
2	Years	=	48/393	=	12%
3	Years	=	33/315	=	10%
5	Years	=	11/199	=	6%
10	Years	=	4/85	=	5%

between 1934 and 1944. In this large group of patients, there is a breakpoint at one year for continuous hospitalization.

This suggests that there are two groups of patients in the study, one of which is chronically hospitalized and the other which is not. The data suggest two psychoses, one which is acute and mainly affective, the other, chronic and mainly schizophrenic. It does not show evidence of a normal distribution. Thus, it is opposed to the idea of continuity of psychoses.

Conclusions

Using the variables of the medical model, the data are opposed to continuity of psychoses but rather in favor of two illnesses, one affective and the other schizophrenic.

References

1. McCabe W, Fowler R, Cadoret R and Winokur G (1971) Psychol. Med. 1: 326–332.
2. Black D, Warrack G and Winokur G (1985) J. Am. Med. Assoc. 253: 58–61.
3. Winokur G, Black D and Nasrallah A (1990): In: Marnaros A and Tsuang M (eds.) Affective and Schizoaffective Disorders: Similarities and Differences. Springer-Verlag, Berlin/Heidelberg, pp. 23–32.
4. Winokur G, Kadrmas A and Crowe R (1986) In: Marnaros A and Tsuang M (eds.) Schizoaffective Mania: Family History and Clinical Characteristics in Schizoaffective Psychoses. Springer-Verlag, Berlin/Heidelberg, pp. 115–122.
5. Morrison J, Winokur G, Crowe R and Clancy J (1973) Arch. Gen. Psychiatry 29: 678–682.

© 1991 Elsevier Science Publishers B.V. All rights reserved.
Biological Psychiatry, Volume 2. G. Racagni et al., editors.

A non-Kraepelinian continuity of affective disorders and schizophrenia is suggested by twin and family studies

E.S. Gershon, W.H. Berrettini, A. Robb, M. Martinez and L.R. Goldin
Clinical Neurogenetics Branch, National Institutes of Mental Health, Bethesda, MD 20892, U.S.A.

The question of continuity or dichotomy cannot have a simple answer in diseases whose inheritance is complex and where genetic and clinical heterogeneity may well be present and uncorrelated with each other. Data from twin, family and adoption studies are useful to determine if some genetic overlap occurs, but do not resolve the issue further. A valid genetic linkage marker, even if valid for only a fraction of cases, could give a definitive answer. That is, one might find that the fifth genetic illness which causes schizophrenia also would cause bipolar illness, but the other four would not.

In the relatives of schizophrenics (SZ), in recent family studies we in the U.S. [1] and Maier et al. [2] in Germany have found increased morbid risk of affective disorders (AD). Schizoaffective (SA) patients have relatives with both AD (including bipolar [BP]) and SZ; no clinical criterion consistently separates the SA patients with SZ relatives from those with AD relatives. Previous family studies did not generally find this, as reviewed elsewhere [1].

Twin studies have repeatedly found some affective disorders in twins of schizophrenics, including monozygotic (MZ) twins, as reviewed elsewhere [3]. We then noted that no MZ pair had been reported where one was schizophrenic and another bipolar, but such pairs have now been reported [4,5]. In a recent review of twins seen at the Maudsley clinic, Farmer et al. [6] applied DSM III criteria to the medical records. Of 18 MZ pairs in which one twin was schizophrenic, the other had schizophrenia in 6 instances and major depressive disorder (without schizophrenia) in 4 instances. In the 22 DZ pairs there were 3 cases of major depressive disorder. Although the MZ-DZ difference in affective disorders is not significant, the results are consistent with the recent family study data.

The adoption data in bipolar illness are meager. In the Danish adoption study of schizophrenia, which now includes a national sample, no excess of affective illness in biological relatives of schizophrenics has been observed (S.S. Kety, personal communication).

Segregation analyses of family study data have not resolved the mode of inheritance of these disorders. Complex inheritance, including genetic heterogeneity, may be present. The possibility that, nonetheless, a linkage marker or a change in a candidate gene may succeed in detecting single genetic loci contributing to schizophrenia and/or affective illness vulnerability has captured the imagination and efforts of many genetics investigators over the past decade. We refer here to the recent positive linkage findings, although we have elsewhere noted our inability to reproduce these findings. In the recent report of linkage of the colorblindness region to manic-depressive illness, no cases of schizophrenia consistent with the illness phase of the linkage markers were observed [7]. In the reported linkage of markers on chromosome 5 segments q11-13 to schizophrenia, linkage was observed to a spectrum of disorders, including affective disorders [8]. The latter report, at least, would suggest genetic overlap between the two entities.

The validity of the chromosome 5 finding has been questioned by McGuffin et al. [9] on the basis that if the Sherrington et al. [8] series is excluded, the remainder of the reported data do not contain any evidence for linkage or heterogeneity. They conclude that the report by Sherrington et al. [8] was a chance finding, perhaps because of the use of multiple disease models [10]. Amos et al. [11] have questioned this conclusion, because considered overall the data are significantly positive for linkage with heterogeneity, the use of multiple models would not have so greatly increased the probability of a false conclusion of linkage (with a very high lod score) and detection of linkage is generally robust to misspecification of parameters of inheritance, although there are conditions where misspecification of the genetic model can lead to a false *exclusion* of linkage. We do not believe that the controversies over the validity of linkage findings are resolvable by statistical argument at this time, and conclusions about genetic overlap which are based on these findings must be considered very tentative.

As we have argued elsewhere [1] numerous interpretations of the family, twin and adoption data are possible, particularly if one assumes complex inheritance, but in none of them is there an unambiguous separation of affective and schizophrenic disorders. We consider BP and SZ to have generally distinct familial vulnerability, but unipolar disorder and schizoaffective disorder are frequently expressed in relatives of both, implying that these disorders can be an expression of the familial causes of either one. The occasional overlap of BP and SZ in families or in MZ twins may point to a distinct (and rare) genetic entity which can be expressed as either disease, or to rare interactions between particular genes and environmental factors in these particular twin pairs.

References

1. Gershon ES, DeLisi LE, Hamovit J, Nurnberger JI Jr, Maxwell ME, Schreiber J, Dauphinais D, Dingman CW II and Guroff JJ (1988) Arch. Gen. Psychiatry 45: 328.
2. Maier W, Hallmayer J, Minges J and Lichtermann D (1990) In: Marneros A and Tsuang MT (eds.) Affective and Schizoaffective Disorders: Similarities and Differences. Springer-Verlag, Berlin, Heidelberg, New York, pp. 201–207.
3. Gershon ES and Rieder RO (1980) In: Belmaker RH and van Praag HM (eds.) Mania: An Evolving Concept. Spectrum Publications Inc., Jamaica, pp. 97–109.
4. Dalby JT, Morgan D and Lee ML (1986) J. Nerv. Mental Dis. 174: 304.
5. Blackwood D, St. Clair D and Muir W (1991) Eur. Arch. Psychiatry Clin. Neurosci. 240: 191.
6. Farmer AE, McGuffin P and Gottesman II (1987) Arch. Gen. Psychiatry 44: 634.

7. Baron M, Risch N, Hamburger R, Mandel B, Kushner S, Newman M, Drumer D and Belmaker RH (1987) Nature 326: 289.
8. Sherrington R, Brynjolfsson J, Petursson H, Poter M, Dudleston K, Barraclough B, Wasmuth J, Dobbs M and Gurling H (1988) Nature 336: 164.
9. McGuffin P, Sargeant M, Hetti G, Tidmarsh S, Whatley S and Marchbanks RM (1990) Am. J. Hum. Genet. 47: 524.
10. Weeks DE, Lehner T, Squires-Wheeler E, Kaufmann C and Ott J (1990) Genet. Epidemiol. 7: 237.
11. Amos CI, Martinez M and Bale SJ (1991) Can a susceptibility locus for schizophrenia be excluded from chromosome 5q11–13? (submitted for publication).

Neuropeptides and psychoneuroimmunoendocrinology

© 1991 Elsevier Science Publishers B.V. All rights reserved.
Biological Psychiatry, Volume 2. G. Racagni et al., editors.

Actions and metabolism of psychotropic gonadal steroids

Christoph Hiemke[1], Markus Banger[1] and Rudolf Knuppen[2]
[1]*Department of Psychiatry, University of Mainz, 6500 Mainz; and* [2]*Department of Biochemical Endocrinology, University of Lübeck, 2400 Lübeck, Germany*

Introduction

Gonadal hormones exhibit psychotropic properties [1]. This view is based on findings showing that alterations in the gonadal state correlate with changes in sexual behavior, aggression, cognition, arousal, sleep or mood [2]. It is currently suggested that psychotropic effects of gonadal steroids are brought about by interactions of the classical sex steroids estradiol, progesterone or dihydrotestosterone with *intracellular* receptors in the brain [3,4]. Gonadal steroids, however, underlie various enigmatic transformations thus leading to multiple metabolites. At least some of the metabolites like the reduced progesterone metabolite 3α-hydroxy-5α-pregnane-20-one (HPO) or 2- or 4-hydroxylated estrogens (catecholestrogens) have been shown to be potent modulators of neuronal activities [5,6]. Moreover, their actions may differ from those of primary sex steroids and be transmitted via *membrane*-associated receptors [6]. Classical sex steroids seem unlikely to play a major role in the occurrence of major depression or schizophrenia; on the other hand, it is unknown whether sex steroid *metabolites* are involved.

In the present investigation we measured the formation and metabolism of estrogen metabolites in male psychiatric patients and healthy subjects to see if psychiatric diseases were associated with alterations in the formation of the estrogen metabolites. In addition, in male subjects the production rates of the reduced progesterone metabolite HPO were determined which has so far not yet been carried out by others. Steroid metabolite concentrations were determined in 24-h urine samples for calculation of endogenous production rates.

Patients and Methods

The study included male healthy subjects and depressed patients. The patients (male, 59 ± 8 years old), who had been drug-free for at least 1 week, had a major depressive episode according to DSM III at the time of investigation. Inclusion criteria required a Hamilton rating score of depression (21 items scale) of at least 19 points as baseline. The healthy volunteers consisted of male subjects who were 22–40 years old or control subjects who were age and body weight matched for the depressed patients.

Table 1. Excretion rates (μg/24 h) and ratio of excretion rates of catecholestrogens and 2-methoxyestrogens in depressed patients and healthy controls. Values given are the mean ± S.D. determined in 24-h urine samples of 6 depressed patients and 12 male healthy controls

Steroid	Healthy controls	Depressed patients	Significance
Primary estrogens	8.8 ± 2.9	6.1 ± 1.5	N.S.
2-Hydroxyestrogens	5.2 ± 2.4	3.1 ± 1.3	N.S.
4-Hydroxyestrogens	1.3 ± 0.5	0.6 ± 0.2	<0.05
2-Methoxyestrogens	8.7 ± 4.8	10.3 ± 3.2	N.S.
2-Methoxyestrogens/ 2-Hydroxyestrogens	1.8 ± 0.7	3.8 ± 1.6	<0.05

Unless otherwise indicated 24-h urine samples were collected from 7.00 to 7.00 a.m. of the next day. The samples were stored frozen (–25°C) until assayed.

The concentrations of estrogens, 2- and 4-hydroxylated estrogens, 2-O-methoxyestrogens and HPO were measured in the urine samples after multiple chromatographic separation steps and determined either by radioimmunoassay or gas chromatography coupled with mass spectrometry as described elsewhere [7,8].

Results

In the depressed patients the production rates of 2- and 4-hydroxylated estrogens and 2-O-methylated catecholestrogens ranged between 0.2 and 48 μg/24 h, thus being similar to the excretion rates of primary estrogens (Table 1). As compared to healthy controls, the production of 4-hydroxyestrogens was significantly lower in the depressed patients. The ratio of excretion rates of 2-methoxyestrogens: 2-hydroxyestrogens, which is considered as an index for 2-O-methylation, was about 2-fold higher in the patients. This difference thus indicated that alterations in methylation or demethylation reactions were associated with depression.

The determinations of HPO showed for the first time that the progesterone metabolite was present in urine samples of all healthy volunteers with high interindividual variations. The mean excretion rate was 14.8 ± 11.8 μg/24 h. There were no indications for diurnal variations when analyzing the production rates for daytime and night hours separately. Furthers studies will show if the formation of this potent steroid acting on the $GABA_A$ receptor complex [6] is altered in psychiatric patients.

Conclusions

Determination of HPO, catecholestrogens and 2-methoxyestrogens in urine samples revealed that the steroid metabolites are formed in low amounts similar to those of primary sex steroids. The analysis of estrogen metabolism in the depressed patients indicated that psychotropic properties should not be restricted to the classical sex steroids. Their metabolism and the resulting metabolites must also be considered. To our knowledge, this is the first study that has revealed distinct alterations in the metabolism of estrogens in depressed patients. The pathognomonic relevance of such disturbances remains to be clarified.

References

1. Herrmann WM and Beach RC (1978) Pharmacopsychiatry 11: 19–26.
2. Hiemke C and Banger M (1990) Clin. Neuropharmacol. (Suppl. 2) 13: 514–515.
3. Quadagno DM and Ho GKW (1975) Horm. Behav. 6: 19–26.
4. Hiemke C, Poetz B and Ghraf R (1985) J. Endocrinol. 106: 37–42.
5. Knuppen R (1980) In: Wuttke W and Horowski R (eds.) Gonadal Steroids and Brain Function. Springer, Berlin pp. 108–117.
6. Schumacher M (1990) Trends Neurosci. 13: 359–362.
7. Banger M, Hiemke C, Knuppen R, Ball P, Haupt M and Wiedemann K (1990) Biol. Psychiatry 28: 685–696.
8. Hiemke C, Banger M, Knuppen R, Haupt O and Jussofie A (1991) J. Neuroendocrinol. 3: (in press).

© 1991 Elsevier Science Publishers B.V. All rights reserved.
Biological Psychiatry, Volume 2. G. Racagni et al., editors.

Modulation of GABAergic neurotransmission by progesterone metabolites

Virendra B. Mahesh, Darrell W. Brann, and Carla D. Putnam
Department of Physiology and Endocrinology, Medical College of Georgia, Augusta, GA 30912-3000, U.S.A.

Introduction

Recent work from our laboratory has shown that progesterone plays a critical role in synchronizing and enhancing the preovulatory surge of gonadotropins to the magnitude required for normal ovulation [1]. Progesterone is extensively metabolized in the body and progesterone metabolites are generally considered as metabolic end-products of degradation of progesterone that are readily conjugated to form water-soluble products for rapid elimination from the body. Work from several laboratories has now demonstrated conclusively that progesterone metabolites may regulate the secretion of gonadotropins [2–6] and inhibit uterine contractions [7,8].

Involvement of GABAergic transmission in gonadotropin release

Two progesterone metabolites, 5α-dihydroprogesterone (5α-pregnane-3,20-dione; 5α-DHP) and 3α,5α-tetrahydroprogesterone (3α-hydroxy-5α-pregnan-20-one; 3α,5α-THP) were shown by Murphy and Mahesh to bring about selective release of FSH [4] and LH [5] respectively in estrogen-primed ovariectomized immature rats. Of these, 5α-DHP could readily bind to the progesterone receptor whereas 3α,5α-THP did not bind to the progesterone receptor from the rat uterus, chick oviduct or the guinea pig uterus. Recent work of several investigators has shown that 3α,5α-THP and many of the 5β-reduced progesterone metabolites are able to bind and modulate the $GABA_A$ receptors in the brain and that this action is responsible for the anesthetic effects of these steroids [9–11]. Therefore the possibility of the action of 3α,5α-THP on the selective release of LH in the estrogen-primed ovariectomized immature rat by the modulation of the $GABA_A$ system was examined by Brann et al. [6]. The results in Table 1 show that in the estrogen-primed ovariectomized immature rat, the administration of 1.6 mg/kg bw of 3α,5α-THP brought about a selective release of LH, whereas serum FSH was not significantly different from the control. The $GABA_A$ receptor antagonist picrotoxin (1 mg/kg bw) [10,12,13] or the progesterone antagonist RU486 did not alter serum LH or FSH levels when administered to the estrogen-primed rats.

Table 1.[a]Inhibition of 3α,5α-tetrahydroprogesterone-induced LH release by the $GABA_A$ antagonist picrotoxin but not by the progesterone antagonist RU486 in estrogen-primed ovariectomized immature rats

Treatment	Serum LH (% control)	Serum FSH (% control)
Vehicle	100	100
RU486	104	106
Picrotoxin	101	97
3α,5α-THP	217[b]	81
3α,5α-THP+RU486	212[b]	109
3α,5α-THP+picrotoxin	80[c]	80

[a]Compiled from Brann et al [6]. 26-day old immature female rats were ovariectomized and injected with 2 μg estradiol for 2 days. On the 3rd day they received either vehicle or RU486 (200 μg) or picrotoxin (1 mg/kg bw) at 8 a.m. and vehicle or 3α,5α-THP (1.6 mg/kg bw) at 9 a.m. Serum gonadotropins were measured at 3 p.m.;
[b]Significantly increased ($P < 0.05$) over vehicle, RU486 and picrotoxin controls;
[c]Significantly decreased ($P < 0.05$) as compared to 3α,5α treatment.

However, when these agents were administered 1 h prior to the 3α,5α-THP administration, the $GABA_A$ receptor antagonist picrotoxin but not RU486 antagonized the selective LH release. These results demonstrated that 3α,5α-THP exerts its biological action through the $GABA_A$ receptor system rather that the classical intracellular progesterone receptor.

Role of GABAergic system in modulating steroid effects on uterine contractility

The concept of the modulation of reproductive function by steroids through mechanisms other than the classical intracellular steroid receptors was intriguing, and it was important to seek confirmation of such effects. The uterus appeared to be an important tissue to study because it contained a high density of $GABA_A$ receptor sites [14] and uterine contractility was inhibited by progesterone metabolites [7]. Therefore the effect of progesterone, 3α,5α-THP, 5β-pregnane-3,20-dione and 3β-hydroxy-5β-pregnan-20-one on uterine contractility were studied in vitro by Putnam et al. [8] in the presence and absence of the progesterone antagonist RU486 and the $GABA_A$ antagonist, picrotoxin. Once again, RU486 and picrotoxin did not have any effect on uterine contractility in the absence of the progestins. As shown in Table 2, progesterone and the three progesterone metabolites significantly inhibited uterine contractility. Progesterone and 5β-pregnane-3,20-dione exerted their effects through the progesterone and not $GABA_A$ receptor because the progesterone receptor antagonist RU486 but not picrotoxin was able to override their inhibitory effects on uterine contractility. On the other hand, the inhibition of uterine contractility by 3α,5α-THP and 3β-hydroxy-5β-pregnan-20-one was mediated through the $GABA_A$ receptor system because picrotoxin but not

Table 2.[a]Inhibition of uterine contractility by progesterone and its metabolites and the effect of the progesterone receptor antagonist RU486 and $GABA_A$ receptor antagonist picrotoxin on steroid-induced uterine contractility

Treatment	Tension g/mg uterine tissue			
	Vehicle	Steroid	Steroid plus RU486	Steroid plus picrotoxin
Progesterone	50 ± 3	34 ± 4[b]	58 ± 8	28 ± 4[d]
5β-pregnane-3,20-dione	46 ± 7	28 ± 1[b]	44 ± 5	18 ± 2[d]
3β-hydroxy-5β-pregnan-20-one	30 ± 5	16 ± 2[b]	21 ± 1[c]	34 ± 5
3α,5α-THP	43 ± 8	17 ± 2[b]	18 ± 1[c]	38 ± 6

[a]Compiled from Putnam et al. [8]. Uterine rings from diestrus-II rats were exposed to vehicle or progesterone (40 μg/ml), 5β-pregnane-3,20-dione (10 μg/ml), 3β-hydroxy-5β-pregnan-20-one (6 μg/ml), 3α,5α-THP (27.5 μg/ml) with or without 16 μg/ml of RU486 or 32 μg/ml picrotoxin;
[b]Significantly different ($P < 0.05$) from vehicle-treated controls;
[c]Steroid effect not reversed by RU486;
[d]Steroid effect not reversed by picrotoxin.

RU486 was able to override their effects. Incidentally, 3β-hydroxy-5β-pregnan-20-one turned out to be the most potent inhibitor of uterine contractility among the four steroids tried [7,8] and its actions were modulated through the $GABA_A$ receptor system.

Conclusions

This study points out the biological importance of progesterone metabolites and the $GABA_A$ receptor system in important reproductive functions such as gonadotropin secretion and uterine contractility. Furthermore, they emphasize alternative mechanisms of steroid hormone action that do not utilize the classical intracellular steroid receptor system.

Acknowledgements

This work was supported by Research Grant HD-16688 from the National Institute of Child Health and Human Development, National Institutes of Health, Bethesda, Maryland, U.S.A.

References

1. Brann DW and Mahesh VB (1991) Front. Neuroendocrinol. 12: 167.
2. Nuti KM and Karavolas HJ (1977) Endocrinology 100: 777.

3. Zanisi M and Martini L (1979) J. Steroid Biochem. 11: 885.
4. Murphy LL and Mahesh VB (1984) Biol. Reprod. 30: 594.
5. Murphy LL and Mahesh VB (1984) Biol. Reprod. 30: 795.
6. Brann DW, Putnam CD and Mahesh VB (1990) Endocrinology 126: 1854.
7. Kubli-Garfias C, Medrano-Conde L, Beyer C and Bondani A (1979) Steroids 34: 609.
8. Putman CD, Brann DW and Mahesh VB (1991) Biol. Reprod. (in press).
9. Simmonds M and Turner J (1987) Neuropharmacology 26: 923.
10. Gee K, Bolger M, Brinton R, Coirini H and McEwen B (1988) J. Pharmacol. Exp. Ther. 246: 803.
11. Majewska M, Harrison N, Schwartz R, Baker J and Paul SM (1986) Science 236: 1004.
12. Harrison N and Simmonds M (1984) Brain Res. 323: 287.
13. Turner D, Ransom R, Yang J and Olsen R (1989) J. Pharmacol. Exp. Ther. 248: 960.
14. Majewska M, Falkay G and Baulieu EE (1989) Eur. J. Pharmacol. 174: 43.

© 1991 Elsevier Science Publishers B.V. All rights reserved.
Biological Psychiatry, Volume 2. G. Racagni et al., editors.

TRH and mood and anxiety disorders

James C. Garbutt

Department of Psychiatry, University of North Carolina, Chapel Hill, NC 27599 and Clinical Research Unit, Dorothea Dix Hospital, Raleigh, NC 27603, U.S.A.

Introduction

The discovery of the chemical structure of thyrotropin-releasing hormone (TRH) in 1969 was followed by the observation that TRH produced behavioral effects in animals independent of its endocrine actions. These observations suggested that manipulation of TRH function in brain might have therapeutic effects in psychiatric disorders, a promise that has only been partly fulfilled.

The purpose of this review is to integrate the basic and clinical evidence suggesting that TRH or TRH analogues may be useful in the treatment of individuals with mood and anxiety disorders.

Basic science studies

Early observations reported that TRH had arousal and activating properties related, in part, to effects on monoaminergic and cholinergic systems (see [1] for review).

Metcalf [2] reviewed data indicating that TRH and centrally acting TRH analogues are active in a variety of antidepressant screening tests in animals, including the Porsolt test [3]. Parallel to these findings it has been reported that antidepressant administration alters the behavioral response to TRH [4] and increases TRH levels in brain [5]. TRH-induced decreases in brain β-adrenergic receptors have been reported by one group [6] but not another (see [2]) and brain 5-HT_2 receptors have been reported not to be reduced by chronic TRH [7].

Though less studied, anxiolytic effects of TRH alone and in combination with benzodiazepines, barbiturates and ethanol have been reported in animal models [8].

Clinical studies

The first clinical trials of TRH in psychiatric patients were the reports by Prange et al. [9] and Kastin et al. [10] in 1972 that intravenous TRH produced a rapid and transient antidepressant and anxiolytic effect in depressed patients. Over the next eight years on the order of 30 studies involving around 550 patients investigated the antidepressant actions of TRH utilizing oral and i.v. routes with different dosages and many different designs. This work has been thoroughly reviewed [11] and in balance, shows an equal distribution between positive and negative studies controlling for length of trial. In 1983 [12] it was reported that the TRH analogue CG 3509 had marginal effects in depressed patients; to my knowledge no therapeutic studies have been completed since.

Two studies have reported that i.v. TRH reduces tension in normal women [13,14]. Therapeutic studies of TRH in anxiety disorders per se have not been reported.

Reducing the clinical trials to a conclusive statement on TRH as an antidepressant is made difficult by differences in study design. As noted by Prange et al. [11] the data are compatible with TRH having some positive effects in some depressed patients but the data do not indicate that TRH is an antidepressant in the same clinical sense as standard antidepressants. However, the problems of TRH dose, duration of administration and other design problems, e.g. use of refractory patients, confound the issue.

Future directions

Though clinical studies to date have been mixed, the positive reports coupled with the continued evidence from animal studies that TRH has antidepressant and anxiolytic actions indicate that further work on the therapeutic uses of TRH in mood and anxiety disorders is indicated.

Two developments outside the field of psychiatry may enable this work to be advanced. First, studies in patients with amyotrophic lateral sclerosis have shown that doses of TRH orders of magnitude higher than those previously used in psychiatry can safely be given to humans. Second, analogues of TRH have been developed that exhibit greater stability and enhanced CNS activity compared to TRH. Several analogues have relatively low potency in stimulating TSH and prolactin release, an important consideration for practical clinical use. Trials with high doses of TRH and with TRH analogues in mood and anxiety disorders are needed.

At a theoretical level is the question of whether TRH could offer any therapeutic advantage over existing antidepressants. The original reports generated excitement, in part because they indicated TRH could produce amelioration of depression in hours. However, it has yet to be demonstrated that lasting remission in depression can be achieved by any means in this time frame. Nevertheless, the likely novel mechanism of action of TRH would be expected to provide new therapeutic options for some types of depression and if TRH exhibits anxiolytic effects in humans its arousing properties would offer a distinct advantage over benzodiazepines.

References

1. Nemeroff CB, Kalivas PW, Golden RN et al. (1984). Pharmacol. Ther. 24: 1–56.
2. Metcalf G (1982) Brain Res. Rev. 4: 389–408.
3. Ogawa N, Mizuno S, Mori A et al. (1984) Peptides 5: 743–746.
4. Bennett GW, Green AR, Leghton C et al. (1986) Br. J. Pharmacol. 88: 129–139.
5. Lighton C, Bennett GW and Marsden CA (1985). Neuropharmacology 2: 401–406.
6. Schmidt BH and Schultz JE (1985) J. Pharmacol. Exp. Ther. 233: 466–472.
7. Pranzatelli MR, Dailey A and Markush (1989) Ann. N.Y. Acad. Sci. 553: 503–504.
8. Witkin JM, Sickle J and Barrett JE (1984). Peptides 5: 809–813.
9. Prange AJ Jr, Wilson IC, Lara PP et al. (1972). Lancet ii: 999–1002.
10. Kastin AJ, Ehrensing RH, Schalch DS et al. (1972) Lancet ii: 740–742.
11. Prange AJ Jr, Loosen PT, Wilson IC et al. (1984) In: Post RM and Ballenger JC (eds.) Neurobiology of Mood Disorders. Williams and Wilkins, Baltimore/London, pp. 11–322.
12. Benkert O and Flohe L (1983) In: Griffiths EC and Bennett GW (eds.) Thyrotropin-Releasing Hormone. Raven Press, New York, p. 353.
13. Wilson IC, Prange AJ Jr, Lara PP et al. (1973) Arch. Gen. Psychiatry 29: 15–21.
14. Winokur A, Amsterdam JD, Mihailovic V et al. (1982) Psychoneuroendocrinology 7: 239–244.

© 1991 Elsevier Science Publishers B.V. All rights reserved.
Biological Psychiatry, Volume 2. G. Racagni et al., editors.

ACTH-related neuropeptides in the treatment of autistic children

Herman van Engeland, Jan Buitelaar, Jan van Ree and Jan van Hooff
Department of Child and Adolescent Psychiatry, University Hospital Utrecht, P.O. Box 85500, 3508 GA Utrecht, The Netherlands

Introduction

Childhood autism is a chronic persisting psychiatric disorder that is pre-eminently marked by deficits in social interaction. Recently psychophysiological information processing research has revealed that autistic children show deficits in the processing of novel, unpredictable and complex stimuli [1,2]. Several authors have conjectured that this information processing deficit has selective effects on the processing of social stimuli, suggesting that in autism an information processing deficit is basic to disturbances in social behaviour. In animal research, ACTH-related peptides definitely have a positive effect on novelty behaviour, attention and learning [3]. In human studies the synthetic adrenocorticotrophic hormone (4-9) positively influences social behaviour [4] as well as information processing [5]. So it is quite conceivable that ACTH-related peptides might be useful in the treatment of autistic children.

Ethology and childhood autism

In a first study, ethological methods for the observation and analysis of behaviour were applied to chart the deficit and the structure of social behaviour of autistic children. The concept of the structure of behaviour refers to the temporo-sequential relationship of various behaviour elements and to the distinction of behavioural systems. This process of pattern detection is based among others on the temporal contingencies of behavioural elements. The social behaviour of 14 autistic children and 10 non-autistic retarded control children was observed in a semi-structured playroom session. The time relationships of single behaviour elements were registered by means of an event recorder. The behavioural elements of the children to be registered included a fine grained scoring of gaze behaviours, talk behaviours, stereotypies, reactions to task behaviour and non-verbal gestures. Temporal contingencies of behaviour elements were assessed on the basis of a matrix of combination frequencies within a time-frame of 5 s. For each cell of this matrix, standardized residuals were calculated which served as an expression of the temporal contingencies. The comparison of the structure of social behaviour between both groups revealed that gaze behaviours of child and experimenter in the control group were showing high temporal contingencies in contrast to the autistic group. This indicates that in the control group gaze behaviours are emitted closely together in time, pointing to the establishment of mutual eye contact. Conversely, gaze behaviours of the autistics were occurring temporarily independently from the gaze behaviour by the experimenter. A second difference concerned the strong contingencies between the verbal initiatives (putting a question, shifting the conversation to a new topic) and stereotypies in the autistic group. Obviously verbal initiative by the autistics was connected strongly with stereotyped behaviours, denoting a rigid way of making verbal initiatives by asking for the same thing again and again [6].

Behavioural effects of ACTH-peptides

The behavioural effects of ORG 2766 (a synthetic analogue of the adrenocorticotrophic hormone (4-9)) in 14 outpatient autistic children were studied in a double-blind placebo-controlled crossover design. Each child was given orally 20 mg ORG 2766 per day during 4 weeks and drug effects were monitored by the above-described ethological playroom observation, as well as by behaviour rating scales, filled out by parents and teachers. Behaviour rating scales did not show significant changes. Ethological playroom observation made clear that ORG 2766 decreased stereotypic behaviour, while increasing amount as well as quality of the social interaction of the autistic children [7].

In a second study ORG 2766 (40 mg per child per day during 8 weeks) was orally administered to 20 autistic children under double-blind placebo-controlled conditions. Parents' behaviour ratings as well as clinicians' behaviour ratings pointed to significant behavioural improvement after ORG 2766 administration, most clearly indicating a decrease in social withdrawal in autistic children. Ethological observation of playroom behaviour showed a significantly increased social interaction of the autistic child and favourable changes in the total amount, the type and the social quality of the children's play behaviour. Gaze coordination between child and the experimenter was improved, while task responding gestural, gaze and verbal communicative behaviours revealed themselves to be more coherently organized in one behaviour cluster after ORG 2766 administration.

Conclusion

The results indicate that specific disturbances in the social behaviour of autistic children are beneficially influenced by ACTH-related peptides. Whether this positive effect of ORG 2766 is mediated by improvement of attentional and information processing mechanisms is still an open question.

References

1. van Engeland H, Roelofs JW, Verbaten MN and Slangen JL (1991) Psychiatr. Res. (accepted).
2. Verbaten MN, Roelofs JW, van Engeland H, Kenemans JL and Slangen JL (1991) J. Autism Dev. Disord. (accepted).
3. De Wied D and Jolles J (1982) Physiol. Rev. 62: 976–1059.
4. van Ree JM (1991) In: Morley JE and Korenman SG (eds.) Problems in Geriatric Endocrinology. Blackwell, Cambridge, U.K.
5. Born J, Kern W, Pietrowsky R, Sittig W and Fehm HL (1989) Psychopharmacology 99: 439–444.
6. Buitelaar JK, van Engeland H, de Kogel CH, de Vries H and van Hooff JARAM (1991a) J. Child Psychol. Psychiatry (accepted).
7. Buitelaar JK, van Engeland H, van Ree JM and de Wied D (1990)· J. Autism Dev. Disord. 20: 467–478.

© 1991 Elsevier Science Publishers B.V. All rights reserved.
Biological Psychiatry, Volume 2. G. Racagni et al., editors.

Neuropeptides in dementia

Per Kragh-Sørensen, Annette Lolk and Henry Nielsen
Department of Psychiatry, Odense University, DK-5000 Odense C, Denmark

Introduction

Studies by de Wied and his colleagues demonstrated the effects of 2 neuropeptides, vasopressin (VP) and adrenocorticotropin (ACTH), on memory and learning processes in rodents [1]; this served as a major impetus to study the role of neuropeptides in neurodegenerative disorders such as Alzheimer's Disease (AD) and Senile Dementia of Alzheimer's Type (SDAT).

The initial clinical trials, mostly uncontrolled, of VP therapy of demented patients were unbelievably promising. Subsequent controlled clinical trials did not prove to be entirely consistent with these initial findings.

In this paper, clinical results of ACTH-like peptides are examined. As dementia is the most serious psychiatric disorder in old age, focus will be placed on the significance of the clinical use of these medications in AD/SDAT. In this context the validity of the clinical diagnosis, its grading of severity and definition of treatment efficacy in demented patients will be discussed.

Clinical trials in man

ACTH and related peptides, in particular Org 2766, have been studied quite extensively in humans in connection with a wide range of cognitive performance tasks.

Studies using acute systemic administration have failed to demonstrate a consistent treatment effect. Findings concerning subchronic oral treatment with Org 2766 appear to improve mood, which leads to increased sociability, feelings of competence and greater co-operation in institutional life. In a recent placebo-controlled study covering 156 patients mildly or moderately demented using 5–80 mg/day for 1 month, Org 2766 induced a small but significant therapeutic effect, mainly on the SCAG total score, but in particular on cognitive and somatic functioning [2]. These effects were almost unrelated to the dose administered and clinically relevant effects were shown in 25% of the patients. Post hoc analysis showed the best effects in mildly demented patients with comparatively good orientation who complained of lack of energy. Because of the very vague although statistically significant results, the authors questioned both the validity of SCAG as a assessment instrument and the validity of the diagnosis in the group of "responders" (DSM III criteria of Primary Degenerative Senile Dementia).

Clinical assessment of diagnosis

There are many difficulties encountered in the clinical diagnosis of dementia in the elderly. In this connection an area of particular interest is mild dementia. Although this term is already in common usage in pharmacological, clinical and epidemiological literature, there are certain difficulties connected with the concept. The need to define homogeneous diagnostic groups with mild dementia is obvious, as potential pharmacological treatment will at that stage most likely prove effective.

A population of 87 patients with mild or moderate degree of dementia of AD/SDAT or vascular dementia (DSM III criteria) were included in a 3-year follow-up study [3]. Of the surviving 57 patients (38 AD/SDAT) evaluated by means of rating scales and psychometric tests, 11 AD/SDAT patients underwent no intellectual deterioration and in 9 AD/SDAT patients cognitive decline remained doubtful. These results underline the problems of early diagnosis of dementia according to the DSM III criteria.

Procedures in evaluating dementia

There are many methods available for assessing drug effects in geriatric psychopharmacology. They can be classified as rating scales, psychometric tests and measures of neurophysiological function. Most of the rating scales available (i.e. SCAG) are not specifically designed for use in AD/SDAT patients. As a result, most of the scales do not evaluate all the symptoms characteristic of and specifically associated with dementia.

Measures of performance on psychometric tests are likely to be the most valid, reliable and sensitive in the assessment of the efficacy of drug treatment of dementia.

In a recent study [4], we had for the first time the opportunity of comparing SCAG with the more recently developed Brief Cognitive Rating Scale (BCRS) [5] and the assessment reached on these 2 rating scales with the results of a psychometric test battery. The results of the statistical analysis (i.e. setwise multiple regression analyses, canonical correlation analysis) questioned the validity of the SCAG as an assessment instrument in psychopharmacological treatment of cognitive decline.

Conclusion

The literature reviewed is confusing, and so are the results. The findings suggest that ACTH-like peptides can affect human behaviour in certain circumstances. It is still an open question whether this effect is specific or non-specific. It is, however, evident that the clinical methodology used in the studies is not optimal. The need to define homogeneous diagnostic groups with mildly demented cases is evident. The present data has emphasized the need for valid rating scales as well as valid psychometric tests, in studies evaluating treatment effects in patients with AD/SDAT.

References

1. De Wied D (1984) Trends Neurosci. 7: 62–67.
2. Kragh-Sørensen P, Bang Olsen R, Lund S, Van Riezen H and Steffensen K (1986) Progr. Neuro-Psychopharmacol. Biol. Psychiatry 10: 479–492.
3. Nielsen H, Lolk A, Pedersen I, Autzen M, Sennef C and Kragh-Sørensen P (1991) The accuracy of early diagnosis and predictors of death in Alzheimer's disease and vascular dementia a follow-up study. Acta Psychiatr. Scand. (accepted for publication).
4. Lolk A, Nielsen H and Kragh-Sørensen P (1988) Acta Psychiatr. Scand. 78: 592–598.
5. Reisberg B, Schneck MK, Ferris SH, Schwartz GE and de Leon MJ (1983) Psychopharmacol. Bull. 19: 47–50.

© 1991 Elsevier Science Publishers B.V. All rights reserved.
Biological Psychiatry, Volume 2. G. Racagni et al., editors.

Do vasopressin-like neuropeptides influence human memory?

Bill E. Beckwith, Thomas V. Petros and Robyn R. Swenson

Psychology Department, University of North Dakota, Box 7187, University Station, Grand Forks, ND 58202, U.S.A.

The belief that vasopressin (VP) influences learning and memory originated with DeWied's early demonstration that removal of the neurohypophysis disrupted avoidance behavior which was corrected after treatment with peripheral administration of pitressin, an extract of the neurohypophysis [1]. Subsequently, it was demonstrated that the active constituent of pitressin was VP and that peripheral administration of VP could both restore normal avoidance in hypophysectomized rats and delay extinction in intact rats. Based on data such as these, DeWied and Bohus [2] were the first to suggest that VP facilitated long-term memory.

Although early clinical studies with humans supported the belief that peripherally administered VP enhanced memory (e.g., [3,4]), subsequent clinical evaluations have not been uniformly successful [5,6]. One explanation for these inconsistencies is that VP improves memory only when degenerative processes in the brain are mild to moderate rather than severe [6]. If the actions of VP are more prominent in less severe disorders of memory and if VP also has the capacity to act on memory in intact systems, then it seems reasonable to assume that one may gain knowledge of the potential of VP to abate disorders of memory by exploring its actions on memory in healthy volunteers [7]. Numerous studies have demonstrated the efficacy of VP in facilitating memory in healthy volunteers [7]. When administered to healthy adult volunteers, VP has been shown to improve the consistency, organization and completeness of recall for structured lists of words [8]; to improve visual, spatial and auditory memory as assessed by a variety of neuropsychological tests [9] and to enhance the primacy effect and impair the recency effect in free recall of lists of unrelated words [10]. In addition, a series of studies has shown that a single 60 μg dose of the VP analog DDAVP enhanced visual discrimination learning [11], memory scanning for digits [12], recall of implicational sentences [13,14] and recall of narrative prose [15].

It is also interesting to note that several of these studies have used the VP analog DDAVP which produced no effect on gross measures of autonomic function; i.e. heart rate, systolic blood pressure and diastolic blood pressure [11]. In addition, although treatment with DDAVP has been shown to increase the concentration of urine in subjects demonstrating changes in memory performance, DDAVP did not alter the concentration of salivary cortisol in these same subjects [16]. Furthermore, neither specific gravity of urine nor salivary cortisol were associated with memory performance in this study. Thus, it appears that the mnemonic effect of VP may be independent of obvious changes in cardiovascular reactivity, renal activity, or modulation of glucocorticoids. This suggests that VP may modulate human memory by some as yet unspecified alteration of CNS function independent of its classical endocrine actions.

Where do we go from here? There are at least two directions that seem useful for future behaviorally-oriented research. First, it is apparent that there are a multitude of methodological factors which enter into the equation for determining whether an effect will be demonstrated and how large an effect may be found. These factors include not only pharmacological variables such as dose, time course, analog, time of day, etc., but also many nonpharmacological variables. For example, it appears important to consider the impact of individual differences in this equation. Gender [13,17] and verbal ability [14] have already been demonstrated to be important factors that modulate the effects of VP on memory. Second, we need models of human memory from which to work, e.g. Cowan [18]. These models will help specify the precise cognitive processes modified by VP which will, in turn, guide the construction of rational clinical trials.

As we gain a more useful understanding of memory systems and of the localization of cognitive operations in the human brain, we need concurrent efforts to describe and to understand the impact of pharmacologically and behaviorally relevant variables on human memory. It is essential that evaluations of the effect of VP on human memory be directed by theory-driven experiments (e.g. [10,15]). This will allow more precise statements indicating how this neuropeptide does and does not guide human information processing. The interaction of important pharmacological and behavioral variables with various treatments is important to disentangle if we are to more clearly understand the mechanism by which VP or other neuropeptides influence human memory and where to look in assessing their clinical utility as a treatment for disorders of memory.

References

1. De Wied D (1965) Int. J. Neuropharmacol. 4: 157–167.
2. De Wied D and Bohus B (1966) Nature 212: 1484–1486.
3. Legros JJ, Gilot P, Seron X, Claessens J, Adam A, Moeglen JM, Audibert A and Berchier P (1978) Lancet i: 41–42.
4. Oliveros JC, Jandeli MK, Trimsit-Berthier M, Remy R, Benzhezal A, Audibert A and Moeglen JM (1978) Lancet i: 42.
5. Tinklenberg JR and Thornton JE (1983) Psychopharmacol. Bull. 19: 199–211.
6. Jolles J (1987) In: Gash DM and Boer GJ (eds.) Vasopressin: Principles and Properties. Plenum Press, New York, pp. 549–578.
7. Beckwith BE, Petros TV, Couk DI and Tinius TP (1990) Ann. N.Y. Acad. Sci. 579: 215–226.
8. Weingartner H, Gold P, Ballenger JC, Smallberg SA, Summers R, Rubinov DR, Post RM and Goodwin FK (1981) Science 211: 601–603.
9. Laczi F, Van Ree JM, Wagner A, Valkusz JS, Jaranhazy T, Kovacs GL, Telegdy G, Szulard J, Laszlo FA and De Wied D (1983) Acta Endocrinol. 102: 205–212.
10. Fehm-Wolfsdorf G, Voigt KH and Fehm HL (1983) In: Endroeczi E, Angelucci L, De Wied D and Scapagnini V (eds.) Neuropeptides and Psychosomatic Processes. Academiai Kiado, Budapest, pp. 81–88.

11. Beckwith BE, Petros TV, Kanaan-Beckwith S, Couk DI, Haug R and Ryan C (1982) Peptides 3: 627–630.
12. Beckwith BE, Couk DI and Till TS (1983) Peptides 4: 707–709.
13. Beckwith BE, Till RE and Schneider V (1984) Peptides 5: 819–822.
14. Till RE and Beckwith BE (1985) Peptides 6: 397–402.
15. Beckwith BE, Petros TV, Bergloff PJ and Staebler R (1987) Behav. Neurosci. 101: 429–432.
16. Beckwith BE, Till RE, Reno CR and Poland RE (1990) Peptides 11: 473–476.
17. Beckwith BE, Petros TV and Knutson KK (1990) Peptides 11: 1313–1315.
18. Cowan N (1988) Psychol. Bull. 104: 163–191.

© 1991 Elsevier Science Publishers B.V. All rights reserved.
Biological Psychiatry, Volume 2. G. Racagni et al., editors.

Overview of peptides and peptide systems with special reference to coexistence with classical transmitters

T. Hökfelt, A. Bean, S. Ceccatelli, Å. Dagerlind, R.P. Elde, M. Goldstein, B. Meister, A.P. Nicholas, M. Pelto-Huikko, V. Pieribone, M. Schalling, V. Verge, M. Villar, Z. Xu and T. Bartfai

Department of Histology, Karolinska Institute, Stockholm; and Department of Biochemistry, Arrhenius Laboratory, Stockholm University, Sweden

It is now evident that numerous molecules may be involved in chemical signalling in the nervous system and that they can be divided into different sub-classes. Thus, in addition to amino acids, such as GABA and glutamate, and biogenic amines, such as dopamine and noradrenaline, neurons produce and release peptides. These neuropeptides represent a heterogeneous group of molecules, the smallest ones built up of only two amino acids with larger peptides consisting of 40 or more amino acids. In fact, it is not quite easy to draw a distinct line between these so-called polypeptides and small protein molecules, for example growth factors which are also present in the nervous system. The interest in neuropeptides has arisen thanks to the pioneering work of Erspamer, Mutt, Leeman, Guillemin, Schally, Vale and others.

The distribution and cellular localization of peptides have been analysed using both radioimmunoassay and immunohistochemistry, and this work revealed that the various peptides show a distinct and highly regional distribution in the nervous system. In most instances they are present in neurons which already contain, for example, a catecholamine, or the cholinergic transmitter acetylcholine or an amino acid transmitter, i.e., compounds which are often referred to as classical transmitters. A large number of such coexistence situations have been described in the literature during the last decade [1]. Examples are the presence of cholecystokinin (CCK) in mesencephalic A10 dopamine neurons and substance P in medullary 5-hydroxytryptamine (5-HT) neurons. Recently, it has been shown that 5-HT/substance P neurons in addition contain glutamate-like immunoreactivity (LI) [2]. Perhaps some neurons operate with three different classes of transmitters – an amino acid, a biogenic amine and one or more peptides.

Our understanding of the functional significance of coexistence of several messengers is not clear. In fact, particularly with regard to the peptides, their role and physiological function still remain to be analyzed in many cases. However, some general principles have emerged concerning the coexistence phenomenon. They may be summarized as follows: a) classical transmitter systems can be subdivided on the basis of specific peptides. For example, the 5-HT neurons projecting to the ventral horn contain substance P and thyrotropin-releasing hormone (TRH), whereas those projecting to the dorsal horn seem to lack these peptides; b) classical transmitters and peptides have a different sub-cellular distribution and are presumably localized in different types of storage vesicles [3]; c) at least in certain systems the release of peptides and classical transmitters is frequency coded, that is whereas classical transmitters are released already at low firing rates, peptides may only be released when neurons are firing at high activity or exhibiting bursting activity [3]. This mechanism is probably related to the differential storage and may operate at least in some systems, and suggests that peptides are only functionally active under certain circumstances. Moreover, it can be predicted that peptide antagonists will not exhibit any marked effects when neurons operate at low activities; and d) classical transmitters and neuropeptides may interact in different fashions. Thus, peptides may be synergistic or antagonistic to the classical transmitter, in the latter case for example by inhibiting the release of the classical transmitter [3].

Here we would like to deal briefly with a few examples of coexistence encompassing 2 peptides, CCK and galanin. CCK-LI occurs in dopamine neurons in the ventral mesencephalon, especially in the ventral tegmental area, i.e., in the A10 dopamine cell group [4]. Using in situ hybridization combined with immunohistochemistry there is now final evidence that in fact dopamine neurons can produce this peptide [5]. A possible role for CCK in dopaminergic mechanisms has therefore been investigated in numerous studies [6]. A wide variety of partly contrasting effects have been reported. It is long known that CCK exerts neuroleptic-like effects [7], and several studies show that CCK may exert an antagonistic action on dopamine transmission. For example, it has been shown that CCK inhibits dopamine release in cat striatum [8]. These findings support the idea that CCK agonists may be used as adjuncts to neuroleptic drugs in treatment of a disease such as schizophrenia. In fact, CCK or CCK analogues have been administered to patients with the diagnosis of schizophrenia [9]. Such studies have raised the question whether or not CCK is indeed present in dopamine neurons in the human brain. Some studies suggest that it is difficult to demonstrate CCK mRNA in human nigral neurons [10,11]. However, in brains from schizophrenic patients treated with neuroleptics such a message could be visualized [11]. This indicates that at least under certain circumstances these neurons have the ability to express the peptide. With regard to other species, CCK mRNA and/or CCK peptide have been shown to occur in mesencephalic dopamine neurons of mouse, cat and monkey but not in guinea pig and hamster [11].

Galanin is a fairly recently discovered peptide built up of 29 amino acids [12]. It has been shown to have a wide distribution in the rat central nervous system [13,14]. One characteristic of certain galanin neurons is that they exhibit a marked plasticity in peptide expression under various experimental manipulations. Thus, after peripheral axotomy there is a marked upregulation of peptide and mRNA levels in sensory ganglia [15], and this also occurs in a number of systems in the brain after various types of lesions. For example, a lesion of the ipsilateral hippocampus causes a distinct upregulation of galanin mRNA and galanin peptide in the cholinergic ventral forebrain neurons [16], and this can be seen also after colchicine treatment [17]. However, an ibotenic acid lesion does not seem to upregulate galanin [16]. The role of galanin in various neurons remains to be established.

The findings discussed here provide evidence that peptides are present in multiple systems and are involved in a wide variety of functions. The recent cloning of several peptide receptors by Japanese and American groups represents further evidence for a physiological role of peptides in neuronal function. The elucidation of such functions will also be greatly facilitated by the recent development of novel non-peptide antagonists which pass the blood-brain barrier. In this way it will be possible to further substantiate the present view that peptides are particularly important under conditions of increased neuronal activity and under pathological conditions.

Acknowledgements

Supported by the Swedish MRC (04X.2887) and NIMH (MH43230).

References

1. Hökfelt T, Millhorn D, Seroogy K, Tsuruo Y, Ceccatelli S, Lindh B, Meister B, Melander T, Schalling M, Bartfai T and Terenius L (1987) Experientia 43: 768.
2. Nicholas AP, Cuello AC, Goldstein M and Hökfelt T (1990) NeuroReport 1: 235.
3. Lundberg JM, Hedlund B, Änggård A, Fahrenkrug J, Hökfelt T, Tatemoto K and Bartfai T (1982) In: Bloom SR, Polak, JM and Lindenlaub E (eds.) Systemic Role of Regulatory Peptides: Co-storage of Peptides and Classical Transmitters in Neurons. K. Schattauer Verlag, Stuttgart-New York, p. 93.
4. Hökfelt T, Skirboll L, Rehfeld JF, Goldstein M, Markey K and Dann O (1980) Neuroscience 5: 2093.
5. Seroogy K, Shalling M, Brené S, Dagerlind Å, Chai SY, Hökfelt T, Persson H, Brownstein M, Huan R, Dixon J, Filer D, Schlessinger D and Goldstein M (1989) Exp. Brain Res. 74: 149.
6. Wang RY, White FJ and Voigt MM (1984) Trends Pharmacol. Sci. 5: 436.
7. Zetler G (1980) Neuropharmacology 19: 415.
8. Markstein R and Hökfelt T (1984) J. Neurosci. 4: 570.
9. Losonczy MF, Davidson M and Davis KL (1987) In: Meltzer HY (ed.) Psychopharmacology: The Third Generation of Progress. Raven Press, New York, p. 715.
10. Palacios JM, Savasta M and Mengod G (1989) Brain Res. 488: 369.
11. Schalling M, Friberg K, Seroogy K, Riederer P, Bird E, Schiffmann SN, Mailleux P, Vanderhaeghen JJ, Kuga S, Goldstein M, Kitahama K, Luppi PH, Jouvet M and Hökfelt T (1990) Proc. Natl. Acad. Sci. U.S.A. 87: 8427.
12. Tatemoto K, Rökaeus Å, Jörnvall H and McDonald TJ (1983) FEBS Lett. 164: 124.
13. Melander T, Hökfelt T and Rökeus Å (1986) J. Comp. Neurol. 248: 475.
14. Skofitsch G and Jacobowitz D (1985b) Peptides 6: 509.
15. Villar MJ, Cortés R, Theodorsson E, Wiesenfeld-Hallin Z, Schalling M, Fahrenkrug J, Emson PC and Hökfelt T (1989) Neuroscience 33: 587.
16. Cortés R, Villar MJ, Verhofstad A and Hökfelt T (1990) Proc. Natl. Acad. Sci. U.S.A. 87: 7742.
17. Cortés R, Ceccatelli S, Schalling M and Hökfelt T (1990) Synapse 6: 369.

© 1991 Elsevier Science Publishers B.V. All rights reserved.
Biological Psychiatry, Volume 2. G. Racagni et al., editors.

Neuropeptides and behavior

David de Wied

Rudolf Magnus Institute, Department of Pharmacology, University of Utrecht, Vondellaan 6, 3521 GD, The Netherlands

A cascade of processes evolves in peptidergic neurons in order to express the genetic information into biologically active neuropeptides. These processes determine the quantities of neuropeptides synthesized and their biological activity through size, form and derivatization. In this way sets of neuropeptides with different opposite and more selective properties are formed from the same precursor. An example of a cell-specific gene expression is the formation of calcitonin in thyroid tissue and that of calcitonin gene-related peptide in the brain by different mRNA from a single gene. The processing of neuropeptide precursors also is a cell-specific phenomenon. Thus, pro-opiomelanocortin (POMC) is processed by corticotrophs of the anterior pituitary to ACTH-(1-39) and a 16-N-terminal fragment, while the melanotrophs in the intermediate lobe convert ACTH(1-39) to α-MSH, ACTH-(18-39), γ-LPH and β-endorphin (βE). Posttranslational modifications as a result of acetylation, sulphation, amidation, glycosylation and phosphorylation again is cell-specific and causes marked alterations in the biological activity of neuropeptides. Thus, acetylation of ACTH-(1-13) to α-MSH markedly enhances the melanotrophic and behavioral effects while reducing their anti-opiate effects. Acetylation of endorphins eliminates their analgesic effects but not their neuroleptic-like effects, while acetylation of vasopressin blocks its peripheral endocrine and central nervous system effects.

Early studies with ACTH on shuttle box avoidance learning in hypophysectomized rats showed that the influence of ACTH on their deficient avoidance learning was not the result of the corticotrophic effect of this polypeptide hormone, but resided in the heptapeptide ACTH-(4-10). This appeared to be a common feature of peptide hormones found in the brain; their CNS effects are dissociated from their classical endocrine influence. Evidence was found that ACTH-(1-39) in the brain is converted into fragments (ACTH-(1-16), α-MSH, ACTH-(4-16), ACTH-(7-16)) which may be responsible for the behavioral effects [1]. The same was found for the neurohypophyseal hormones [2]. Vasopressin and oxytocin are converted to behaviorally active fragments such as [pGlu^4, Cyt^6] AVP-(4-9): OXT-(4-9) e.o. [3] which have lost their classical endocrine effect but act much more potently than the parent molecules on memory processes. These peptides also lack certain CNS effects of vasopressin such as those on thermoregulation, barrel rotation and epilepsy. Other examples of differential effects of neuropeptides derived from the same precursor are CCK-8, which has neuroleptic-like activity and CCK-4, which was found to be anxiogenic. Intraaccumbal injection of substance P (SP-(1-11)) inhibits extinction of pole-jumping avoidance behavior, while the fragment SP-(7-11) has the opposite effect [4]. βE-(1-31) possesses opiate-like effects, while βE-(1-27) is an opiate antagonistic neuropeptide. It also generates non-opiate fragments which possess neuroleptic-like (γ-type endorphins), amphetamine-like (α-type endorphins) or serotonin-like effects (βE-(10-16)) [5]. ACTH/MSH and vasopressin and related neuropeptides which have a positive effect on avoidance behavior, act in an opposite manner on pilocarpine-induced epilepsy. ACTH-(4-10), but not ACTH-(1-24) attenuates, while vasopressin but not the fragment [pGlu^4,Cyt^6]AVP-(4-9) potentiates pilocarpine-induced epilepsya. The effect of vasopressin could be blocked by a V_2 antagonist only, suggesting that the effect is mediated by V_2 receptors. These, however, are not identical to the V_2 receptor found in the kidney [6,7]. Neuropeptide Y (NPY), a 36-amino acid peptide, acts on feeding and memory [8] and injected intracranially increases feeding and improves retention of avoidance behavior in a T-maze. The influence on feeding was found only with the intact peptide, while the effect on retention could be elicited by the intact peptide and the fragment NPY-(20-36). Interestingly a smaller fragment, NPY-(26-36) was without effect. NPY effects on feeding seem to be mediated through postsynaptic (Y_1) NPY receptors, while effects on memory are mediated by presynaptic (Y_2) NPY receptors. In addition, similar CNS effects of different neuropeptides may be caused by their structural relationship. Thus ACTH-(4-10), LHRH and TRH may affect avoidance behavior as a result of the presence of a number of similar amino acid residues [8].

Many behavioral studies are performed with neuropeptides in relatively high amounts. Effects induced by the massive flooding of the brain through the ventricular system may be mediated also by the simultaneous release of endogenous ligands with profound behavioral effects. Thus the administration of vasopressin either following intraventricular or systemic administration causes a measurable increase in IRβE in the CSF [10]. It has been suggested that neuropeptides come into play only following intense stimulation, but not under normal stimulatory conditions. NPY in the sympathetic nerve ending is released only following intense stimulation but not under normal stimulatory conditions. CRH is a powerful stimulant of the sympathetic nervous system. This influence is of central origin and is induced in supraphysiological amounts. This suggests that CRH affects the sympathetic nervous system only in situations of stress [11]. Besides these effects, CRH has CNS effects independent of the influence on the autonomic nervous system. In doses as low as 0.1 ng i.c.v. which do not affect heart rate or core temperature in free-moving rats, CRH attenuates passive avoidance behavior. The antagonist α-CRH-(9-41) blocks the attenuating influence of CRH. One should realize that more than 40 neuropeptides have been found so far in the brain and that these might generate a multitude of biologically active principles, many of which have not yet been discovered.

The long fiber systems which carry POMC, or the precursor molecules of vasopressin and oxytocin from the sites of production in the hypothalamus to extrahypothalamic brain sites, seem to modulate the whole spectrum of central nervous system functions. Neuropeptides generated from these precursors affect learning and memory processes, pain, mood, aggression, social, sexual and maternal behavior, drug-seeking behavior, maintenance behavior (grooming), stretching and yawning. These neuropeptides are involved in the regulation of the autonomic nervous, the cardiovascular, and the respiratory system, body temperature, cerebral blood flow, brain metabolism and sleep-waking cycle.

The limbic system plays an important role in learning and memory processes. The system is richly innervated by fibres containing the classical neurotransmitters such as the monoamines, acetylcholine and serotonin as well as the excitatory (glutamate) and inhibitory amino acid neurotransmitters and inhibitory amino acid neurotransmitters γ-aminobutyric acid (GABA). Besides it is innervated by POMC, vasopressin, oxytocin and CRH-containing nerve fibres. Behavioral studies have shown that neuropeptides related to ACTH/MSH peptides, the endorphins, vasopressin, oxytocin, CRH and other stress hormones, modulate learning and memory processes.

Many other neuropeptides affect learning and memory processes. Interestingly, the gut hormones (CCK, bombesin, gastrin-releasing peptide, pancreastatin) exhibit U-shaped dose-dependent and time-dependent effects on retention of avoidance behavior and prevent amnesia induced by protein synthesis inhibition or scopolamine. Such peptides may mediate the memory effects of feeding and probably act through the vagus nerve [12].

References

1. De Wied D and Jolles J (1982) Physiol. Rev. 62: 976–1059.
2. De Wied D, Joëls M, Burbach JPH, De Jong W, De Kloet ER, Gaffori OWJ, Urban IJA, Van Ree JM, Van Wimersma Greidanus TJB, Veldhuis HD, Versteeg DHG and Wiegant VM (1988) In: Negro-Villar A and Conn PM (eds.) Peptide Hormones: Effects and Mechanisms of Action. CRC Press, Boca Raton, pp. 97–140.
3. Burbach JPH, Kovács GL, De Wied D, Van Nispen JW and Greven HM (1983) Science 221: 1310–1312.
4. Gaffori O, Stewart JM and De Wied D (1984) Experientia 40: 89–91.
5. Van Ree JM, Verhoeven WMA and De Wied D (1987) Prog. Brain Res. 72: 249–267.
6. Wamil A, Croiset G, Kleinrok Z and De Wied D (1989) Neurosci. Res. Commun. 4: 109–116.
7. Croiset G and De Wied D (1990) Eur. J. Pharmacol. 183: 506.
8. Flood JF and Morley JE (1989) Peptides 10: 963–966.
9. De Wied D, Witter A and Greven HM (1975) Biochem. Pharmacol. 24: 1463–1468.
10. Wiegant VM and Sweep CGJ (1990) In: Distler W and Beck L (eds.) Endorphins in Reproduction and Stress. Springer-Verlag, Berlin, pp. 81–91.
11. Diamant M and De Wied D (1991) Endocrinology (in press).
12. Flood JF, Smith GE and Morley JE (1987) Science 236: 832–834.

© 1991 Elsevier Science Publishers B.V. All rights reserved.
Biological Psychiatry, Volume 2. G. Racagni et al., editors.

Neuropeptides in the brain

France Javoy-Agid
INSERM U 289, Hôpital de la Salpêtrière, 47, Bd de l'Hôpital, 75651 Paris Cédex 13, France

One approach to understanding peptide function in mature brain is to study neurodegenerative diseases in the human brain after autopsy to establish correlations between dysfunction of peptidergic neurons, pathological evidence of neuronal damage, and symptoms. Peptides have been investigated in several diseases. Of special interest are the diseases characterized by intellectual disorders. In Alzheimer's disease (AD) histopathological lesions lie essentially in cerebral cortex and hippocampus. AD is clinically diagnosed on intellectual deterioration sufficiently severe to interfere with social or occupational functions, memory impairment, impaired abstract thinking or judgement, aphasia, apraxia or agnosia, personality changes. Parkinsonian syndromes, where cell loss occurs in deep gray matter rather than cerebral cortex, are characterized by movement disorders and may be associated with cognitive deficits distinguished by two essential characteristics: memory disorders associated with frontal-lobe like deficits, absence of aphasia, apraxia and agnosia. Two clinical paradigms will be considered: Parkinson's disease (PD) with neuronal loss in the substantia nigra, and progressive supranuclear palsy (PSP) with additional lesion of the striato-pallidal complex [1].

Accumulation of such studies might give some insight into the anatomical organization of human brain, on the basis of correlations with neuronal damage, as well as into the physiological implication, on the basis of correlations with clinical symptoms.

Several peptides have been radioimmunoassayed in cerebral cortex and/or hippocampus, where they are found within intrinsic neurons (cholecystokinin (CCK), vasoactive intestinal polypeptide (VIP), neuropeptide Y (NPY)) and/or intrinsic or ascending projections (substance P, methionine-enkephalin, thyrotropin-releasing-hormone, neurotensin). Their levels did not markedly differ from controls in AD [2] and demented PD patients [3]. In subcortical areas, no changes were observed related to cognitive deficits. Thus the corresponding neurons are most likely not implicated in these intellectual disorders.

Two peptides, galanin and somatostatin (SS), have stimulated particular attention since alterations of these neuronal systems may be involved in AD and PD cognitive dysfunctions.

Galanin, although distributed throughout the human brain, is present in neuronal cells largely restricted to the basal forebrain. Immunocytochemical and in situ hybridization methods have shown that galanin and galanin gene are expressed in a minor number of cholinergic projection neurons in the basal forebrain as well as in local interneurons. The interneurons form terminal networks which innervate somata and dendrites of the cholinergic cells. Fibers are more widespread, particularly in the hippocampus and scattered throughout the cortex [4].

In AD, the presence of galanin mRNA-labelled cells (small neurons and occasionally large magnocellular) suggests a preservation of the galanin neurons in the basal nucleus of Meynert. The increase in galanin gene expression compared to controls [5], in keeping with above normal peptide levels [4] may indicate a plastic response of galanin system in AD brain. The unaffected cortical and hippocampal concentrations of galanin in AD and PD dementia patients [6] was surprising, since galanin is found in the cholinergic neurons that innervate the cerebral cortex and hippocampus. Indeed, the cholinergic neurons of the basal forebrain, the major source of cholinergic input to the cerebral cortex and hippocampus, are known to degenerate in patients with AD as in PD dementia [1]. It may be, among other hypotheses, that the cholinergic neurons containing galanin are the ones that survive. Galanin could normally subserve a protective or a trophic function. Given the inhibitory actions of galanin on cholinergic function in animal, particularly in basal forebrain-lesioned rats [4], it has been hypothesized [7] that increased galanin transmission during the progression of AD could serve to further inhibit the functions of remaining cholinergic neurons in anatomical pathways relevant to memory. The inhibitory actions of galanin may be greatest in disease states in which cholinergic neurons are damaged or degenerating. From a therapeutic point, galanin could prevent cholinergic drugs from exerting their intended efficacy.

Somatostatin (SS) is widely distributed in the human brain, particularly in intrinsic neurons in the cerebral cortex. In AD, SS levels are consistently reduced in cortical and hippocampal areas, but are preserved in subcortical regions [2]. Similar data were reported in brains of demented PD when compared to non-demented patients [1]. The data suggest that intellectual impairment is associated with alterations of cortical and hippocampal SS transmission. Whether decreased SS levels indicate a change in peptide metabolism or loss of SS neurons remains controversial. Quantitative immunocytochemical analyses of AD brains have reported that the number of SS positive neurons is preserved in hippocampus and cortex of patients while others have shown a loss in SS neurons in cortex with alterations in their morphology. In fact, the loss of a subset of SS neurons suggests a selective vulnerability of some SS neurons [8]. Interestingly, cortical NPY-containing neurons, which frequently colocalize SS, seem to be relatively spared in AD. NPY levels were not different from controls in cortex of AD [2] or PD dementia [3] patients. In addition, immunocytochemical data have shown a sparing of NPY and NPY-SS cortical neurons in AD, indicating that they are less vulnerable. Thus a particular phenotype of cortical SS neurons may degenerate in AD. A particular phenotype may not be sufficient, however, to determine the vulnerability of the neurons, which also depends on their laminar distribution in the cortical layers [8].

In summary, intellectual deterioration in AD and PD is associated with some common neurochemical deficits. However, per se, these neurochemical deficits cannot account for cognitive dysfunction. Indeed, in PSP, characterized by a dramatic intellectual deterioration, cortical cholinergic transmission was mildly affected, if at all; in contrast, a severe subcortical cholinergic deficit was found. In addition, various peptides investigated in the different cortical and subcortical areas of these patients postmortem were not affected; of particular interest, neocortical and hippocampal somatostatin levels were preserved [9].

References

1. Agid Y, Ruberg M, Dubois B and Pillon B (1987) In: Stahl SM, Iversen SD and Goodman EC (eds.) Cognitive Neurochemistry. Oxford Science Publication, pp. 248–271.
2. Rossor MN, Emson PC, Dawbarn D, Mountjoy CQ and Roth M (1986) In: Emson PC, Rossor MN and Tohyama M (eds.) Progress in Brain Research Vol. 66, pp. 143–159.
3. Agid Y and Javoy-Agid F (1985) Trends Neurol. Sci. 8, 1: 30–35.
4. Crawley JN and Wenk GL (1989) Trends Neurol. Sci. 12, 8: 278–282.
5. Chan-Palay V, Ernfors P and Persson H (1990) Dementia 1: 192–196.
6. Beal MF, MacGarvey U and Swartz KJ (1990) Ann. Neurol. 28: 157–161.
7. Hökfelt T, Millhorn D, Seroogy K, Tsuruo Y, Ceccatelli S, Lindh B, Meister B, Melander T, Schalling M, Bartfai T and Terenius L (1987) Experientia 43: 768–780.
8. Gaspar P, Duyckaerts C, Febvret A, Benoit R, Beck B and Berger B (1989) Brain Res. 490: 1–13.
9. Ruberg M, Hirsch EH and Javoy-Agid F (1991) In: Litvan I and Agid Y (eds.) Progressive Supranuclear Palsy. Oxford University Press, New York (in press).

© 1991 Elsevier Science Publishers B.V. All rights reserved.
Biological Psychiatry, Volume 2. G. Racagni et al., editors.

Neuropeptides and mental illness: Focus on affective disorders

Garth Bissette, Michael J. Owens and Charles B. Nemeroff

Departments of Psychiatry and Pharmacology, Box 3859, Duke University Medical Center, Durham, NC 27710, U.S.A.

The advent of neuropeptide research opened the way for a completely new area of investigation into possible neurochemical substrates of depression. Because many of the original neuropeptide discoveries involved endocrine releasing factors and because of the historical recognition that affective disorders often present with endocrine alterations, the hypothalamic releasing factors and inhibiting factors were some of the first neuropeptide systems to be investigated. For these and other reasons, the neuropeptides most often associated with alterations in major depression are corticotropin-releasing factor (CRF), thyrotropin releasing hormone (TRH) and somatotropin release inhibiting factor (SRIF), also known as somatostatin.

The ability of stress to precipitate or exacerbate depressive symptoms and the work of Selye [1] and others in elucidating the role of the hypothalamic-pituitary-adrenal (HPA) axis in responses to stress have made this axis a natural target of investigation. The seminal work of Sachar and colleagues [2] in discovering the hypercortisolemia often present in major depression and the work of Carroll and associates [3] in demonstrating that depressed patients exhibit early escape from dexamethasone suppression of ACTH release, set the stage for investigation of the hypothalamic component of the HPA axis. After Vale isolated and characterized CRF [4], investigations of cerebrospinal fluid (CSF) concentrations of CRF established that it is elevated in drug-free patients with major depression [5–7]. This hypersecretion of CRF seems to be a “state” marker of depression as a regimen of electroconvulsive therapy reduces elevated CSF concentrations of CRF toward the normal range [8]. Although neither CRF concentrations or CRF receptors in temporal or occipital cortex in postmortem brain tissue of patient diagnosed during life with depression was altered in a report from Ferrier’s group [9], the depressive state at the time of death was not documented and patients were taking medication at death. Receptors for CRF are decreased in number in the frontal cortex of suicides compared to homicide controls [10], which may represent down-regulation of these receptors in response to hypersecreted CRF.

The thyroid axis also has been demonstrated to play a role in responses to stress and thyroid hormone imbalance can induce depressive symptoms in certain patients. Thyrotropin (TSH) and thyroid hormone (T_4) concentrations are often increased in patients with major depression [11] and an increased incidence of autothyroid antibodies has been reported in depressed populations [12]. Approximately 25% of depressed patients exhibit a blunted TSH response to exogenously administered TRH [13] adumbrating possible down-regulation of TRH receptors on pituitary thyrotrophs due to increased secretion of TRH from the hypothalamus. Two separate studies have demonstrated that depressed patients have significantly increased CSF concentrations of TRH [14,15]. The amount of TRH in CSF did not correlate with other thyroid indicators, however. It is not known whether increased CRF concentrations of TRH is a "state" or "trait" marker of depression, although both electroconvulsive shock [16] and antidepressant drug treatment [17,18] have been shown to alter TRH concentrations in discrete brain regions of laboratory animals.

Somatostatin inhibits the release of growth hormone, thyrotropin and prolactin from the anterior pituitary and insulin from the pancreas. It is co-localized within gamma-aminobutyric acid containing neurons of the cortex [19] and usually produces inhibition of firing when applied iontophoretically to neurons. Two forms, $SRIF_{14}$ and $SRIF_{28}$ exist in neurons, with $SRIF_{14}$ being the predominant species in CSF [20]. Somatostatin concentration has been found to be decreased in the CSF of patients with major depression by a variety of investigators [21–26], but CSF concentrations of SRIF are also reduced in patients with Alzheimer's disease [24–26], demented Parkinson's disease patients [27], multiple sclerosis [28], etc. Temporal and parietal cortex concentrations of somatostatin have been reported to be reduced in major depressives post-mortem [29] and exhibited the same general pattern of deficits seen in Alzheimer's disease, although depletions were not as severe. These findings were not replicated in a similar study [30].

These data indicate that CRF, TRH and SRIF are often altered in CSF and brain tissue of patients with major depression. What role these alterations play in the specific symptoms of depression remains obscure. Peripherally-administered CNS receptor antagonists for CRF and TRH or agonists for SRIF would be obvious candidates for clinical trials in the treatment of major depression.

Acknowledgements

Supported by NIMH grants MH-42088 and MH-45975.

References

1. Selye H (1936) Nature 138: 32.
2. Sachar E, Hellman L and Roffvarg H (1973) Arch. Gen. Psychiatry 28: 19–24.
3. Carroll BJ, Feinberg M, Greden JF, Tarika J, Albala AA, Haskett RF, James NM, Kronfol Z, Lohr N, Steiner M, deVigne JP and Young E (1981) Arch. Gen. Psychiatry 38: 15–22.
4. Vale W, Speiss J, Rivier C and Rivier J (1981) Science 213: 1394–1397.
5. Nemeroff CB, Widerlov E, Bissette G, Walleus H, Karlson I, Eklund K, Kilts CD, Loosen PT and Vale W (1984) Science 226: 1342–1344.
6. Banki CM, Bissette G, Arato M, O'Connor L and Nemeroff CB (1987) Am. J. Psychiatry 144: 873–877.
7. Risch SC, Lewine RJ, Kalin NH, Jewart RD, Risby ED, Caudle JM, Stipetic M, Turner J, Eccard MB and Pollard WE (1991) Neuropsychopharmacology (in press).

8. Nemeroff CB, Bissette G, Akil H and Frank M (1991) Br. J. Psychiatry 158: 59–63.
9. Leake A, Perry EK, Perry RH, Fairbain AF and Ferrier IN (1990) Biol. Psychiatry 28: 603–608.
10. Nemeroff CB, Owens MJ, Bissette G, Andorn AC and Stanley M (1988) Arch. Gen. Psychiatry 45: 577–579.
11. Kirkegaard C, Korner A and Faber J (1990) Biol. Psychiatry 27: 472–476.
12. Haggerty JJ, Simon JS, Evans DL and Nemeroff CB (1987) Am. J. Psychiatry 114: 1491–1493.
13. Loosen PT (1985) Psychoneuroendocrinology 10: 237–260.
14. Kirkegaard C, Faber J, Hummer L and Rogodwski P (1979) Psychoneuroendocrinology 4: 227–235.
15. Banki CM, Bissette G, Arato M and Nemeroff CB (1988) Am. J. Psychiatry 145: 1526–1531.
16. Kubek MJ, Low WC, Sattin A, Morzorati SL, Meyerhoff JL and Larsen SH (1989) N.Y. Acad. Sci. 553: 286–303.
17. Przegalinski E and Jaworska L (1990) Psychoneuroendocrinology 15: 147–153.
18. Lighton C, Bennett GW and Marsden CA (1985) Neuropharmacology 5: 401–153.
19. Lin CS, Lu SM and Schmechel DE (1986) J. Comp. Neurol. 244: 369–383.
20. Rissler K, Cramer H, Schaudt D, Strubel D and Gattaz WF (1986) Neurosci. Res. 3: 213–225.
21. Gerner RH and Yamada T (1982) Brain Res. 238: 298–302.
22. Rubinow DR, Gold PW, Post RM, Ballenger JC, Crowdry R, Bollinger J and Reichlin S (1983) 40: 409–412.
23. Agren H and Lundqvist G (1984) Psychoneuroendocrinology 9: 233–248.
24. Bissette G, Widerlov E, Walleus H, Karlsson I, Eklund K, Forsman A and Nemeroff CB (1986) Arch. Gen. Psychiatry 43: 1148–1151.
25. Sunderland T, Rubinow DR, Tariot PN, Cohen RM, Newhouse PA, Mellow AM, Mueller EA and Murphy DL (1987) Am. J. Psychiatry 144: 1313–1316.
26. Davis KL, Davidson M, Yang R-K, Davis BM, Siever LJ, Mohs RC, Ryan T, Coccaro E, Bierer L and Targum SD (1988) Biol. Psychiatry 24: 710–712.
27. Epelbaum J, Ruberg M, Moyse E, Javoy-Agid F, Dubois B and Agid Y (1983) Brain Res. 278: 376–379.
28. Sorensen KV, Christensen SE, Dupont E, Hansen AP, Pederson E and Orskov H (1980) Acta Neurol. Scand. 61: 186–191.
29. Bowen D, Najlerahim A, Procter AW, Francis PT and Murphy E (1989) Proc. Natl. Acad. Sci. U.S.A. 86: 9504–9508.
30. Charlton BG, Leake A, Wright C, Fairbairn AF, McKeith IG, Candy JM and Ferrier IN (1988) J. Neurol. Neurosurg. Psychiatry 51: 719–721.

© 1991 Elsevier Science Publishers B.V. All rights reserved.
Biological Psychiatry, Volume 2. G. Racagni et al., editors.

Neuropeptides in affective disorders: An introduction

Arthur J. Prange Jr.

Department of Psychiatry, University of North Carolina School of Medicine, Chapel Hill, North Carolina, U.S.A.

Peptides consist of amino acids connected in either a linear or cyclic fashion by so-called peptide bonds, wherein the nitrogen terminal of one amino acid is joined to the carboxyl group of the next. When many, many amino acids are connected, the substance is called a protein.

The smallest possible peptide consists of only two amino acids, and such a peptide is carnosine, which occurs in muscle and the olfactory bulb. The latter location suggests that carnosine has a role in olfaction, and through it, in behavior, a prospect that deserves more study than it has received.

Peptide P was discovered many decades ago, but the modern era of neuropeptidology began in 1978 when Guillemin [1] and Schally [2], working independently, announced the structure of thyrotropin-releasing hormone (TRH). One of the sites of concentration of this widely-distributed tripeptide is the hypothalamus. From there it enters the portal venous system, reaches the anterior pituitary gland and causes the release of thyroid stimulating hormone (TSH). Thus, TRH was the first so-called hypothalamic-hypophysiotropic hormone to be identified. Others in this series, all of them peptides, are corticotropin-releasing hormone (CRH), which stimulates ACTH release and gonadotropin-releasing hormone (GnRH), which stimulates follicle-stimulating hormone and luteinizing hormone release. These three tripartite, hierarchical systems are referred to as the hypothalamic-anterior pituitary-target gland axes. They are, of course, the hypothalamic-pituitary-thyroid (HPT) axis, the hypothalamic-pituitary-adrenal (HPA) axis and the hypothalamic-pituitary-gonadal (HPG) axis.

Some endocrine transactions between the hypothalamus and the anterior pituitary are not part of the target gland system. Thus, growth hormone (GH) comes from the pituitary and has many functions in many tissues. It is regulated by at least two hypothalamic peptides, somatostatin or somatotropin-release *inhibiting* factor (SRIF) and by growth hormone releasing hormone (GHRH), which *stimulates* GH release. Dopamine, a biogenic amine rather than a peptide, appears to be the chief regulator, through inhibition, of the pituitary secretion, prolactin. By and large, the peptides that come from the hypothalamus are quite small, while the peptides that they influence in the anterior pituitary are relatively large.

The regulation of ACTH secretion may be more complex than is generally appreciated. Recently Page et al. [3] have shown in normal humans that an infusion of oxytocin prevents CRH from releasing ACTH, while all other hypothalamic-pituitary transactions are unaffected. However, in the rat, including the infant rat

[4], oxytocin may facilitate ACTH release. Regulation of ACTH release is important in part because the HPA axis has been a focus of interest in studies of patients with affective disorders.

Oxytocin may be important in another way in depression. Like many other peptides, oxytocin exerts behavioral effects that are independent of, but harmonious with, their endocrine effects. The classical tissue effects of oxytocin, of course, are contraction of the uterus and ejection of milk from the breast. A few years ago it was shown that direct injection of the peptide into the lateral ventricle of estrogen-primed virgin rats would cause them to display a full spectrum of maternal behavior toward pups [5]. But more germane to the context of affective disorder, oxytocin has now been shown to act like antidepressant drugs in two animal screening tests used to identify such substances [6,7].

One other example of a neuropeptide of the endocrine system that has direct behavioral effects is TRH. This substance will potentiate the excitement shown by rats if they are pretreated with L-dopa and an MAO inhibitor. It will do this even if they have been hypophysectomized [8]. TRH, of course, has received trials as a clinical antidepressant.

In view of the oxytocin and TRH findings cited above, one could consider therapeutic uses as well as diagnostic uses for peptides in affective disorders. However, no peptide has yet been found to be competitive with standard treatments for depression or mania.

In the study of affective disorders peptides are almost always used diagnostically, though it would be more accurate to refer to this use of peptides as "descriptive". It is true that peptides can be used to diagnose frank endocrine disorders, but in psychiatric patients one is more often interested in subtle changes. In such cases peptides can be used as independent variables or as dependent variables. One example of the former is the administration of TSH and the subsequent measurement of TSH, as in the so-called TRH test. In such case, of course, TSH becomes a dependent variable. Among their descriptive uses, peptides can be used to describe not only endocrine state but also mental state of patients. Thus, for example, one might compare the amnestic effects of oxytocin between patients and controls.

Finally, it should be noted that just as many elements of the endocrine system are peptides, so are many elements of the immune system. Clearly, brain cells can elaborate the former; recent evidence suggests they can elaborate at least one of the latter as well, interleukin 1 [9]. Thus, peptides may be among the languages by which the organism achieves integration between its communication systems.

References

1. Guillemin R (1978) Science 202: 390–402.
2. Schally AV (1978) Science 202: 18–23.

3. Page SR, Ang VTY, Jackson R, White A, Nussey SS and Jenkins JS (1990) Clin. Endocrinol. 32: 307–313.
4. Noonan LR, Pedersen CA, Mason GA and Prange AJ Jr (1989) ACNP Abstr.
5. Pedersen CA and Prange AJ Jr (1979) Proc. Natl. Acad. Sci. U.S.A. 76: 6661–6665.
6. Arletti R and Bertolini A (1987) Life Sci. 41: 1725–1730.
7. Meisenberg G (1981) Peptides 2: 1–8.
8. Plotnikoff NP, Prange AJ Jr, Breese GR, Anderson MS and Wilson IC (1972) Science 178: 417–418.
9. Breder CD, Dinarello CA and Saper CB (1988) Science 240: 321.

© 1991 Elsevier Science Publishers B.V. All rights reserved.
Biological Psychiatry, Volume 2. G. Racagni et al., editors.

The role of corticotropin-releasing factor (CRF) in the pathophysiology of depression

Charles B. Nemeroff[1], Garth Bissette[2] and K. Ranga R. Krishnan[2]
[1]*Department of Psychiatry, Emory University School of Medicine, Box AF, Atlanta, GA 30322; and* [2]*Departments of Psychiatry and Pharmacology, Box 3859, Duke University Medical Center, Durham, NC 27710, U.S.A.*

Introduction

Because the hypothalamic-pituitary-adrenal (HPA) axis plays an integral role in the pathophysiology of stress, and stress has long been thought to precipitate episodes of affective disorder in genetically vulnerable individuals, it has been the best studied of all the endocrine axes in psychiatric disorders.

At the level of the anterior pituitary corticotroph, a number of factors regulate the secretion of ACTH. These include corticotropin-releasing factor (CRF), vasopressin, somatostatin, vasoactive-intestinal polypeptide, catecholamines (both α and β-adrenergic mechanisms) angiotensin and glucocorticoids.

Corticotropin-releasing factor (CRF), a 41 amino acid-containing peptide, was finally characterized, sequenced, and synthesized approximately 10 years ago [1]. It stimulates the synthesis of the ACTH and β-endorphin precursor pro-opiomelanocortin (POMC), as well as the release of ACTH and other adenohypophyseal products of POMC. Vasopressin also releases ACTH from corticotrophs, though its effect is minimal compared to the effect of CRF. However, vasopressin potentiates the action of CRF on the corticotroph, amplifying the effect 3-fold. In addition, there is negative feedback effect of glucocorticoids on the adenohypophyseal corticotroph. Glucocorticoid feedback also occurs at extra-hypothalamic sites, primarily the hippocampus.

The vast majority of studies have indicated that patients with affective disorders during the depressed phase exhibit increased secretion of cortisol as measured by 24-h urinary free cortisol, and elevated plasma corticosteroid concentrations which are generally highest in the most severely depressed subjects.

A number of investigators have measured the ACTH response to exogenously administered CRF. CRF, when administered at a dose of 1 μg/kg, produces a robust ACTH and cortisol response in humans [2]. Ovine CRF (oCRF) has a longer half-life in man than human CRF and has been used in most studies of psychiatric patients. The oCRF-induced ACTH response is blunted in drug-free depressed patients compared to normal subjects [3]. Gold et al. [3] suggested that this finding of an attenuated response to CRF in depression was due to the negative feedback effects of elevated cortisol concentrations. This was supported by their finding of a significant inverse correlation between basal plasma cortisol concentrations and the ACTH response to CRF. The blunted ACTH response to CRF has been confirmed by other authors [4], and a similar finding has been reported using human CRF [5]. The blunted ACTH response is seen only in the evening [5], during the quiescent phase of HPA axis activity. This response is state-dependent and returns to normal after successful treatment of depression [6]. A recent study by Holsboer et al. [7], and a similar study by our group indicate that after dexamethasone pretreatment, depressed patients have higher ACTH and cortisol responses after exogenous CRF than normal subjects. Lisansky et al. [8] and von Bardeleben et al. [9] have also shown the ACTH response to CRF after metyrapone administration (metyrapone is used to inhibit cortisol synthesis and therefore eliminate feedback) is increased in depressed patients compared to controls. These data, taken together, indicate that the blunted ACTH response to CRF in depression is not merely due to the hypercortisolemia and resultant negative feedback. Animal studies indicate that chronic CRF administration can lead to an increase in the number and volume of corticotrophs [10,11]. It is therefore possible that there is an increase in pituitary gland size in depression. Indeed, utilizing magnetic resonance imaging, we have recently shown in a study of 19 depressed patients and 19 age- and sex-matched controls, that the pituitary gland is enlarged in depressed patients [12].

The role of corticotropin releasing factor (CRF) in the pathogenesis of depression

Once the chemical identity of CRF was elucidated (vide supra), immunohistochemical and radioimmunoassay methods were utilized to determine the distribution of the peptide in the mammalian CNS. In brief, CRF is found not only within the hypothalamus but in extrahypothalamic brain areas that subserve affective, cognitive and autonomic functions. These areas include the locus caeruleus, dorsal motor nucleus of the vagus, hippocampus, cerebral cortex, amygdala and certain parts of the basal ganglia. There is little doubt that CRF functions as a neurotransmitter substance in the CNS.

Because CRF is the major physiological regulator of the HPA axis, by virtue of its potent action on ACTH secretion, it was of interest to determine whether CRF hypersecretion contributes to the hypercortisolemia observed in patients with major depression. In addition, a further impetus to assess a role for CRF in depression comes from studies in laboratory animals that have demonstrated that direct central administration of CRF produces behavioral effects remarkably similar to the cardinal signs and symptoms of major depression including decreased libido, decreased appetite, psychomotor alterations and disturbed sleep. These findings led to the measurement of CRF in cerebrospinal fluid (CRF) of drug-free patients with major depression, and patients with other psychiatric diagnoses. Our group has conducted 6 studies. In our first study, we measured the CSF concentration of CRF in 10 normal controls, 23 depressed patients, 11 schizophrenics and 29 demented patients. The CSF concentration of CRF was elevated in the depressed patients compared to all of the other groups; 11 of the 23 depressed patients had CSF CRF concentrations higher than the highest normal controls [13]. In our second study we measured the CSF concentration of CRF in 54 depressed women, 138 neurological controls, 23 schizophrenic patients and 6 manic patients. The depressed patients exhibited a marked 2-fold elevation in CSF CRF concentrations [14]. In a third study we reported that patients with major depression had higher CSF CRF levels than patients with chronic pain [15]. Our fourth study, conducted in Budapest, also found increased CSF CRF concentrations in depressed patients [16]. A fifth study was conducted in which we measured CSF CRF concentrations collected postmortem from the intracisternal space in depressed suicide victims and sudden death controls. Again CSF CRF concentrations were elevated in the depressed group [17]. Finally, we have recently shown that the increase in CSF CRF concentrations that occurs in depression, such as the concomitant hypercortisolemia, normalizes upon recovery [18]. Nine drug-free psychotically depressed patients had elevated CSF CRF concentrations that were significantly reduced after electroconvulsive therapy and clinical improvement. The increase in CSF CRF concentrations have been confirmed by Risch et al. [19], by Kathol et al. [20] and by Roy et al. [21] in DST non-suppressors.

In order to determine whether chronic CRF hypersecretion results in CRF receptor down-regulation, we measured the number and affinity of CRF receptors in the frontal cortex of 26 suicide victims and 29 controls [22]. The suicide victims exhibited a marked decrease in CRF receptor number, consistent with the hypothesis that chronic hypersecretion of the peptide produced a long-lasting reduction in CRF receptor density.

This concatenation of findings supports the hypothesis that CRF is hypersecreted in depressed patients, resulting in both behavioral signs and symptoms, and increased HPA axis activity. In subsequent studies, measurement of CRF mRNA levels in discrete postmortem brain areas will provide information as to which CRF neuronal systems are hyperactive in depression.

References

1. Vale W, Spiess J, Rivier C and Rivier J (1981) Science 213: 1394–1395.
2. Schuemeyer H, Avgerinos PC, Gold PW, Gallucci WT, Tomai TP, Cutler GB, Loriaux DL and Chrousos GP (1984) J. Clin. Endocrinol. Metab. 59: 1103–1108.
3. Gold PW, Chrousos GP, Kellner CH, Post RM, Roy A, Augerinas P, Schulte H, Oldfield EH and Loriaux DL (1984) Am. J. Psychiatry 141: 619–627.
4. Kathol RG, Haeckle RS, Lopez JF and Muller WH (1980) Br. J. Psychiatry 155: 468–478.
5. Holsboer F, Haack D, Gerken A and Vecoci P (1984) Biol. Psychiatry 19: 281–291.
6. Amsterdam JD, Maislin G, Winokur A, Berwish N, Kling M and Gold P (1988) J. Affective Disord. 14: 213–222.
7. Holsboer F, Wiedemann K and Boll E (1986) Arch. Gen. Psychiatry 43: 813–815.
8. Lisansky J, Peake GT, Strassman R, Qualls C, Meikle AW, Risch SC, Fava GA, Zownir-Brazis M, Hochla P and Britton D (1989) Arch. Gen. Psychiatry 46: 641–643.

9. Von Bardeleben U, Benker O and Holsboer F (1987) Pharmacopsychiatry 20: 28–34.
10. Westlund KN, Aguilera G and Childs GV (1987) Endocrinology 120: 381–388.
11. Gertz BJ, Cantreras LN, McDomb DJ, Kovacs K, Tyrrell JB and Dallman MF (1987) Endocrinology 120: 381–388.
12. Krishnan KRR, Doraiswamy PM, Venkataraman S, Reed D and Ritchie JC (1991) In: McCubbin J, Kaufman P and Nemeroff CB (eds.) The Role of Neuropeptides in Stress Pathogenesis and Disease. Academic Press, New York, pp. 19–35.
13. Nemeroff CB, Widerlov E, Bissette G, Walleus H, Karlsson I, Eklund K, Kilts CD, Loosen PT and Vale W (1984) Science 226: 1342–1344.
14. Banki CM, Bissette G, Arato M, O'Connor L and Nemeroff CB (1987) Am. J. Psychiatry 144: 873–877.
15. France RD, Urban B, Krishnan KRR, Bissette G, Banki CM, Nemeroff CB and Spielman FJ (1988) Biol. Psychiatry 23: 86–88.
16. Arato M, Banki CM, Nemeroff CB and Bissette G (1986) Ann. N.Y. Acad. Sci. 487: 263–270.
17. Arato M, Banki CM, Bissette G and Nemeroff CB (1989) Biol. Psychiatry 25: 355–359.
18. Nemeroff CB, Bissette G, Akil H and Fink M (1991) Br. J. Psychiatry 158: 59–63.
19. Risch SC, Lewine RJ, Kalin NH, Jewart RD, Risby ED, Caudle JM, Stipetic M, Turner J, Eccard MB and Pollard WE (1991) Neuropsychopharmacology (in press).
20. Kathol RG, Haeckle RS, Lopez JF, Muller WH (1989) Br. J. Psychiatry 155: 468–478.
21. Roy A, Pikar D, Paul S, Doran A, Chrousos GP and Gold PW (1987) Am. J. Psychiatry 144: 641–645.
22. Nemeroff CB, Owens MJ, Bissette G, Andron AC and Stanley M (1988) Arch. Gen. Psychiatry 45: 577–579.

© 1991 Elsevier Science Publishers B.V. All rights reserved.
Biological Psychiatry, Volume 2. G. Racagni et al., editors.

Somatostatin in affective disorders

David R. Rubinow
Section on Behavioral Endocrinology, Biological Psychiatry Branch, National Institute of Mental Health, Bldg. 10, Room 3N238, 9000 Rockville Pike, Rockville, Maryland, U.S.A.

Introduction

Somatostatin is a hypothalamic tetradecapeptide that modulates central nervous system activity and that appears in abnormal concentrations in the brains and CSF of patients with a variety of neuropsychiatric illnesses. In addition to the localization of somatostatin and somatostatin receptors throughout the CNS, somatostatin displays neurophysiologic effects and regulatory interactions with brain neurotransmitters and peptides. It acts in the CNS as a neuromodulator, if not a neurotransmitter. Central administration of somatostatin has been observed to alter many behaviors that are disturbed in depression, including appetite, sleep, pain sensitivity and cognition [1]. These behavioral effects of somatostatin are particularly intriguing in light of the decreased concentrations of somatostatin found in the CSF and brains of patients with neurologic (Alzheimer's disease, Parkinson's disease, multiple sclerosis) and psychiatric (depression) illness.

Among psychiatric disorders, evidence is clearest for a change in central somatostatin concentration in affective illness. Gerner and Yamada [2] and Rubinow et al. [1] described significant decreases in CSF somatostatin in medication-free depressed patients compared with normal controls. These initial findings were subsequently replicated by Agren and Lundqvist [3], Black et al. [4], Bissette et al. [5] and Davis et al. [6] in groups of 21, 18, 17 and 8 medication-free depressed patients, respectively. In an extension of a study by Sunderland et al. [7], Molchan et al. [8] described significantly lower CSF somatostatin in 18 elderly depressed patients and in 60 Alzheimer's disease patients compared with 12 age-matched controls. This group further described a significant negative correlation between severity of depressed mood in the Alzheimer's disease patients and CSF somatostatin levels, as well as a trend toward a negative correlation between CSF somatostatin and Hamilton Depression Scale scores in the patients with major depression. Alzheimer's disease patients who were also depressed were noted to have significantly lower CSF somatostatin than did non-depressed Alzheimer's disease patients. Finally, in an extension of earlier findings, Rubinow [9] reported significantly lower CSF somatostatin values in 49 medication-free depressed patients compared with 47 volunteers and 23 patients with affective illness in the improved or euthymic state. In a study of 8 medication-free depressed patients and controls who underwent both morning and evening lumbar punctures, highly similar evening CSF somatostatin levels were observed in the patients and controls. Thus, detection of decreased CSF somatostatin levels in depressed patients relative to normals appears dependent on time of day at which the samples were obtained and, therefore, may represent disturbed circadian or total somatostatin secretion.

Decreased CSF somatostatin may, in the neuropsychiatric disorders characterized by this abnormality, reflect a common central neuroregulatory disturbance or mediate a common manifestation of these disorders. For example, somatostatin appears to facilitate learning and memory in a number of animal studies, with depletion of somatostatin resulting in diminished performance [10]. As such, it is noteworthy that cognitive impairment is a common feature of those neuropsychiatric disorders associated with decreased CSF somatostatin, i.e. Alzheimer's disease, depression, multiple sclerosis, Parkinson's disease and Cushing's disease. Further, decreases in CSF somatostatin have been correlated with the degree of cognitive impairment in patients with Alzheimer's disease [6,7] or Parkinson's disease [11] in some but not all studies.

In addition to the potential role for somatostatin in the symptoms of depression, alterations in somatostatin function may mediate some of the physiologic disturbances described in depression. A variety of reciprocal regulatory interactions exist between the hypothalamic pituitary adrenal (HPA) axis and brain somatostatin. Thus, the ability of somatostatin to inhibit stimulated ACTH secretion [12] and/or stress-induced CRH secretion [13] provides the possibility that reduced CSF somatostatin might contribute to the disinhibition of the HPA axis seen in depression. Consistent with this possibility are the observations of a significant negative correlation between CSF somatostatin and post-dexamethasone plasma cortisol levels in depressed and schizophrenic patients [14], Alzheimer's disease patients [15], and in underweight anorexics [16]. Several recent clinical [17,18] and in vitro [19] studies suggest that this negative relationship between somatostatin and HPA activity may reflect hypercortisolemia-induced decreases in somatostatin. Nonetheless, a growing body of evidence suggests that the relationship between the somatostatinergic and HPA systems is physiologically meaningful and may further our understanding of those disorders characterized by dysregulation of these systems.

Conclusion

Decreases in brain and/or CSF somatostatin have been identified and replicated in several neuropsychiatric disorders, including Alzheimer's disease and depression. While the decreases in Alzheimer's disease appear to be the product of a degenerative process, the somatostatin dysregulation seen in depression is transient and reversible, and appears to reflect functional alterations in somatostatin secretion or metabolism or both. Clarification of the precise mechanisms involved in the somatostatin alterations and their consequences should provide valuable insights into normal and pathological CNS function.

References

1. Rubinow DR, Gold PW, Post RM, Ballenger JC, Cowdry RW, Bollinger J and Reichlin S (1983) Arch. Gen. Psychiatry 40: 409.
2. Gerner RH and Yamada T (1982) Brain Res. 238: 298.
3. Agren H and Lundqvist G (1984) Psychoneuroendocrinology 9: 233.
4. Black PM, Ballantine HT, Carr DB, Beal MF and Martin JB (1986) Biol. Psychiatry 21: 1077.
5. Bissette G, Widerlov E, Walleus H, Karlsson I, Eklund K, Forsman A and Nemeroff CB (1986) Arch. Gen. Psychiatry 43: 1148.
6. Davis KL, Davidson M, Yank RK, Davis BM, Siever LJ, Mohs RC, Ryan T, Coccaro E, Bierer L and Targum SD (1983) Biol. Psychiatry 24: 710.
7. Sunderland T, Rubinow DR, Tariot P, Cohen RM, Newhouse PA, Mellow AM, Mueller EA and Murphy DL (1987) Am. J. Psychiatry 144: 1313.
8. Molchan SE, Lawlor BA, Hill JL, Martinez RA, Davis CL, Mellow AM, Rubinow DR and Sunderland T (1990) Biol. Psychiatry (in press).
9. Rubinow DR (1986) Biol. Psychiatry 21: 341.
10. Vecsei L and Widerlov E (1990) Psychoneuroendocrinology 15: 139.
11. Epelbaum J, Ruberg M, Moyse E, Javoy-Agid F, Dubois B and Agid Y (1983) Brain Res. 278: 376.
12. Heisler S, Reisine T, Hook V and Axelrod J (1982) Proc. Natl. Acad. Sci. U.S.A. 79: 6502.
13. Brown MR, Rivier C and Vale W (1984) Endocrinology 114: 1546.
14. Doran A, Rubinow DR, Roy A and Pickar D (1986) Arch. Gen. Psychiatry 43: 365.
15. Serby M, Richardson SB, Rypma B, Twente S and Rotrosen JP (1986) Biol. Psychiatry 21: 971.
16. Kaye W, Rubinow DR, Gwirtsman H, Tomai T, Chrousos G and Gold PW (1988) Psychoneuroendocrinology 13: 265.
17. Wolkowitz OM, Rubinow DR, Breier A, Doran AR, Davis C and Pickar D (1987) Life Sci. 41: 1929.
18. Kling MA, Rubinow DR, Chrousos GP, Doran AR and Gold PW (1986) Abstr. Soc. Biol. Psychiatry No. 92.
19. Cote GJ, Palmer WN, Leonhart K, Leong SS and Gagel RF (1986) J. Biol. Chem. 261: 12930.

© 1991 Elsevier Science Publishers B.V. All rights reserved.
Biological Psychiatry, Volume 2. G. Racagni et al., editors.

The role of thyrotropin-releasing hormone in depression

Garth Bissette

Department of Psychiatry, Box 3859, Duke University Medical Center, Durham, NC 27710, U.S.A.

Thyrotropin-releasing hormone (TRH) was the first hypothalmic releasing factor to be purified and sequenced and was the first endogenous neuropeptide commercially available for pharmacologic investigation. The arduous efforts of competing research teams using tedious bulk processing techniques yielded less than 2 mg of TRH from over one half [1,2] million sheep and pig hypothalami and even this amount represented a respectable 20% recovery. The endocrine releasing-factor actions of TRH when released from neurons of the hypothalamic paraventricular nucleus result in secretion of thyroid stimulating hormone (TSH) and prolactin from the anterior pituitary gland [3]. The rat TRH gene consists of 3 exons and 2 introns with five copies of the TRH sequence contained on exon 3 [4]. Brain and pituitary TRH receptors are similar but not identical, [5,6] and both use a G-protein-coupled protein kinase C to activate phosphoinositol turnover with subsequent concomitant release of inositol triphosphate and diacylglycerol as the second messenger system activated by the receptors binding TRH. Prange and coworkers established that TRH had direct central nervous system effects after intraperitoneal or intracisternal injection [7]. These effects were not confined to the hypothalamic-pituitary-thyroid axis and included potentiation of DOPA-stimulated locomotor activity in mice [8] and reversal of the sedation and hypothermia associated with either pentobarbital [9,10] or alcohol [11] intoxication. The location of TRH analeptic activity has been mapped to the septal region of rats [12]. These neurons are part of the population of TRH neurons that extend from the anterior hypothalamus through the pre-optic, diagonal band and septal regions and finally end on the olfactory bulb of rats [13]. TRH concentration is decreased in the frontal cortex, septum, amygdala and pons-medulla by immobilization stress, while TRH receptor binding is decreased in the septum, amygdala and hypothalamus [14]. Cold stress, however, increases TRH content of the hypothalamus [15]. The ability of TRH to reverse the effects of CNS depressant drugs and the recognition of the major role of the thyroid axis in response to stress led to early clinical trials of TRH as an antidepressant. Despite initial encouraging reports indicating that TRH has some antidepressant activity in women [7], later clinical trials were not able to reproduce this finding. However, the hypothalamic-pituitary-thyroid axis is definitely altered in major depression [16,17]. Two reports have now confirmed that the cerebrospinal fluid concentrations TRH are elevated in drug-free patients with major depression compared to non-depressed controls [18,19]. Both of these studies obtained similar concentrations of TRH in the depressed and control groups. Neither group was able to correlate the CSF concentration of TRH to other thyroid axis indicators and the CNS source of CSF TRH remains obscure. Approximately 25% of depressed patients show a blunted TSH response to an intravenous TRH challenge, indicating down-regulation of pituitary TRH receptors possibly due to endogenous TRH hypersecretion. A significant proportion of patients with major depression have autoantibodies to thyroid hormone [21], which is also consistent with a TRH-induced hyperactivity of the thyroid axis. Thus, several lines of evidence converge to indicate a centrally overdriven thyroid axis in major depression. It is, as yet, unclear whether this TRH hypersecretion represents a state or trait marker of major depression. The concentrations of TRH are increased in the rat nucleus accumbens and striatum by antidepressant drug treatment [22,23] and TRH potentiates the effects of imipramine on swimming behaviors [24] and serotonin [25] and catecholamine [26] metabolism in rats. Electroconvulsive shock increases TRH concentrations in the hippocampus and amygdala-piriform cortex of rats [27]. Although these TRH increases are the opposite of the alterations expected of TRH as a state marker, these data indicate that TRH neuronal systems are indeed altered by currently successful treatments for symptoms of major depression. Whether TRH is a state or trait marker of depression awaits clinical trials in which CSF concentrations of TRH are assessed before and after successful antidepressant or electroconvulsive therapies. Based on the current clinical data, a TRH receptor antagonist with specificity for and access to brain TRH receptors would be a potential candidate for clinical trials of antidepressant activity.

Acknowledgement

Supported by NIMH Grant MH-45975.

References

1. Boler J, Enzmann F, Folker K, Bowers CY and Schally AV (1969) Biochem. Biophys. Res. Commun. 37: 705–710.
2. Burgus R, Dunn T, Desiderio D and Guilleman R (1969) C.R. Acad. Sci. (Paris) 269: 1870–1873.
3. Koch Y, Goldhaber G, Fireman I, Zor U, Shai J and Tal E (1977) Endocrinology 100: 1476.
4. Lee SL, Sevarino K, Roos BA and Goodman RH (1989) N.Y. Acad. Sci. 553: 14–28.
5. Sharif NA (1989) N.Y. Acad. Sci. 553: 147–175.
6. Hinkle PM (1989) N.Y. Acad. Sci. 553: 176–187.
7. Prange AJ Jr, Wilson IC, Lara PP, Alltop LB and Breese GR (1972) Lancet ii: 999–1002.
8. Plotnikoff NP, Prange AJ Jr, Breese GR, Anderson MS and Wilson LC (1972) Science 178: 417–418.
9. Prange AJ Jr, Breese GR, Cott JM, Martin BR, Cooper BR, Wilson IC and Plotnikoff NP (1974) Life Sci. 14: 447–455.
10. Breese GR, Cott JM, Cooper BR, Prange AJ Jr, Lipton MA and Plotnikoff NP (1975) J. Pharmacol. Exp. Ther. 193: 11–22.

11. Cott JM, Breese GR, Cooper BR, Barlow TS and Prange AJ Jr (1976) J. Pharmacol. Exp. Ther. 196: 594–604.
12. Kalivas PW, Simasko SM and Horita A (1981) Brain Res. 222: 253–265.
13. Jackson IMD and Reichlin S (1974) Endocrinology 95: 854.
14. Takayama H, Ota Z and Ogawa N (1986) Reg. Peptides 15: 239–248.
15. Lin MT, Wang PS, Chuang J, Fan LJ and Won SJ (1989) Neuroendocrinology 50: 177–181.
16. Joffe RT, Roy-Byrne PP, Uhde TW and Post RM (1984) Biol. Psychiatry 19: 1685–1691.
17. Joffe RT, Blank DW, Post RM and Uhde TW (1985) Biol. Psychiatry 20: 922–925.
18. Kirkegaard C, Faber J, Hummer L and Rogodwski P (1979) Psychoneuroendocrinology 4: 227–235.
19. Banki CM, Bissette G, Arato M and Nemeroff CB (1988) Am. J. Psychiatry 145: 1526–1531.
20. Loosen PT (1985) Psychoneuroendocrinology 10: 237–260.
21. Haggerty JJ, Simon JS, Evans DL and Nemeroff CB (1987) Am. J. Psychiatry 144: 1491–1493.
22. Przegalinski E and Jaworska L (1990) Psychoneuroendocrinology 15: 147–153.
23. Lighton C, Bennett GW and Marsden CA (1985) Neuropharmacology 5: 401–406.
24. Reny-Palasse V and Rips R (1985) Br. J. Pharmacol. 85: 463–470.
25. Rastogi RB, Singhal RL and Lapierre YD (1981) Brain Res. Bull. 7: 449–451.
26. Rastogi RB, Singhal RL and Lapierre YD (1980) Psychopharmacology 72: 85–91.
27. Kubek MJ, Low WC, Sattin A, Morzorati SL, Meyerhoff JL and Larsen SH (1989) N.Y. Acad. Sci. 553: 286–303.

© 1991 Elsevier Science Publishers B.V. All rights reserved.
Biological Psychiatry, Volume 2. G. Racagni et al., editors.

Effects of dexamethasone, adrenocorticotropic hormone and corticotropin releasing hormone on dopamine activity in man

Alan F. Schatzberg[1], Joel A. Posener[1] and Anthony J. Rothschild[2]
[1]*Massachusetts Mental Health Center, 74 Fenwood Road, Boston, MA 02115; and* [2]*McLean Hospital, 115 Mill Street, Belmont, MA 02178, U.S.A.*

In this paper, we discuss a program of research investigating interactions between the hypothalamic-pituitary-adrenal (HPA) axis and dopamine (DA) systems, particularly as they may play a role in the pathogenesis of delusions in depressed patients. Abnormalities of the HPA axis in association with depression are well known and there have been a number of observations that, in comparison with non-psychotic depression, psychotic (i.e. delusional) depression is characterized by greater elevations in baseline plasma cortisol, higher rates of non-suppression on the dexamethasone suppression test and extremely high postdexamethasone cortisol levels. In contrast to non-psychotic depression, psychotic depression is also characterized by: elevated CSF levels of homovanillic acid (HVA), the principal dopamine metabolite; lower levels of serum dopamine-β-hydroxylase; and response to the combination of neuroleptics with tricyclic antidepressants (TCA's) but not to TCA's alone. In part on the basis of these observations, we proposed the hypothesis that delusions in depressed patients may be due to an increase in mesolimbic dopamine activity driven by elevated levels of plasma corticosteroids [1].

We and others have reported that glucocorticoids increase DA activity in man. In one study [2], 12 healthy volunteers, free of all medication, had blood drawn for catecholamine levels at 8:00 a.m. and 4:00 p.m. and were administered 1 mg dexamethasone at 11:00 p.m. Plasma was collected for catecholamine determinations at 8:00 a.m. and 4:00 p.m. the following day. Although dexamethasone (DEX) had no effect on levels of norepinephrine and epinephrine, increases in DA levels were noted. At baseline, plasma free dopamine was not detectable in most cases. Following dexamethasone, plasma dopamine was detectable in all cases and mean dopamine levels were significantly higher at both time points after dexamethasone in comparison to pre-DEX values. The interpretation of plasma dopamine levels is not straightforward, as plasma DA is derived from both central and peripheral sites, but the findings do support the effect of a synthetic glucocorticoid on dopamine in man. Wolkowitz and colleagues have also reported DEX increases 4:00 p.m. plasma HVA levels in healthy controls [3].

Evidence for increases in cortisol activity resulting in increases in DA activity has come from preclinical research. Our group has reported that intraperitoneal injection of dexamethasone produces significantly elevated DA levels in the hypothalamus and nucleus accumbens of rats [4] and others have reported that peripherally administered glucocorticoids increase homovanillic acid (HVA) levels in the rat caudate [5]. Research has begun to elucidate the mechanisms governing these interactions. Administration of dexamethasone has been reported to increase the activity of tyrosine hydroxylase (TH), the rate-limiting enzyme in dopamine synthesis, in rodent nervous system preparations. Glucocorticoids also increase levels of TH mRNA in the human adrenal. Other studies have suggested that glucocorticoids may directly affect dopamine uptake and receptors. Glucocorticoid administration elevates dopamine levels in synaptosomes devoid of glucocorticoid receptors, and glucocorticoids down-regulate dopamine receptor-complex adenylate cyclase activity.

Preliminary clinical investigations by our group have supported the association between hyperactivity of the HPA axis and increased dopamine activity in psychotic depression [6,7]. Comparing psychotic depressives, non-psychotic depressives and normal control subjects, we found that at baseline patients with psychotic depressions had higher plasma levels of both cortisol and dopamine than did non-psychotic depressives or controls. In response to 1 mg DEX, all of our small sample of patients with psychotic depression failed to suppress cortisol, a rate significantly higher than for non-psychotic depressives. After receiving dexamethasone, the psychotic depressives had higher cortisol levels than non-psychotic depressives or controls and higher levels of dopamine than patients with non-psychotic depression.

In another study, 10 healthy volunteers, determined to be without personal history of Axis I or Axis II disorders, had blood collected at 8:00 a.m. and 4:00 p.m. for plasma HVA levels prior to administration of 1 mg dexamethasone at 11:00 p.m. HVA levels were subsequently determined at 8:00 a.m. and 4:00 p.m. the day following dexamethasone and at 8:00 a.m. on the next day. Baseline values showed a diurnal variation with HVA at 8:00 a.m. significantly higher than at 4:00 p.m. Following dexamethasone, HVA at 8:00 a.m. was significantly lower than at baseline. However, at 4:00 p.m. postdexamethasone, HVA was significantly higher than at 4:00 p.m. on the baseline day. Moreover at 8:00 a.m. on the second day postdexamethasone, HVA was even higher. Thus, dexamethasone appears to exert complex time-related effects on HVA. These data suggest that dexamethasone affects DA via more than one mechanism.

In this study, we have also explored the effects of different dexamethasone doses on dopamine activity. After the ten subjects were studied with a 1 mg dose of DEX, they were studied two more times (each one month apart) using the same protocol with the exception that subjects received either 2 or 4 mg of DEX. Subjects were randomly assigned to receive, under double-blind conditions, 2 mg or 4 mg of DEX. One month later, the protocol was repeated; those subjects who had previously received 2 mg DEX were given 4 mg and vice versa. Results of this study will determine whether and how responses of HVA to dexamethasone are affected by different doses of dexamethasone.

A recent report by Risch's group [8] may shed further light on the mechanism of

HPA axis-dopamine interactions. These investigators administered metyrapone, an inhibition of adrenal cortisol synthesis, to healthy control subjects at 11:00 p.m. and at 8:00 a.m. and 12:00 noon the following day. Blood was collected at 4:00 p.m. on the baseline day and at regular intervals the following day. Following metyrapone, cortisol was decreased and ACTH was increased as expected. HVA was increased the morning following metyrapone and gradually returned to baseline by 4:00 p.m. These observations suggest that ACTH rather than cortisol may be the major determinant of HVA levels.

In an ongoing study, we are attempting to determine the effects of ovine corticotropin releasing hormone (oCRH) and adrenocorticotropin (ACTH) on dopamine activity. Ten volunteers, who were free of both personal and family history of psychiatric illness, had no significant medical problems, and were not taking medication, have been studied. On the first day, blood was drawn for determination of cortisol and HVA at 8:00 a.m. and at 15-min intervals between 1:00 p.m. and 4:00 p.m. On a subsequent day, baseline samples were drawn for determination of cortisol, HVA and ACTH at 8:00 a.m. and 8:30 a.m., and at 8:35 a.m. synthetic ACTH (Co-syntropin) 0.25 mg was administered by i.v. push. Blood was then collected for the same determinations of cortisol, HVA, and ACTH at 30-min intervals from 9:00 a.m. until 12:00 noon. On another day, at least one week later than the day of the ACTH protocol, subjects had baseline blood samples collected for cortisol, ACTH, and HVA determinations at 6:30 p.m. and 6:45 p.m. At 7:00 p.m., ovine corticotropin releasing hormone (oCRH), 1 mcg/kg body weight, was administered by i.v. push. Blood was collected for the determination of cortisol, ACTH, and HVA at 15-min intervals until 8:00 p.m. and at 30-min intervals from 8:00 p.m. to 11:00 p.m.

Results of this study will help to define the nature of HPA axis/DA interactions. Integrated sampling for cortisol and HVA over time may clarify associations in the diurnal rhythms of the two systems. Our studies with synthetic ACTH and oCRH will help to determine whether activation at higher levels of the HPA axis can directly increase DA activity. A better understanding of HPA axis/DA interactions in normal humans will help pinpoint specific sites of dysregulation and may help to develop alternative treatment strategies for various depressive disorders, particularly delusional depression.

Acknowledgements

This work was supported in part by grants from the National Institute of Mental Health (MH38671, MH15413, and MH16259) and the Poitras Charitable Foundation. Ms. Linda Messier prepared this manuscript.

References

1. Schatzberg AF et al. (1985) J. Psychiatr. Res. 19: 57–64.
2. Rothschild AJ et al. (1984) J. Psychiatr. Res. 18: 217–2232.
3. Wolkowitz OM et al. (1987) Arch. Gen. Psychiatry 44: 782–789.
4. Rothschild AJ et al. (1985) Life Sci. 36: 3491–2501.
5. Wolkowitz OM et al. (1986) Eur. J. Pharmacol. 122: 329–338.
6. Rothschild AJ et al. (1987) Psychiatr. Res. 20: 143–153.
7. Schatzberg AF et al. (1987) Psychiatr. Res. 20: 155–164.
8. Richter RA et al. (1990) Plasma HVA increases after metyrapone administration. American Psychiatric Association Annual Meeting, New Research Abstracts, NR16.

© 1991 Elsevier Science Publishers B.V. All rights reserved.
Biological Psychiatry, Volume 2. G. Racagni et al., editors.

Elevated Le^y antigen expression in T lymphocytes of schizophrenic patients

Masahiro Kokai [1,2], Ichiro Hirata[2], Masakazu Adachi[2], Takehiko Tachibana[1], Noboru Hatotani[3] and Sen-Ichiro Hakomori[4]

[1]Department of Immunology, Institute for Tuberculosis and Cancer, Tohoku University, Sendai; [2]Japan Immunoresearch Laboratories, Takasaki; [3] Minakuchi Hospital, Shiga, Japan; and [4]The Biomembrane Institute and University of Washington, Seattle, U.S.A.

Introduction

The autoimmune mechanism and viral agents have been postulated as causal factors of schizophrenia based on findings of immunological abnormalities. As one of these, the appearance of atypical lymphocytes supposed to be immunologically activated in peripheral blood of schizophrenic patients are reported [1,2]. Since lymphocyte activation is an essential stage of immune responses in general, this phenomenon should be intensively studied in psychiatry for further understanding of immunological involvement. We examined the expression of carbohydrate antigen, Le^y, as an activation marker, in peripheral lymphocytes of psychiatric patients as the increase in Le^y antigen expression in T-cell subpopulations has been observed in HIV (human immunodeficiency virus) infected-lymphocytes and peripheral lymphocytes of AIDS patients [3].

Materials and Methods

The patients were diagnosed by DSM III-R and were all hospitalized. They were free of physical diseases and history of autoimmune diseases. The schizophrenic patients were chronic and divided into 2 groups: 24 were active types (they present prominent psychotic symptoms; 13 male, 13 female; mean age 37.0 ± 9.6 years) and 11 residual types (6 male, 5 female; mean age 39.6 ± 8.1 years). The bipolar disorder patients (11 male, 12 female; mean age 39.4 ± 8.8 years) included 12 manic and 11 depressed types. Neuroleptic medication was continued throughout this study. Twenty-six medical staff members (17 male, 9 female; mean age 33.8 ± 6.5 years) at these 2 hospitals were included as the normal control. Informed consents were obtained from all the patients.

Heparinized peripheral blood was drawn early in the morning, centrifuged over Ficoll-Hypaque. The purified lymphocyte fraction was reacted with anti-Le^y mouse monoclonal antibody (BM-1; IgM: Jimro, Takasaki, Japan) followed by reaction with FITC labelled anti-mouse IgM (F[ab]$_2$ fragment: Tago Inc, Burlingame, CA, U.S.A.). The lymphocyte suspension was washed with PBS and mixed with 1 of 2 types of phycoerythrin-labelled monoclonal antibodies: anti-CD4 (helper/inducer T-cell) or anti-CD8 (suppressor/killer T-cell) (Becton Dickinson and Co., Mountain View, U.S.A.). The mixtures were washed with PBS. Then, 2-color flowcytometric analysis was carried out. The data were evaluated by Lepage test.

Results

T-cell subsets number and their Le^y antigen expression rate

See Table 1 and Fig. 1.

Statistical analysis on Le^y antigen expression rate

Le^y antigen expression rate was significantly higher in both CD4 and CD8 positive T-cells in active-type schizophrenia compared with Le^y antigen expression in bipolar disorder (CD4 and CD8: $P < 1.29$ and 0.36%) and the normal control ($P <$ 0.01 and 0.01%) and a significant difference was found between residual type schizophrenia and normal control ($P < 0.08$ and 0.96%). Bipolar disorder group had a significantly higher expression both in CD4 and CD8 positive T-cells compared with the normal controls ($P < 3.11$ and 0.01%). There was no significant difference between active and residual type schizophrenia, and between bipolar disorder and residual type both in CD4 and CD8 positive T-cells.

Discussion

Our results demonstrated that Le^y antigen expression in T-cell subpopulations of schizophrenic patients were higher than in the normal control and the patients with bipolar disorder. Since Le^y antigen is reported to be expressed by aberrant fucosyltransferase activity on the cell surface of cancer, embryo, and Con-A

Table 1. T-cell subsets and their Le^y expression rate in subject groups

Groups	T-cell subset (%)		Le^y expression (%) in:	
	CD4	CD8	CD4	CD8
Schizophrenia				
– active type	47.9 ± 6.6	28.1 ± 7.5	21.9 ± 11.9	25.7 ± 11.6
– residual tye	49.5 ± 6.3	26.6 ± 6.7	13.2 ± 6.1	18.8 ± 7.0
Bipolar disorder	46.7 ± 10.4	26.1 ± 7.9	13.5 ± 4.8	15.2 ± 10.5
Normal control	47.1 ± 11.3	28.4 ± 7.8	10.2 ± 3.5	11.6 ± 6.5

No significant difference among subject groups in CD4 and CD8 positive T-cell subset number.

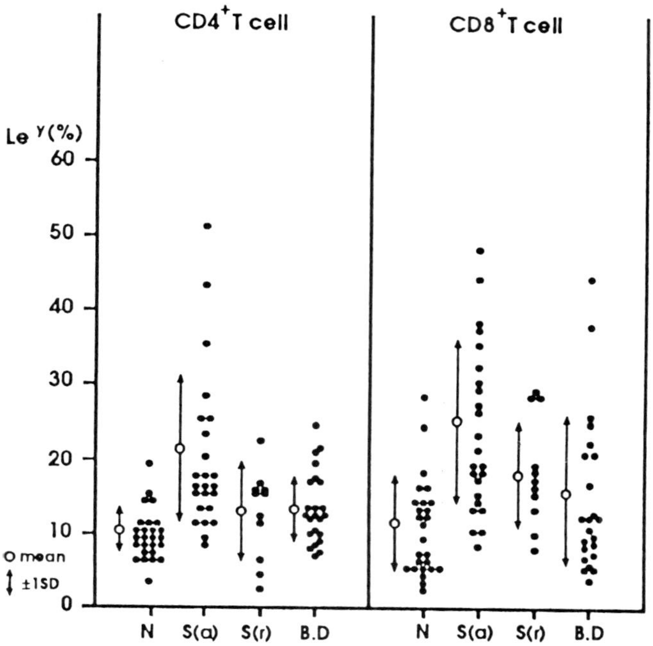

Fig. 1 Le^y antigen expression in T-cell subpopulations. CD4: helper/inducer T-cell; CD8: suppressor/killer T-cell; n, normal control; S(a), schizophrenia (active type); S(r), schizophrenia (residual type); B.D., bipolar disorder.

stimulated lymphocytes, Le^y antigen could be used as an index of cell-activated states and proliferations [3,4]. These findings may suggest the existence of the increased number of activated lymphocytes in schizophrenia. Lymphocyte activation is a crucial step in immune responses in general. The HLA-DR antigen expression, that is an activation marker of T lymphocytes, is reported to be higher in schizophrenia [5]. There may be no gross abnormality of fundamental immunological functions in our psychiatric patients, since no difference in CD4/CD8 T-cell subsets ratio was found among subject groups (Table 1). The mechanism regulating Le^y antigen expression is not clear, but an interaction with viral infection is suspected. Le^y higher expression in HIV (human immunodeficiency virus)-infected T-cell line and peripheral blood lymphocytes of AIDS patients were reported [3]. Hence results in our study may support the hypothesis that viral infection could be one of causal factors of schizophrenia. About 30% of active type schizophrenics showed the Le^y antigen elevation and this may reflect that schizophrenia could be comprised of groups with heterogeneous etio-pathogeneses. Since there are 2 manic and 1 depressed types of patient presenting higher Le^y rate compared with the highest value of normal controls, we may have to consider viral factors also in some part of bipolar disorder. Influence of neuroleptic medication in this study remains unknown. Psychotropic drugs happen to provoke allergic reactions, while neuroleptics mainly used during this study are known to suppress the activation and proliferation of lymphocytes [6]. Longitudinal study of non-medicated patients for the expression of Le^y antigen is needed.

Acknowledgements

The authors are indebted to several individuals for assistance in the collection of specimens: Dr. Takesuke Aoki, Dr. Jumei Yoshida, Dr. Toulu Ohtani and Dr. Masando Sugama; and for the statistical calculation, Dr. Takashi Suzuki.

References

1. Fessel WJ and Hirata-Hibi M (1963) Arch. Gen. Psychiatry 9: 601–613.
2. Hirata-Hibi M, Higashi S, Tachibana T and Watanabe N (1982) Arch. Gen. Psychiatry 39: 82–87.
3. Adachi M, Hayami M, Kashiwagi N, Mizuta T, Ohta Y, Gill JM, Matheson SD, Tamaoki T, Shiozawa C and Hakomori S (1988) J. Exp. Med. 67: 323–331.
4. Fenderson BA, Holmes EH, Fukushi Y and Hakomori S (1986) Dev. Biol. 114: 12–21.
5. Rabin BS, Ganguli R, Kelly RH, Lyte M and Ragu U (1987) Ann. N.Y. Acad. Sci. 469: 675–685.
6. Munyon MW, Salo R and Briones FD (1987) Psychopharmacology 91: 182–188.

Address for correspondence: Masahiro Kokai, Division of Psychobiology, The Sakamoto Institute of Psychopathology, 7–17 Nishikamikosaka Higashioska City, Osaka 577, Japan.

© 1991 Elsevier Science Publishers B.V. All rights reserved.
Biological Psychiatry, Volume 2. G. Racagni et al., editors.

Catecholamines, neuropeptide Y and immune function in Alzheimer caregiver stress

Michael Irwin, Marvin Brown, Tom L. Patterson, Richard L. Hauger, Margaret Quayhagen, Mary Quayhagen and Igor Grant

Departments of Psychiatry, San Diego Veterans Affairs Medical Center and University of California, San Diego, La Jolla, CA 92093, U.S.A.

Introduction

Alterations of the immune system have been described during life stress [1,2]. One laboratory assay of immune function that has received considerable attention is natural killer (NK) cell activity. NK cells are a lymphocyte subset involved in the recognition and destruction of virus-infected cells and their cytotoxic activity may be of in vivo relevance to health [3].

The link between psychological processes and changes in cellular immunity has not been fully explored, although a number of preclinical and clinical studies suggest that it is unlikely that activation of the pituitary adrenal axis solely mediates stress-associated changes in immunity [1,4,5]. Another pathway that may have a physiologic role in the modulation of immunity is the sympathetic nervous system [6]. Noradrenergic fibers extensively innervate lymphoid tissue and central administration of corticotropin-releasing factor activates the sympathetic nervous system and produces a reduction in splenic NK activity in the rat [1,6,7]. However, in humans the relationship between sympathetic activity and cellular immunity during life stress has not yet been examined.

The purpose of this report is to evaluate the association between sympathetic nervous system activity and NK cytotoxicity in persons undergoing chronic life stress. To test the hypothesis that sympathetic activation is inversely correlated with immune function, NK activity was assayed and basal and dynamic levels of epinephrine, norepinephrine and neuropeptide Y were determined following orthostatic challenge in Alzheimer spousal caregivers.

Methods

Subjects

The subjects included in this study were Alzheimer spousal caregivers (n = 43; 19 men and 24 women) with a mean ± SD age of 72.0 ± 7.9 (range: 55 to 92 years). Subjects were in good medical health and were not taking any psychotropic medications or any medications known to influence the immune system, blood pressure, or cardiovascular function.

Procedures

Subjects were asked to refrain from using alcohol, tobacco, or any caffeinated beverages for at least 12 h before the testing. Between 8 and 11 a.m., a heparinized catheter was inserted into a foreman vein and serial samples of blood (5 ml) were drawn during an orthostatic challenge at 15 and 30 min supine and after 2, 5, and 10 min of standing.

Assay of plasma catecholamines, NPY, and NK activity

Plasma concentrations of epinephrine and norepinephrine were measured using radioenzymatic methods [8]. Measurement of plasma concentrations of neuropeptide Y (NPY) used previously described radioimmunoassay procedures [8]. For assay of NK activity, peripheral blood lymphocytes were isolated by density gradient sedimentation and cytotoxicity was measured in a standard 3-h chromium release assay [2].

Results

In this group of Alzheimer spousal caregivers, mean ± S.D. NK activity was 12.8 ± 14.1 lytic units. Responses of epinephrine and norepinephrine, but not neuropeptide Y, showed significant ($P < 0.01$) increases from supine to standing position. Mean plasma concentration of epinephrine was 34.4 ± 16.9 pg/ml at rest and 41.5 ± 21.9 pg/ml upon standing; whereas mean circulating norepinephrine was 433.4 ± 197.7 pg/ml supine and 816.4 ± 292.2 pg/ml standing. Mean level of neuropeptide Y across the five intervals of assessment was 133.0 ± 54.4 pg/ml.

To evaluate the relationship between NK activity and plasma levels of catecholamines and neuropeptide Y, values of cytotoxicity were correlated with resting and dynamic responses of epinephrine and norepinephrine and with levels of neuropeptide Y. NK cytotoxicity was not correlated with either baseline or peak levels of epinephrine ($r = -0.15$, $P = 0.32$; $r = -0.24$, $P = 0.14$) or with baseline or peak levels of norepinephrine ($r = -0.24$, $P = 0.13$; $r = -0.29$, $P = 0.07$). In contrast, Fig. 1 illustrates the negative correlation between NK activity and neuropeptide Y in the Alzheimer caregivers ($r = -0.32$, $P < 0.04$). This study has evaluated the association between sympathetic activity and NK cytotoxicity in life stress. Circulating levels of the sympathetic neurotransmitter neuropeptide Y, but not the catecholamines epinephrine or norepinephrine, are inversely correlated with NK activity in life stress. These data suggest that activation of the sympathetic nervous system with release of neuropeptide Y may have a role in the modulation of immune function during the condition of chronic life stress.

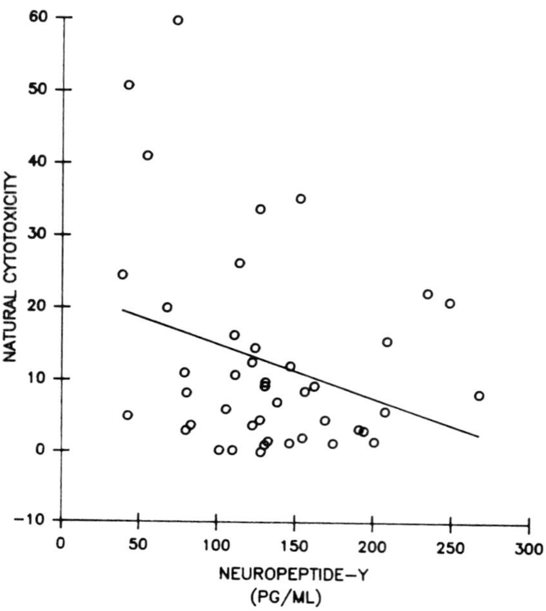

Fig. 1. The relationship between plasma levels of NK cell activity and plasma neuropeptide Y in Alzheimer spousal caregivers (r = −0.32, $P < 0.04$).

Acknowledgements

This work was supported by grants from the Veterans Affairs Merit Review (M.I.), the National Institutes of Mental Health (NIMH) Grant (M 44275-02 to M.I.), NIMH Mental Health Clinical Research Center Grant (MH30914), GCRC Grant (MOI RR00827), Alzheimer Caregiver Grant (MH42840-03) and the National Institutes of Health Grant (HL 43154).

References

1. Irwin MR and Hauger RL (1991) In: Lewis M (ed.) Child and Adolescent. Psychiatry: A Comprehensive Textbook. Williams and Wilkins, Baltimore, MD, pp. 51–63.
2. Irwin M, Daniels M, Bloom ET, Smith TL and Weiner H (1987) Am. J. Psychiatry 144: 437–441.
3. Biron CA, Byron KS and Sullivan JL (1989) N. Engl. J. Med. 320: 1731–1735.
4. Irwin M, Vale W and Rivier C (1990) Endocrinology 126: 2837–2844.
5. Jain R, Zwickler D, Hollander CS, Brand H, Saperstein A, Hutchinson B, Brown C and Audhya T (1991) Endocrinology 128: 1329–1336.
6. Felten DL, Felten SY, Bellinger DL, Carlson SL, Ackerman KD, Madden KS, Olschowka JA and Livnat S (1987) Immunol. Rev. 11: 225–260.
7. Irwin MR, Jones L, Provencio M, Hauger RL and Britton KT (1990) J. Pharmacol. Exp. Ther. 255: 101–107.
8. Brown MR, Allen R, Fisher LA (1989) In: Conn PM (ed.) Methods in Enzymology, Vol. 168. Academic Press, New York, pp. 431–443.

© 1991 Elsevier Science Publishers B.V. All rights reserved.
Biological Psychiatry, Volume 2. G. Racagni et al., editors.

Depression and the immune system*

Steven E. Keller[1], Steven J. Schleifer[1] and Antonio Andreoli[2]
[1]Department of Psychiatry, University of Medicine and Dentistry, New Jersey Medical School, 185 South Orange Avenue, MSB E561, Newark, New Jersey, U.S.A.; and [2]Department of Psychiatry, University of Geneva, Geneva, Switzerland

Introduction

It has been hypothesized that the development of affective disturbances of syndromal proportions may be involved in the immune effects of bereavement and other stressors. It is well known that the affective changes and neurovegetative symptoms found in the bereaved often suggest the presence of a clinical affective disorder [1–3]. Moreover, depression, like bereavement, has been associated with increased medical mortality [4–7] and with an increased prevalence of neoplastic and infectious diseases [6–8]. Neuroendocrine functions, including those relating to the hypothalamic-pituitary-adrenal and the hypothalamic-pituitary-thyroid axes, as well as peripheral and central noradrenergic and other neurotransmitter processes, are altered in depressed patients [9–12]. These systems have been shown to modulate immune function [1].

Studies by our group and others have demonstrated a complex relationship between syndromal depressive disorder and the immune system. In our (S.E.K. and S.J.S.) initial studies of depression and immunity, we found significantly decreased responses to the mitogens PHA, ConA and PWM in hospitalized patients with major depressive disorders (MDD) compared with age and sex-matched controls [14]. All subjects were healthy and were not taking drugs, including antidepressant agents, known or likely to effect immune function. A second study of ambulatory patients with MDD found, in contrast, no differences between depressed patients and matched controls [15]. Hospitalized drug-free patients with schizophrenia and otherwise healthy patients hospitalized for elective herniorrhaphy also showed no immunologic changes [15]. These studies suggested that psychoimmunologic effects are specific to subgroups of patients with depressive disorders and, furthermore, are not simply a consequence of the nonspecific distress associated with psychiatric disturbance or hospitalization.

The different immune effects among hospitalized and ambulatory depressed patients suggested several possible intervening variables. These included hospitalization itself, including loss of control, isolation and activity restriction, severity of the depression, gender and age (the hospitalized patients being older and more predominantly male). This was elucidated in a more extensive study of hospital-

*In part from: Directions in Psychiatry, April, 1991.

ized and ambulatory unipolar, MDD patients and age and sex-matched controls [16]. While we found no significant overall differences between our sample of 91 depressed patients and 91 matched controls for any of an extended battery of immune measures, significant patient-control differences were revealed, however, when age, sex, severity of depression and hospitalization were considered.

An association between MDD and altered lymphocyte activity was found in relation to the age of the depressed patient. In contrast to increasing mitogen responses across the adult age range in the healthy controls, MDD patients showed a progressive age-related decrement in lymphocyte activity. A similar age-related difference been MDD patients and controls was found for the number of $CD4^+$ (T-helper) cells. Specifically, with increasing age in the middle and later years, patients with MDD, compared with controls, had concurrent and progressive deficits in the number of $CD4^+$ cells as well as in lymphocyte proliferative activity. In contrast, depressed young adults compared with matched controls appeared to have similar or possibly increased numbers of $CD4^+$ cells and increased lymphocyte activity. The parallel age-related immunologic effects in depression on $CD4^+$ cells and on mitogen-induced lymphocyte proliferation are consistent with a mechanism involving a primary defect in T-helper cells and consequent functional changes in the lymphocyte in MDD.

The age-related immune changes in MDD may represent an interaction between processes associated with major depression and those associated with aging. Decreased lymphocyte proliferation in older depressed patients may result from age- and depression-related hormonal and monoaminergic abnormalities impacting on an aging immune system at the limits of its adaptive capacity [17,18]; the same depression-related factors in younger patients would impact on an immune system with greater residual and adaptive capacity. The age-related effects may also be a consequence of a syndromal disparity between younger and older MDD patients. For example, differential familiar loading in early- and late-onset depression has been demonstrated [19], suggesting that these may be biologically distinct disorders. The length of time in depression or the number of depressive episodes may also be involved in the age effects.

In addition to the association between age and altered immunity in depression, we found an association, independent of age, between the extent of depressive symptoms (measured by the Hamilton Depression Scale [20]) and lower mitogen responses. This indicated that several factors may be operative in the immune alterations found in MDD, including age-dependent changes associated with the syndrome of MDD and effects of affective distress that may, as discussed above, be common to a variety of syndromal and non-syndromal states.

Our findings with respect to NK cell activity are less clear. There was an age-related pattern of change in NK activity similar to that found for mitogen response; however, these relationships did not reach traditional levels of significance but were suggestive of a trend ($P < 0.08$). The NK findings are of further interest considering the findings by several other groups of lower NK activity in MDD patients (e.g. Irwin et al. [21]).

In another study we (S.E.K. and A.A.) examined affective components within MDD. Specifically we compared depressed patients with co-morbid panic disorder to depressed patients without panic disorder. Those patients with co-morbid panic disorder had mitogen responses and numbers of T-cells higher than those depressed patients without a panic component to their affective makeup. These data strongly suggest that the quality of the depression is important in understanding immune relationships in MDD.

Conclusion

The growing psychoimmunologic literature has served to emphasize that the relationship between behavioral states and the immune system is far from simple. There is, nevertheless, evidence suggesting that depressive affective states are an important psychoimmunologic factor in many settings. A variety of neuroendocrine and other mechanisms may contribute to immune system changes as a consequence of stress or depression.

References

1. Clayton PJ, Halikes JA and Maurice WL (1972) Br. J. Psychiatry 120: 71.
2. Parkes CM (1972) Bereavement: Studies of Grief in Adult Life. Int. Univ. Press, New York.
3. Osterweis M, Solomon F and Green M (eds.) (1984) Bereavement: Reactions, Consequences and Care. National Academy Press, Washington D.C.
4. Avery D and Winokur G (1976) Arch. Gen. Psychiatry 33: 1029–1037.
5. Murphy JM, Monson RR, Olivier DC et al. (1987) Arch. Gen. Psychiatry 44: 473–480.
6. Shekelle RB, Raynor WJ, Ostfeld AM et al. (1982) Psychosomat. Med. 43: 1017–1022.
7. Odegaard O (1952) Acta Psychiatr. Scand. 27: 353–387.
8. Cappel R, Gregoire F, Thiry L and Sprecher S (1978) J. Clin. Psychiatry 39: 266–268, .
9. Sachar EJ, Hellman L, Roffwarg HP et al. (1973) Arch. Gen. Psychiatry 134: 493–501.
10. Carroll BJ, Curtis GC and Mendels J (1976) Arch. Gen. Psychiatry 33: 1051–1058.
11. Whybrow PC and Prange AJ (1981) Arch. Gen. Psychiatry 38: 106–113.
12. Mann JJ, Brown RP, Halper JP et al. (1985) N. Engl. J. Med. 313: 715–720.
13. Stein M, Schliefer SJ and Keller SE (1987) In: American Psychiatric Association Annual Review, Vol. 6. pp. 210–234.
14. Schliefer SJ, Keller SE, Meyerson AT et al. (1984) Arch. Gen. Psychiatry 41: 484–486.
15. Schliefer SJ, Keller SE, Siris SG et al. (1985) Gen. Psychiatry 42: 129.
16. Schliefer SJ, Keller SE, Bond RN et al. (1989) Arch. Gen. Psychiatry 46: 81–87.
17. Weksler ME and Huttaroth TH (1974) J. Clin. Invest. 53: 99–104.
18. Weksler ME (1983) Ann. Int. Med. 98: 105–107.
19. Weissman M, Wickramarative P, Merikangas K et al. (1984) Arch. Gen. Psychiatry 41: 1136–1143.
20. Hamilton M (1967) Br. J. Soc. Clin. Psychol. 6: 278–296.
21. Irwin M, Patterson T, Smith TL et al. (1990) Biol. Psychiatry 27: 22–30.

© 1991 Elsevier Science Publishers B.V. All rights reserved.
Biological Psychiatry, Volume 2. G. Racagni et al., editors.

Depression, aging and psychoimmunology: Focus on the pituitary-thyroid axis

Charles B. Nemeroff[1] and Garth Bissette[2]

[1]Department of Psychiatry, Emory University School of Medicine, Box AF, Atlanta, GA 30322; and [2]Departments of Psychiatry and Pharmacology, Duke University Medical Center, Box 3859, Durham, NC 27710, U.S.A.

Introduction

Although it has long been appreciated [1] that patients with primary hypothyroidism exhibit many of the signs and symptoms of major depression, work conducted over the past decade is concordant with the view that many drug-free depressed patients exhibit more subtle abnormalities in the hypothalamic-pituitary-thyroid (HPT) axis. The HPT axis is organized hierarchically. Thyrotropin-releasing hormone (TRH), a tripeptide [2], is the hypothalamic releasing hormone that is synthesized within the hypothalamus, and released from nerve endings in the median eminence. Once released, TRH is humorally transported to the anterior pituitary gland within the vessels of the portal system. TRH binds to TRH receptors on the thyrotrophs, resulting in release of thyroid-stimulating hormone (TSH), into the systemic circulation. At the thyroid, TSH causes the release of the two major thyroid hormones, tri-iodothyronine (T_2) and thyroxine (T_4). Thyroid hormones feed back to inhibit TSH release and to inhibit TRH release and synthesis [3].

Tests of HPT function to diagnose hypothyroidism

In primary or grade I hypothyroidism, plasma concentrations of the thyroid hormones are decreased, plasma TSH concentrations are increased (due to loss of negative feedback), and the TRH-induced TSH response is markedly exaggerated. In grade II hypothyroidism, plasma concentrations of T_3 and T_4 are still within the normal range but basal plasma TSH concentrations are elevated, and the TRH-induced TSH response is exaggerated. In grade III (subclinical) hypothyroidism, plasma concentrations of both TSH and thyroid hormones are normal, but the TRH response to TSH is exaggerated [4].

The TSH response to TRH in depression

Shortly after the discovery of TRH, a TRH stimulation test was standardized. TRH (500 μg) is administered intravenously and blood samples are obtained at 30-min intervals for 2–3 h. Several investigators, beginning with the pioneering observations of Prange [5], have observed that approximately 25% of depressed patients, though euthyroid by any of the usual endocrinological criteria, exhibit a subnormal or blunted TSH response to TRH [6].

One mechanism to explain the blunted TSH response to TRH in drug-free depressed patients is hypersecretion of TRH which theoretically could result in a reduced number of TRH receptors, so-called "down-regulation", on the thyrotrophs. In laboratory rats, chronic administration of TRH results in down-regulation of TRH receptors in the anterior pituitary gland, as assessed by decreased plasma concentrations of TSH, T_3 and T_4, and a blunted TSH response to TRH [7]. Kirkegaard et al. [8] reported that depressed patients had elevated CSF concentrations of TRH. This supported the hypothesis that TRH is hypersecreted in depressed patients, but there were problems with the TRH radioimmunoassay used. We have now measured the concentration of CSF TRH in 14 drug-free patients with major depression, 12 controls with peripheral neurological disease, 4 patients with somatization disorder and 2 manic patients. The depressed patients exhibited markedly higher CSF TRH concentrations [9]. All of the depressed patients in our study were severely depressed, and 13 of 14 were either melancholic or psychotic. Eleven of the 14 depressed patients had higher CSF TRH concentrations that the highest concentration found in the controls.

We have begun to scrutinize the specificity of the elevated CSF concentrations of TRH in depressed patients. In drug-free patients with anorexia nervosa, CSF TRH is not increased [10], nor do patients with Alzheimer's disease or anxiety disorders show any alterations in CSF TRH [11]. Recently, Adinoff et al. [12] found a significant inverse relationship between the integrated TSH response to TRH and CSF TRH concentrations in 13 drug-free male alcoholics, a group that also exhibits TSH blunting to TRH. These data, taken together, represent compelling evidence that TRH hypersecretion may underlie the diminished TSH response to TRH.

Symptomless autoimmune thyroiditis and depression

Although the blunted TSH response to TRH in depressed patients is well established, approximately 15% of depressed patients exhibit an exaggerated TSH response to TRH [13]. This finding has led to the realization that many depressed patients with exaggerated TSH responses to TRH and normal baseline plasma TSH and thyroid hormone concentrations have, by definition, grade III hypothyroidism. Gold et al. [14] reported that of 15 patients with clearly supranormal TSH responses to TRH, 9 had detectable circulating antimicrosomal thyroid and/or antithyroglobulin antibodies. This was the first report that depressed patients suffer from a greater than expected incidence of symptomless autoimmune thyroiditis (SAT), which likely underlies the high incidence of subclinical (grade III) hypothyroidism.

We have studied the prevalence of antithyroid antibodies in depressed patients in detail. In our first study [15], we measured the presence of antimicrosomal and antithyroglobulin thyroid antibodies in 45 psychiatric inpatients with prominent depressive symptoms (28 with DSM III major depression). Nine of the patients (20%) had detectable titers of antithyroid antibodies, a rate considerably higher than the 5–10% observed in the normal population. In a second study [16] the relationship between the presence of antithyroid antibodies and an abnormal DST was studied in depressed patients. DST non-suppression is thought to represent a measure of disease severity by some investigators. A total of 124 adolescent and adult inpatients were studied. Of the 102 patients who fulfilled criteria for major affective disorder (major depression, mixed bipolar disorder, etc.), 20% exhibited detectable thyroid antibodies. DST non-suppressors were more likely than suppressors to exhibit thyroid abnormalities.

In a third study [17] we sought to determine the prevalence rate of autoimmune thyroiditis in subtypes of affective disorder. We studied 173 consecutively admitted psychiatric inpatients. Patients with bipolar illness had a higher rate of symptomless autoimmune thyroiditis when compared to patients with unipolar depression.

Discussion

In spite of years of concerted study, it is almost remarkable how little we know concerning the role of the HPT axis in the pathophysiology of affective disorders. However, it is evident that a sizeable proportion of depressed patients, in particular those with bipolar illness, exhibited relatively high rates of autoimmune thyroiditis, as evidenced by the presence of antithyroid antibodies. Early in the course of autoimmune thyroid disease, plasma TSH concentrations are increased in order to maintain normal plasma T_3 and T_4 concentrations as the negative feedback of thyroid hormones is decreased. I would propose that this pathophysiological condition may also be associated with TRH hypersecretion, necessary to increase TSH secretion and secondary to lack of T_3 and T_4 feedback on TRH neurons in the hypothalamus. Clearly, CSF TRH concentrations should be measured in depressed patients with autoimmune thyroiditis to test this hypothesis.

The issue of treatment of depressed patients with symptomless autoimmune thyroiditis remains an issue of paramount importance. Is treatment with exogenous thyroid hormone alone sufficient to normalize their mood state? There are anecdotal accounts of treating such patients successfully with T_4 alone, and we should remember the seminal observations of Prange and coworkers [18] demonstrating reduced effectiveness of tricyclic antidepressants in patients with frank hypothyroidism. Moreover, Targum et al. [19] reported that depressed patients refractory to tricyclic antidepressants who responded to T_3 supplementation had an increased prevalence rate of subclinical hypothyroidism. Such questions are not trivial, as Gold et al. [13] have reported that 10% of unselected depressed or anergic patients referred to psychiatrists have Grades 1, 2 or 3 hypothyroidism.

The high rate of autoimmune thyroiditis and subclinical hypothyroidism in bipolar patients is of interest in view of the landmark studies by Whybrow and colleagues [20] exhibiting therapeutic responses of rapid-cycling bipolar patients to high doses of thyroid hormones.

The blunted TSH response to TRH observed in approximately 25% of depressed patients, as well as in abstinent alcoholics remains mechanistically enigmatic. However, our studies suggest that chronic TRH hypersecretion as evidenced by increased CSF TRH concentrations results in adenohypophyseal TRH receptor down-regulation.

Careful longitudinal clinical studies and family studies should be designed to answer the many questions that remain in our knowledge of the role of the HPT axis in affective disorders.

Acknowledgements

Supported by NIMH MH-42088 and MH-39415.

References

1. Whybrow PW, Prange AJ and Treadway C (1969) Arch. Gen. Psychiatry 20: 48–62.
2. Burgus R, Dunn TF, Desiderio D, Vale W and Guillemin R (1969) C.R. Acad. Sci. 269: 226–228.
3. Morley JE (1981) Endocr. Rev. 2: 396–436.
4. Gold MS and Kronig MH (1984) In: Hall RCW and Beresford TO (eds.) Handbook of Psychiatric Diagnostic Procedures, Vol. I. Spectrum Press, New York, pp. 29–45.
5. Prange AJ, Wilson IC, Lara PP, Alltop LB and Breese GR (1972) Lancet ii: 999–1002.
6. Loosen PT (1987) In: Nemeroff CB and Loosen PT (eds.) Handbook of Clinical Psychoneuroendocrinology. Guilford Press, New York, pp. 336–350.
7. Nemeroff CB, Bissette G, Martin JB, Brazeau P, Vale W, Kizer JS and Prange AJ Jr (1980) Neuroendocrinology 30: 193–199.
8. Kirkegaard C, Faber J, Hummer L and Rogowski P (1979) Psychoneuroendocrinology 4: 227–235.
9. Banki CM, Bissette G, Arato M and Nemeroff CB (1990) Am. J. Psychiatry 145: 1526–1531.
10. Lesem MD, Kaye WH, Bissette G, Jimerson DC and Nemeroff CB (1990) Proc. 143rd Ann. Meeting Am. Psychiatr. Assoc., NR504, p. 240.
11. Fossey M, Lydiard RB, Larara MT, Bissette G, Nemeroff CB and Ballenger JC (1990) Biol. Psychiatry 27 (Suppl.): 167A.
12. Adinoff B, Nemeroff CB, Bissette G, Martin PR and Linnoila M (1991) Am. J. Psychiatry (in press).
13. Gold MS, Pottash A and Extein I (1981) J. Am. Med. Assoc. 245: 1919–1921.
14. Gold MS, Pottash ALC and Extein I (1982) Psychiatr. Res. 6: 261–269.
15. Nemeroff CB, Simon JS, Haggerty JJ and Evans DL (1990) Am. J. Psychiatry 144: 1491–1493.
16. Haggerty JJ, Simon JS, Evans DL and Nemeroff CB (1987) Am. J. Psychiatry 144: 1491–1493.
17. Haggerty JJ, Evans DL, Golden RN, Pederson CA, Simon JS and Nemeroff CB (1990) Biol. Psychiatry 27: 51–60.
18. Prange AJ, Jr, Wilson IC, Breese GR and Lipton MA (1976) In: Sachar EJ (ed.) Hormones, Behavior and Psychopathology. Raven Press, New York, pp. 41–67.
19. Targum AD, Greenberg RD and Harmon RL (1984) J. Clin. Psychiatry 45: 345–346.
20. Bauer MS and Whybrow PC (1990) Arch. Gen. Psychiatry 47: 435–442.

© 1991 Elsevier Science Publishers B.V. All rights reserved.
Biological Psychiatry, Volume 2. G. Racagni et al., editors.

Cellular immunity and immune genetics in schizophrenia

Manfred Ackenheil, Elisabeth Hofchuster and Norbert Müller
Psychiatric Hospital, University of Munich, Nussbaumstr. 7, 8000 Munich 2, Germany

Introduction

Alterations of the immune system of psychiatric patients have been described [1,2] and might play a role in the pathogenesis of such disorders. These alterations concern the number of subgroups of T- and B-lymphocytes [3–5], the immune function of T-lymphocytes [6,7], the secretion of cytokines, such as interleukin-2 [8], the production of antibrain antibodies [9,10] and the protein contents and pattern in CSF [11]. Other alterations of the lymphocytes, the significance of which is unclear, such as increased spiperone binding [12] and different patterns of membrane phospholipids, are described as well. Although the mode of inheritance is unknown, genetic transmission occurs at least in subgroups of psychiatric patients. Biological markers, such as spiperone binding [12] and the HLA system, are also genetically determined. Altered frequencies of HLA class I and II antigens, the genetic basis of immune functions, are reported, too [13,7]. The present study investigated the number of subtypes of T-cells, the immune function, distribution of HLA antigens of schizophrenic patients and of patients with affective disorders as compared to controls in relation to genetic parameters.

Subjects and investigations

Forty-eight schizophrenics (ICD 9: 295.1, 295.3, 295.6) and 7 schizoaffectives (ICD 9: 295.7), without neuroleptic medication were investigated. Twenty-four of them (12 F, 12 M), mean age 32 years, were studied again after improvement. Family history was recorded. Fifty-one mentally and somatically healthy subjects (22 F, 29 M), age: 22 to 55 years (mean age 29 years) served as controls. WBC differential count, HLA-A, -B, -C typing, T-cell numbers and subsets (OKT3, OKT4, and OKT8 were analyzed (for details see [15]). Immune function: antigen and mitogen stimulation and suppressor cell activity were analyzed as described earlier [14]. A cluster analysis of cases was carried out according to K-means method over HLA-A, -B and -C-loci in two healthy control groups [15]. Due to statistical criteria, two independent HLA clusters of healthy controls were performed. The schizophrenic patients and a second group of patients with affective psychosis (n = 27; HLA- and T-cell and T-cell subgroup data were analyzed) were reclustered according to the cluster criteria obtained in healthy controls. Interactions between the affiliation to the HLA cluster and the family history of psychiatric diseases were investigated by a two-way analysis of variance.

Results

Compared to healthy controls (CD3 absolute: 1016 ± 457; CD3%: 45 ± 12; CD4 abs.: 697 ± 312; CD4%: 31 ± 9) schizophrenic patients showed more CD3 (abs.: 1324 ± 551; CD3%: 54 ± 11; $P < 0.000–0.006$) and CD4 cells (abs.: 883 ± 409 CD4%: 36 ± 10; $P < 0.017–0.025$). After clinical improvement we still observed an elevation of CD3 (abs.: 1522 ± 636; CD3%: 58 ± 9; $P < 0.000–0.000$) and CD4 cells (abs.: 1012 ± 448; CD4%: 39 ± 9; $P < 0.001–0.003$) as compared to controls. No significant difference was found between healthy controls and schizophrenic patients in the absolute number and the percentage of CD8 cells, but a higher number of CD8 cells was observed in medicated schizophrenics (CD8 abs.: 638 ± 313) as compared to acute schizophrenics (CD8 abs.: 498 ± 218; $P < 0.05$). The T4/T8 ratio was slightly increased in acute schizophrenics (1.83 ± 0.77) in comparison to controls (1.52 ± 0.62; $P < 0.04$). Suppressor cell activity was significantly reduced both in schizophrenic and in depressive patients (Fig. 1).

With regard to the HLA genes two different immunogenic clusters of controls with significant differences on HLA-A1, -A2, -A3, -A28, -B8, -B12, -B17 and -B21 were calculated [15]. Patients were distributed in two clusters according to the cluster criteria found in our controls. Seventy-four percent of the controls belonged to cluster 1 and 26% to cluster 2. Similarly, patients with endogenous psychosis were found in cluster 1 (74%) and in cluster 2 (26%). No significant

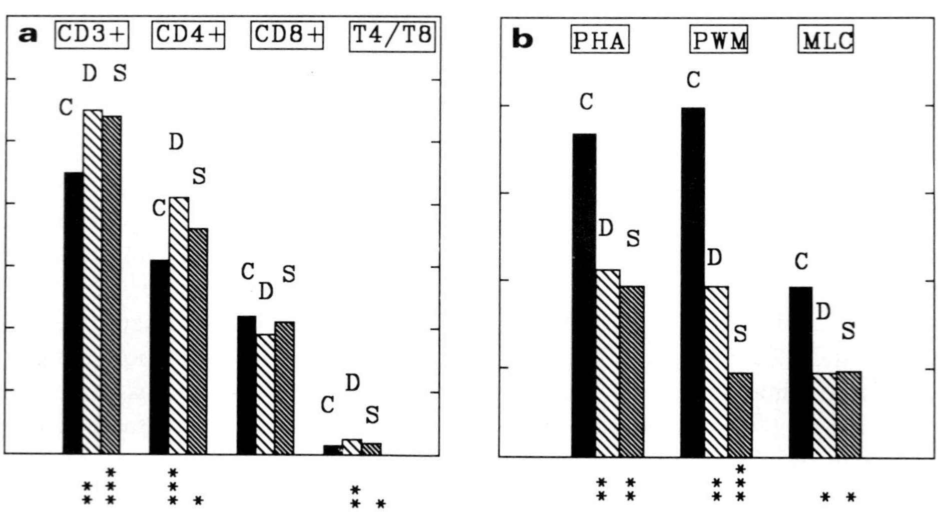

Fig. 1. Cell number (a) and suppressor cell activity (b) in schizophrenics (S), depressives (D) and controls (C). $*P < 0.05$; $**P < 0.01$; $***P < 0.001$ (Student's *t*-test).

differences between schizophrenic patients (cluster 1: 78%, cluster 2: 22%) and affective disorders (cluster 1: 63%, cluster 2: 37%) were found. With regard to the family history of psychiatric diseases, there was a significant difference between cluster 1 and cluster 2; in cluster 1 were significant more family history negative patients (87%) than in cluster 2 (13%; $P < 0.03$).

The affiliation to the clusters and the family history showed significant differences. CD3- and CD4-cells were high in family history positive patients in cluster 2 and in family history negative patients in cluster 1 ($P < 0.03$–0.02; Table 1). CD8-cells were low in family history negative patients in cluster 2 and in family history positive patients in cluster 1 ($P < 0.007$).

Discussion

Elevated CD3- and CD4-cells were found both, before and during neuroleptic treatment in comparison to controls. This elevation of CD3-cells might be due to the elevated CD4-cells, similar to the increased T4/T8 ratio. The increased T-cell compartment and especially the T-helper cells may reflect a state of enhanced reactivity of the immune system. Findings of enhanced IL-2 receptors [9,10], reduced serum-IL-2 [11,12], increased activated helper cells [8], and reduced suppressor cell activity [15] point in the same direction. Enhanced CD4-cells and reduced suppressor cell activity were also found in patients with affective psychosis [16] and no relevant difference in HLA-gene distribution and in cluster analysis could be observed between patients suffering from schizophrenia and affective psychosis. Therefore, HLA data of both types of endogenous psychosis were analyzed together. The significant differences in the two-way analysis of variance show that family history of psychiatric diseases and HLA distribution play a role in the expression of the number of CD3- and CD4-cells in endogenous psychosis. On the other hand, correlations between CD3- and CD4-cells and psychopathology after clinical improvement demonstrate that these parameters might be related to the long-term course of psychopathological symptoms and thus might reflect the tendency of the disease to progress to the chronic stage [16]. Since an increase of

Table 1. Distribution of patients to cluster 1 and 2 in relation to T-cell numbers and family history of psychotic diseases (2-way interaction analysis of variance; $P < 0.03$)

Family history	Cluster 1		Cluster 2			
+	$CD3^+$↔ $CD4^+$↔ $CD8^+$↔	30 (68%)	$CD3^+$↑ $CD4^+$↑ $CD8^+$↑	14 (32%)	44	(100%)
–	$CD3^+$↑ $CD4^+$↑ $CD8^+$↑	39 (87%)	$CD3^+$↔ $CD4^+$↔ $CD8^+$↔	6 (13%)	45	(100%)

cell numbers was found both, before and during neuroleptic treatment, these changes seem unlikely to be a result of neuroleptic therapy. It seems possible that alterations of immunological parameters and psychopathology are different expressions of the same underlying process, in which family history of psychiatric diseases play a role.

References

1. Knight JG (1982) Lancet: 1073–1076.
2. Crow TJ (1984) Br. J. Psychiatry 18: 113–119.
3. DeLisi LE, Goodman S, Neckers LM and Wyatt RJ (1982) Biol. Psychiatry 17: 1003–1009.
4. Ganguli R, Rabin BS and Kelly RH (1989) In: Hadden JW, Masek K and Nisticò G (eds.) Interactions Among CNS, Neuroendocrine and Immune Systems. Pythagora Press, Rome/Milan, pp. 365–384.
5. Rapaport MH, McAllister CG, Pickar D, Nelson DL and Paul SM (1989) Arch. Gen. Psychiatry 46: 291–292.
6. Kay WA, Adri MN, Soeldner JS, Rabinowe SK, Kaldany A, Kahn CR, Bristian B, Srikanta S, Ganda OP and Eisenbarth GS (1986) N. Engl. J. Med. 315: 930.
7. Rabin BS, Ganguli R, Cunnick JE and Lysle DT (1988) Clin. Lab. Med. 8: 253–268.
8. Villemain F, Chatenoud L, Guillibert E, Pelicier Y and Bach JF (1987) In: Iancovic BD, Marcovic BM and Spector NH (eds.) Ann. N.Y. Acad. Sci. 496: 669–675.
9. Kelly RH, Ganguli R and Rabin BS (1987) Biol. Psychiatry 22: 1488–1491.
10. DeLisi LE, Weber RI and Pert CB (1985) Biol. Psychiatry 20: 94–119.
11. Wildenauer D, Körschenhausen D, Hoechtien W, Ackenheil M, Kehl M and Lottspeich F (1991) Electrophoresis (in press).
12. Bondy B and Ackenheil M (1987) J. Psychiatr. Res. 21: 521–529.
13. Miyanaga K, Machiyama Y and Juji T (1984) Biol. Psychiatry 19: 121–129.
14. Müller N, Ackenheil M, Eckstein R, Hofschuter E and Mempel W 1987) In: Jancovic BD, Marcovic BM and Spector NH (eds.) Ann. N.Y. Acad. Sci. 496: 686–690.
15. Muller N, Hofschuster E and Ackenheil J (1990) In: Stefanis et al. (eds.) Psychiatry: A World Perspective II. Elsevier, pp. 174–179.
16. Muller N, Ackenheil M, Hofschuster E, Eckstein R and Mempel W (1988) Psychopharmacology (Suppl.) 96: 221.

© 1991 Elsevier Science Publishers B.V. All rights reserved.
Biological Psychiatry, Volume 2. G. Racagni et al., editors.

Psychoimmunoendocrine aspects of panic disorder

F. Brambilla[1], L. Bellodi[2], G. Perna[2], M. Battaglia[2], G. Sciuto[2], G. Diaferia[2], F. Petraglia[3], A. Panerai[4] and P. Sacerdote[2]

[1]Osp. Psichiatrico Pini, Milan; [2]Ist. Sci. S. Raffaele, Dip. Sci. Neuropsichiche, Milan; [3]Clin. Ostetrica-Ginecol. Univ., Modena; and [4]Dip. Farmacologia Univ., Milan, Italy

Introduction

Neuroimmunoendocrine investigation of panic disorder has given controversial results, possibly due to heterogeneity of the population examined, which included patients with major depressive comorbidity [1–3]. We have recently studied immune and neuroendocrine functions of a selected group of patients with pure panic disorder without depressive comorbidity. We measured lymphocyte proliferative response to phytohaemagglutinin (HPA), lymphocyte beta-endorphin (β-EP) levels, ACTH, cortisol β-EP plasma concentrations before and after stimulation with corticotropin-releasing hormone (CRH). Cortisol response to dexamethasone inhibition (DST) was also examined.

The aim of the investigation was to determine whether impairments of the immune system occurred in the mental disorder and if the alterations could be related to derangement of the hypothalamo-pituitary-adrenal (HPA) axis and of lymphocyte β-EP secretion, which are known to modulate the immune function [4,5]. All the tests were repeated after 30 days of alprazolam therapy, to see if a pharmacologically-induced psychological improvement could be accompanied by changes in the immunoendocrine parameters, thus confirming the existence of a link between the 3 systems.

Materials and Methods

Seventeen outpatients with pure panic disorder without depressive comorbidity according to the DSM III-R criteria and 14 psychophysically healthy controls, matched for sex and age, entered the study. Patients were 8 men and 9 women, aged 17–47 years, with a history of the disease of 3 months to 7 years duration and 1–14 panic attacks per week. They had been drug free for at least 15 days.

Both patients and controls were given the CRH test (1 mcg/kg b.w. i.v.) at 9:00 a.m. ACTH, cortisol, β-EP plasma concentrations were measured at 15–30-min intervals for 2 h, by RIA using commercial kits for ACTH and cortisol and the method of Facchinetti et al. [6] for β-EP, which includes a chromatographic separation of the peptide by G 75 column. In parallel, before and 30 min after the CRH administration we measured the mitogenic response of T-lymphocyte to PHA and lymphocyte β-EP concentrations [7–9]. Psychological assessment of patients and controls included the SCID-UP and SIDP-R interviews for diagnosis of panic disorder and of personality features, respectively. Anxiety was monitored by the Hamilton Rating Scale for Anxiety, by the Fear Questionnaire, by the Agoraphobic Cognition Questionnaire and by the State-Trait Anxiety Inventory. Severity and frequency of panic attacks and of anticipatory anxiety were monitored by the Panic Attack and Anticipatory Anxiety Scale, and depression by the Hamilton Rating Scale for Depression.

Data were analyzed statistically by the 2V program of the Software Package BMDP, by ANOVA for repeated measures and by the Student's t-test.

Results

β-EP and cortisol basal concentrations and ACTH, β-EP, cortisol responses to CRH stimulations were not significantly different in patients and controls, either before or after 30 days of alprazolam therapy. Instead, ACTH basal levels were higher in patients than in controls (22.5 ± 1.3 vs. 13.5 ± 6.7 pg/ml; $P = 0.02$) and decreased at 30 days of alprazolam therapy (16.4 ± 13.3). Moreover, the ratio between ACTH and cortisol responses to CRH stimulation examined as area under the curve (AUC), was significantly lower in patients than in controls (0.9 ± 0.7 vs 1.4 ± 0.6; $P = 0.02$) and returned to normal after therapy (1.6 ± 0.5). The DST was blunted in 23.5% of the cases.

T-lymphocyte proliferative responses to PHA stimulation were not significantly different in patients and controls in basal conditions and after CRH stimulation, either before or after alprazolam therapy. T-lymphocyte basal β-EP concentrations and their response to CRH stimulation were also not significantly different in controls and in patients, both before and after alprazolam therapy.

Anxiety and phobias were severe before therapy and significantly reduced by 30 days' alprazolam therapy. In parallel, the minor depressive symptomatology presented by patients disappeared. The pharmacological treatment significantly reduced the weekly number and severity of panic attacks.

Discussion and Conclusions

Our data suggest that immune function, or at least T-lymphocyte proliferative response to mitogen stimulation, is well preserved in panic disorder. The difference with the data in the literature [1–3], which has reported increased or decreased responses to mitogenic stimulation, is probably due to the selection of patients, which often included subjects with depressive comorbidity, while our group suffered from pure panic disorder. In fact, immune impairments have been repeatedly reported in depressed patients [10,11]. The study of the HPA function showed hyperactivity of the axis, as revealed by the increased ACTH basal plasma levels and by the decreased ratio between ACTH and cortisol responses to CRH stimulation. The dissociation between HPA hypersecretion and normal immune function suggests that the neuroendocrine impairment is possibly not mandatory for inducing immune suppression in panic disorder. Alternatively, it is possible that other factors have balanced the HPA hormone suppressive effect on immune function, including the normal secretion of plasma and T-lymphocyte β-EP, which is known to stimulate the immune function [5]. The effect of alprazolam therapy, with normalization of psychological and HPA function and no changes in the immune parameters, confirms the existence of a link between psychological and hormonal parameters, while the immune system, or at least part of its function, does not seem to be involved in the psychoneuroendocrine alteration.

References

1. Schleifer SJ, Keller SE, Scott BJ and Vecchione J (1990) Biol. Psychiatry (Suppl. 9/A) 27: 172 A.
2. Andreoli A, Keller SE, Taban C, Rabaeus M and Garrone G (1990) Biol. Psychiatry (Suppl. 9A) 27: 95 A.
3. Ramesh C, Yeragani VK, Balan R and Pohl R (1990) Biol. Psychiatry (Suppl. 9A) 27: 65 A.
4. Irwin M, Daniels M, Risch SC, Bloom E and Weiner H (1988) Biol. Psychiatry 24: 173–178.
5. Stefano GB (1989) Prog. Neurobiol. 33: 149–159.
6. Facchinetti F and Genazzani AR (1979) In: Albertini A, Da Prada M and Peskar BA (eds.) Radio-immunoassay of Drugs and Hormones in Cardiovascular Medicine. Elsevier, Amsterdam, pp. 347–354.
7. Barcellini W, Borghi MO, Sguotti C, Palmieri R, Frasca D, Meroni PL and Zanussi C (1988) Clin. Immunol. Immunopathol. 47: 142–151.
8. Panerai AE, Martini A, Di Giulio AM, Fraioli F, Vegni C, Pardi G, Marini A and Mantegazza P (1983) J. Clin. Endocrinol. Metab. 57: 537–544.
9. Sacerdote P, Rubboli F, Locatelli L, Ciciliato I, Mantegazza P and Panerai AE (1991) J. Neuroimmunol. (in press).
10. Schleifer SJ, Keller SE, Camerino M, Thorton JC and Stein M (1983) J. Am. Med. Assoc. 250: 374–377.
11. Irwin M, Patterson T, Smith TL, Caldwell C, Brown SA, Gillin JC and Grant I (1990) Biol. Psychiatry 27: 22–30.

© 1991 Elsevier Science Publishers B.V. All rights reserved.
Biological Psychiatry, Volume 2. G. Racagni et al., editors.

Neuropeptides in the immune system: A new tool?

Alberto E. Panerai[1], Paola Sacerdote[1], Barbara Manfredi[1], Luisa Locatelli[1], Mauro Bianchi[1], Gabriele Panza[2] and Francesca Brambilla[3]

[1]Department of Pharmacology; and [2]Department of Psychiatry, University of Milan; and [3]Ospedale Psichiatrico, "P. Pini", Milan, Italy

Introduction

Recent experimental evidence suggests that neuropeptides participate in the modulation of the immune system [1,2], and many neuropeptides have been shown to be present and constitutively synthesized in cells of the immune system. In our studies, we investigated the concentrations of β-endorphin (βE), vasoactive intestinal peptide (VIP), and cholecystokinin (CCK) in peripheral blood mononuclear cells (PMNC) in human and animal models. Firstly, we investigated the possibility of modulating the concentrations of βE, CCK, and VIP in PMNC with the same drugs which we knew could modulate the concentrations of neuropeptides in the brain. Finally, we began investigating the changes in the patterns of PMNC VIP, CCK, and βE in patients suffering from chronic pain or schizophrenic subjects before and during treatment.

Pharmacological modulation of PMNC neuropeptides

Table 1 illustrates the effect of pharmacological treatments on βE concentrations in PMNC. Chronic pharmacological treatments aimed to potentiate the serotoninergic system increase, and the concomitant treatment with the serotoninergic antagonist metergoline decreases, the concentrations of βE. Also in normal subjects or depressed patients treated with chlorimipramine, βE concentrations increase after treatment with chlorimipramine.

Drugs that increase the dopaminergic tone induce a decrease of βE concentrations in rat PMNC, while the concentrations increase after the administration of the dopaminergic antagonist haloperidol. The same effect was also observed after administration of haloperidol for 2 or 15 days to schizophrenic subjects not previously treated with neuroleptics.

Finally, βE concentrations were decreased in rat PMNC by the GABA agonist sodium valproate; similar results were observed in epileptic subjects chronically treated with the drug.

Interestingly, the modulation of βE concentrations in PC obtained with drugs affecting the GABAergic, dopaminergic or serotoninergic systems appears to be totally superimposable on the modulation of βE in the hypothalamus [3–5].

Table 1. Effect of treatment with serotoninergic, dopaminergic and GABAergic drugs on βE concentrations in rat PBMC

Saline 24.2 ± 5.1[a]	5-HTP 150.2 ± 8.10	MCE 5.3 ± 5.2	MCE + 5-HTP 40.4 ± 6.2
Saline 26.6 ± 6.1	BCE 6.4 ± 2.1	HALO 50.4 ± 10.2	BCE + HALO 8.1 ± 1.1
Saline 28.4 ± 8.3	Sodium valproate 4.5 ± 1.1		

[a] = Mean ± S.D.; [b] = pg/10^6 cells; MCE = metergoline; 5-HTP = 5-hydroxytryptophan; HALO = haloperidol: BCE = bromocriptine.

It is very important to underline that none of the pharmacological treatments applied in vivo or in vitro affected CCK or VIP concentrations in PC (data not presented).

PMNC concentrations of neuropeptides in diseases of the nervous system

Chronic pain

We measured βE in PC obtained from rats suffering from experimental arthritis and in this model we observed decreased concentrations of the opioid, similarly to what we previously reported in CSF of patients suffering from chronic recurrent low back pain [6].

Schizophrenia

βE, VIP and CCK concentrations were measured in schizophrenic subjects (DSM III-R) at the first visit to the hospital, who had not previously been treated for the disease, and after two or fifteen days of treatment with haloperidol, at the doses required by each patient for control of the disease. The concentrations of the three neuropeptides were correlated to haloperidol doses and clinical development of the disease. The results obtained are summarized in Table 2.

Basal concentrations of βE were not different in controls and schizophrenic patients, and increased in a dose and clinical improvement related fashion. CCK concentrations were significantly higher in schizophrenic patients than in controls and decreased together with disease symptoms, but in a dose unrelated fashion. Finally, VIP concentrations were lower in schizophrenic subjects than in controls and remained unchanged during treatment.

Two observations are of particular interest. Similarly to what was observed in PMNC, VIP, CCK and βE showed decreased, increased and unchanged concentrations respectively, in CSF and brain samples obtained from patients or autopsies [7]. This observation also confirms in schizophrenia the parallelism

Table 2. β-endorphin, cholecystokinin and vasoactive intestinal peptide concentrations in PMNC of control subjects and schziphrenic patients before and at 2 and 15 days of treatment with haloperidol

Controls	Before	2 days	15 days
β-endorphin			
25.6 ± 5.2[a]	30.0 ± 10.1	58.1 ± 15.3	82.4 ± 8.6
Cholecystokinin			
38.5 ± 4.1	98.2 ± 20.0	74.3 ± 12.4	60.2 ± 8.2
Vasoactive intestinal peptide			
40.2 ± 2.0	10.1 ± 2.2	15.0 ± 1.0	8.2 ± 5.1

[a] = $pg/10^6$ cells.

between CNS and PMNC behavior of VIP, CCK and βE. The second observation is that, since we previously showed that haloperidol does not change per se the concentrations of CCK, and the decrease observed during therapy does not correlate to the doses of the neuroleptic, the decrease mirrors the clinical improvement.

Conclusions

Our observations offer ground for new studies and perspectives. An interesting point put forward by the results reported here is the apparently complete parallelism between the modulation of the three neuropeptides in PMNC and CNS, both in physiological and pathological conditions. If this observation is further confirmed in other experimental models and/or for other neuropeptides, it will open up an interesting field of investigation. It will be possible, in fact, to consider the behavior of neuropeptides in PMNC as a mirror of CNS and this will allow their study on peripheral tissue. For instance, the measurement of PMNC neuropeptides might become a useful tool in the hands of the psychiatrist in order to follow the progression of schizophrenia or response to therapy.

References

1. Blalock JE (1989) Physiol. Rev. 69:1.
2. Morley JE, Kay NE, Solomon GF and Plotnikoff NP (1987) Life Sci. 41: 527.
3. Locatelli V, Petraglia F, Penalva A and Panerai AE (1983) Life Sci. 33: 1711.
4. Martini A, Sacerdote P, Mantegazza P and Panerai AE (1984) J. Neurochem. 43: 871.
5. Sacerdote P, Brini A, Mantegazza P and Panerai AE (1987) Pharmacol. Biochem. Behav. 26: 153.
6. Panerai AE, Martini A, Abbate D, Villani R and DeBenedittis G (1983) In: Bonica JJ, Lindblom O and Iggo A (eds.) Advances in Pain Research and Therapy. Raven Press, New York, pp. 543–547.
7. Rafaelsen OJ and Gjerris A (1985) Prog. Neurol. Psychopharmacol. Biol. Psychiatry 9: 533.

Neurotransmitters, receptor molecular biology, brain signal transductions and behaviour

© 1991 Elsevier Science Publishers B.V. All rights reserved.
Biological Psychiatry, Volume 2. G. Racagni et al., editors.

Molecular genetic studies in psychiatry

J. Mendlewicz

Department of Psychiatry, Erasme Hospital, Free University of Brussels, route de Lennik 808, 1070 Brussels, Belgium

Recent advances in molecular behavioral genetics have attracted much attention and provided a new insight into the pathophysiology of affective illness [1,2].

The identification and precise localisation of a major vulnerability gene in the transmission of affective illness could lead to better phenotype characterisation and insight into the genetic etiology of these mental disorders. In this linkage method, one tries to test a potential linkage relationship between a known genetic marker and a character which is known to be genetically determined, but has not yet been mapped on the chromosome. It has been used successfully in the genetic study of several hereditary conditions, and recently to test the hypothesis of genetic linkage in manic-depressive illness.

Reich et al. [3] studied 2 large families assorting for colour blindness (an X-linked recessive marker) and bipolar illness, while Mendlewicz et al. [4] reported on seven such families. In both studies, the marker and the illness failed to show independent assortment.

Mendlewicz and Fleiss [5] were able to demonstrate close linkage between bipolar illness and both deutan and protan colour blindness in 17 informative pedigrees and the absence of such linkage in 11 unipolar pedigrees. Recent linkage data confirm a linkage relationship between colour blindness and bipolar manic-depressive illness [6–9], and are at variance with the report of Gershon et al. [10], who did not find such a linkage. A more comprehensive study – part of the Biological Psychiatry Collaborative Programme of the World Health Organisation – was conducted in four collaborative centres (Bethesda, Basel, Brussels and Copenhagen) on 16 informative families, the overall results being consistent with the presence of linkage between bipolar illness and colour blindness. Some families showed an X-linked pattern of inheritance, while others did not, this last observation suggesting the hypothesis of genetic heterogeneity in manic-depressive illness [11,12].

A comprehensive analysis of linkage data from the available literature shows that X-linkage between color blindness and bipolar illness is indeed demonstrated in a large sample of families, despite the presence of genetic heterogeneity [13–15].

Mendlewicz et al. [16] reported a positive linkage between bipolar illness and glucose-6-phosphate dehydrogenase deficiency (G6PD), a genetic marker on the X-chromosome.

Recently, Del Zompo et al. [8] have studied two pedigrees for bipolar illness, colour blindness, and G6PD deficiency, which is closely linked with colour blindness on the X-chromosome [17]. Their results are also consistent with X-linkage in bipolar illness. Like Kruger et al. [18], Risch and Baron [13] also suggested genetic heterogeneity to explain discrepancies in X-linkage studies.

The DNA recombinant method and more recently the polymerase chain reaction (PCR) for gene amplification permit exploration of DNA polymorphisms in various regions of the human genome [19]. Presently, linkage with DNA markers in manic-depression has been reported in two distinct chromosomal regions, the distal part of the short arm of chromosome 11 (11p 15) and the subterminal region of the long arm of the X chromosome (Xq 26-28).

Chromosome 11

Egeland et al. [20], studying a large pedigree of the Amish community, reported a positive linkage between manic depression and the C-Harvey-ras-A (HRAS) oncogene as well as the insulin (INS) marker on the short arm of chromosome 11. This linkage, however, could not be confirmed in American bipolar pedigrees of non Amish origin [21] and in other pedigrees of bipolar disorders [22–25] as well as in pedigrees of unipolar disorder [26,27]. Furthermore, a reanalysis of the original Amish pedigree with 2 unaffected subjects becoming ill in the core pedigree and including a lateral extension, could almost exclude the probability of linkage of affective illness to the 11p 15 region of chromosome 11 [28].

These apparently conflicting results could perhaps be explained on the following grounds: the vulnerability to affective illness could be linked to more than one gene (genetic heterogeneity), and this may also be the case in the extended family of the Amish isolate.

Chromosome X

Previous linkage studies with classical X-chromosome markers have been confirmed by the finding of positive linkage between bipolar illness and the factor IX (hemophilia B) in region Xq27 in 10 Belgian pedigrees [29]. Negative linkage findings with DNA markers located in the color blindness and G6PD region (Xq28) have been reported by one group [30], but these last results have been obtained in a limited sample of small-sized families with polymorphic psychiatric disturbances and few bipolar cases, the presence of affective illness on both the paternal and maternal sides, and apparent transmission of illness from father to son in several families, despite positive linkage scores for the ST 14 probe (Xq 28 region) in 2 families, which renders these negative results less convincing. An association between the fragile X syndrome (Fra-X) and affective illness has also been observed [31,32] and recently confirmed in one family [33]. Another gene of interest in the Xq 28 region is the gene of the 3 subunit of the GABA receptor ($GABAR^3$) [34] which makes it a candidate gene for the genetic study of manic depression.

Thus the overall linkage data confirm the presence of a major locus of transmission of bipolar illness in the Xq27–28 region on the long arm of the X chromosome.

Positive X-linkage results have now been confirmed in 14 different samples in a total of 59 pedigrees collected in 7 centres located in various countries such as the U.S. (n = 3), Israel (n = 2), Belgium (n = 1) and Italy (n = 1).

The prevalence rate the X-linked form of bipolar illness in the general population and its clinical phenotypical characteristics remain to be defined. Some data suggest that X-linked bipolar affective illness may be associated with an early onset (before age 30) [35,36] and a greater psychiatric morbidity, as suggested by an increased relapse rate and a greater loading of bipolar disorders in relatives [36]. As for unipolar illness, chromosomal linkage studies have so far rejected the presence of a locus on chromosome X and chromosome 11 in this affective disorder [5,26,27]. The X-linked form of bipolar illness has now been substantiated by several family studies and numerous linkage studies using classical and DNA markers in the Xq27–28 region of the X-chromosome. Non-X-linked forms of the illness are most likely to be present (genetic heterogeneity), but the transmission of a major susceptibility gene on the short arm of chromosome 11 is at present not confirmed.

The identification and separation of genetic subgroups of the affective disorders with the use of genetic markers and candidate genes could allow a better clinical, biochemical and therapeutic approach to these complex behavioral disorders. Caution should be taken in making premature claims of linkage, due to the possibility of spurious linkage when dealing with selective ascertainment of frequent disorders and common genetic markers, as seems to be the case in the area of psychiatric disorders. The study of the interaction between genetic and non genetic vulnerability factors remains a major challenge for future research strategies in affective illness.

References

1. Mendlewicz J and Rainer JD (1977) Nature 268: 327–329.
2. Mendlewicz J (1988) Br. J. Psychiatry 153(3): 16–25.
3. Reich T, Clayton PJ and Winokur G (1969) Am. J. Psychiatry 125: 1358–1359.
4. Mendlewicz J, Fleiss J and Fieve RR (1972) J. Am. Med. Assoc. 222(13): 1624–1627.
5. Mendlewicz J and Fleiss JL (1974) Biol. Psychiatry 9: 261–294.
6. Baron M (1977) Arch. Gen. Psychiatry 34: 721–725.
7. Mendlewicz J, Linkowski P, Guroff JJ and Van Praag HM (1979) Arch. Gen. Psychiatry 36: 1442–1447.
8. Del Zompo M, Bocchetta A, Goldin LR and Corsini GU (1984) Acta Psychiatr. Scand. 70: 282–287.
9. Baron M, Risch N, Hamburger R, Mandel B, Kushner S, Newman M and Belmaker RH (1987) Nature 326: 289–292.
10. Gershon ES, Targum SD, Matthyse S and Bunney WE Jr (1979) Arch. Gen. Psychiatry 36: 1423–1431.
11. Gershon ES, Mendlewicz J, Gastpar M, Bech P, Goldin LR, Kielholz P, Rafaelsen OJ, Vartanian F and Bunney WE Jr (1980) Acta Psychiatr. Scand. 61: 319–338.
12. Mendlewicz J (1974) Évol. Psychiatr. 2: 411–416.
13. Risch N, Baron M (1982) Ann. Hum. Genet. 46: 153–166.
14. Risch (1989) Genet. Epidemiol. 6: 187–189.

15. Van Eerdewegh P (1989) Genet. Epidemiol. 6: 271–276.
16. Mendlewicz J, Linkowski P and Wilmotte J (1980) Br. J. Psychiatry 137: 337–342.
17. Siniscalco M, Filippi G and Latte B (1964) Nature 204: 1061–1064.
18. Kruger SD, Turner JW and Kidd KK (1982) Biol. Psychiatry 17: 1081–1099.
19. Bolstein D, White RL, Skolnick M and Davis RW (1980) Am. J. Human Genet. 32: 314–331.
20. Egeland JA, Gerhard DS, Paul DC, Sussex JN, Kidd KK, Allen CR, Hostetter AM and Housman DE (1987) Nature 325: 783–787.
21. Detera-Wadleigh SD, Berrettini WH, Goldin LR, Boorman D, Anderson S and Gershon ES (1987) Nature 325: 806–807.
22. Hodgkinson S, Sherrington R, Gurling H, Marchbanks M, Reeders S, Mallet J, Mc Innis M, Peturson H and Brynjolsfson J (1987) Nature 325: 805–806.
23. Gill M, McKeon P and Humphries P (1988) J. Med. Genet. 25: 634–637.
24. Mitchell P, Wraters B, Morrison N, Shine J, Donald J and Eisman J (1991) J. Affective Disord. 21: 23–32.
25. Mendlewicz J, Leboyer M, Malafosse A, Sevy S, Hirsch D, Babron MC, Van Broeckhoven C and Mallet J (1991) No linkage between chromosome 11p 15 markers and manic depressive illness in a Belgian pedigree (submitted).
26. Neiswanger K, Slaugenhaulst SA, Hughes HB, Frank E, Frankel DR, Mc Carthy MI, Chakravarti A, Zubenko GS, Kupfer DJ and Kaplan BB (1990) Biol. Psychiatry 28: 63–72.
27. Wesner RB, Tanna VL, Palmer PJ, Goedken RJ, Crowe RR and Winokur G (1990) Eur. Arch. Psychiatr. Neurol. Sci. 239: 356–360.
28. Kelsoe JR, Ginns EI, Egeland JA, Gerhard DS, Golstein AM, Bale SJ, Pauls DL, Long RJ, Kidd KK, Conte G, Housman DE and Paul SM (1989) Nature 342: 238–243.
29. Mendlewicz J, Simon P, Sevy S, Charon F, Brocas H, Legros S and Vassart GP (1987) Lancet: 1230–1232.
30. Berrettini WH, Goldin LR, Gelernter J, Gesman PV, Gershon ES and Detera-Wadleigh (1990) Arch. Gen. Psychiatry 47: 366–373.
31. Pascalis G, Teyssier JR and Carre-Pigeon F (1985) Ann. Méd. Psychol. 146: 594–595.
32. Reiss AL, Feinstein C, Toomey KE, Goldsmith B, Rosenbaum K and Caruso MA (1986) Am. J. Med. Genet. 23: 394–401.
33. Mendlewicz J and Hirsch D (1991) Biol. Psychiatry 29: 295–308.
34. Buckle VJ, Fujita N, Ryder-Cook AS, Derrz J, Barnard PJ, Lebo RV, Schofield PR, Seeburg PH, Bateson AN, Darlison MG and Barnard EA (1989) Neuronology 3: 647–654.
35. Mendlewicz J and Simon P (1987) Lancet ii No. 8554: 345.
36. Baron M, Hamburger R, Sandkuyl LA, Risch N, Mandel B, Endicott J, Belmaker RH and Ott J (1990) Acta Psychiatr. Scand. 82: 196–203.

© 1991 Elsevier Science Publishers B.V. All rights reserved.
Biological Psychiatry, Volume 2. G. Racagni et al., editors.

Prevention and treatment of age-associated dementia: Theoretical and pragmatic issues

Kazuo Hasegawa
Department of Psychiatry, St. Marianna University, Kawasaki, Japan 216

Introduction

The recent advances in medicine, universal availability of health care and other enlightened social programs have all contributed to extending longevity in our society. As the population ages, the prevalence rate of such as age-associated dementia increases as well. How to cope with age-associated dementia is the most urgent issues for mental health of the elderly. Biological psychiatry has been recently contributing a great deal to the elucidation of pathogenesis of age-associated dementia, especially Alzheimer's disease (AD). However, the first strategy is to have good data on the epidemiological study of age-associated dementia. It is of essential importance in establishing social strategies to know the pattern of illnesses causing dementia and it is indispensable for prevention of age-associated dementia to elucidate its risk factors. The second is a rather direct issue: i.e., to develop the pharmacological treatment against age-associated dementia. Both issues need international collaborative studies. World Health Organizations and other academic international organizations should be encouraged to enhance the cross-national research and work in these two areas.

Epidemiological issues

The WHO Special Program of Research on Aging (WHO-Spra) set up the multicentre epidemiological studies on age-associated dementia in 1988, co-ordinated by Florence WHO collaborating center (L. Amaducci). The value of cross-national studies is considerable. Differences in prevalence rate of, for example, Alzheimer's disease, might be explained by differences in culture, environment, genetic make-up or in health-care delivery. Furthermore, cross-national studies could enhance our understanding of the fundamental biology of aging and dementia and could enhance the efficacy of means for preventing, treating and caring for dementia sufferers. The involvement of countries in a research program could also facilitate the development of resources for prevention and care. Recently we have had a substantial increase in knowledge about the prevalence of age-associated dementia from many places in the world. Jorm et al. [1] were able to integrate the findings and reach to the following 4 conclusions, based on 47 published surveys:

1. the estimated prevalence of dementia increases exponentially with age;
2. the overall prevalence of dementia is the same in men and women;
3. there is greater variation in the estimates of prevalence;
4. there is higher prevalence rates for vascular dementia (VD) in Japan and China.

Since 1974, when the first large scale prevalence study on dementia was carried out by the author in Tokyo [2], about 21 local governments throughout Japan have administered well-organized population surveys of 65-year olds and over. Interesting findings have emerged. The prevalence of VD was consistently higher than those of AD in most of Japanese surveys [3], which appears to be the opposite western surveys, as mentioned earlier. However, when we compare the actual prevalence rates of both types of dementia in Japanese and Western surveys, it appears that the prevalence of VD does not differ significantly between the two surveys but the prevalence of AD was much less in Japan than Europe or the U.S.: from 0.6 to 2.7% vs. 0.6 to 10.3%. Several hypotheses to explain the differences (including constitutional or environmental factors) have been discussed. However, no reasonable conclusion has been reached. This is the reason why cross-national surveys with comparable protocols and instruments should be conducted. In recent Japanese epidemiological studies on dementia, there was a nice example of how preventive measures for causative disease of dementia might effect the decrease in the overall prevalence of dementia. There were the repetitive surveys of age-associated dementia carried out with identical methods and by the same investigators in 1980 and 1988 in Tokyo metropolitan areas [4]. The prevalence of the first survey was 4.6% in 1980 and the second survey revealed 4.0% in 1988. It should be considered that the elderly population over 65 increased from 871,163 (7.6%) to 1,101,144 (9.4%) during these eight years. Taking into consideration the increased elderly population in 1988 compared with that in 1980, the presumed prevalence rate was 5.3% in 1988. Therefore the actual prevalence was below the presumed prevalence. The first reason was the decrease in prevalence of cerebrovascular disorders from 7.2% to 6.4% and death rate due to CVD also decreased from 109.0 to 86.8 per 100,000. The changes might be due to the immense effort by local health care centers where the early detection of high blood pressure as well as preventive life counselling has been administered by health professionals. These findings provide us with some evidence that the preventive effort toward cerebrovascular disease would be of great value for preventing VD.

Development of antidementia drugs

Another important strategy against age-associated dementia is to develop antidementia drugs. Since the discovery in the late 1970s that cholinergic neurons in the basal forebrain degenerate in AD, much of the research on the treatment of AD has relied on traditional neuropharmacological approaches designed to ameliorate defects in cholinergic mechanisms. However, the early enthusiasm for the cholinergic hypothesis has been tempered by the results of subsequent research such as: the defects in membrane changes in metabolism; the role of growth factors; gene expression and abnormal proteins, etc. In spite of the complexities and difficulties in theoretical and methodological issues, the opportunities for clinical trials on the safety and efficacy of new biological agents are increasing as we learn more about the changes in brain structures and functioning affected by AD.

The first and most important issue is again to have adequate protocols and instruments for measuring cognitive changes which might be elicited by the agents administered. This task needs international collaborative study, especially so that culture fair instruments may be adapted to a range of cultures and nations.

References

1. Jorm AF, Korten AE and Henderson AS (1987) Acta Psychiatr. Scand. 76: 465–479.
2. Hasegawa K, Iwa H, Amamoto H et al. (1979) The Commemorative Publication for Professor Shinfuku N. Tokyo, Department of Psychiatry, Jikei University, 342–354 (in Japanese).
3. Hasegawa K, Homma A and Imai Y (1986) Int. J. Geriatr. Psychiatry 1: 45–55.
4. Karasawa A (1989) Shinkei Kenkyu no Shinpo (Adv. Neurol. Sci. Jpn. 3: 131–139. (in Japanese).

© 1991 Elsevier Science Publishers B.V. All rights reserved.
Biological Psychiatry, Volume 2. G. Racagni et al., editors.

Animal models of anxiety

Sandra E. File
Psychopharmacology Research Unit, Guy's Hospital, London SE1 9RT, U.K.

Introduction

There are 2 related reasons for using animal tests to detect anxiolytic action. One is to screen new compounds for their potential clinical use; the second is to study the neural substrates of anxiety. In both cases it is essential to maintain contact with the clinical literature, with regard to both the efficacy of new products and to the issues of diagnostic classification. The heterogeneity of anxiety disorders is clinically accepted, which raises the question as to whether there are distinct neurobiological substrates and whether different animal tests might be sensitive to different types of anxiety.

Classification of animal tests

The wide range of animal tests has been recently discussed [1]. Several are based on *punishment:* Some use the actual delivery of punishment to suppress an ongoing response [2] e.g. lever-pressing for food (Geller-Seifter test); drinking (Vogel test); or locomotor activity. Others are based on the anticipation of punishment, following a prior period of conditioning [3]. Others are based on *loss of reward:* In these tests the animal has been trained to respond (usually with a lever press) for reward. This is then either withdrawn (extinction) or reduced (successive negative contrast). These behavioural tests may be better described as animal models of frustration or disappointment [4]. Finally, there are several *ethologically based tests:* In these, anxiety is generated by situations or stimuli that are naturally aversive to the animal concerned [5]. These tests can be based on measuring the effect of an aversive stimulus on a rodent's exploratory behaviour (e.g. black-white transitions, elevated plus-maze) or on social behaviour of rodents or primates.

Validity of animal tests

Physiological versus pathological anxiety

Anxiety can exist in a pathological or physiological form. In all animal tests of anxiety the animal's response to the test situation is adaptive, and thus reflects a physiological rather than a pathological state. If the biochemical changes in physiological and pathological anxiety are the same, differing only in intensity and frequency, then these tests should have predictive value for the pathological state. This is likely to be the case for generalised anxiety, but it is a matter of controversy whether or not the biochemical mechanisms that underlie panic disorder are quite distinct.

State versus trait anxiety

Potentially more worrying is the difference between state (relating to a particular time or event) and trait (enduring over long time periods and probably at least partly genetically determined) anxiety. Most patients requiring drug treatment for anxiety are those with a high trait anxiety (albeit perhaps augmented by a temporary increase in their state anxiety due to adverse events). However, all animal tests are based on conditions that generate changes in state anxiety. There has been remarkably little work on possible genetic differences in animal tests of anxiety and this would clearly be an important area for future development.

Pharmacological validation

The validation of an animal test might seem to be an essential part in its development, but at its worst the logic behind the use of some of the tests is as follows: diazepam is an anxiolytic; diazepam has behavioural action A; drug X has behavioural action A; therefore drug X is an anxiolytic. The flaw in this argument arises from the assumption that behavioural action A necessarily reflects an anxiolytic action. However, this is in no way to decry the importance of extensive pharmacological validation of animal tests of anxiety, since it is a necessary (although not sufficient) requirement.

Behavioural validation

To be confident that a given behavioural test is detecting anxiolytic activity, it is necessary to attempt a behavioural as well as a pharmacological validation. This is difficult because of the lack of clinical data on the aetiology of anxiety disorders and it is really only the ethologically based tests of state anxiety that have attempted this form of validation [5]. Our main method of behavioural validation is to exclude alternative explanations for a given behavioural change. This can be attempted statistically, by taking more than one behavioural measurement in the test and using analysis of covariance, or by a factor analysis study (see later section). Alternatively, the effects of a given drug, brain lesion or hormone manipulation can be assessed in a variety of animal tests that are designed to measure other behavioural effects.

Sex and age differences

There is a higher incidence of anxiety disorders in women than in men and it is therefore interesting to see whether there are sex differences in the behavioural tests used to detect anxiolytic action in animals. Johnston and File [6] tested male and female rats of equal weight in 3 different tests (social interaction; elevated plus-maze; punished drinking), but no systematic sex differences emerged. Furthermore, the relative insensitivity of female social interaction to changes in the familiarity of the test arena led to a questioning of whether the social interaction test was a valid test of anxiety for female rats. The test had been developed and validated with male rats and the function of social interaction may well be different in males and females.

With age, humans become more sensitive to the sedative effects of the benzodiazepines and similar findings have been reported in the rat [7,8]. However, old rats are less sensitive to the anxiolytic effects of diazepam [7,8]; and additionally, old rats had scores in the plus-maze indicative of increased anxiety [8].

Factor analysis of animal tests of anxiety

Do the different animal tests provide different measures of the same state, or do the different tests measure different states of anxiety? This question can be approached using a factor analysis of the various behavioural parameters obtained in different tests used to detect anxiolytic action. This provides a description of the relationships between different variables, which helps in interpreting the various behavioural parameters. The results from such analyses [1,9] suggest an encouraging ability to separate measures of anxiety from those of motor activity or exploration. However, there was also a complete separation of the "anxiety" factors as measured in the social interaction, elevated plus-maze and Vogel punished drinking tests [1]. This raises the interesting possibility that different animal tests are sensitive to different states of anxiety. Whereas an anxiolytic action of benzodiazepines can be detected in all the tests, it may be that some of the novel compounds will be active against only a subset of anxiety states. It will be particularly important to try and exploit these differences among the animal tests to develop tests that correspond with different clinical states.

References

1. File SE (1991) In: Elliott JM (ed.) Experimental Approaches to Anxiety and Depression. John Wiley, London (in press).
2. Howard JL and Pollard GT (1991) In: File SE (ed.) Psychopharmacology of Anxiolytics and Antidepressants, Pergamon Press, New York, pp. 131–153.
3. Davis M (1991) In: *Op. cit.* pp. 187–212.
4. Flaherty CF (1991) In: *Op. cit.* pp. 213–230.

5. Lister RG (1991) In: *Op. cit.* pp. 155–185.
6. Johnston AL and File SE (1991) Physiol. Behav. 49: 245–250.
7. Komiskey HL, Buck MA, Mundinger KL, McSweeney FK, Farmer-Dougan VA and Dougan JD (1987) Psychopharmacology 93: 443–448.
8. File SE (1990) Human Psychopharmacol. 5: 169–173.
9. Lister RG (1987) Psychopharmacology 92: 180–185.

© 1991 Elsevier Science Publishers B.V. All rights reserved.
Biological Psychiatry, Volume 2. G. Racagni et al., editors.

Animal models and alcoholism

Richard G. Lister

Laboratory of Clinical Studies, National Institute on Alcohol Abuse and Alcoholism, DICBR, Building 10, Room 3C102, 9000 Rockville Pike, Bethesda, MD 20892, U.S.A.

In discussing whether there is currently an animal model of alcoholism it is important to consider what we understand by the term "model". The purpose that a model is intended to serve determines the criteria by which it is evaluated [1]. It seems most unlikely that a "substitutive" model [2] will ever be developed in animals that reproduces all the features of human alcoholism. However, animal studies have contributed to our understanding of a number of different aspects of alcoholism. For example, researchers have been successful in developing models that allow an investigation of the mechanisms underlying some of alcohol's behavioral effects (e.g. its ataxic, anxiolytic, hypothermic and hypnotic effects). There has also been considerable success in the development of animal models of alcohol tolerance and alcohol withdrawal. The latter allows an examination of potential treatments for humans undergoing alcohol withdrawal. Less successful have been attempts to develop models that cast light on the etiology of alcoholism. Much research has focused on genetic mechanisms following human studies in the 1970s indicating that individuals who had an alcoholic biological parent had an increased risk of becoming alcoholics. Many selective breeding programs have begun in which animals have been bred for sensitivity and insensitivity to a variety of alcohol's behavioral effects. For example, mice have been bred for differing sensitivity to alcohol-induced hypnosis, alcohol-induced hypothermia, alcohol-induced locomotor stimulation and alcohol withdrawal seizures and rats have been bred that differ in their tendency to self-administer alcohol [3,4].

It is clear that the ability to develop an animal model of a disorder is critically dependent on the knowledge of the disorder in humans. Recent research in humans has led a number of workers to suggest that alcoholism may not be a single disorder but exist in two or more different forms. Cloninger, for example, has distinguished between two different types of alcoholism. Type I is characterized by a late onset, low novelty seeking, high harm avoidance and high reward dependence. In contrast, Type II alcoholism is associated with an early onset, high novelty seeking, low harm avoidance and low reward dependence [5]. Type II alcoholics frequently have a history of fighting and arrests while drinking. A disorder of serotonin metabolism may be associated with Type II alcoholism [6,7].

Rather than examine individual differences in alcohol self-administration or differences in behavioral response to alcohol, an alternative approach involves an examination of the neurobiology of traits associated with different types of alcoholism. Over a period of time in our laboratory we have observed that in some cages of our group-housed mice, one mouse in the cage inflicts bite-marks on the backs and tails of its cage mates, but lacks any signs of being attacked itself. We have compared the behavior of these "α" mice with that of the subordinate cage mates, and of controls housed in cages where no fighting is observed [8]. The α mice spent a shorter time immobile in Porsolt's swim test than either of the other groups, but did not differ in their behavior in a plus-maze test. Subordinate mice had higher concentrations of 5-HIAA in brain stem, hippocampus and hypothalamus than the other groups. However, the α mice did not appear to differ from controls in their serotonin metabolism. More recently we have found that the difference in behavior in the swim test appears to follow, rather than precede, the social interactions, and therefore may not reflect a trait difference between the groups [9]. In a recent study we have assessed alcohol preference in mice before and after the group-housing period. Mice were divided into three groups according to whether they became α, were mildly attacked by the α, or were severely attacked by the α. A marked increase in alcohol self-administration was observed in those mice that were severely attacked by the α mice but not in the α or in those that were only mildly attacked (Hilakivi-Clarke and Lister, in preparation).

While the differences in behavior observed in the above studies appear to reflect the effects of environmental variables, we are also examining the behavior of a large battery of inbred strains of mice in tests of fear, anxiety, aggression and alcohol consumption. Reports [10,11] that some anxiety disorders are associated with alcoholism (Cloninger's Type I) would suggest that increased alcohol preference might be observed in strains of mice that appear 'anxious' in animal models of anxiety. Our studies to date, however, have failed to find such an association.

References

1. Overmier JB and Patterson J (1988) In: Simon P, Soubrie P and Wildlocher D (eds.) Animal Models of Psychiatric Disorders. Karger, Basel, pp. 1–35.
2. Suomi S (1987) In: Gittelman R (ed.) Anxiety-Like Disorders in Young Non-Human Primates. Guilford, New York, pp. 1–23.
3. Phillips TJ, Feller DJ and Crabbe JC (1989) Experientia 45: 805–827.
4. Li T-K, Lumeng L, McBride WJ and Waller MB (1979) Drug Alcohol Depend. 4: 45–60.
5. Cloninger CR (1986) Science 236: 410–416.
6. Linnoila M, Virkkunen M, Scheinin M, Nuutila A, Rimon R and Goodwin FK (1983) Life Sci. 33: 2609–2614.
7. Virkkunen M, Nuutila A, Goodwin FK and Linnoila M (1987) Arch. Gen Psychiatry 44: 241–247.
8. Hilakivi LA, Lister RG, Durcan MJ, Ota M, Eskay R, Mefford I and Linnoila M (1989) Brain Res. 502: 258–266.
9. Hilakivi-Clarke LA and Lister RG (1991) J. Comp. Psychol. (in press).
10. Mullaney JA and Trippett CJ (1979) Br. J. Psychiatry 135: 565–573.
11. George DT, Nutt DJ, Dwyer BA and Linnoila M (1990) Acta Psychiatr. Scand. 81: 97–107.

© 1991 Elsevier Science Publishers B.V. All rights reserved.
Biological Psychiatry, Volume 2. G. Racagni et al., editors.

Animal models of Alzheimer's disease

Bernadette Earley
C.N.S. Research Unit, Pharmacology Department, University College, Galway, Ireland

Alzheimer's disease (AD) is the most common dementing disease of the elderly and a definite diagnosis can only be made at autopsy. Neurochemical and histopathological findings in Alzheimer's disease primarily involve the cholinergic system, as manifested by reductions in choline acetyltransferase activity (CAT) in cortex and hippocampus, and degeneration of cholinergic neurons. Memory impairment and cognitive decline are commonly recognized as being the most serious symptoms of ageing and dementia [1]. Therefore, an animal model facilitating the evaluation of putative agents for the treatment of the cognitive deficits in Alzheimer's disease would be of immense importance. However, it is widely accepted that non-humans do not suffer from Alzheimer's disease and that no acceptable animal model exists.

In vivo animal models of ageing fall into 2 main categories; studies using the aged rat and lesioning studies in young animals. The aged rat model is widely used to study age-related cognitive disturbances and is based on the underlying premise that the more an animal mimics the aetiology and behavioural aspects of the aged human brain, the greater will be its predictive value in drug screening for cognitive dysfunction. Progress in evaluating the behavioural changes produced in the rat by experimentally-induced lesion of the basal forebrain cholinergic system (BFCS) has provided useful information for understanding the mechanisms underlying memory loss.

It is generally accepted that the hippocampus plays a major role in spatial or working memory and that lesions of the medial septal nucleus or the fornix which transects the cholinergic pathway to the hippocampus impairs learning and memory in rats in the Morris water maze, radial arm maze and delayed alternation tasks. Lesions of the nucleus basalis of Meynert (NMB) using the excitotoxins, ibotenic acid or kainic acid, induces severe depletions in cortical CAT activity which are consistent with impairments in learning and memory tasks. Thus, neurotoxins are capable of simulating one or more of the pathological changes associated with diseases causing memory dysfunction. However, one problem relating to lesion studies is the lack of site-directed specificity of most toxins which are used to produce memory deficits. The cognitive and biochemical changes associated with dementia can be reproduced in animals using compounds that are not neurochemically specific but are selectively toxic to neurons.

Trimethyltin (TMT), an organotin compound, is a potent neurotoxicant producing rapid and extensive damage to the central nervous system. A single related to the concept of pharmacological isomorphism as discussed by Matthysse [2]. The actual behaviour displayed by the animal in the model can be (and generally is) totally unrelated to the actual disease process.

Examples of such animal models with predictive validity are conditioned avoidance behaviour, intracranial self stimulation, the dopamine induced locomotor activation and the paw test. Important in analysing the validity of these models is the presence of a set of validating criteria [1,3]. Apart from general criteria (such as the absence of false negatives and positives) these criteria must include some characteristics of neuroleptic drugs. Matthysse [2] has suggested that anticholinergics (at least in low doses) and chronic treatment while not influencing the therapeutic efficacy do reduce the extrapyramidal side-effects. Recently we have developed a new animal model, on the basis of the similarities and dissimilarities between the classical neuroleptic haloperidol and the atypical neuroleptic clozapine [4]. This animal model, the paw test, seems to fulfill all criteria for animal models with predictive validity. Thus this animal model may allow us to study the neuronal mechanism underlying the therapeutic and extrapyramidal side-effects of classical and atypical neuroleptics.

Animal models with face validity

The next class of animal models are the models with *face validity*. These models assess the phenomenological similarity of the disease they model and are similar to the concept of symptom similarity of Matthysse [2]. Given the discussion in the introduction, it may seem obvious that very few animal models with face validity for schizophrenia exist. Among these models are the dopamine agonist-induced stereotypies and some models for catatonia.

Animal models with construct validity

The highest class of animal models are those which aspire to construct validity. In these models, one tries to model the psychopathological construct underlying the disease process. Although the psychopathological construct underlying schizophrenia is still largely unknown, we have recently argued that many literature data are consistent with the hypothesis that schizophrenic patients have difficulty in distinguishing between relevant and irrelevant stimuli [1].

This perceptual disturbance provides us with a psychopathological construct which can be represented in an animal model. Indeed, it has recently been shown that several animal models with construct validity are based on this principle [1]. Among these models are the latent inhibition and the blocking paradigm, which are both based on the proposition that animals have to learn to ignore irrelevant stimuli. Other animal models with construct validity are the acoustic startle response, in which both the habituation and the prepulse inhibition may be relevant for schizophrenia and the amphetamine-induced social isolation in monkeys, in which both positive and negative symptoms seem to be present.

Conclusions and Prospects

Studying animal models in a more theoretical way may help us analyse the usefulness of the different models presently available. Thus animal models with predictive validity may help us develop new and potentially more useful drugs for treating schizophrenia. Moreover, they may help us study the neuronal mechanisms underlying the clinical effects of these drugs. However, these models will probably not increase our knowledge of the disease process underlying schizophrenia. The animal models with construct validity may, on the other hand, help us in studying the neuronal mechanism underlying the psychopathological construct possibly underlying the disease. In this respect it is interesting that the hippocampus-amygdala-ventral striatum circuitry has been implicated in latent inhibition, blocking, prepulse inhibition and monkey social isolation [1]. Thus these data may possibly increase our insight into the disease process underlying schizophrenia.

References

1. Ellenbroek BA and Cools AR (1990) Behav. Pharmacol. 1: 469–490.
2. Matthysse S (1986) Prog. Brain Res. 65: 259–270.
3. Willner P (1984) Psychopharmacology 83: 1–16.
4. Ellenbroek BA and Cools AR (1988) Life Sci. 42: 1205–1213.

© 1991 Elsevier Science Publishers B.V. All rights reserved.
Biological Psychiatry, Volume 2. G. Racagni et al., editors.

Animal models for schizophrenia

Bart A. Ellenbroek and Alexander R. Cools
Psychoneuropharmacology Research Unit, Catholic University of Nijmegen, P.O. Box 9101, 6500 HB Nijmegen, The Netherlands

Introduction

Developing animal models for psychiatrical disturbances is a complicated process. This is due to a number of different reasons. First of all, our knowledge on the etiology, as well as the pathology of psychiatric disorders is in general rather limited. Second, the core symptoms of most psychiatric disorders are of a cognitive nature, which makes modelling in animals difficult. Thirdly, most psychiatric disorders lack a pathognomic symptom, being predictive of and unique to the disease.

These problems seem to be particularly true for schizophrenia, which is one of the most severe psychiatrical disturbances. With respect to the etiology of schizophrenia, it seems evident now that genetic predisposition plays an important role. However, it appears equally evident that genetics alone cannot completely explain the occurrence of schizophrenia. Equally unclear is the pathology of schizophrenia. Although with the help of newer techniques (like PET scan, MRI and regional cerebral blood flow) many intriguing data have been gathered in recent years, we are still far from understanding which disturbances in the brain are responsible for the development of schizophrenia in general or schizophrenic symptoms in particular. With respect to the symptomatology of schizophrenia, it seems clear that modelling such core symptoms as hallucinations, delusion or formal thought disturbances in animals is impossible. Moreover, the fact that many schizophrenic symptoms can also occur in a number of other disturbances, indicates that modelling a single symptom may not provide much information on the disease process underlying schizophrenia.

Given these problems, it seems worthwhile to investigate the numerous animal models proposed to study schizophrenia and to analyse their validity in a systematic way. In order to do this it has proven useful to subdivide animal models into three hierarchically organised classes [1–3].

Animal models with predictive validity

The lowest class of animal models are those which aspire only to *predictive validity*. These models are only concerned with the success of the predictions they can make with respect to pharmacological manipulations and as such are closely intraperitoneal administration of TMT, over a dose range of 6, 7 and 8 mg/kg to rats causes a dose-related destruction of the hippocampus and olfactory cortical areas (olfactory tubercle, amygdala and entorhinal cortex). Animals administered TMT also show a large decrease in cholinergic muscarinic receptor density and a decrease in acetylcholinesterase (AChE) staining in several brain regions [2]. Neurological and behavioural changes include aggression, hyperirritability, tremor, hyperactivity, deficits in passive avoidance and memory impairment in the Morris water maze task [3].

Of particular interest is the characteristic hippocampal damage which represents the most consistent morphological feature of TMT intoxication. Significant neuronal loss in the pyramidal cell of the hippocampal Ammon's horn in rats is a characteristic features of TMT intoxication.

The distribution of TMT-induced neurotoxicity in rats is consistent with the pattern of behavioural and biochemical changes that have been collectively called the "TMT syndrome".

In summary, TMT produces a select and chronic hypofunction of the cholinergic system which is behaviourally manifested by learning and memory impairments. Thus, rats treated with TMT may provide a useful model system for elucidating the underlying mechanisms of Alzheimer's disease and for assessing potentially useful therapeutic strategies.

References

1. Bartus RT, Dean RL III, Beer B and Lippa AS (1982) Science 217: 408–417.
2. Earley B, Biegon A and Leonard BE (1989) Neurochem. Int. 15: 475–483.
3. Earley B, Burke M, Leonard BE, Gouret CJ and Junien JL (1990) Neuropharmacology 29: 8, 695–703.

© 1991 Elsevier Science Publishers B.V. All rights reserved.
Biological Psychiatry, Volume 2. G. Racagni et al., editors.

Animal models of depression

B.E Leonard
Pharmacology Department, University College, Galway, Ireland

Introduction

Although the neuroanatomical and neurochemical structures of all mammalian brains are essentially similar, there is no convincing evidence to suggest that even the most developed subhuman animal suffers from a major mental illness. For this reason, the development of animal models of psychiatric disease are fraught with difficulties.

Discussion will be restricted to those models which only detect antidepressants following their chronic administration. Furthermore, comment will be restricted to rodent models as these are understandably the most widely used. Nevertheless, the relevance of primate models, largely based on separation behaviour resulting from the removal of infant monkeys from their mothers, are particularly important despite their very limited practicality [1,2].

Stress models of depression

Chronic (4–6 weeks) social isolation of mature rats causes a disruption of co-operative social behaviour which may be attenuated by chronic treatment [3] with drugs such as floxetine or imipramine. In premature rats, prolonged social isolation (up to 1 year!) results in hyperactivity which may be reversed by the acute treatment of either typical or atypical antidepressants [4]. The long duration of isolation necessary before the acute effects of antidepressants can be detected limits the usefulness of the latter approach.

Chronic unpredictable severe stress (3 weeks exposure to random electric shocks, immersion in cold water, immobilisation, reversal of the light-dark cycle) has been developed as a model by Katz and Sibel [5], but the limited specificity of the model (anticholinergic drugs are active) and the unacceptability of such a model on ethical grounds precludes its application. A more interesting model has been provided by Willner et al. [6] in which rats are subject to chronic unpredictable mild stress for several weeks (short periods of food and water deprivation, slight reduction in the ambient temperature, changes in the housing conditions etc.). Such mild stress results in a reduction in the consumption of a sucrose solution, an effect which is reversed by chronic tricyclic antidepressant treatment. Recent evidence suggests that such changes in behaviour following chronic mild stress are attributable to an enhanced postsynaptic dopamine receptor sensitivity [7].

A change in central dopaminergic activity has also been detected following the chronic administration of antidepressants to non-stressed rats. Thus Serra et al. [8] have shown that chronic antidepressants attenuate the hypomotility that follows the acute administration of a low dose of apomorphine (0.1 mg/kg). Hasan and Leonard [9] showed that both typical and atypical antidepressants are active in this test.

Brain lesion models

Although there are preliminary reports in the literature that lesions of the internal capsule and septum produce behaviours which may be corrected by antidepressants, the most extensively studied lesion model is the olfactory bulbectomised rat (OB) model. This model was first described by Cairncross [10] and has been extensively reviewed recently by Van Riezen and Leonard [11]. In brief, bilateral removal of the olfactory bulbs leads to a deficit in exploratory, passive avoidance and conditioned taste avoidance behaviours which are attenuated by chronic, but not acute, antidepressants. Psychotropic drugs lacking antidepressant activity are inactive.

In the rat, the olfactory bulbs form part of the limbic system and the behavioural and neurochemical defects appear to be related to the destruction of the main inhibitory pathway that projects from the bulbs to the amygdala. Lesions of the bulbs by selective neurotoxins suggest that the serotonergic system may be partly responsible for the behavioural deficits, but that defects in the amino acid neurotransmitters seem to be responsible for most of the deficits.

Recently, Butler et al. [12] showed that bulbectomy results in a reduction in the ^{3}H-^{5}HT transport into the platelets which is normalised by the chronic administration of antidepressants that shows selectivity for either the noradrenergic or serotonergic uptake site. These changes are qualitatively similar to those occurring in depressed patients [13]. Finally, neutrophil phagocytosis has been shown to be defective in both depressed patients and the OB rat, an abnormality which may be reversed by chronic antidepressant treatment [14].

Conclusion

The chronic stress models and the OB rat model of depression, which enable antidepressants to be selected following their chronic administration after a period which approximates to that necessary to obtain a therapeutic response, seem to be of particular value in the detection and investigation of the mode of action of putative antidepressants. The OB model would appear to be the most extensively investigated so far and appears to show qualitatively similar changes in neurochemical and immunological parameters to those found in the depressed patients.

References

1. Hrdina PD, Von Kulmiz P and Stretch R (1979) Psychopharmacology 64: 89–93.
2. Lewis JK, McKinney WT, Young LD and Kraemer GW (1976) Arch. Gen. Psychiatry 33: 699–705.
3. Willner P, Sampson D, Phillips G, Fichera R, Foxlow P and Muscat R (1989) Behav. Pharmacol. 1: 85–90.
4. Garzon J and Del Rio J (1981) Eur. J. Pharmacol. 74: 287–294.
5. Katz RJ and Sibel M (1982) Pharmacol. Biochem. Behav. 16: 973–977.
6. Willner P, Towell A, Sampson D, Sophokleous S and Muscat R (1987) Psychopharmacology 93: 358–364.
7. Willner P (1991) In: Willner P (ed.) Behavioural Models in Psychopharmacology. Cambridge University Press, Cambridge pp. 91–125.
8. Serra G, Argiolas V, Fadda F and Gessa GL (1979) Pharmacol. Res. Commun. 12: 619–624.
9. Hasan F and Leonard BE (1983) In: McKenheil M and Matussek N (eds.) Special Aspects of Psychopharmacology. Expansion Scientifique Francaise, Paris, pp. 67–82.
10. Cairncross KD (1984) In: Bond NW (ed.) Animal Models in Psychopathology. Academic Press, New York, pp. 99–128.
11. Van Riezen H and Leonard BE (1991) In: File SE (ed.) Psychopharmacology of Anxiolytics and Antidepressants. Pergamon Press, New York, pp. 231–1250.
12. Butler J, Tannion M and Leonard BE (1988) Progr. Neuropsychopharmacol. Biol. Psychiatry 12: 585–594.
13. Healy D, O'Halloran B, Carney PA and Leonard BE (1985) J. Affective Disord. 9: 285–296.
14. O'Neill B and Leonard BE (1990) J. Affective Disord. 19: 265–272.

© 1991 Elsevier Science Publishers B.V. All rights reserved.
Biological Psychiatry, Volume 2. G. Racagni et al., editors.

From Golgi impregnation to in situ hybridization histochemistry: Is neuroanatomy still the mother of neurophysiology?

M. Kawata, K. Yuri, M. Hirakawa, Y. Hirayama and K. Kumamoto

Department of Anatomy, Kyoto Prefectural University of Medicine, Kawaramachi-Hirokoji, Kamigyo-ku, Kyoto 602, Japan

With increasing knowledge, neuroanatomy and neurophysiology came closer to each other in terms of the methods available to scientists studying the nervous system. Even today, the Golgi method remains a fruitful and indispensable technique in neuroanatomical investigations, whether used alone or in combination with immunohistochemistry or electron microscopy. Impregnated neurons by the Golgi method may be revealed in their entirety and in the finest detail, and we can trace the afferent and/or efferent connections of stained neurons. It is characteristic of the Golgi method that a very small proportion of less than 5% shows successful staining.

Pathway tracing techniques using labeled tracers have proved to be a good tool for elucidating neuron connections. The tracers used for anterograde, retrograde and transneuronal transport are HRP, HRP-WGA, PHA-L, DiI, DiL, cholera and tetanus toxins, and herpes simplex viruses. Although this method is very useful for identifying the origin of specific terminals, retrogradely transported tracers within the neurons do not give us an entire neuronal configuration of dendritic arborization.

More recent study demonstrates that the peculiar shape of the neuron largely depends on the proteins constituting the cytoskeleton such as actin, neurofilaments, microtubules, MAPs and tau. In addition, these proteins serve as a mediator for the movement of organelles and chemical transmitter substances for neuronal transmission from one region of the neuron to the other. They also work as anchor-membrane constituents for receptors or ion channels.

All of the macromolecule proteins of a neuron are synthesized in the perikaryon from each specific mRNA that is transcribed from genomic DNA in the nucleus. The mRNAs that encode the cytosolic proteins for cytoskeleton and enzymes and the mitochondrial proteins become associated with ribosomes to form polysomes, while the mRNAs for membrane proteins and secretory products are translated on the rERs. There are now extremely powerful histochemical techniques for localizing neuroactive peptides, transmitter substances and proteins. Chemical transmitter substances including peptides and synthesizing enzymes for small-molecule neurotransmitter can be localized within neurons by using immunohistochemistry in conjunction with specific antibodies. It is now also possible to histochemically identify neurons in which the gene for a particular transmitter enzyme or peptide precursor is active by an in situ hybridization method. In in situ hybridization histochemistry, labeled probes (cDNA, cRNA, oligonucleotide) are applied to tissue sections under appropriate conditions suitable for hybridizing with endogenous mRNA. When using radiolabeled probes, autoradiogram reveals not only the location of neurons that contain the hybridization complex formed by the labeled probes and the mRNAs, but also the copy numbers of mRNA by counting the silver grains on the neurons.

Steroid hormones activate many developmental and physiological processes in brain functions by altering expression of particular genes (Fig. 1A). Based on these regulations, steroid hormone obviously changes the morphological characteristics of dendritic branching pattern. For instance, the number, morphology and connectivity of neurons in the preoptic nucleus are regulated by the action of estrogen. In fact, neurons containing tyrosine hydroxylase (TH)-immunoreactivity in the periventricular preoptic nucleus (PPN) of ovariectomized rat have numerous dendrites, while estrogen-treated rat shows dendritic retraction of TH-immunoreactive neurons in the PPN (Fig. 1B). On the contrary, enkephalin- and CGRP-immunoreactive nerve fibers in the PPN of estrogen-treated rat are increased in number compared to those of ovariectomized rat. These findings show steroid-induced plasticity of neuronal configuration.

Using in situ hybridization histochemistry with radiolabeled probe and a com-

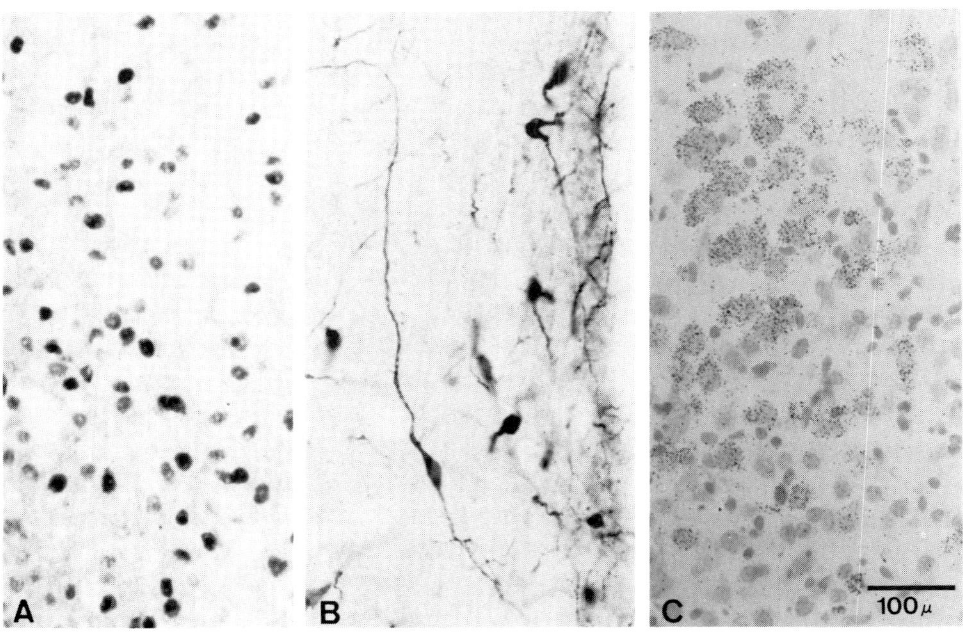

Fig. 1. A: Estrogen receptor-immunoreactive neurons in the periventricular preoptic nucleus of ovariectomized rat; B: Tyrosine hydroxylase-immunoreactive neurons in the periventricular preoptic nucleus of ovariectomized rat; C: Oxytocin mRNA-containing neurons in the paraventricular nucleus of progesterone-treated estrogen-primed rat.

puter-assisted image analysis system, it was found that statistic analysis shows progesterone treatment of estrogen-primed ovariectomized rat does not affect hybridization for oxytocin mRNA in neurons of the supraoptic nucleus, whereas prolonged progesterone exposure significantly increases the number of silver grains in neurons of the paraventricular nucleus. Among the sub-divisions of the paraventricular nucleus, the posterior ventromedial part shows a particularly strong increase in oxytocin mRNA levels (Fig. 1C). These results suggest that progesterone, working in concert with estrogen priming, has an effect on oxytocin mRNA levels in that portion of the paraventricular nucleus which might be relevant for the control of female reproductive behavior.

References

1. Kawata M, McCabe JT, Harrington C, Chikaraishi D and Pfaff DW (1988) J. Comp. Neurol. 270: 528–536.
2. Kawata M, McCabe JT and Pfaff DW (1988) Brain Res. Bull. 20: 693–697.
3. Kawata M, McCabe JT, Pfaff DW and Sano Y (1988) In: Yoshida S and Share L (eds.) Recent Progress in Posterior Pituitary Hormone. Elsevier, Amsterdam, pp. 249–255.
4. Kawata M, Yuri K and Kumamoto K (1990) Acta Histochem. Cytochem. 23: 307–325.
5. McCabe JT, Kawata M, Sano Y, Pfaff DW and Descharnais RA (1990) Cell Mol. Neurobiol. 10: 59–71.
6. Kawata M, Yuri K and Sano Y (1991) Comp. Biochem. Physiol. 98C: 41–50.
7. Harbuz M, Russell JA, Sumner BEH, Kawata M and Lightman SL (1991) Mol. Brain Res. 9: 285–291.
8. Yuri K and Kawata M (1991) Brain Res. (in press).

© 1991 Elsevier Science Publishers B.V. All rights reserved.
Biological Psychiatry, Volume 2. G. Racagni et al., editors.

Structural integration of neural networks

M. Réthelyi

Second Department of Anatomy, Semmelweis University Medical School, Tüzoltó utca 58, H-1094 Budapest, Hungary

Neural networks consist of neurons interconnected by synapses. From a structural standpoint, a network can be characterized: a) by the geometry of the neuronal processes (random vs. oriented); and b) by the complexity of the synapses. The elements of the networks (terminal axon arborizations or neurons with dendritic trees) seem to be integrated as individual or as common components of the network depending on the nature of the synapses.

The network of neurons in the dorsal horn of the spinal grey matter presents several structural features. These are: a) the regular longitudinal orientation of the vast majority of neuronal processes (dendrites and axons); b) the laminar distribution of the terminal arborizations; and c) a rich variety of synapses from simple to complex glomerular arrangements.

The spinal dorsal horn, defined as laminae I–IV of Rexed, consists of neurons of various size, shape and dendritic arborizations, and receives terminal axon arborizations from the dorsal root ganglia (primary afferent terminals, PAF) and from supraspinal sources. The axons of the dorsal horn neurons arborize entirely and/or give off collateral branches within the area [4].

Synapses in the dorsal horn were studied by ultrastructural analysis of functionally characterized and horseradish peroxidase (HRP)-labeled neurons. In one series of experiments the presynaptic components (axon terminals), in another series of experiments the postsynaptic components (perikarya and dendrites) were analysed and labeled.

Fine myelinated high-threshold mechanoreceptor fibers terminated with two separate arborizations. The majority of the terminal branches arborized in lamina I and in the outer portion of lamina II (IIo), while collateral branches of the parent fibers ran to the junction between laminae IV and V. The ultrastructure of the terminal boutons showed individual, regional and species-specific variations. In the cat the primary afferent terminals formed complex synapses and synapsed mostly with numerous dendritic protrusions in lamina I and IIo. Small size axons and vesicle containing profiles resembling presynaptic dendrites synapsed with the primary afferent boutons. In the monkey no presynaptic dendrites were seen in the complex synapses. Boutons of the deep arborizations of the fibers synapsed with 1 or 2 dendrites and received many axo-axonic synapses. Another type of fine myelinated afferent fibers, the sensitive D-hair afferents terminated in lamina III and synapsed with dendritic protrusions in the form of complex glomerular synapses in the cat. Among the dendritic protrusions many contained synaptic vesicles and synapsed with the adjacent protrusions. Axo-axonic synapses were frequently encountered in the synaptic complex [2].

Large caliber myelinated PAF arborizing in laminae III and IV were found to terminate in boutons which formed mostly simple axo-dendritic synapses. Axo-axonic synapses were frequently seen in connection with the primary afferent boutons [1].

The analysis of the presynaptic components showed that myelinated PAF of various caliber and functional significance differed in termination area, branching pattern and also in synaptic ultrastructure. The only common feature was that a large majority of the terminal boutons received one or several synapses from small-size axon terminals.

In the second series functionally characterized neurons excited by slowly conducting myelinated primary afferent fibers were labeled with HRP. The injection of the enzyme stained the perikaryon and the dendritic tree of the neurons. In several cases the initial portion of the axon arborization of the neurons with numerous small-size en passant boutons were stained, too. The ultrastructural analysis of the stained cells showed that dendrites of a given neuron received identical types of synapses, while other types of synapses regularly present in the dorsal horn neuropil were not seen in connection with the dendritic branches. Typical synapses could be described by the site, size and vesicle content of the axon terminals, and by the complexity of the synapses. Axo-somatic synapses occurred relatively infrequently, but when present, were numerous. Dendro-dendritic synapses between a stained and an unstained neuron were seen in some neurons, but also in these few cases they occurred frequently along the entire dendritic tree. The single common feature for all neurons with stained axon was the uniformly small size of the *en passant* boutons. They formed simple axo-dendritic synapses [3].

The above two studies showed that within a network the synaptic connections are determined by the geometry of the pre- and postsynaptic components, i.e. by the respective orientation of axon arborizations and dendritic trees. Due to the structural peculiarities of the primary afferent boutons (complex synapses, axo-axonic and occasional dendro-axonic contacts), they seem to be the specific (individualized) components of the network. The *en passant* boutons of the dorsal horn neurons seem to be distributed uniformly, and their simple synapses could be interpreted as non-specific (generalized) components of the network. On the other hand, each neuron could be described by a certain combination of synaptic connections distributed on the perikaryon and along the dendrites. Thus, each neuron seems to be an individual entity within the network.

References

1. Maxwell DJ and Réthelyi M (1987) Trends Neurol. Sci. 10: 117–123.
2. Réthelyi M, Light AR and Perl ER (1982) J. Comp. Neurol. 207: 381–393.
3. Réthelyi M, Light AR and Perl ER (1989) J. Neurosci. 9:1846–1863.
4. Willis WD and Coggeshall RE (1978) Sensory Mechanisms of the Spinal Cord. Plenum Press, New York, London.

© 1991 Elsevier Science Publishers B.V. All rights reserved.
Biological Psychiatry, Volume 2. G. Racagni et al., editors.

Synaptic connections of nigrostriatal neurones

I.P. Bolam
MRC Anatomical Neuropharmacology Unit, Department of Pharmacology, South Parks Road, Oxford, U.K.

Introduction

The basal ganglia are a group of subcortical structures that are critically involved in the control of movement. Information flows from all regions of the cortex to the major division of the basal ganglia, the striatum; this is then integrated with the many other inputs and then passed to the output stations of the basal ganglia, the pallidal complex and the substantia nigra. The basal ganglia influence movement by these regions projecting to the thalamus and then back to the cortex or by projecting to subcortical premotor regions. The dopaminergic nigrostriatal neurones represent a major modulatory feedback system of the basal ganglia. Thus the output of the cortico-striato-pallidal and the cortico-striato-nigral pathways is modulated by the dopaminergic neurones that project to the striatum. The importance of this feedback is exemplified by the marked motor disturbances that occur in Parkinson's disease. Their role as a modulatory feedback system is dependent on the site of release of dopamine from their terminals in the striatum, i.e. the nature of the neurones with which the dopaminergic terminals make synaptic contact. The release of dopamine at these synapses is in turn dependent on the activity of the nigral axons and ultimately on the activity and nature of the afferent synaptic input to the dendrites and perikarya of the parent neurones in the substantia nigra. The object of this paper is to review first the known afferent synaptic input to the dendrites and cell bodies of dopaminergic nigrostriatal neurones, i.e. the input that ultimately controls the release of dopamine in the striatum, and secondly the known synaptic targets of the dopamine terminals in the striatum, i.e. the sites where their modulatory role is exerted.

Synaptic input to dopaminergic neurones

Ultrastructural analysis of neurones in the substantia nigra pars compacta (i.e. the location of the dopaminergic neurones) [1–3] or of identified dopaminergic neurones labelled by tyrosine hydroxylase (TH) immunocytochemistry [4,5] reveals that they receive an abundant and complex array of afferent synaptic terminals. On the basis of anterograde synaptic degeneration it has been demonstrated that the dopaminergic neurones, identified by TH immunocytochemistry or by retrograde labelling from the striatum, receive symmetrical synaptic input from terminals derived from the striatum [5,6], globus pallidus [7] and the nucleus tegmenti pedunculopontinus [8]. The transmitter characteristics of the afferent terminals of identified dopaminergic neurones have been examined in some detail. The major input, consisting of at least 70% of all afferent terminals, are those that are immunoreactive for glutamate decarboxylase, the synthetic enzyme for GABA, or are immunoreactive for GABA itself [9,10]. The possible sources of these terminals are: 1) the striatum; 2) the globus pallidus; and 3) local GABA-containing projection neurones or interneurones.

Dopaminergic neurones also receive synaptic input from terminals that display immunoreactivity for substance P [11–14], some of which display GABA immunoreactivity as well [9]. The origin of at least some of the substance P-containing terminals, especially those that also contain GABA, is likely to be the striatum, since it well established that these substances are present in the striatonigral pathway. Further experiments have shown that dopaminergic neurones receive input from terminals that display immunoreactivity for neurotensin [15], enkephalin [16], 5-hydroxytryptamine (derived from the raphe) [17] and choline acetyltransferase (probably derived from brainstem cholinergic neurones) [18].

Synaptic output of dopaminergic neurones

It is clear from ultrastructural analyses of dopaminergic axons in the striatum, identified by immunocytochemistry for TH or for dopamine itself, that dopaminergic terminals make symmetrical synaptic contacts with striatal neurones, the majority of which are spiny neurones that project back to the substantia nigra. By a combination of Golgi impregnation, retrograde labelling and immunocytochemistry for TH, it has been shown directly that this is indeed the case; the major target of dopaminergic terminals are the spiny neurones of the striatum that project back to the substantia nigra [19]. The majority of the dopaminergic terminals in contact with the spiny projection neurones do so on the necks of dendritic spines. The spines are also postsynaptic to other terminals that form asymmetrical synapses and are probably derived from the cortex. This relationship between dopaminergic input, cortical input and spines has be confirmed by a combination of anterograde degeneration and immunocytochemistry for TH [20]. The arrangement provides an anatomical substrate for a very selective effect of the dopaminergic terminals on cortical input to the striatum, not at a presynaptic site, but on the *postsynaptic* structure, i.e. the spine. The input to spiny neurones has been confirmed by the analysis of neurones immunostained for the putative transmitters (or related enzymes) of spiny neurones, namely GAD, enkephalin and substance P [21–23]. In addition to the spiny output neurones, populations of striatal interneurones, including those that utilize GABA [23], acetylcholine [24] and neuropeptide Y [25,26] as transmitter substances, also receive synaptic input from the dopaminergic nigrostriatal terminals.

In summary, it is evident that the dopaminergic neurones in the substantia nigra that give rise to the projection to the striatum are under complex synaptic control from a rich diversity of terminals of different chemical characteristics and different origins. The output of the dopaminergic neurones in the striatum will thus depend upon the activity and spatial relationships of each of the afferent terminals. Dopaminergic neurones will then influence information flow through the basal ganglia by an action in the striatum at synaptic specializations on both the spiny output neurones and interneurones.

References

1. Hajdu F, Hassler R and Bak IJ (1973) Z. Zellforsch. 146: 207–221.
2. Rinvik E and Grofova I (1970) Exp. Brain Res. 11: 229–248.
3. Schwyn RC and Fox CA (1974) J. Hirnforsch. 15: 95–126.
4. Bolam JP, Freund TF, Bjorklund A, Dunnet SB and Smith AD (1987) Exp. Brain Res. 68: 131–146.
5. Wassef M, Berod A and Sotelo C (1981) Neuroscience 6: 2125–2139.
6. Somogyi P, Bolam JP, Totterdell S and Smith AD (1981) Brain Res. 217: 245–263.
7. Smith Y and Bolam JP (1990) J. Comp. Neurol. 296: 47–64.
8. Tokuno H, Moriizumi T, Kudo M and Nakamura Y (1988) Neurosci. Lett. 85: 1–4.
9. Bolam R and Smith Y (1990) Brain Res. 529: 57–78.
10. Van den Pol AN, Smith AD and Powell JF (1985) Brain Res. 348: 146–154.
11. Chang HT (1988) Brain Res. 448: 391–396.
12. Kawai Y, Takagi H, Kumoi Y, Shiosaka S and Tohyama M (1987) Brain Res. 401: 371–376.
13. Mahalik TI (1988) Synapse 2: 508–515.
14. Mendez I, Elisevich K and Flumerfelt BA (1989) Soc. Neurosci. Abstr. 15: 810.
15. Woulfe J and Beaudet A (1989) Brain Res. 479: 402–406.
16. Bolam JP and Smith Y (1991) In: Bemardi G, Carpenter MB and DiChiara G (eds.) The Basal Ganglia III. Plenum Press, New York, pp. 117–129.
17. Nedergaard S, Bolam JP and Greenfield SA (1988) Nature 333: 174–177.
18. Bolam JP, Francis CM and Henderson Z (1991) Neuroscience 41: 483–494.
19. Freund TF, Powell J and Smith AD (1984) Neuroscience 13: 1189–1215.
20. Bouyer JJ, Park DH, Joh TH and Pickel VM (1984) Brain Res. 302: 267–275.
21. Kubota Y, Inagaki S, Kito S, Takagi H and Smith AD (1986) Brain Res. 367: 374–378.
22. Kubota Y, Inagaki S and Kito S (1986) Brain Res. 375: 163–167.
23. Kubota Y, Inagaki S, Kito S and Wu J-Y (1987) Brain Res. 406: 147–156.
24. Kubota Y, Inagaki S, Shimada S, Kito S, Eckenstein F and Tohyama M (1987) Brain Res. 413: 179–184.
25. Kubota Y, Inagaki S, Kito S, Shimada S, Okayama T, Hatanaka H, Pelletier G, Takagi H and Tohyama M (1988) Brain Res. 458: 389–393.
26. Vuillet J, Kerkerian L, Kachidian P, Bosler O and Nieoullon A (1989) Neurosci. Lett. 100: 99–104.
27. Flumerfelt BA, Mendez I and Elisevich K (1989) Soc. Neurosci. Abstr. 15: 582.
28. Grofova I and Rinvik E (1970) Exp. Brain Res. 11: 249–262.

© 1991 Elsevier Science Publishers B.V. All rights reserved.
Biological Psychiatry, Volume 2. G. Racagni et al., editors.

Electrophysiological and pharmacological responses of nigral and striatal neurons

G. Bernardi, P. Calabresi and N.B. Mercuri

Clinica Neurologica, II Universita' degli Studi di Roma, Via O, Raimondo n. 8, Rome 00173, Italy

Introduction

Neurons of the substantia nigra pars compacta and the striatum are part of a circuit that initiates and controls the execution of movements. It is well known that pathological processes producing a degeneration of substantia nigra pars compacta neurons and striatal cells determine Parkinson's and Huntington's disease respectively. In the past few years a great deal of interest has been generated by the possibility of recording the response properties of individual substantia nigra and striatal neurons in in vitro brain slice preparations. Thus the electrophysiological responses to dopamine and dopaminergic agents in the substantia nigra and striatum have been studied.

Results

Membrane properties of nigral cells

In the substantia nigra pars compacta of rat (maintained in vitro) two types of cells can be recorded intracellularly [1]:

a) Principal cells (presumed to be dopaminergic), having resting membrane potential around –55 mV, spike duration more than 1.5 ms, spontaneous firing (0.3–10 Hz) and pronounced afterhyperpolarization. The principal cells exhibited anomalous inward rectification with the hyperpolarization of the membrane;
b) Secondary neurons (presumed to be non-dopaminergic and interneurons), having shorter duration action potential (less than 1 ms), spontaneous firing activity higher than 10 Hz. The secondary cells did not show anomalous rectification with the hyperpolarization of the membrane.

Responses to direct and indirect dopaminergic agonists

Dopamine acting on D_2 autoreceptors inhibited the firing of the principal cells by hyperpolarizing the membrane. This hyperpolarization (outward current, in voltage clamp experiments at holding potential between –50 and –60 mV) was due to receptor-mediated activation of a G-protein and to a subsequent increase in potassium conductance. The same conductance was also activated by $GABA_b$ receptors [2]. The electrical properties of secondary cells were not affected by dopamine [1]. Psychotropic (amphetamine and cocaine), antidepressant (amineptine, nomifensine) and antiparkinsonian (levodopa) agents, all have clear inhibitory effects on the principal cells by increasing the extracellular level of dopamine in the substantia nigra. A blockade of the dopamine uptake process by cocaine and amineptine slowly hyperpolarized the substantia nigra pars compacta cells and potentiated the responses to the application of exogenous dopamine [3–4]. A calcium-independent increase in the efflux of dopamine explained the hyperpolarizing effect of amphetamine [5]. Differently to cocaine and amineptine, amphetamine did not potentiate the responses to added dopamine. Levodopa also hyperpolarized dopaminergic cells by increasing the efflux of neosynthesized dopamine in the substantia nigra [6]. The electrophysiological effects of levodopa were dependent on the presence of calcium in the superfusate.

Membrane properties of striatal cells

Membrane properties of striatal cells have been previously described both in vivo [7] and in vitro [8–10] preparations. Neostriatal neurons intracellularly recorded in vitro showed very negative resting membrane potential (–85 mV in 2.5 mM KCl and –75 mV in 5 mM KCl). Spontaneous action potentials were not observed at resting level. During injection of depolarizing current pulses (0.5–1 nA) a tonic firing discharge was activated. Current voltage plots showed membrane rectification in depolarizing and hyperpolarizing directions.

Responses to dopaminergic agonists

Application of dopamine (1–30 μM) or of SKF 38393 (1–10 μM), a D_1 selective agonist, causes an inhibition of the action potential evoked by depolarizing pulses in the absence of membrane potential changes. This inhibitory effect was antagonized by SCH 23390 (1–3 μM), but not by (–) sulpiride (1–3 μM) [11]. Under control conditions, activation of D_2 receptors by quinpirole (0.1–10 μM) did not produce significant electrophysiological effects. Since it has been shown that either chronic haloperidol treatment or dopamine-depleting procedures (reserpine or lesion of the homolateral substantia nigra) produce supersensitivity of D_2 receptors, we have studied the effect of D_2 receptor activation under these conditions. In treated animals we observed a potent presynaptic inhibitory effect of quinpirole (0.1–10 μM) on the excitatory synaptic potentials recorded in the striatal neurons following cortical activation [12]. These potentials were blocked by CNQX, an antagonist of non-NMDA glutamate receptors.

Conclusions

We have shown that under control conditions activation of nigral D_2 receptors inhibits dopaminergic neurons by activating a K^+ conductance. After the induction of D_2 receptor supersensitivity, activation of D_2 receptors in the striatum causes a presynaptic inhibitory effect on cortico-striatal glutamatergic fibers.

References

1. Lacey MG, Mercuri NB and North RA (1989) J. Neurosci. 9: 1233–1241.
2. Lacey MG, Mercuri NB and North RA (1988) J. Physiol. 401: 437–454.
3. Lacey MG, Mercuri NB and North RA (1990) Br. J. Pharmacol. 99: 731–735.
4. Mercuri NB, Stratta F, Calabresi P and Bernardi G (1991) Br. J. Pharmacol. (submitted).
5. Mercuri NB, Calabresi P and Bernardi G (1989) Br. J. Pharmacol. 98: 127–134.
6. Mercuri NB, Calabresi P and Bernardi G (1990) Br. J. Pharmacol. 100: 257–260.
7. Calabresi P, Mercuri NB, Stefani A and Bernardi G (1990) J. Neurophysiol. 63: 651–662.
8. Calabresi P, Mercuri NB and Bernardi G (1990) J. Neurophysiol. 63: 663–675.
9. Calabresi P, Misgeld U and Dodt U (1987) Neuroscience 20: 293–303.
10. Calabresi P, De Murtas M, Mercuri NB and Bernardi G (1991) J. Physiol. (in press).
11. Calabresi P, Mercuri NB, Stanzione P, Stefani A and Bernardi G (1987) Neuroscience 20: 757–771.
12. Calabresi P, Benedetti M, Mercuri NB and Bernardi G (1988) Neuroscience 27: 145–157.

© 1991 Elsevier Science Publishers B.V. All rights reserved.
Biological Psychiatry, Volume 2. G. Racagni et al., editors.

Functional heterogeneity of the striatum: Presynaptic regulation of dopamine release in striosomes and matrix

Jacques Glowinski, Marie-Odile Krebs, Marcel Desban, Christian Gauchy and Marie-Lou Kemel

Laboratoire Neuropharmacologie, INSERM U114, Collège de France, 75231 Paris Cedex 05, France

Introduction

Accumulating evidence indicates that the striatum of mammals including man is a heterogeneous structure in which two main anatomical compartments can be distinguished, the striosomes and the matrix. These striatal substructures have been identified by several biochemical markers and also differ in the identity or the origin of their afferent fibers and the target areas of their efferent neurones [1]. In addition, as shown in the cat or the rat in particular, the striosomes and the matrix are innervated by different populations of mesencephalic dopaminergic (DA) neurones. Although a population of the A_9 DA cells of the substantia nigra pars compacta innervates both compartments, those located in the so-called densocellular zone project only into the striosomes. Furthermore, the matrix (but not the striosomes) is innervated by DA fibers originating from the A_{10} and A_8 groups of DA cells [2,3]. These anatomical findings led us to investigate the existence of differences in the presynaptic control of DA release in the striosomes and matrix.

Materials and Methods

Using acetylcholinesterase staining as a matrix marker in the cat and naloxone binding for the visualization of striosomes in the rat, striosome maps were performed in the striatum of both species on sagittal and frontal sections. Good reproducibility of the localization of a large proportion of striosomal areas was found from one animal to another. Therefore, a new in vitro superfusion procedure allowing estimation of the release of ^{3}H-DA continuously synthesized from ^{3}H-tyrosine in striosomal and matrix-enriched areas could be devised [4]. Using this highly sensitive approach on either frontal or sagittal sections, the effects of NMDA and ACh were compared in both striatal compartments in either the rat (NMDA) or the cat (ACh) [4,5] (Fig. 1). These agonists were used since cortico-striatal glutamatergic neurones innervate the striosomes and the matrix and also regulate cholinergic interneurones by acting on NMDA receptors. Finally, although the cholinergic interneurones are mainly located in the matrix, they could

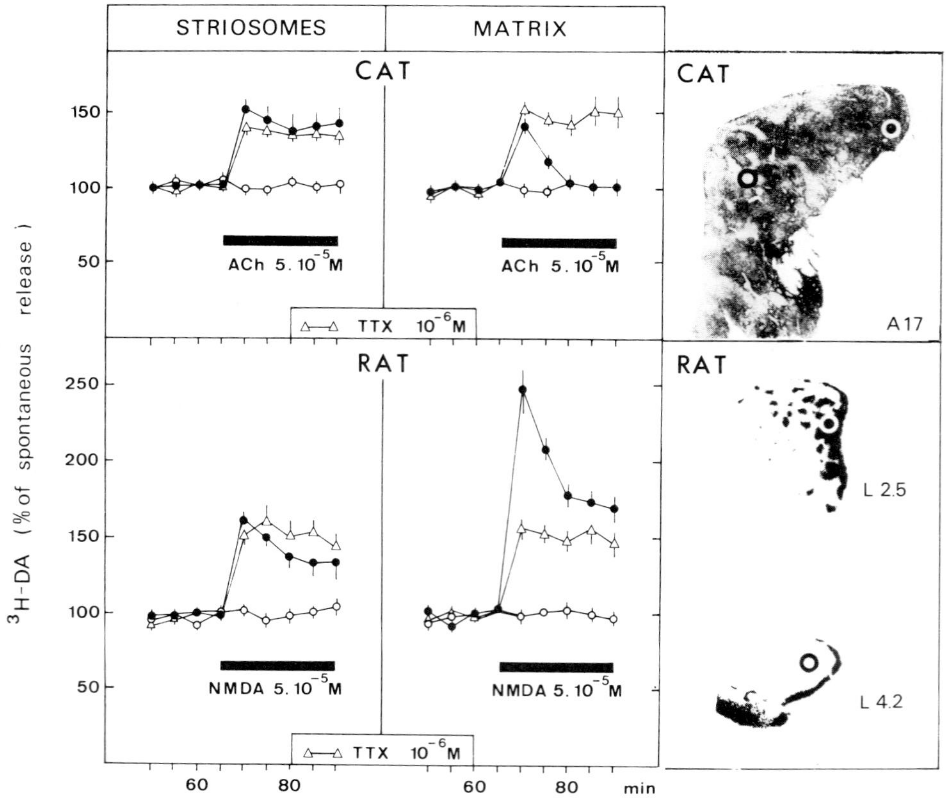

Fig. 1. Tetrodotoxin-sensitive and -insensitive effects of ACh and NMDA on AH-DA release in striosomal- and matrix-enriched area.
Using microsupertusion devices, the release of ^{3}H-DA continuously synthesized from ^{3}H-tyrosine was estimated in striosomal- and matrix-enriched striatal zones of frontal or sagittal brain slices from the rat or the cat. ACh or NMDA (5×10^{-5} M) were applied 65 min after the onset of superfusion with ^{3}H-tyrosine. When applied, TTX (10^{-6} M) was added in the superfusion medium from the beginning of the experiment. Results (mean ± S.E.M., n = 7–11) are expressed as a percentage of the mean spontaneous release of ^{3}H-DA determined in the four fractions preceding the application of either NMDA or ACh. In all cases, NMDA- and ACh-evoked responses (in the presence or absence of TTX) were significantly different from respective controls (○). *$P < 0.05$ effect of ACh or NMDA (●) when compared to the effect of the agonists in the presence of TTX (Δ). The right part of the figure illustrates the localizations of the superfused areas (black or white circles) in the cat and the rat, superposed on the anatomical determination of striosomal and matrix areas. In the cat, these compartments were revealed on frontal slices by the histochemical visualization of AChE activity (striosomes: AChE-poor zone, clear; matrix: AChE-rich zone, dark). In the rat, the striosomes (dark) and the matrix (clear) were identified using ^{3}H-naloxone binding performed on sagittal sections.

contribute to the transfer of information from one compartment to the other, since some of their neurites innervate the striosomes.

Results and Discussion

The presence in both compartments of NMDA and muscarinic receptors on DA nerve terminals involved in a direct presynaptic facilitatory control of DA release was first demonstrated in experiments carried out in the presence of tetrodotoxin (TTX, a neurotoxin which prevents indirect effects by blocking sodium channels). Under these conditions, NMDA (in the presence of Mg^{2+}) and ACh stimulated the release of ^{3}H-DA, the effects of each agonist being of similar amplitude and duration in striosomal and matrix-enriched areas. TTX-resistant NMDA-evoked responses were blocked by MK-801 or Mg^{8+}, while TTX-resistant ACh-evoked responses were antagonized by atropine (Fig. 1).

In contrast, important differences were seen when experiments were carried out in the absence of TTX, indicating that local circuits play a much more important role in the presynaptic control of DA transmission in the matrix.

1. In the rat striatum, the stimulatory effect of NMDA on ^{3}H-DA release was of much larger amplitude in the matrix than in striosomes and this difference was still observed when NMDA-evoked responses were potentiated by glycine. In addition, in the matrix only, the NMDA-evoked release of ^{3}HDA was potentiated in the presence of atropine and pempidine, indicating that the stimulation of cholinergic interneurones reduces the NMDA-evoked responses and suggesting that ACh stimulates inhibitory neurones.
2. In the cat caudate nucleus, the ACh-evoked release of ^{3}H-DA was of short duration in the matrix but not in the striosomal area. In addition, as revealed by experiments performed with either atropine, pempidine or both types of cholinergic antagonists, two opposite indirect regulations of DA release triggered by ACh were demonstrated selectively in the matrix. One is facilitatory and involves nicotinic receptors located on as yet unidentified neurones. The other, more prominent, is inhibitory and mediated by muscarinic receptors (in agreement with data obtained in NMDA experiments). As shown by experiments carried out with naloxone or bicuculline, depending on the localization of the matrix area investigated, the ACh-evoked inhibitory response is mediated by dynorphin-containing neurones or GABA neurones.

These results add complementary information on the heterogeneity of the matrix and raise some questions concerning the mechanisms involved in cotransmission processes, GABA and dynorphin being co-localized in a population of striatal efferent neurones.

References

1. Graybiel AM (1990) Trends Neurol. Sci. 13: 244–254.
2. Jimenez-Castellanos J and Graybiel AM (1987) Neuroscience 23: 223–242.
3. Gerfen CR, Herkenham M and Thibault J (1987) J. Neurosci. 7: 3915–3934.
4. Kemel ML, Desban M, Glowinski J and Gauchy C (1989) Proc. Natl. Acad. Sci. U.S.A. 86: 9006–9010.
5. Krebs MO, Trovero F, Desban M, Gauchy C, Glowinski J and Kemel ML (1991) J. Neurosci. (in press).

© 1991 Elsevier Science Publishers B.V. All rights reserved.
Biological Psychiatry, Volume 2. G. Racagni et al., editors.

Dysfunction of the dopaminergic nigrostriatial system in humans

France Javoy-Agid
INSERM U 289, Hôpital de la Salpêtrière, 47, Bd de l'Hôpital, 75651 Paris Cedex 13, France

The dopaminergic deficit in the mesostriatal pathway is a common feature of parkinsonian syndromes such as Parkinson's disease (PD) associated with neuronal loss in the substantia nigra, and progressive supranuclear palsy (PSP), with additional lesions in the striato-pallidal complex [1]. Neurochemical examination of the brains of patients deceased with such neurodegenerative diseases might bring some insight into the anatomical organization of the dopamine system in the human brain, as well as into the physiological implication of these neurons by establishing correlations between development of symptoms, pathological evidence of neuronal damage and under-representation of known neurotransmitters.

The organization of the human mesostriatal system is more complex than previously thought [2]. In the mesencephalon, tyrosine hydroxylase immunocytochemistry shows the existence of several dopamine-containing cell groups. Dopaminergic neurons were most densely distributed in the substantia nigra pars compacta, many also appeared in the substantia nigra pars lateralis, the ventral tegmental area, the paramedian tegmentum and central grey substance. The dopamine-containing cell groups differed markedly from each other in the percentage of neuromelanin-pigmented they contain: very high for neurons of the substantia nigra to very low in the central grey substance and intermediate in the ventral tegmental area [3]. In view of experiments in animals, it is most likely that in the human, the different dopaminergic cell groups have distinguishable connections. Among the population of dopaminergic neurons, subpopulations of melanized neurons were the most vulnerable in PD, while there was a greater relative sparing of the non-pigmented neurons [3]. Marked variations from patient to patient occurred in the severity and pattern of neuronal loss.

The striatum, the area of projection of the midbrain dopaminergic neurons, has a compartmental neurochemical architecture [3]. In animals, the striatal compartments in striosomes and matrix are zones known to have different inputs or outputs. In the human brain, tyrosine hydroxylase immunoreactive fibers, representing the dopaminergic mesostriatal innervation, are distributed according to a striosome/matrix pattern as are other neurotransmitter and neuropeptidergic systems. In PD, despite the severe dopamine denervation, the fundamental neurochemical division of the striatum is preserved [1,3,4]. This finding is of clinical interest because it suggests that the neuronal organization of the striatum remains intact. In particular, survival of postsynaptic constituents may account for the success of levodopa therapy. This is not the case in all parkinsonian syndromes, however. In PSP, the local circuitry of the striatum is affected [5]. The reduction in density of D_2 dopamine receptors, a consequence of the degeneration of dopaminoceptive cholinergic neurons might explain why most if not all patients with PSP are insensitive to levodopa treatment.

The severity of the striatal dopaminergic denervation is variable from individual to individual and is not always a function of duration of the disease, indicating that the rate of nerve cell death is not the same in all patients. Dopaminergic denervation progresses in the course of the disease with a twice more rapid rate than in the normal ageing. The continuous progression does not seem related to age of onset of the disease [6]. These observations suggest that dopamine neurons are exposed to a permanent pathogenic factor. A number of metabolic abnormalities can be evidenced postmortem in the substantia nigra which support the concept of an ongoing pathogenic insult in the brains of patients. Data indicate that an increased level of lipid peroxydation continues to occur up to the time of death, perhaps because of continued exposure of nigral cells to excess free radicals derived from some endogenous or exogenous neurotoxic species [7].

It is well admitted that the nigrostriatal dopamine deficiency plays a major role in the genesis of motor symptoms (akinesia, tremor, rigidity) [1]. The notion is based on examination of cases of parkinsonism produced in man and monkeys by MPTP intoxication, a drug thought to selectively destroy the nigrostriatal dopaminergic neurons. It is less clear whether the striatal dopamine deficit alone is responsible for all symptoms. Does the nigrostriatal dopamine deficiency contribute to the development of cognitive disorders in parkinsonian patients [1]? The question is still debated, but the notion has been put forward. Moderate mental deficits similar to that observed in the idiopathic disease have been described in MPTP-induced parkinsonism. The beneficial effects of levodopa in some patients suggest brain dopamine deficit might contribute to reduction of alertness, bradyphrenia and depression.

Finally, the anatomical characteristics of the organization of dopaminergic nigrostriatal system in man, the heterogeneous pattern of neuronal loss among parkinsonian patients, the evidence that the disease continuously progresses in the course of life, at variable rates among individuals, are a number of factors which could account for the marked individual differences which appear in the symptoms expressed in the parkinsonian patients, as estimated by retrospective analysis of clinical findings.

References

1. Agid Y, Javoy-Agid F, Ruberg M and Hirsch E (1989). In: Quinn N and Jenner P (eds.) Disorders of Movement. Academic Press Limited, pp. 85–100.
2. Graybiel AM (1990) Trends Neurol. Sci. 13, 7: 244–253.
3. Hirsch EC, Graybiel AM and Agid Y (1988) Nature 334, 6180: 345–348.
4. Hirsch EC, Graybiel AM, Hersh LB, Duyckaerts C and Agid Y (1989) Neurosci. Lett. 96: 145–150.

5. Ruberg M, Hirsch EH and Javoy-Agid F (1991). In: Litvan I and Agid Y (eds.) Progressive Supranuclear Palsy. Oxford University Press, New York (in press).
6. Scherman D, Desnos C, Darchen F, Pollak P, Javoy-Agid F and Agid Y (1989) Ann. Neurol. 26: 261–265.
7. Dexter DT, Carter CJ, Wells FR, Javoy-Agid F, Agid Y, Lees A, Jenner P and Marsden CD (1989) J. Neurochem. 52: 381–389.

© 1991 Elsevier Science Publishers B.V. All rights reserved.
Biological Psychiatry, Volume 2. G. Racagni et al., editors.

Delusional status and abnormally methylated compounds

J. Ciprian-Ollivier

Carrera de Postgrado de Especialistas en Psiquiatría, Unidad Académica Docente Moyano, Facultad de Medicina, UBA, Centro de Psiquiatría Biológica, Francisco de Vittoria 2324, (1425) Buenos Aires, Argentina

Transmethylation processes have been focused on by biological psychiatry with oscillatory interest [1,2]. We started their study in the early seventies following the investigation by Fischer et al. [3]. At that time the possibility of explaining some symptoms of schizophrenic syndromes through the hyperproduction or insufficient catabolization of methylated derivatives of serotonin, tryptamine and dopamine appeared as an alternative to the ever dominant dopaminergic theory [4]. We referred specially to the disperceptive and/or hallucinatory but not auditory symptoms, and the possible correlation with thought disorders, considering the former as the input for the latter.

We had left behind the sixties and the violent irruption in the western culture of the so-called hallucinogenic drugs and so we had an excellent experimental field for studying experimental psychosis in volunteers who, using these drugs, provided an extremely valid model for a better understanding of the clinical and biological intimacy of genuine endogenous psychosis.

The remarkable biochemical similarity between well-known hallucinogenic molecules and those resulting from the methylation of neurochemically active indoles found in body fluids of psychotic patients [5,6], provided the possibility for a coherent explanation of broad aspects of symptomatology marked by perception alterations, ranging from the propioceptive spectrum to time and field notions.

These aspects of the clinical picture of endogenous psychosis do not always deserve the consideration that their importance in terms of diagnosis and follow-up merit. This is possibly due to the fascination that alterations in the thinking process exert on the observer, although formal disperception, interceptions and "déraillements" might also be explained by alterations in the quality of the molecule in charge of transmitting information.

We have continued studying the relationship between the clinical aspects of perceptual disorders and their possible biological origins, through the action of endogenous hallucinogens such as bufotenin (dimethylserotonin), O-methyl-bufotenin (5-methoxy-NN-dimethyltryptamine) and NN-dimethyltryptamine [7], in spite of the fact that, as we have mentioned, the endotoxin theories passed through an out-of-scientific-fashion period [8,9]. This was probably due to the technical difficulties that the rapid turnover of these substances imply in the insufficient study of their metabolites as was recently remarked [10]. On the other hand, significant investments have been made following the dopaminergic, peptidergic and other very suitable theories [4].

We claimed that considering the broad spectrum that endogenous psychosis represents, it was very probable that each of these leading theories might account in explaining only one part of the symptomatology for some nosologic subgroups which will probably be better defined in the future, as far as clinical-laboratory research supports these categorizations.

We have consistently verified the existence of a sort of gradient between the increased urinary excretion of these methylated compounds and the possibility of the clinical picture under study to produce psychotic symptomatology, in particular disperceptions. In schizophrenics excretion is higher, and we found no statistical difference with the control group and minor depressions where urinary excretion is the lowest [5]. This gradient has a very interesting degree of sharpness demonstrated by the fact that it is possible for us to differentiate in a group of bipolar patients between manic subjects and those with hypomania according to DSM III-R by evaluating the urinary excretion of methylated compounds and perceptual disorders.

Here we have evaluated three pathological groups, middle-aged and of both sexes, classified according to DSM III-R as follows: 23 bipolars with manic episodes, 27 bipolars with hypomanic episodes and 30 major depressives. Brain impairment, renal or hepatic failure were exclusion criteria. An age-sex matched control group of 30 healthy volunteers was included. All were drug-free 10 days prior to the study and under a uniform diet during the biochemical determinations. All were aware of the aims of the study.

The four groups were submitted to psychiatric evaluation including Hoffer-Osmond Diagnostic Test [10] in order to quantify their perceptual status (PerS). The 24-h urinary excretion of abnormal methylated compounds bufotenin, O-methyl bufotenin and NN-dimethyltryptamine was measured concomitantly.

The results, statistically processed by ANOVA followed by the Tukey Test were found to be significant for PerS and NNDMT ($P < 0.05$) as shown in Fig. 1.

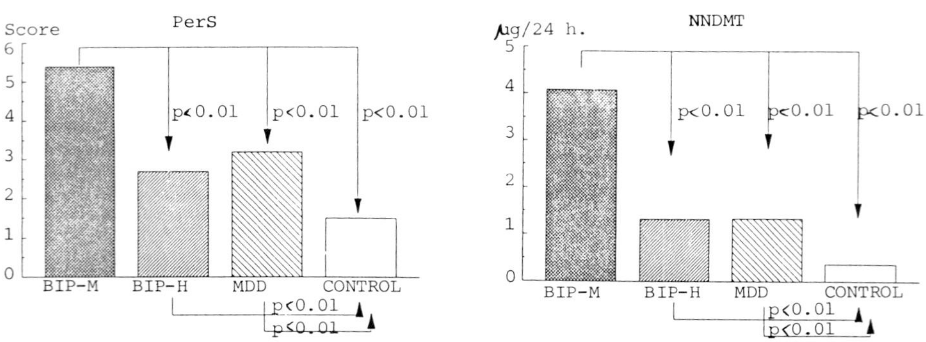

Fig. 1.

Finally we would like to remark that the hypoactivity of MAO in some of these psychoses, especially in schizophrenia, has been clearly demonstrated. This hypoactivity occurs peripherically at liver and platelet level [12]. Methylated compounds are a preferential substrate of this active catalytic enzyme so its hypoactivity might account for their abnormal increase and accumulation.

We are of the opinion that the possibility of an extracerebral genetic metabolic error might lead to an abnormal peripheral production of endogenous hallucinogens acting secondarily on the CNS. The capacity of some of them to cross the blood-brain barrier with ease is well known [13]. Taking this fact into account we consider that transmethylation processes and their incidence in psychiatric illnesses still deserve some special attention in future research.

References

1. Andreoli VM et al. (1978) Transmethylation and the Central Nervous System. Springer-Verlag, Heidelberg.
2. Smythies JR (1983) Psychol. Med. 13: 711–714.
3. Fischer E et al. (1971) Psychosomatics 12: 278–280.
4. Ciprian-Ollivier J (1988) Psiquiatría Biológica. Fundamentos y Aplicación Clínica (Compilador). Interamericana. Buenos Aires, Argentina.
5. Ciprian-Ollivier J et al. (1981) In: Struwe G (ed.) Abstracts of the III World Congress of Biological Psychiatry. Stockholm, Sweden, Vol. 2, F1014.
6. Buscaino G et al. (1969) Acta Neurol. 24(2): 113–118.
7. Spatz H (1967) Prensa Med. Argent. 54: 2116.
8. Ciprian-Ollivier J (1982) In: Belgrano (ed.) Correlaciones Psicobiológicas. Buenos Aires, Argentina, pp. 33–39.
9. Ciprian-Ollivier J et al. (1985) In: Shagass C et al. (eds.) Biological Psychiatry. Elsevier, New York, pp. 243–245.
10. Sitaram BR and Mc Leod WR (1990) Biol. Psychiatry 28: 841–848.
11. Kelm H (1973) In: Hawkins D and Pauling L (eds.) Orthomolecular Psychiatric Treatment of Schizophrenia. Freeman and Co., San Francisco, pp. 327–341.
12. Tachiki KH et al. (1986) Biol. Psychiatry 21: 59–68.
13. Wyatt RJ and Gillin JG (1976) Psychiatr. Ann. 6(1): 33–49.
14. American Psychiatric Association (1988) DSM III-R. Manual Diagnóstico y Estadistico de los Trastornos Mentales. Masson, Barcelona.
15. Friedhoff AJ and Van Winkle E (1962) Nature 194: 897–898.

© 1991 Elsevier Science Publishers B.V. All rights reserved.
Biological Psychiatry, Volume 2. G. Racagni et al., editors.

S-Adenosyl-L-methionine (AdoMet) as an antidepressant

Vittorino Andreoli
Department of Psychiatry, Ospedale San Giovanni Battista, Soave, Verona, Italy

In an open study conducted in 1971, I was able to show the effect of AdoMet, discovered by G. Cantoni [1] in depressive syndromes, still using Wittenborn's Rating Scale for evaluation [2]. On the basis of such clinical evidence, I immediately started investigations in an attempt to further support these data, using a still more suitable assessment criterion such as the Hamilton Rating Scale for Depression. The results of this study were published in 1972 [3]. In order to support such an extraordinary finding, a profitable collaboration arose between my research group in Verona and that in Rome, the latter including Cornelio Fazio, Alessandro Agnoli and Massimo Casacchia. The first joint study was published in Italy in 1973 and on IRCS in 1974, with 49 depressed patients evaluated in an open trial [4] [5]. The relevant data are summarized in Fig. 1.

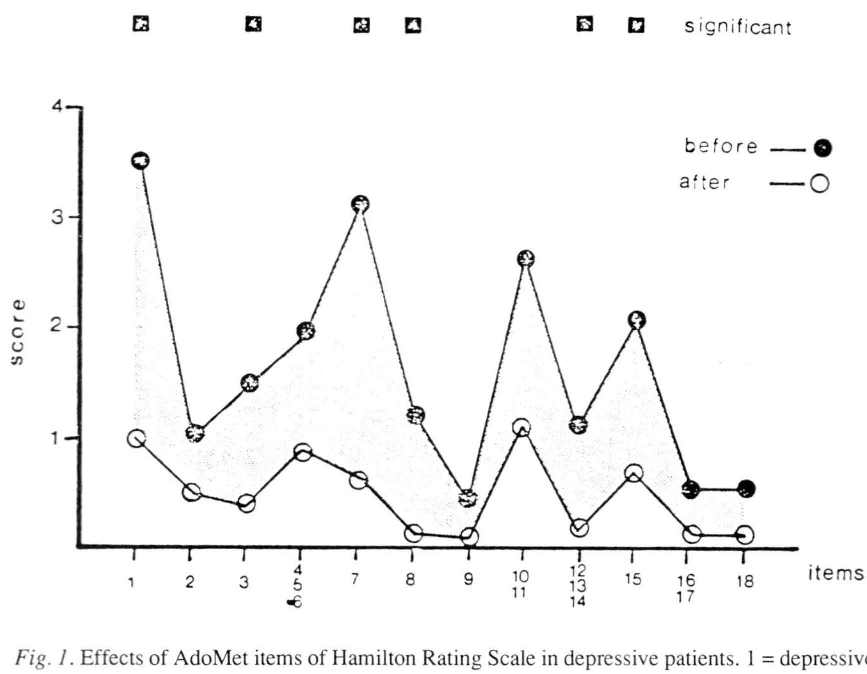

Fig. 1. Effects of AdoMet items of Hamilton Rating Scale in depressive patients. 1 = depressive mood ($P < 0.001$); 3 = depression suicide ($P < 0.001$); 4, 5 and 6 = insomnia initial, middle, delayed ($P < 0.01$); 7 = work and interest ($P < 0.001$); 8 = retardation ($P < 0.001$); 12, 13 and 14 = somatic symptoms ($P < 0.01$); 15 = hypochondriasis ($P < 0.001$) [4].

Table 1. Clinical trials of AdoMet in depressive syndromes: years 1971–1990

Country	Open trials	Double-blind vs. placebo	Double-blind vs. antidepressants
Italy	14	5	7
Spain	4	1	–
U.K.	2	1	–
Austria	–	–	1
U.S.A.	2	2	3
Total	22	9	11

This is the very beginning of the clinical trials which have now been extended as summarized in Table 1.

The double-blind vs. placebo studies are indicated in Table 2. They constantly show the significant effect of AdoMet vs. placebo in a total of 139 patients. Table 3 reports the studies comparing AdoMet with other antidepressants. As may be seen, AdoMet has been shown to possess similar or superior activity vs. imipramine, cloimipramine, amitriptiline, nomifensine, and minaprine. These double-blind controlled studies enrolled 157 patients treated with AdoMet.

A particular aspect of the clinical picture is represented by the switching from depression to hypomania/mania. This is an event occurring in the natural course of depression (namely without any treatment) and is peculiar to the bipolar form. Here it is necessary to speak about this just because this event is particularly important in the AdoMet treatment. Not only does this occurrence stimulate discussion on this subject, but it is also extremely suggestive of the drug activity. The relative data are summarized in Table 4.

Another clinically remarkable aspect regards the action of AdoMet in healthy volunteers. In this connection, only a controlled study is available, which was conducted by A. Agnoli, C. Fazio, V. Andreoli et al. [6] in 1975. Ten subjects

Table 2. AdoMet vs. placebo double-blind trials in patients with depressive syndromes

References	Pts on AdoMet (n)	HRS-D score
Fasio et al. 1973 [5]	14	S > P
Agnoli et al. 1976 [6]	20	S > P
Muscettola et al. 1982 [7]	9	S > P
Gonzales 1982 [8]	15	S > P
Carney 1986 [9]	16	S > P (endogenous)
De Leo 1987 [10]	19	S > P
Caruso et al. 1987 [11]	30	S > P
Janicak et al. 1988 [12]	7	S > P
Kagan et al. 1990 [13]	9	S > P
Total	139	

Table 3. AdoMet vs. antidepressant double-blind trials in patients with depressive syndromes

References	Pts on AdoMet (n)	HRS-D score
Mantero et al. 1975 [14]	16	S = IMI
Scarsella et al. 1978 [15]	10	S > CLO d.7; S = CLO d.14
Del Vecchio et al. 1978 [16]	14	S = CLO
Barbieri et al. 1978 [17]	10	S = AMI
Miccoli et al. 1978 [18]	44	S = CLO
Scaggian et al. 1982 [19]	9	S > NOMI
Kufferle et al. 1982 [20]	9	S = CLO
Bell et al. 1988 [21]	9	S > IMI
Janicak et al. 1988 [12]	7	S = IMI
Potkin et al. 1988 [22]	9	S = IMI
Cerutti et al. 1988 [13]	20	S = MINA
Total	157	

received AdoMet for a period of 10 days and were evaluated before and after treatment using the Nowlys Mood Scale, after ruling out the presence of depressive symptoms by the Minnesota Multiphasic Personality Inventory (MMPI). The Nowlys Mood Scale is a self-rating scale which enables daily changes in 11 items to be evaluated. No item was significantly altered during treatment, except for that related to "fatigue".

My purpose was to give you an up-to-date outline of the clinical activity of AdoMet, and I wish to conclude with the hope that this drug may play the desired major role in future too, when novel therapeutic strategies will be strongly required in the frame of a new cultural and psychiatric environment. Thus, soon there will be an increasing need for drugs with the following features:

- easy to administer;
- rapid effect;
- moderate side-effects;
- capable of being taken for long periods of time without inducing dependence;
- enabling the patient to pursue his activities as much as possible in his normal environment.

Table 4. Occurrence of switching to hypomania/mania on AdoMet treated patients – a comparison with other antidepressants

Various conditions	Switch (%)
Pts on AdoMet	14.19
Spontaneously occurring switch (untreated pts)	10.14
Pts on TCs	8.60
Pts on MAOIs	11.10

We believe that AdoMet possesses some of these peculiarities. Moreover, this drug has acquired a particular interest for deeper research work both as regards its clinical activity and its mechanism of action.

The lack of side-effects makes it as an ideal candidate for the pharmacological prevention of depressive syndromes.

References

1. Cantoni GL (1952) J. Am. Chem. Soc. 74: 2942.
2. Andreoli V (1970/71) Quad. Ter. Sper. Biochem. Biol. Sper. (Suppl. 4) 9: 1.
3. Pinzello A and Andreoli V (1972) Quad. Ter. Sper. Biochem. Biol. Sper. (Suppl. 2) 10: 3.
4. Fazio C et al. (1974) IRCS 2: 1015.
5. Fazio C et al. (1973) Min. Med. 64: 1515.
6. Agnoli A et al. (1975) Clin. Ter., 75: 567.
7. Muscettola G et al. (1982) In: Costa E and Racagni G (eds.) Typical and Atypical Antidepressants: Clinical Practice. Raven Press, New York, p. 151.
8. Gonzales-Quiros P (1982) Psicopatologia 3: 265.
9. Carney MWP et al. (1986) Clin. Neuropharmacol. 9: 235.
10. De Leo (1987) Curr. Ther. Res. 41: 865.
11. Caruso I et al. (1987) Clin. Trials J. 24: 305.
12. Janicak PG et al. (1988) Alabama J. Med. Sci. 25: 306.
13. Kagan BL et al. (1990) Am. J. Psychiatry 147 (5): 591.
14. Mantero M et al. (1975) Min. Med. 66: 4098.
15. Scarzella R and Appiotti A (1978) Freniatria 102: 344.
16. Del Vecchio M et al. (1978) Freniatria 102: 344.
17. Barberi A and Pusateri C (1978) Min. Psich. 19: 235.
18. Miccoli L et al. (1978) Acta Neurol. 33: 243.
19. Scaggion G et al. (1982) Min. Psich. 23: 93.
20. Küfferle B and Grünberger J (1982) In: Costa E and Racagni G (eds.) Typical and Atypical Antidepressants: Clinial Practice. Raven Press, New York, p. 175.
21. Bell KM et al.(1988) Am. J. Psychiatry 145: 1110.
22. Potkin SG et al.(1988) Alabama J. Med. Sci. 25: 313.

© 1991 Elsevier Science Publishers B.V. All rights reserved.
Biological Psychiatry, Volume 2. G. Racagni et al., editors.

Biopterin in psychiatric illness

J.A. Yaryura-Tobias, M. Baker and F. Neziroglu
Bio-Behavioral Psychiatry, 935 Northern Boulevard, Great Neck, NY 10021, U.S.A.

A faulty metabolism in the aminergic pathway has been hypothesized for schizophrenia [1], depressive illness [2], and obsessive-compulsive disorder [3]. Furthermore, the synthesis and biodegradation of monoamines requires biopterin, a substance already related to the pathophysiology of neuropsychiatric disorders [4]. Tetrahydrobiopterin (BH_4) is the cofactor for the regulation of tyrosine hydroxylase, tryptophan hydroxylase, and phenylalanine hydroxylase, which are the rate-limiting enzymes in the biosynthesis of catecholamines and indolamines [5]. Because of this essential role, we have measured biopterin plasma levels, a compound related to BH_4, in patients suffering from various psychiatric illnesses.

Subjects and Methodology

Fifty-two females and 51 males (mean age 34.7 ± 14.80 years) participated in the study. Patients were diagnosed according to DMS III-R classification [6] with obsessive-compulsive disorder (n = 55), schizophrenia (n = 15), dementia of the Alzheimer type (n = 15), generalized anxiety disorder (n = 13) and major depression, recurrent (n = 5). Patients were tested during their acute or subacute phase; no patients were in remission. Seventy patients were medication-free for at least 3 months or had never been medicated, and 33 patients were on antidepressants, antipsychotics, or anxiolytics. The control group consisted of 50 females and 50 males without mental illness. Complete blood count with differential, liver and thyroid profile, electrolytes, plasma glucose and urea, uric acid and urinalysis were done. Blood samples for biopterin were drawn at 9:00 a.m., following 12 h fasting. Biopterin was measured by the bioassay based on the growth-stimulating effect for *Crithidia fasciculata* [7]. This bioassay is sensitive (less than 1 ng/ml) and specific for 6-hydroxyalkypterins.

Results

A Z-test was performed to compare biopterin levels between controls and diagnostic groups. The results indicated that both obsessive-compulsive (M = 1.13 ± 0.42 ng/ml) and schizophrenic patients (M = 1.34 ± 0.61 ng/ml) had significantly higher biopterin levels than controls (M = 0.9 ± 0.20 ng/ml). The Z scores were Z =

4.02, $P < 0.01$ and $Z = 2.70$, $P < 0.01$, respectively. A t-test was performed to compare biopterin levels between medicated ($M = 1.41 \pm 0.65$ ng/ml) and drug-free patients ($M = 1.12 \pm 0.45$ ng/ml). The results indicated that medicated patients had significantly higher biopterin levels than drug-free patients ($t(1,45) = 2.65$, $P < 0.009$). Significantly higher biopterin levels were found in the drug-free patients than in the controls ($t(2,168) = 4.40$, $P < 0.01$). The same was also true between the medicated patients ($M = 1.41 \pm 0.65$) and controls ($t(2,130) = 6.89$, $P < 0.01$). Blood chemistries and urinalysis results were within normal limits.

Discussion

High plasma BH_4 in OCD and schizophrenia suggests its involvement in the physiopathology of these disorders. Other reports have shown no significant differences between schizophrenics and controls in CSF pterin cofactor levels [8], and in neopterin and biopterin urinary output [9]. While our findings were significantly negative for depression, perhaps due to a small sample size, other authors have found significantly elevated total plasma biopterin levels in depression and hypomania [10], significantly higher neopterin and biopterin urinary output in unipolar depression [9] and significantly higher BH_4 urinary output levels in depression [11]. We found no significant changes in biopterin levels in patients with dementia of the Alzheimer type (DAT), as previously reported in CSF biopterin concentrations [12]. Our findings also indicated that patients on medication had significantly higher levels of plasma biopterin than patients without medication, as previously reported in patients with unipolar or bipolar depression taking tricyclics and lithium [13]. However, in female patients suffering from depression and maintained on lithium therapy ($n = 51$) and benzodiazepines ($n = 21$), urinary biopterin levels were significantly lower than in controls [14]. Among the caveats to be considered are: 1) few studies have been conducted; 2) most samples are quite small; 3) measuring biopterin in different fluids makes comparison difficult; and 4) some patients were medicated.

References

1. Yaryura-Tobias JA, Diamond B and Merlis S (1970) Curr. Ther. Res. 12: 528–531.
2. Coppen A (1967) Br. J. Psychiatry 113: 1237–1252.
3. Yaryura-Tobias JA, Bebirian RJ, Neziroglu F and Bhagavan HN (1977) Psychol. Psychiatr. Behav. 2: 279–286.
4. Nagatsu T, Matsuura S and Sugimoto T (1989) Med. Res. Rev. 1(9): 25–44.
5. Kaufman S and Fisher BD (1974) In: Hayaishi O (ed.) Academic Press, New York.
6. The American Psychiatric Association (1978) DSM III-R.
7. Baker M, Frank O, Bacci CJ and Hutner SH (1974) Am. J. Clin. Nutr. 27: 1247–1253.
8. Garbutt JC, van Kammen DP, Levine RA, Sternberg DE, Murphy DL, Ballenger J, Bunney WE Jr and Lovenberg WM (1982) Psychiatr. Res. 6: 145–151.

9. Duch DS, Woolf JH, Nichol CA, Davidson JR and Garbutt JC (1984) Psychiatr. Res. 11: 83–89.
10. Hashimoto R, Ozaki N, Ohta T, Kasahara Y, Kaneda N and Nagatsu T (1990) Biol. Psychiatry 28: 526–528.
11. Garbutt JC, Duch DS, Nichol CA and Woolf JH (1985) Psychiatr. Res. 16: 181–187.
12. Kaye JA, May C, Daly E, Atack JR, Sweeney DJ, Luxenberg JS, Kay AD, Kaufman S, Milstien S, Friedland RP and Rapoport SI (1988) Neurology 38: 554–557.
13. Leeming RJ, Blair JA and Walters J (1982) Psychol. Med. 12: 191–192.
14. Coppen A, Swade C, Jones SA, Armstrong RA, Blair JA and Leeming RJ (1989) J. Affective Disord. 16: 103–107.

© 1991 Elsevier Science Publishers B.V. All rights reserved.
Biological Psychiatry, Volume 2. G. Racagni et al., editors.

Isatin: An anxiogenic endocoid

Vivette Glover, A. Clow, A. Przyborowska, J. Halket, S.K. Bhattacharya and M. Sandler

Department of Chemical Pathology, Queen Charlotte's and Chelsea Hospital, Goldhawk Road, London W6 OXG, U.K.

Isatin (2,3-dioxoindole), a recently discovered endocoid [1], has a discrete tissue distribution. In the rat brain, highest levels have been found in hippocampus and cerebellum (0.13 and 0.11 µg/g respectively), significantly higher than the 0.04 µg/g in the frontal cortex [2]. In the human striatum, even higher concentrations have been noted of about 0.6 µg/g (or 4 µM). This concentration is nearer that of the neurotransmitter monoamines than that of the "trace amines".

The functional role, if any, of isatin is still not clear. In vitro, its most potent action described to date is as a monoamine oxidase (MAO) inhibitor, where it has a selective action on MAO-B (IC_{50}, 3 µM), compared with MAO-A (IC_{50}, 60 µM) [1]. It thus may function as an endogenous (–)-deprenyl-like agent. Its action on benzodiazepine receptors is much less potent, as it is on 5-hydroxytryptamine (5-HT) uptake, imipramine binding and 5-HT_{1A} receptors (unpublished observations).

In vivo, at doses of 15–20 mg/kg, isatin appears to be anxiogenic in rodents [3]. In mice, it induces similar behavioural responses to those of yohimbine in the open field and elevated plus maze, whilst in rats its responses resemble those of yohimbine in the social interaction and thirst conflict tests [3]. It also attenuates the effects of diazepam in these models [3]. At higher doses isatin has a different profile of action and can become sedative. It is unlikely that these effects derive from MAO inhibition. It thus seems likely that isatin, or its metabolites, act on a wider spread of enzyme systems and/or receptors than had previously been suspected.

The anxiogenic agent, pentylenetetrazole, significantly increases brain isatin concentration in both rabbit [4] and rat (in preparation). In the rabbit, levels in liver were also measured but were unchanged.

Little is known about either the biosynthetic or metabolic pathways for isatin. We have recently examined tissue and urinary concentrations in rats reared in a germ-free environment, compared with conventionally reared controls (submitted for publication). The levels in urine were very much reduced in the germ-free animals, but those in tissue were unchanged. This finding suggests that isatin in rat urine is predominantly synthesised by the gut flora (absent in the germ-free animals), but that the relatively low amounts in the tissues derive from another source, presumably synthesized endogenously, in that levels in the diet are very low. Loading rats with the possible precursors tyrosine, tryptophan or phenyl-alanine has no influence on brain concentrations (in preparation).

We still have little information about isatin output in different clinical conditions. We first identified this compound as the major component of tribulin (endogenous MAO inhibitory activity) in normal human urine. Tribulin output is raised in a range of clinical states associated with stress or anxiety, such as general anxiety disorder [5] and lactate-induced panic attacks [6]. In a series of urine samples taken from migraine patients where isatin and tribulin were measured in parallel, the correlation between the two was 0.69 ($P < 0.001$) [7]. However, tribulin and isatin levels do not always mirror each other, and we suspect that there may be other components of tribulin activity.

In summary, isatin is present in the brain and other tissues. Its levels are raised by the anxiogenic agent, pentylenetetrazole, and the compound itself is anxiogenic in rodents. Whether it forms part of a novel anxiogenic system of physiological significance remains to be established.

References

1. Glover V, Halket JM, Watkins PJ, Clow A, Goodwin BL and Sandler M (1988) J. Neurochem. 51: 656–659.
2. Watkins P, Clow A, Glover V, Halket J, Przyborowska A and Sandler M (1990) Neurochem. Int. 17: 321–323.
3. Bhattacharya SK, Rai An, Mitra SK and Achary SB (1991) J. Pyschopharmacol. (in press).
4. Clow A, Davidson J, Glover V, Halket JM, Milton AS, Sandler M and Watkins P (1989) Neurosci. Lett. 107: 327–330.
5. Clow A, Glover V, Sandler N and Tiller J (1988) Psychopharmacology 95: 378–380.
6. Clow A, Glover V, Weg MW, Walker PL, Sheehan DV, Carr DB and Sandler M (1988) Br. J. Psychiatry 152: 122–126.
7. Jarman J, Przyborowska A, Glover V, Davies PTG, Clifford Rose F and Sandler N (1991) J. Neural Transm. (in press).

© 1991 Elsevier Science Publishers B.V. All rights reserved.
Biological Psychiatry, Volume 2. G. Racagni et al., editors.

Evidence for a dual origin of naturally occurring benzodiazepines in the mammalian brain

J.H. Medina[1], C. Peña[2], M. Piva[2], C. Wasowski[2], M.L. de Stein[1], C. Wolfman[1] and A.C. Paladini[2]

[1]Instituto de Biologia Celular, Fac. Medicina, Bs.As., Argentina; and [2]IQUIFIB, Fac. Farmacia y Bioquimica, Bs.As., Argentina

Introduction

De Blas and colleagues demonstrated in 1986 the occurrence of n-desmethyl-diazepam in bovine brain [1]. Since then, several BDZs, as well as other incompletely characterized BDZ-like molecules, have been found in brain, peripheral organs, plasma and cerebrospinal fluid of BDZ-free humans and animals [2–5]. Laboratory contamination was rigorously excluded in all these experiments; furthermore, it was recently found that diazepam and other BDZs were present in human brain samples stored prior to the introduction of BDZs into the market (1960) and also in food products harvested in 1958 [6]. It is then very unlikely that environmental pollution by synthetic BDZs could account for their presence in biological samples.

Since it seems well established that natural BDZs exist in several mammalian tissues including brain, an important question to be answered is the origin of these compounds. On discussing possible explanations for these findings, two main hypotheses, not mutually exclusive, must be considered:

a) BDZs are biosynthesized by microorganisms and/or plants and are incorporated in mammals via the food chain;
b) BDZs are biosynthesized totally or partially by mammalian tissues. The former hypothesis is supported by recent studies showing the presence of BDZs in cow milk, vegetables, grains and plants [3,5–7].

Evidence for an exogenous origin of natural BDZs

Based on the well-known findings that BDZ nucleus [1,4] can be synthesized by microorganisms such as Penicillium ciclopium and Streptomyces refuineus [6], and on the existence of BDZs in bovine brain and milk [2], we decided to carry out a series of experiments using the bovine rumen as a biosynthetic reactor where the ruminal flora could synthesize BDZs using precursors provided by the forage ingested. The rationale of this study is mainly based on two findings from our laboratory: 1) that BDZs are present in the ruminal content; and 2) that two particular forages eaten by the cattle when analyzed contained either non-detectable quantities of BDZ-like molecules or 10 times lower amounts of these substances than those observed in the ruminal content a few hours after their ingestion (submitted for publication).

The in vitro incubation of ruminal microorganisms with the forages *Festuca arundinacea* plus *Trifolium repens* during 4 h in anaerobic conditions, showed a 9-fold increase in the content of BDZ-like molecules (Figs. 1A and B). In addition, it is evident from Fig. 1 that three new active fractions appear after the incubation. Further purification of the active fractions shown in Fig. 1B yielded homogenous peaks which share physico-chemical and immunological properties with BDZs.

These preliminary results clearly show that BDZs-like molecules can be synthesized by ruminal microorganisms. It follows then, that these molecules should be constantly absorbed and through the blood reach the brain and the mammary gland [3].

Evidence for an endogenous origin of natural BDZs in rat brain

Control experiments including rat brain incubates at 0°C, non-incubated tissue, or use of preboiled brain tissue revealed basal levels of BDZ-like molecules of 0.08 ± 0.01 ng diazepam equivalents/g of wet weight tissue (n = 6). The incubation of rat brain or cerebral cortex homogenates during 2–4 h at 37°C with a nutritive medium (GIBCO Dulbecco's modified Eagle's medium) increased by 800% the content of BDZ-like molecules. One of these molecules purified by reverse-phase HPLC on

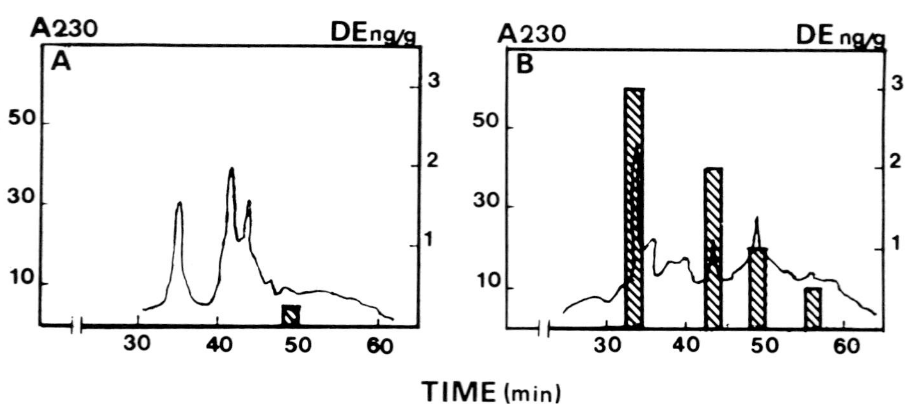

Fig. 1. The grasses *Festuca arundinacea* or *Trifolium repens* were incubated anaerobically with rumen microorganisms. Alcoholic extracts of these incubates, or of the fresh grasses, were purified by counter-current distribution, silica gel filtration and HPLC. A and B show the HPLC results obtained with F. arundinacea before and after incubation. The C_4 analytical column used was eluted with an increasing gradient of ACN in water. The bars indicate BDZ-like molecules detected by immunoassay using monoclonal antibody to BDZs. No BDZ-like material was found in T. repens extracts. DZE: diazepam equivalent; A_{230}: absorbency at 230 nm.

C_{18} and C_4 columns, eluted just before authentic diazepam, inhibited the binding of ^{3}H-flunitrazepam to both the central type benzodiazepine receptor and to the specific antibenzodiazepine monoclonal antibody mAb 21-7F9 and had a low molecular weight as determined by gel permeation HPLC. The small amount of purified BDZ-like substance precluded its chemical identification. However, its physico-chemical, pharmacological and immunological properties are quite similar to those of BDZs.

In conclusion, although many questions about natural BDZs remain to be answered, particularly those related to the biological role of the compounds present in brain, our results suggest that a dual source of BDZs might account for their occurrence in mammalian brain. Since the seminal work of De Blas group, a wealth of new and exciting data has emerged [6]; but further intensive investigations are needed to clarify the role played by natural BDZs.

References

1. Sangameswaran L, Fales HM, Friedrich P and De Blas A (1986) Proc. Natl. Acad. Sci. U.S.A. 83: 9236–9240.
2. Medina JH, Peña C, Piva M, Paladini AC and De Robertis E (1988) Biochem. Biophys. Res. Commun. 152: 534–539.
3. Medina TN (1990) Comm. Biol. 8: 217–234.
4. Unseld E, Fischer C, Rothemud E and Klotz U (1990) Biochem. Pharmacol. 39: 210–212.
5. Wildman J (1989) Pharmacol. Res. 21: 673–682.
6. Klotz U (1991) Life Sci. 48: 209–215.
7. Medina JH, Peña C, Levi de Stein M, Wolfman C and Paladini AC (1989) Biochem. Biophys. Res. Commun. 165: 547–553.

© 1991 Elsevier Science Publishers B.V. All rights reserved.
Biological Psychiatry, Volume 2. G. Racagni et al., editors.

Putative endogenous inhibitor of the tritiated imipramine binding site in depressed patients

K.R.R. Krishnan, D.G. Blazer, D.L. Knight, D. Benjamin, L.R. Meyerson and C.B. Nemeroff

Psychiatry Department, Duke University Medical Center, Box 3215, Durham, NC 27710, U.S.A.

Introduction

High-affinity binding sites for imipramine have been demonstrated in the brain. These binding sites are specific site of action of the drug and are associated with the uptake of serotonin [1–3]. Similar imipramine binding sites are found in the platelets [3]. Many studies have demonstrated that untreated severely ill depressed patients have a lower density of binding sites in their platelets compared to normal control subjects [3,4]. Density of imipramine binding sites in platelets of depressed patients is state-dependent [5]. On the basis of the studies cited above, a number of investigators have attempted to identify modulators and inhibitors of the imipramine binding site. α_1-acid glycoprotein (AGP) has been identified by Abraham et al. as an endogenous modulator of the tritiated imipramine serotonin transporter site in human platelets [6]. The same group has reported that in normal human volunteers, there is a diurnal concordance of human AGP and platelet serotonin content [7]. AGP is known to increase during periods of physical stress such as trauma, surgery, myocardial infarction, cancer and other major medical conditions [8]. An early study carried out by Brinkschulte et al. [9] demonstrated no difference in AGP concentration between depressed patient and normal controls.

Our group studied the role of AGP and platelet imipramine binding in depressed patients. Fifty-one patients who met DSM III diagnosis criteria of major depression and 36 normal controls were studied [10]. The diagnosis was made on the basis of both the clinical interview and the Duke Depression Evaluation Schedule. The final diagnosis was a LEAD diagnosis (Longitudinal Evaluation of All Available Data). Severity of depression was assessed using Montgomery-Asberg Depression Rating Scale. Normal volunteers were included through the Center for the Study of Aging. Volunteers were interviewed in a manner similar to that used for the depressed patients and before collection of specimens for AGP and platelet imipramine binding. Depressed patients also received a standard 1 mg dexamethasone suppression test. Patients received 1 mg of dexamethasone at 11 p.m., and plasma cortisol was measured the next day at 3 p.m. and 10 p.m. AGP was measured using a radial immunodiffusion assay [10]. The plasma samples were assayed without knowledge of the diagnosis and identity of the samples. Platelet tritiated imipramine binding was obtained in a standard fashion, as described previously [4]. Depressed patients had a significant increase in plasma AGP concentration compared with control subjects [10]. Fourteen of the 51 depressed patients had AGP concentrations that were higher than the highest normal control value [10]. There was a positive correlation between AGP concentration and the highest postdexamethasone cortisol concentration ($r = 0.38$, $P = 0.004$) [10]. There was no correlation between AGP and imipramine binding site density. Age was negatively correlated to plasma AGP ($r = -0.33$, $P = 0.02$). AGP concentrations were also positively correlated to Montgomery-Asberg Depression Rating Scale total score ($r = 0.37$, $P = 0.02$) [10].

The study demonstrates that the putative endogenous modulator of the imipramine binding site AGP is increased in depressed patients compared to control subjects [10]. The finding that it is not related to imipramine uptake binding site density might reflect the fact that tritiated imipramine binding site number represents the mean of platelets of different age. Thus the length of time platelets have been exposed to increased plasma concentration of the endogenous AGP and the age of the platelets are important confounding factors, and there is no easy way of determining platelet age. Kehoe et al. [11] reported that AGP concentrations were found to be significantly elevated in 15 depressed patients compared to controls. This study supports the results of our study in demonstrating that there is an elevation of AGP in the acute phase of depression. The physiological basis for the increase in AGP is unknown. The increase of AGP is not only involved in the modulation of platelet binding of imipramine, but may also reduce the free fraction of imipramine and this may be important in the initial phases of treatment with antidepressant medications. Whether this finding has much to do with the delay in response after starting antidepressants is unknown. In view of the well-established stress model of affective disorders, it is of interest that stress increases plasma concentrations of AGP [12]. Whether AGP regulates the central nervous system imipramine binding site and plays a role in the etiology or pathogenesis of major depression requires further study.

References

1. Langer SZ, Raisman R, Sechter D, Gay C, Loo H and Zarifian E (1984) In: Usdin E, Asberg M, Bertilsson L and Sjogvist F (eds.) Frontiers in Biochemical and Pharmacological Research in Depression. Raven Press, New York, pp. 113–125.
2. Langer SZ, Galzin AM, Lee CR and Schoemaker H (1986) CIBA Found. Symp. 123: 3–29.
3. Briley MS, Langer SZ, Raisman R, Sechter D and Zarifian E (1980) Science 209: 303–305.
4. Nemeroff CB, Knight DL, Krishnan KRR, Slotkin TA, Bissette G, Melville ML and Blazer DG (1988) Arch. Gen. Psychiatry 45: 919–923.
5. Stanley M, Virgilio J and Gershon S (1982) Science 216: 1337–1339.
6. Abraham KI, Ieni JR and Meyerson LR (1987) Biochem. Biophys. Acta 932: 8–21.
7. Meyerson LR, Strano R and Ocheret D (1989) Pharmacol. Biochem. Behav. 32: 1043–1047.
8. Kremer JM, Wilting J and Janssen LH (1988) Pharmacol. Rev. 40: 1–46.

9. Brinkschulte M, Gaertner HJ, Schied HW and Breyer-Pfaff U (1982) Eur. J. Clin. Pharmacol. 22: 367–373.
10. Nemeroff CB, Krishnan KRR, Blazer DG, Knight DL, Benjamin D and Meyerson LR (1990) Arch. Gen. Psychiatry 47: 337–340.
11. Kehoe WA, Kwentus JA, Sheffel WB and Harralson AF (1991) Biol. Psychiatry 29: 489–493.
12. Schmid K (1975) In: Putnam FW (ed.) The Plasma Proteins. Academic Press Inc., Orlando, FL, pp. 184–228.

© 1991 Elsevier Science Publishers B.V. All rights reserved.
Biological Psychiatry, Volume 2. G. Racagni et al., editors.

Neurotrophic effects on gene expression and function in the brain

Fred H. Gage, Gerald A. Higgins, Mark H. Tuszynski, Kazunari Yoshida, Michael D. Kawaja and Karen S. Chen

Department of Neurosciences, University of California, San Diego, La Jolla, CA, U.S.A.

Introduction

Nerve growth factor (NGF) is a protein that is known to promote the survival, differentiation and process extension of a number of neuronal systems to various degrees during development, and in some cases, in mature organisms [1]. Deficits in the NGF-responsiveness of basal forebrain cholinergic neurons may contribute to pathological changes following damage and in the aged CNS. The goals of the studies summarized here are to understand the molecular, cellular and behavioral effects of NGF on neuronal tissue.

Methods and Materials

The methods and materials used here are those that have been described in detail in the manuscripts listed in the reference section. In vitro and in vivo models are used to assess the effects of NGF. Furthermore, both rodent and primates are used as in vivo subjects. All experiments are undertaken with NIH-approved animal protocols.

Results

Lesion and aging studies in non-primate mammals have shown that chronic intracerebroventricular NGF infusions can prevent or reverse degenerative changes in central nervous system basal forebrain cholinergic neurons [2–4]. Since some human neurodegenerative conditions result in the loss of basal forebrain cholinergic neurons, we sought in the first experiment to determine in a separate study whether lesion-induced damage to primate basal forebrain cholinergic neurons can be prevented by intracerebroventricular NGF infusions. Our results demonstrate that NGF substantially reduces lesion-induced cholinergic neuron degeneration in the non-human primate Macacas fascicularis [5]. The use of neurotrophic therapy in human neurodegenerative studies requires a more complete understanding of actions of NGF on gene expression and functional measures in the rat and non-human primate.

One gene whose expression appears to be regulated by NGF is the amyloid protein precursor (APP), which encodes the β/A4 protein component of amyloid deposits in aged and Alzheimer's diseased brain [6]. In order to understand the regulation of APP gene expression by NGF in the basal forebrain of adult and aged rats we have initiated studies using in situ hybridization and quantitative mRNA analysis of different APP transcripts, NGF receptor (NGF-R) and choline acetyltransferase (ChAT). NGF or vehicle was infused into aged and adult rats. In young adult rats, chronic NGF infusion produces robust increases in APP mRNA hybridization, NGF-R mRNA hybridization, NGF-R immunoreactivity, ChAT mRNA hybridization and hypertrophy of ChAT immunoreactive and mRNA-positive neurons [7,8]. NGF has been shown to increase APP expression in developing and adult brain [6,9]. Aged rats with spatial memory deficits show increased levels of APP-751 mRNA in the forebrain as compared to aged behaviorally non-impaired or young adult rats [10]. We are currently examining whether chronic NGF administration in young adult rats can induce APP expression in aged animals can effect changes in APP gene expression associated with behavioral impairment.

In a final set of experiments we have studied methods of long-term stable delivery of neurotrophic molecules to the brain through implantation of genetically modified cells [11,12]. At present we have determined that the autologous primary fibroblasts can be stably transfected with the NGF cDNA. These cells can transcribe the NGF mRNA, translate the NGF protein and secrete NGF. Furthermore, following intracerebral grafting these cells survive for at least 6 months and result in clear long-lasting effects on cholinergic neurons in the adult brain.

Studies directed at the mechanisms and functions of neurotrophic factors will lead to important insights into the basic principles of brain development and function, as well as potential therapies for CNS disorders.

Acknowledgements

This study was supported by NIH AGO6088, AGO8514.

References

1. Levi-Montalcini R (1987) Science 237: 1154–1162.
2. Hefti F (1986) J. Neurosci. 6: 2155–2162.
3. Williams LR, Varon S, Peterson GM, Wictorin K, Fisher W, Bjorklund A and Gage FH (1986) Proc. Natl. Acad. Sci. U.S.A. 83: 9231–9235.
4. Fischer W, Wictorin K, Bjorklund A, Williams LR, Varon S and Gage FH (1987) Nature 329: 65–68.
5. Tuszynski MH, U HS, Amaral DG and Gage FH (1990) J. Neurosci. 10(11): 3604–3614.
6. Mobley WC, Neve RL, Prusiner SB and McKinley MP (1988) Proc. Natl. Acad. Sci. U.S.A. 85: 9811–9815.
7. Gage FH, Batchelor P, Chen KS, Chin D, Higgins GA, Koh S, Deputy S, Rosenberg MB, Fischer W and Bjorklund A (1989) Neuron 2: 1177–1184.
8. Higgins GA, Koh S, Chen KS and Gage FH (1989) Neuron 3: 247–256.
9. Higgins GA, Neve RL, Chen KS and Gage FH (1989) Soc. Neurosci. Abstr. 15: 1378.

10. Higgins GA, Oyler GA, Neve RL, Chen KS and Gage FH (1990) Proc. Natl. Acad. Sci. U.S.A. 87: 3032–3036.
11. Gage FH, Wolff JA, Rosenberg MB, Xu L, Yee J-K, Shults C and Friedmann T (1987) Neuroscience 23(3): 795–807.
12. Rosenberg MB, Friedmann T, Robertson RC, Tuszynski M, Wolff JA, Breakefield XO and Gage FH (1988) Science 242: 1575–1578.

© 1991 Elsevier Science Publishers B.V. All rights reserved.
Biological Psychiatry, Volume 2. G. Racagni et al., editors.

NGF in CNS: From physiology to pharmacology

Guido Vantini, Mariella Fusco and Alberta Leon
Fidia Research Laboratories, 35031 Abano Terme, Padua, Italy

Among neurotrophic factors (i.e. proteins capable of affecting survival, differentiation, proper target innervation and/or function of neuronal cell populations), nerve growth factor (NGF) represents the most intensively studied. The enormous amount of information on the biochemistry, biological properties and effects of NGF has also led to the assumption that, like other naturally-occurring protein molecules, this neurotrophic factor might have the potential to become a pharmaceutical agent in pathological conditions affecting both the CNS and PNS [1,2]. More recently, other molecules, namely brain-derived neurotrophic factor (BDNF) [3,4] and hippocampal-derived neurotrophic factor (HDNF, also designated NGF-2, neurotrophin-3 or neuronotrophin-3: NT-3) [5–10] which are structurally and functionally related to NGF, have been purified and partially characterized. Although less is known about NT-3 and BDNF, one can assume, as with NGF, that these latter two molecules have the potential to become pharmacological agents.

In the CNS, the presence of NGF and its capability of affecting in vitro and, more importantly, in vivo basal forebrain cholinergic neurons was reported in the early 1980s [11–13]. Since these initial reports, many experiments have strengthened the notion that forebrain cholinergic neurons use NGF as a trophic factor [1,14–16]. It has been shown that these neurons respond to exogenous NGF with a prominent and selective increase of choline acetyltransferase (ChAT) activity both in vitro and in vivo. In addition, measurable levels of NGF, NGF receptors and the corresponding mRNAs, and their regional distribution in the brain suggests that NGF may regulate the function of the above-mentioned cholinergic neurons. Disconnection, removal or lesion of the target region (e.g. hippocampus or cortex) by surgical procedures result in shrinkage, disappearance and/or death of cholinergic neurons. These alterations can be partially or totally prevented by NGF administration.

These data have generated a great deal of interest because the cholinergic neuronal pathways that respond to NGF in animals correspond to nerve tracts found to degenerate in the brain of Alzheimer patients [1]. Thus it has been hypothesized that NGF-related mechanisms may be involved in the pathogenesis of the disease. In addition, the potential use of NGF, or compounds mimicking its action in the treatment of cholinergic deficit-related symptoms of Alzheimer's disease has been hypothesized [17]. To further evaluate the functional role and the pharmacological potential of NGF in the CNS, a series of studies carried out in our laboratories have provided the following results.

Rabbit anti-NGF IgG administered intracerebroventricularly (i.c.v.) to both neonatal and adult rats induced a significant decrease in ChAT activity in brain regions shown to be sensitive to exogenous NGF [18,19]. In addition, in neonatal animals, similar cholinergic alterations were observed following treatment with monoclonal anti-NGF and anti-NGF receptor antibodies. Taken together, these findings directly support the notion that NGF plays a physiological role in the CNS.

Continuous i.c.v. infusion of NGF in adult rat brain induces a dose-dependent and long-lasting increase of ChAT activity in forebrain cholinergic neurons [20,21]. For example, in both septum and hippocampus, a significant increase in ChAT activity was still observable in response to NGF (100 μg, i.c.v. infusion for 2 weeks) 35 days after termination of treatment. In the septum of both neonatal and adult animals, the increase in ChAT activity after NGF administration is, at least in part associated with an increase in ChAT mRNA as evaluated by the polymerase chain reaction [22].

An important concomitant in relation to i.c.v. administration of NGF is the ability to amplify the expression of NGF receptor mRNA and NGF receptor-related immunoreactivity in basal forebrain [23] as well as in other areas expressing the NGF receptor. Interestingly, the ability of NGF to modulate the level of its receptor was also observed in the brain of aged animals.

Taken together, our results corroborate a functional, physiological role for NGF in the control of forebrain cholinergic neurons throughout the lifespan of an animal and, in general terms, are consistent with the rationale for the use of NGF in Alzheimer's disease. Noteworthy is that studies on NGF effects in the non-human primate CNS are now available [24,25] and clinical trials of NGF infusion into the brain of patients with Alzheimer's disease have recently begun [26].

References

1. Hefti F, Hartikka J and Knusel B (1989) Neurobiol. Aging 10: 515.
2. Seckel BR (1990) Muscle Nerve 13: 785.
3. Barde Y-A, Edgar D and Thoenen H (1982) EMBO J. 1: 549.
4. Leibrock J, Lottspeich F, Hohn A, Hofer M, Henderer B, Masiakowski P, Thoenen H and Barde Y-A (1989) Nature 341: 149.
5. Enfors P, Ibanez CF, Ebendal T, Olson L and Persson H (1990) Proc. Natl. Acad. Sci. U.S.A. 87: 5454.
6. Hohn A, Leibrock J, Bailey K and Barde Y-A (1990) Nature 344: 339.
7. Jones KR and Reichardt LF (1990) Proc. Natl. Acad. Sci. U.S.A. 87: 8060.
8. Kaisho Y, Yoshimura K and Nakahama K (1990) FEBS Lett. 266: 187.
9. Maisonpierre PC, Belluscio L, Squinto S, Ip NY, Furth ME, Lindsay RM and Yancopoulos GD (1990) Science 247: 1446.
10. Rosenthal A, Goeddel DV, Nguyen T, Lewis M, Shih A, Laramee GR, Nikolics K and Winslow JW (1990) Neuron 4: 767.
11. Honegger P and Lenoir D (1982) Dev. Brain Res. 3: 229.
12. Crutcher KA and Collins F (1982) Science 217: 67.
13. Gnahn H, Hefti F, Schwab ME and Thoenen H (1983) Dev. Brain Res. 9: 45.
14. Thoenen H, Bandtlow C and Heumann R (1987) Rev. Physiol. Biochem. Pharmacol. 109: 145.

15. Whittemore SR and Seiger A (1987) Brain Res. Rev. 12: 439.
16. Barde Y-A (1989) Neuron 2: 1525.
17. Marx J (1990) Science 247: 408.
18. Vantini G, Schiavo N, Di Martino A, Polato P, Triban C, Callegaro L, Toffano G and Leon A (1989) Neuron 3:267.
19. Fusco M, Schiavo N, Bigon L, Fabris M, Leon A and Vantini G (1989) Soc. Neurosci. (Abstr.) 15: 954.
20. Fusco M, Oderfeld-Nowak B, Vantini G, Schiavo N, Gradkowska M, Zaremba M and Leon A (1989) Neuroscience 33: 47.
21. Fusco M, Tria MA, Schiavo N, Leon A and Vantini G (1990) Neurosci. Res. Commun. 7: 97.
22. Cavicchioli L, Flanigan TP, Dickson JG, Vantini G, Dal Toso R, Fusco M, Walsh FS and Leon A (1991) Mol. Brain Res. 9: 319.
23. Cavicchioli L, Flanigan TP, Vantini G, Fusco M, Polato P, Toffano G, Walsh FS and Leon A (1989) Eur. J. Neurosci. 1: 258.
24. Tuszynski MH, Sang UH, Amaral DG and Gage FH (1990) J. Neurosci. 10: 3604.
25. Koliatsos VE, Nauta HW, Clatterbuck RE, Holtzman DM, Mobley WC and Price DL (1990) J. Neurosci. 10: 3801.
26. Olson L, Nordberg A, von Holst H, Alafusoff I, Amberla C, Backman L, Ebendal T, Hartvig P, Lilja A, Lundquist H, Langstrom B, Meyerson B, Viitanen M, Winblad B and Seiger A (1991) Abstr., 2nd International Springfield Symposium on Advances in Alzheimer Therapy.

© 1991 Elsevier Science Publishers B.V. All rights reserved.
Biological Psychiatry, Volume 2. G. Racagni et al., editors.

NGF levels in plasma and CNS following psychosocial stress in adult mice

Enrico Alleva[1] and Luigi Aloe[2]
[1]*Section of Behavioural Pathophysiology, Laboratorio di Fisiopatologia di Organo e Sistema, Istituto Superiore di Sanità, Viale Regina Elena 299, I-00161, Rome; and* [2]*Institute of Neurobiology, CNR, Viale Marx 15, I-00156, Rome, Italy*

In 1983 together with Rita Levi-Montalcini we started a new line of research, aimed at assessing whether or not a series of behavioural states could cause NGF release from male salivary glands into the bloodstream. This idea arose from several papers, claiming or negating NGF presence in the bloodstream of adult mice. It appeared to us that such a series of conflicting results could be produced by some uncontrolled (behavioural) variable. Moreover, Bing and co-workers [1] found that renin, another protein molecule exerting marked regulatory properties (also stored in male mouse salivary glands), was released into the bloodstream following intermale aggressive behaviour caused by a prolonged period of individual housing. (A more detailed overview of these initial efforts and the rationale behind them is reported in a recent review [2].)

Psychosocial stress and salivary NGF release

Intraspecific fighting induced by 6–8 weeks of social isolation resulted in massive release of nerve growth factor (NGF) into the bloodstream of adult male mice. The amount of circulating NGF was highly correlated with the number of fighting episodes. Biological, radioimmunological, immunohistochemical and ultrastructural studies showed that NGF is discharged from the salivary gland into the blood within minutes after fighting and reaches the highest level 3–4 h later. Denervation of adrenergic inputs to salivary gland (immunosympathectomy or neonatal 6-hydroxydopamine administration) or adrenalectomy did not abolish the NGF release. Likewise, corticotropic hormones did not induce NGF increase in the blood. Ten daily administrations of highly purified mouse NGF (3 μg per g body weight) resulted in a considerable increase in adrenal volume. More interestingly, we found that only psychosocial stressors (intraspecific fighting or sexual arousal) caused NGF release, while non-psychosocial stressors, such as inescapable or escapable footshock, cold water swim, forced biting, restraint stress etc., were ineffective [3]. A further step was to characterize the blood NGF level of dominant and subordinate male mice. We found a marked difference between the two social conditions, since following repeated fighting, subordinates showed higher NGF levels than dominant animals [4] in agreement with previous reports relating mouse social conditions and adrenal gland volume changes (see e.g. [5]). It appears, therefore, that in male mice adrenal activation produced as a result of high levels of circulating NGF is finely tuned by the quality and frequency of psychosocial stressful events.

Stress-induced NGF increase in the hypothalamus

The effects of intermale aggressive behaviour induced by social isolation on the level of $mRNA^{NGF}$ and protein were investigated in central and peripheral mouse tissues [6]. A large increase in both $mRNA^{NGF}$ and protein was observed in hypothalamus, with no changes in cerebral cortex, hippocampus, or cerebellum. No change in $mRNA^{NGF}$ levels was found in heart, spleen, vas deferens or submaxillary salivary gland. The cellular localization of $mRNA^{NGF}$ investigated by in situ hybridization showed that numerous nerve cells were specifically labelled in preoptic and ventrolateral nuclei of the hypothalamus, as well as in the cornu ammonis region of the hippocampus and throughout all layers of the cerebral cortex, with the highest concentration in layer III. The results of this study firmly established that nerve cells constitute an important source of NGF in the brain.

In a second series of anatomical and immunohistochemical studies [7], NGF immunoreactivity was detected in the hypothalamus of adult male mice. NGF-immunoreactive cell bodies were examined through consecutive brain sections, and it was found that most of the NGF-positive cells were located in the dorso-medial and medio-lateral portions of the hypothalamus. Tissue culture bioassays showed that hypothalamic extract elicits neurite outgrowth from both chick sensory ganglia and rat superior cervical ganglia neurons, and that these effects are inhibited by addition of NGF antibodies. Our results also showed that intermale aggressive behaviour induced an NGF increase in the hypothalamic area, which is not abolished by sialoadenectomy, suggesting that the increased brain NGF is locally synthesized and does not come from salivary sources. Likewise, the level of NGF in the hypothalamus of adrenalectomized fighting mice increased, although to a much lesser extent, when compared to hypothalamic levels of sham-operated fighting controls. These results and the previous report showing that aggressive behaviour causes an increase of $mRNA^{NGF}$ in specific hypothalamic areas [6] also seemed to indicate that, in the CNS, sites of NGF synthesis and sites of NGF presence, as revealed by immunoreactivity, do not fully overlap.

NGF as a link between the nervous, endocrine and immune systems

Mast cells and lymphocytes express NGF receptors and may be activated by NGF. Fighting-induced NGF release into the bloodstream resulted in marked mast cell degranulation and in peritoneal histamine increase [8]. These results and an increasing body of new findings support the hypothesis that NGF exerts a modulatory role in neuroimmunendocrine functions of vital importance in the regulation of homeostatic processes [9,10].

Future directions

A rather speculative explanation for the sudden increase in brain NGF level following a psychosocial stressful event is that NGF could serve some still unknown process leading to a renewal of brain plasticity at the adult stage. In fact, it is known that stress can rapidly change behavioural responding, promoting e.g. imprinting-like phenomena in adults, in which some environmental stimuli suddenly become relevant and produce long-lasting behavioural alterations [2]. Hypothalamic NGF could in fact represent a functional link between the "emotional" status caused by a psychosocial stressor and the biological needs of the organism (and of its brain) to "remember" the events leading to an appropriate (or inappropriate) coping with the stressor itself. NGF could shift backwards some still unknown brain zones to an "immature-like stage", by renewing neuronal plasticity or sprouting.

Acknowledgements

Supported, in part, by National Research Council (CNR), Target Project "Prevention and Control of Disease Factors"; Subproject: Stress.

References

1. Bing J, Poulsen K, Hackenthal E, Rix E and Taugner R (1980) J. Histochem. Cytochem. 28: 874–880.
2. Alleva E and Aloe L (1989) Int. J. Comp. Psychol. 2: 147–163.
3. Aloe L, Alleva E, Bohm A and Levi-Montalcini R (1986) Proc. Natl. Acad. Sci. U.S.A. 83: 6184–6187.
4. Maestripieri D, De Simone R, Aloe L and Alleva E (1990) Physiol. Behav. 47: 161–164.
5. Hucklebridge FH, Gamal-el-Din L and Brain PF (1981) Behav. Neural. Biol. 33: 345–363.
6. Spillantini MG, Aloe L, Alleva E, De Simone R, Goedert M and Levi-Montalcini R (1989) Proc. Natl. Acad. Sci. U.S.A. 86: 8555–8559.
7. Aloe L, Alleva E and De Simone R (1990) Behav. Brain Res. 39: 53–61.
8. De Simone R, Alleva E, Tirassa P and Aloe L (1990) Brain Behav. Immun. 4: 74–81.
9. Abramchik GV, Yermakova SS, Kaliunov VN, Tanina RM and Tumilovich MK (1988) J. Neurosci. Res. 19: 349–356.
10. Levi-Montalcini R, Aloe L and Alleva E (1990) Prog. NeuroEndocrinol. Immunol. 3: 1–10.

© 1991 Elsevier Science Publishers B.V. All rights reserved.
Biological Psychiatry, Volume 2. G. Racagni et al., editors.

Expression of NGF receptor by retinal ganglion cells in the adult rat

G. Carmignoto, R. Canella, P. Candeo and M.C. Comelli
Fidia Research Laboratories, 35031 Abano Terme (PD), Italy

Introduction

Nerve growth factor (NGF) is essential for the development and maintenance of peripheral sympathetic and neural crest-derived sensory neurons [1,2] and probably also plays a physiological role for central cholinergic neurons in the mammalian forebrain nuclei [3]. Additional neuronal populations might be targets for NGF action, since NGF receptors have been detected on many other central nervous system (CNS) neurons [4].

Here we present evidence for the expression of NGF receptor (NGFR) on retinal ganglion cells (RGCs) of the adult rat and of the occurrence of the retrograde transport of ^{125}I-NGF by retinal ganglion cell axons. We will also briefly discuss the hypothesis that NGF or an NGF-like molecule plays an important role in the adult mammalian visual system.

Materials and Methods

Iodinated NGF (specific activity 70–90 μCi/μg) was injected into either the right superior colliculus or lateral geniculate nucleus of anaesthetized adult rats using a glass micropipette. Both optic nerves were then ligated (6–0 silk) at a site approximately 3 mm from the eye. Twenty-four hours after injection the animals were decapitated, the optic nerves dissected and the radioactives of the segments proximal and distal to the ligation site determined.

Results

Messenger RNA for the NGFR is expressed in the retina of many animal species, including primates [5]. In the rat retina NGFR mRNA is expressed both during development and in adulthood [6]. The NGFR protein is localized at the level of two retinal cell populations [6]. The first population is found in the RGC layer. Morphological criteria allows a part of these cells to be classified as RGCs. The second population of cells labeled by ^{192}-IgG antibody is made up of cells with soma located in the inner nuclear layer. Immunopositive radial fibers from these cells were observed to terminate with characteristic end-feet at the level of the ganglion cell layer. These cells are likely Müller cells, the main class of glial cells in the retina.

From these results it can be inferred that the NGFR is expressed on RGC axonal terminals to bind NGF or an NGF-like molecule produced by the target tissue. NGF is then internalized and retrogradely transported to the cell bodies of NGF responsive neurons as an NGF-NGFR complex [7]. Intense immunostaining for the NGFR has indeed been observed in many target regions of RGCs [4].

We have found that following ligation of the optic nerve, 192-IgG immunopositive material accumulates both proximally and distally to the site of ligation, suggesting that the NGFR is both anterogradely and retrogradely transported by RGC axons [6].

We also investigated whether the administration of ^{125}I-NGF into the target regions of RGCs results in its uptake by RGC axonal terminals and its subsequent retrograde transport by RGC axons. A small quantity of ^{125}I-NGF was injected into the superior colliculus or lateral geniculate nucleus and a ligation applied to both optic nerves. Twenty-four hours later, radioactive material had accumulated proximally to the site of ligation of the optic nerve contralaterally, but not ipsilaterally, to the injection site (Fig. 1). Similar results were obtained after injection into the

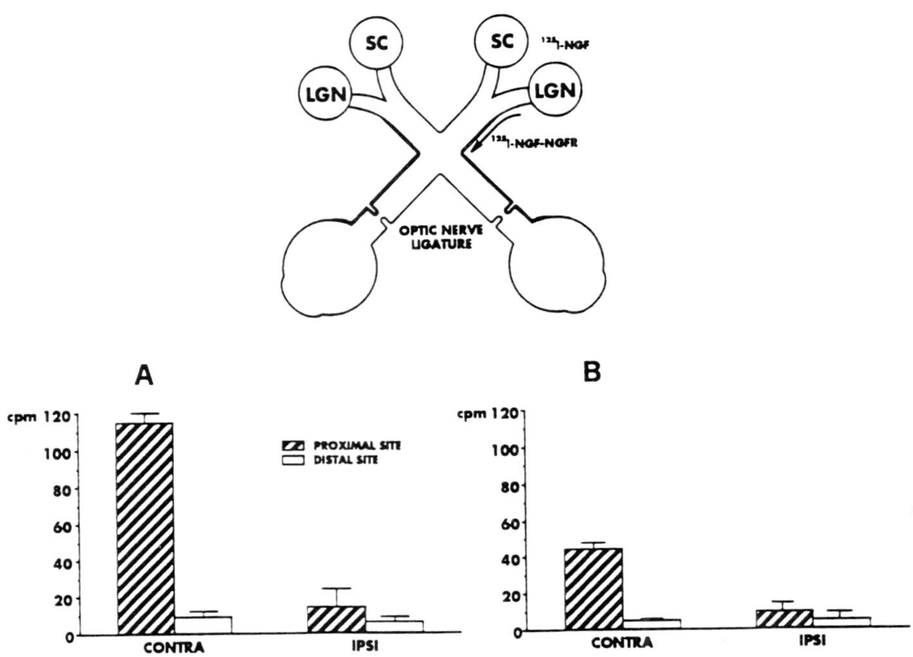

Fig. 1. Retrograde transport of ^{125}I-NGF was analyzed 24 h after injection of 4.2 ng, corresponding to 942,000 cpm (A) and 1.4 ng, corresponding to 324,000 cpm (B) into the right superior colliculus of four and 2 rats, respectively.

lateral geniculate nucleus. The retrograde transport of ^{125}I-NGF is specific, since it is blocked by co-injection of an excess of unlabeled NGF.

Discussion

The expression of NGFR by RGCs and its anterograde and retrograde transport by RGC axons suggest that RGCs might be sensitive to the action of NGF. Before accepting this conclusion, it should be noted that our immunocytochemical studies do not allow for any conclusions about the presence of the high-affinity NGFR which is believed to be responsible for the internalization and biological effects of NGF [8]. Indeed, ^{192}-IgG monoclonal antibody recognizes only the low affinity form of the NGFR [9]. The evidence for the retrograde transport of ^{125}I-NGF by RGC axons obtained in this study and the rescuing effect of NGF on RGCs after optic nerve section in adult rat [10], however, support the hypothesis that the high-affinity form of the NGFR is present in the rat retina, as already found for chicken retina [11]. Binding studies and/or affinity labeling with ^{125}I-NGF and chemical cross-linking [9] will be necessary to clarify whether or not rat RGCs express the high-affinity NGFR.

References

1. Levi-Montalcini R and Angeletti PU (1968) Physiol. Rev. 48: 534–569.
2. Greene LA and Shooter EM (1980) Ann. Rev. Neurosci. 3: 353–402.
3. Thoenen H, Bandtlow C and Heumann R (1987) Rev. Physiol. Pharmacol. 109: 145–171.
4. Yan Q and Johnson EM Jr (1989) J. Comp. Neurol. 290: 585–598.
5. Schatteman GC, Gibbs L, Lanahan AA, Claude P and Bothwell M (1988) J. Neurosci. 8: 860–873.
6. Carmignoto G, Comelli MC, Candeo P, Cavicchioli L, Yan Q, Merighi A and Maffei L (1991) Exp. Neurol. 111: 302–311.
7. Thoenen H and Barde YA (1980) Physiol. Rev. 60: 1284–1335.
8. Sutter A, Riopelle RJ, Harris-Warrick RM and Shooter EM (1979) J. Biol. Chem. 254: 5972–5982.
9. Meakin SO and Shooter EM (1991) Neuron 6: 153–163.
10. Carmignoto G, Maffei L, Candeo P, Canella R and Comelli MC (1989) J. Neurosci. 9: 1263–1272.
11. Escandon E and Chao MV (1990) Dev. Biol. 142: 293–300.

© 1991 Elsevier Science Publishers B.V. All rights reserved.
Biological Psychiatry, Volume 2. G. Racagni et al., editors.

Biological and immunological properties of nerve growth factor and related proteins: Clinical possibilities in dementia

Ted Ebendal[1], Stine Söderström[1], Finn Hallböök[1], Ingrid Stromberg[2], Cynthia Wetmore[2], Lars Olson[2], Patrik Ernfors[3], Carlos Ibáñez[3] and Håkan Persson[3]

[1]*Department of Developmental Biology, Biomedical Center, Uppsala University, Uppsala;* [2]*Department of Histology and Neurobiology; and* [3]*Department of Medical Chemistry , Karolinska Institute, Stockholm, Sweden*

Introduction

Nerve growth factor (NGF) serves functions in the central nervous system (CNS) to support the development and maintenance of cholinergic neurons in the basal forebrain [1,2]. NGF is a basic 118 amino acid protein acting as a trophic factor for many sensory and sympathetic neurons in the peripheral nervous system [2–4].

An enzyme immunoassay for NGF recognizing the human recombinant NGF protein

A valuable method in NGF research is the sensitive two-site enzyme immunoassay (EIA) introduced to allow for reliable determinations of the low levels of NGF present in peripheral and CNS tissues [5–7]. One major obstacle in assessing the function of NGF in neurodegenerative conditions such as Alzheimer's disease [8] is the lack of a sensitive EIA for the human NGF protein. It would be of interest to study the distribution of NGF in the human brain, especially since the cholinergic neurons are severely deteriorated in Alzheimer's disease [9–11]. The monoclonal antibody 27/21 to mouse NGF [5] was shown to effectively block the activity of both the human recombinant NGF and mouse native NGF, and a two-site EIA using monoclonal antibody 27/21 was optimized [12]. Under the conditions used, the EIA detected the human recombinant NGF with the same sensitivity (1–2 pg/ml) as shown for the mouse NGF [12]. It should now be possible to test this EIA on homogenized tissue to examine human NGF in brain samples from Alzheimer patients or age-matched controls.

Molecular cloning of novel neurotrophic proteins with similarities to β-nerve growth factor

The known nucleotide sequences [13,14] of NGF and the related BDNF (brain-derived neurotrophic factor) have made it possible to predict conserved domains of the proteins and to design degenerated probes for polymerase chain reaction. We have reported the cloning of a novel member of this family [15]. From the nucleotide sequence a 282 amino acid long protein with about 45% similarity to BDNF and NGF was deduced. The activity profile of the recombinant protein shows that the function of this new factor, termed hippocampal-derived neurotrophic factor (HDNF) or neurotrophin-3 (NT-3) [16–18] may be supplementary to that of NGF and BDNF.

Thus, NGF, BDNF and HDNF/NT-3 each has unique biological activities and represent different members of a family of neurotrophic factors that may cooperate to support the development and maintenance of the vertebrate nervous system, and have functions in human brain development and neurodegenerative disease.

Construction of cell lines stably producing human recombinant NGF

We have isolated primary cell lines from different organs of rat and human fetuses to serve in expression of recombinant NGF family members. The growth and transplantation properties of these cell lines are currently being studied. We [19] have shown that cell lines can be genetically modified to secrete large amounts of NGF. The cells can be grafted to the brain and exert effects on NGF-sensitive neurons.

We have isolated several mouse 3T3 cell and rat cell cones stably producing the human βNGF. The methods used were similar to those previously used by us in creating the 3E cell line [19]. Thus a mammalian expression vector [19] containing a synthetic oligonucleotide encoding a metal responsive element in conjunction with a rabbit β-globin promoter was used to establish such cell lines.

We suggest that implantation of genetically modified cells producing NGF should make it possible to study the effects of human NGF on brain repair. Furthermore, the availability of cell lines producing high levels of human NGF will allow for homogenous preparations of biologically active, recombinant human NGF for clinical purposes.

Clinical applications of NGF: Experience of first clinical trial on intracranial infusion of nerve growth factor to support adrenal medullary autografts in Parkinson's disease

Recently, a first Parkinson patient has been given NGF infusions to the putamen in connection with autologous transplantation of adrenal medullary tissue [20]. The patient, a 63 year-old woman, shows improvements in the scores for Parkinson symptoms and has not reacted negatively to the administered NGF. Purified mouse NGF was infused for 23 days at a total dose of 3.3 mg. The experiment has shown long-lasting positive effects of adrenal autografts supported initially by NGF infusion in a patient with severe Parkinson's disease [20]. Temporary NGF infusion to meet different clinical conditions merits further scientific exploration on the basis of these findings.

References

1. Ebendal T (1989) Growth Factor Res. 1: 143–159.
2. Thoenen H, Bandtlow C and Heumann R (1987) Rev. Physiol. Biochem. Pharmacol. 109: 145–178.
3. Levi-Montalcini R (1987) Science 237: 1154–1162.
4. Thoenen H and Barde Y-A (1980) Physiol. Rev. 60: 1284–1335.
5. Korsching S and Thoenen H (1983) Proc. Natl. Acad. Sci. U.S.A. 80: 3513–3516.
6. Korsching S and Thoenen H (1987) Methods Enzymol. 147: 167–185.
7. Lärkfors L and Ebendal T (1987) J. Immunol. Methods 97: 41–47.
8. Hefti F and Weiner WJ (1986) Ann. Neurol. 20: 275–281.
9. Bartus RT, Dean RL, Beer B and Lippa AS (1982) Science 217: 408–417.
10. Coyle JT, Price DL and DeLong MR (1983) Science 219: 1 184–1190.
11. Wilcock GK, Esiri MM, Bowen DM and Smith CCT (1982) J. Neurol. Sci. 57: 407–417.
12. Söderström S, Hallböök F, Ibáñez CF, Persson H and Ebendal T (1990) J. Neurosci. Res. 27: 665–677.
13. Ullrich A, Gray A, Berman C and Dull TJ (1983) Nature 303: 821–825.
14. Leibrock J, Lottspeich F, Hohn A, Hofer M, Hengerer B, Masiakowski P, Thoenen H and Barde Y-A (1989) Nature 341: 149–152.
15. Ernfors P, Ibáñez CF, Ebendal T, Olson L and Persson H (1990) Proc. Natl. Acad. Sci. U.S.A. 87: 5454–5458.
16. Hohn A, Leibrock J, Bailey K and Barde Y-A (1990) Nature 344: 339–341.
17. Maisonpierre PC, Belluscio L, Squinto S, Ip NY, Furth ME, Lindsay RM and Yancopoulos GD (1990) Science 247: 1446–1451.
18. Rosenthal A, Goeddel DV, Nguyen T, Lewis M, Shih A, Laramee GR, Nikolics K and Winslow JW (1990) Neuron 4: 767–773.
19. Ernfors P, Ebendal T, Olson L, Mouton P, Strömberg I and Persson H (1989) Proc. Natl. Acad. Sci. U.S.A. 86: 4756–4760.
20. Olson L, Backlund E-O, Ebendal T, Freedman R, Hamberger B, Hansson P, Hoffer B, Lindblom U, Meyerson B, Strömberg I, Sydow O and Seiger Å (1991) Arch. Neurol. (in press).

© 1991 Elsevier Science Publishers B.V. All rights reserved.
Biological Psychiatry, Volume 2. G. Racagni et al., editors.

Regulation of receptor gene expression: General aspects and role of protein phosphorylation

Patrick Rogue, Guy Vincendon and Anant N. Malviya
Laboratoire de Neurobiologie Moléculaire des Interactions Cellulaires du CNRS, Centre de Neurochimie, 5 rue Blaise Pascal, 67084 Strasbourg, France

Receptor responsiveness is regulated dynamically at many levels. Thus, the activation of certain receptors is associated with feed-back phosphorylations which alter their sensitivity to ligands [1]. Regulation of responsiveness also involves modulation of the expression of the receptor genes. For example, exposure to agonists modifies NGF receptor mRNA availability [2]. Similarly, chronic exposure to antagonists alters the level of dopamine receptor mRNA in the rat striatum [3]. Change in gene expression implies that the information transduced by the activated receptor is transferred to the nucleus. How these transmission pathways operate is not well understood. In some cases (steroid hormones) the receptors themselves move to the nucleus and function as ligand-regulated transcription factors. In other cases (G-protein or tyrosine-kinase associated receptors) transcription is influenced through nuclear factors ("third messengers") which are controlled in particular by cytoplasmic second messengers. They bind specifically to short cis-acting nucleotide sequences ("response elements"), the presence of which in the promotor region of target genes (including the genes of the receptors whose activation determines the signalling cascade) confers inducibility. Prominent amongst these transcription factors is AP-1, which recognizes the TRE ("TPA responsive element"). The TRE is necessary for gene induction by phorbol esters, tumor promoters which are also potent activators of protein kinase C (PKC). AP-1 is a dimer made up of the products of the proto-oncogenes c-fos and c-jun. These can form c-Fos-c-Jun heterodimers or c-Jun-c-Jun homodimers. As for several other transcription factors, both c-Fos (c-Fos, FosB, ΔFosB, Fra-1 and –2) and c-Jun (c-Jun, JunB and D) belong to families of proteins. The number of possible combinations between the members makes it difficult to correlate the composition of AP-1 and its transcriptional activity (stimulatory or inhibitory). The genes for these peptides are induced upon cell stimulation (some of the promotors include TRE's). There is a specific pattern for each (some are induced quickly: "immediate early genes", IEG), so that the composition of AP-1 also changes in time. Inhibitors (IP-1) have recently been identified [4].

Thus AP-1 is highly regulated. Post-translational modifications, in particular phosphorylations, play a role in this regulation. For instance, the induction of IEG's by TPA can occur in the absence of protein synthesis and probably involves a change in the state of phosphorylation of pre-existing AP-1 factors. Both c-Fos and c-Jun are known to be phosphorylated in vivo and phosphorylation can change transcriptional activity [5]. Focus in this area has been on serine/threonine kinases activated by second messengers, which seem to intervene at several levels. They can influence the transport of newly-translated transcription factors from the cytoplasm to the nucleus. This transport involves cytoplasmic "anchor" proteins which free the bound factor upon phosphorylation. One example is I-kB with NF-kB. Recently, a cytoplasmic protein which inhibits the nuclear transport of c-Fos has been described [6]. Several serine/threonine kinases are present in the nucleus also, where they intervene in nuclear function. In this context, we will focus mainly on nuclear PKC. Several nuclear proteins are substrates of PKC, suggesting a prominent role for nuclear PKC in the regulation of nuclear events. We have shown that nuclei isolated from resting liver cells and devoid of any cytoplasmic contaminant contain the type II isoform of PKC [7], confirming that the enzyme is present in the nucleus independently of translocation from the cytoplasm. There is a differential tissue and subcellular distribution for the various PKC isoforms, which may also occur at the level of the nucleus since non-liver tissues have been found to contain another isoform [8]. Isolated nuclei possess the necessary elements for the activation of PKC, and the enzyme can indeed be activated by incubating the nuclei with ligands which have receptors located in the nucleus, such as erythropoietin [9]. We have recently shown that nuclei also possess functional inositol 1,4,5-triphosphate (IP_3) receptors [10]. IP_3 can stimulate PKC activity in isolated nuclei [11]. Thus the intimate relationship between PKC and IP_3 receptors (phosphorylated by several protein kinases including PKC [12]) may also exist at the nuclear level, where it may be involved in the control of third messenger systems. The pool of PKC in the nucleus allows a rapid regulation of transcription and several factors which modulate gene expression through PKC (such as erythropoietin with c-myc) may do so by activating the nuclear enzyme.

Protein phosphatase (PP) have an equally important part to play. Cells contain a latent form of phosphorylated (by glycogen synthetase kinase 3 in particular) c-Jun incapable of dimerization and which cannot efficiently bind to the TRE [13]. PKC stimulation by TPA results in the rapid dephosphorylation of c-Jun at sites which negatively regulate its DNA-binding activity, probably through stimulation of a PP. Activation of PKC also leads to the rapid and transient expression of c-Fos. Okadaic acid (an inhibitor of PP type 1 and 2A) produces a more delayed and sustained increase in c-fos expression, probably through the inhibition of a PP responsible for reversing the phosphorylation catalyzed by PKC [14].

These mechanisms participate in the transcriptional regulation of genes which code for receptors, in particular those coupled to G-proteins. Activation of various receptors induces the transcription of IEG's, with a pattern which is probably specific for each [15]. The promoters of receptor genes contain the cis-acting response elements which confer responsiveness to third messengers. For instance, CRE's ("cAMP responsive element") are present in several promotor regions such as those of the adrenergic α_{2A}, β_2, and TSH receptor genes. AP-1 sites have been found in the promotor of the human M1 muscarinic receptor gene [16]. Many psychotropic drugs manifest a clinical effect only after a period of several days, a delay during which receptor adaptation at the level of transcription probably occurs. Thus the mechanisms briefly outlined here appear as fundamental aspects of the new molecular psychopharmacology, and offer novel approaches for drug design.

References

1. Rogue P, Zwiller J, Malviya AN and Vincendon G (1990) Biochem. Int. 22: 575–582.
2. Cavicchioli L, Flanigan TP, Vantini G, Fusco M, Polato P, Toffano G, Walsh FS and Leon A (1989) Eur. J. Neurosci. 1: 258–262.
3. Rogue P, Hanauer A, Zwiller J, Malviya AN and Vincendon G (1991) Eur. J. Pharmacol. (in press).
4. Auwerx J and Sassone-Corci P (1991) Cell 64: 983–993.
5. Ofir R, Dwarki VJ, Rashid D and Verma IM (1990) Nature 348: 80–82.
6. Roux P, Blanchard J-M, Fernandez A, Lamb N, Jeanteur P and Piechaczyck M (1990) 63: 341–351.
7. Rogue P, Labourdette G, Masmoudi A, Yoshida Y, Huang FL, Huang KP, Zwiller J, Vincendon G and Malviya AN (1990) J. Biol. Chem. 265: 4161–4165.
8. Hagiwara M, Uchida C, Usuda, Nagata T and Hidaka H (1990) Biochem. Biophys. Res. Commun. 168: 161–168.
9. Mason-Garcia M, Weill CL and Beckman BS (1990) Biochem. Biophys. Res. Commun. 168: 490–497.
10. Malviya AN, Rogue P and Vincendon G (1990) Proc. Natl. Acad. Sci. U.S.A. 87: 9270–9274.
11. Martelli AM, Gilmour S, Manzoli FA and Cocco L (1990) Biochem. Biophys. Res. Commun. 174: 149–155.
12. Ferris CD, Huganir REL, Bredt DS, Cameron AM and Snyder SH (1991) Proc. Natl. Acad. Sci. U.S.A. 88: 2232–2235.
13. Boyle WJ, Smeal T, Defize LHK, Angel P, Woodgett JR, Karin M and Hunter T (1991) Cell 64: 573–584.
14. Schönthal A, Tsukitani Y and Feramisco JR (1991) Oncogene 6: 423–430.
15. Dwarki K, Sukhatme VP, Shubeita HE and Chien KR (1990) J. Biol. Chem. 265: 13809–131817.
16. Busch SJ, Richards M, Jones and Leppik R (1991) J. Cell Biochem. 45: 167.

© 1991 Elsevier Science Publishers B.V. All rights reserved.
Biological Psychiatry, Volume 2. G. Racagni et al., editors.

Regulation of muscarinic receptors primary cultures of cerebellar granule neurons of rat

W.J. Wojcik[1], I. Holopainen[1], S.W. McLeskey[1], P. Longone[1], M. Riva[2] and I. Mocchetti[2]

[1]Fidia Georgetown Institute for the Neurosciences; and [2]Anatomy and Cell Biology Department, Georgetown University, Washington D.C., 20007, U.S.A.

Introduction

Neurotransmitter receptors usually desensitize after an exposure to receptor agonist. The rates of desensitization vary among the many known receptors; however, mechanisms of desensitization have been successfully identified for only a few receptors such as the β-adrenergic receptor. Briefly, the mechanism of desensitization for the β-adrenergic receptor proceeds in two steps [1]. The first and most rapid step involves the phosphorylation of the receptor by β-adrenergic receptor kinase (βARK) and protein kinase A. This signals internalization of the receptor from the plasma membrane [2]. The second, slower step involves a change in the mRNA content that encodes the β-adrenergic receptor. It is not clear whether this process is typical of other receptors. The following studies attempt to uncover the mechanism of desensitization of neuronal muscarinic receptors which inhibit cyclic AMP formation. A primary cell culture of cerebellar granule cells, which do not synthesize acetylcholine, was selected for these studies in order to avoid the complication of endogenous agonist production.

Muscarinic receptors that inhibit cyclic AMP formation have been recently categorized as muscarinic m_2 and/or m_4 receptor subtypes. Of the five reported subtypes of muscarinic receptors, the remaining muscarinic m_1 m_3 and m_5 receptors have been shown to stimulate the hydrolysis of inositol phospholipids [3,4]. Cerebellar granule neurons express both muscarinic m_2 and m_3 receptor subtypes [5]. When these primary cultures were exposed to carbachol (100 μM), a muscarinic receptor agonist, desensitization of the m_2 receptor occurred within 1 h. The $T_{1/2}$ of desensitization was between 20 and 30 min. This receptor desensitization had short-term and long-term components. The short-term component was characterized by a rapid resensitization (within 1 h) after a 1 h treatment with carbachol. When the cell cultures were treated with carbachol for more than 1 h, a rapid resensitization was not observed, indicating that a more permanent change had occurred.

Methods

Primary cell cultures of rat cerebellar granule cells

Primary cell culture of rat cerebellar granule cells were prepared as previously described [6]. Isolated cells were added to 24-well plates (Nunc) at a density of 7.5 $\times 10^5$ cells/well. The cultures were kept in a humidified environment containing 6% CO_2/air for 7 days.

Antisense oligodeoxynucleotide treatment of cerebellar granule cells

The antisense oligonucleotides βARK-1 (5'-GCG-CTC-ATT-CAG-GGC-3') and βARK-2 (5'-GGC-CTC-GGA-GAA-GAC-3') were synthesized by Research Genetics, Huntsville, Alabama. Antisense oligonucleotides (25 μM) were added 1 day after plating the granule cells and its effectiveness in blocking carbachol (100 μM)-mediated inhibition of cyclic AMP formation in intact cells was tested 6 days later. The incubation solution was an isotonic salt solution (pH 7.3) containing forskolin (5 μM) and 3-isobutyl-1-methyl xanthine (0.5 mM). After a 5 min-incubation, the cyclic AMP was extracted and quantified by the automated radioimmuno assay/Gamma FLO instrument [7].

^{3}H-Propylbenzilylcholine mustard (PBCM) labeling of m_2 and m_3 receptors

Irreversible labeling of muscarinic receptors on cerebellar granule cells with ^{3}H-PBCM has been previously described [6].

mRNA measurement using ^{32}P-cRNA probes for m_2 receptors

Plasmids containing the cDNA for human and rat m_2 receptors were provided by Drs. Bonner (NIMH) and Venter (NIH). The preparation of labeled cRNA probes and hybridization to Northern blots of poly-A^+ mRNA were by standard methods that have been described previously [8]. All results were normalized to the amount of cyclophilin mRNA present on each blot using the labeled P1B15 cDNA probe.

Results and Discussion

We tested whether the first event in the short-term process of desensitization might involve the activation of endogenous βARK. Since no inhibitors of βARK are known, the synthesis of endogenous βARK was prevented by adding to these primary cultures antisense oligonucleotides composed of a specific base sequence. This “antisense strategy” [9], as it is now called, involves the binding of an antisense oligonucleotide to a specific segment of mRNA that encodes βARK. The

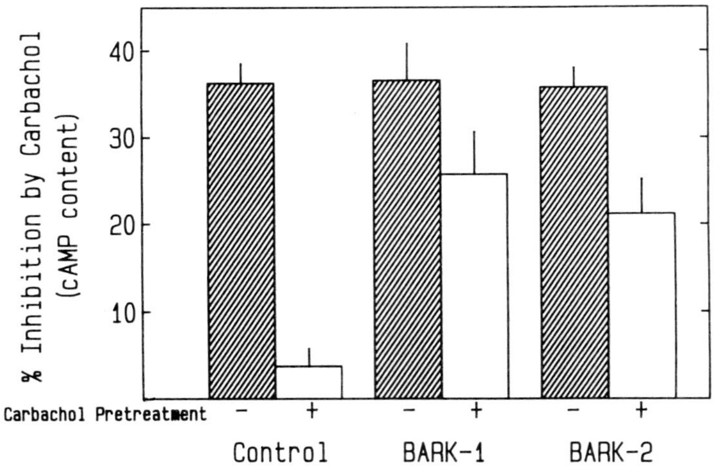

Fig. 1. Antisense oligonucleotides βARK-1 and βARK-2 prevent the carbachol-induced desensitization of muscarinic m_2 receptors. The results are shown as the percent of inhibition of cyclic AMP formation and represent the mean ± S.E. for three experiments performed in duplicate. Desensitization of m_2 receptors resulted from a 1-h pretreatment of the cell cultures with carbachol (100 μM). The carbachol-containing solution was washed from the wells before the assay measuring receptor responsiveness to cyclic AMP formation. Neither antisense oligonucleotides nor the carbachol pretreatment altered basal cyclic AMP levels.

binding of antisense oligonucleotide to mRNA encoding βARK decreases the synthesis (translation) of βARK. Figure 1 shows the actions of carbachol at normal and desensitized (1 h carbachol pretreatment) muscarinic m_2 receptors present on control (no antisense) and βARK antisense oligonucleotide-treated cell cultures. From data not presented, we know that both antisense oligonucleotides entered these cells intact and were present within the cells for at least three days after their application to the cell culture medium. The highest concentration was observed within the first day after application to the cell cultures. These studies suggest that βARK may phosphorylate m_2 receptors, which has been reported to decrease receptor affinity for agonists (resulting in desensitization).

After the cell cultures were treated (1 h) with carbachol, we also observed that the m_2 receptors were no longer detectable by binding with the irreversible ligand ^{3}H-PBCM (Fig. 2). Since ^{3}H-PBCM is non-selective for muscarinic m_2 and m_3 receptor subtypes, both receptors were labeled with ^{3}H-PBCM. However, only the m_2 receptor was decreased. These results suggest that either the m_2 receptor was converted into a low affinity state or that it was sequestered within the cell.

Finally, the long-term consequences of agonist treatment might involve changes at the level of gene expression for the muscarinic m_2 receptor. After a 1, 3, 6, 9, 12, and 24-h treatment with carbachol (100 μM), a statistically significant decrease in the mRNA content for the m_2 receptor was observed. The maximal reduction in message was about 50% at 9 h. After 9 h of exposure to carbachol, the mRNA

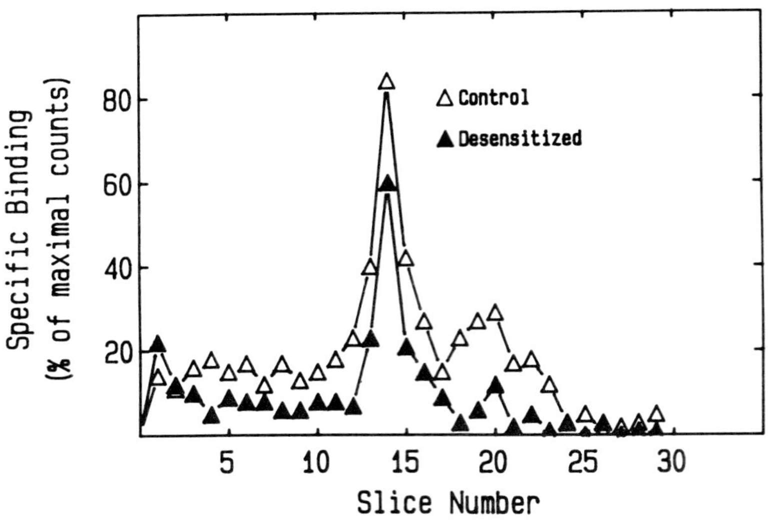

Fig. 2. Irreversible labeling of m_2 and m_3 receptors with ^{3}H-PBCM and separation of proteins by SDS-PAGE. Crude plasma membranes were prepared from cell cultures that were either pretreated for 1 h with vehicle (Δ) or carbachol at 100 μM (▲). The radiolabeled proteins were separated into two molecular sizes, a 92 kDa (m_3, left pèak) and a 66 kDa (m_2, right peak) protein. Results are plotted as the average specific binding of ^{3}H-PBCM for two experiments. Specific binding was obtained by subtracting non-specific binding of ^{3}H-PBCM to proteins in the presence of atropine (1 μM) from total binding of ^{3}H-PBCM. Each point represents the amount of radioactivity present in a 3-mm slice of polyacrylamide gel.

content for the m_2 receptor increased surpassing the baseline value by the 24th hour. The decrease in m_2 mRNA content may reflect a secondary mechanism to diminish the number of m_2 receptors present on the plasma membrane. Further work is necessary to complete our understanding of the steps involved in the long-term regulation of muscarinic m_2 receptors, expecially those events that involve gene expression of the m_2 receptor subtype.

In conclusion, these studies show that the desensitization of the neuronal muscarinic m_2 receptor present on cerebellar granule cells in primary cultures involves multiple processes. Short-term processes involve the activation of βARK and the loss of receptors from the plasma membrane, while long-term processes appear to include changes in mRNA levels within the cell. It is still unclear as to whether the change in mRNA content reflects a change in transcription or stabilization of the mRNA itself.

References

1. Hausdorff WP, Caron MG and Lefkowitz RJ (1990) FASEB J. 4: 2881–2889.
2. Chuang DM and Costa E (1979) Proc. Natl. Acad. Sci. U.S.A. 76: 3024–3028.
3. Kerlavage AR, Fraser CM and Venter JC (1987) Trends Pharmacol. Sci. 8: 426–431.

4. Bonner TI, Young AC, Brann MR and Buckley NJ (1988) Neuron 1: 403–410.
5. Fukamauchi F, Hough C and Chuang D-M (1991) J. Neurochem. 56: 716–719.
6. McLeskey SW and Wojcik WJ (1990) Neuropharmacology 29: 861–868.
7. Brooker G, Terasaki WL and Price MG (1976) Science 194: 270–276.
8. Mocchetti I, DeBernardi M, Szekely AM, Alho H, Brooker G and Costa E (1989) Proc. Natl. Acad. Sci. U.S.A. 86: 3891–3895.
9. Dolnick BJ (1990) Biochem. Pharmacol. 40: 671–675.

© 1991 Elsevier Science Publishers B.V. All rights reserved.
Biological Psychiatry, Volume 2. G. Racagni et al., editors.

Transcriptional and post-transcriptional pathways regulate G protein-coupled receptor expression

Sheila Collins, Joachim Altschmied, Jacek Ostrowski, Brenda Lilly, Robert J. Lefkowitz and Marc G. Caron
HHMI, Duke University Medical Center, Durham, NC 27710, U.S.A.

Introduction

The family of G protein-coupled receptors (GPCR) are an important group of transmembrane signalling molecules and the β_2-adrenergic receptor (β_2AR)/adenylyl cyclase system has been studied extensively to explore the mechanisms regulating receptor-mediated hormonal responsiveness. Studies of catecholamine-induced "desensitization" of ARs have shown that β_2AR phosphorylation by the cAMP-dependent protein kinase (PKA) and an adrenergic receptor-specific kinase (βARK) contribute to the rapid uncoupling of the receptor from G_S [1] and adenylyl cyclase. In addition to these rapid and essentially reversible effects upon the receptor protein, expression of the β_2AR and other GPCR is also under complex and dynamic regulation.

Results and Discussion

Short-term exposure to agonists or cAMP analogues increases β_2AR mRNA levels due to direct cAMP-dependent stimulation of β_2AR gene transcription [2]. Similar results have recently been obtained for the luteinizing hormone/chorionic gonadotropin receptor (LH/CGR) [3,4] and the D_1 dopamine receptor (D_1R) [5]. For several genes regulated by cAMP, this transcriptional response has been localized to a distinct DNA sequence in the promoter region termed the cAMP response element (CRE; [6]), which is recognized by a 43 kDa phosphoprotein (CRE binding protein, CREB). CREB's ability to enhance transcription is regulated by phosphorylation [6], thus linking receptor-ligand interactions at the cell surface with regulation of gene expression. We explored the possibility that GPCR are under the control of CREB due to similarities between a sequence in the β_2AR promoter (GTACGTCA) and the CRE consensus (TGACGTCA). By site-directed mutagenesis (Fig. 1), DNAse I footprinting and gel shift analysis with purified CREB protein, the β_2AR element is defined as a CRE [7]. Thus, β_2AR gene expression is stimulated in an autoregulatory manner by the same second-messenger pathway that this receptor activates.

During more prolonged exposure to agonists, down-regulation results in dra-

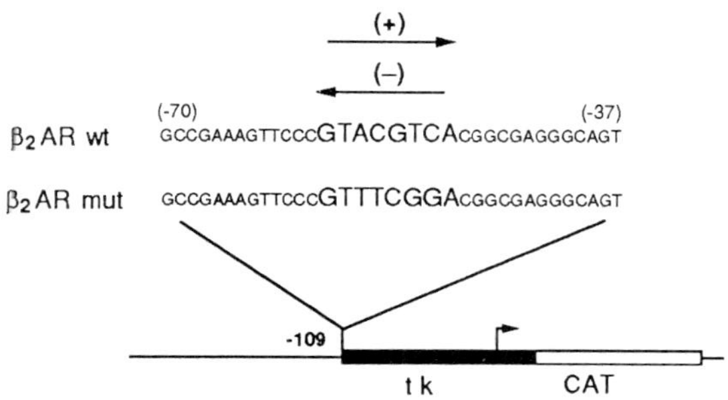

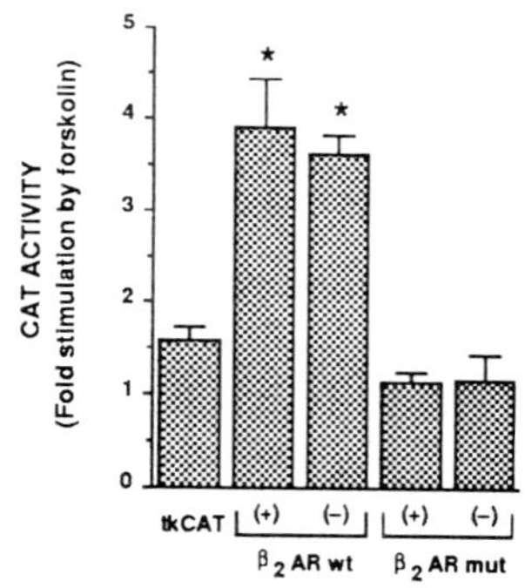

Fig. 1. Wild-type and mutant cAMP-responsive sequences cloned into tkCAT vector (left) and CAT activity of constructs (right).

matic reductions in receptor number and effector stimulation. For the β_2AR, we and others [2,8] have found that down-regulation is accompanied by a 50% reduction in β_2AR mRNA. Recent studies of the LH/CG-R and D_1R show similar decreases in receptor mRNA [4–6]. In each case this effect can be mimicked by cAMP analogues or forskolin. These results implicate PKA in mediating the reduction of receptor mRNAs. At least for the β_2AR, message destabilization has been proposed as one mechanism involved [9]. Changes in mRNA stability have been described for some other cAMP regulated genes [2].

Interestingly, most genes that are transcriptionally regulated by cAMP have relatively short-lived mRNAs (min vs. h, [10]), so that a change in gene transcription can rapidly manifest itself in new steady-state levels of the protein product. In agreement with this paradigm, we find that the half-life of the β_2AR mRNA is 40–60 min in several cell lines ([2]; and manuscript in preparation). In addition, the half-life of the substance P receptor (SPR), another GPCR, has been reported to be 30 min [11]. One feature associated with highly-regulated, unstable mRNAs is a high proportion of A&U residues in their 3' untranslated regions (UTR; [12]). Examples include the proto-oncogenes *c-fos* and *c-myc*. Inspection of the 3' UTRs of the β_2AR, SPR, and several other GPCR indicates a similar high abundance of A&U residues.

We explored the role of this region in conferring mRNA instability by construct

Table 1. Half-life of β-globin and β_2-adrenergic receptor mRNAs

Construct	Glo	β_2AR	β_2Glo	Gβ_2AR
$t_{1/2}$* (h)	$8.42^a \pm 0.43$ (4)	$2.90^b \pm 0.70$ (4)	$9.00^b \pm 0.70$ (2)	$2.70^b \pm 0.60$ (4)

*Data presented as the mean ± S.E.M. for the number of experiments shown (n); mean values with same letter ^{a} or ^{b} are not different, whereas ^{a} differs significantly ^{b} ($P < 0.0001$).

Table 2. Density of β_2AR in cells expressing construct β_2AR and β_2Glo

Construct	β_2AR	β_2Glo
[^{125}I] CYP binding[a]	487 ± 70	4848 ± 588

[a]Data expressed as mean ± S.E.M. of 3 experiments in fmol/mg protein.

ing chimeras between human β_2AR and β-globin, the latter being a highly stable (>10 h) mRNA. Table 1 shows that the β_2AR 3' UTR has a dominant destabilizing effect upon mRNA half-life.

When the density of β_2AR is compared in cells expressing β_2AR or β_2Glo, a 10-fold difference is observed (Table 2), demonstrating the power of 3' UTR sequences to control receptor expression.

These data demonstrate that GPCRs are dynamically regulated by multiple pathways, including autoregulation of receptor gene expression.

References

1. Lefkowitz RJ et al. (1990) Trends Pharmacol. Sci. 11: 190.
2. Collins S et al. (1989) Proc. Natl. Acad. Sci. U.S.A. 86: 4853.
3. Segaloff DL et al. (1990) Mol. Endocrinol. 4: 1856.
4. Wang H et al. (1991) J. Biol. Chem. 266: 780.
5. Silvia C and Collins S (1991) (in preparation).
6. Gonzalez GA et al. (1989) Nature 337: 749.
7. Collins et al. (1990) J. Biol. Chem. 265: 19330.
8. Hadcock JR and Malbon CC (1988) Proc. Natl. Acad. Sci. U.S.A. 85: 5201.
9. Hadcock JR et al. (1989) J. Biol. Chem. 264: 19928.
10. Roesler WJ et al. (1988) J. Biol. Chem. 263: 9063.
11. Ihara H and Nakanishi S (1990) J. Biol. Chem. 265: 22441.
12. Cleveland D and Yen TJ (1989) New Biol. 1: 121.

© 1991 Elsevier Science Publishers B.V. All rights reserved.
Biological Psychiatry, Volume 2. G. Racagni et al., editors.

Structure and function of NGF receptors

M. Chao, M. Barkett, M. Benedetti, M. Berg, M. Einarson, J. Huber, K. Hsu, D. Battleman, J. Lown, H. Yan and B. Hempstead

Department of Cell Biology and Anatomy, Hematology/Oncology Division, Cornell University Medical College, 1300 York Avenue, NY 10021, U.S.A.

Introduction

The many physiological effects of nerve growth factor (NGF) on selective neuronal populations in the central and peripheral nervous systems [1,2] are the result of its initial interaction with cell surface receptors. Our laboratory has emphasized the role of the NGF receptor in mediating the trophic and differentiative effects of NGF. To this end, knowledge of the structure, function, and regulation of the functional NGF receptor complex is essential to understanding the mechanism of action of NGF in responsive cells.

Equilibrium binding of ^{125}I-NGF to cells reveals two distinct affinity states for the NGF receptor [3,4]. In most responsive cells, such as sympathetic neurons or pheochromocytoma PC12 cells, approximately 10–15% of the receptors display high affinity binding with a K_d of 10^{-11} M, with the remainder of the receptors possessing a low affinity K_d of 10^{-9} M. Biological responsiveness to NGF depends upon interactions with the high affinity form. This difference implies that the molecular events that change NGF receptor affinity are involved in the signal transduction mechanism of NGF.

Results

Using affinity crosslinking of ^{125}I-NGF with carbodiimide agents, the major radioiodinated complex isolated from neurons and tumor cell lines has an apparent molecular weight of 100,000 Da. Subtraction of the molecular weight of the β-dimer of NGF from the crosslinked complex gives an apparent molecular weight for the receptor of 75,000 Da ($p75^{NGFR}$). Crosslinking studies have demonstrated that the 75,000 Da receptor species appears in cells with both high and low affinity forms of the NGF receptor [5,6].

The $p75^{NGFR}$ is a glycosylated transmembrane protein, rich in cysteine residues and negatively charged [7,8]. Of 28 cysteine residues in the predicted amino acid sequence, 24 cysteines are found in four canonical repeats in the NH_2-terminal region. Similar cysteine-rich repeats have been detected in the extracellular domains of a number of proteins including TNF receptors, the B-cell activation molecule, CDw40, and the T-cell molecule, OX40 [9].

The existence of this family of diverse cell surface molecules implies that common mechanisms may serve to mediate signal transduction. A highly conserved domain exists in the transmembrane and cytoplasmic domains of the $p75^{NGFR}$. The construction of chimeric receptors between the extracellular domain of the human EGF receptor and the conserved domains of $p75^{NGFR}$ indicates that these intracellular domains of the p75 receptor are required for the initial steps of NGF-mediated neuronal differentiation [10].

A second receptor species of 135,000–158,000 Da can be identified by crosslinking ^{125}I-NGF using the heterobifunctional and relatively lipophilic reagent hydroxysuccinimidyl-4-azido benzoate, HSAB [11,12]. This crosslinked species was observed only on cells which express high as well as low affinity receptors (PC12 cells and neurons). Recent HSAB crosslinking has firmly identified the 158 K_d species as the product of the *trk* proto-oncogene [13] crosslinked to NGF. This receptor protein has been shown to respond to NGF in PC12 cells by autophosphorylation on tyrosine residues [14].

The *trk* proto-oncogene was originally identified as a rearranged oncogene from a colon carcinoma [15], however, normal *trk* expression in vivo was observed only in sensory ganglia [16]. *Trk* encodes a receptor tyrosine kinase that exists as a transmembrane glycoprotein of mw 140,000 ($p140^{prototrk}$) The exquisite developmental expression of *trk* [16] and stimulation of $p140^{prototrk}$ autophosphorylation by NGF [14] lead to the identification of $p140^{prototrk}$ as a receptor for NGF [13]. It is worth noting that the extracellular sequence of $p140^{prototrk}$ differs substantially from the p75 receptor ligand binding domain. In particular, cysteine repeats are absent in $p140^{prototrk}$ and affinity crosslinking agents exist that can crosslink ^{125}I-NGF to $p75^{NGFR}$, but do not crosslink ^{125}I-labeled NGF to $p140^{prototrk}$ [17]. Therefore, different protein-protein interactions are made between NGF and each of the 2 receptors.

Both $p140^{prototrk}$ and $p75^{NGFR}$ bind ^{125}I-NGF with a similar low affinity(10^{-9} M) K_d [6,13]. Reconstitution experiments by membrane fusion and transfection of cloned cDNAs for *trk* and $p75^{NGFR}$ in heterologous cells [6,17] indicate that high affinity NGF binding requires co-expression and binding to both the $p75^{NGFR}$ receptor and the tyrosine kinase *trk* gene product. These studies concerning the two cellular receptors for NGF reveal a new growth factor receptor-mediated mechanism of cellular differentiation, involving $p140^{prototrk}$ and $p75^{NGFR}$.

References

1. Thoenen H and Barde YA (1980) Physiol. Rev. 60: 1284–1335.
2. Levi-Montalcini R (1987) Science 237: 1154–1164.
3. Sutter A, Riopelle RJ, Harris-Warrick RM and Shooter EM (1979) J. Biol. Chem. 254: 5972–5982.
4. Schechter A and Bothwell MA (1981) Cell 24: 867–874.
5. Green SH and Greene LA (1986) J. Biol. Chem. 261: 15316–15326.
6. Hempstead BL, Schleifer LS and Chao MY (1989) Science 243: 373–375.

7. Johnson D, Lanahan A, Buck CR, Sehgal A, Morgan C, Mercer E, Bothwell M and Chao M (1986) Cell 47: 545–554.
8. Radeke MJ, Misko TP, Hsu C, Herzenberg LA and Shooter EM (1987) Nature 325: 593–597.
9. Smith CA, Davis T, Anderson D, Solam L, Beckmann MP, Jerzy R, Dower SK, Cosman SD and Goodwin RG (1990) Science 248: 1019–1023.
10. Yan H, Schlessinger J and Chao MY (1991) Science 252: 561–563.
11. Massague J, Guilette BJ, Czech MP, Morgan CJ and Bradshaw RA (1981) J. Biol. Chem. 256: 9419–9424.
12. Hosang M and Shooter EM (1985) J. Biol. Chem. 260: 655–662.
13. Kaplan DR, Hempstead BL, Martin-Zanca D, Chao MY and Parada LF (1991) Science 252: 554–558.
14. Kaplan DR, Martin-Zanca D and Parada LF (1991) Nature 350: 158–160.
15. Martin-Zanca D, Hughes SH and Barbacid M (1986) Nature 319: 743–748.
16. Martin-Zanca D, Barbacid M and Parada LF (1990) Genes Dev. 4: 683–694.
17. Hempstead BL, Martin-Zanca D, Kaplan DR, Parada LF and Chao MY (1991) Nature 350: 678–683.

© 1991 Elsevier Science Publishers B.V. All rights reserved.
Biological Psychiatry, Volume 2. G. Racagni et al., editors.

Cloning and characterization of dopaminergic receptors

Pierre Falardeau[1,2], Mario Tiberi[1], Keith Jarvie[1], Chris Silvia[1], Jay Gingrich[1], Robert T. Fremeau[1], Michael D. Bates[1] and Marc G. Caron[1]

[1]*Department of Cell Biology, Duke University Medical Center, Durham, NC, 27710, U.S.A.; and* [2]*Génétique Moléculaire and School of Pharmacy, CHUL, Laval University, Ste-Foy, Quebec G1V 4G2, Canada*

Introduction

No longer than 5 years ago, we could explain pharmacologically and biochemically most of the dopaminergic signalling by the existence of only 2 different classes of dopaminergic receptors, D_1 and D_2. D_1 dopamine receptors were coupled to the stimulation of adenylyl cyclase and D_2 receptors were either linked or not linked to the inhibition of adenylyl cyclase. Since the molecular cloning of the first dopaminergic receptor by Civelli's group in 1988 [1], we started to understand better the signalling of the dopaminergic transmission. Two isoforms of D_2 dopamine receptors were cloned and shown to differ only by the insertion of an additional 29 amino acids in the third cytoplasmic loop [1–3]. These 2 receptors display the same pharmacological and signalling properties. They are both coupled to the inhibition of adenylyl cyclase and to the opening of the potassium channel via a G protein. Moreover, the 2 isoforms of D_2 receptors are found in both pre- and postsynaptic neurons. Last year, 2 other receptors were cloned: a dopamine receptor termed D_3 and a D_1 dopamine receptor. Although D_3 receptor has a higher structural and pharmacological homology to D_2 receptors, the distribution of its mRNA and its chromosomal localization are clearly different [4]. In contrast with the D_2-like receptors, the cloned D_1 receptor is intronless and is coupled in a positive manner to adenylyl cyclase (AC) through a G protein but not to the stimulation of phosphatidylinositol (PI) metabolism [5]. Moreover, the tissue distribution of D_1 dopamine receptor mRNA included most importantly the caudate with lower levels of message found in cortex, hippocampus and cerebellum.

Several observations are consistent with the idea that subtypes of D_1 receptors may exist [6]. For example, it has been demonstrated that injection of rat striatal mRNA into Xenopus oocytes directs the expression of a D_1 dopamine receptor coupled to the activation of phospholipase C and (PI) metabolism, whereas the cloned D_1 receptors do not couple to that effector. In addition, previous studies have documented the presence of D_1 receptors in the kidney coupled to either AC or phospholipase C, although no message for the cloned D_1 receptor was found in kidney [5]. Here, we describe the molecular cloning of a new D_1 dopamine receptor that we termed D_{1B} as opposed to D_{1A} for the previously cloned D dopamine receptor.

Methods and Results

Degenerate primers corresponding to the 5th and 6th transmembrane (TM) regions of the human D_{1A} were used in the polymerase chain reaction (PCR) to amplify human genomic DNA. PCR products were subcloned into the sequencing vector pBluescript II SK+ (Stratagene), isolated, and sequenced. A product (V-15), showing a significant homology with the region corresponding to the 3rd intracellular loop of the human D_{1A} receptor, was used to screen a rat genomic library. A 4.2 Kb EcoRI fragment was isolated, subcloned, and sequenced from one clone (DR5). It displayed an open reading frame of 1425 bp coding for a protein of 475 amino acids with a calculated molecular weight of 52834 Da. This protein possesses several features characteristic of G protein-coupled receptors. Seven putative TM regions which has 80% identity with D_{1A} receptor, whereas the amino and carboxy termini are the most divergent regions (< 20% identity). Furthermore, an aspartate residue (Asp 118) in the 3rd TM region and 2 serine residues (Ser 224 and 227) in the 5th TM region are conserved in every cloned catecholamine receptor and have been shown to interact with the amino and catechol hydroxyl groups of catecholamines respectively [7]. Putative glycosylation sites are found in the extracellular portion of the receptor (Asn 7 and 194). A cysteine residue (Cys 370) found in the carboxy tail, near the 7th TM, is also conserved in several G protein-coupled receptors and has been shown to be palmitoylated in the β_2 adrenergic and rhodopsin receptors [8].

The 4.2 Kb EcoRI fragment was subcloned into an expression vector (pCMV5) and transiently transfected in Cos-7 cells by the DEAE-dextran sulfate procedure. Ligand binding studies on membranes of the transfected cells showed that [^{125}I] SCH 23982 bound specifically to the expressed receptor with a dissociation constant (K_d) of 0.41 ± 0.01 nM. Table 1 summarizes the K_d values of dopaminergic agonists and antagonists for the binding of [^{125}I] SCH 23982 for the new D_1 receptor (D_{1B}) compared to the previously cloned D_1 receptor (D_{1A}). Both receptors showed a similar pharmacological profile and potency for agonists and antagonists when transfected into a human embryonic kidney cells (293), the cloned receptor is positively coupled to AC but not to phospholipase C. Dopamine and the selective agonist fenoldopam stimulated AC activity by 2–3-fold. This effect is blocked by the D_1 selective antagonist SCH 23990, but not by adrenergic or D_2 selective antagonists.

Using fluorescent in situ hybridization, we determined the chromosomal localization of the human homologue of this novel receptor. Thus, only the chromosome 4 (4p16) location was specifically labelled. The tissue distribution of the rat D_{1B} receptor mRNA was examined by PCR analysis. A specific 339 bp fragment was amplified using primers in the 3' untranslated area of the gene for D_{1B} receptor and total mRNA of different nuclei of the brain and peripheral tissues. The most prominent signals were observed in hippocampus and hypothalamus, weak signals being present in striatum and cerebellum. No detectable signal was observed in frontal cortex, kidney, liver and heart. Northern blot analysis of hippocampal

Table 1. Equilibrium dissociation constant values (K_d) of dopaminergic compounds for [^{125}I]-SCH 23982 binding in Cos-7 cell membranes

	Human D_{1A} receptor (nM)	Rat D_{1B} receptor (nM)	D_{1B}/D_{1A}
Antagonists			
SCH 23390	0.17	0.11	0.6
Cis-Piflutixol	0.65	2	3.1
(+) Butaclamol	1	6	6.0
Cis-Flupentixol	4	7	1.8
SCH 23388	15	10	0.7
Haloperidol	24	35	1.5
Fluperlapine	75	510	6.8
Spiperone	450	2600	5.8
Agonists			
Fenoldopam	17	11	0.6
SKF 38393	135	100	0.7
Apomorphine	360	240	0.7
NPA	1540	1050	0.7
Dopamine	12000	3900	0.3

Binding parameters shown are the result of two independent experiments conducted in triplicate determination. For each drug, the two competition curves were co-analysed and fitted to a one site model.

polyA$^+$ RNA revealed a hybribizing band at 3.0 Kb. In situ hybridization of rat brain revealed a more precise distribution of the message for D_{1B} receptor. Prominent labelling was found in the lateral mammillary nuclei, the anterior pretectal nuclei and in several layers of the hippocampus. In contrast, little or no message was detected in striatum, nucleus accumbens and olfactory tubercle, regions in which D_{1A} is abundant. Interestingly, the mammillary bodies, anterior pretectal nuclei, and hippocampus which express high levels of message for D_{1B}, have been shown to contain very low levels of receptor binding [9]. These observations raise the possibility that this receptor is synthesized in cell bodies where the mRNA is found and transported to nerve terminals elsewhere in the brain.

Conclusion

From our results, we conclude that we have cloned a novel D_1 dopamine receptor which stimulates AC and has a similar pharmacology and signalling system to the previously described D_1 dopamine receptor. For now, the most interesting aspect of this receptor gene is its highly restricted expression when compared to the D_{1A} receptor gene. This particular expression pattern suggests that this receptor might mediate a specific subset of dopaminergic functions. In particular, the presence of mRNA in the anterior pretectal area suggests a possible role of this receptor in the visual processes. Moreover, its specific expression in the limbic nuclei, suggests a role for the D_{1B} receptor in the physiology of the limbic system. The testing of drugs that will discriminate between these different subtypes of dopamine receptors will help us to better understand the implication of each of those receptors in the physiology of the dopaminergic transmission.

References

1. Bunzow JR et al. (1988) Nature 336: 783.
2. Giros B, Sokolof P, Martres MP, Riou JF, Emorine LJ and Schwartz JC (1989) Nature 342: 923.
3. Dearry A, Falardeau P, Shores C, and Caron MG (1991) Cell. Mol. Neurobiol. (in press).
4. Sokolof P, Giros B, Martres MP, Bouthenet ML and Schwartz JC (1990) Nature 347: 146.
5. Dearry A, Gingrich JA, Falardeau P, Fremeau RT, Bates MD and Caron MG (1990) Nature 347: 72.
6. Andersen PH, Gingrich JA, Bates MD, Dearry A, Falardeau P, Senogles SE and Caron MG (1990) Trends Pharmacol. Sci. 11: 231.
7. Dixon R et al. (1987) Nature 326: 73.
8. O'Dowd BF, Hnatovich M, Caron MG, Lefkowitz RJ and Bouvier M (1989) J. Biol. Chem. 264: 7564.
9. Schofield P, Shivers B and Seeburg P (1990) Trends Neurosci. 13: 8.

© 1991 Elsevier Science Publishers B.V. All rights reserved.
Biological Psychiatry, Volume 2. G. Racagni et al., editors.

The dopamine D_3 receptor: A novel target for neuroleptics

J.C. Schwartz[1], P. Sokoloff[1], B. Giros[1], M.P. Martres[1], M. Andrieux[1], R. Besancon[1] and M.L. Bouthenet[2]

[1]*Unité de Neurobiologie et Pharmacologie (U.109) de l'INSERM, Centre Paul Broca, 2ter rue d'Alésia, 75014 Paris; and* [2]*Laboratoire de Physiologie, Faculté de Pharmacie, Université René Descartes, Paris, France*

We have repeatedly raised the idea that dopamine (DA) interacts with more than 2 receptor subtypes [1]. However, the dual classification of DA receptors (D_1 and D_2) was, until recently, widely accepted and neuroleptics were believed to derive their antipsychotic activity from selective interaction with D_2 receptors.

The situation has started to be modified with the cloning of the cDNA encoding the D_2 receptor and the identification in several laboratories of 2 splice products of the corresponding gene. These 2 isoforms, however, display similar pharmacology.

More recently we have cloned in rats [2] and humans [3] a novel DA receptor, the D_3 receptor, whose localization and pharmacology both suggest that it may constitute an important target for antipsychotics.

Molecular structure of the rat and human D_3 receptors

The D_3 receptor sequence contains 7 putative transmembrane domains (TMs) which indicate its belonging to the superfamily of G protein-coupled receptors. It comprises 446 amino acid residues in the rat but only 400 residues in human. The D_3 receptor resembles the D_2 receptor by: a) the occurrence of several exons; and b) the high amino acid sequence homology at the level of the TMs where dopaminergic ligands presumably bind.

The D_3 receptor is subject to the process of alternative splicing which occurs at the level of TM_3 and TM_5. However no dopaminergic binding activity is associated with these shorter variants [4].

The human D_3 receptor gene was assigned to the long arm of chromosome 3, i.e. in 3q13.3 [3,5] which also contains the genes of cholecystokinin, enkephalinase and rhodopsin.

Anatomical distribution of D_3 receptor mRNA in rat brain

The distribution of D_3 receptor gene transcripts markedly differs from those of the D_2 receptor gene. Only a weak hybridization signal was detected in the striatum, which contains the highest densities of D_2 receptor mRNA. No signal was detected in the pituitary. By contrast, the D_3 receptor mRNA is highly expressed in the "limbic or ventral striatum" i.e. olfactory tubercle – island of Calleja complex, bed nucleus of stria terminalis and nucleus accumbens, a territory receiving afferents from the prefrontal or allocortex and amygdala and its major DA inputs from the A10 cell group in the ventral tegmental area. It projects, to the prefrontal cortex via the ventral pallidum and mediodorsal thalamic nucleus.

D_2 receptor mRNA is also highly expressed in these limbic areas but there is *no strict overlap* with D_3 receptor mRNA distribution. This suggests a major participation of postsynaptic D_3 receptors in dopaminergic transmissions in limbic areas known to be associated with cognitive, emotional and endocrine functions.

The D_3 receptor as a second autoreceptor

After degeneration induced by local injection of 6-OHDA, we found a marked ipsilateral reduction of the PCR-generated signal for both the D_2 and D_3 receptors in both the substantia nigra and the ventral tegmental area [2]. This suggests that both play the role of autoreceptors. Such a role for the D_3 receptor is consistent with its high apparent affinity for dopamine and its pharmacological profile (see below).

Many distinct functions were previously attributed to dopamine autoreceptors, i.e. inhibition of impulse flow, dopamine synthesis and release at either nerve terminals or dendrites and co-transmitter release. D_2 and D_3 autoreceptors might variously participate in all these actions and in various brain areas. Finally, the question as to whether a single DA neuron expresses both D_2 and D_3 receptors remains to be answered.

Pharmacology and signalling system of the D_3 receptor

When expressed in CHO cells, human D_2 and D_3 receptors were both labeled by $[^{125}I]$-iodosulpride with K_d values of 0.5 and 1.3 nM, allowing their pharmacology to be compared. Dopamine was 24 times more potent at D_2 than at D_3 receptors in the absence of added guanylnucleotide and the ratio became $\approx$60 in the presence of Gpp(NH)p, a difference reflecting the larger shift at the D_2 receptor. Whereas apomorphine was equipotent at the 2 receptors, most other DA agonists, particularly those considered as "autoreceptor-selective", e.g. TL 99 or quinpirole, were much more potent at D_3 than at D_2 receptors.

Antipsychotics generally displayed nanomolar potency at the D_3 receptor but 2 main groups of compounds could be distinguished: those which were up to 5 times more potent at D_2 than at D_3 receptors, e.g. haloperidol and prochlorperazine and those which were less than twice as potent, e.g. pimozide, pipotiazine, carpipramine or amisulpride. The latters appear to correspond to "atypical" antipsychotics, displaying less extrapyramidal side-effects and more disinhibitory properties than the former. This may suggest that the differential recognition of D_2 and D_3 receptors could partly account for the clinical profile of antipsychotics.

The only antagonists that were more potent at D_3 than at D_2 receptors were AJ 76 and UH 232, designated by A. Carlsson and his colleagues as "autoreceptor-selective" drugs. Their preferential recognition by D_3 receptors might account for their previously reported original behavioural properties.

Activation of the human or rat D_3 receptor in CHO cells resulted only in a weak inhibition of the forskolin-stimulated formation of cyclic AMP: it was maximally 30–40% and inconstant, which contrasts with the robust and reproducible inhibition mediated by D_2-receptors also expressed in CHO cells. This suggests that D_2 and D_3 receptors couple to distinct G proteins.

In conclusion, the D_3 receptor appears to be an important target for antipsychotics in the limbic system but the exact delineation of its functional role requires development and testing of selective D_3 antagonists in psychiatry. These data should then be compared to those obtained for drugs interacting with the various other DA receptor subtypes.

References

1. Schwartz JC, Delandre M, Martres MP, Sokoloff P, Protais P, Vasse M, Costentin J, Laibe P, Wermuth CG, Gulat C and Lafitte A (1984) In: Usdin E, Carlsson A, Dahlstrom A and Engel J (eds.) Catecholamines: Neuropharmacology and Central Nervous System – Theoretical Aspects. Alan R. Liss, New York, pp. 59–72.
2. Sokoloff P, Giros B, Martres MP, Bouthenet ML and Schwartz JC (1990) Nature 347: 146–151.
3. Giros B, Martres MP, Sokoloff P and Schwartz JC (1990) C.R. Acad. Sci. (Paris) 311: 501–508.
4. Giros B, Martres MP, Pilon C, Sokoloff P and Schwartz JC (1991) Biochem. Biophys. Res. Commun. (in press).
5. Le Coniat M, Hillion J, Sokoloff P, Martres MP, Giros B, Pilon C, Schwartz JC and Berger R (1991) Hum. Genet. (in press).

© 1991 Elsevier Science Publishers B.V. All rights reserved.
Biological Psychiatry, Volume 2. G. Racagni et al., editors.

Regulation of D_2 dopamine receptor mRNA following denervation or chronic haloperidol treatment

Ian Creese and Shouxi Xu

Center for Molecular and Behavioral Neuroscience, Rutgers, The State University of New Jersey, Newark, NJ 07102, U.S.A.

Introduction

D_2 dopamine (DA) receptors in rat striatum are up-regulated by a number of manipulations. Denervation of postsynaptic striatal D_2 receptors, chronic treatment with D_2 receptor antagonists or the DA depleter, reserpine, produce reversible increases in receptor density with no change in their affinity [1]. Understanding the molecular mechanisms involved in this regulation has been recently facilitated by the cloning of the D_2 receptor [2]. D_2 receptor mRNA has 2 forms, long and short, produced by differential splicing [3–5]. The long form contains an additional 87 bases which encode 29 amino acid residues in the third intracellular loop between transmembrane regions 5 and 6. Here, we present the response of D_2 receptor mRNA levels compared with receptor density changes following treatments with the D_2 receptor antagonist, haloperidol, or lesion of the nigro-striatal pathway.

Methods

Treatments

Chronic antagonist treatments. Male Sprague-Dawley rats were injected s.c. with 0.5 mg/kg/day haloperidol or vehicle and sacrificed 2 h after a single drug injection and the day following 7, 14, or 21 daily injections and 21 daily injections plus 3 days withdrawal. Striata were dissected and stored at −70°C. One striatum from each rat was used for mRNA quantification and the other for D_2 receptor binding.

Denervation. Rats were injected stereotaxically with 6-OHDA HCl (8 μg in 4 μl) into the right substantia nigra. Two weeks later the efficacy of the lesion was assessed by examining apomorphine-induced contralateral rotations. The rats were sacrificed 1 week later.

Molecular analyses

D_2 receptor binding. Striata were homogenized in 50 volumes (w/v) of ice-cold 50

mM Tris-HCl (pH 7.7 at 25°C) and washed by centrifugation twice. Duplicate tubes containing striatal membranes (1.5–2 mg wet wt), 0.4 nM [^{3}H]spiperone in an assay buffer of 50 mM Tris-HCl, 5 mM $MgSO_4$, 0.5 mM EDTA (pH 7.4 at 37°C), 40 nM ketanserin to block 5-HT_2 receptors, ± 1 μM cis-flupentixol to define nonspecific binding, were incubated for 30 min at 37°C. Membranes were filtered and washed under vacuum and trapped radioactivity counted by liquid scintillation spectrometry.

Probes. Three 48-base oligodeoxynucleotide probes (gift from NEN Research products) were generated complementary to regions of the rat D_2 receptor mRNA which encode the N-terminal, the third cytoplasmic loop and the C-terminal. Their sequences were complementary to bases 4–51, 766–813 and 901–948. The sequence of a 48-base oligodeoxynucleotide probe for the mRNA complementary to the insert sequence in the long form of the D_2 receptors was derived from the insert amino acids 242–257 (gift from David R. Sibley). A cDNA probe to β-actin mRNA was used to correct for RNA preparation errors.

Northern blot analyses. RNA was prepared by homogenization of striata in 1.5 ml 4 M guanidine thiocyanate buffer (GIT), extracted with equal amount of phenol/chloroform and centrifuged at 10,000 × g (20 min at 4°C). The aqueous phase was collected, extracted with phenol/chloroform and recentrifuged. Five to 8 μg of RNA denatured in formaldehyde was fractionated by electrophoresis on 1% agarose gel containing 2% formaldehyde and 20 mM MOPS and then transferred to nylon membranes which were baked at 80°C for 2 h. The membranes were prehybridized in 6 × SSC, 5 × Derhardt's solution, 50% formamide, 100 μg/ml denatured salmon sperm DNA, 100 μg tRNA/ml and 0.1% SDS at 42°C for 2–4 h and then hybridized at 42°C overnight in 6 × SSC, 4 × Denhardt's solution, 50% formamide, 100 μg DNA/ml and 1% SDS with oligodeoxynucleotide probes (10^7 dpm/ml hybridization mixture), end-labelled with [α–^{32}P]dATP. The membranes were washed in 2 × SSC, 0.1% SDS and 1 × SSC, 0.1% SDS at room temperature for 15 min, respectively. Finally, they were washed in 0.5 × SSC, 0.1% SDS at 55°C for at least 15 min and then exposed to Kodak XAR-2 film with 2 intensifying screens at –70°6 for 4–20 h in order to ensure that all comparisons were made within the linear sensitivity range of the film. The membranes were rehybridized for β-actin measurement. The optical densities of the bands were measured with the Drexel University Microcomputer Image Analysis System.

Results and Discussion

Northern blot analyses revealed that the chronic haloperidol treatment had no significant effect on the levels of D_2 and receptor mRNA (total), or D_2 receptor mRNA (long form) in rat striatum at any time point, although there were significant up-regulations (+16–30%) of D_2 receptor densities from day 7–21 (df = 5,18;

$P < 0.001$). In contrast, 21 days following the 6-OHDA lesion of the nigro-striatal pathway, the levels of striatal D_2 receptor mRNA (total) and D_2 receptor mRNA (long form) were increased by 52.4% and 54% (df = 1,12; $P < 0.02$), with striatal D_2 receptors significantly increased by 38.2% (df = 1,8; $P < 0.001$).

We had previously found that a 21-day treatment with selective D_2 receptor antagonists had no effect on rat striatal D_2 receptor mRNA levels [6], suggesting that chronic D_2 receptor blockade may not influence striatal D_2 receptor gene transcription, in spite of a receptor up-regulation. However, a 5-day administration with haloperidol was reported to lead to a significant increase in rat neurointermediate pituitary lobe D_2 receptor mRNA [7]. This may indicate a tissue-specific difference in gene regulation, reflect the different treatment schedule or differences in the regulation of the short and long forms of D_2 receptor mRNAs. The present study supports the first hypothesis since no increase in either form of D_2 receptor mRNA was seen, even at the shorter treatment periods, whether or not a receptor increase had occurred. In contrast, 21 days following the 6-OHDA lesion of the nigro-striatal pathway, D_2 receptors and both D_2 receptor mRNA forms were significantly increased.

These findings suggest that the D_2 receptor increase following denervation is the result of an increase in D_2 receptor gene transcription, while different molecular mechanisms must be responsible for receptor up-regulation following chronic haloperidol treatment. Previous research studying DA receptor turnover rates with EEDQ also suggested that while denervation increased receptor production rate, receptor blockade *decreased* receptor production and, to an even greater extent, receptor degradation [9]. Chronic receptor blockade by antagonists, denervation or depletion of DA by reserpine have been considered to be functionally equivalent, leading to an increase in D_2 receptor density and behavioural supersensitivity to DA agonists. These present studies demonstrate that the lack of stimulation of a receptor by its natural ligand may not be biochemically equivalent, at the level of gene regulation, to chronic receptor blockade with an antagonist.

Acknowledgements

Supported by ADAMHA DA 04612, MN 44211 "Neuroscience Center for Research in Schizophrenia" and RSA MH 00316. Part of this research will appear in the conference proceedings of "Dopamine 90", XIth International Conference of Pharmacology.

References

1. Creese I, Sibley DR, Hamblin MW and Leff SE (1983) Ann. Rev. Neurosci. 6: 43.
2. Bunzow JR, Van Tol HHM, Grandy DK, Albert P, Salon J, Christie M, Machida CA, Neve KA and Civelli O (1988) Nature 336: 783.

3. Monsma FJ, McVittie LD, Gerfen CR, Mahan LC and Sibley DR (1989) Nature 342: 926.
4. Giros B, Sokoloff P, Martres MP, Riou JF, Emorine LJ and Schwartz JC (1989) Nature 342: 923.
5. Grandy DK, Marchionni MA, Makam H, Stofko RE, Alfano M, Frothingham L, Fischer JB, Burke-Howie KJ, Bunzow JR, Server AC and Civelli O (1989) Proc. Natl. Acad. Sci. U.S.A. 86: 9762.
6. Van Tol HHM, Riva M, Civelli O and Creese I (1990) Neurosci. Lett. 111: 303.
7. Autelitano DJ, Snyder L, Sealfon SC and Roberts JL (1989) Mol. Cell Endocrinol. 67: 101.

© 1991 Elsevier Science Publishers B.V. All rights reserved.
Biological Psychiatry, Volume 2. G. Racagni et al., editors.

Pharmacological basis for dopamine D_2 receptor diversity

M. Memo, A. Valerio, M. Pizzi, C. Missale, M.O. Carruba and P.F. Spano

Department of Biomedical Sciences and Biotechnology, Section of Pharmacology, Toxicology and Experimental Therapeutics, University of Brescia, Via Valsabbina 19, 25124 Brescia, Italy

Several lines of evidence are consistent with the existence of multiple signal processing pathways activated by dopamine (DA) through D_2 receptor stimulation [1–3]. The isolation of distinct cDNAs encoding proteins that share binding profiles indicative of D_2 receptors, clearly indicates multiple forms of D_2 receptors [4]. Based on functional and pharmacological studies, we have proposed the existence of 2 distinct subtypes of dopamine D_2 receptors, which differ in their structure, G protein coupling, effector systems and drug sensitivity in rat lactotroph cells. The former, named D_{2A} receptor, appears to be associated to calcium-dependent K^+ channels via inhibition of adenylate cyclase activity; the latter, D_{2B} receptor, operates the activation of voltage-dependent K^+ channels [5]. We have also observed that the dopamine agonist BHT 920 [6] by activating mammotroph D_2 receptors, selectively stimulates voltage-dependent K^+ fluxes without modifying adenylate cyclase activity [7], thus representing a possible pharmacological tool for studying dopamine D_{2B} receptor subtype.

Although most of the evidence on dopamine receptors was obtained in pituitary cells, the presence of multiple transduction mechanisms for D_2 receptors was also proposed in brain [8–10]. We conducted studies to assess the presence of DA-activated K^+ channels in rat striatum and to analyze the selectivity of BHT 920 for possible cerebral subtypes of DA D_2 receptors. We found that BHT 920, contrary to other D_2 receptor agonists like bromocriptine, failed to inhibit forskolin-

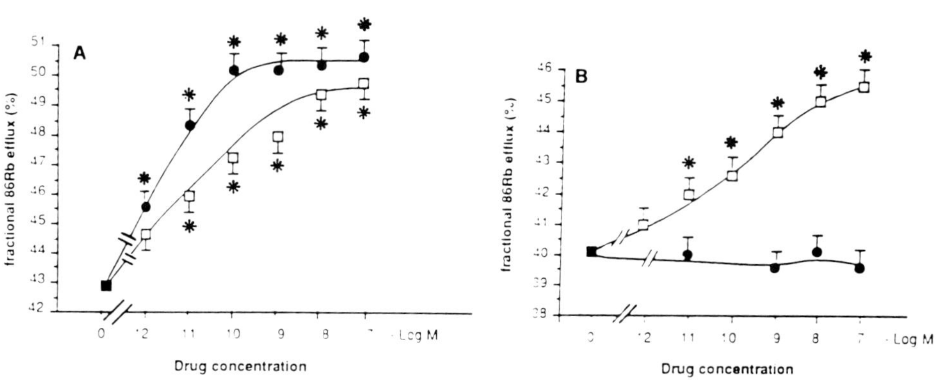

Fig. 1. Effects of quinpirole (❏) and BHT 920 (●) on voltage-dependent (A) and calcium-activated (B) K^+ channel activity. ■, no drug. Points represent means ± S.E.M. for 3 experiments run in triplicate. $*P < 0.01$ vs. no drug values.

stimulated cyclic AMP formation in striatal homogenates. By measuring $^{86}Rb^+$ efflux as an index of K^+ channel activity in a preparation of presynaptic nerve terminals from rat striatum, we showed that the D_2 agonist quinpirole significantly activated both voltage-dependent and calcium-dependent (cyclic AMP-sensitive) K^+ channels. In contrast, BHT 920 induced a significant stimulation of the voltage-regulated K^+ fluxes and was completely ineffective in modifying the calcium-activated K^+ channel activity (Fig. 1).

Our results indicate that BHT 920 selectively stimulates a subtype of D_2 receptors uncoupled to adenylate cyclase mojety and linked to voltage-dependent K^+ channels, thus providing a useful pharmacological tool for studying the D_{2B} receptor subtype in the central nervous system. Moreover, our data suggest that the multiple molecular form of D_2 receptors may share different pharmacological and functional profiles. The preferential action of putative new drugs on a specific subtype of DA D_2 receptors may disclose new clinical applications in psychiatric disorders including depression and related diseases.

References

1. Memo M, Castelletti L, Missale C, Valerio A, Carruba MO and Spano PF (1986) J. Neurochem. 47: 1689–1695.
2. Memo M, Missale C, Carruba MO and Spano PF (1986) J. Neural Transm. 22 (Suppl.): 19–32.
3. Vallar L and Meldolesi J (1989) Trends Pharmacol. Sci. 10: 74–77.
4. Strange PG (1991) Trends Neurosci. 14(2): 43–45.
5. Castelletti L, Memo M, Missale C, Spano PF and Valerio A (1989) J. Physiol. 410: 251–265.
6. Anden NE, Nilson H, Ross E and Thornstrom U (1983) Acta Pharmacol. Toxicol. 52: 51–56.
7. Pizzi M, Valerio A, Benarese M, Missale C, Carruba MO, Memo M and Spano PF (1990) Mol. Neuropharmacol. 1: 37–42.
8. Memo M, Missale C, Carruba MO and Spano PF (1986) Neurosci. Lett. 71: 192–196.
9. Freedman JE and Weight FF (1988) Proc. Natl. Acad. Sci. U.S.A. 85: 3618–3622.
10. Bowyer J and Weiner N (1989) J. Pharmacol. Exp. Ther. 248: 514–520.

© 1991 Elsevier Science Publishers B.V. All rights reserved.
Biological Psychiatry, Volume 2. G. Racagni et al., editors.

New trends in the molecular biology and pharmacology of dopaminergic transmission

Arvid Carlsson, Nicholas Waters, Kjell Svensson and Lena Löfberg
Department of Pharmacology, University of Göteborg, P.O. Box 33031, S-400 33 Göteborg, Sweden

Introduction

The recent development in receptor cloning has reinforced the notion derived from behavioral and biochemical pharmacology that the heterogeneity of dopamine receptors extends far beyond the currently recognized D_1/D_2 dichotomy. About a year ago we learned about the D_3 subtype [1] and more recently reports on the D_4 subtype are forthcoming. Our group immediately became interested in the D_3 subtype, since 2 compounds developed by us, namely (+)-AJ76 and (+)-UH232, were reported to be the only antagonists with a distinct 3- to 4-fold preference for D_3 in relation to D_2. In the present paper we will discuss some recent observations on the actions of these compounds, which show an unusual pharmacological profile. Moreover, we will present evidence that these 2 compounds differ significantly from each other. Thus it seems unlikely that a preference for the D_3 subtype can entirely explain our data.

(+)-AJ76 and (+)-UH232: Preferential dopamine autoreceptor antagonists

These 2 agents are mild behavioral stimulants and their stimulating action depends almost entirely on the integrity of the dopaminergic system. Like classical neuroleptics they stimulate the firing of dopaminergic neurons as well as the synthesis, release and metabolism of dopamine. This effect is apparently due to blockade of dopaminergic autoreceptors, which are now known to belong to both the D_2 and the D_3 subtypes. These agents are also capable of blocking postsynaptic dopamine receptors, as indicated by blockade of apomorphine and amphetamine stimulation. The balance between pre- and postsynaptic receptor blockade appears to be dependent on the baseline activity, as indicated by behavioral data. A low behavioral baseline, induced by habituation to the environment favors a stimulatory response, whereas behavioral inhibition can be seen at a high baseline activity, induced, for example, by dopaminergic agonists [2].

Microdialysis data on dopamine release

Microdialysis from the nucleus accumbens of unanesthetized rats shows that

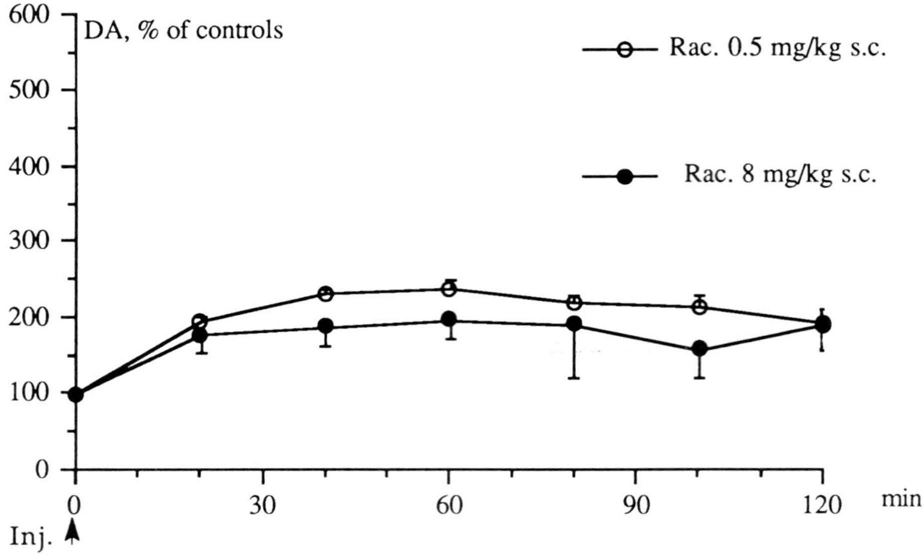

Fig. 1. Effect of raclopride, 0.5 or 8 mg/kg s.c. on the efflux of dopamine from rat nucleus accumbens.

(+)-UH232 has a dose-response curve for the efflux of dopamine similar to those of raclopride (Fig. 1) and classical neuroleptics, with a maximal increase of up to 200%. However, the maximal increase in dopamine efflux, induced by (+)-AJ76 is much higher, i.e. about 300–400%. In both cases the effect is calcium-dependent. If the dopamine D_2 antagonist raclopride is given in a dose of 0.5 mg/kg s.c., this results in a doubling of the dopamine efflux. If then (+)-AJ76 is superimposed in a dose of 50 μmol/kg s.c., a further increase in dopamine efflux is seen, such as to reach the same levels as would be attained by (+)-AJ76 alone (Fig. 2). However, if the dose of raclopride is elevated to 8 mg/kg, it can prevent the increase induced by (+)-AJ76, so that the level of dopamine efflux remains at 200% of control. Haloperidol has also been tried and seems to be able to antagonize the excessive rise of dopamine induced by (+)-AJ76, although perhaps not as completely as raclopride.

Thus it would appear that one dopamine receptor antagonist, i.e. (+)-AJ76, is capable of inducing a greater efflux of dopamine than classical neuroleptics and that a classical neuroleptic can prevent the additional efflux induced by (+)-AJ76. This remarkable result may tentatively be explained as follows. (+)-AJ76 occupies the same dopamine receptor site as e.g. raclopride, as indicated by the ability of the latter agent to block the additional effect of the former agent. To account for the ability of one antagonist to block the action of another antagonist, we propose that (+)-AJ76 acts like an inverse agonist, capable of an opposite action to that of an agonist on e.g. an ion channel. Thus, if dopamine retards the passage of an ion through a channel, this action can be blocked by a classical neuroleptic, which has

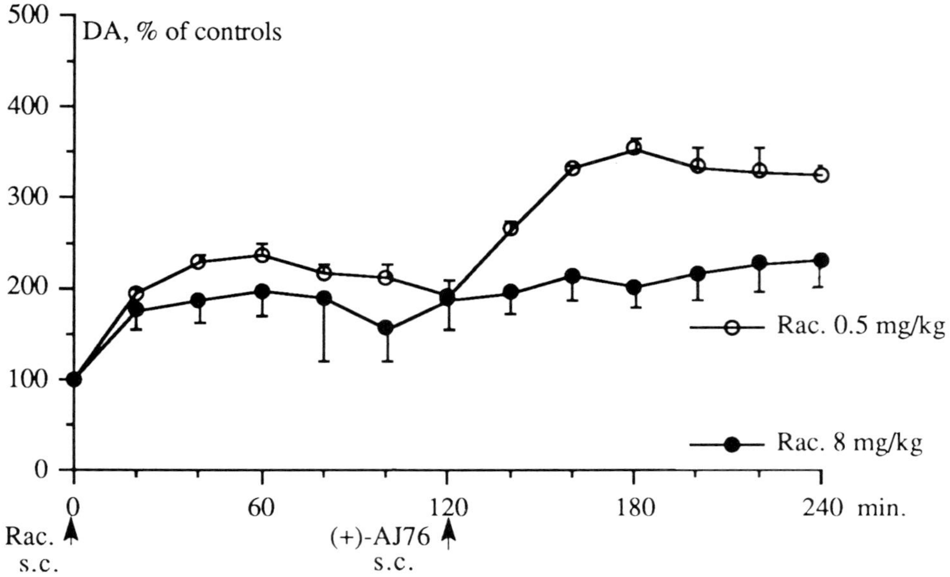

Fig. 2. Blockade by 8 but not by 0.5 mg/kg raclopride of the (+)-AJ76-induced increase in dopamine efflux from rat nucleus accumbens.

no effect on the ion channel other than being able to block the action of an agonist. (+)-AJ76, on the other hand, when occupying the same site in the ion channel not only blocks the action of dopamine but is, in addition, capable of enhancing the passage of ions through the channel, resulting in excessive release of neurotransmitter.

Needless to say, further work is needed to confirm or reject this hypothesis. In any event, it seems to emphasize the heterogeneity of the dopamine receptor family. For example, the difference in dopamine efflux described here does not seem to have a counterpart when the stimulation of dopamine synthesis is measured. Thus the autoreceptors controlling dopamine synthesis and release may be different.

References

1. Sokoloff P, Giros B, Martres M-P, Bouthenet M-L and Schwartz J-C (1990) Nature 347: 146–151.
2. Svensson K (1986) Dopamine Autoreceptor Antagonists. A New Class of Central Stimulants. Thesis, University of Göteborg, Sweden, pp. 1–6.

© 1991 Elsevier Science Publishers B.V. All rights reserved.
Biological Psychiatry, Volume 2. G. Racagni et al., editors.

The role of dopaminergic mechanisms in antidepressant action

J. John Mann and Shitij Kapur
Western Psychiatric Institute and Clinic, 3811 O'Hara Street, Pittsburgh, PA 15213, U.S.A.

The evidence available from animal and human experiments implicating dopamine in depression, the antidepressant effect of dopaminergic agents and the dopaminergic effects common to antidepressant agents are reviewed.

Role of dopamine in depression

Animal models of depression

"Learned helplessness" is an animal model of depression where animals exposed to inescapable stressors exhibit decreases in performance and activity. Brain studies reveal dopamine depletion. Prior treatment with a dopamine agonist prevented, and prior treatment with dopamine antagonists worsened this state. Learned helplessness can be reversed by treatment with antidepressant medications and ECS. Similar evidence is available to support the role of dopamine in the "behavioral despair" animal model of depression [1].

Human studies in depression

Studies of the synthesis, storage and catabolism of dopamine have not revealed any reliable abnormality in patients with depressive disorders [2]. Neuroendocrine studies do not suggest any major functional abnormality in the dopamine system function. Most studies of CSF HVA have found a decrease in the CSF HVA in patients with depression, especially in a subgroup of patients with severe psychomotor retardation [3].

Agents that deplete CNS dopamine or block dopamine receptors

Reserpine, which exerts most of its behavioral effects in animals via the dopaminergic system, is associated with a higher incidence of depression. α-Methyl dopa, an antihypertensive which displaces dopamine from its storage vesicles, is also associated with depression [2,3]. Neuroleptic agents, all of which block dopamine receptors, have reported to cause depression in many studies, especially in patients with non-psychotic depression with psychomotor retardation [1,3].

Parkinson's disease

Parkinson's disease is an idiopathic disorder characterized by rigidity, akinesia and tremor, with degeneration of the nigrostriatal dopaminergic system and loss of projections of the midbrain, limbic and cortical projections. The incidence of depression (about 40–50%) in Parkinson's disease is significantly higher even when compared with equivalently disabled controls. This argues for a neurobiological basis of the depression in Parkinson's disease. However, a direct relation between dopamine and depression in Parkinson's disease has not been established, and a role for an alteration in the serotonin mechanism is becoming increasingly evident [4].

The antidepressant effects of dopaminergic agents

Dopamine precursors

Several studies have explored the antidepressant efficacy of L-dopa in depression. Its antidepressant efficacy in an unselected population is unimpressive [5]. L-dopa may have efficacy as an antidepressant in a subset of patients with psychomotor retardation or with a low pretreatment CSF HVA. Tyrosine, a catecholamine precursor, has been tried as an antidepressant in one controlled and one uncontrolled study and found to be useful [5].

Dopamine agonists

Bromocriptine has significant dopamine agonist properties and controlled studies in patients with depression report antidepressant efficacy equivalent to standard tricyclic antidepressants [6]. Piribedil is predominantly a dopamine agonist at higher doses with little effect on the noradrenergic or serotonergic system; in a study of depressed patients in doses where it functions as a dopamine agonist, it has been found to exert an antidepressant effect, especially in a subset of patients with low CSF HVA [7].

Dopamine reuptake blockers

Nomifensine is a dopamine reuptake inhibitor which also inhibits the reuptake of norepinephrine. Numerous double-blind placebo controlled studies have consistently demonstrated the antidepressant efficacy of nomifensine. Scheyen et al. observed that psychomotor retardation responds more to nomifensine, and that the levels of CSF HVA are lower in responders [8]. Bupropion is a weak reuptake blocker of dopamine without any appreciable effect on the norepinephrine or the serotonin system [9]. It has been found to be superior to placebo as an antidepressant, but the relationship between its dopaminergic action and antidepressant effect needs clarification [10]. Deprenyl (selegiline) irreversibly inhibits the monoamine oxidase subtype MAO-B. The overall effect of the drug is to increase the levels of DA content in the striatonigral system and to enhance the sensitivity of the dopaminergic neurons [11]. While multiple open trials have established the efficacy of selegiline as an antidepressant, it is unclear whether this effect is seen at MAO-B selective doses [12].

The dopaminergic effect of antidepressant agents

Electroconvulsive therapy

Spontaneous locomotor activity and stereotypic behaviors in rats are mediated by the mesolimbic and striatonigral pathway respectively, and increase in response to dopaminergic agents [13]. Only convulsive not subconvulsive, repeated not single, and both bilateral and unilateral ECS consistently potentiate the dopaminergic activation of these behaviors [14]. While the enhancement of dopaminergic function by ECS seems well established, the site and the relevance of this change to the antidepressant effect remain to be clarified.

Pharmacological antidepressants

Multiple studies confirm the potentiation of dopamine-agonist induced locomotor behavior, which reflects dopaminergic activity in the meso-limbic region, by chronic administration of typical and atypical antidepressants [1]. However, the enhancement of dopaminergic responses is unaccompanied by any change in dopamine turnover, receptor number or sensitivity, suggesting that the enhancement of physiological sensitivity may be at site distal to the receptors [15].

Conclusion

In summary, evidence from animal and human sources suggests that perturbations may exist in the dopaminergic system in depression. Most agents which enhance dopaminergic transmission exert some antidepressant effect and antidepressants of biochemically unrelated classes and ECT enhance dopaminergic effects. Further research will be spurred by the cloning of three different dopamine receptors, the availability of selective dopaminergic agents for antidepressant trials and the use of PET and SPECT scan to study in vivo dopamine receptors.

References

1. Willner P (1983) Brain Res. Rev. 6: 225.

2. Willner P (1983) Brain Res. Rev. 6: 211.
3. Randrup A, Munkvad I, Fog R, Gerlach J, Molander L, Kjellberg B and Scheel-Kruger J (1975) In: Essman WB and Valzelli L (eds.) Current Developments in Psychopharmacology, Vol. 2. Spectrum Publications, New York, pp. 206–248.
4. Mayeux R (1990) J. Clin. Psychiatry 51 (Suppl. 7): 20.
5. Gelenberg AJ, Gibson CJ and Wojcik JD (1982) Psychopharmacol. Bull. 18: 7.
6. Theohar C, Fischer-Cirnelssen K, Akesson HO, Ansari J, Gerlach J, Harper P, Ohman R, Ose B and Stegink AJ (1981) Curr. Ther. Res. 30: 830.
7. Post RM, Gerner RH, Carman JS, Gillin JC, Jimerson DC, Goodwin FK and Bunney WE (1978) Arch. Gen. Psychiatry 35: 609.
8. Van Scheyen JD, Van Praag HM and Korf J (1977) Br. J. Clin. Pharmacol. 4: 179S.
9. Ferris RM, Cooper BR and Maxwell RA (1983) J. Clin. Psychiatry 44 (5 Sec. 2): 74.
10. Zung WWK (1983) J. Clin. Psychiatry 44 (5 Sec.2): 104.
11. Knoll J (1983) Acta Neurol. Scand. (Suppl.) 95: 57.
12. Mann JJ, Aarons SF, Wilner PJ, Kelip JG, Sweeney JA, Pearlstein T, Frances AJ, Kocsis J and Brown RP (1989) Arch. Gen. Psychiatry 46: 45.
13. Willner P (1983) Brain Res. Rev. 6: 237.
14. Gulati A, Srimal RC, Dhawan KN and Dhawan BN (1987) Neuropharmacology 16: 1733.
15. Heal DJ and Green AR (1978) Neuropharmacology 17: 1085.

© 1991 Elsevier Science Publishers B.V. All rights reserved.
Biological Psychiatry, Volume 2. G. Racagni et al., editors.

Distribution and alterations of the various 5-HT receptor subtypes in control and pathological human brain

J.M. Palacios, G. Mengod, M. Pompeiano and C. Waeber
Preclinical Research, Sandoz Pharma Ltd., 4002 Basle, Switzerland

Introduction

A multiplicity of 5-HT receptors appears to exist in the mammalian brain. Up to 12 different types have been proposed. The genes or cDNAs coding for 4 of these receptors are now cloned. Radioligands exist for at least 6 well defined subtypes: 5-HT_{1A}, 5-HT_{1B}, 5-HT_{1C}, 5-HT_{1D}, 5-HT_2 and 5-HT_3. With the exception of the 5-HT_{1B} receptors, the other 5 sites have been demonstrated in the human brain [1]. This communication reviews briefly the main features of these receptors, their localization and possible involvement in pathologies of the human brain.

Material and Methods

Brain tissues were collected at autopsy, dissected into blocks and kept frozen until use. Tissues used in the experiments reported here were obtained from the Dept. of Neuropathology, Univ. Basel (Prof. A. Probst) and from the Human Brain Tissue Resource Ctr., Harvard Univ. (Prof. E. Bird). In parallel with human tissues, tissues from various laboratory animals were also examined.

The blocks were then brought to –20°C and 10-μm thick sections were cut using a microtome-cryostat and mounted onto gelatin-coated microscope slides. Tissue sections were incubated with different radiolabeled ligands in defined conditions for the labeling of receptors.

Tritium-sensitive films were exposed to the labeled sections along with radioactive standards for different amounts of time to generate autoradiograms. Analysis of autoradiograms was carried out using a computerized image-analysis systems [5,6]. Several of these systems are commercially available.

Results and Discussion

Distribution of 5-HT receptors in human brain

5-HT_{1A}: These receptors were visualized using ^{3}H-[8-hydroxy di-N-propylamino]-tetralin (8-OH-DPAT), an agonist ligand. The pharmacological characteristics of these receptors in human brain are very similar to those found in the rat brain. 5-HT$_{1A}$ sites are particularly concentrated in limbic areas such as the hippocampus and amygdala. In addition, the raphe nuclei, the region containing the cell bodies of the serotoninergic neurons, also present high densities of 5-HT$_{1A}$ sites. Other brain areas, such as the substantia gelatinosa of the spinal cord also present 5-HT$_{1A}$ sites. In contrast, basal ganglia and associated areas are poor in 5-HT$_{1A}$ binding [2].

5-HT$_{1D}$ receptors, the equivalent of the 5-HT$_{1B}$ receptor found in rats and mice, are particularly enriched in the basal ganglia, where they are predominant in the two segments of the globus pallidus [2,3]. The highest concentration of 5-HT$_{1D}$ sites in the human brain is found in the substantia nigra pars reticulata. Until recently, no selective ligand was available for the labeling of 5-HT$_{1D}$ receptors. ^{3}H-5-HT was used in the presence of blocker such as 8-OH-DPAT and mesulergine to prevent binding to 1A and 1C sites. These sites were consequently defined by exclusion as "non-1A non-1C". However, Segu and collaborators [4] have recently developed a new selective ligand, ^{125}I serotonin-O-carboxy-methyl-glycyl-tyrosinamide, that allows the direct visualization of 5-HT$_{1D}$ sites. This new ligand has permitted confirmation of the localization of 5-HT$_{1D}$ sites in human brain.

5-HT$_{1C}$ and 5-HT$_2$ receptors are closely related in pharmacological and molecular aspects. ^{3}H-mesulergine and ^{3}H-ketanserine can be used to label 1C and 2 sites, respectively. Recently ^{125}I-DOI, an agonist at both 1C and 2 receptors, has been developed as a ligand. As in the rat, the tissue presenting the highest density of 5-HT$_{1C}$ sites in the human brain is the choroid plexus of the brain ventricles. 5-HT$_{1C}$ receptors are also found in the basal ganglia and substantia nigra. Differential labeling of these sites is obtained with agonists and antagonists, probably due to the existence of different affinity states. 5-HT$_2$ receptors are concentrated in the neocortex. Using ligand agonists, a heterogeneous distribution in patches of the striatum has been observed (Waeber and Palacios, in preparation).

Finally, the availability of ligands such as ^{3}H-ICS 205-930 and ^{3}H-(S)zacopride has made the visualization of *5-HT$_3$* receptors in the human brain possible [6]. Initially described in the peripheral nervous system, these receptors have been found to be particularly enriched in regions such as the substantia gelatinosa of the spinal cord and the trigeminal nerve as well as in the dorsal nucleus of the vagus. In limbic areas of the forebrain, 5-HT$_3$ sites were found in the hippocampus, amygdala and also in the "matrix" compartment of the caudate and putamen.

Cellular localization of 5-HT receptor mRNAs

In situ hybridization studies in the rat brain have provided detailed insight into the cells expressing the different 5-HT receptor mRNAs. Because of the similarities in the distribution of these receptors in rat and human brain, some of these observations are probably extrapolatable to the human brain.

We have used oligonucleotide probes derived from the published sequences of four 5-HT-receptors (5-HT$_{1A}$, 5-HT$_{1C}$, 5-HT$_{1D}$ and 5-HT$_2$) to characterize the cells expressing the corresponding mRNAs. For both 5-HT$_{1A}$ and 5-HT$_2$ receptors, we have observed a very good correspondence between the degree of expression of the mRNA and binding densities. Furthermore, the results show that these receptors are expressed by, for example, the serotoninergic cells of the raphe nuclei and pyramidal and granule cells of the hippocampus, in the case of 5-HT_{1A} receptors or cortical cells and motor neurons of the cranial nerve nuclei for 5-HT_2 receptors. No such good correlation has been found for 5-HT_{1C} sites. While the density of 5-HT_{1C} binding sites is very low in many brain areas, high levels of 5-HT_{1C} receptor mRNA have been observed. No expression of the cloned 5-HT_{1D} receptor has been detected in brain tissue until now. These results suggest that either other receptor subtypes, not yet identified, exist or that important differences in mRNA and/or receptor protein could occur in the different receptors [7].

Alterations of 5-HT receptors in pathologies of the human brain

The techniques for receptor visualization have been applied to the study of 5-HT receptor alterations in several neurodegenerative diseases. In Alzheimer's disease (AD), decreases in both 5-HT_{1A} and 5-HT_2 receptors have been reported [8]. Clear decreases in hippocampal 5-HT_{1A} have been observed associated with loss of neurons [1]. In the temporal cortex, reduction in these sites has also been reported. 5-HT_2 sites were dramatically decreased in the AD cortex in several studies. However, recent evidence has questioned these findings. The studies on 5-HT_{1D} sites in basal ganglia pathologies have been more informative. A dramatic decrease in 5-HT_{1D} binding has been observed in Huntington's chorea but not in Parkinson's disease (PD) [9]. These findings have been reproduced in animal models of these diseases and provided evidence for a localization of 5-HT_{1D} receptors in the cell bodies and terminals of the striato-nigral pathway but not in the ascending dopaminergic pathway. Similar losses of striatal 5-HT_2 sites have been found in HD but not in PD. The effects of disease on 5-HT_3 receptors is currently under investigation in our laboratory.

References

1. Palacios JM, Waeber C, Hoyer D and Mengod G (1990) Ann. N.Y. Acad. Sci. 600: 36–52.
2. Pazos A, Probst A and Palacios JM (1987) Neuroscience 21: 97–122.
3. Hoyer D, Pazos A, Probst A and Palacios JM (1986) Brain Res. 376: 85–96.
4. Boulenguez P, Chaveau J, Segu L, Morel A, Lanoir J and Delaage M (1991) Eur. J. Pharmacol. 194: 91–98.
5. Pazos A, Probst A and Palacios JM (1987) Neuroscience 21: 123–139.
6. Waeber C, Hoyer D and Palacios JM (1989) Neuroscience 31: 393–400.
7. Palacios JM, Waeber C, Mengod G and Hoyer D (1991) Neurochem. Int. 18: 17–25.
8. Cross AJ (1990) Ann. N.Y. Acad. Sci. 600: 405–417.
9. Waeber C and Palacios JM (1989) Neuroscience 32: 337–347.

© 1991 Elsevier Science Publishers B.V. All rights reserved.
Biological Psychiatry, Volume 2. G. Racagni et al., editors.

Behavioural, endocrine and other physiological effects in humans of drugs acting on 5-HT receptor subtypes

Dennis L. Murphy, K. Peter Lesch and Teresa M. Pigott
Laboratory of Clinical Science, National Institute of Mental Health, NIH Clinical Center 10/3D41, Bethesda, MD 20892, U.S.A.

This paper summarizes the effects in humans of two major groups of agents with selective actions at serotonin receptor subtypes. It focuses on data from single-dose studies of l-arylpiperazines administered as probes of the functions of central nervous system serotonin receptors, and of alterations in the functional status of these receptors in patients with neuropsychiatric disorders prior to and during treatment of these disorders. The studies described in this paper have been comprehensively reviewed by us in 1990 and 1991, and the primary citations, which are too numerous to list here, can be found in the reference lists of these reviews [1,2].

As indicated in Table 1, one group of arylpiperazines, the azapirones (e.g. ipsapirone, buspirone, gepirone and tandospirone), which have high, selective affinity for brain 5-HT$_{1A}$ receptors in vitro and which have well-defined pharmacological properties as 5-HT$_{1A}$ agonists in animals, were found to yield a consistent pattern of effects when given to healthy volunteers in oral doses of 15–90 mg. Plasma cortisol, ACTH and growth hormone were increased, and body temperature was decreased. Plasma prolactin was increased by buspirone and gepirone but not ipsapirone. Behavioral effects and side-effects were minimal, with drowsiness and mild nausea most commonly noted.

Antagonism of the neuroendocrine effects of ipsapirone and buspirone and of the temperature effects of ipsapirone followed pretreatment with the 5-HT$_{1A}$ (and β-adrenergic) antagonist, pindolol and, to some extent, the non-selective serotonin antagonist, metergoline, but not by the selective β-adrenergic antagonist, betaxolol.

In studies comparing the neuroendocrine and temperature responses to ipsapirone in patients with neuropsychiatric disorders vs. controls, patients with depression or panic disorder had diminished ACTH, cortisol and temperature responses, while patients with obsessive-compulsive disorder (OCD) had responses no different from controls. However, treatment of the OCD patients with the selective serotonin uptake inhibitor, fluoxetine, led to a partial attenuation of the neuroendocrine and temperature responses to ipsapirone.

Another group of arylpiperazines, including m-chlorophenylpiperazine (m-CPP), other substituted phenylpiperazines, and a related piperazine, MK-212, have been found in animal studies to consistently increase plasma cortisol, ACTH, prolactin and vasopressin and to elevate body temperature [2]. They have relatively

Table 1. Responses to different arylpiperazines given to healthy human volunteers

Azapirones	Response							
	Cortisol	ACTH	Prl	GH		Temp.		Behavior
Ipsapirone	I	I	O	I		D		Drowsy, mild nausea
Buspirone	I	I	I	I				Mild sedation
Gepirone	I	I	I	I		D		
Tandospirone				I				
Other arylpiperazines	Response							
	Cortisol	ACTH	Prl	GH	NE	Temp.	BP	Behavior
m-CPP (oral)	I	I	I	O	O	I	O	Anxious, activated, mild nausea
m-CPP (i.v.)	I	I	I	I	I	I	I	Very anxious, cognitive impairment
MK-212	I		I	O			I	Anxious, difficulty thinking
Quipazine	I		O	O				Nausea, GI symptoms
2-MPP							D	Marked sedation, cognitive impairment

Abbreviations: I = increased; D = decreased; O = no response; A = completely antagonized; PA = partially antagonized.

high affinity for 5-HT_3 and 5-HT_{1C} sites, but their serotonin receptor selectivity is both less and more variable than that of the azapirones for 5-HT_{1A} sites.

As indicated in Table 1, m-CPP, MK-212 and quipazine increased plasma cortisol in humans, m-CPP and MK-212 increased plasma prolactin and blood pressure, and m-CPP had other neuroendocrine effects and also elevated body temperature. These agents had notable behavioral effects depending upon dosage and route of administration, producing anxiety, behavioral activation, cognitive impairment and, to a variable extent, nausea and gastrointestinal symptoms. Many of the neuroendocrine effects as well as the temperature elevation produced by orally-administered m-CPP were antagonized by metergoline or methysergide.

In studies comparing the responses to m-CPP in neuropsychiatric patients vs. controls, a few patient groups (panic disorder, seasonal affective disorder) manifested greater neuroendocrine responses than controls, while OCD patients had some evidence of diminished neuroendocrine responses which were not consistent across all studies but which were also observed with MK-212. Alzheimer's disease patients had diminished temperature responses to m-CPP. Most noteworthy, however, was the overall tendency for m-CPP to elicit greater subjective and behavioral responses in the patient groups than the controls, with the responses often times taking the form of the patients' disorder, e.g. panic episodes in panic disorder patients, migraine headaches in individuals with a personal or family history of migraine and an exacerbation of OCD or schizophrenic symptoms in patients with those disorders. In the case of OCD, the symptom exacerbation elicited by m-CPP was suppressed by pretreatment with metergoline or chronic treatment with fluoxetine or clomipramine. Preliminary data suggest that ritanserin or clozapine (but not fluphenazine) pretreatment mitigates m-CPP's effects in schizophrenic patients.

These results with direct serotonin agonists and antagonists provide more specific information about serotonin-mediated CNS functions in humans beyond that previously available from indirect agents such as L-tryptophan, 5-hydroxytryptophan and fenfluramine. They also provide some additional evidence suggestive of serotonergic subsystem alterations in patients with neuropsychiatric disorders which will be interesting to investigate further with more selective agonists, antagonists and with ligands for brain imaging studies of serotonin receptor subtypes.

References

1. Murphy DL (1990) Neuropsychopharmacology 3: 457–471.
2. Murphy DL, Lesch KP, Aulakh C and Pigott T (1991) Pharmacol. Rev. (in press).

© 1991 Elsevier Science Publishers B.V. All rights reserved.
Biological Psychiatry, Volume 2. G. Racagni et al., editors.

5-HT receptor ligands and conflict behavior

W. Koek* and F.C. Colpaert*

Neurobiology Division, Fondax – Groupe de Recherche Servier, 7 rue Ampere, 92800 Puteaux, France

The various behavioral procedures commonly used in the preclinical evaluation of the potential anxiolytic activity of drugs have in common that a particular response is followed by different stimuli that act, in a conflicting manner, to increase and decrease its frequency. In the first of such procedures to be characterized pharmacologically, Geller and Seifter [1] trained rats to press a lever for food under a multiple schedule consisting of two components: a schedule of food reinforcement and a schedule in which every response was reinforced by food, but also punished by electric shock. Of the psychoactive drugs that were studied at that time, only those having documented clinical anxiolytic activity (i.e. barbiturates and benzodiazepines) increased punished responding.

During the past decade, variants of the conflict paradigm (e.g. social interaction test and elevated plus maze) have been introduced that, more so than the Geller-Seifter procedure, have provided evidence that serotonergic agents exert putative anxiolytic activity (e.g. [2]). A major limitation of these variants, however, is the variability of their outcome [3], perhaps related to the limited ability to control the stimulus conditions in these procedures.

Barrett and colleagues [4] recently introduced a variant of the Geller-Seifter conflict procedure, implemented in pigeons, that appears to be unique among the currently available models of anxiety in combining the following two features. First, the response is under the influence of stimuli that can be strictly controlled. Second, the procedure would seem to reveal anticonflict activity not only of benzodiazepines but also of clinically active, serotonergic anxiolytics, i.e. buspirone [5] and ritanserin [6]. Together, these features suggest that this procedure may provide a reproducible, valid assay of anxiolytic potential.

It was shown recently that the pigeon conflict procedure indeed yields results that are reproducible across laboratories. In agreement with previous observations [7], we found chlordiazepoxide, buspirone and ritanserin to increase punished responding in this procedure [8]. Further, the pigeon conflict procedure appeared to be more sensitive to the effects of non-benzodiazepine anxiolytics than prominent conflict procedures in rats (i.e. Geller-Seifter, Vogel [9]), which revealed antipunishment effects of chlordiazepoxide, but not of buspirone and ritanserin [8]. Finally, the pigeon conflict procedure appeared able to differentiate the anticonflict effects of the compounds tested: whereas buspirone increased punished responding

*Present address: Centre de Recherche Pierre Fabre, 17 avenue Jean Moulin, 81106 Castres, France.

to levels (i.e. 3839% of the control rate) similar to those produced by chlordiazepoxide (i.e. 3332%), ritanserin increased punished responding to a lesser extent (i.e. 2259%).

A second series of experiments examined further the activity of 5-HT_2 receptor ligands in the pigeon conflict procedure. Punished responding was increased significantly not only by ritanserin, but also by other 5-HT_2 antagonists, i.e. ICI 169,369 and risperidone [10]. As was the case with ritanserin, the maximum effect of ICI 169,369 and risperidone (i.e. 1331% and 943%, respectively) was lower than that observed with chlordiazepoxide. Previously, 5-HT_3 antagonists were shown to exert less antipunishment activity than 5-HT_2 antagonists in the pigeon conflict procedure, if any at all [7]. The extent to which 5-HT_{1A} ligands (i.e. the agonists, 8-OH-DPAT, (+)–flesinoxan, buspirone; the putative antagonists, BMY 7378, NAN 190) increased punished responding which varied among the compounds tested, their maximum effects being 4381%, 3868%, 3839%, 2297% and 593%, respectively [11]. The magnitude of the antipunishment effects of these compounds corresponded with their apparent in vivo efficacy in producing 5-HT_{1A} agonist actions in rodents.

It is concluded that: 1) the pigeon conflict procedure may constitute the method of choice in characterizing the anxiolytic potential of compounds; 2) the role of 5-HT_{1A} receptors in punished behavior may be more significant than that of either 5-HT_2 or 5-HT_3 receptors; and 3) the anxiolytic potential of 5-HT_{1A} ligands may be positively related to their efficacy at 5-HT_{1A} receptors.

References

1. Geller I and Seifter J (1960) Psychopharmacologia 1: 482–492.
2. Gardner CR (1986) Pharmacol. Biochem. Behav. 24: 1479–1485.
3. Chopin P and Briley M (1987) Trends Pharmacol. Sci. 8: 383–388.
4. Barrett JE and Witkin JM (1990) In: Tunnicliff G, Eison AS and Taylor DP (eds.) Buspirone: Mechanisms and Clinical Aspects. Academic Press, New York.
5. Rickels K, Weissman K, Norstad N, Singer M, Stoltz D, Brown A and Danton J (1982) J. Clin. Psychiatry 43: 81–86.
6. Ceulemans DLS, Hoppenbrauwers ML, Gelders YG and Reyntjens AJM (1985). Pharmacopsychiatry 18: 303–305.
7. Gleeson S, Ahlers ST, Mansbach RS, Foust JM and Barrett JE (1989) J. Pharmacol. Exp. Ther. 250: 809–817.
8. Brocco MJ, Koek W and Colpaert FC (1990) Behav. Pharmacol. 1: 403–418.
9. Vogel JR, Beer B and Clody DE (1971) Psychopharmacologia 21: 1–7.
10. Koek W, Jackson A and Colpaert FC (1991) (submitted).
11. Colpaert FC, Millan MJ, Koek W, Lehmann J, Rivet JM, Lejeune F, Canton H, Bervoets K, Laubie M and Lavielle G (1991) (submitted).

© 1991 Elsevier Science Publishers B.V. All rights reserved.
Biological Psychiatry, Volume 2. G. Racagni et al., editors.

Serotonin receptor regulation: Implications for drug action

Josee E. Leysen and Petrus J. Pauwels
Department of Biochemical Pharmacology, Janssen Research Foundation, B-2340 Beerse, Belgium

Properties of 5-HT receptor subtypes

Serotonin receptors have been classified, mainly based on radioligand binding or signal transduction measurements, into at least 7 subtypes; their characteristics are summarized in Table 1.

The various 5-HT receptor subtypes have a particular distribution in the brain and also occur in peripheral tissues (see Palacios et al., this volume). Exogenous agonists for 5-HT_{1A}, 5-HT_2, 5-HT_3 and 5-HT_4 receptors elicit marked centrally mediated and/or peripheral effects. 5-HT_{1A} agonists produce hypothermia, clonic seizures, discriminative stimulus, sleep decrease, hyperphagia, hypotension. Partial 5-HT_{1A} agonists (buspirone, ipsapirone) have therapeutic effects in anxiety, depression and alcohol craving. 5-HT_2 agonists produce head twitches, clonic seizures, sleep decrease and discriminative stimulus in rodents, malignant hyperthermia in susceptible pigs, hallucinations and vivid dreams in man. 5-HT_3 agonists induce a reflex fall in blood pressure and heart rate and 5-HT_4 agonists have gastrokinetic effects. In contrast, selective antagonists for these receptor subtypes, at dosages which produce full receptor blockade, have very minor effects. Bromo-N-[4-pindolol l-methyl cyclohexyl]acetamide (BPMCA), one of the rare selective 5-HT_{1A} antagonists, was reported to produce no observable behavioural change. Selective 5-HT_2 antagonists (pipamperone, cinanserin) or mixed 5-HT_2/5-HT_{1C} antagonists (e.g. ritanserin) cause *no* disturbance of motor, autonomic or intellectual functions. However, they increase slow wave sleep in laboratory animals and humans. In rats they abolish behavioural inhibition induced by natural aversive stimuli and they reduce learned preferences for drugs of abuse (alcohol, cocaine, fentanyl). In patients, ritanserin and pipamperone have thymostenic effects and they reduce negative symptoms of schizophrenia and neuroleptic-induced extrapyramidal symptoms. 5-HT_3 antagonists also have no directly observable behavioural effects, but they antagonize chemo- and radiotherapy-induced emesis. No selective 5-HT_{1B}, 5-HT_{1D} and 5-HT_{1C} antagonists have thus far been described; hence the consequences of blocking these receptors are not yet known.

Regulation of 5-HT receptor subtypes

Destruction of raphe 5-HT neurones reduced 5-HT_{1A} receptors in the raphe, indicat-

Table 1. 5-HT receptor subtypes: binding affinities (K_i, nM) of 5-HT and of relatively selective compounds, agonist-induced signal transduction, electrophysiological and neurochemical effects

	5-HT	Agonist	K_i	Antagonist	K_i	Signal transduction	Electrophysiology	Neurochemical effects
5-HT_{1A}	2.1	8-OHDPAT Ipsapirone	0.66	NAN-190 BPMCA	1.22 0.71	AC ~ cAMP↓	Hyperpolarization K^+ conductance↑	Soma dendrites 5-HT neuronal activity↓
5-HT_{1B}	2.1	CP 93129	15	Not known		AC ~ cAMP↓		Nerve terminals: 5-HT-, NE release↓
5-HT_{1D}	1.8	Sumatriptan	13	Not known		AC ~ cAMP↓		Nerve terminals: 5-HT-, NE release↓
5-HT_{1C}	13	DOB	16	Mesulergine Ritanserin	1.4 0.58	PLC ~ IP_3,DAG↑		
5-HT_2	380	DOB	52	Pipamperone Ritanserin	0.99 0.30	PLC ~ IP_3,DAG↑ PLA_2 ~ arachidonic acid↑	Depolarization K^+ conductance↓	
5-HT_3	180	mCPBG	15	Zacopride ICS 205930 Odansetron	0.44 0.65 8.3	Cation channel opening	Depolarization Na^+, K^+ conductance↑	Sympathetic: NE release↑ Parasympathetic: ACh release↑ CNS: DA release↑
5-HT_4	93	Cisapride	72	ICS 205930	1000	AC ~ cAMP↑	Neuronal excitation	Ileum myenteric plexus: ACh release↑

DOB: 1-(4-Bromo-2, 5-dimethoxyphenyl)2-amino propane; mCPBG: metachlorophenyl biguanide; AC: adenylate cyclase; PL: phospholipase.

ing the existence of somatodendritic 5-HT_{1A} autoreceptors, but it did not cause alterations in 5-HT_{1A} [1] or 5-HT_2 [2] receptors in any other brain area. Development of supersensitivity or up-regulation of these receptors was not apparent.

5-HT_{1A} receptors appeared to have no or poor propensity to desensitize. Chronic treatment of rats with monoamine oxidase inhibitors, specific 5-HT uptake blockers or 5-HT_{1A} agonists caused no change of postsynaptic 5-HT_{1A} receptors, either measured by electrophysiological or biochemical means. In some studies desensitization of somatodendritic electrophysiological responses was found, but this was not corroborated in neurochemical or receptor binding studies [1]. Chronic treatment with tricyclic antidepressants was reported to cause no change of somatodendritic 5-HT_{1A} receptors, but to reduce postsynaptic 5-HT_{1A} receptor responses [1]. We found that cloned human 5-HT_{1A} receptors expressed in HeLa cells did not desensitize during culture in serum-supplemented medium containing 5-HT, and Andrade and Araneda [3] observed no desensitization of 5-HT_{1A} receptor-mediated membrane hyperpolarization in pyramidal cells of layer V of rat frontal cortical slices.

In contrast, 5-HT_2 receptors revealed a very rapid, profound and long-lasting desensitization via homologous (i.e. by direct 5-HT_2 receptor stimulation) and heterologous mechanisms. Repeated administration of 2,5-dimethoxyphenyl 2-amino propane derivatives (DOM, DOI) or LSD to rats caused significant to complete desensitization (homologous) of the head twitch response after the second and fourth injection, respectively and a concomitant significant reduction of up to 40% of 5-HT_2 receptor binding sites, assayed by ex vivo radioligand binding in the frontal cortex [4]. In aortic smooth muscle cells in culture, the 5-HT_2 receptor-mediated phosphatidyl inositol hydrolysis completely desensitized within 2 h in the presence of 5-HT or DOM [5] and also the 5-HT_2 receptor-mediated membrane depolarization in pyramidal cells of layer V in frontal cortical slices was reported to rapidly desensitize [3]. Chronic treatment with 5-HT_2 antagonists, tricyclic antidepressants, non-selective neuroleptics (the latter 2 types of compounds have multiple effects amongst which potent 5-HT_2 receptor blockade) and 5-HT_{1A} agonists, also caused desensitization (heterologous) of the 5-HT_2 receptor-mediated behavioural response and a concomitant decrease in brain 5-HT_2 receptor numbers (reviewed in [6]). Following down-regulation, the restoration of 5-HT_2 receptor numbers occurred slowly over more than 24 h in vitro [5] or more than 6 days in vivo [4].

Finally also 5-HT_3 and 5-HT_4 receptors appeared to desensitize very rapidly.

Conclusions and hypothesis

The above information, together with findings on the serotonergic neurone anatomy and activity, showing that only a minor part of serotonergic dorsal raphe neurones form synaptic contacts [7] and that these neurones only exert a low regular activity which is not influenced by various strong environmental or physiologic stimuli [8], led us to propose the following hypothesis. 5-HT neurones in mammalian brain show a very low activity under normal physiological conditions: 5-HT release rapidly leads to auto-inhibition via high affinity, not readily desensitizing, 5-HT receptors at the somatedendritic (5-HT_{1A}) and nerve terminal level (5-HT_{1B}, 5-HT_{1D}). Post-synaptic 5-HT receptors, particularly the excitatory 5-HT_2 and probably also 5-HT_3 receptors, for which 5-HT shows μM affinity, are likely only scarcely and very transiently activated. Higher stimulation readily leads to detrimental responses and must be prevented. A rapid and prolonged desensitization of these receptors is a natural protective mechanism. In certain pathological or pharmacological conditions, post-synaptic (excitatory) 5-HT receptor stimulation may be enhanced and/or the desensitization mechanism may be impaired. In such conditions, 5-HT_2 or 5-HT_3 antagonists are side-effect-free therapeutic agents, which restore the physiological condition, acutely by blocking the receptors and in case of the 5-HT_2 receptor, chronically by down-regulating them.

References

1. Hamon M, Gozlan H, El Mestikawy S, Emerit MB, Bolaños F and Schechter L (1990) Ann. N.Y. Acad. Sci. 600: 114–131.
2. Leysen JE, Van Gompel P, Verwimp M and Niemegeers CJE (1983) In: Mandel P and Defeudis FV (eds.) CNS Receptors – From Molecular Pharmacology to Behaviour. Raven Press, New York, pp. 373–383.
3. Araneda R and Andrade R (1991) Neuroscience 40: 399–421.
4. Leysen JE and Pauwels PJ (1990) Ann. N.Y. Acad. Sci. 600: 183–193.
5. Pauwels PJ, Van Gompel P and Leysen JE (1990) Life Sci. 47: 2009–2020.
6. Conn PJ and Sanders-Bush E (1987) Psychopharmacology 92: 267–277.
7. Descarries L, Audet M-A, Doucet G, Garcia S, Oleskevich S, Séguéla P, Soghomonian J-J and Watkins KC (1990) Ann. N.Y. Acad. Sci. 600: 81–92.
8. Jacobs BL, Fornal CA and Wilkinson LO (1990) Ann. N.Y. Acad. Sci. 600: 260–271.

© 1991 Elsevier Science Publishers B.V. All rights reserved.
Biological Psychiatry, Volume 2. G. Racagni et al., editors.

Is 5-HT$_3$ receptor blockade able to prevent dopaminergic activation by stress?

Michel Hamon[1], Emma Kidd[1], Henri Gozlan[1] and Patrick Martin[2]

[1]*INSERM U.288, Neurobiologie Cellulaire et Fonctionnelle; and* [2]*Département de Pharmacologie, CHU Pitié-Salpêtrière, 75634 Paris Cedex 13, France*

Introduction

Since the discovery of central 5-HT$_3$ receptors by Kilpatrick et al. [1] in 1987, numerous investigations have been carried out to try and identify which physiological functions they control in the brain. Electrophysiological, biochemical and behavioural studies showed that the stimulation of central 5-HT$_3$ receptors exerts an excitatory influence on mesolimbic dopaminergic systems, and conversely, 5-HT$_3$ receptor blockade may prevent the activation of these systems by various treatments [2]. These observations led to the proposal that selective 5-HT$_3$ antagonists might be of potential therapeutic value in the treatment of disorders associated with a hyperactivity of mesolimbic dopaminergic systems such as schizophrenia and addiction to drugs of abuse [3]. However, the exact nature of the interactions between serotonin (5-HT) and dopamine (DA) through 5-HT$_3$ receptors is still controversial. For instance Blandina et al. [4] reported that 5-HT$_3$ receptor stimulation enhances the *spontaneous* outflow of DA from superfused rat striatal slices whereas in vivo investigations led to the conclusion that this effect exclusively concerns the amine release *evoked by impulse flow* in DA cells [5]. In addition, Koulu et al. [6] have shown that 5-HT$_3$ receptor blockade (by ondansetron) did not modify the haloperidol-induced activation of central DA turnover, whereas Carboni et al. [7] found that the increased release of DA within the nucleus accumbens of haloperidol-treated rats could be prevented by prior administration of a 5-HT$_3$ receptor antagonist (ICS 205-930).

In most of the studies performed so far, the effects of 5-HT$_3$ receptor ligands on DA neurotransmission have been examined after the administration of drugs which activate DA release through various non-physiological mechanisms [2,7]. Therefore uncontrolled drug-drug interactions might have occurred, leading to erroneous conclusions regarding the actual involvement of 5-HT$_3$ receptors in the control of central DA neurotransmission. One possible way to avoid such artifacts may consist of investigating the effects of 5-HT$_3$ receptor ligands on DA systems activated by non-drug treatments. A stressful situation would be particularly relevant in this respect because stress is generally associated with a marked activation of meso-cortico-limbic DA systems [8], and 5-HT$_3$ antagonists have been claimed to possess anxiolytic-like properties in rats [2]. We therefore examined whether the 5-HT_3 receptor antagonist ondansetron was able, like benzodiazepines [8], to alter stress-induced activation of meso-cortico-limbic DA systems in rats.

Materials and Methods

Ondansetron (GR 38032F, Glaxo, 1 mg/kg, i.p.) or saline was administered 30 min before immobilizing adult male Sprague-Dawley rats in a cylinder made of iron mesh, for 1 h. They were immediately decapitated thereafter, and the nucleus accumbens was dissected in coronal brain sections and homogenized in 10 vol (v/w) of 0.1 M $HClO_4$ for the determination of 5-HT, DA and their metabolites, 5-hydroxy-indole acetic acid (5-HIAA), dihydroxyphenylacetic acid (DOPAC) and homovanillic acid (HVA) by HPLC coupled to electrochemical detection [9]. Other rats (controls) were treated with ondansetron or saline and kept in their home-cages for 90 min before sacrifice.

Results

A marked increase in the levels of DOPAC (+24%) and HVA (+44%) was found in the nucleus accumbens of restrained rats as compared to controls (Table 1). 5-HIAA levels were also significantly elevated (+42%), but those of 5-HT and DA remained unchanged after a 1 h immobilization stress.

As shown in Table 1, ondansetron affected neither the amines nor their metabolites' concentrations in control unstressed animals. Furthermore immobilization stress produced the same increases in the levels of DOPAC (+30%), HVA (+43%) and 5-HIAA (+54%) in the nucleus accumbens of ondansetron-treated rats as in those receiving saline (Table 1).

Table 1. Effects of restraint stress on the levels of DA, 5-HT and their metabolites in the nucleus accumbens of rats treated with ondansetron or saline. Each value (in µg/g fresh tissue) is the mean ± S.E.M. of at least 6 independent determinations

	Saline		Ondansetron	
µg/g	Control	Restraint stress	Control	Restraint stress
DA	5.13 ± 0.24	5.70 ± 0.28	5.31 ± 0.37	5.89 ± 0.35
DOPAC	0.745 ± 0.041	0.922 ± 0.053[a]	0.860 ± 0.062	1.115 ± 0.034[a]
HVA	0.538 ± 0.026	0.774 ± 0.026[a]	0.597 ± 0.035	0.855 ± 0.043[a]
5-HT	0.321 ± 0.014	0.317 ± 0.024	0.299 ± 0.026	0.352 ± 0.040
5-HIAA	0.418 ± 0.013	0.592 ± 0.032[a]	0.378 ± 0.023	0.581 ± 0.032[a]

[a]$P < 0.05$ when compared to respective control values (Student's t-test).

Discussion

The present data confirmed for the nucleus accumbens that the systemic administration of a 5-HT_3 antagonist, e.g. ondansetron, does not affect the turnover of DA in mesolimbic areas in control unstressed rats [6]. Similar observations have been made after systemic treatments with other 5-HT_3 antagonists (ICS 205-930: 0.05–1.0 mg/kg i.p., or zacopride: 0.05–1.0 mg/kg i.p., unpublished data). A marked acceleration of mesolimbic DA and 5-HT turnover resulted in significant increases in the levels of their metabolites, DOPAC, HVA and 5-HIAA, in the nucleus accumbens of stressed rats. Ondansetron did not prevent the stress-induced activation of DA and 5-HT systems since the relative increases in DOPAC, HVA and 5-HIAA levels were as pronounced after the administration of this 5-HT_3 antagonist as after saline. Similarly, zacopride (0.1–1.0 mg/kg, i.p.) also failed to affect DA and 5-HT turnover in the nucleus accumbens and other brain areas in stressed rats (data not shown). Therefore 5-HT_3 antagonists differ from benzodiazepines which have been shown to reverse stress-induced activation of DA meso-cortico-limbic systems in rats [8].

In conclusion, the anti-DA effects of 5-HT_3 antagonists probably do not involve a presynaptic mechanism since DA turnover remains unaffected by these drugs. Indeed, binding studies with [^{3}H]zacopride revealed no loss of 5-HT_3 binding sites after the extensive degeneration of DA fibres and terminals, in line with the absence of 5-HT_3 receptors on DA neurones at the presynaptic level (unpublished data). Instead, 5-HT_3 receptor blockade might prevent DA neurotransmission through a postsynaptic mechanism, which would explain why ondansetron suppresses the hyperactivity triggered by the infusion of DA directly into the nucleus accumbens or the amygdala in rats [2]. Whether DA inhibition at the postsynaptic level is associated with the anxiolytic-like properties of ondansetron and other 5-HT_3 antagonists [2] deserves further investigation.

Acknowledgements

Supported by grants from INSERM and DRET: Contract No. 901085.

References

1. Kilpatrick GJ, Jones BJ and Tyers MB (1987) Nature 330: 746–748.
2. Costall B, Naylor RJ and Tyers MB (1988) Rev. Neurosci. 2: 41–65.
3. Tricklebank MD (1989) Trends Pharmacol. Sci. 10: 127–129.
4. Blandina P, Goldfarb J, Craddock-Royal B and Green JP (1989) J. Pharmacol. Exp. Ther. 251: 803–809.
5. Jiang LH, Ashby CR Jr, Kasser RJ and Wang RY (1990) Brain Res. 513: 156–160.
6. Koulu M, Sjöholm B, Lappalainen J and Virtanen R (1989) Eur. J. Pharmacol. 169: 321–324.
7. Carboni E, Acquas E, Frau R and Di Chiara G (1989) Eur. J. Pharmacol. 169: 515–519.

8. Lavielle S, Tassin JP, Thierry AM, Blanc G, Hervé D, Barthélémy C and Glowinski J (1978) Brain Res. 168: 585–594.
9. Hamon M, Fattaccini CM, Adrien J, Gallissot MC, Martin P and Gozlan H (1988) J. Pharmacol. Exp. Ther. 246: 745–752.

© 1991 Elsevier Science Publishers B.V. All rights reserved.
Biological Psychiatry, Volume 2. G. Racagni et al., editors.

5-HT receptors involved in sleep regulation

Christine Dugovic[1] and Joelle Adrien[2]

[1]*Department of Neuropsychopharmacology, Janssen Research Foundation, Beerse, Belgium; and* [2]*INSERM U288, CHU Pitié-Salpêtrière, 91 Bd de l'Hôpital, 75013 Paris, France*

The development of increasing numbers of specific agonists and antagonists acting on different 5-HT receptor populations provides attractive opportunities to understand the role of serotonin in the regulation of sleep and wakefulness. Recent pharmacological investigations indicate that 5-HT_1, 5-HT_2 and possibly 5-HT_3 receptors may be implicated in this physiological process. However, the majority of these pharmacological tools is now known to be only relatively selective with respect to the multiple 5-HT receptor sites. In the light of these new data, the present review attempts to clarify whether the various 5-HT receptor subtypes are specifically involved in the modulation of the sleep-wakefulness states.

5-HT_1 receptor subtypes and wakefulness

In rats and cats, an increase of wakefulness seems to be a common response to the stimulation of various 5-HT_1 receptor subtypes. Indeed, these effects were observed following the administration of the 5-HT_{1A} agonists 8-OH-DPAT [8-hydroxy-2-(di-n-propylamine) tetralin], buspirone and ipsapirone, the mixed 5-HT_{1B}/5-HT_{1A} agonist RU24969 [5-methoxy-3-(1,2,3,6-tetrahydro-4-pyridinyl) 1H-indole] and the mixed 5-HT_{1C}/5-HT_{1B} agonist mCPP (m-chlorophenylpiperazine) [1–4]. The ipsapirone-induced sleep-wakefulness changes in rats reflect an activation of post- rather than pre-synaptic 5-HT_{1A} receptors since similar effects were obtained after 5,7-dihydroxytryptamine lesions of the nucleus raphe dorsalis (Adrien et al., this congress). With regard to clinical studies, buspirone has been shown to cause no impairment of daytime wakefulness [5], whereas prominent behavioral effects that interfered with sleep have been reported in healthy volunteers given m-CPP [6].

Thus, serotonergic mechanisms may play a role in wakefulness processes through 5-HT_1 receptors. However, whether the arousing effects of 5-HT_1 agonists can be counteracted by specific antagonists remains to be elucidated. On the other hand, the activation of the 5-HT_1 receptor by using 8-OH-DPAT, RU24969 and mCPP elicits behavioral changes such as impaired motor activity [7] that probably contribute to the increase of wakefulness observed with these drugs.

5-HT_2 receptor-mediated slow wave sleep regulation

The mixed 5-HT_2/5-HT_{1C} antagonist ritanserin increased the duration of deep slow wave sleep (SWS) in humans [8] and in rats [9–11]. Conversely, the mixed 5-HT_2/5-HT_{1C} agonist methoxyphenethylamines DOM, DOB and DOI produced a deep SWS deficit in rats. This effect could be dose-dependently reversed by ritanserin as well as by the selective 5-HT_2 antagonist cinanserin [9–11]. However, sleep-wakefulness alterations observed after administration of the mixed 5-HT_{1C}/5-HT_{1B} agonist mCPP were not modified by ritanserin or cinanserin pretreatment. This suggests that serotonin may exert an inhibitory control on deep SWS through 5-HT_2 receptors. In addition, ritanserin did not influence the sleep-wakefulness changes elicited by 8-OH-DPAT and RU24969 [9,11], indicating no functional interaction between 5-HT_2 and 5-HT_{1A} or 5-HT_{1B} receptors.

Further investigations on the functional activity of 5-HT_2 receptors revealed diurnal variations in sensitivity depending on the day-night cycle and/or the melatonin rhythm. Sleep-wakefulness changes induced by ritanserin as well as DOM were only evident during the physiological rest period of the rat (when melatonin levels are low) and could be counteracted by melatonin pretreatment [12]. In humans, the SWS-promoting action of ritanserin was also optimal during the natural sleep period [13], thus in association with high melatonin levels in this species. The 5-HT_2 receptor system may exhibit a phasic activity with a low sensitive state during the active period and a high sensitive state during the sleep period (light phase for rats and dark phase for humans).

Are 5-HT_3 receptors involved in sleep-wakefulness regulation?

To date, a number of 5-HT_3 antagonists (MDL 72222, ICS 205-930 and ondansetron) and putative 5-HT_3 agonists (phenylbiguanide, 2-methyl-5-HT) have been tested but failed to reveal any major modifications of sleep-wakefulness patterns in rats and cats [3–4]. Thus, 5-HT_3 receptors appear to play only a minor role in sleep-wakefulness modulation. However, MDL 72222 could prevent the effects of ipsapirone in cats but not in rats [3–4]. These results indicate a functional interaction between 5-HT_3 and 5-HT_{1A} receptors in particular species.

5-HT receptors and paradoxical sleep regulation

Both agonists and antagonists at either the 5-HT_1 or the 5-HT_2 receptor, and in general most drugs which alter serotonin-mediated transmission, reduced paradoxical sleep (PS). However, the effects of 5-HT_{1A} agonists were biphasic with an initial inhibition of PS and a secondary rebound [4,14]. Regarding the 5-HT_2 receptor system, the PS-suppressing effects of agonists were reversed by antagonists in the immature but not in the adult rat [9–11]. For 5-HT_3 antagonists, a moderate enhancement of PS could be observed at some doses [4]. Thus, several 5-HT receptor subtypes may participate in the regulation of PS.

Conclusions

The hypothesis emerges that each 5-HT receptor subtype may be differently involved in the control of the sleep-wakefulness states. In fact, it is premature to precisely define their respective role because of the paucity of selective agents at a given 5-HT receptor site. In addition, the only selective ligands for 5-HT_1 receptors which are the 5-HT_{1A} agonists (8-OH-DPAT, buspirone, ipsapirone) may act as full or partial agonists depending on the location of their target in the brain. Furthermore, regarding sleep-wakefulness regulation, the precise site of action for most 5-HT receptor ligands is not known, especially with respect to potential hypnogenic targets located in the hypothalamus [15].

Finally, several 5-HT receptor-active drugs (5-HT_{1A} agonists, 5-HT_2/5-HT_{1C} antagonists and 5-HT_3 antagonists) are presently being developed as potential anxiolytic agents [16]. However, in spite of such common anxiolytic properties these compounds have different actions on sleep and wakefulness.

References

1. Lerman JA, Kaitin KI, Dement WC and Peroutka SJ (1986) Neurosci. Lett. 72: 64–68.
2. Dzoljic MR, Saxena PR and Ukponmwan OE (1987) Sleep Res. 16: 88.
3. Adrien J, Davenne D, Jolas T and Hamon M (1990) In: Horne J (ed.) Sleep '90. Pontenagel Press, Bochum, pp. 123–125.
4. Tissier MH, Franc B, Hamon M and Adrien J (1990) In: Horne J (ed.) Sleep '90. Pontenagel Press, Bochum, pp. 126–128.
5. Seidel WF, Cohen SA, Bliwise NG and Dement WC (1985) Psychopharmacology 87: 371–373.
6. Lawlor BA, Newhouse PA, Balkin TJ, Molchan SE, Mellow AM, Murphy DL and Sunderland T (1991) Biol. Psychiatry 29: 281–286.
7. Tricklebank MD (1985) Trends Pharmacol. Sci. 6: 403–407.
8. Idzikowski C, Mills FJ and Glennard R (1986) Brain Res. 378: 164–168.
9. Dugovic C, Wauquier A, Leysen JE, Marrannes R and Janssen PAJ (1989) Psychopharmacology 97: 436–442.
10. Davenne D, Dugovic C, Frank B and Adrien J (1989) In: Wauquier A, Dugovic C and Radulovacki M (eds.) Slow Wave Sleep: Physiological, Pathophysiological and Functional Aspects. Raven Press, New York, pp. 21–30.
11. Monti JM, Pineyro G, Orellana C, Boussard M, Jantos H, Labraga P, Olivera S and Alvarino F (1990) Biog. Amines 7: 145–151.
12. Dugovic C, Leysen JE and Wauquier A (1989) Neurosci. Lett. 104: 320–325.
13. Ujzdszi J (1990) In: Horne J (ed.) Sleep '90. Pontenagel Press, Bochum, pp. 460–462.
14. Depoortere H (1988) In: Koella WP, Obál F, Schulz H and Visser P (eds.) Sleep '86. Gustav Fischer Verlag, Stuttgart, New York, pp. 346–348.
15. Denoyer M, Sallanon M, Kitahama K, Aubert C and Jouvet M (1989) Neuroscience 28: 83–94.
16. Murphy DL (1990) Neuropsychopharmacology 3: 457–471.

© 1991 Elsevier Science Publishers B.V. All rights reserved.
Biological Psychiatry, Volume 2. G. Racagni et al., editors.

An extract from cerebral cortex interacts selectively with 5-HT_1 receptors

Gilles Fillion, Jean-Claude Rousselle, Emilie Zifa and Olivier Massot
Pharmacologie NIE, Institut Pasteur, 28 rue du Dr Roux, F75015 Paris, France

Introduction

The serotonergic cerebral system plays an important role in depression and anxiety. Various types of 5-HT receptors are involved in its function (5-HT_1, 5-HT_2, 5-HT_3, 5-HT_4). Endogenous ligands have been presented which may interact with the 5-HT_2 cerebral receptors [1,2] and with the neuronal transport system for 5-HT [2]. The present studies were undertaken in an attempt to isolate and purify a non-monoaminergic cerebral extract that would interact selectively with 5-HT_1 receptors.

Materials and Methods

Horse brains were dissected out on ice 2 h after the sacrifice of the animal to isolate cortex, striatum and hippocampus. These tissues were homogenized in 5 volumes (w/v) of a medium containing acetic acid (1 M), EDTA (2 mM), phenylmethyl sulfonylfluoride (PMSF) (0.1 mM), and aprotinin (5 U/l) for 1 min. The homogenate was centrifuged (17,500 g for 90 min) and the supernatant was lyophilized then resuspended in 1 volume of distilled water containing EDTA (2 mM), aprotinin (5 U/l) and PMSF (0.1 mM), and extracted with 3 volumes of acetone. After filtration on a glass filter the filtrate was evaporated and extracted, using 90% isopropanol, centrifuged (17,500 g for 20 min) and the supernatant evaporated under vacuum.

The cerebral extracts resuspended in water were subjected to HPLC with reverse-phase (nucleosil 300-5-C_4 and nucleosil 100-5-C_{18}) and gel filtration (TSK HW 40 S, 30 × 1.6 cm) columns.

The binding assays for different radioligands were performed according to the literature. Proteins were measured by the method described by Lowry et al. [3].

Results

Extraction with acetic acid, acetone and isopropanol resulted in a fraction that dose-dependently inhibited [^{3}H]5-HT binding. This extract was also able to alter

Table 1. Displacing activity of the semipurified fraction

Receptor sites	Ligand	C_{18} Reverse phase	TSK Gel filtration
5-HT_1	[^{3}H]5-HT (5 nM)	0 ± 2.6	19.3 ± 18
5-HT_{1A}	[^{3}H]DPAT (1 nM)	–	70 ± 16
5-HT_2	[^{3}H]ketanserin (1 nM)	100 ± 2	130 ± 19
Muscarinic	[^{3}H]QNB (3 nM)	100 ± 1.7	99 ± 2
Histaminergic H_1	[^{3}H]mepyramine (5 nM)	53 ± 7	68 ± 14
Opioids	[^{3}H]naloxone (2 nM)	106 ± 15	–
Dopaminergic	[^{3}H]spiperone (2 nM)	90 ± 15	80 ± 7
Benzodiazepine	[^{3}H]FNZP (3 nM)	127 ± 3	92 ± 0.5
β_1 adrenergic	[^{3}H]DHA (3 nM)	100 ± 12	86 ± 7
α_1 adrenergic	[^{3}H]prazosin (2 nM)	109 ± 17	119 ± 5
5-HT uptake	[^{3}H]paroxetine (0.2 nM)	118 ± 6	–

Specific binding in the presence of the fraction is expressed as % of control.

(–40% to –60%) the binding of specific ligands to other neurotransmitter receptors.

The first chromatographic step on the C_4 reverse-phase column allowed the separation of a polar fraction displacing [^{3}H]5-HT from its 5-HT_1 sites with an EC_{50} = 19 μg equivalent protein/ml. A total displacement of [^{3}H]5-HT was observed at 60 μg/ml. At that concentration, the fraction did not significantly alter the binding of other ligands: [^{3}H]spiperone, [^{3}H]ketanserin, [^{3}H]QNB, [^{3}H]DHA, [^{3}H]prazosin, [^{3}H]naloxone, except for [^{3}H]mepyramine (32 ± 7%) and flunitrazepam (FNZP) (126 ± 3%). After C_{18} reverse-phase separation, the fraction dose-dependently inhibited the [^{3}H]5-HT binding with an EC_{50} = 5 μg/ml.

At a concentration totally displacing the [^{3}H]5-HT binding, other bindings were not significantly altered with the exception of [^{3}H]mepyramine (53 ± 7%) and FNZP (127 ± 3%).

After gel filtration on TSK HW 40 S, a single fraction was isolated which selectively inhibited the [^{3}H]5-HT binding with an apparent EC_{50} close to 2 μg equivalent protein/ml. The bindings of [^{3}H]spiperone, [^{3}H]ketanserin, [^{3}H]QNB, [^{3}H]DHA, and [^{3}H]FNZP were not significantly affected (Table 1); at a concentration of the extract totally inhibiting the [^{3}H]5-HT binding, the binding of [^{3}H]DPAT was decreased by 30%. The fraction corresponded to an apparent molecular weight close to 4000. The fraction did not significantly alter the [^{3}H]paroxetine binding at any step of the purification.

Discussion

The enriched fraction obtained through the HPLC and gel filtration procedure was able to inhibit totally the binding of [^{3}H]5-HT to the 5-HT_1 receptor sites. The selectivity of the effect increased along with the purification steps. The serotonergic specificity of this fraction was indicated by the fact that the binding of [^{3}H]5-HT to 5-HT$_1$ receptors subtypes (including 5-HT$_{1A}$) was strongly reduced, whereas the binding of other ligands, with the exception of mepyramine, was unaffected.

The displacing effect of the fraction was not due to the endogenous 5-HT, since the latter was separated and discarded during the C$_4$-HPLC chromatography.

The fact that [^{3}H]paroxetine binding was not altered indicated that the serotonergic transport site was not a target for this fraction under these experimental conditions.

The nature and the molecular mechanism of interaction of the fraction at the 5-HT$_1$ sites have not yet been determined; it is not excluded that this 4000-Da polar fraction may be peptidergic. Experiments are currently underway to further purify this fraction.

References

1. Apud JA and Ito Y (1991) J. Chromatogr. 538: 177–185.
2. Barbaccia ML, Costa E and Guidotti A (1988) Ann. Rev. Pharmacol. Toxicol. 28: 451–476.
3. Lowry OH, Rosebrough NJ, Farr AL and Randall RJ (1951) J. Biol. Chem. 193: 263–275.

© 1991 Elsevier Science Publishers B.V. All rights reserved.
Biological Psychiatry, Volume 2. G. Racagni et al., editors.

Electrophysiology of pre- and postsynaptic 5-HT$_{1A}$ receptors

G.K. Aghajanian

Departments of Psychiatry and Pharmacology, Yale University School of Medicine, 34 Park Street, New Haven, CT 06508, U.S.A.

Introduction

By autoradiography, a high density of 5-HT$_{1A}$ receptors has been found both presynaptically on 5-HT neurons of the dorsal raphe nucleus and postsynaptically in certain areas such as the hippocampus [1]. To date, molecular studies have revealed the presence of only one member of the 5-HT$_{1A}$ receptor gene family [2]. Nevertheless, as reviewed below, electrophysiologic studies show marked differences in the responses of presynaptic neurons of the dorsal raphe nucleus and postsynaptic neurons of the hippocampus to selective 5-HT$_{1A}$ ligands, suggesting that multiple 5-HT$_{1A}$ receptor subtypes may exist in the central nervous system.

Presynaptic 5-HT$_{1A}$ autoreceptors

Somatodendritic autoreceptors on 5-HT neurons in the dorsal raphe nucleus appear to be of the 5-HT$_{1A}$ subtype, as indicated by the fact that a variety of drugs with 5-HT$_{1A}$ selectivity (e.g. buspirone, ipsapirone and 8-OH-DPAT) share the ability to potently inhibit raphe cell firing [3–5]. The efficacy of 5-HT$_{1A}$ ligands has been further demonstrated by the fact that they fully mimic 5-HT in producing a hyperpolarizing effect in association with a decrease in input resistance [4]. The inhibitory/hyperpolarizing effect of 5-HT in the dorsal raphe nucleus results from an opening of K channels which is mediated via a pertussis toxin-sensitive G protein [6,7]. Consistent with its 5-HT$_{1A}$ binding properties, the inhibitory effect of ipsapirone in the dorsal raphe nucleus is also blocked by pertussis toxin [8].

Postsynaptic 5-HT$_{1A}$ receptors: Hippocampus

In contrast to their potent agonist activity in the dorsal raphe nucleus, 5-HT$_{1A}$ agonists (e.g. 8-OH-DPAT and ipsapirone) are relatively ineffective in suppressing the spontaneous activity of CA$_1$ hippocampal pyramidal cells [9]. Similarly, 5-HT$_{1A}$ agonists by themselves elicit relatively weak changes in membrane potential and input resistance [10–12]. Interestingly, prior exposure to 5-HT$_{1A}$ agonists occludes the full agonist effect of 5-HT itself. Taken together, these studies suggest that selective 5-HT agonists in the hippocampus have only a partial agonist action.

In the hippocampus, as in the dorsal raphe nucleus, pertussis toxin-sensitive G proteins have been shown to block the hyperpolarizing effect of 5-HT [13]. Furthermore, although 5-HT is negatively coupled to adenylate cyclase, the hyperpolarizing effect of 5-HT on membrane potential does not involve cAMP either in the hippocampus [13] or dorsal raphe nucleus [14]. Thus, a difference in transduction mechanisms does not appear to account for differences in the efficacy of 5-HT_{1A} agonists in the 2 areas.

Summary and Conclusions

Electrophysiologic studies from a number of laboratories have shown that selective 5-HT_{1A} ligands are potent and full agonists in the dorsal raphe nucleus but only partial agonists in the hippocampus. These findings raise the possibility that there may be distinct 5-HT_{1A} subtypes that are differentially expressed in the dorsal raphe nucleus, hippocampus and perhaps in other regions as well. Alternatively, it is conceivable that the differences in receptor reserve ("spare receptors"), rather than receptor subtype, account for the apparently greater efficacy of 5-HT_{1A} agonists in the dorsal raphe. Consistent with such a possibility is biochemical evidence for a large 5-HT_{1A} receptor reserve in the dorsal raphe nucleus [15]. Thus, in the dorsal raphe nucleus, if only a small fraction of receptor occupancy were required for a maximum response, a partial agonist could give the appearance of being a full agonist. Furthermore, if there were a greater receptor reserve in the dorsal raphe than hippocampus, sensitivity to 5-HT as well as 5-HT_{1A} should be enhanced. However, the electrophysiologic results are inconsistent with this prediction since sensitivity to 5-HT itself is identical in the dorsal raphe nucleus and hippocampus [9]. Thus, it is concluded that the differences in the efficacy of 5-HT_{1A} agonists in the 2 regions are more easily explained by multiple receptor subtypes rather than a difference in receptor reserve. If proven, the existence of multiple 5-HT_{1A} receptors would open up the possibility of developing new classes of subtype-selective pharmacologic agents.

References

1. Pazos A and Palacios JM (1985) Brain Res. 346: 205–230.
2. Hartig PR, Kao H-T, Macchi M, Adham N, Zgombick J, Weinshank R and Branchek T (1989) Neuropsychopharmacology 3: 335–347.
3. de Montigny C, Blier P and Chaput Y (1984) Neuropharmacology 23: 1511–1520
4. Sprouse JS and Aghajanian GK (1987) Synapse 1: 3–9.
5. VanderMaelen CP, Matheson GK, Wilderman RC and Patterson LA (1990) Eur. J. Pharmacol. 129: 123–130.
6. Aghajanian GK, Sprouse JS, Sheldon P and Rasmussen K (1990) Ann. NY Acad. Sci. 600: 93–103.
7. Bobker DH and Williams JT (1990) Trends Neurosci. 13: 169–173.
8. Innis RB and Aghajanian GK (1987) Eur. J. Pharmacol. 143: 195–204.
9. Sprouse JS and Aghajanian GK (1988) Neuropharmacology 27: 707–715.

10. Andrade R and Nicoll RA (1987) J. Physiol. (Lond.) 394: 99–124.
11. Colino A and Halliwell JV (1986) Eur. J. Pharmacol. 130: 151.
12. Segal M, Azmitia EC and Whitaker-Azmitia PM (1989) Brain Res. 502: 76–74.
13. Andrade R, Malenka RC and Nicoll RA (1986) Science 234: 1261–1265.
14. Innis RB, Nestler EJ and Aghajanian GK (1988) Brain Res. 459: 27–36.
15. Meller E, Goldstein M and Bohmaker K (1990) Mol. Pharmacol. 37: 231–237.

© 1991 Elsevier Science Publishers B.V. All rights reserved.
Biological Psychiatry, Volume 2. G. Racagni et al., editors.

Effects of sustained administration of tandospirone on serotonin and noradrenergic neurotransmissions

Pierre Blier, Roger Godbout and Claude de Montigny

Neurobiological Psychiatry Unit, Department of Psychiatry, Faculty of Medicine, McGill University, Montreal, Quebec, Canada H3A 1A1

Animal studies have shown that agonists of the 5-HT$_{1A}$ receptor subtype display potent anxiolytic- and antidepressant-like activities [1,2]. The therapeutic efficacy of these non-benzodiazepine 5-HT$_{1A}$ ligands of the azapirone family has now been confirmed in generalized anxiety and depressive disorders [3–5]. In contrast to the immediate anxiolytic effect of benzodiazepines, that of 5-HT$_{1A}$ agonists occurs only 1 to 2 weeks after the initiation of treatment [3–6]. This suggests that their efficacy might be related to adaptive changes in the 5-HT system due to long-term 5-HT$_{1A}$ receptor activation or to the accumulation of a clinically active metabolite. In support of the former proposal is the recent demonstration that, in the rat, long-term administration of gepirone reduces the sensitivity of the somatodendritic 5-HT autoreceptor [7]. This autoreceptor, which is of the 5-HT$_{1A}$ subtype, exerts a negative feedback control of the firing activity of 5-HT neurons. All compounds of the azapirone class share a common metabolite, 1-(2-pyrimidinyl)-piperazine (1-PP), which is an α_2-adrenoceptor antagonist [8,9]. It is possible, therefore, that alterations in noradrenergic neurotransmission might, at least in part, mediate the anxiolytic/antidepressant effects of these drugs. The present studies were performed in chloral hydrate-anesthetized rats to characterize the effects of acute and long-term administration of the 5-HT$_{1A}$ agonist tandospirone (SM-3997) on the efficacy of 5-HT and NE neurotransmissions in the rat brain [10,11].

The acute intravenous administration of tandospirone decreased the firing rates of dorsal raphe 5-HT neurons (ED$_{50}$ = 9.1 ± 1.1 μg/kg). A two-day tandospirone treatment (10 mg/kg/day, s.c.) markedly reduced their firing activity; this was followed by a partial recovery after seven days and by a complete recovery after 14 days of treatment. Following a 14-day tandospirone treatment (10 mg/kg/day, s.c.), the responsiveness of 5-HT neurons to intravenous LSD was reduced, suggesting that somatodendritic 5-HT autoreceptors had desensitized. The suppressant effects of microiontophoretically-applied tandospirone on the firing activity of CA$_3$ hippocampus pyramidal neurons was blocked by the intravenous injection of the 5-HT$_{1A}$ antagonist BMY-7378, showing that tandospirone exerts an agonistic action on postsynaptic 5-HT$_{1A}$ receptors. However, the suppressant effect of microiontophoretically applied 5-HT to these same neurons was markedly reduced by concurrent application of tandospirone, suggesting that the latter acts as a partial agonist at postsynaptic 5-HT$_{1A}$ receptors. The 14-day administration of tandospirone (10 mg/kg/day, s.c.) altered neither the effectiveness of microiontophoretically applied 5-HT and tandospirone nor that of endogenous 5-HT released by the electrical stimulation of the afferent 5-HT pathway in suppressing the firing activity of hippocampus pyramidal neurons, suggesting that postsynaptic 5-HT_{1A} receptors had not desensitized. Long-term tandospirone treatment also left unaltered the sensitivity of the terminal 5-HT autoreceptors. It is concluded that the desensitization of somatodendritic 5-HT autoreceptors permits 5-HT neurons to regain their physiologic rate of firing during long-term treatment and, consequently, to release a normal amount of 5-HT into the synaptic cleft. This, combined with the sustained activation of normosensitive postsynaptic 5-HT_{1A} receptors by tandospirone during such a treatment, should result in an enhanced tonic activation of postsynaptic 5-HT_{1A} receptors.

At low doses, 1-PP ($ED_{50} = 75 \pm 9$ µg/kg, i.v.) reversed the suppressant effect of the α-adrenoceptor agonist clonidine (20 µg/kg, i.v.) on the firing activity of noradrenergic neurons of the locus coeruleus (LC). Following 14-day treatment with tandospirone (10 mg/kg/day, s.c.), the responsiveness of these NE neurons to intravenous clonidine was decreased, but their mean firing frequency remained within the control range. The intravenous administration of 1-PP (2 to 8 mg/kg) reduced the effect of microiontophoretically applied NE on CA_3 dorsal hippocampus pyramidal neurons without affecting their responsiveness to GABA and 5-HT. The effect of the electrical stimulation of LC NE neurons in reducing pyramidal neuron firing activity, which is mediated by postsynaptic α_1-adrenoceptors, was increased by 47% following acute administration of 1-PP (4 mg/kg, i.v.), presumably as a result of terminal α_1-autoreceptor blockade. The effectiveness of the LC stimulation was unchanged following long-term treatment with tandospirone. The decrease in the effectiveness of LC stimulations obtained by increasing the frequency from 1 to 5 Hz, a phenomenon due to an increased activation of terminal α_2-adrenergic autoreceptors by endogenous NE, remained unaltered following long-term treatment with tandospirone. In addition to its initial suppressant effect, LC stimulation induces a late activation of these neurons which is mediated by ß-adrenoceptors. The degree of activation induced by LC stimulation was similar in control and long-term tandospirone-treated rats. From the effects of the acute administration of 1-PP, it is concluded that it acts as an antagonist at somatodendritic and terminal α_2-adrenergic autoreceptors as well as at postsynaptic α_2-adrenoceptors in the CNS of the rat. However, from the results obtained with long-term administration of the parent compound tandospirone, it is concluded that the levels of 1-PP attained are insufficient to modify the function of pre- and postsynaptic α_2-adrenoceptors, leaving unaltered the efficacy of NE neurotransmission.

In conclusion, the present electrophysiologic data suggest that the anxiolytic/antidepressant effect of tandospirone might be attributable to an enhanced activation of postsynaptic 5-HT_{1A} receptors, rather than to a modification of NE neurotransmission.

References

1. Traber J and Glaser T (1987) Trends Pharmacol. Sci. 8: 432–437.
2. Wieland S and Lucki I (1990) Psychopharmacology 101: 497–504.
3. Feighner JP, Merideth CH and Henrichson GA (1982) J. Clin. Psychiatry 43 (Sect. 2): 103–107.
4. Rickels K, Weisman K, Norstad N, Singer M, Stolz D, Brown A and Danton I (1982) J. Clin. Psychiatry 43 (Sect. 2): 81–86.
5. Robinson DS, Rickels K, Feighner J et al. (1990) J. Clin. Psychopharmacol. 10 (Suppl. 3): 67–76.
6. Jenkins SW, Robinson DS, Fabre LF, Andary JJ, Messina ME and Reich LA (1990) J. Clin. Psychopharmacol. 10 (Suppl. 3): 77–85.
7. Blier P and de Montigny C. (1987) Synapse 1: 470–480.
8. Engberg G (1989) J. Neural. Transm. 76: 91–98.
9. Sanghera MK, Coke JA, Williams HL and McMillen BA (1990) Brain Res. Bull. 24: 17–22.
10. Godbout R, Chaput Y, Blier P and de Montigny C (1991) Neuropharmacology (in press).
11. Blier P, Curet O, Chaput Y and de Montigny C (1991) Neuropharmacology (in press).

© 1991 Elsevier Science Publishers B.V. All rights reserved.
Biological Psychiatry, Volume 2. G. Racagni et al., editors.

Antidepressant-like behavioral effects of 5-HT_{1A} agonists

Irwin Lucki and Scott Wieland

Departments of Psychiatry and Pharmacology, University of Pennsylvania, 207 Piersol Building, Philadelphia, PA 19104-4283, U.S.A.

Introduction

Buspirone and chemical-related derivatives, such as gepirone, ipsapirone and tandospirone compose a new class of compounds termed azapirones that exert clinical anxiolytic and antidepressant effects [1]. These drugs demonstrate high affinity for 5-HT_{1A} receptors [2], which may be associated with their clinical effects [3]. The purpose of this study was to examine whether the azapirones demonstrated behavioral effects in animals that were similar to those produced by established antidepressant drugs and to study the pharmacologic mechanisms underlying those behavioral effects.

The azapirones were compared with the tricyclic antidepressants desipramine and imipramine for their ability to produce antidepressant-like effects on the forced swimming test [4]. The pharmacologic mechanism underlying the antidepressant-like behavioral effects was studied by examining the ability of the 5-HT_{1A} agonist 8-OH-DPAT to produce effects similar to those of the azapirones. Putative 5-HT_{1A} antagonists, such as pindolol or NAN-190, were examined for the ability to produce antidepressant-like effects when given alone or to block the effects of the azapirones when administered in combination. The involvement of presynaptic versus postsynaptic serotonergic mechanisms was examined by studying whether para-chlorophenylalanine (PCPA), an inhibitor of 5-HT synthesis, was able to mimic the effects of the azapirones or to alter their effects when given in combination.

Materials and Methods

Male rats were used in the forced swimming test [5] as described previously [6]. Two swim sessions were conducted: an initial 15-min pretest was followed 24 h later by a 5-min test. Drugs were administered 3 times during the period between the pretest and test sessions: 0.5, 19, and 23 h after the start of the pretest. The test sessions were videotaped and scored by an experienced rater. A rat was judged to be immobile when it remained floating in the water without struggling and making only those movements necessary to keep its head above water.

The ability of the drugs to alter the locomotor activity of rats was also examined as described previously [7]. Rats were placed in the locomotor activity chambers for 30 min after receiving drug treatments that were identical to those administered in the forced swimming test.

The following drugs were given subcutaneously in a volume of 1 ml/kg, except for imipramine and desipramine (4 ml/kg): tandospirone (5, 10, 15, and 20 mg/kg); buspirone (10 mg/kg); gepirone (10 mg/kg); ipsapirone (10 and 20 mg/kg); imipramine (5, 10, and 15 mg/kg); desipramine (5, 10, and 15 mg/kg); and 8-OH-DPAT (0.12, 0.25, 0.5, and 1.0 mg/kg).

Results

The 5-HT_{1A} agonist 8-OH-DPAT and tandospirone both produced dose-dependent reductions of immobility time in the forced swimming test [6]. These results were similar to those obtained with the established tricyclic antidepressants desipramine and imipramine. In addition, the other 5-HT_{1A} agonists buspirone, gepirone, and ipsapirone also produced reductions of behavioral immobility in the forced swimming test.

The ability of these drugs to alter locomotor activity was examined to determine whether nonspecific stimulant effects might mediate their effects in the forced swimming test. None of the drugs produced increases in activity when compared with saline.

Neither pindolol nor NAN-190 altered behavioral immobility in the test when given alone. However, pretreatment with either pindolol or NAN-190 blocked the anti-immobility effects of 8-OH-DPAT.

PCPA alone produced no effect on immobility time when compared with saline. Administration of PCPA prior to treatment with 8-OH-DPAT, tandospirone, or desipramine did not prevent or alter the magnitude of the reduction of immobility time produced by these drugs.

Discussion

This study demonstrated that drugs with high affinity for 5-HT_{1A} receptors produced antidepressant-like behavioral effects in rats. The 5-HT_{1A} agonist 8-OH-DPAT, and the azapirone compounds tandospirone, buspirone, gepirone, and ipsapirone, each produced reductions of behavioral immobility time, an effect similar to that produced by the established tricyclic antidepressants.

Pindolol and NAN-190, drugs with high affinity for 5-HT_{1A} receptors but weak efficacy, have been characterized as partial agonists or antagonists. These two drugs failed to alter behavioral immobility when given alone. When given in combination with 8-OH-DPAT, these drugs blocked the anti-immobility effects of the 5-HT_{1A} agonist. The 5-HT synthesis inhibitor PCPA was used to examine the role of 5-HT neurotransmission in the effects of antidepressant drugs on the forced swimming test. The reduction of 5-HT content by PCPA failed to mimic an antidepressant-like behavioral effect on the forced swimming test. Furthermore, PCPA pretreatment did not alter the anti-immobility effects of the 5-HT_{1A} agonists 8-OH-DPAT or tandospirone or the tricyclic antidepressant desipramine.

In conclusion, these data support the hypothesis that the 5-HT_{1A} agonist effects of the azapirones and 8-OH-DPAT mediate the antidepressant activity of these compounds. The observation that presynaptic depletion of 5-HT does not influence the effect of 5-HT_{1A} agonists on the forced swimming test provides further evidence that direct agonist effects of these compounds mediate their antidepressant effects.

Acknowledgements

This research was supported by USPHS Grants MH 36262 and MH 14654 and by Pfizer Inc.

References

1. Rickels K, Amsterdam JD, Clary C, Puzzuoli G and Schweizer E (1991) J. Clin. Psychiatry 52: 34–38.
2. Hamik A, Oksenberg D, Fischette C and Peroutka SJ (1990) Biol. Psychiatry 28: 99–109.
3. Lucki I and Wieland S (1990) Neuropsychopharmacology 3: 481–493.
4. Borsini F and Meli A (1988) Psychopharmacology 94: 147–160.
5. Porsolt RD, Anton G, Blavet N, Deniel M and Jalfre M (1978) Eur. J. Pharmacol. 47: 379–391.
6. Wieland S and Lucki I (1990) Psychopharmacology 101: 497–504.
7. Lucki I, Ward HR and Frazer A (1989) J. Pharmacol. Exp. Ther. 249: 155–164.

© 1991 Elsevier Science Publishers B.V. All rights reserved.
Biological Psychiatry, Volume 2. G. Racagni et al., editors.

Stimulation of prolactin release by 5-HT$_{1A}$ agonists

Kenneth J. Kellar[1], Susan E. Mulroney[1], Bridget Hulihan-Giblin[1], Laurie A. Pabreza[1], Caroline M. Skudlarek[1], and Anne Shemer[2]
[1]Georgetown University School of Medicine, Washington D.C.; and [2]Pfizer Inc., New York, New York, U.S.A.

Introduction

Serotonin (5-HT) agonists stimulate prolactin release in the rat [1,2]. The specific subtype of brain 5-HT receptor(s) that mediates this effect is controversial. For example, several studies found that the 5-HT$_{1A}$ agonist 8-hydroxy-2-(di-n- propyl-amino) tetralin (8-OH-DPAT) stimulates prolactin release, but this effect did not appear to be dose-related [3,4]. Furthermore, two recent studies [5,6] reported that, in contrast to other direct and indirect 5-HT agonists, 8-OH-DPAT did not increase plasma prolactin levels at all.

The main purpose of our studies was to examine the effects of 5-HT$_{1A}$ agonists on prolactin release in the rat. To do this, the time-course and dose-response relationships for prolactin release by 8-OH-DPAT, 5-methylurapidil (5-MeU) and tandospirone (SM-3997) were studied in awake rats in which a jugular vein cannula allowed multiple sampling of blood over time. In addition, the effects of 5-HT antagonists on prolactin release induced by 8-OH-DPAT, 5-MeU and tandospirone were assessed and the capacity of the agonists to desensitize the prolactin response mediated by 5-HT$_{1A}$ receptors was determined.

Methods

Male Sprague-Dawley rats (≈350 g) were anesthetized with sodium pentobarbital. A cannula made from Silastic tubing was placed in the jugular vein, inserted to the level of the heart atrium and secured with a suture. The free end of the cannula was passed under the skin and out through the dorsal surface of the neck. The cannula was filled with heparinized saline and closed with a knot. The next day, the cannula was connected to a syringe via a 38-cm length of tubing, and blood sampling and drug injections were begun at least 1 h later. Drugs were injected intravenously, and baseline blood samples were collected before each injection. Beginning ≈2 min after each drug injection, timed blood samples were collected periodically for at least 60 min. Plasma prolactin was measured by RIA using prolactin standards (RP-2 and RP-3) supplied by the National Hormone and Pituitary Program of NIDDK.

Results

Following an intravenous injection of 8-OH-DPAT, 5-MeU, or tandospirone, the plasma prolactin level increased rapidly, peaked at approximately 6 times the baseline level within 10 min after injection and returned to baseline values within 30 min after injection. The stimulation of prolactin release by each of these drugs was dose-related. The ED_{50} values for 8-OH-DPAT and 5-MeU were less than 50 μg/kg and that for tandospirone was approximately 300 μg/kg. At higher doses of tandospirone (>2 mg/kg), there appeared to be an additional increase in prolactin release which was not studied here. The tandospirone metabolite 1-pyrimidinyl piperazine (1-PP) did not increase plasma prolactin levels at a dose of 10 mg/kg.

Methysergide (3 and 5 mg/kg) and metergoline (0.3 to 3 mg/kg) both increased prolactin levels, possibly by blocking dopamine receptors in the pituitary. But within 60 min, the prolactin levels had returned to baseline levels. Pretreatment with methysergide (5 mg/kg) 60 min before agonist completely blocked the prolactin responses to 8-OH-DPAT and 5-MeU. Similarly, metergoline (3 mg/kg) nearly completely blocked the prolactin responses to 8-OH-DPAT and tandospirone.

The rapid time-course of the effects of these 5-HT_{1A} agonists on prolactin release suggested that the 5-HT_{1A} receptors that mediate the effect might desensitize rapidly. Consistent with this possibility, pretreatment with 200 μg/kg 8-OH-DPAT decreased the response to a second injection of 8-OH-DPAT given 60 to 90 min later. Similarly, pretreatment with 8-OH-DPAT decreased the response to tandospirone that was administered 1 h later. This desensitization of the effect of tandospirone by 8-OH-DPAT is further evidence that tandospirone releases prolactin by acting at 5-HT_{1A} receptors.

Discussion

The dose-response relationship for prolactin release by 8-OH-DPAT, 5-MeU and tandospirone, and the blockade of this effect by pretreatment with methysergide and metergoline, are consistent with involvement of 5-HT_{1A} receptors in prolactin release. The failure of previous studies to detect a dose-response relationship for 8-OH-DPAT-stimulated prolactin release is most likely related to the rapid time-course of this effect. That is, according to the studies presented here, if blood is sampled 15 min or more after injection, the plasma prolactin level could have returned more than 60% toward baseline from its peak. In addition, because maximum prolactin responses are seen after an intravenous dose of 8-OH-DPAT of about 200 μg/kg, a dose-response relationship could be obscured at higher doses of 8-OH-DPAT. Furthermore, the possibility of receptor desensitization may lead to diminished responses to subsequent doses of 5-HT_{1A} agonists.

These studies indicate that the plasma prolactin response to drugs such as tandospirone could be a useful measurement of 5-HT_{1A} receptor function in brain, and that the 5-HT_{1A} receptor may desensitize after high doses of agonists.

Acknowledgement

Supported by a grant from Pfizer Inc.

References

1. Clemens JA, Roush ME and Fuller RW (1978) Life Sci. 22: 2209.
2. Meltzer HY, Wiita B, Tricou BJ, Simonovic M, Fang V and Manov G. In: Ho BT (ed.) (1982) Serotonin in Biological Psychiatry. Raven Press, New York, pp. 117–138.
3. Simonovic M, Gudelsky GA and Meltzer HY (1984) J. Neural Transm. 59: 143.
4. Aulakh CS, Wozniak EM, Haas M, Hill JL, Zohar J and Murphy DL (1988) Eur. J. Pharmacol. 146: 253.
5. Van de Kar LD, Lorens SA, Urban JH and Bethea CL (1989) Neuropharmacology 28: 299.
6. Di Renzo G, Amoroso S and Targlialatela M. (1989) Eur. J. Pharmacol. 162: 371.

© 1991 Elsevier Science Publishers B.V. All rights reserved.
Biological Psychiatry, Volume 2. G. Racagni et al., editors.

Serotonin neuronal regulation of neuroendocrine function and behavior in psychiatric disorders

Dennis S. Charney, Pedro L. Delgado, John H. Krystal, Scott W. Woods, Lawrence H. Price and George R. Heninger

West Haven VA Medical Center and Yale University School of Medicine, 960 Campbell Avenue, West Haven, CT 06516, U.S.A.

Introduction

One of the most commonly used methods to assess brain serotonin (5-HT) function in human subjects has been the measurement of neuroendocrine and behavioral responses to drugs with action on 5-HT neurons. The neuroendocrine and behavioral effects of 5-HT precursors (tryptophan, 5-HTP), 5-HT reuptake inhibitors (chlorimipramine), 5-HT releasing agents (fenfluramine) and 5-HT receptor agonists (MCPP, MK-212, gepirone, isapirone, tandospirone), have been determined in healthy subjects and patients with major depression, obsessive-compulsive disorder (OCD), schizophrenia and panic disorder.

Major depression

Several research groups have reported that the prolactin and growth hormone responses to tryptophan are reduced in some depressed patients [1,2]. Consistent with these findings are the blunted neuroendocrine responses to fenfluramine [3] and chlorimipramine [4]. In contrast, the neuroendocrine and behavioral effects of the non-selective postsynaptic 5-HT receptor agonist, M-chlorophenylpiperazine (MCPP) are not altered [5]. Recent findings suggest that the hypothermic responses to the 5-HT_{1A} receptor agonist, ipsapirone, may be reduced in depressed patients [5].

Considered together, the available data suggest that presynaptic regulation of serotonin function may be abnormal in depression. These results may be related to the recent demonstration that rapid depletion of plasma tryptophan and consequently, brain 5-HT, by administration of an amino acid drink produces a temporary relapse in patients remitted on antidepressant drugs [7].

Obsessive-compulsive disorder

The hypothesis that the pathophysiology of OCD is associated with an abnormality of 5-HT function is primarily based on the therapeutic effectiveness of potent serotonin reuptake inhibitors. Challenge studies with MCPP in OCD patients have yielded mixed results. Several groups have found that oral MCPP exacerbates OCD symptoms. The cortisol and in some cases, the prolactin responses to oral MCPP and MK-212, and fenfluramine have been reported to be blunted in OCD [8]. However, low and high doses of intravenous MCPP produce similar neuro-endocrine and behavioral effects in OCD patients and healthy subjects [9].

Schizophrenia

Interest in 5-HT function in schizophrenia has been sparked by the demonstration that clozapine is a superior antipsychotic drug. It has been speculated that clozapine's efficacy may relate to an ability to antagonize 5-HT_2 and 5-HT_{1C} receptors. Several groups have recently studied the effects of MCPP (which is a 5-HT_{1C} receptor agonist) in schizophrenic patients, and there are indications that MCPP may have psychotomimetic effects in these patients [10]. If this work is replicated, it supports the view that some serotonin receptor subtypes may be involved in the pathophysiology and treatment of schizophrenia.

Panic disorder

Preclinical studies of the neurobiology of anxiety and fear and the antianxiety properties of 5-HT_{1A} agonists and serotonin reuptake inhibitors implicate a role for 5-HT in anxiety disorders. Intravenous tryptophan and MCPP (high- and low-dose) produce similar neuroendocrine and behavioral effects in patients with panic disorder as in healthy subjects. On the other hand, oral MCPP and fenfluramine may produce increased anxiogenic and neuroendocrine responses in panic disorder patients [11]. Ongoing studies are determining the neuroendocrine and behavioral effects of serotonin agents in patients with Post-Traumatic Stress Disorder and Generalized Anxiety Disorder.

Concluding comments

Extensive preclinical and clinical investigations indicate that serotonin neurons are involved in a wide range of behavioral and somatic functions. The complexity of the involvement of serotonin in the central nervous system is supported by the discovery of at least 7 different 5-HT receptor subtypes. It is likely that in the future, dysfunction of the 5-HT system will more specifically be defined in several neuropsychiatric disorders. Moreover, the numerous 5-HT receptor subtypes offer an excellent opportunity for the discovery of novel therapeutic agents.

References

1. Deakin JFW, Pennell I, Upadhyaya AJ and Lofthouse R (1990) Psychopharmacology 101: 85–92.
2. Heninger GR, Charney DS and Sternberg DE (1984) Arch. Gen. Psychiatry 41: 398–402.
3. Siever LJ, Murphy DL, Slater S, de la Vega E and Lipper S (1984) Life Sci. 34: 1029–1039.
4. Golden RN, Hsiao JK, Lane E et al. (1990) Psychiatr. Res. 31: 39–47.
5. Kahn RS, Wetzler S, Asnis GM, Papolos D and van Praag HM (1990) Biol. Psychiatry 28: 358–362.
6. Lesch KP, Mayer S, Disselkamp-Tietze J, Hoh A, Schoelnhammer G and Schulte HM (1990) Life Sci. 46: 1271–1277.
7. Delgado PL, Charney DS, Price LH, Aghajanian GK, Landis H and Heninger GR (1990) Arch. Gen. Psychiatry 47: 411–418.
8. Murphy DL, Zohar J, Benkefat C, Pato MT, Pigott TA and Insel TR (1989) Br. J. Psychiatry 155: 15–24.
9. Insel TR (1990) Psychiatr. Ann. 20: 560–562.
10. Deutch AY, Moghaddam B, Inis RB, Krystal JH, Aghajanian GK, Bunney BS and Charney DS (1991) Schizophr. Res. 4: 121–156.
11. Charney DS, Krystal JH, Southwick SM, Nagy LM, Woods SW and Heninger GR (1990) Psychiatr. Ann. 20: 593–602.

© 1991 Elsevier Science Publishers B.V. All rights reserved.
Biological Psychiatry, Volume 2. G. Racagni et al., editors.

Glutamate receptors and nitric oxide formation

John Garthwaite

Department of Physiology, University of Liverpool, Brownlow Hill, P.O. Box 147, Liverpool L69 3BX, U.K.

Nitric oxide (NO) is a novel messenger molecule which is being found to operate in an increasing number of tissues. In blood vessels, for example, it is responsible for endothelium-dependent vasodilation [1]; when produced by macrophages and other phagocytic cells, NO contributes to their cytostatic and cytotoxic effects [2]. In the nervous system, NO was first identified as the intercellular messenger which mediates the actions of glutamate on cyclic GMP levels in the cerebellum [3]. Since then, knowledge of the way that NO operates in brain and peripheral nerve has increased substantially.

It is now clear that there are at least two enzymes (synthases) responsible for the formation of NO. In both cases, NO is produced from one of the two guanidino nitrogens of the amino acid, L-arginine, and the reaction requires NADPH and molecular oxygen. However, the brain and endothelial type enzyme is constitutively active and strictly Ca^{2+}-dependent, whereas the macrophage type is inducible (by, for example, endotoxin) and is Ca^{2+}-independent [4–6]. It is not known if macrophage-type cells (microglia) in the central nervous system can express the inducible enzyme, or if there are different isoforms of the Ca^{2+}-dependent enzyme in different brain areas.

Two models for the way that NO functions in the nervous system have emerged. In one, glutamate (and possibly other) receptor activation activates a postsynaptic NO synthase by eliciting Ca^{2+} influx or mobilization. Unlike with conventional second messenger systems, the NO so-formed does not appear to act within the neurones that produce it. This is probably because, even though they may contain NO-sensitive guanylate cyclase, the same concentrations of Ca^{2+} (100 to 500 nM) that activate the NO synthase, inhibit the guanylate cyclase [4]. Instead, due to the rapid diffusion of NO through membranes, the molecule appears designed to act on neighbouring cells and thus serves as a novel mediator of cell-cell communication. The targets appear to be both neuronal and glial.

In the second model, NO is produced presynaptically, presumably in response to action potential-dependent Ca^{2+} influx, and then diffuses to its target cells which, again, may be neuronal or glial. There are now many examples of NO functioning in the peripheral nervous system in such a transmitter-like capacity to evoke muscle relaxation [7].

The brain area in which the NO system has been studied most vigorously is the cerebellum. There are at least two pathways associated with NO formation. One is the mossy fibre-granule cell pathway. Here glutamate is the likely neurotransmitter and it activates both NMDA and AMPA receptors on granule cells. However, NO formation appears to be linked selectively to NMDA receptors, presumably because of the high Ca^{2+} permeability of their associated ion channels. In the developing cerebellum, NO formation is dominated by this linkage to NMDA receptors; indeed, this link is present remarkably early on, well before any synapses have been formed. The targets of the NO include other granule cells, the afferent mossy fibre terminals, and adjacent astrocytes [7].

The other main locus of the NO system is in the molecular layer where climbing fibres, which make powerful excitatory synapses with Purkinje cells, represent one source of NO [8]. These fibres are believed to be involved in the triggering of long-term changes in synaptic strength at other excitatory synapses with Purkinje cells, those of the granule cell axons, or parallel fibres. This long-term depression of parallel fibre-Purkinje cell synaptic transmission is thought to represent a cellular correlate of cerebellar learning behaviour. Recent evidence suggests that the NO released from climbing fibres plays a necessary role in this phenomenon [9].

Acknowledgement

Research on NO was funded by the Medical Research Council.

References

1. Moncada S, Palmer RMJ and Higgs EA (1989) Biochem. Pharmacol. 38: 1709–1715.
2. Marletta MA (1989) Trends Biochem. Sci. 14: 488–492.
3. Garthwaite J, Charles SL and Chess-Williams R (1988) Nature 336: 385–388.
4. Knowles RG, Palacios M, Palmer RMJ and Moncada S (1989) Proc. Natl. Acad. Sci. U.S.A. 89: 5159–5162.
5. Bredt DS, Hwang PM and Snyder SH (1990) Proc. Natl. Acad. Sci. U.S.A. 87: 682–685.
6. Tayeh MA and Marletta MA (1989) J. Biol. Chem. 264: 19654–19658.
7. Garthwaite J (1991) Trends Neurosci. 14: 60–67.
8. Southam E and Garthwaite (1991) Eur. J. Neurosci. 3: 379–382.
9. Shibuki K and Okada D (1991) Nature 349: 326–328.

© 1991 Elsevier Science Publishers B.V. All rights reserved.
Biological Psychiatry, Volume 2. G. Racagni et al., editors.

Regulation of neuronal Ca^{2+} by excitatory amino acids

Richard J. Miller

Department of Pharmacological and Physiological Sciences, The University of Chicago, 947 East 58th Street, Chicago, IL 60637, U.S.A.

Introduction

Glutamate is the neurotransmitter at the majority of excitatory synapses within the central nervous system. Not only is glutamate responsible for fast excitatory neurotransmission, but it is also responsible for a variety of longer-term plastic changes in synaptic strength such as long-term potentiation and long-term depression. Furthermore, excessive stimulation of glutamate receptors can lead to the death of neurons in the brain [1]. Many of the longer-term effects of glutamate require the participation of second messenger molecules, particularly Ca^{2+} [2]. I shall summarize the various ways by which activation of glutamate receptors can increase intracellular Ca^{2+} levels, $(Ca^{2+})_i$ in neurons.

Kainate/AMPA receptors

These types of glutamate receptor are responsible for the actions of the glutamate agonists, kainate, quisqualate and AMPA and antagonists such as CNQX and DNQX [3]. AMPA and quisqualate appear to act as partial agonists at these receptors. A traditional view of the kainate receptor is that it activates an ion channel that is only permeable to monovalent cations such as Na^+ and K^+, but is impermeable to divalents such as Ca^{2+} [2,4]. Activation of kainate receptors at glutamatergic synapses is responsible for fast synaptic transmission. However, molecular biological experiments have revealed an increased complexity for these types of glutamate receptor. Five kainate receptor subunits have now been cloned. These have been named GluR1 to GluR5 [5–9]. All of these appear to be related to each other, particularly the first four. It is thought likely that kainate receptors formed in vivo are made up of combinations of these subunits, although all of them can form ion channels when expressed by themselves in oocytes. Experiments on the first three types of kainate receptor have been particularly interesting. For example, kainate receptors that contain the GluR2 subunit in combination with either of the others form a traditional kind of kainate receptor with a linear I/V curve and very low permeability to Ca^{2+}. However, when kainate receptors are formed from GluR1, GluR3 or combinations of the two, an ion channel is formed that shows high degree of inward rectification as well as a high permeability to Ca^{2+} [10]. Such Ca^{2+}-permeable kainate channels have in fact been observed in hippocampal [11] and Purkinje neurons (unpublished observations) in culture. It is therefore quite likely that at some synapses where NMDA receptors are not found, glutamate-mediated phenomena that require the participation of Ca^{2+} ions may utilize these Ca^{2+}-permeable kainate receptors.

NMDA receptors

Glutamate receptors that are activated by the glutamate agonist, N-methyl-D-aspartate acid (NMDA) have been very intensively studied. These receptors regulate an ion channel that has a very high permeability to Ca^{2+} [2]. In fact, it is about 10 times more permeable to Ca^{2+} ions than to Na^+. Activation of these receptors by glutamate therefore allows the entry of a large amount of Ca^{2+} into the nerve cell directly, in addition to producing cell depolarization. It is thought likely that in many cases the NMDA receptor is responsible for supplying the Ca^{2+} that mediates phenomena such as long-term potentiation (LTP) and nerve cell degeneration. NMDA receptors have a well developed pharmacology, being blocked by competitive antagonists such as APV as well as by non-competitive antagonists that have binding sites within the NMDA-gated ionophore [3]. These include molecules such as PCP and MK-801. NMDA receptors are generally found to be inhibited by prevailing physiological concentrations of Mg^{2+}. However, the block of the receptor is voltage-dependent and can be relieved by cell depolarization. Thus, NMDA receptors are generally thought to be utilized most when synapses are being strongly activated, to an extent that is great enough to relieve the Mg^{2+} block of the receptor. In addition to Mg^{2+}, several other regulatory substances such as glycine, Zn^{2+} and polyamines have been identified, all of which can produce profound effects upon the receptor in vitro. Each of these binding sites has its own individual pharmacology.

The metabotropic glutamate receptor

This glutamate receptor differs from the others by virtue of the fact that it is not a ligand-gated ionophore. This type of glutamate receptor is linked via G-proteins to various effector mechanisms [12,13]. The first kind of effector to which the metabotropic glutamate receptor was found to be linked was the enzyme phospholipase C. Activation of this enzyme produced increased intracellular levels of IP_3 and subsequently Ca^{2+} mobilization. Indeed, glutamate-mediated Ca^{2+} mobilization has been observed in a number of neuronal types [14]. However, it has recently been observed that activation of metabotropic glutamate receptors can also give rise to other cellular responses such as cell depolarization due to the turning off of a variety of K^+ conductances and also possibly due to stimulation of Na^+/Ca^{2+} exchange [13]. Metabotropic glutamate receptors have now been cloned [15]. They are found in various parts of the brain, but are particularly highly concentrated in the granule and Purkinje cells of the cerebellum as well as in certain portions of the hippocampus. The physiological role of these receptors is not really clear at present. No reliable antagonist has yet been identified. However, a rather specific agonist, "trans ACPD", has been synthesized [12] and its use is currently been widely employed in order to further understand the physiological role of this kind of glutamate receptor.

References

1. Mayer ML and Miller RJ (1990) Trends Pharmacol. Sci. 11: 254–260.
2. Choi DW (1990) J. Neurosci. 10: 2493–2501.
3. Watkins JL, Krogsgaard-Larsen P and Honoré T (1990) Trends Pharmacol. Sci. 11: 25–34.
4. Barnard EA and Henley JM (1990) Trends Pharmacol. Sci. 11: 500–507.
5. Hollman M, O'Shea-Greenfield A, Rogers SW and Heinemann S (1989) Nature 342: 643–648.
6. Boulter J, Hollmann M, O'Shea-Greenfield A, Hartley M, Deneris E, Maron C and Heinemann S (1990) Science 249: 1033–1037.
7. Keinanen K, Wisden W, Sommer B, Werner P, Herb A, Verdoorn TA, Sakmann B and Seeburg PH (1990) Science 249: 556–560.
8. Nakanishi N, Schneider NA and Axel R (1990) Neuron 5: 583–595.
9. Bettler B, Boulter J, Hermans-Bourgmeyer I, O'Shea-Greenfield A, Deneris ES, Moll C, Bourgmeyer V, Hollmann M and Heinemann S (1990) Neuron 5: 583–595.
10. Hollmann M, Hartley M and Heinemann S (1991) Science (in press).
11. Iino M, Ozawa S and Tsuzuki K (1990) J. Physiol. 424: 151–165.
12. Schoepp D, Bockaert J and Sladeczek F (1990) Trends Pharmacol. Sci. 11: 508–515.
13. Charpak S, Gähwiler BH, Do KQ and Knöpfel T (1990) Nature 347: 765–767.
14. Murphy SN and Miller RJ (1989) Mol. Pharmacol. 35: 671–680.
15. Masu M, Tanabe Y, Tsuchida K, Shigemoto R and Nakanishi S (1991) Nature 349: 760–765.

© 1991 Elsevier Science Publishers B.V. All rights reserved.
Biological Psychiatry, Volume 2. G. Racagni et al., editors.

Ganglioside antagonism of neuronal Ca^{2+} homeostasis destabilization induced by excitotoxic amino acids

Hari Manev, Alessandro Guidotti and Erminio Costa

Fidia-Georgetown Institute for the Neurosciences, Georgetown University Medical School, Washington D.C. WA 20007, U.S.A.

Introduction

Glutamate and other excitatory amino acids (EAAs) can cause neuronal death through a process of excitotoxicity (ET) that stems in a non-physiological, paroxysmal, "abusive" glutamate receptor stimulation [1,2]. This occurs when the glutamate concentration of interstitial fluids is abnormally high due to the increased glutamate release and the impaired glutamate re-uptake, triggered by the damage or the death of glutamatergic neurons (brain ischemia, trauma). The most explored strategy for the treatment of the ensuing pathology has been the use of receptor antagonists – the potential clinical advantages of such an approach being shadowed by:

a) difficulties in obtaining a simultaneous blockade of multiple subtypes of glutamate receptors [3];
b) side-effects that result from a generalized blockade of glutamate receptors in the CNS which include a complex deficit in cardiorespiratory and blood pressure functions, motor disorders, and cognitive imbalance [4,5];
c) antagonist-induced primary neuronal damage [6].

A new therapeutic alternative to this approach is the strategy of the receptor abuse-dependent antagonism (RADA) that selectively targets drugs downstream from the receptor, i.e. to the site where neuronal homeostatic mechanisms are destabilized by paroxysmal receptor stimulation.

This avoids that identical receptors, attending to a variety of functions – some of them of a potential compensatory value in the pathology such as ischemic brain damage – are blocked simultaneously throughout the brain [7,8].

Materials and Methods

Experiments were performed in primary cultures of newborn rat neurons (cerebellar granule and cerebral cortical neurons) [9]. Biochemical, electrophysiological and morphological assays were performed as previously described [7–9].

Results and Discussion

In the intracellular expression of the homeostatic destabilization (Table 1) triggered by persistent glutamate receptor stimulation, the sustained destabilization of $[Ca^{2+}]_i$ homeostasis, which is triggered by a protracted membrane translocation of PKC, appears to be a crucial event – at least when abusive stimulation of NMDA-selective glutamate receptors contributes to excitotoxicity. Gangliosides, and even more potently their synthetic derivatives (LIGA4, LIGA20), protect from glutamate ET without affecting the basal or agonist-stimulated activity of ionotropic and metabolotropic glutamate receptors (Table 1). In vivo, in the photochemical model of stroke [1]) induced by injecting the rats intravenously with 80 mg/kg rose Bengal and focally illuminating the scull, the resulting behavioral deficit can be recovered by pretreatment (1 day) with GM1 or LIGA4 (50 and 10 mg/kg, i.v., respectively), followed by a subcutaneous post-treatment (4 days) [16]. This suggests that the RADA profile of these drugs is also operative in vivo.

Table 1. RADA of glutamate excitotoxicity (ET) is achieved through the stabilization of EAA-impaired homeostasis of protein kinase C (PKC) translocation and intraneuronal free Ca^{2+}

Signal transduction step (STS)	Drug	Effect on STS	Effect on ET	Reference
PKC	TPA	Down-regulation	Protection	10
	GM1, GT1b, LIGA4 LIGA20, PKS3	Inhibition of protracted translocation	Protection	7,9,11
$[Ca^{2+}]_iH$	EGTA	Reversal of protracted increase	Protection	11,12
	GM1, LIGA4	Reversal of protracted increase	Protection	11,12
Calpain I	Leupeptin, NAN	Inhibition	No	13
	GM1, LIGA4	Indirect inhibition	Protection	13
ODC	DFMO	Inhibition	No	14
	GM1	No	Protection	14
NO	SNP	Inhibition	Protection from NMDA/potentiation of kainate	14

RADA: receptor abuse-dependent antagonism; ET: excitotoxicity; STS: signal transduction step; PKC: protein kinase C; TPA: phorbol 12-myristate 13 acetate; $[Ca^{2+}]_iH$: intraneuronal free calcium homeostasis; GM1, GT1b: natural gangliosides; LIGA4, LIGA20, PKS3: synthetic sphingolipids; NAN: N-acetyl-Leu-Leu-norleucinal; DFMO: difluoromethylornithine; ODC: ornithine decarboxylase; NO: nitric oxide; SNP: sodium nitroprusside; NMDA, N-methyl-D-aspartate.

Acknowledgement

This work was supported in part by NIH Grant PO1 NS28130.

References

1. Olney JW and Sharpe LG (1968) Science 166: 386–388.
2. Choi DW (1990) In: Guidotti A (ed.) Neurotoxicity of Excitatory Amino Acids. Raven Press, New York, pp. 235–242.
3. Wroblewski JT and Danysz W (1989) Ann. Rev. Pharmacol. Toxicol. 29: 441–474.
4. Abrahams TP, Gillis RA, Hamosh P and Taveria Da Silva AM (1988) Soc. Neurosci. Abstr. 14: 937.
5. Luby ED, Cohen RC, Rosenbaum B, Gottlieb JS and Kelly R (1959) Arch. Neurol. Psychiatry 81: 363–369.
6. Olney JW, Labruyere J and Price MT (1989) Science 244: 1360–1362.
7. Manev H, Favaron M, Vicini S, Guidotti A and Costa E (1990) J. Pharmacol. Exp. Ther. 252: 419–427.
8. Manev H, Costa E, Wroblewski JT and Guidotti A (1990) FASEB J. 4: 2789–2797.
9. Favaron M, Manev H, Siman R, Bertolino M, Ferret B, Guidotti A and Costa E (1988) Proc. Natl. Acad. Sci. U.S.A. 85: 7351–7355.
10. Favaron M, Manev H, Siman R, Bertolino M, Sly AM, DeErausquin G, Guidotti A and Costa E (1990) Proc. Natl. Acad. Sci. U.S.A. 87: 1983–1987.
11. Manev H, Favaron M, Guidotti A and Costa E (1989) Mol. Pharmacol. 36: 106–112.
12. DeErausquin GA, Manev H, Guidotti A, Costa E and Brooker G (1990) Proc. Natl. Acad. Sci. U.S.A. 87: 8017–8021.
13. Manev H, Favaron M, Siman R, Guidotti A and Costa E (1991) J. Neurochem. (in press).
14. Manev H, Caredda S, Lombardi G, Guidotti A and Costa E (1991) In: Barnard EA and Costa E (eds.) Transmitter Amino Acid Receptors: Structures, Transduction and Models for Drug Development, Raven Press, New York, (in press).
15. Dietrich WD, Watson BD, Busto R, Ginsberg MD and Bethea JR (1987) Acta Neuropathol. (Berl.) 72: 315–325.
16. Manev H, Lombardi G, Francioni S, Armstrong DM, Guidotti A and Costa E (1991) Soc. Neurosci. Abstr. (in press).

© 1991 Elsevier Science Publishers B.V. All rights reserved.
Biological Psychiatry, Volume 2. G. Racagni et al., editors.

Tryptophan metabolites, NMDA receptors and neuropsychiatric disorders

P. Russi[1], G. Lombardi[1], R. Pellicciari[2], M. Alesiani[1], G. Cherici[1] and F. Moroni[1]
[1]*Department of Pharmacology, University of Florence, Viale Morgagni 65, 50134 Florence; and* [2]*Department of Medicinal Chemistry, Via del Liceo 3, 06100 Perugia, Italy*

Introduction

The brain contains several electrophysiologically active tryptophan (TRP) metabolites such as 5-HT, quinolinic (QUIN) and kynurenic (KYNA) acids. While 5-HT has been widely investigated in pharmacological and psychiatric research during the last 40 years, information on the possible role of QUIN and KYNA in brain function is sparse. This paucity exists in spite of several observations published in the early sixties reporting modifications of TRP metabolism in affective and schizophrenic disorders [1] and the largely diffused knowledge that a TRP-poor diet is associated with a variety of mental disturbances (typically present in cases of pellagra) which cannot be explained by a decrease of 5-HT formation. In fact, these disturbances are different from those obtained with treatments with agents able to inhibit TRP-hydroxylase, the rate-limiting enzyme for 5-HT formation.

The possibility that mental and neurologic disturbances due to a TRP-poor diet could be ascribed to abnormal regulation of QUIN and KYNA synthesis and release has been recently proposed [2]. One of the problems in studying the role of QUIN and KYNA in experimental models of brain pathology is their peculiar electrophysiological activity. QUIN is an NMDA agonist while KYNA antagonizes glutamate (and QUIN) induced excitation by interacting with the glycine recognition site of the NMDA receptor ion channel complex. Thus when both QUIN and KYNA accumulate in the brain, the experimental results may be partially obscured by their mutually antagonistic actions. Recently significant changes in the brain content of QUIN and KYNA have been described in hepatic encephalopathy [3], Huntington's chorea [4] and in AIDS-associated dementia [5]. In our opinion a better knowledge of the mechanisms controlling the formation and the release of QUIN and KYNA in the brain is necessary before proposing their causal involvement in brain disorders.

Selective changes of QUIN and KYNA content in the brain

The presence and distribution of QUIN and KYNA in the mammalian brain have been carefully reported [6,7]. In rats and humans QUIN is more concentrated in the cortex and KYNA in the brain-stem. Both of them accumulate in the brain of aged mammals and a circadian rhythm for brain KYNA content has been described in rats. QUIN and KYNA are substrates for the organic acid transport system and their concentration in the brain increases in probenecid-treated animals [6,7]. However, the relative importance of this transport or of other metabolic mechanisms involved in their inactivation has not been studied. The regulation of their synthesis is also a matter of debate. Thus it is clear that TRP administration to different animal species results in increased content of both QUIN and KYNA (see Table 1).

However, a metabolic pathway leading to QUIN formation independent of TRP has been reported [8] and it has been shown that the brain concentration of QUIN may increase in rats fed a TRP-free diet for 15 days. Nevertheless, several indirect observations suggest that TRP may be the main source of brain QUIN and KYNA under normal nutritional conditions. Two different enzymes can open the indole ring of TRP and start the formation of the kynurenines. The first of these enzymes is TRP-pyrrolase (E.C.1.13.11.11). It is located exclusively in the liver and may be induced by repeated steroid administration. The second enzyme is indoleamine-2,3, dioxygenase (IDO, E.C.1.13.11.11). It is present in most organs including the brain, and may be induced by bacterial toxins through a mechanism involving the formation of intermediaries of the immune system such as interferons and interleukins. While the induction of TRP-pyrrolase decreased brain QUIN content, the induction of IDO, obtained by administering endotoxins, increased the cortical content of both QUIN and KYNA (see Table 1). The endotoxin-induced accumulation of both QUIN and KYNA in the brain could explain the neuropsychiatric symptomatology present during different infectious diseases. We attempted to separate the accumulation of brain QUIN from that of KYNA by inhibiting kynurenine hydroxylase, one of the enzymes leading to QUIN formation. This was performed by using nicotinilalanine (NAL), an analogue of kynurenine, described in the early sixties [9]. Another approach to selectively increased brain KYNA content was the administration of IPA, a cheto analogue of TRP [10]. As reported in Table 1, IPA selectively increased brain KYNA content and NAL facilitated the

Table 1. Relative changes of QUIN and KYNA content in rat cortex

	KYNA	QUIN	Ratio
Controls	100	100	1.0
LPS (250 μg/kg i.p.)	140[a]	130[a]	1.1
LPS + NAL (200 mg/kg i.p.)	230[ab]	110	2.1
TRP (200 mg/kg i.p.)	190[a]	430[a]	0.4
IPA (250 mg/kg i.p.)	200[a]	130[a]	1.5
TRP + NAL	450[ac]	180[ac]	2.5

The content of KYNA in the cortex of 2–3 month-old rats was 33 ± 5 pmol/g tissue and that of QUIN 350 ± 40 pmol/g tissue. LPS were injected 24 h before, while NAL, TRP and IPA 2 h before sacrifice; [a]$P < 0.05$ vs. control; [b]$P < 0.01$ vs. LPS; [c]$P < 0.01$ vs. TRP.

accumulation of KYNA induced by endotoxins or TRP administration. Furthermore, HAL reduced QUIN neosynthesis. In separate experiments we observed that HAL had several pharmacological properties (it antagonized audiogenic or kynurenine-induced seizures and it prevented ethanol withdrawal syndrome), which supports the hypothesis of specific roles for both QUIN and KYNA in brain function.

References

1. Cazzullo CL, Mangoni A and Mascherpa G (1966) Br. J. Psychiatry 112: 157–161.
2. Stone TW (1990) In: Quinolinic Acid and the Kynurenines. CRC Press, Boca Raton, Florida.
3. Moroni F, Lombardi G, Carla' V, Pellegrini D, Carassale GL and Cortesini C (1986) J. Neurochem. 46: 869–874.
4. Schwarcz R, Okuno E, White RJ, Bird ED and Whetsell WO (1988) Proc. Natl. Acad. Sci. U.S.A. 84: 4079–4081.
5. Heyes MP, Brew B, Martin A, Markey SP, Price R and Salazar A (1989) Ann. Neurol. 26: 589–592.
6. Moroni F, Lombardi G, Carla' V and Moneti G (1984) Brain Res. 295: 352–355.
7. Moroni F, Russi P, Lombardi G, Beni M and Carla' V (1988) J. Neurochem. 51: 177–181.
8. Baran H and Schwarcz R (1990) J. Neurochem. 55: 738–744.
9. Decker RH, Brown RR and Price JM (1963) J. Biol. Chem. 238: 1049–1053.
10. Russi P, Carla' V and Moroni F (1989) Biochem. Pharmacol. 38: 2405–2409.

© 1991 Elsevier Science Publishers B.V. All rights reserved.
Biological Psychiatry, Volume 2. G. Racagni et al., editors.

Phencyclidine, σ binding sites and the NMDA receptor complex

Patricia Boksa, Isabelle Chaudieu, Howard Mount, Yvan Dumont and Remi Quirion
Douglas Hospital Research Center and Departments of Psychiatry, and Pharmacology and Therapeutics, Faculty of Medicine, McGill University, 6875 Blvd. LaSalle, Verdun, Quebec, H4H 1R3, Canada

Introduction

Phencyclidine (PCP) is a well known drug of abuse interacting with multiple targets in the CNS [1–3]. However, most of its unique pharmacological profile is now believed to be due to the modulatory actions of PCP on the N-methyl-D-aspartate (NMDA) receptor complex [1–3], and to a lesser extent on the dopamine uptake system [4] and the σ receptor [1,2,5].

Recently, we demonstrated that NMDA as well as non-NMDA receptors modulate dopamine release in rat cultured mesencephalic cells [6–9]. Thus, this appeared as a good model to investigate functional interactions between PCP and the NMDA receptor complex. Additionally, we also evaluated possible interactions between PCP/NMDA, σ and neuropeptide Y (NPY) receptor systems on the basis of recent evidence suggesting interactions between NMDA and σ receptors [10], and between PCP, σ and NPY binding sites [11,12], respectively.

Materials and Methods

Dissociated cell cultures were prepared from anterior ventral mesencephalic tissue of gestation day 15 Sprague-Dawley rat fetuses [6]. Cultures were grown in Dulbecco's modified Eagle's medium, supplemented with 10% v/v fetal calf serum and 20 mM KC1. After 6 days, cells were rinsed and loaded with [^{3}H]dopamine (DA, 50 nM, 20 Ci/mmol, New England Nuclear, Boston, MA) in the presence of desipramine (50 μM) to block uptake of DA by noradrenergic neurons [6]. Effects on [^{3}H]DA release of various concentrations of PCP and related drugs, alone or in the presence of 10 μM NMDA or kainate were determined as described earlier [7–9]. Evoked [^{3}H]DA release was expressed as a percent of the total [^{3}H]DA uptake into cells and data analyzed as described before [7–9]. In another series of experiments, possible interactions between PCP, σ, NPY and PYY receptor sites in the rat brain were assessed as described before [13] using 2 nM [^{3}H]TCP, 2 nM [^{3}H]DTG, 40 pM [^{125}I]Bolton-Hunter NPY or 40 pM [^{125}I]PYY as radioligands. Sources of drugs used here have been reported elsewhere [9,13].

Results and Discussion

We have previously shown that excitatory amino acids stimulate [^{3}H]dopamine release by acting on NMDA as well as non-NMDA receptors in rat mesencephalic cell cultures [7]. In that model, PCP and related drugs such as MK-801, as well as competitive NMDA receptor antagonists (CPP and APV) blocked, in a concentration-dependent manner, NMDA-stimulated (100 μM) [^{3}H]DA release without affecting that of kainate [7]. The antagonistic effects of PCP and MK-801 on NMDA-stimulated [^{3}H]DA release were observed at concentrations ranging between 5–50 μM (IC_{50}; 2.0 μM) and 1–5 μM (IC_{50}; 0.3 μM), respectively [7]. DTG, a purported σ ligand [14] was unable to enhance NMDA-stimulated [^{3}H]dopamine release at concentrations up to 100 nM while at higher doses (1–10 μM), it blocked NMDA-induced [^{3}H]DA release, a PCP-like effect. This suggests the lack of direct interactions between NMDA and σ receptor sites in our model, in contrast to other preparations [5,10]. This indicates that modulation of NMDA-receptor sensitivity by σ-related drugs is a region-dependent phenomenon.

In regard to the possible interaction of NPY and related peptides with PCP and/or σ receptors [11], we investigated the effects of these peptides on NMDA and kainate-induced [^{3}H]DA release in mesencephalic cell culture and in CNS binding assays. At relatively high concentrations (μM) both NPY and PYY were able to significantly block NMDA-stimulated [^{3}H]DA release [13]. However, in contrast to PCP and MK-801, both peptides also blocked, with similar efficacies, kainate-induced [^{3}H]dopamine release. In binding assays, we failed to obtain direct evidence for interactions between [^{3}H]TCP, [^{3}H]DTG, [^{125}I]BH-NPY and [^{125}I]-PYY sites since NPY and PYY failed to compete for PCP and σ bindings; PCP and DTG being unable to compete for either NPY and PYY receptors [13]. Taken together, these results provide evidence against the existence of direct interactions between the NMDA/PCP receptor complex and NPY receptors.

At concentrations ≥100 μM, PCP and related compounds induced, by themselves, [^{3}H]DA release in rat mesencephalic cells (Table 1). Thus these drugs have 2 opposing effects in this model, namely an inhibition of NMDA-stimulated [^{3}H]DA release at low concentrations and direct stimulatory action at higher ones [7,9]. The direct stimulating effect of high concentrations of PCP (1 mM, 4.5 ± 0.3% of intracellular stores of [^{3}H]DA) was shared by congeners including TCP (1 mM, 6.2 ± 0.4%) and MK-801 (1 mM 3.1 ± 0.2%) and the σ ligand DTG (1 mM, 3.2 ± 0.2%) but not by the competitive NMDA antagonist APV the dopamine uptake blocker, GBR 12909. This suggests that the NMDA receptor complex and the dopamine uptake site are not mediating the direct effects of PCP and related drugs on [^{3}H]DA release. In order to assess further the possible involvement of the σ receptor, the effects of 2 prototypical ligands, namely (+)- and (−)-SKF10,047 were evaluated. At high concentrations (1 mM) both stimulated, in a naloxone-insensitive manner, the release of [^{3}H]DA ((+)SKF10,047: 6.2 ± 0.4%; SKF10,047: 6.4 ± 0.3%). This is rather atypical of known σ receptors on which the (+)stereoisomer is generally found to be more active [2,5].

PCP has also been found to block K^+ channels at relatively high concentrations (10–100 μM) [15,16]. We observed that 4-aminopyridine, a K^+ channel blocker [17], induced [^{3}H]DA release in our preparation (1 mM, 4.9 ± 0.4%). Thus, It may be that K^+ channels are involved, at least partly, in the mediation of [^{3}H]DA release induced by high concentrations of PCP and congeners.

In summary, PCP and analogues, via their blockade of the NMDA receptor-associated channel, antagonize the stimulating effects of NMDA receptor agonists on [^{3}H]DA release in fetal mesencephalic cells. Additionally, these drugs, can, at higher concentrations directly stimulate [^{3}H]DA release, possibly by acting on K^+ channels. These opposite actions of PCP-like drugs on dopaminergic systems could have an important functional implication in view of the eventual uses of PCP-related analogues in neurological and psychiatric disorders.

References

1. Quirion R (1986) In: Boulton AA, Baker GB and Hrdina P (eds.) Neuromethods, Vol. IV. Humana Press Inc., New Jersey, pp. 499–542.
2. Quirion R, Chicheportiche R, Contreras PC, Johnson KM, Lodge D, Tam SW and Woods JH (1987) Trends Neurosci. 10: 444–446.
3. Wood PL and Rao TS (1989) Prog. Neuro-Psychopharmacol. Biol. Psychiatry 13: 519–523.
4. Chaudieu I, Vignon J, Chicheportiche M, Kamenka JM, Troiller G and Chicheportiche R (1989) Pharmacol. Biochem. Behav. 32: 699–705.
5. Su TL (1991) Eur. J. Biochem. (in press).
6. Mount H, Welner S, Quirion R and Boksa P (1989) J. Neurochem. 52: 1300–1310.
7. Mount H, Quirion R, Kohn-Alexander J and Boksa P (1990) Synapse 5: 271–280.
8. Mount H, Quirion R, Chaudieu I and Boksa P (1990) J. Neurochem. 55: 268–275.
9. Mount H, Boksa P, Chaudieu I and Quirion R (1990) Can. J. Physiol. Pharmacol. 68: 1200–1206.
10. Monnet FP, Debonnel G and de Montigny C (1990) Eur. J. Pharmacol. 179: 441–445.
11. Roman FJ, Pascaud XP, Duffy O, Vauché D, Martin B and Junien JL (1989) Eur. J. Pharmacol. 174: 301–302.
12. Monnet FP, Debonnel G and de Montigny C (1990) Eur. J. Pharmacol. 182: 207–208.
13. Quirion R, Mount H, Chaudieu I, Dumont Y and Boksa P (1991) In: Kameyama T, Nabeshima T and Domino EF (eds.) NMDA Receptor Related Agents: Biochemistry, Pharmacology and Behavior. NPP Books, Michigan (in press).
14. Weber E, Sonders M, Quarm M, McLean S, Poo S and Keana JFW (1986) Proc. Natl. Acad. Sci. U.S.A. 83: 8784–8788.
15. Albuquerque EX, Aguayo LG, Warnick JE, Weinstein H, Glick SD, Maayani S, Ickowicz RK and Blaustein MP (1981) Proc. Natl. Acad. Sci. U.S.A. 78: 7792–7796.
16. Sorensen RG and Blaustein MP (1988) Biochem. Pharmacol. 37: 511–519.
17. Bowman WC and Savage AO (1981) Rev. Pure Appl. Pharmacol. Sci. 2: 317–371.

© 1991 Elsevier Science Publishers B.V. All rights reserved.
Biological Psychiatry, Volume 2. G. Racagni et al., editors.

Electrophysiological characterization of the NMDA receptor

Jon W. Johnson[1] and Philippe Ascher[2]
[1]*Department of Behavioral Neuroscience, University of Pittsburgh, Pittsburgh, PA 15260, U.S.A.; and*
[2]*Laboratoire de Neurobiologie, Ecole Normale Supérieure, 46 rue d'Ulm, 75230 Paris, France*

Fast synaptic communication within vertebrate nervous systems relies on a relatively small number of receptor classes. Receptors activated by L-glutamate comprise the major class of receptors involved in fast excitatory neurotransmission. Although it has been known for more than 30 years that glutamate can excite central vertebrate neurons, our present knowledge of glutamate-activated responses in vertebrates rests largely on the surge of interest and research that has taken place over the past decade. The realization that there are numerous types of glutamate receptors was an important advance that has helped propel recent research.

The number of different types of known glutamate responses is in a growth phase. A primary division can be made into those responses that appear to be mediated through G-proteins and second messenger systems ("metabotropic" responses), and those that are mediated by ligand-gated ion channels ("ionotropic" responses, analogous to the nicotinic acetylcholine response). There is a well described metabotropic response in brain neurons that is linked to the phosphatidylinositol second messenger system, and at least one other type of metabotropic response found in retina that may be linked to intracellular cyclic-GMP concentration. Among the ionotropic responses, the clearest division is between those receptors activated specifically by N-methyl-D-aspartate (termed NMDA receptors) and a probably more diverse group of receptors that are specifically activated by other ligands (non-NMDA receptors). The agonists that have been most commonly used to identify non-NMDA receptors are quisqualate, kainate, and AMPA. This group of receptors is now being studied by molecular biological as well as pharmacological approaches and results from both approaches suggests that the group exhibits great diversity. The final class of glutamate receptors, NMDA receptors, is the subject of this presentation.

The NMDA receptor has numerous qualities that clearly distinguish it from other ligand-gated ion channels. The first described unusual property is a strong voltage dependence under normal physiological conditions. Voltage dependence at hyperpolarized voltages results in the near complete blockage of NMDA responses at a neuron's normal resting potential. This block is due to the entry of extracellular Mg^{2+} into the channel associated with the NMDA receptor (the NMDA channel), preventing the flow of current through the channel [1,2]. Depolarization favors the absence of Mg^{2+} in the channel, and so relieves the block. Thus, whereas most neurotransmitter receptors are activated simply by the presence of agonist, the activation of the NMDA response requires two signals: the presence of agonist, and depolarization. In addition to the block by extracellular Mg^{2+} that is increased with hyperpolarization, the NMDA channel is subject to a voltage-dependent block by intracellular Mg^{2+} [3]. This block is increased by cell depolarization. The requirement for two signals has allowed the NMDA receptor to play an important role in some models of associative memory formation, a process in which synaptic strength has been proposed to increase only when two signals arrive at the same postsynaptic cell at the same time.

A second important property of the NMDA response is its high Ca^{2+} permeability [4]. The large increase in intracellular Ca^{2+} concentration that results from opening of the NMDA channel can result in the activation of numerous Ca^{2+}-dependent enzymes. This property provides a potential link between receptor activation and changes in the long-term characteristics of a cell by the activity of Ca^{2+}-dependent enzymes. This link is hypothesized to be important for physiological processes such as the establishment of proper synaptic connections during development, and strengthens the possibility that NMDA receptors are involved in the induction of some forms of memory. The Ca^{2+} permeability of the NMDA receptor is also thought to contribute to neuronal death following a variety of insults to the nervous system, such as anoxia, and may be involve in the etiology of some nervous system diseases.

A third property of the NMDA receptor that sets it apart from other known agonist-activated channels is its dependence on agonist binding at the glycine site [5]. Ligand-gated ion channels usually have more than one agonist binding site, but in general the same agonist acts at each site. The NMDA receptor depends not only on agonist binding at the NMDA site, but also on the binding of a different agonist at a site that has high affinity for glycine. The physiological importance of this site is not at present clear. However, study of the interaction of glycine with the NMDA receptor is fundamental to understanding of NMDA receptor function. There also may be potential for exploitation of the glycine site for pharmaceutic modulation of NMDA receptor activity.

Due to the probable involvement of the NMDA receptor in numerous pathologies of the nervous system, sites at which it can be blocked may be of clinical significance. Along with the NMDA and glycine binding sites, a third site at which there is potential for drugs to limit NMDA channel activity is the PCP site [6]. Numerous compounds, including PCP, MK-801 and ketamine, have high affinity for a site thought to be located close to or within the NMDA channel. The binding of these drugs prevents current flow through the NMDA channel, possibly by a mechanism similar to that by which Mg^{2+} blocks the channel. Their inhibitory action resembles that of Mg^{2+} in that both exhibit strong voltage dependence, but the slow kinetics of block at the PCP site distinguish it from the block by Mg^{2+}.

NMDA receptor activity can be modulated at numerous other sites. The known actions of Zn^{2+}, polyamines, agents that change the oxidation-reduction state of the receptor and hydrogen ions all can modulate channel activity at apparently distinct sites. Investigation of the diverse and growing number of modulatory sites on the

NMDA receptor is rapidly expanding our understanding of its functioning. In addition, these sites may eventually provide novel means of changing NMDA receptor function therapeutically.

References

1. Nowak L, Bregestovski P, Ascher P, Herbet A and Prochiantz A (1984) Nature 307: 462–465.
2. Mayer M, Westbrook GL and Guthrie PB (1984) Nature 309: 261–263.
3. Johnson JW and Ascher P (1990) Biophys. J. 57: 1085–1090.
4. MacDermott AB, Mayer ML, Westbrook GL, Smith SJ and Barker JL (1986) Nature 321: 519–522.
5. Johnson JW and Ascher P (1987) Nature 325: 529–531.
6. Lodge D and Anis NA (1982) Eur. J. Pharmacol. 77: 203–204.

© 1991 Elsevier Science Publishers B.V. All rights reserved.
Biological Psychiatry, Volume 2. G. Racagni et al., editors.

Psychopharmacological effects and therapeutic potential of NMDA antagonists

D.J. Sanger, G. Perrault, D. Joly and E. Morel
Synthélabo Recherche (LERS), 31 ave P.V. Couturier, 92220 Bagneux, France

The NMDA receptor has several sites at which different pharmacological agents act. In recent years a number of compounds have been described with affinity for the transmitter recognition site (e.g. AP7, CPP, CGS 19755, LY 2330053), the associated ion channel (dizocilpine, phencyclidine, ketamine), the strychnine-insensitive glycine site (7-chlorokynurenate, HA-966, ACPC) and the polyamine site (ifenprodil, SL 82.0715). The in vivo pharmacological profiles of some of these compounds have been subjected to systematic experimental analysis and the results of such studies indicate several potential therapeutic activities for NMDA antagonists.

Anticonvulsant activity

Compounds acting at all 4 sites associated with the NMDA receptor complex have been found to have anticonvulsant effects in experimental animals [1]. Procedures used in this research include seizures induced by electroshock, pentylenetetrazol, NMDA and electrical kindling and convulsions seen in photosensitive baboons and sound-sensitive mice (DBA/2). Thus, NMDA antagonists have broad-spectrum anticonvulsant activity which may be indicative of clinical potential in the treatment of epilepsy. However, for many of these compounds, the therapeutic index is relatively low, as other undesirable pharmacological effects occur at doses similar to or only slightly higher than those showing anticonvulsant activity. Non-competitive NMDA antagonists acting at the ion channel, such as dizocilpine and the dissociative anesthetics, produce excitation in rodents including increased locomotion, stereotyped movements and ataxia whereas many competitive antagonists have marked muscle relaxant activity [2]. In contrast, non-competitive antagonists which act at the polyamine site (ifenprodil, SL 82.0715) produce muscle relaxation at doses higher than those showing anticonvulsant activity and have not been observed to produce stimulant effects.

Anxiolytic effects

A number of recent studies have described the effects of NMDA antagonists in behavioural tests used for evaluating anxiolytic drugs. Both competitive (e.g. CPP) and non-competitive (e.g. dizocilpine) antagonists have been found to increase rates of punished responding, although effects often show considerable variation and seem less consistent and smaller than those typically observed with clinically active anxiolytics such as the benzodiazepines [3]. It has recently been reported, however, that in at least one experimental model, separation-induced vocalizations in rat pups, compounds acting at the glycine site produce anxiolytic-like activity at doses considerably lower than those producing a general disruption of behaviour [4]. The polyamine site ligands ifenprodil and SL 82.0715 are inactive in several tests in rats and mice predictive of clinical anxiolytic activity.

Learning and memory

Long-term potentiation, a neurophysiological phenomenon which has been associated with different forms of neural plasticity including learning and memory, is known to be disrupted by NMDA antagonists. It has also been shown that both competitive and non-competitive NMDA antagonists disrupt learning in several procedures including passive avoidance and spatial tasks [5,6]. Such results may indicate that the therapeutic use of some NMDA antagonists would be compromised by the production of cognitive disturbances. However, it has also been proposed that compounds with partial agonist activity at the NMDA receptor might be used in the treatment of cognitive disorders. Another possibility is that antagonists acting at different sites might differentially affect memory processes. Ifenprodil and SL 82.0715, for example, did not disrupt the acquisition of a passive avoidance response in mice even at doses which produced substantial decreases in exploratory behaviour [7].

Discriminative stimulus effects

Non-competitive NMDA antagonists acting at the ion channel produce characteristic discriminative stimuli in several species of experimental animals (rats, pigeons, rhesus monkeys [2,8]). There is cross-generalization between different drugs in this class (e.g. phencyclidine and dizocilpine), indicating that compounds acting at the ion channel may all produce similar subjective effects. The extent to which competitive antagonists (AP7, CPP, CGS 19755) or compounds acting at the glycine site (HA-966, L 687,414) substitute for phencyclidine, ketamine or dizocilpine has shown considerable variation although results are never as consistent as those reported with different non-competitive antagonists [8]. Ifenprodil and SL 82.0715 are not generalized by rats trained to discriminate either phencyclidine or dizocilpine [9], suggesting that they will not give rise to phencyclidine-like subjective effects and are unlikely to be abused.

Conclusions

Compounds acting at different sites within the NMDA receptor complex exhibit both similarities (e.g. anticonvulsant activity) and differences (e.g. stimulus properties) in their pharmacological effects. Thus, given the physiological importance of NMDA receptors and the complex and differential psychopharmacological profiles of different antagonists it is likely that compounds will be identified with therapeutic potential at doses widely separated from those giving rise to undesirable side-effects.

References

1. Chapman AG (1991) In: Meldrum BS (ed.) Excitatory Amino Acid Antagonists. Blackwell, London, pp. 265–286.
2. Woods JH, Koek W, France CP and Moerschbaecher JM (1991) In: Meldrum BS (ed.) Excitatory Amino Acid Antagonists. Blackwell, London, pp. 237–264.
3. Sanger DJ and Jackson A (1989) J. Pharmacol. Exp. Ther. 248: 1215–1221.
4. Kehne JH, McCloskey TC, Baron BM, Chi EM, Harrison BL, Whitten JP and Palfreyman MG (1991) Eur. J. Pharmacol. 193: 283–292.
5. Morris RGM (1989) J. Neurosci. 9: 304–3057.
6. Venable N and Kelly PH (1990) Psychopharmacology 100: 214–221.
7. Sanger DJ and Joly D (1991) Psychopharmacology (in press).
8. Willetts J, Balster RL and Leander JD (1990) Trends Pharmacol. Sci. 11: 423–428.
9. Sanger DJ and Jackson A (1988) Psychopharmacology 96: 87–92.

© 1991 Elsevier Science Publishers B.V. All rights reserved.
Biological Psychiatry, Volume 2. G. Racagni et al., editors.

Glutamate receptor pharmacology: A novel approach to the treatment of schizophrenia

Arvid Carlsson, Maria Carlsson and Anders Svensson
Department of Pharmacology, University of Göteborg, P.O. Box 33031, S-400 33 Göteborg, Sweden

Introduction: Anatomical considerations

This paper will discuss the hypothesis that excitatory amino acids (EAA), despite their excitatory action at the level of the cell membrane, may nevertheless serve important inhibitory functions at the behavioral level. In particular, the question will be addressed of whether the traditionally assumed inhibitory influence of the cerebral cortex on subcortical structures may be exerted via corticofugal, notably corticostriatal glutamatergic/aspartatergic pathways.

We have postulated the existence of a negative feedback loop (or rather a series of parallel feedback loops), starting out in the cerebral cortex and passing through the striatum and pallidum (including both their dorsal and ventral, "limbic" portions) to the thalamus on which an inhibitory action is postulated, resulting in a restriction of the sensory information relayed to the cortex as well as reduced arousal [1]. Since the number of inhibitory GABAergic neurons from the striatum to the thalamus is assumed to be uneven, the excitatory influence of the cortico-striatal pathway on the striatum will be converted into an inhibitory influence on the thalamus. The neuronal chain from the striatum to the thalamus includes: 1) one GABAergic neuron from the striatum to the lateral globus pallidus; 2) one GABAergic neuron from the latter structure to the subthalamic nucleus; 3) one glutamatergic neuron from the latter structure to the medial globus pallidus; and 4) one GABAergic neuron from the latter structure to the thalamus (see Carlsson et al., this volume and [2]). The thalamic nuclei involved are the ventrolateral, dorsomedial and intralaminar nuclei. The ventrolateral nucleus is connected to the dorsal striatum and may be chiefly involved in the control of motor functions, whereas the dorsomedial nucleus belongs to the "limbic" system. The intralaminar nuclei belong to an unspecific system involved in the control of cortical arousal. The mesencephalic reticular formation may form part of this negative feedback system. The thalamocortical fibers appear to be predominantly glutamatergic.

The glutamatergic-dopaminergic balance

The dopaminergic pathways from the mesencephalon to the dorsal and ventral striatum appear to be important modulators of this negative feedback loop. They appear to exert an inhibitory influence on the striatum and are thus antagonistic to the corticostriatal glutamatergic pathways. Hyperdopaminergia should thus result in reduced striatal inhibition on the thalamus and thus in an opening of the thalamic filter and increased arousal. Excessive hyperdopaminergia is known to be psychotogenic and may mimic schizophrenia. Conversely, hypoglutamatergia induced by the NMDA receptor antagonist PCP (phencyclidine, "angel dust") is likewise psychotogenic and is capable of mimicking schizophrenia even more faithfully than dopaminergic agonists.

According to our hypothesis, the striatum is fundamentally involved in sensorimotor gating and perhaps especially in the habituation mechanism. Closely related to habituation is apparently the so-called prepulse inhibition of the startle response. This inhibition is antagonized both by dopaminergic agonists and by PCP given systemically. In addition, local administration of dopamine into the nucleus accumbens has the same effect [3].

Considerations on the pathogenesis of schizophrenia will thus have to take into account not only a hyperdopaminergic but also a hypoglutamatergic dysfunction. Possibly some of the cognitive defects and negative symptoms of schizophrenia may be more easily understood in terms of a hypoglutamatergic dysfunction.

We have investigated the behavioral interactions of the glutamatergic and other aminergic systems in mice. Even in the absence of monoamines in the brain, NMDA antagonists can induce movements which occur independently of monoaminergic mechanisms. In addition, NMDA antagonists can dramatically increase the responsiveness of dopaminergic and α-adrenergic receptors to their respective antagonists. Cholinergic mechanisms are also involved in these interactions. From these studies, it may be concluded that glutamatergic pathways in cooperation with cholinergic pathways are capable of inhibiting psychomotor activity independently of monoaminergic mechanisms but that they are also capable of strongly suppressing the responsiveness of monoaminergic receptors. In addition, they may cause inhibition of monoaminergic transmitter release (see Carlsson et al., this volume and [2]).

The obvious therapeutic implications of these findings are that glutamatergic agonists may have antipsychotic properties. A problem here is the excitotoxic actions of the EAA. Partial agonists or the development of agonists acting on glutamatergic receptor subtypes not involved in excitotoxicity may be strategies to circumvent this obstacle. Therapeutic trials in schizophrenic patients with glycine, which has glutamatergic agonist properties by acting on an allosteric site on the NMDA receptor, have yielded partly encouraging results. Whereas the glycine precursor milacemide was ineffective when given to otherwise untreated patients [4], glycine given to patients on neuroleptic treatment caused significant though marginal improvement [5]. Given the interactions described above, glycine in combination with neuroleptics might be expected to be more efficacious than glycine alone.

References

1. Carlsson A (1988) Neuropsychopharmacology 1: 179-186
2. Carlsson M and Carlsson A (1990) Trends Neurosci. 13: 272–276.
3. Geyer MA, Swerdlow NR, Mansbach RS and Braff DL (1990) Brain Res. Bull. 25: 485–498.
4. Tamminga CA (1990) Paper read at ACNP Satellite Conference on New Research Directions in the Development of Atypical and Other Novel Antipsychotic Medications, San Juan, Puerto Rico, December 15, 1990.
5. Potkin S (1990) Paper read at ACNP Satellite Conference on New Research Directions in the Development of Atypical and Other Novel Antipsychotic Medications, San Juan, Puerto Rico, December 15, 1990.

© 1991 Elsevier Science Publishers B.V. All rights reserved.
Biological Psychiatry, Volume 2. G. Racagni et al., editors.

Neuroprotective potential of NMDA receptor antagonists

Bernard Scatton, Christopher Carter and Jesus Benavides
Synthélabo Recherche (LERS), Department of Biology, 31 Avenue Paul Vaillant-Couturier, 92220 Bagneux, France

Introduction

Stroke is the third leading cause of morbidity and mortality in the western world today. With both ischaemic and haemorrhagic stroke, the outcome is a severe reduction in cerebral blood flow which deprives the affected area of the brain of glucose and oxygen thus leading to tissue death with as consequence severe neurological deficits. At present there is no treatment which can limit brain damage during an acute stroke episode. However, recent animal experiments have shown that pharmacological blockade of a subclass of glutamate receptor, the N-methyl-D-aspartate (NMDA) receptor, may offer a promising therapeutic perspective for the treatment of stroke patients.

The excitotoxic hypothesis of ischaemic brain injury

Recent studies have suggested that an overactivity of excitatory amino acid transmitter systems plays a cardinal role in the pathogenesis of ischaemic neuronal injury (see [1–4] for review). Following brain ischaemia, large quantities of glutamate and aspartate accumulate in and around the ischaemic zone and cause an overexcitation of NMDA receptors, with as consequence a massive entry of calcium ions (through NMDA receptor gated calcium channels) at toxic levels into the target cell. Raised intracellular calcium concentrations promote delayed neuronal death by activating intracellular proteases and phospholipases and by causing irreversible mitochondrial and cytoskeletal damage. During ischaemia, not only is the NMDA receptor overstimulated by the build-up of extracellular glutamate/aspartate but the control mechanisms that normally prevent its use (voltage-sensitive blockade by magnesium ions of the channel, energy-dependent ion pumping mechanisms) are overridden by the increase in extracellular potassium and energy failure. Another late factor that could contribute to the deregulation of the NMDA receptor in brain ischaemia is an increase in polyamine metabolism [3–5]. The levels of endogenous polyamines and the activity of the polyamine synthesizing enzyme ornithine decarboxylase are increased following cerebral ischaemia in several animal species. Moreover, NMDA receptor activation selectively increases extracellular levels of spermine and spermidine in the rat striatum in vivo. It is thus possible that excessive release of polyamines following ischaemia contributes to neurotoxic damage and to the propagation of the phenomenon of delayed neuronal death through their inherent neurotoxic properties and/or via their interaction with the modulatory polyamine site on the NMDA receptor.

Anti-ischaemic potential of NMDA receptor antagonists

NMDA receptor antagonists markedly reduce neuronal damage observed in vivo in animals after focal or global ischaemia and in vitro in neuronal cultures deprived of oxygen and/or glucose (see ref. [1–5] for review). In models of focal ischaemia in the rat, cat and mouse, all types of NMDA receptor antagonists (recognition site antagonists, channel blockers, glycine and polyamine antagonists) very effectively reduce the infarct size (assessed histochemically) either when given before or after the occlusion of the middle cerebral artery. The degree of neuroprotection afforded by NMDA antagonists is very large. For example, when given following focal ischaemia in mice MK-801 and SL 82.0715 can reduce cortical infarction (assessed by measuring glial proliferation) by 93 and 72%, respectively. NMDA antagonists also reduce hippocampal damage after global ischaemia induced by bilateral carotid occlusion in the gerbil and after bilateral carotid occlusion with induced hypotension in the rat. The fact that a considerable reduction in ischaemic brain damage has been achieved when NMDA antagonists were administered several hours after the onset of ischaemia supports the existence of a late (or progressive) ischaemic neuronal death and suggests that there is a window of opportunity for successful therapeutic intervention, though limited to the initial hours that follow the primary insult. The neuroprotective potential of NMDA antagonists is not limited to brain ischaemia as this class of drugs is also capable of affording protection against traumatic brain and spinal injury [6] and against methamphetamine-induced neurotoxicity [7].

A serious problem with non-competitive NMDA receptor antagonists acting at the channel site is the possible occurrence of psychotomimetic effects, memory disturbances [8] and apparent neurotoxicity in specific populations of rat cortical neurons [9]. However, these undesirable side-effects of NMDA receptor antagonists appear to depend on the specific component of the NMDA receptor with which they interact, as a number of other compounds that block the effects of NMDA at other sites (glycine, polyamine) do not possess such properties.

Conclusion

NMDA receptor blockers may provide a novel attractive approach for the treatment of cerebral ischaemia and brain trauma. In view of the suspected involvement of an overactivity of excitatory amino acid systems and NMDA receptors in the pathophysiology of a number of chronic degenerative diseases and AIDS dementia, the neuroprotective ability of NMDA antagonists may be relevant to a large number of neurological disorders.

References

1. Albers GW, Goldberg MP and Choi W (1989) Ann. Neurol. 25: 398–403.
2. Rothman SM and Olney JW (1986) Ann. Neurol. 19: 105–111.
3. Scatton B, Carter C, Benavides J and Giroux C (1991) Cerebrovasc. Dis. 1: 121–135.
4. Scatton B and Carter C (1989) Circ. Métab. Cerveau 6: 185–210.
5. Carter C, Benavides J, Dana C, Schoemaker H, Perrault G, Sanger D and Scatton B (1991) In: Meldrum BS (ed.) Excitatory Amino Acid Antagonists. Blackwell Scientific Publications, London, pp. 130–163.
6. Faden AI, Demediuk P, Panter SS and Vink R (1989) Science 244: 798–800.
7. Sonsalla PK, Nicklas J and Heikkila R (1989) Science 243: 398–400.
8. Willetts J, Balster RL and Leander JD (1990) Trends Pharmacol. Sci. 11: 423–428.
9. Olney JW, Labruyere J and Price MT (1989) Science 24: 1360–1362.

© 1991 Elsevier Science Publishers B.V. All rights reserved.
Biological Psychiatry, Volume 2. G. Racagni et al., editors.

Early stroke trial (EST): Study protocol and results of the adjudication process

A. Carolei, C. Fieschi, C. Argentino, G.L. Lenzi, E. Bottacchi, S. Muntoni, D. Inzitari, E. Ott, F. Gerstenbrand, J. Bogousslavsky, A. Portera-Sanchez, S. Horowitz, G.L. Brambilla, U. Senin, A. Bes, D. Gambi, G. Kraemer, K. Einhaeupl, A. Mamoli and R. Bruno
Istituto di Scienze Neurologiche, Università degli Studi di Siena, Siena, Italy

Introduction

GM1-Ganglioside is a complex glycolipid normally present in the cell membranes of mammalian nervous tissue. The parenteral administration of exogenous GM1 demonstrated a definite role in nervous tissue repair process, by means of its favorable influence on many functional, biochemical, and behavioural parameters after traumatic or ischemic lesions [1–7].

On the basis of these data we designed a clinical trial to evaluate safety and efficacy of GM1 in patients affected with acute ischemic stroke.

Patients and Methods

The Early Stroke Trial (EST) is a randomized, stratified, double-blind placebo-controlled trial to assess the effect of GM1-monosialotetraexosilganglioside in reducing the rate of mortality and change in the Canadian Neurological Scale (CNS) score at 4 months, in patients who have had an acute ischemic stroke in the carotid territory (within 5 h from the onset of symptoms).

The EST organization included 16 clinical centers (8 in Italy, 1 in the U.S.A., 2 in Germany, 2 in Austria, 1 in Switzerland, 1 in Spain and 1 in France), a coordinating and clinical monitoring center and appropriate policy, adjudication and monitoring committees.

The steering committee had overall responsibility for the study. A central adjudication committee was responsible for validating the eligibility of patients entered into the study and the outcome events reported by the investigators. An independent advisory-review and treatment effects monitoring committee (ARTEMC) with necessary expertise was responsible for ongoing monitoring of safety and efficacy.

Potentially eligible patients were those admitted to the emergency room of one of the participating centers because of a focal cerebral deficit of acute onset in the carotid territory. A computed tomogram (CT) brain scan was required, primarily to rule out disease processes other than cerebral infarction.

Patients included were those evaluated, randomized and treated with the first dose of GM1 (or placebo) within 5 h from the onset of stroke. Excluded patients were the following: younger than 35 or older than 80 years; subjects with stupor or coma; with diseases which might interfere with the neurological assessment or with survival during the follow-up period; pregnant women; with clinical or CT evidence of intracerebral hemorrhage, brain tumor, subarachnoid hemorrhage or subtentorial lesion; involved in any other experimental trial; refusing participation in the trial or with a CNS score greater than 8.5.

GM1 was supplied in glass ampoules containing a 2-ml solution of 100 mg of monosialotetraexosilganglioside. The placebo ampoules were identical in appearance and packaging. The treatment regimen was two 100-mg ampoules, to be administered as a single intravenous dose no later than 5 h from the onset of stroke and a second intravenous dose of 100 mg, 12 h after the first. Afterwards the patients received a daily dose of 100 mg intravenously from day 2–10 and finally an intramuscular dose of 100 mg from day 11–21.

Eligible patients giving informed consent were allocated to either GM1 or placebo according to a randomization chart generated separately for each of the clinical centers.

The initial clinical assessment included a general physical and neurological examination, medical history and details of the qualifying stroke together with application of the Barthel Scale assessed by history, the Canadian Neurological Scale (CNS) and the Toronto Scale.

Clinical follow-up assessments were made daily by means of these scales, from day 1–15, at day 21 and at 2 and 4 months. At these follow-up visits general physical and neurological examinations, newly-observed signs and symptoms, concomitant therapies and adverse experiences were recorded.

Laboratory examinations, ECG and brain CT scan were performed on admission (within 5 h from the onset of stroke) and during the follow-up period. Compliance was assessed by the responsible physician. Cerebral angiography of the symptomatic carotid district was performed following brain CT scan, within 5 h from the onset of stroke. When angiography could not be performed or was contraindicated, Doppler sonography of neck arteries and transcranial Doppler (TCD) were performed.

The primary analysis of efficacy was based on mortality rate and changes in the CNS score at 4 months.

Results

The study lasted 40 months, from May 1987 to August 1990. A screening of 8,781 patients was performed. The main characteristics of these patients were recorded in the stroke registry. Only 833 subjects (9.4%) were eligible for the study. Twenty-

Table 1. Accrual by center of randomized patients (n = 805)

Center	Pts. (n)	Center	Pts. (n)
Rome	121	Lausanne	37
Cagliari	114	Madrid	37
Perugia	103	Mainz	34
Bergamo	67	Florence	26
Aosta	56	Toulouse	25
New York	54	Munich	20
Chieti	54	Graz	9
Innsbruck	42	Pavia	6

eight of them refused to be included. As a consequence, the 16 participating centers enrolled a total of 805 patients (Table 1). At entry 13 of these 805 randomized patients (1.6%) were ruled truly ineligible (without the disease of interest) and 22 (2.7%) technically ineligible (with minor protocol violations).

Seventeen patients (2.1%) did not complete the treatment (early discontinuation), 44 (5.5%) lacked one or more of the requested examinations but were alive at 4 months (incomplete data) while 5 patients (0.6%) were definitely lost at 2–4 months follow-up.

The demographic characteristics of the enrolled patients, with the expected sex differences for myocardial infarction, smoking and alcohol abuse are reported in Table 2.

The final distribution of patients, according to the assumed stratification factors (age, sex and severity of the neurological deficit, assessed by means of the CNS at entry) is reported Table 3.

One hundred and sixty-three patients (20.2%) have died. The highest mortality rates were reached in the OFS (39.2%) and OMS (27.0%) strata. The 30-day mortality represented 69% of the total rate. Sixty-nine (42.4%) patients had a

Table 2. Demographic characteristics and risk factors at entry

	Female	Male
Sex (%)	44.5	55.5
Mean age (yrs)	69.5	66.2
Severity (CNS score)	5.1	5.5
Diabetes (%)	10.1	9.6
Hypertension (%)	29.1	28.3
Previous TIA-RIND (%)	9.7	12.5
Congestive heart failure (%)	2.5	2.4
Myocardial infarction (%)	3.5	6.9
Atrial fibrillation (%)	12.2	11.1
Smoking (%)	5.2	27.8
Alcohol abuse (%)	0.7	7.2

Table 3. Patient distribution (%) according to stratification factors

Female	44.5	>65 years	65.8	CNS >5	53.5
Male	55.5	≤65 years	34.2	CNS ≤5	46.5
Y= ≤65 years		F = Female		L (Less severe)	= CNS >5
O= >65 years		M= Male		S (Severe)	= CNS ≤5

cerebral cause of death, 39 (23.9%) a cardiac or sudden death, 53 (32.5%) a non-vascular death and 2 (1.2%) an unknown cause of death.

References

1. Leon A, Dal Toso R, Presti D et al. (1988) J. Neurosci. 8: 746–753.
2. Favaron M, Manev H, Alho H et al. (1988) Proc. Natl. Acad. Sci. U.S.A. 85: 7351–7355.
3. Toffano G, Benvegnù D, Bonetti AC et al. (1980) J. Neurochem. 35(4): 861–866.
4. Karpiak SE, Li YS and Mahadik SP (1987) Stroke 18: 184–187.
5. Bassi S, Albizzati MG, Sbacchi M, Frattola L and Massarotti M (1984) J. Neurosci. Res. 12: 493–498.
6. Argentino C, Sacchetti ML, Toni D et al. (1989) 20: 1143–1149.
7. Reivich M, Dora E, Tanaka K et al. (1984) Clin. Neuropharmacol. 7(1): 597.

Study organization

Chairman: Cesare Fieschi (Rome)

Participating centers: C. Argentino (Rome), E. Bottacchi (Aosta), S. Muntoni (Cagliari), D. Inzitari (Florence), E. Ott (Graz), F. Gerstenbrand (Innsbruck), J. Bogousslavsky (Lausanne), A. Portera-Sanchez (Madrid), S. Horowitz (New York), G.L. Brambilla (Pavia), U. Senin (Perugia), A. Bes (Toulouse), D. Gambi (Chieti), G. Kraemer (Mainz), K. Einhaeupl (Munich) and A. Mamoli (Bergamo).

Steering committee: C. Fieschi (Chairman), G.L. Lenzi (Study Coordinator), R. Bruno, F. Dorsey and W. Rocca.

ARTEMC (Advisory-review and treatment effect monitoring committee): M. Walker (Chairman), J.D. Easton, M. Gent and R. Roberts.

Central adjudication committee: A. Carolei (Chairman), A. Ardia, C. Argentino, R. Bruno (Project Leader), G. Sancesario and E. Olivi.

Analysis center: F. Grigoletto (University of Padua)

Clinical monitoring: T. Alonso (1st year), F. Berni, A. Bianchetti, J. Klesing, C. Martinazzo, D. Poonian and G. Salvato.

© 1991 Elsevier Science Publishers B.V. All rights reserved.
Biological Psychiatry, Volume 2. G. Racagni et al., editors.

Study of the psychomotor, mnesic and subjective effects of SL 82.0715, a new anti-ischaemic NMDA antagonist, in healthy subjects

P. Danjou[1], A.J. Puech[2], D. Warot[2], T. Hergueta[3] and P.L. Morselli[1]

[1]Synthélabo Recherche (LERS), 58 rue de la Glacière, 75013 Paris, France; [2]Hôpital de la Pitié Salpétrière, Départment de Pharmacologie Clinique, 47 bd de l'Hôpital, 75013 Paris; and [3]Thérapharm Recherches, 59 rue de Billancourt, 92100 Boulogne Billancourt, France

Introduction

The therapeutic possibilities in the treatment of acute stroke are virtually limited to the prevention of risk factors and intensive care. No pharmacotherapy is available. In that perspective NMDA receptor antagonists bring an interesting and promising alternative, as these compound are potential treatments for ischemic brain injury [1].

One of the problems encountered in developing NMDA antagonists is related to the deleterious effect on CNS functioning, either mediated by some direct effects on the NMDA receptor-coupled channel or by indirect effects such as the increase of dopamine turnover following MK801. The behavioral resulting effects being therefore agitation/delusions (PCP, ketamine, MK801) or sedation (dextrometorphan). In animals the disruption of NMDA transmission by MK801 and CPP also leads to a decreased memory storage [2] and a decreased long-term potentiation [3], in electrophysiology, after AP5. SL 82.0715, which interacts with a polyamine modulatory site, does not increase locomotor activity and does not affect active avoidance in mice [4]. From this, it can be inferred that SL 82.0715 would have no or only minor effects on CNS functioning. We therefore conducted a double-blind study assessing the psychomotor, mnesic and subjective effects of SL 82.0715 with respect to a placebo and a positive control (midazolam 15 mg).

Experimental design

The 3 treatment placebos, SL 82.0715 30 mg and midazolam 15 mg were administered according to a 3×3 latin square design.

Subjects and Methods

Eleven male healthy subjects were included in the study. The population characteristics were: age: 24.27 ± 1.18 (18–30) years; weight: 74.45 ± 2.62 (65–94) kg; and height: 179.36 ± 1.75 (172–193) cm.

Assessment

CNS arousal and psychomotor performance
Critical flicker fusion was determined by a ZAK™.
Choice reaction time was measured using a ZAK™.

Short-term memory
A paired word test was used, reading a list of 10 pairs of words at a constant rate. A clued recall was then immediately performed by naming the first name of the pair. *Sternberg Scanning memory test* was performed using a paradigm derived from the initial publication of Sternberg [5].

Long-term memory
The 12-picture test used was the one advocated by Warot [6]. A set of 12 pictures was presented at the rate of a new picture every 10 s. Thirty minutes later subjects had to recall this picture within 90 s and a recognition among 24 pictures. Self-assessment was performed using the Leeds Analog Rating Scales [7].

EKG was recorded before, 3 and 8 h post-dosing using a 12-lead Hewlett-Packard apparatus, as in previous studies (178 healthy subjects). SL 82.0715 was shown to induce a dose-dependent, concentration-dependent, reversible increase of cardiac repolarization (QTc).

Results

Midazolam but not SL 82.0715 affected CNS arousal and psychomotor function at 1 and 3 h post-dosing (decreased CFF (Fig. 1) and increased CRT (Fig. 2).

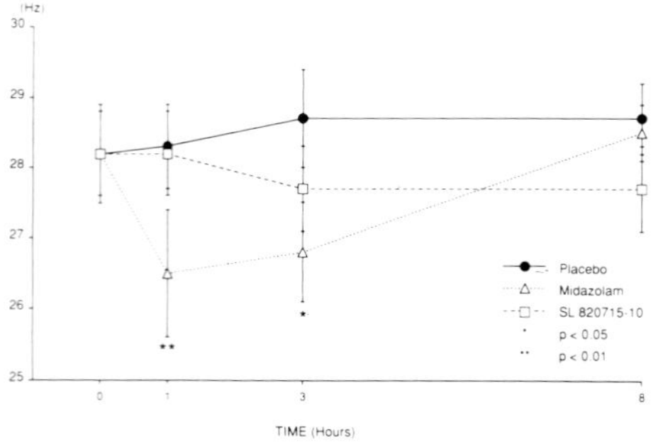

Fig. 1.

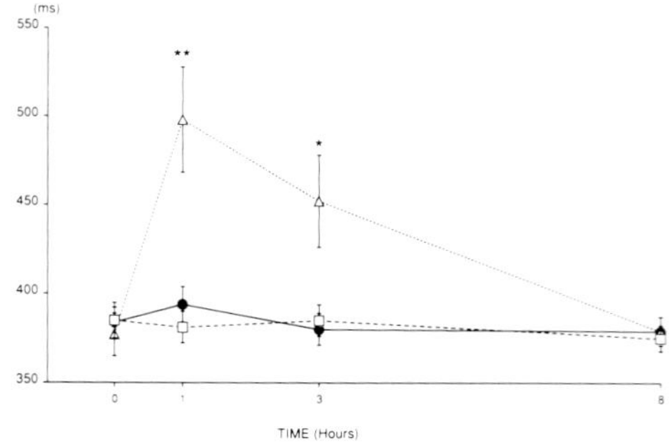

Fig. 2.

Short-term memory measured by paired-word test was impaired 1 and 3 h after midazolam (Fig. 3) dosing. In the Sternberg paradigm, the response time was increased by midazolam 1 and 3 h postdosing. SL 82.0715 was inactive on both tests. Long-term memory assessed by the picture test showed an impairment 1 and 3 h after midazolam but not SL 82.0715 (Fig. 4). Self-assessment showed subjective changes, maximal 2 h postmidazolam dosing (Fig. 5). SL 82.0715 significantly increased QTc, 3 h postdosing (Fig. 6).

Discussion and Conclusions

The results observed under midazolam are characteristic of benzodiazepines which induce sedation and anterograde amnesia in acute dosing in healthy subjects. The magnitude of effect after the dose of midazolam used (15 mg) is consistent with previous results. This dose, according to Sostmann [8], is equipotent to 0.5 mg of triazolam, impairing psychomotor function and CNS arousal.

No such effects were in evidence with SL 82.0715 which indicates that no stimulant, no sedative and no memory-impairing effects exist at the dose used (30 mg). This is probably related to the fact that contrary to MK801, PCP or ketamine,

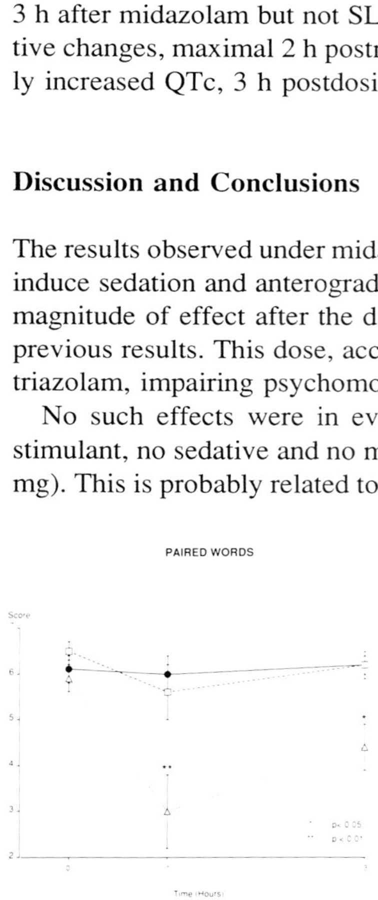

Fig. 3.

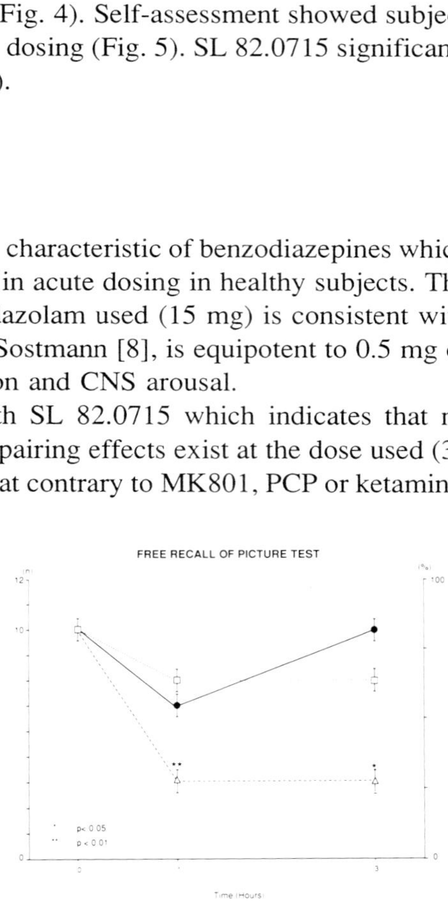

Fig. 4.

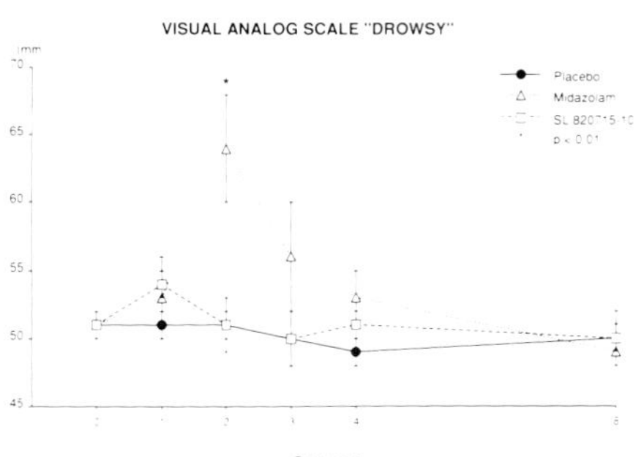

Fig. 5.

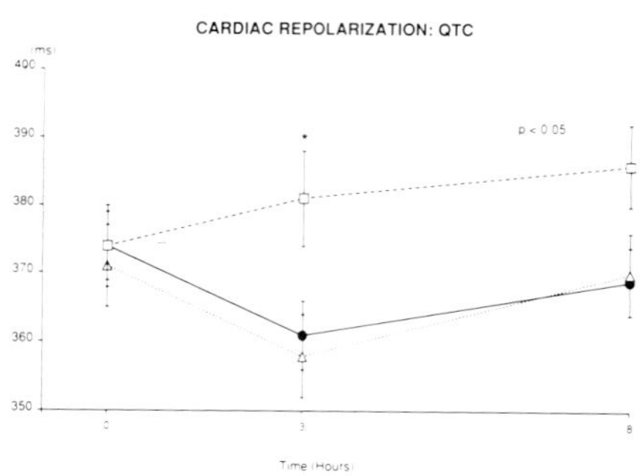

Fig. 6.

SL 82.0715 acts through a modulatory site (polyamine site) but not as a channel blocker.

The effect of SL 82.0715 on cardiac repolarization was the one expected from safety studies, the difference with placebo (20 ms) was clinically non-significant and none of the subjects had an abnormal QTc postdosing (i.e. >450 ms); this effect is related to an interaction within the Ca/Na channel [9].

From the present data, it can be concluded that SL 82.0715 at high dosage (30 mg) does not alter CNS functioning, either when vigilance or memory are assessed.

References

1. Scatton B, Carter C, Benavides J and Giroux C (1990) NMDA receptor antagonists: A novel therapeutic perspective for the treatment of ischaemic brain injury. Cerebrovasc. Dis. (in press).
2. Perrault G, Morel E, Sanger DJ and Zivkovic B (1989) Br. J. Pharmacol. 97: 580.
3. Morris RG, Anderson E, Lynch GS and Baudry M (1986) Nature 319: 774–776.
4. Sanger DJ and Joly D (1990) The effect of NMDA antagonists on punished exploration in mice. Behav. Pharmacol. (in press).
5. Sternberg S (1969) Am. Sci. 55: 421–457.
6. Warot D, Bensimon G, Danjou P and Puech AJ (1987) Fundam. Clin. Pharmacol. 1: 145–152.
7. Hindmarch I, Hank S and Hewet AJ (1977) Br. J. Clin. Pharmacol. 4: 573–578.
8. Sostmann HJ, Sostmann H, Crevorsier C and Bicher J (1989) Eur. J. Clin. Pharmacol. 36: 181–187.
9. Grosset A (1991) Cardiac actions of a new cerebral anti-ischaemic agent: SL 82.0715. Meeting of the British Pharmaceutical Society, Lyon 25–27, April 1991, France.

© 1991 Elsevier Science Publishers B.V. All rights reserved.
Biological Psychiatry, Volume 2. G. Racagni et al., editors.

Excitotoxicity: Relevance to brain disorders in both youth and old age

John W. Olney
Department of Psychiatry, Washington University, St. Louis, Missouri, U.S.A.

Introduction

Significant progress has been made recently in understanding the neurotoxic (excitotoxic) properties of glutamate (Glu) and related excitatory amino acids (EAA). Three EAA receptor subtypes that convey excitotoxicity (N-methyl-D-aspartate (NMDA), kainic acid (KA), quisqualic acid (Quis)) have been identified, drugs with anti-excitotoxic actions have been discovered and evidence for the potential complicity of both exogenous and endogenous excitotoxins in neuro-degenerative disorders has begun to unfold. There now is substantial evidence for the involvement of each EAA receptor subtype in at least one human neuro-degenerative syndrome and recent findings suggest that EAA receptors are sensitive mediators of excitotoxicity at both ends of the age spectrum.

NMDA receptor-mediated syndromes

Excessive activation of NMDA receptors may play a critical role in acute neuronal degeneration associated with hypoxia-ischemia, hypoglycemia, epilepsy and CNS trauma [1]. These conditions cause excessive release of endogenous excitotoxins (Glu and aspartate) from the intra to extracellular compartment of brain which brings these excitotoxins in direct contact with EAA receptors through which they can induce excitotoxic neuronal death. It has been shown in animal studies that NMDA receptor antagonists can mitigate brain damage associated with each of these three conditions. However, as discussed below, NMDA antagonists may prove more effective in preventing hypoxic/ischemic brain damage in the immature than mature CNS, the postulated reason being that hypoxic/ischemic damage may be mediated almost exclusively by NMDA receptors in the immature CNS but by all three EAA receptor types in the adult CNS [1–4].

In addition to the acute conditions mentioned above, a more chronic neuro-degenerative disease, parkinsonism, has been linked to abnormal NMDA receptor activation. This link is supported by evidence that NMDA antagonists protect the dopaminergic nigrostriatal system against the neurotoxic effects of MPP^+ [5] or methamphetamine [6], two drugs that induce parkinsonian syndromes in animals.

There is also basis for postulating the combined involvement of both NMDA and non-NMDA receptors in several chronic neurodegenerative disorders (see below).

Non-NMDA receptor-mediated syndromes

In addition to the possible involvement of both KA and Quis receptors in hypoxic/ischemic brain damage and CNS trauma in adulthood, there is evidence for selective involvement of each of these non-NMDA receptor subtypes in at least one other adult human neurodegenerative syndrome. BOAA (β-N-oxalylamino-L-alanine), an environmental excitotoxin implicated in neurolathyrism, exerts excitotoxic activity exclusively through Quis receptors (Olney and Price, unpublished observations). Domoic acid, an environmental excitotoxin implicated in a recent food poisoning incident [7] that killed some individuals and left others demented, exerts its excitotoxic activity exclusively at KA receptors [8].

Speculation that endogenous excitotoxins might play a role in Parkinson's and Huntington's diseases was recently strengthened by the finding [9] that L-DOPA and its ortho-hydroxylated derivative 6-OH-DOPA have excitotoxic activity. This activity is mediated specifically at non-NMDA receptors. Thus, it is reasonable to propose that L-DOPA, or one of its derivatives, acting as endogenous excitotoxins at non-NMDA receptors, could be responsible for neuronal degeneration in either Huntington's or Parkinson's disease.

Disorders in which both NMDA and non-NMDA receptors may be involved

Evidence is just beginning to emerge in support of the concept that excitotoxins that activate more than one subtype of EAA receptor may be particularly good candidates for complicity in chronic neurodegenerative disorders. L-cysteine, an excitotoxin that penetrates blood-brain barriers and induces hypoxia/ischemia-like lesions in the developing CNS [10], was recently implicated in adult onset neurological disorders by evidence [11] suggesting a disturbance in cysteine metabolism resulting in abnormally increased ratios of cysteine to sulfate in the blood of patients with amyotrophic lateral sclerosis, parkinsonism and Alzheimer's dementia. Interestingly, natives of the Mariana islands (e.g. Guam) were plagued earlier in this century with an endemic disease syndrome comprising features of all three of these disorders, and a causal factor in this syndrome may be BMAA (β-methylamino-L-alanine), an excitotoxin to which these people were exposed in their diet. In addition to being linked to the same three neurological disorders, BMAA and L-cysteine share other interesting characteristics in common. Both molecules activate Quis as well as NMDA receptors, both lack the ω acidic terminal possessed by other excitotoxins, a factor that may facilitate blood-brain barrier penetration and both display markedly enhanced excitotoxicity in the presence of bicarbonate. Finally, the action of either molecule at Quis receptors may serve to relieve the voltage block to which NMDA receptors are ordinarily subject, thereby increasing the chances that even normal levels of stimulation would induce abnormal current flow through the NMDA receptor ion channel.

Vulnerability to excitotoxic mechanisms in youth and old age

Recent evidence [1,3] suggests that during development NMDA receptors are hypersensitive to excitotoxic stimulation (relative to other developing EAA receptor subtypes or to more mature NMDA receptors). In addition, NMDA receptors on different neuronal groups reach peak sensitivity at different developmental ages [3]. Therefore, during development it may not require a very strong excitotoxic stimulus to trigger NMDA receptor-mediated brain damage and an excitotoxin acting at NMDA receptors (e.g. endogenous Glu or cysteine [10]) might induce various patterns of neuronal degeneration depending on which NMDA receptor-bearing neuronal populations are at peak sensitivity at the time of insult. It follows that different clinical syndromes might ensue (e.g. ranging from cerebral palsy to schizophrenia) depending on developmental age at the time of injury.

Involvement of EAA receptor systems in neuropsychiatric disorders of old age may be postulated based on evidence pertaining to domoic acid poisoning. Although individuals poisoned by domoic acid ranged in age from 20 to 89 years, severe neuropsychological impairment (profound anterograde amnesia) occurred primarily in those over 60 years of age [7]. This suggests that KA receptors are sensitive mediators of excitotoxic neuropathology in the aging human brain. It is noteworthy, however, that domoic acid, like KA, is a powerful convulsant that induces brain damage primarily by a seizure mechanism and that seizure-mediated brain damage of the type induced by KA can be largely prevented by blockade of NMDA receptors [12]. The postulated basis for this is that, although KA receptor activation is the mechanism by which domoic acid induces persistent seizure activity, much of the ensuing brain damage stems from seizure-mediated release of endogenous Glu at NMDA receptors. Thus, the domoic acid poisoning incident indicates that both NMDA and KA receptors may be sensitive mediators of excitotoxic pathology in the aged human brain.

References

1. Olney JW (1989) Biol. Psychiatry 26: 505–525.
2. McDonald JW, Silverstein FS and Johnston MV. Brain Res. 459: 200–203.
3. Ikonomidou C, Mosinger JL, Shahid Salles K, Labruyere J and Olney JW (1989) J. Neurosci. 9: 2809–2818.
4. Mosinger JL and Olney JW (1989) Soc. Neurosci. Abstr. 15: 45.
5. Turski L, Bressler K, Tettig K-J, Loschmann P-A and Wachtel H (1991) Nature 349: 414–418.
6. Sonsalla PK, Nicklas WJ and Heikkila RE (1989) Science 243: 398–400.

7. Perl TM, Bedard L, Kosatsky T, Hockin JC, Todd ECD and Remis RS (1990) N. Engl. J. Med. 322: 1775–1780.
8. Stewart GR, Zorumski CF, Price MT and Olney JW (1990) Exp. Neurol. 110: 127–138.
9. Olney JW, Zorumski CF, Stewart GR and Price MT (1990) Exp. Neurol. 108: 269–272.
10. Olney JW, Zorumski C, Price MT and Labruyere J (1990) Science 248: 596–599.
11. Heafield MT, Fearn S and Steventon GB (1990) Neurosci. Lett. 110: 216–220.
12. Clifford DB, Olney JW, Benz AM, Fuller TA and Zorumski CF (1990) Epilepsia 31: 382–390.

© 1991 Elsevier Science Publishers B.V. All rights reserved.
Biological Psychiatry, Volume 2. G. Racagni et al., editors.

Environmental excitotoxins: Role in acute and chronic neurodegenerative disorders

Charles F. Zorumski
Department of Psychiatry, Washington University Medical School, St. Louis, Missouri, U.S.A.

Introduction

The excitatory amino acid (EAA), glutamate (Glu), is currently the leading neurotransmitter candidate at the majority of fast excitatory synapses in the vertebrate central nervous system (CNS), participating in processes important for the understanding of CNS physiology and pathology. In addition to functioning in normal synaptic transmission, prolonged exposure to Glu has neurotoxic consequences, leading to both acute and delayed forms of neurodegeneration. The excitatory and toxic actions result from the flow of ions across neuronal membranes. Under normal circumstances this flow of ions produces the depolarization characteristic of Glu-induced excitation. When the ion flux is prolonged, Glu becomes toxic to neurons. Acute neurodegeneration results from the influx of cations and the passive redistribution of chloride and water. Delayed neurodegeneration involves the influx of Ca^{2+} and the presumed activation of intracellular Ca^{2+}-dependent processes [1]. The relationship between excitatory and toxic properties of EAAs has prompted their designation as “excitotoxins”.

Neurodegenerative syndromes produced by excitotoxins can arise from either the endogenous actions of EAAs or from the ingestion of environmental analogues. Excitotoxins are found naturally in certain foods and have flavor-enhancing properties which invite their use as food additives. In this paper, evidence will be reviewed suggesting the involvement of specific environmental excitotoxins in three human neurodegenerative disorders – β-N-methylamino-L-alanine (BMAA) in the amyotrophic lateral sclerosis (ALS)-parkinsonism-dementia complex of Guam, β-N-oxalylamino-L-alanine (BOAA) in neurolathyrism and domoate in shellfish poisoning.

BMAA and the Guamanian ALS syndrome

The incidence of ALS among the Chamorro population of Guam and the Mariana Islands has been found to be significantly greater than in other countries. This syndrome consists of spastic limb weakness and bulbar dysfunction with muscle fasciculations and atrophy. Some subjects manifest signs of parkinsonism and develop the cognitive changes typical of dementia. Epidemiological studies have linked the syndrome to the ingestion of the false sago palm (Cycas circinalis). The cycad plant contains several potential neurotoxins including BMAA, an agent with weak excitotoxic properties [2].

The toxic actions of BMAA have been studied in vivo and in vitro. In monkeys, daily feeding of BMAA for several weeks produces tremors, weakness and a slowed, shuffling gait. Pathologically, these animals exhibit lesions in the motor cortex and spinal cord which are similar to those found in the human disorder [2]. In cell culture, BMAA exerts actions at several EAA receptors. Antagonists of N-methyl-D-aspartate (NMDA) or kainate/quisqualate ionotropic receptors partially protect against the toxicity while more complete protection is seen using combinations of agents. Other studies indicate that BMAA has effects at metabotropic EAA receptors linked to the phosphoinositide (PI) second messenger system [3], raising the possibility that the release of intracellular Ca^{2+} may be important in the toxicity.

A puzzling feature of BMAA is that the molecule lacks the dicarboxylic acid structure typical of other excitotoxins. Weiss and Choi [4] have demonstrated that the excitatory and toxic actions of BMAA depend on the presence of bicarbonate ions and have suggested that bicarbonate may transform BMAA into a molecule with greater potency. Recent evidence demonstrating that BMAA, in the presence of bicarbonate, forms an α-aminocarbamate resembling NMDA supports this hypothesis [5].

BOAA and neurolathyrism

Neurolathyrism is a crippling upper motor neuron disorder endemic to parts of Africa and Asia. Signs of the disorder include lower extremity weakness, cramps, tremulousness and coarse movements. Like the Guamanian ALS syndrome, neurolathyrism is marked by a slow progression of symptoms over time. Epidemiological studies have linked the disorder to ingestion of the chickling pea (Lathyrus sativus). During periods of famine, this legume becomes a dietary staple in regions where the disorder is endemic [6]. The seeds of the pea contain BOAA, an agent which has selective actions at quisqualate receptors [7].

Within months after starting a diet containing BOAA, monkeys develop features of neurolathyrism. The animal syndrome, like the human disorder, appears to be self-limiting with improvement in symptoms after discontinuation of the toxin. In cell culture, BOAA is a relatively slow-acting toxin, taking days of exposure at moderate concentrations to produce neurodegenerative effects [8]. The slowness may result from the profound desensitization of quisqualate receptors which BOAA induces [7]. Additionally, the delayed toxicity produced by agents acting at non-NMDA receptors is partially inhibited by L-type calcium channel blockers [9]. Non-NMDA agonists do not gate these channels directly and may require chronic exposure to produce sufficient Ca^{2+} influx. BOAA also appears to have preferential actions on quisqualate receptors in motor cortex [10], which may partially explain the regional selectivity of lesions.

Domoate and shellfish poisoning

In 1987, an outbreak of food poisoning in eastern Canada affected more than 100 individuals. This poisoning produced acute neurological symptoms including memory impairment and seizures. Some survivors were left with severe defects in anterograde memory. Among cases coming to autopsy, prominent neuronal loss was found in the hippocampus and amygdala. The syndrome was traced to the ingestion of cultured mussels harvested from estuaries on Prince Edward Island. These mussels had filter fed on a marine plankton (Niachia pungens) which, when in full bloom, synthesizes large quantities of domoate, a potent analogue of the excitotoxin, kainate [11,12].

The human domoate syndrome is reminiscent of symptoms produced by kainate and domoate in experimental animals. After systemic injection, these excitotoxins produce recurring limbic seizures and brain damage involving the hippocampus and amygdala among other areas [13]. Kainate receptors are heavily concentrated in the CA3 hippocampal region which may explain the limbic seizures and hippocampal damage. Both kainate and domoate activate large non-desensitizing responses in CNS neurons and produce dramatic acute neuronal damage during a 30-min exposure [13]. These features may account for the rapid onset of the syndrome. However, based on analogy to the kainate syndrome in rodents, it is likely that much of the damage in regions outside the hippocampus results from the recurring seizures and is mediated by NMDA receptors [14].

Discussion

These studies support a role for environmental excitotoxins in human neurodegenerative disorders. The data are most compelling for neurolathyrism and domoate poisoning. In the case of the Guamanian ALS syndrome the evidence is suggestive but not conclusive. These disorders have important implications for the recognition and regulation of potential dietary excitotoxins.

Acknowledgements

This work was supported in part by NIMH Physician Scientist Award MH00630 and Grants MH45493 and AG05681.

References

1. Olney JW (1990) Ann. Rev. Pharmacol. Toxicol. 30: 47–71.
2. Spencer PS, Nunn PB, Hugon J, Ludolph AC, Ross SM, Roy DN and Robertson RC (1987) Science 237: 517–522.
3. Copani A, Canonico PL and Nicoletti F (1990) Eur. J. Pharmacol. 181: 327–328.
4. Weiss JH and Choi DW (1988) Science 241: 973–975.
5. Nunn PB, Davis AJ and O'Brien P (1991) Science 251: 1619.
6. Spencer PS, Ludolph A, Dwivedi MP, Roy DN, Hugon J and Schaumbure HH (1986) Lancet ii: 1066–1067.
7. Zorumski CF, Thio LL, Clark GD and Clifford DB (1990) Neuron 5: 61–66.
8. Weiss JH, Koh JY and Choi DW (1989) Brain Res. 497: 64–71.
9. Weiss JH, Hartley DM, Koh JY and Choi DW (1990) Science 247: 1474–1477.
10. Ross SM, Roy DN and Spencer PR (1989) J. Neurochem. 53: 710–715.
11. Perl TM, Bedard L, Kosatsky T, Hockin JC, Todd ECD and Remis SC (1990) New Engl. J. Med. 322: 1775–1780.
12. Teitelbaum JS, Zatorre RJ, Carpenter S, Gendron D, Evans AC, Gjedde A and Cashman NR (1990) New Engl. J. Med. 322: 1781–1787.
13. Stewart GR, Zorumski CF, Price MT and Olney JW (1990) Exp. Neurol. 110: 127–138.
14. Clifford DB, Olney JW, Benz A, Fuller TA and Zorumski CF (1990) Epilepsia 31: 382–390.

© 1991 Elsevier Science Publishers B.V. All rights reserved.
Biological Psychiatry, Volume 2. G. Racagni et al., editors.

Excitatory amino acid receptors: Role in schizophrenia

Daniel C. Javitt and Stephen R. Zukin

Departments of Psychiatry and Neuroscience, Albert Einstein College of Medicine; and Bronx Psychiatric Center, 1300 Morris Park Avenue, F111, Bronx, NY 10461, U.S.A.

Introduction

Phencyclidine (1,1-phenylcyclohexylpiperidine; PCP; "angel dust"), originally developed as a general anesthetic in the late 1950s, was found to produce loss of consciousness and analgesia sufficient for the performance of surgical procedures while not causing significant respiratory or cardiovascular depression [1–3]. However, a significant proportion of patients subjected to PCP anesthesia developed psychotic episodes typically lasting 12–72 h but occasionally as long as 7–10 days. These episodes were characterized by excitation, unmanageability, paranoia, concreteness of thought [1,2] and "maniacal episodes" [3]. Subanesthetic doses (0.1 mg/kg i.v.) were subsequently found to induce psychotic episodes in normal volunteers and to rekindle presenting symptomatology in recompensated schizophrenic subjects [4]. In addition, subanesthetic doses of PCP, but not LSD, amobarbital or amphetamine, could induce abnormalities in tests of abstract reasoning, cognitive processing, attention, motor function and proprioception in normal volunteers which closely resembled those seen in patients with chronic schizophrenia [5]. These findings led to the proposal that the mechanisms of action of PCP may be relevant to the pathogenesis of schizophrenia [6].

PCP binds with high affinity to a specific brain PCP receptor [7,8]. Several lines of evidence indicate that the PCP receptor is a site within the ion channel gated by the NMDA-type excitatory amino acid receptor. First, PCP and NMDA receptors are colocalized in the central nervous system [9]. Second, PCP receptor ligands have been shown to inhibit NMDA receptor-mediated conductances noncompetitively [10] in a voltage- and use-dependent fashion [11,12]. Finally, binding of PCP receptor ligands is enhanced by NMDA receptor agonists, such as L-glutamate or NMDA, and is diminished by competitive NMDA receptor antagonists such as D(-)-2-amino-5-phosphonovaleric acid (D(-)AP5) [13]. Such data suggest a model in which NMDA and PCP receptors represent distinct sites associated with a supramolecular NMDA receptor complex. The identification of non-competitive inhibition of NMDA receptor function as the mechanism underlying the psychotomimetic effects of PCP suggests that elucidation of the functioning of the NMDA receptor complex may reveal mechanisms relevant to the pathogenesis and treatment of schizophrenia.

Studies in our laboratory have established that PCP-like drugs manifest two exponentials of association with their binding site within the NMDA channel, and that the Hill coefficient for stimulation of PCP receptor binding by L-glutamate is significantly greater than unity [14]. A model of NMDA receptor functioning which could account for these findings is one involving the existence of two independent sets of agonist recognition sites within each functional NMDA receptor complex. Occupation of both sets by agonist would be required for channel activation and fast [^{3}H]MK-801 binding. Partial activation would not permit channel opening but would permit slow diffusion of [^{3}H]MK-801 to its binding site via a hydrophobic path. In the total absence of agonist, however, the channel would remain closed and in a conformation to which PCP receptor ligands could not bind. This model is similar to models which have been proposed to account for the functioning of nicotinic acetylcholine [15] and $GABA_A$ [16] receptors. If future studies confirm a functional similarity between NMDA and nicotinic receptors, this may indicate that NMDA receptors are structurally homologous to receptors of the Class I superfamily of ligand-gated channels, which includes nicotinic, $GABA_A$, and strychnine-sensitive glycine receptors [17].

Role of NMDA receptors in PCP psychosis

Several lines of evidence support a unique role of the PCP receptor in eliciting schizophreniform psychosis. First, PCP receptors have been shown to mediate the discriminative stimulus effects of PCP in rodents [24]. The rank order of potency with which a large number of drugs from distinct chemical classes can induce the PCP response in animals trained to discriminate PCP from saline corresponds to their rank order of binding to PCP receptors and inducing NMDA receptor blockade [18]. By contrast, agents which selectively bind to the sigma and/or dopamine reuptake sites neither induce PCP-like discriminative stimulus effects nor antagonize the discriminative stimulus effects induced by PCP receptor ligands [18]. These findings suggest that PCP receptors mediate the introceptive cues induced by PCP and PCP-like agents. Second, psychotomimetic effects similar to those induced by PCP can be induced by ketamine, a related arylcyclohexylamine derivative [19]. The psychotomimetic effects of ketamine are induced by doses approximately 10-fold greater than PCP [19], which is consistent with its 10-fold lower potency of binding to PCP receptors [7,8]. By contrast, ketamine is essentially inactive at both DA re-uptake [20] and sigma sites [8]. Finally, PCP-induced psychosis has been found to be associated with serum concentrations of PCP as low as 20 nM, while serum concentrations greater than 400 nM are associated with gross impairments in consciousness [21]. PCP receptors have been shown to bind PCP with an affinity of approximately 30–50 nM [22,23], suggesting a highly significant degree of receptor occupancy by levels of PCP present during low-dose PCP psychosis. By contrast, sigma binding sites and DA reuptake sites have been shown to bind PCP with affinities of approximately 600 [23] and 700 [20] nM, respectively. The affinity of PCP for these sites is thus significantly lower than its affinity for PCP receptors. Furthermore, the affinity of PCP for these sites suggests that they would be affected only to a limited extent by concentrations of PCP that have been demonstrated to cause robust psychotomimetic effects.

In summary, PCP induces psychotomimetic effects that closely resemble those of schizophrenia. Our experimental data from experiments measuring the effects of NMDA receptor activation on binding of [^{3}H]MK-801 to PCP receptors support a model of NMDA receptor functioning in which two molecules of agonist are required for NMDA receptor activation. This model is similar to models which have been proposed for the nicotinic acetylcholine receptor, suggesting the possibility of functional and structural homology between NMDA receptors and members of the Class I superfamily of ligand-gated channels. The psychotomimetic effects of PCP are observed at serum concentrations similar to the concentration at which PCP binds to the NMDA-associated PCP receptor. These findings suggest that endogenous dysfunction or dysregulation of NMDA receptor-mediated neurotransmission may contribute to the pathogenesis of schizophrenia, and that novel agents influencing NMDA receptor functioning could prove of interest as potential treatments for schizophrenia.

Acknowledgements

This work was supported in part by USPHS Grants DA-03383 to S.R.Z. and MH-00631 to D.C.J., grants from the Ritter Foundation and the David Berg Family Fund for Research in Manic Depressive Illness to S.R.Z., and by the generous support of the department of psychiatry of the Albert Einstein College of Medicine, Herman M. van Praag, M.D., Ph.D., Chairman.

References

1. Greifenstein FE, Yoskitake J, DeVault M and Gajewski JE (1958) Anesth. Anal. 37: 283–294.
2. Meyer JS, Greifenstein F and DeVault M (1959) J. Nerv. Ment. Dis. 129: 54–61.
3. Johnstone M, Evans V and Baigel S (1958) Br. J. Anaesth. 31: 433–439.
4. Davies BM and Beech HR (1960) J. Ment. Sci. 106: 912–924.
5. Luby ED, Cohen BD, Rosenbaum F, Gottlieb J and Kelley R (1959) Arch. Neurol. Psychiatry 81: 363–369.
6. Luby ED, Gottlieb JS, Cohen BD, Rosenbaum G and Domino EF (1962) Am. J. Psychiatry 119: 61–65.
7. Rosenbaum G, Cohen BD, Luby ED, Gottlieb JS and Yelen D (1959) Arch. Gen. Psychiatry 1: 651–656.
8. Cohen BD, Rosenbaum G, Luby ED and Gottlieb JS (1962) Arch. Gen. Psychiatry 6: 79–85.
9. Domino EF and Luby ED (1981) In: Domino EF (ed.) PCP (Phencyclidine): Historical and Current Perspectives. NPP Books, Ann Arbor, MI, pp. 400–418.
10. Zukin SR and Zukin RS (1979) Proc. Natl. Acad. Sci. U.S.A. 76: 5372–5376.
11. Vincent JP, Kartalovski B, Geneste P et al. (1979) Proc. Natl. Acad. Sci. U.S.A. 76: 4678–4682.
12. Reynolds IJ, Murphy SN and Miller RJ (1987) Proc. Natl. Acad. Sci. U.S.A. 84: 7744–7748.
13. Maragos WF, Penny JB and Young AB (1988) J. Neurosci. 8: 493–501.
14. Anis NA, Berry SC, Burton NR and Lodge D (1983) Br. J. Pharmacol. 79: 565–575.

15. Honey CR, Miljkovic Z and MacDonald JF (1985) Neurosci. Lett. 61: 135–139.
16. Huettner JE and Bean BP (1988) Proc. Natl. Acad. Sci. U.S.A. 85: 1307–1311.
17. Javitt, DC, Jotkowitz A, Sircar R and Zukin SR (1987) Neurosci. Lett. 78: 193–198.
18. Fagg GE (1987) Neurosci. Lett. 76: 221–227.
19. Loo PS, Braunwalder AF, Lehmann J, Williams M and Sills MA (1987) Mol. Pharmacol. 32: 820–830.
20. Javitt DC and Zukin SR (1991) Bi-exponential kinetics of [^{3}H]MK-801 binding: evidence for access to closed and open *N*-methyl-D-aspartate receptor channels. Mol. Pharmacol. (in press).
21. Hess GP, Cash DJ and Aoshima H (1983) Ann. Rev. Biophys. Bioeng. 12: 443–473.
22. Aoshima A, Anan M, Ishii, H, Iio H and Kobayashi S (1987) Biochemistry 26: 4811–4816.
23. Barnard EA, Darlison MG and Seeburg P (1987) Trends Neurosci. 10: 502–509.
24. Su TP, London ED and Jaffe JH (1988) Science 240: 219–221.
25. Smith RC, Meltzer HY, Arora RC and Davis JM (1977) Biochem. Pharmacol. 26: 1435–1439.
26. Garey RE and Heath RG (1976) Life Sci. 18: 1105–1107.
27. Browne RG (1986) In: Clouet DH (ed.) Phencyclidine: An Update. NIDA Res. Monogr. #64. Dept. of Health and Human Services, Rockville, MD, pp. 134–147.
28. Sircar R, Rappaport M, Nichtenhauser R and Zukin SR (1987) Brain Res. 435: 235–240.
29. Wong EHF, Knight AR and Woodruff GN (1988) J. Neurochem. 50: 274–281.

© 1991 Elsevier Science Publishers B.V. All rights reserved.
Biological Psychiatry, Volume 2. G. Racagni et al., editors.

Excitatory amino acids in Alzheimer's disease

Nunzio Pomara, James C.Y. Chou, Rajkumar Singh and Dennis Deptula
Nathan S. Kline Institute for Psychiatric Research, Orangeburg, NY 10962, U.S.A.

There is growing interest in the hypothesis that excitatory amino acids (EAAs), particularly glutamate, may have a role in Alzheimer's disease (AD) [1–3]. EAAs were theoretically implicated in AD because of three major reasons: a) the NMDA receptor, a subtype of glutamate receptor, has an important role in long-term potentiation, a synaptic analogue of learning and memory; b) histopathological changes characteristic of AD, and reduced neuronal RNA content, as is found in AD, can be induced in vitro by EAAs; and histopathological changes characteristic of AD have been found in other neurodegenerative disorders which may be caused by exogenous EAAs presumably through excitoxic effects; and c) the anatomical distribution of AD pathology closely parallels EAA pathways.

Data supporting the glutamate hypothesis of AD have been provocative, although incomplete. Free glutamate levels in postmortem brains have been found to be decreased in AD in most [4–7] but not all [2,8] studies. NMDA receptors in the cortex and hippocampus have also been found to be decreased in AD in some [2,9,10] but not all [11–12] studies, and the degree of receptor loss may be related to severity of AD pathology [1,10,11,13]. Phencyclindine binding sites (NMDA ion channel) have also been found to be decreased in cortex and hippocampus in AD brain [1,6,14]. Glutamate uptake sites as measured by [^{3}H] aspartate binding have been found to be decreased in AD as well [14-17].

Together, this evidence argues strongly for a loss of glutamatergic neurons in AD. However, these studies were mostly performed on postmortem brains, probably representing the end-stages of AD and provide little information about which changes occur in earlier stages of AD. CSF studies provide the advantage of evaluating AD subjects in vivo before AD has progressed to its final stages.

Several investigators have measured CSF EAAs levels in AD. Smith [18] compared CSF from histopathologically confirmed cases of AD (n = 11) ranging in severity from mild to severe with control subjects who had other neurological disorders. The AD subjects were free of psychotropic drugs for one week. The controls were not age-matched. They found that glutamate levels were not different between the two groups. However, within a subset of the AD group (n = 9) CSF glutamate levels did correlate positively with severity of dementia.

Procter [7] compared CSF EAAs in 15 AD patients and 15 controls with other neurological disorders. The control group was age-matched with the AD patients. They also found that glutamate was unchanged in the AD patients. They also measured CSF aspartate and found no difference.

Degrell [19] measured CSF EAAs in 30 demented patients and compared levels with 16 young "neurotics" who had somatic complaints which warranted lumbar puncture. The demented group included both AD and MID. Severity of dementia and drug status were not reported. They found no differences in glutamate, aspartate, or glutamine between the 2 groups.

We have recently presented preliminary data that CSF glutamate levels are increased in *early* AD [20]. We collected CSF from 10 mild to moderately demented *drug-free* probable AD patients (although not histopathologically confirmed) and compared levels to *normal controls* of similar age who were free of medical or psychiatric diagnoses. This report has several advantages over existing studies in that: a) no subjects had been treated with antidepressants or antipsychotics; b) control subjects were normals of similar age; and c) AD subjects were only of mild to moderate severity. CSF glutamate was found to be slightly but significantly ($P < 0.005$) elevated in AD patients compared to controls.

Our preliminary finding of elevated CSF glutamate in AD should be interpreted with caution because of the small sample size. While plasma glutamate levels are thought to contribute little to CSF glutamate [21] the precise origin of CSF glutamate is not known. Metabolic glutamate not involved in neurotransmission represents the majority of brain glutamate and probably contributes substantially to CSF levels. There may be differential contributions from brain and spinal cord.

Our finding of elevated glutamate in early AD appears to contrast with those reported by others [7,18,19]. However, our samples differed from these earlier reports in that the AD subjects were completely drug-free and were only mildly to moderately demented. Also, the control group was not suffering from neurological conditions and was of similar age.

Although considerable evidence exists that glutamatergic neurons are lost in end-stage AD, our finding of an elevation in CSF glutamate is consistent with increased glutamatergic activity in early AD. The glutamate hypothesis of AD [1,2] suggests that increased glutamatergic activity in early stages of AD, through excitotoxic effects, may lead to the loss of glutamatergic neurons in later stages of the disease. Although considerable data exists documenting loss of glutamatergic systems in end stages of AD, more research is needed to describe the progressive changes in glutamatergic systems in early AD.

References

1. Maragos WF, Greenamyre JT, Penny JB et al. (1987) Trends Neurosci. 10: 65–68.
2. Greenamyre JT and Young AB (1989) Neurobiol. Aging 10: 593–602.
3. Olney JW (1989) Biol. Psychiatry 26: 505–525.
4. Arai H, Kobayashi K, Ichimiya Y et al. (1985) Neurosci. Res. 2: 486–490.
5. Sasaki H, Muramoto O, Kanazawa I, Arai H, Kosaka K and Iizuka R (1986) Ann. Neurol. 19: 263–269.
6. Hyman BT, Van Hoeren GW and Damasio AR (1987) Ann. Neurol. 22: 37–38.
7. Procter AW, Palmer AM, Francis PT et al. (1988) J. Neurochem. 50: 790–802.

8. Tarbit I, Perry EK, Perry RH et al. (1980) J. Neurochem. 35: 1246–1249.
9. Greenamyre JT, Penney JB, Young AB et al. (1985) Science 227: 1496–1499.
10. Represa A, Duyckaerts C, Tremblay E et al. (1988) Brain Res. 457: 355–359.
11. Geddes JW and Cotman CW (1986) Neurosci. Res. 3: 672–679.
12. Cowburn R, Hardy J, Roberts P and Briggs R (1988) Brain Res. 452: 403–407.
13. Monaghan DT, Geddes JW, Yao D, Chung C and Cotman CW (1987) Neurosci. Lett. 73: 197–200.
14. Simpson MDC, Royston MC, Cross AJ, Slater P, Mann DMA, Deakin JFW and Reynolds GP (1987) Br. J. Pharmacol. 92: 609.
15. Cross AJ, Slater P, Simpson M et al. (1987) Neurosci. Lett. 79: 213–217.
16. Hardy J, Cowburn R, Barton A et al. (1987) J. Neurol. Neurosurg. Psychiatry 50: 356–357.
17. Procter AW, Palmer AM, Stratman GC and Bowen DM (1986) N. Engl. J. Med. 26: 1711–1712.
18 Smith CCT, Bowen DM, Francis PT et al. (1985) J. Neurol. Neurosurg. Psychiatry 48: 469–471.
19. Degrell I, Hellsing K, Nagy E et al. (1989) Arch. Gerontol. Geriatr. 9: 123–135.
20. Pomara N, Singh R, Deptula D, Chou JCY, Schwartz MB and LeWitt PA (1991) Am. J. Psychiatry (in press).
21. Fonnum F (1984) J. Neurochem. 42: 1–11.

© 1991 Elsevier Science Publishers B.V. All rights reserved.
Biological Psychiatry, Volume 2. G. Racagni et al., editors.

Investigations of hypothalamic-pituitary-adrenal (HPA) axis and eicosanoid interrelationships

A.A. Mathé[1], M. Thorén[2], N.H. Kalin[3], S.E. Shelton[3], B. Apéria[1], C. Stenfors[1] and P. Bergman[1]

[1]Psychiatry and [2]Endocrinology, Karolinska Institute, Stockholm, Sweden; and [3]Psychiatry, University of Wisconsin Medical School, Madison, Wisconsin, U.S.A.

Introduction

A wealth of investigations has shown intricate relationships between the HPA axis and eicosanoids [1–3]. As demonstrated in a variety of tissues and species [4,5] cortisol decreases eicosanoid synthesis by inhibiting PLA_2 activity. On the other hand, prostaglandin E and some lipoxygenase products can enhance or inhibit release of ACTH from the pituitary and augment synthesis of adrenal corticosteroids [6–8]. Moreover, in contrast to these inverse types of relationships, in certain conditions such as pregnancy and parturition as well as toxic shock, and also following electroconvulsive treatment [9] both an HPA axis activation and eicosanoid increases are found. The aim of the present study was to further explore the HPA axis – eicosanoid interrelationships in a series of parallel human and animal experiments.

Method

Cortisol, ACTH, 11-deoxycortisol and 15-keto-13, 14-dihydro-PGE (measured as its bicyclic product, 11-deoxy-15-keto-13,14-dihydro-11B,16E-cyclo-PGE; PGEM) were determined in plasma samples by RIAs established in our laboratories. Results are expressed as means ± S.D.

Experimental design and results

Dexamethasone suppression test (DST)

1. 1 mg dexamethasone (dex) was given at 23 h orally to 10 subjects (1 male, 9 females) admitted to the endocrinology department for diagnostic work-up. Plasma samples were obtained at 08 h on the day before and after the drug administration. Cortisol concentration decreased: 510 ± 77 to 108 ± 6 nmol/l, $P < 0.001$. PGEM increased in 8/10 subjects for all subjects the values were: 157 ± 16 to 186 ± 11 pg/ml, $P < 0.05$. In a confirmation study, samples were

drawn at 08, 12 and 16 h before and again after peroral dex. Cortisol levels were suppressed and PGEM levels increased (in preparation).

2. Similar DST was performed on 7 rhesus monkeys (4 males, 3 females) who were injected i.m. with 150 μg/kg dex at 23 h. Both cortisol and ACTH were decreased: 483 ± 146 to 69 ± 25 nmol/l, $P < 0.001$; 45 ± 9 to 17 ± 2 pg/ml, $P < 0.03$, respectively. PGEM changed from 88 ± 12 to 104 ± 13 pg/ml, $P = 0.1$. Positive correlations were found between pre-DST cortisol and pre-DST PGEM ($r = 0.84$, $P < 0.02$) and pre-DST cortisol and post-DST PGEM ($r = 0.85$, $P < 0.02$). Pre-DST and post-DST PGEM concentrations were also correlated ($r = 0.7$, $P < 0.05$). Furthermore, the baseline cortisol levels in the DST study and in the stress experiments (see below) were not different and were positively correlated. In parallel, baseline PGEM levels in the two experiments did not differ and were positively correlated.
3. Additional assessment of HPA function in 4 monkeys was performed by bolus i.v. injection of 2 mg dex. Sequential pre- and post-injection samples were collected. While both plasma ACTH and cortisol decreased, PGEM increased: 63 ± 4 and 69 ± 14 (time: −30 and 0) to 102 ± 12 and 89 ± 13 (+ 15 and + 30 min) pg/ml, $P < 0.01$. PGEM concentrations at all time points before and after dex administration showed a high degree of correlation (all r's > 0.90).

Metyrapone test

Metyrapone (an inhibitor of adrenal 11-β-hydroxylase) 250–1000 mg, depending on the body weight, was given Q4h for 20 h to 10 patients as a part of the diagnostic workup. Samples were collected at 06, 08 (baselines) and 18 h on day 1 and 06 h on day 2. Metyrapone decreased cortisol: 289 ± 42 to 42 ± 3 nmol/l, $P < 0.001$ (at 06 h on day 1 and 2). It also elevated 11-deoxycortisol; before the test: not detectable; after the test: >150 nmol/l in all patients, max. concentration 484 nmol/l. PGEM was also increased; baselines: 115 ± 12 and 121 ± 11 , and 10 and 22 h after the first metyrapone dose: 154 ± 17 and 150 ± 17 pg/ml, $P < 0.05$.

ACTH test

1. In the first open study, 10 subjects (1 male, 9 females) received a bolus injection of 25IE (1–24) ACTH. Blood samples were obtained before and 90 and 120 min after ACTH. While there was a marked rise in plasma cortisol, PGEM showed only a trend ($P < 0.09$) to decrease.
2. In a double-blind experiment, a bolus injection of 25IE (1–24) ACTH or placebo was injected i.v. at 08 h to 9 healthy subjects (3 males, 6 females) and the samples collected before and at regular intervals for 4 h after the injection. Cortisol concentrations for baseline, +120 min, and +240 min were: following ACTH 462 ± 81, 942 ± 66, and 631 ± 95, $P < 0.001$; and after placebo 474 ± 100, 273 ± 42, and 284 ± 32 nmol/l. Corresponding PGEM concentrations were:

for ACTH procedure 197 ± 19, 173 ± 17, and 183 ± 20, $P < 0.05$; for placebo procedure 153 ± 80, 161 ± 20, and 154 ± 20 pg/ml.

CRH test

1. Eight healthy subjects (4 males, 4 females) received a bolus injection of 100 μg human CRH. Samples were obtained before (–20, –10 and 0 min) and after (+15, 30, 45, 60, 90, 120 min) the injection. Max. ACTH increase occurred at 30 min: 22 ± 5 to 48 ± 8 pmol/l; max. cortisol elevation at 60 min: 330 ± 7 to 479 ± 28 nmol/l. PGEM concentrations were not changed.
2. One hundred milligrams of CRH was given as i.v. bolus injection to 5 rhesus monkeys and samples collected at –30, 0, +15, 30 and 60 min. In parallel to human studies, both cortisol and ACTH were significantly increased ($P < 0.016$ and <0.024) following CRH injection. However, no significant PGEM changes were found.
3. In an experiment on 4 chair-restrained monkeys, counterbalanced for day and procedure, each animal received i.c.v.: vehicle, 20 μg CRH and 180 μg CRH (ovine). Serial plasma samples were obtained. Concentrations of ACTH and cortisol were increased and PGEM decreased (ANOVA for PGEM: time = $P < 0.002$, dose × time = $P < 0.02$).

Stress test

Two non-invasive stress procedures were carried out.

1. 18 rhesus monkeys (14 males, 4 females) were tested on 4 separate occasions, 1 week apart, counterbalanced for treatment and day.
   a) Baseline: animal taken from home cage and sampled immediately;
   b) +15: confined to a small cage for 15 min before sampling;
   c) +30: confined to a small cage for 30 min before sampling;
   d) +60: confined to a small cage for 30 min, returned to home cage for 30 min and then sampled.

   Plasma was obtained by femoral venipuncture within 7 min of ketamine anesthesia (10 mg/kg i.m.). Previous experience with ketamine in our laboratory has shown that within this period of time there is little if any effect on cortisol levels. This confinement stress increased PGEM, cortisol and ACTH. PGEM: 118 ± 24 to 139 ± 31 and 151 ± 38 pg/ml, $P < 0.004$; cortisol: 499 ± 27 to 706 ± 30 and 863 ± 36 nmol/l, $P < 0.001$; ACTH: 28 ± 2 to 44 ± 2 and 49 ± 5 pg/ml, $P < 0.001$. At 60 min cortisol and PGEM remained elevated, while ACTH returned to baseline.
2. Seven rhesus monkeys (4 males, 3 females), single-cage housed, were manually restrained and the blood samples taken by femoral venipuncture within 3 min of approaching the animal (time 0) and at +30 min. There was a parallel increase in plasma PGEM, cortisol and ACTH. PGEM: 83 ± 8 to 129 ± 16 pg/ml, $P < 0.005$; cortisol: 601 ± 72 to 960 ± 58 nmol/l, $P < 0.005$; ACTH: 73 ± 9 to 94 ± 4 pg/ml,

$P < 0.04$. Pre-stress cortisol was correlated both to pre-stress PGEM ($r = 0.78$, $P < 0.04$) and to post-stress PGEM ($r = 0.79$, $P < 0.04$). Furthermore, pre-stress and post-stress PGEMs were also correlated ($r = 0.83$, $P < 0.02$).

Comment

Our results are in line with and extend the previous data and hypotheses that the HPA axis-eicosanoid interaction takes place on all three axis levels and that the relationships, in general, are of inverse nature. Thus, corticosteroids inhibit eicosanoids, while eicosanoids enhance and in some circumstances inhibit ACTH and cortisol and possibly also CRH release. In addition, under some specific conditions (c.f. Introduction) and as shown here for non-invasive stress, both systems can be activated in parallel and simultaneously.

Acknowledgements

Supported in part by the Karolinska Institute, Swedish Society of Medicine and Groschinsky Foundation. We thank K. Renk and A. Knall for expert technical help.

References

1. Ojeda SR, Negro-Vilar A and McCann SM (1981) In: RL Soto (ed.) Physiopathology of Endocrine Disease and Mechanism of Hormone Action. pp. 229–247.
2. Weidenfeldt J, Siegal RA, Conforti N, Feldman S and Chowers I (1981) Endocrinology 109: 205–209.
3. Vlaskovska M, Hertting G and Knepel W (1984) Endocrinology 115: 895–903.
4. Russo-Marie F and Duval D (1980) In: P. Ramwell (ed.) Prostaglandin Synthetase Inhibitors: New Clinical Applications. pp. 13–29.
5. Lewis GD, Campbell WB and Johnson AR (1986) Endocrinology 119: 62–69.
6. Carr BR, Mason JI, Parker CR Jr and Simpson ER (1983) Steroids 41: 663–674.
7. Gupta OP, Lahlou B, Botella J and Porthé-Nibelle J (1985) Exp. Biol. 43: 201–212.
8. Lihrmann I, Delarue C, Homo Delarche F, Netchiatailo P, Leboulenger F and Vaudry H (1986) Prostaglandins 32: 127–131.
9. Mathé AA, Bergman P, Apéria B and Wetterberg L (1987) Progr. Neuro-Psychopharmacol. Biol. Psychiatry 11: 701–707.

© 1991 Elsevier Science Publishers B.V. All rights reserved.
Biological Psychiatry, Volume 2. G. Racagni et al., editors.

Astroglial cells as sources of eicosanoids: Role of receptor-mediated phosphatidyl-inositol breakdown

András Seregi, Birgitta Noe and Georg Hertting
Institute of Pharmacology, University of Freiburg, Hermann-Herder Straße 5, D-7800 Freiburg, Germany

Introduction

Eicosanoids are enzymatic products derived from arachidonic acid. They include prostaglandins (PGs) and thromboxanes (TX) formed by the cyclooxygenase pathway as well as hydro[per]oxy fatty acids and leukotrienes which are due to the lipoxygenase activity. The synthesis of eicosanoids under in vitro and in vivo conditions in brain tissue has been widely confirmed [1]. Little is known about the molecular events leading to increased eicosanoid formation in specific brain cells. Astroglial cells are probably the major source of these substances [2]. They are capable of synthesizing large amounts of prostanoids (mainly PGD_2) upon stimulation with the Ca^{2+}-ionophore A23187 in primary cultures [3]. This suggests the involvement of a Ca^{2+}-dependent phospholipase (PL) A_2 in astroglial eicosanoid synthesis. Diacylglycerol (DAG)-mimetic phorbol-esters amplify PG formation when applied together with subthreshold doses of A23187, suggesting a cooperation between PLA_2 and PLC in this process [4]. However, among neurotransmitters which stimulate phosphatidylinositol (PI) breakdown in astrocytes, solely ATP is able to induce arachidohic acid liberation and prostanoid formation [5–7]. We now compare in detail the ATP-, noradrenaline (NA)- and carbachol (CCh)-stimulated astroglial PI breakdown, in order to find out whether differences between the effects of these agonists on PI metabolism exist that could explain their ability or inability to elicit prostanoid synthesis.

Methods

Primary astroglial cultures

Cells were grown from neonatal rat brain hemispheres in Dulbecco's minimum essential medium (DMEM) supplemented with 10% endotoxin-free fetal calf serum plus 10 ng lipopolysaccharide/ml and cultured for 20 days with two changes of media per week as described previously [4,5].

Labeling of cultures

Cultures were prelabeled for 48 h in serum-free DMEM in the presence of $[^3H]$-(myo)-inositol (1 µCi/ml).

Incubation of cultures

Cultures were washed 3 times in Dulbecco's phosphate buffered saline (DPBS), pH 7.4, and preincubated for 15 min in the same medium at 37°C. Then they were incubated in 1 ml DPBS with agonists for another 15 min. Preincubations and incubations were performed in the presence of 5 mM LiCl. Reactions were stopped with 0.3 M perchloric acid. Radioactive inositol phosphates (IPs) in neutralized perchloric acid extracts were separated by anion exchange chromatography [8].

Results and Discussion

Stimulation of astroglial receptors by noradrenaline, carbachol or ATP all resulted in enhanced phosphatidylinositol (PI) breakdown. NA and CCh, which are incapable of inducing prostanoid synthesis in astrocytes [9], concentration-dependently increased total inositolphosphate (IP) formation (IC_{50} ca. 10^{-6} M for NA and 10^{-4} M for CCh, respectively). The effect of NA was inhibited by prazosine (IC_{50} ca. 10^{-7} M) and the effect of CCh by pirenzepine (IC_{50} ca. 10^{-8} M) indicating the involvement of an α_1-adrenoceptor and an M_1 muscarinic receptor respectively. ATP, as well as ATP[γS] and ADP in a concentration of 10^{-3} M markedly stimulated total IP formation (221.6% ± 20.5, 214.3% ± 11.3 and 196.9% ± 23.2 of the unstimulated control, respectively). Adenosine was less potent and AMP was ineffective. This rank order of potency closely resembles the effects of these compounds on PGD_2-formation [6], suggesting that both processes are initiated via the same or similar P_{2Y}-receptors. The effect of ATP was also concentration-dependent (IC_{50} ca. 2×10^{-4} M). The effect of NA on total IP formation was more pronounced than that of CCh or ATP. This finding seemed to contradict the hypothesis that PI breakdown products participate in the stimulation of PG synthesis.

A detailed analysis of the time-course of formation of IP_3, IP_2 and IP_1 showed that the three different agonists (i.e. ATP, NA or CCh) induced markedly different responses (Table 1). There was a rapid and transient increase of IP_3 liberation upon ATP stimulation, while NA and CCh caused much smaller or negligible IP_3 formation. IP_1 levels reached nearly maximal values at 0.5–1 min after ATP-stimulation, whereas they increased almost continuously following CCh- or NA-stimulation.

These results strongly suggest that the astroglial purinoceptor is coupled to PLC, releasing the Ca^{2+}-mobilizing IP_3 and simultaneously the PKC activator DAG. Stimulation of the α_1-adrenoceptor or the muscarinic M_1-receptor, on the other

Table 1. Time-course of ATP-, carbachol- and noradrenaline-induced formation of individual inositol phosphates in cultured astrocytes

IP	Agonist	0 s	15 s	30 s	1 min	5 min	10 min
IP_1	ATP	4.6 ± 0.4	7.0 ± 0.5	7.2 ± 0.3	7.7 ± 0.4	7.8 ± 0.6	8.9 ± 0.9
	CCh	4.3 ± 0.3	5.5 ± 0.6	5.7 ± 0.4	6.1 ± 0.5	8.3 ± 0.6	10.8 ± 0.7
	NA	4.6 ± 0.6	6.1 ± 0.8	6.6 ± 0.7	6.8 ± 0.6	11.5 ± 2.1	19.8 ± 3.5
IP_2	ATP	1.0 ± 0.1	2.9 ± 0.2	2.1 ± 0.1	2.4 ± 0.2	1.5 ± 0.1	1.9 ± 0.3
	CCh	1.4 ± 0.1	1.7 ± 0.1	1.9 ± 0.2	2.2 ± 0.2	2.3 ± 0.1	2.7 ± 0.2
	NA	0.9 ± 0.1	1.8 ± 0.4	1.9 ± 0.3	2.2 ± 0.4	2.3 ± 0.5	2.7 ± 0.6
IP_3	ATP	1.5 ± 0.1	3.3 ± 0.3	2.5 ± 0.3	2.6 ± 0.3	1.8 ± 0.2	1.7 ± 0.3
	CCh	1.4 ± 0.2	1.6 ± 0.2	1.5 ± 0.2	1.5 ± 0.2	1.7 ± 0.2	1.3 ± 0.1
	NA	1.4 ± 0.2	2.1 ± 0.4	1.6 ± 0.3	1.9 ± 0.3	1.6 ± 0.3	1.9 ± 0.5

Cells were stimulated by ATP (10^{-3} M), CCh (10^{-3} M) or NA (10^{-4} M) for different times, as indicated. Results are means of six independent experiments performed in triplicate (n = 18) ± S.E.M. and expressed as c.p.m. × $10^{-3}/10^{6}$ intracellular free inositol.

hand, predominantly increases IP_1 (and possibly phosphatidic acid or DAG). These latter intracellular signals appear not to increase free intracellular Ca^{2+} sufficiently to activate PLA_2 which would then mobilize arachidonic acid for PG synthesis. This would explain, why NA or CCh are incapable of inducing PG synthesis in astrocytes.

Thus, simultaneous release of free DAG and a sufficient amount of IP_3 seem to be necessary for the induction of receptor-mediated astroglial prostanoid synthesis. ATP may fulfill these criteria by acting on P_{2Y}-purinoceptors which are coupled to a PIP_2-specific PLC. NA and CCh may interact with receptors coupled to a PLC, which preferentially hydrolyzes PI/PIP, or probably even to PLD, which does not supply IP_3 and DAG from PIP_2. Direct coupling of the purinoceptor to PLA_2, however, cannot be excluded to date.

References

1. Hertting G and Seregi A (1989) Ann. N.Y. Acad. Sci. 559: 84–99.
2. Seregi A, Keller M and Hertting G (1987) Brain Res. 404: 113–120.
3. Keller M, Jackisch R, Seregi A and Hertting G (1985) Neurochem. Int. 7: 655–665.
4. Gebicke-Haerter PJ, Seregi A, Schobert A and Hertting G (1988) Neurochem. Int. 4: 475–480.
5. Gebicke-Haerter PJ, Wurster S, Schobert A and Hertting G (1989) Naunyn-Schmiedeberg's Arch. Pharmacol. 338: 704–707.
6. Pearce B, Murphy S, Jeremy J, Morrow C and Dandona P (1989) J. Neurochem. 52: 971–977.
7. Bruner G and Murphy S (1990) J. Neurochem. 55: 1569–1575.
8. Berridge MJ, Downes CP and Hanley MR (1982) Biochem. J. 206: 587–595.
9. Keller M, Seregi A, Jackisch R and Hertting G (1987) Neurochem. Int. 10: 433–443.

© 1991 Elsevier Science Publishers B.V. All rights reserved.
Biological Psychiatry, Volume 2. G. Racagni et al., editors.

Modulation of arachidonic acid metabolism in astroglial cells by n-6 and n-3 fatty acids

A. Petroni, M. Blasevich, P. Grossi and C. Galli
Institute of Pharmacological Sciences, University of Milan, via Balzaretti 9-20133 Milan, Italy

Introduction

The activation of phospholipases in the SNC results in the formation of products such as platelet activating factor (PAF) and arachidonic acid (AA) metabolites which are mediators in different pathological events such as ischemia, convulsions or inflammation [1-3]. Astroglial cells in the SNC, participate in the onset of various pathological diseases and in repair processes. These cells are very active in generating AA metabolites and PAF is a potent agonist of this metabolic cascade [4]. The aim of our study was thus to investigate the activation of AA metabolism through the cyclo- (CO) and the lipo- (LO) oxygenases in a primary culture of astroglial cells stimulated by PAF and to evaluate the effects of the PAF antagonist BN 52021 on these processes. PAF stimulation was compared with the effect of the calcium-ionophore A 23187, a potent activator of phospholipases. Moreover, since glial cells in culture appear to be depleted of long-chain polyunsaturated fatty acids (PUFA) compared to brain tissue, we have studied the incorporation of docosahexaenoic acid (DHA) in cell phospholipids and the consequent effect on AA metabolism stimulated by A 23187. DHA is a 22:6, n-3 fatty acid which is present in the brain in very high concentrations, especially in the retina and in synaptic membranes.

Materials and Methods

Primary cultures of astroglial cells were prepared from cerebral hemispheres of newborn rats [5] and used at confluence (12–14 days). The purity was checked by the presence of glial fibrillary acidic protein (> 95% astrocytes) [6].

PAF and calcium-ionophore were incubated with the cells at different concentrations and time periods of stimulation. In some experiments the cells were labeled with tritiated AA (1μ Curies/well) to evaluate the products of phospholipid hydrolysis free fatty acids (FFA) and diacylglycerol (DAG), separated by mono and bidimensional thin layer chromatography. The metabolic conversion of AA through the CO was monitored by measuring 6-keto-$PGF_{1\alpha}$ and thromboxane B_2 (TxB_2), the stable metabolites of prostacyclin and thromboxane A_2 respectively, by enzymatic immunoassay. The effects of the PAF antagonist BN 52021 was investigated by incubating the cells with BN 52021 for 15 min before the stimulation with the agonists. LO metabolites were monitored by HPLC connected with a variable UV detector to monitor the compounds produced by the endogenous pool and connected with an on-line radiodetector to evaluate the labeled metabolites: 12 and 15-hydroxyeicosatetraenoic acids (HETE).

To study the incorporation of DHA in cell phospholipids the cells were grown for 72 h before the incubation with Eagle basal medium containing 5 μM DHA. The relative concentrations and absolute amounts of DHA were measured by quantitative gas chromatography. The effects of the incorporation of DHA in cells on AA metabolism were evaluated by measuring the products generated by cells prelabeled for 4 h with tritiated AA and stimulated with A 23187.

Results and Discussion

PAF and eicosanoid production in astrocytes

When the arachidonic acid labeled cells were stimulated with PAF a marked increase of DAG was detected after 2 and 30 min of stimulation, some elevation of AA occurred only at 30 min, suggesting that PAF primarily activates phospholipase C. In contrast the marked accumulation of free AA after A 23187 stimulation indicates that phospholipase A_2 was primarily activated. After PAF stimulation, AA was metabolized by LO, but the formation of 12 and 15-HETE could be detected only when cells were labeled with tritiated AA. No LTC_4 appeared to be produced after PAF stimulation. Accumulation of 12 and 15-HETE and of LTC_4 was instead also detected in unlabeled cells when stimulated with A 23187. The stimulation by PAF and A 23187 of the formation of CO metabolites is shown in Fig. 1. The two agonists were incubated at 1 μM concentration for 15 min. At this

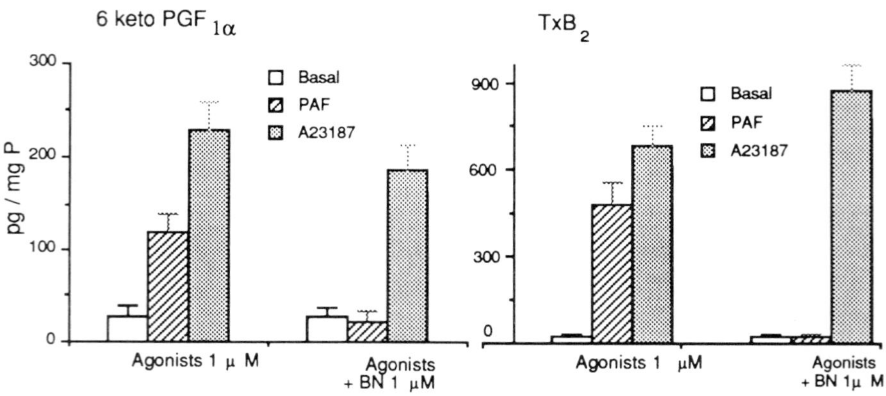

Fig. 1. Left panel: Levels of 6-keto-$PGF_{1\alpha}$ (pg/mg protein) in astroglial cells incubated with BN 52021 for 15 min and stimulated with PAF and A 23187 (1 μM) for 15 min. Right panel: Levels of TxB_2 in astroglial cells incubated with BN 52021 for 15 min and stimulated with PAF or A 23187 (1 μM) for 15 min.

Table 1. Levels of TxB_2 and 6-keto-$PGF_{1\alpha}$ in preparation of control and DHA-enriched glial cells after stimulation with the calcium ionophore A23187

Preparations	TxB_2 (pg/mg P)	6-keto-$PGF_{1\alpha}$ (pg/mg P)
Control	918 ± 130	687 ± 80
DHA	554 ± 31[a]	475 ± 1

concentration PAF was very active, although less potent than A 23187 in stimulating both TxB_2 and 6-keto-$PGF_{1\alpha}$. The PAF antagonist BN 52021 very specifically inhibited the production of CO metabolites, whereas it did not inhibit the effects of A 23187 on the eicosanoid cascade.

Effect of DHA on eicosanoid production in glial cells

The primary cultures of astroglial cells had a concentration of DHA, as percent of total fatty acids of about 2, lower than that measured in lipid extracted from brain tissue (about 8–9). The cells were thus grown for 72 h with 5 μM DHA and the levels of this fatty acid under these conditions increased up to a relative concentration of about 5–6%. Cells were then labeled for 4 h with tritiated AA before stimulation with A 23187 (1 μM) for 15 min.

In the stimulated cells levels of the eicosanoids were markedly elevated (Table 1) over those, almost undetectable, in the non-stimulated preparations. When the concentration of DHA in the cells was raised after 72 h of incubation, the production of the two eicosanoids was markedly reduced. Our studies show that PAF, a compound which is involved in various processes of inflammatory nature, is a potent stimulant of the eicosanoid cascade in astrocytes, and this suggests a possible role of PAF in glial cell activation during brain damage.

In addition, supplementation of DHA, in order to restore the levels of this long chain PUFA in cells which appear to be depleted of this fatty acid in culture, resulted in a very pronounced modification of arachidonic acid metabolism, indicating possible modulation of this cascade by n-3 fatty acid in the CNS.

References

1. Benveniste J, Henson PM and Cochrane CG (1972) J. Exp. Med. 136: 1356–1377.
2. Gaudet RJ, Alam I and Levine L (1980) J. Neurochem. 35: 653–658.
3. Kumar R, Harvey SAK, Kester M, Hanahan DJ and Olson MS (1988) Biochim. Biophys. Acta 963: 375–383.
4. Petroni A, Blasevich M, Visioli F, and Galli C (1990) In: B Samuelsson et al. (ed.) Adv. Prost. Thromb. Leuk. Res. Raven Press Ltd, New York, U.S.A. 743–747.
5. Booher J and Sensenbrenner M (1972) Neurobiology 2: 97–105.
6. Gebicke-Haerter PJ, Althaus HH, Schwartz P and Neuhoff V (1981) Dev. Brain Res. 1: 497–518.

© 1991 Elsevier Science Publishers B.V. All rights reserved.
Biological Psychiatry, Volume 2. G. Racagni et al., editors.

Effect of nutritive factors on docosahexaenoic acid metabolism to hydroxy docosahexaenoate (HDHE)

John W. Karanian, Hee Yong Kim and Norman Salem Jr.
Laboratory of Clinical Studies, DICBR, NIAAA, Bldg. 10/3C-102, 9000 Rockville Pike, Bethesda, MD 20892, U.S.A.

The metabolism of docosahexaenoic acid (22:6w3) to its hydroxy derivatives has been observed in several mammalian cells and tissues, including basophils [1] macrophages [2], liver [3] and brain [4]. This fatty acid is highly localized in excitable membranes such as those of the brain and retina. In the human platelet, both the 11- and 14-hydroxy derivatives are formed in vitro from exogenously administered 22:6w3 [5]. Hydroxylation of 22:6w3 to all 10 positional isomers has also been observed in mammalian brain [6]. Both inhibitor profiles and stereochemical analyses suggests that the platelet products are enzymatically produced via a 12-lipoxygenase enzyme, whereas the brain products are mainly produced through a peroxidation process [6]. Whether these metabolites are produced from endogenous substrate under physiological conditions and are of biological significance in the human is still an open question.

Croset et al. [7] have reported a relatively specific antagonism of thromboxane-induced platelet aggregation by HDHEs. A similar antagonism by HDHE of thromboxane-induced vascular smooth muscle contraction has also been shown [8]. Concentrations as low as 250 pmoles inhibit the contractile effects and aggregatory effects of a thromboxane agonist, U46619. In addition, recent data indicate these hydroxy derivatives are capable of stimulating leukotriene production from macrophages, neutrophils and airway smooth muscle (Karanian et al., unpublished results). It is possible the hydroxylated metabolites of 22:6w3 may be physiologically active in cell-cell interactions of vascular beds such as the cerebral microvasculature [9] and in the pathology of cerebral ischemia [10].

Effects of alcohol and dietary ω_3 supplementation on 22:6w3 content and HDHE production

A deficiency in the precursor fatty acid, 22:6w3 has been associated with neurological diseases, visual impairment and learning deficiencies [11]. The brain, compared to other organs, is considered resistant to dietary-induced changes in lipid composition. Nevertheless, several investigators have demonstrated that ethanol exposure can lead to decreases in 22:6w3 in brain [12–14]. Although there is, in a few cases, disagreement concerning the degree and direction of the changes

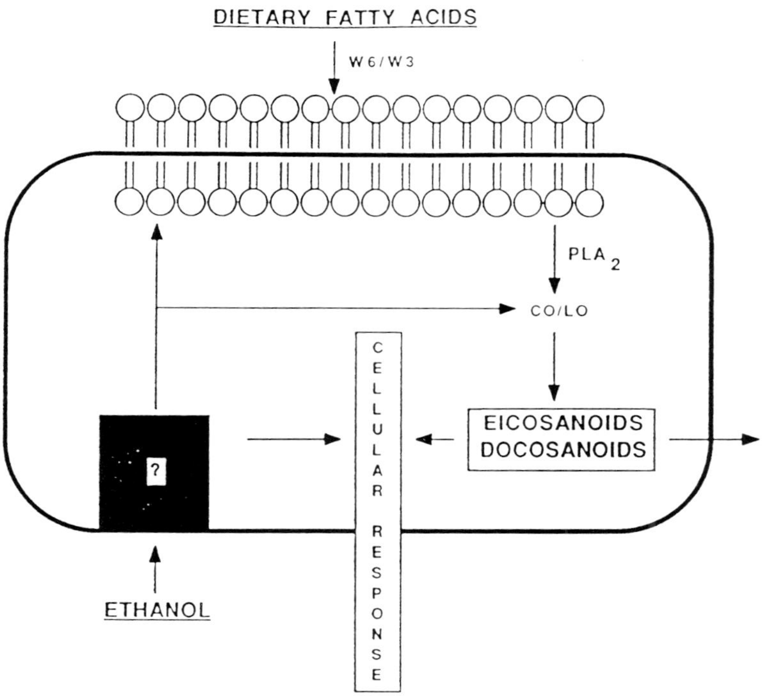

Fig. 1. Effects of nutritive factors on cellular function.

[15], most evidence favours the proposition that ethanol exposure leads to a decline in polyunsaturated fatty acyl content of cell membranes [16].

The proposition that moderate alcohol consumption increases eicosanoid production and that this change is related to the biological effects of alcohol [17,18] may also be the case for docosanoids. For example, marked stimulation of 22:6w3 lipoxygenation by rat platelet to HDHE was observed following 7 days of moderate ethanol inhalation [19].

It is a common observation that w-3 supplementation of the diet results in an increase in w-3 polyunsaturates with a concomitant decrease in w-6 polyunsaturates [20]. Recent studies in our laboratory and others [21] have demonstrated that 22:6w3 content in brain increases with w-3 supplementation and decreases with w-6 supplementation in young rats.

We have shown that marked increases in 22:6w3 in rat platelets after an w-3 rich diet correlated with increases in docosanoid production to levels which may be of biological significance [22]. Platelets obtained from these rats produce as much as 3 nmoles of these w-3 hydroxy derivatives which are clearly active in this concentration range.

The physiological significance of changes in 22:6w3 content together with its lipoxygenation to HDHE requires further study; however, current findings indicate that 22:6w3 and its lipoxygenase products are altered by dietary permutations such as alcohol and w-3 supplementation. Whether fatty acid supplementation can counter fatty acid deficiencies caused by chronic alcohol exposure or alter eicosanoid/docosanoid mediated cellular responses in brain and other organs will be further tested through carefully designed dietary studies and experimental models of alcoholism (Fig. 1).

References

1. Corey E, Shih C and Cashman JR (1983) Proc. Natl. Acad. Sci. U.S.A. 80: 3581–3584.
2. Rigaud M (1984) Prostaglandins 27: 358–361.
3. van Rollins M, Baker RC, Sprecher HW and Murphy RC (1984) J. Biol. Chem. 259: 5776–5783.
4. Shingu T, Karanian JW, Kim HY, Yergey JA and Salem N Jr (1988) Adv. Alcohol Subst. Abuse 7: 235–240.
5. Alvedano MI and Specher HW (1983) J. Biol. Chem. 258: 9339–9643.
6. Kim NY, Karanian JW, Shingu T and Salem N Jr (1990) Prostaglandins 140: 473–490.
7. Croset M, Sala A, Folco G and Lagarde M (1988) Biochem. Pharmacol. 37: 1275–1280.
8. Karanian JW, Kim NY, Shingu T and Salem N Jr (1988) Biomed. Biochim. Acta 47: S79–S82.
9. Karanian JW, Kim NY, Shingu T and Salem N Jr (1989) In: Schror K and Sinzinger H (eds.) Prostaglandins in Clinical Research: Cardiovascular System. A.R. Liss, pp. 511–515.
10. Shingu T, Karanian JW, Kim HY and Salem N Jr (1989) Ann. NYAS 559: 482–484.
11. Salem N Jr, Kim HY and Yergey JY (1986) In: Simopoulis A and Kifer R (eds.) Health Effects of PUFA in Seafoods. Academic Press, pp. 217–263.
12. Littleton JM, John GR and Grieve SJ (1979) Alcoholism 3: 50–56.
13. Harris BA, Baster DM and Mitchell MA (1984) Mol. Pharmacol. 25: 401–419.
14. Aloia RC, Paxton J, Daviau JS, van Geib O, Miekusch W, Truppe W, Meyer JA and Brauer FS (1985) Life Sci. 36: 1003–1017.
15. Sun GY and Sun AY (1979) Res. Commun. Chem. Path. Pharmacol. 24: 405–408.
16. Salem N Jr, Hun F, Yoffe A, Karanian JW and Kim HY (1988) In: B Samuelsson, P Wong and F Sun (eds.) Adv. Prostaglandins, Thromboxane, Leukotriene Res. Plenum Press 19: 103–108.
17. Horrobin DF (1980) Med. Hypothesis 6: 929–942.
18. Karanian JW and Salem N Jr (1987) In: Gallo L (ed.) Cardiovascular Disease. Plenum Press, pp. 299–321.
19. Salem N Jr and Karanian JW (1989) Adv. Alcohol Subst. Abuse 45: 183–197.
20. Salem N Jr (1989) In: Spiller G and Scala J (eds.) New Protective Roles for Selected Nutrients. A.R. Liss, pp. 213–332.
21. Connor WE, Neuringer M and Lin D (1985) Clin. Chem. 33: 598A–603A.
22. Karanian JW, Kim HY and Salem N Jr (1990) Int. Con. Prostaglandins and Related Compounds. p. 44.

© 1991 Elsevier Science Publishers B.V. All rights reserved.
Biological Psychiatry, Volume 2. G. Racagni et al., editors.

Arachidonic acid breakdown as a modulatory system for neurotransmission

A. Volterra, D. Trotti, P. Cassutti, C. Tromba and G. Racagni
Center of Neuropharmacology and Institute of Pharmacological Sciences, University of Milan, Via Balzaretti 9, 20133 Milan, Italy

12-Lipoxygenase metabolites of arachidonic acid cause synaptic inhibition by increasing K^+ channel activity in Aplysia

In the marine mollusk Aplysia Californica the neuropeptide FMRFamide induces presynaptic inhibition at sensorimotor synapses utilizing 12-lipoxygenase metabolites of arachidonic acid as second messengers [1]. The peptide exerts its inhibitory action mostly by increasing the activity of a class of outward K^+ channels (S channels) in the sensory cell. As a consequence, membrane potential hyperpolarization and action potential shortening are achieved.

Lipoxygenase derivatives are produced by sensory cells following FMRFamide receptor stimulation. Among them, 12-hydroperoxyeicosatetraenoic acid (12-HPETE) proves very effective in mimicking the inhibitory action of the peptide and in increasing the opening of the S channels. 12-HPETE acts on S channels even in membrane patches isolated from the remainder of the cell and lacking the internal cell medium. This evidence suggests that its modulatory action on the channel may be direct [2]. Downstream metabolites of 12-HPETE, possibly compounds produced by the cytochrome P_{450} pathway such as hepoxilins, are also effective in opening S channels in excised patches [3]. On the contrary, 12-HETE, 15-HPETE and arachidonic acid are almost completely ineffective.

Glutamate synapses in the CNS: Arachidonic acid involvement in synaptic potentiation and intercellular communication

Glutamate synapses in the CNS can undergo plasticity phenomena involving long-term changes in synaptic efficacy. Among these, long-term potentiation (LTP) is the best characterized. Following brief high frequency stimulation of afferent fibers, glutamate synapses show increased excitatory responsiveness which can last for hours. Studies of LTP in area CA_1 and dentate gyrus of the hippocampus indicate that LTP is started by activation of NMDA-type glutamate receptors and Ca^{2+} entry through the related channel in the postsynaptic cell [4]. Ca^{2+} can then trigger a series of biochemical events leading to changes in synaptic function. Among these, up-regulation of postsynaptic glutamate receptors and\or enhancement of presynaptic glutamate release could be responsible for LTP expression.

In order for presynaptic changes to take place, it has been hypothesized that NMDA receptors induce the release of a "retrograde messenger" bringing adaptive information from the postsynaptic element to the presynaptic one. Arachidonic acid is a candidate for this role. Thus, different laboratories have shown arachidonate release upon NMDA receptor stimulation (e.g. [5]). We find that neuronal cell cultures from rat cortex or hippocampus but not glial cultures respond to glutamate or NMDA with an extracellular release of pre-incorporated ^{3}H-arachidonic acid. Also, free arachidonate levels in the hippocampus are enhanced following LTP induction and phospholipase inhibitors seem able to prevent LTP [6].

Arachidonic acid does enhance glutamate release from hippocampal synaptosomes, leading to increased synaptic availability of the transmitter [7]. We show a different and synergic mechanism through which arachidonic acid may lead to the same effect: inhibition of glutamate reuptake. Both presynaptic neuronal terminals and perisynaptic astrocytes possess high-affinity uptake systems for glutamate. Clearance from the synaptic space via diffusion and uptake is the major mechanism for the termination of glutamate synaptic actions. Arachidonic acid significantly reduces uptake rate both in synaptosomes and astrocytes (Fig. 1). Its action is fast: 30 s after arachidonate application uptake inhibition is already present. Maximal effect is reached within 5–10 min. Arachidonate is maximally effective (up to 50% inhibition) at concentrations between 50–100 μM. However, significant uptake reduction is also seen with 1 μM.

Albumin, a free fatty acid-binding protein, completely reverses arachidonate-induced inhibition. This observation has 2 implications: a) arachidonate does not need incorporation in the target membrane phospholipids to act; b) arachidonate acts from the outer side of the membrane. Thus, its effect is reversed by albumin,

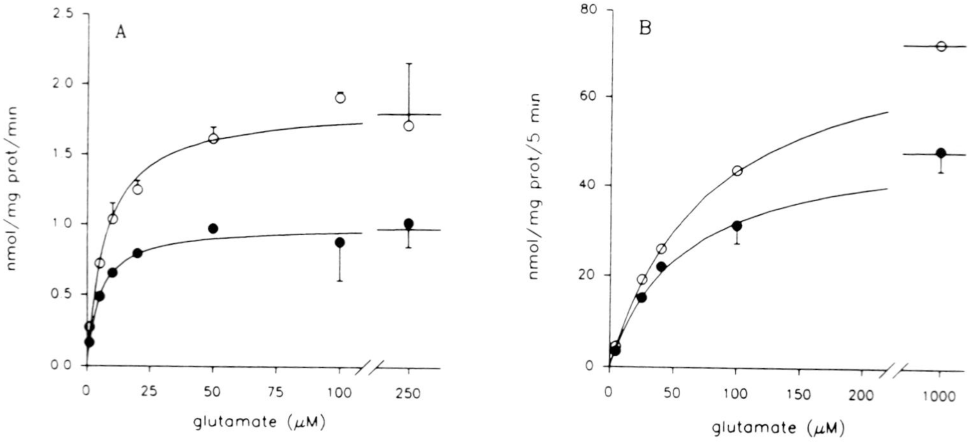

Fig. 1. High-affinity glutamate uptake inhibition by arachidonic acid in cortical synaptosomes (A) and astrocytes (B); open circles: basal glutamate uptake; filled circles: glutamate uptake in the presence of 100 μM arachidonic acid.

which cannot cross cell membranes. Therefore, our data reinforce the idea that arachidonic acid could be a fast intercellular messenger at glutamate synapses. It may be released outside the postsynaptic neuron following NMDA receptor activation. By diffusing in the synaptic space arachidonate may target the presynaptic element and inhibit glutamate uptake with a simple one-step mechanism. In addition, it can initiate a multiple-step process to enhance glutamate release. Both effects would eventually lead to accumulation of the transmitter in the synaptic space. In this situation, glutamate synaptic levels could still be decreased by diffusion in the perisynaptic area. However, here, uptake in astrocytes may also be impaired by arachidonate, with the final result of a significantly reduced glutamate clearance. More transmitter would then be available to activate its receptors and potentiate synaptic transmission. Indeed, recent functional evidence indicates that the excitatory postsynaptic current of CA_1 pyramidal neurons in response to afferent glutamatergic fibers stimulation is increased in the presence of glutamate uptake inhibitors such as dihydrokainate [8].

References

1. Piomelli D, Volterra A, Dale N, Siegelbaum SA, Kandel ER, Schwartz JH and Belardetti F (1987) Nature 328: 38.
2. Buttner N, Siegelbaum SA and Volterra A (1989) Nature 342: 553.
3. Belardetti F, Campbell WB, Falck JR, DeMontis GC and Rosolowsky M (1989) Neuron 3: 497.
4. Kennedy MB (1989) Cell 59: 777.
5. Dumuis A, Sebben M, Haynes L, Pin JP and Bockaert J (1988) Nature 336: 68.
6. Lynch MA, Errington ML and Bliss TVP (1989) Neuroscience 30: 693.
7. Freeman EJ, Terrian DM and Dorman RV (1990) Neurochem. Res. 15: 743.
8. Hestrin S, Sah P and Nicoll RA (1990) Neuron 5: 247.

© 1991 Elsevier Science Publishers B.V. All rights reserved.
Biological Psychiatry, Volume 2. G. Racagni et al., editors.

Neuronal Ca^{2+} homeostasis and its control by neurotransmitters

Richard J. Miller

Department of Pharmacological and Physiological Sciences, The University of Chicago, 947 East 58th Street, Chicago, IL 60637, U.S.A.

Introduction

Intracellular Ca^{2+} signals, $[Ca^{2+}]_i$, are extremely important in the control of nerve cell function. For example, changes in the $[Ca^{2+}]_i$ control neurotransmitter release and nerve cell excitability. In the longer-term they also control neuronal gene expression, synaptic plasticity and nerve cell viability. Thus, it is extremely important for us to understand the molecular mechanisms which regulate the shaping of neuronal Ca^{2+} signals.

Ca^{2+} signals in nerve cells basically depend on a balance between processes that can increase $[Ca^{2+}]_i$ and those that serve to decrease it. Basically, increases in intracellular Ca^{2+} are normally produced either by Ca^{2+} influx from the extra-cellular space through Ca^{2+} channels or by release from intracellular stores of various types. On the other hand, the buffering of intracellular Ca^{2+} is usually the result of activation of either intracellular or plasma membrane localized Ca^{2+} pumps, of Na^+/Ca^{2+} exchange mechanisms, of Ca^{2+} uptake into mitochondria or of Ca^{2+} binding to intracellular proteins.

Increases in intracellular Ca^{2+}

The following processes are capable of producing increases in $[Ca^{2+}]_i$ in nerve cells.

Voltage-sensitive Ca^{2+} channels

Nerve cells possess a variety of voltage-sensitive Ca^{2+} channels. There appear to be at least four types, but in all probability the actual number of channels will probably be proved to be much larger [1,2]. These channels have considerable differences in both their biophysical properties and also their pharmacology. Ca^{2+} influx via voltage-sensitive Ca^{2+} channels, which open during neuronal activity, produce important changes in $[Ca^{2+}]_i$ that can regulate neurotransmitter release and cell excitability. Many kinds of voltage-sensitive Ca^{2+} channels can also be modified by the action of neurotransmitters either directly through G-proteins or through the actions of diffusible intracellular messenger molecules.

Receptor-operated Ca^{2+} channels

A number of neurotransmitters can directly open ion channels which are permeable to Ca^{2+}. The best studied example of this phenomenon is the NMDA type of glutamate receptor [3]. Activation of this receptor by glutamate directly opens an ion channel which is about 10 times more permeable to Ca^{2+} than to Na^+. When excitatory glutamate-mediated synaptic transmission occurs at high frequency, such channels may be opened allowing glutamate to activate a large Ca^{2+} influx via this route. In addition to the NMDA receptor, it may be that certain types of kainate/AMPA-type glutamate receptors also exhibit a permeability to Ca^{2+} [4]. Recent observations suggests that the Ca^{2+} permeability of these glutamate receptors will depend critically on the subunit composition of the particular receptor. There are also other types of ligand gated ion channels found in the brain such as nicotinic receptors which may also be permeable to Ca^{2+} ions.

Na^+/Ca^{2+} exchange

Many neurons possess a Na^+/Ca^{2+} exchange system in their cell membranes [5]. This process may be important for removing Ca^{2+} that has accumulated in nerve cells. However, under some conditions it may also reverse and allow Ca^{2+} influx into nerve cells (see below). This is because the Na^+/Ca^{2+} exchange is voltage dependent. Depolarization of the neuron will favor the movement of Ca^{2+} into the cell in exchange for Na^+ moving outward. It is not clear at this point how often this process actually occurs under physiological conditions.

Intracellular Ca^{2+} release

Neurons possess at least two types of intracellular Ca^{2+} storage sites [6]. These both appear to correspond to vesicular elements which are associated with the endoplasmic reticulum. Ca^{2+} is pumped into these vesicles by means of a Ca^{2+} pump and bound within them by a Ca^{2+} binding protein such as calreticulin. It is quite likely that these two types of Ca^{2+} storage vesicles are differentially localized within nerve cells and serve different functions. For example, IP_3-sensitive storage sites release Ca^{2+} in response to IP_3 synthesized as the result of stimulation of receptors in the cell plasma membrane by a variety of neurotransmitters. On the other hand, the second type of Ca^{2+} storage vesicle, which contains the ryanodine receptor, appears to participate in the process of Ca^{2+}-induced Ca^{2+} release similar to that found in cardiac muscle [7]. This is a process by which small cytoplasmic Ca^{2+} signals can be furthered amplified. These events have been described in both peripheral and central neurons.

Intracellular Ca^{2+} buffers

Once intracellular Ca^{2+} has been increased by one of the processes described above, various elements in the cell are responsible for decreasing it again until resting levels are obtained. The precise mechanisms for buffering intracellular depend on the nerve cell and the size of the rise in $[Ca^{2+}]_i$. The following processes all seem to be important.

Ca^{2+} binding proteins

There are a number of Ca^{2+} binding proteins which are found to be highly concentrated in neurons [8]. In addition to calmodulin, which is found to one extent or another in most cells, high concentrations of calbindin, calretinin and parvalbumin have been described in unique neuronal populations. It is quite likely that these proteins perform very rapid Ca^{2+} buffering when intracellular Ca^{2+} first enters the cytoplasm.

Ca^{2+} pumps

Ca^{2+} ATPases are found on the plasma membrane and also on the membranes of intracellular Ca^{2+} storage vesicles as described above [9]. These Ca^{2+} pumps have a quite high affinity for Ca^{2+} (in the micromolar and submicromolar range), particularly under the most optimal conditions. It is thought likely that these Ca^{2+} pumps are responsible for setting the resting Ca^{2+} levels in the neuronal cytoplasm. However, they have a relatively low capacity and cannot rapidly handle very large Ca^{2+} loads.

Na^+/Ca^{2+} exchanger

This has been described above and is a fairly low-affinity, but high-capacity system for handling intracellular Ca^{2+} [5]. The system found in the cell plasma membrane is also voltage-dependent and can allow Ca^{2+} to enter the cell under some conditions. However, when Ca^{2+} rises within the cell to fairly high levels (>1 μM), Na^+/Ca^+ exchange may be responsible for the removal of a large portion of the Ca^+ from the cell.

The mitochondria

The mitochondria contain a Ca^{2+}-permeable uniporter in the membrane of the inner mitochondrial matrix [10]. Large amounts of Ca^{2+} may enter the mitochondria under some circumstances and it is quite likely that when Ca^{2+} levels rise appreciably within the cytoplasm that considerable amounts of the Ca^{2+} may enter mitochondria. The Ca^{2+} entering the mitochondria has an important role to play, as it can regulate the activity of a number of important metabolic enzymes within the mitochondrial matrix. It may therefore be a mechanism for connecting the metabolic activity of the cell to its electrical activity. Eventually, Ca^{2+} must leave the mitochondrial matrix once again, a process which also utilizes a Na^{+}/Ca^{2+} exchange mechanism found in the matrix membrane. Once it has re-entered the cytoplasm, Ca^{2+} can be furthered removed by one of the other Ca^{2+} buffering processes described above.

References

1. Miller RJ (1990) FASEB J. 4: 3291–3300.
2. Tsien RW and Tsien RY (1990) Ann. Rev. Cell. Biol. 6: 715–760.
3. Mayer ML and Miller RJ (1990) Trends Pharmacol. Sci. 11: 254–260.
4. Hollmann M, Hartley M and Heinemann S (1991) Science (in press).
5. Blaustein MP (1988) Trends Neurosci. 11: 438–443.
6. Thayer SA, Perney TM and Miller RJ (1988) J. Neurosci. 8: 4089–4097.
7. Thayer SA, Hirning LD and Miller RJ (1988) Mol. Pharmacol. 34: 669–673.
8. Celio MR (1990) Neuroscience 35: 375–475.
9. Carafoli E (1987) Ann. Rev. Biochem. 56: 395–433.
10. Crompton M (1985) Curr. Top. Membr. Transp. 25: 231–276.

© 1991 Elsevier Science Publishers B.V. All rights reserved.
Biological Psychiatry, Volume 2. G. Racagni et al., editors.

Regulation of glutamatergic synaptic transmission by intracellular calcium

Arthur Konnerth and Jörg Dreessen
Max-Planck-Institut für Biophysikalische Chemie, Am Fassberg, 3400 Göttingen, Germany

The role of calcium in signal-transduction at glutamatergic synapses is well established. Of special interest are N-methyl-D-aspartate (NMDA)-receptor channels which are thought to be important for activity-dependent changes in intracellular calcium [1,2]. There is, however, increasing evidence that also non-NMDA glutamatergic receptors involve changes in cytosolic calcium concentration ($[Ca^{2+}]_i$) for their physiological responses.

A particularly suitable preparation for the study of $[Ca^{2+}]_i$-changes induced by non-NMDA receptors are the cerebellar Purkinje cells. These cells receive 2 major excitatory synaptic inputs, consisting of axons of the parallel fiber (PF) and the climbing fiber (CF) systems. Both inputs have been shown to exert their effect exclusively through the activation of glutamate receptors of the non-NMDA type [3–5]. Nevertheless, activation of glutamate receptors of cerebellar Purkinje cells involves transient changes of $[Ca^{2+}]_i$ arising from various sources.

Activation of CFs is strongly associated with what has been termed CA-electroresponsiveness of Purkinje cells [6]. By combining whole-cell patch-clamp recordings with fura-2 video imaging applied to cerebellar slices, we could demonstrate that the CF-induced Ca-transients are caused primarily by the activation of voltage-gated Ca-channels [7]. The CF-induced $[Ca^{2+}]_i$-changes were spatially non-uniform, being largest in the peripheral dendrites and lowest in the cell somata. Conjunctive stimulation of PFs and CFs is known to induce a long-lasting form of cerebellar learning which consists of a long-lasting depression of the PF-responses and which has been named long-term depression (LTD) [8]. Our data indicate that a transient rise in $[Ca^{2+}]_i$ associated with PF-stimulation is a necessary and sufficient condition for the induction of LTD in cerebellar slices [7].

A second possible mechanism contributing to the rises in $[Ca^{2+}]_i$ in Purkinje cells involves the activation of the metabotropic glutamate receptors which induce their effect through a chain of second messengers leading eventually to the release of Ca^{2+} from intracellular stores [for review see 9]. Indeed, bath application of quisqualate (1 μM) or glutamate (100 μM) induces large increases in $[Ca^{2+}]_i$ in the dendrites of Purkinje cells. These $[Ca^{2+}]_i$-transients persist in Ca^{2+}-free (EGTA-containing) extracellular solutions, indicating that they result from the release of Ca^{2+} from intracellular stores. The dendritic location of this Ca^{2+}-signals may suggest that under physiological conditions metabotropic receptors are activated by synaptically-released glutamate [10].

A third pathway for Ca^{2+} entering Purkinje cells is the ionotropic glutamate receptors themselves. Recent work on recombinant AMPA/kainate [11,12] demonstrates that certain receptor subtypes are highly permeable for Ca^{2+}. A similar mechanism seems to be present in Purkinje cells, where upon bath application of kainate or AMPA, under conditions in which the contribution of voltage-gated Ca^{2+}-channels is absent, dendritic changes in $[Ca^{2+}]_i$ can be observed.

In conclusion, these findings indicate that even in the absence of NMDA-receptors, the function of glutamatergic synapses is linked in a complex and powerful fashion to Ca^{2+} and other second messengers. More work is required in order to establish the precise mechanisms by which Ca^{2+}-signals are linked to the intracellular machinery during normal function and the induction of LTD at glutamatergic non-NMDA synapses.

Acknowledgements

This work was supported by grants from the Bundesministerium für Forschung und Technologie (Projektgruppen Neurobiologie) and the Deutsche Forschungsgemeinschaft (SFB 236).

References

1. Collingridge GH and Bliss TVP (1987) Trends Neurosci. 10: 288–293.
2. Mayer M and Westbrook G.
3. Kano M and Kato M (1987) Nature 325: 276–279.
4. Konnerth A, Llano I and Armstrong CM (1989) Proc. Natl. Acad. Sci. U.S.A. 87: 2662–2665.
5. Llano I, Marty A, Armstrong CM and Konnerth A (1991a) J. Physiol. 434: 183–213.
6. Llinas R and Sugimori M (1980) J. Physiol. 305: 197–213.
7. Konnerth A, Dreessen J and Augustine G (1991) (submitted).
8. Ito M (1989) Ann. Rev. Neurosci. 12: 85–102.
9. Mayer ML and Miller RJ (1990) Trends Pharmacol. Sci. 11: 254–260.
10. Llano I, Dreessen J, Kano M and Konnerth A (1991b) (submitted).
11. Hollmann M, Hartley M and Heinemann S (1991) Science (in press).
12. Keller BU, Hollmann M, Heinemann S and Konnerth A (1991) (submitted).

© 1991 Elsevier Science Publishers B.V. All rights reserved.
Biological Psychiatry, Volume 2. G. Racagni et al., editors.

Voltage-operated calcium channels and synaptic pathology

Emanuele Sher, Maria Passafaro, Erminio Biancardi and Francesco Clementi
CNR Center of Cytopharmacology, Department of Medical Pharmacology, University of Milan, via Vanvitelli 32, 20129 Milan, Italy

Introduction

Different subtypes of voltage-operated calcium channels are known to be co-expressed in single cells [1–2]. They open in response to plasma membrane depolarization and allow Ca^{2+} entry from the extracellular medium into cell cytoplasm because of the steep electrochemical gradient present for this ion. Ca^{2+} entry will then activate a number of different Ca^{2+}-dependent processes, one of which is the Ca^{2+}-dependent release of neurotransmitters from the nerve-terminals.

There is a human pathology of neurotransmission, the Lambert-Eaton myasthenic syndrome (LEMS), which is characterized by the presence of autoantibodies, directed against presynaptic antigens. The patients suffer from symptoms related to the deficit in the Ca^{2+}-dependent release of neurotransmitters in both the voluntary and autonomic nervous system.

The aim of our study was to characterize the different subtypes of VOCCs expressed in human neuronal cells, to define the VOCC subtypes controlling Ca^{2+} influx in the nerve terminals and finally identify the molecular target for LEMS autoantibodies.

Materials and Methods

Cell culture

IMR human neuroblastoma cells were cultivated and differentiated as described in [3]. Differentiation was achieved by adding to the culture medium 1 mM Bt_2cAMP or 25 μM 5 BrdU or both.

^{125}I-ω-Conotoxin binding assay

The specific binding of ^{125}I-ω-conotoxin (^{125}IωCTx) to IMR32 cells was studied as described in [4]. Increasing concentrations of ^{125}I-ωCTx (1–200 pM) were added to a fixed amount of tissue (100–200 μg) in a final volume of 100 μl and left for 2 h at room temperature. In parallel tubes, non-specific toxin binding was evaluated for each concentration, in the presence of an excess (1 μM) of unlabeled toxin. At

Table 1. ^{125}I-ωCTx binding in neuronal cell lines

IMR_{32}	(Human neuroblastoma)	5.0 ± 3.1
SK-N-BE	(Human neuroblastoma)	4.5 ± 2.0
SK-N-SH	(Human neuroblastoma)	9.0 ± 3.5
SH-SY5Y	(Human neuroblastoma)	11.5 ± 6.0
NIE-115	(Mouse neuroblastoma)	1.1 ± 0.2
NG-108-15	(Mouse neuroblastoma × rat glioma)	3.4 ± 1.9
PC_{12}	(Rat pheochromocytoma)	7.4 ± 5.4

the end of the incubation the samples were centrifuged, the pellets washed twice and finally counted.

Calcium channel immunoprecipitation

A homogenate of IMR_{32} was prepared and VOCCs labeled with a saturating (100 pM) concentration of ^{125}I-ωCTx. After reaching equilibrium, 1% Triton was added in order to solubilize the channel-toxin complexes. After centrifugation at 15,000 rpm for 30 min in order to remove particulate material, the supernatant was used as source of labeled antigen, in an immunoprecipitation assay performed as described in [5].

Results

Properties of ^{125}I-ωCTx binding to IMR_{32} cells

ωCTx binds specifically to a saturable number of binding sites present in the human neuroblastoma cell line IMR_{32}. The binding is of high affinity, having a K_d of 10–20 pM. Similar binding sites were detectable in other human neuroblastoma cell lines and related non-human cell clones (Table 1).

The binding was almost irreversible. Although classical organic calcium antagonists (like nitrendipine, verapamil and diltiazem) did not compete with ^{125}I-ωCTx binding, both neomycin and Ca^{2+} ions were potent antagonists of ^{125}I-ωCTx binding to its target (K_i = 1 μM and 5 mM, respectively). In both Bt_2cAMP and 5BrdU treated IMR_{32} cells there was an increase in ^{125}I-ωCTx binding sites (Fig. 1). When the two agents were given together, the induction was faster but not higher (Fig. 1). We have previously shown that under these culture condition IMR_{32} cells become secretion-competent [3] and that more high voltage-activated calcium currents can be observed [6].

Immunoprecipitation of calcium channels from IMR_{32} cells

When increasing concentrations of control or LEMS patients' serum were added to

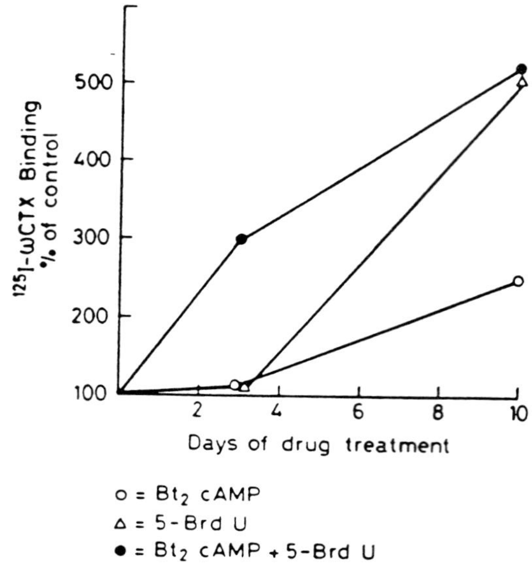

Fig. 1. ωCTx binding sites in differentiating human neuroblastoma cells (IMR_{32}).

the prelabeled VOCCs extracted from IMR_{32} cells, a dose-dependent precipitation of toxin-channel complexes was detected (Fig. 2).

The antibody titer (expressed as pmol of toxin binding sites precipitated per liter of serum) was relatively low (between 20 and 300 pM, 20 pM being the threshold of specificity with respect to control sera) especially when compared to the titer of antinicotinic receptor autoantibodies (up to 1 μM) found in myasthenia gravis (MG), another disease of neurotransmission.

However, none of the LEMS patients had antinicotinic receptor antibodies, and

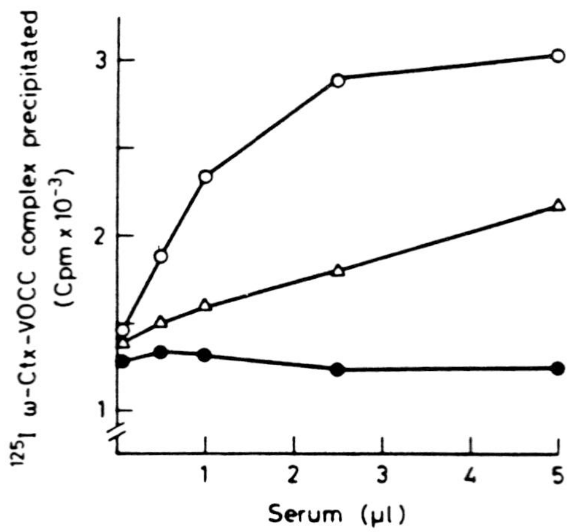

Fig. 2. Precipitation of ω-type VOCCs by LEMS autoantibodies.

vice versa, MG patients did not have anti-VOCC antibodies. LEMS autoantibodies induced a rapid internalization and degradation of surface VOCCs in IMR_{32} cells (manuscript in preparation) and this reduction in functional VOCCs is probably the main mechanism by which LEMS autoantibodies impair the presynaptic control of neurotransmitter release.

Discussion

We have described that different neuronal cell lines in vitro, and in particular a human neuroblastoma cell line, IMR_{32}, express VOCCs labeled by ωCTx. By both pharmacological and functional experiments with Fura2 [4] and patch clamp techniques [6], we have demonstrated that ωCTx binds specifically to one subtype (ω-type) of the three (or more) expressed by these cells.

Together with a number of other molecules and organelles involved in neurotransmitter release [3], the ωCTx-sensitive channels are also increased after in vitro differentiation of IMR_{32} cells.

A crucial role for this channel subtype in the presynaptic control of neurotransmitter release was also recently suggested by our morphological finding that ωCTx-sensitive channels, at the frog neuromuscular junction, are clustered, presynaptically, in sites possibly related to the active zones.

The importance of the ω-type VOCCs in neurotransmitter release was further inferred by our results indicating that the autoantibodies of LEMS patients immunoprecipitate this particular type of channel. Up to now we have not found LEMS patients' sera able to immunoprecipitate L-type, dihydropyridine-labeled VOCCs of IMR_{32} cells.

In conclusion, the availability of cultured neuronal cells of human origin expressing VOCCs, and their sensitivity to ωCTx, is very helpful for both molecular and pharmacological studies and for defining the immunopathogenesis of a human disease of synaptic function.

References

1. Bean B (1989) Ann. Rev. Physiol. 51: 367–384.
2. Sher E and Clementi F (1991) Neuroscience 42: 1–7.
3. Sher E, Denis-Donini S, Zanini A, Bisiani C and Clementi F (1989) J. Cell. Biol. 108: 2291–2300.
4. Sher E, Pandiella A and Clementi F (1988) FEBS Lett. 235: 178–182.
5. Sher E, Gotti C, Canal N, Scoppetta C, Piccolo G, Evoli A and Clementi F (1989) Lancet ii: 640–643.
6. Carbone E, Sher E and Clementi F (1990) Pflügers Arch. 416: 170–179.
7. Torri Tarelli F et al. (1991) Brain Res. 547: 331–334.

© 1991 Elsevier Science Publishers B.V. All rights reserved.
Biological Psychiatry, Volume 2. G. Racagni et al., editors.

Intracellular Ca^{2+} stores in neurons

J. Meldolesi[1], A. Villa[1], P. Podini[1], A. Ciardo[1], P. Volpe[2] and T. Pozzan[2]
[1]*Department of Pharmacology, CNR Cytopharmacology and B. Ceccarelli Centers, S. Raffaele Scientific Institute, University of Milan; and* [2]*Institute of General Pathology, University of Padua, Padua, Italy*

As in all other cells, most of the calcium contained within neurons is not free in the cytoplasm but segregated within membrane-bound stores. Extensive evidence [1] indicates that at least part of these stores are not stable, but can release their calcium (in the form of Ca^{2+}) to the cytoplasm, and thus increase $[Ca^{2+}]_i$. Conversely, when $[Ca^{2+}]_i$ is increased (for example, via the activation of the specific channels in the plasma membrane) the stores can rapidly accumulate considerable quantities of Ca^{2+}, and thus contribute to the buffering of the elicited response. Finally, these rapidly-exchanging stores are believed to sustain the $[Ca^{2+}]_i$ oscillations that have been described in a variety of cells, including neurons.

Since $[Ca^{2+}]_i$ plays a major role in the control of fundamental functions in neurons (from membrane potential, via the activations of Ca^{2+}-dependent channels, to transmitter release; from axonal transport to nerve fiber growth; from long-term potentiation, and thus memory, to neuronal death) Ca^{2+} stores should be regarded as key physiological and structural elements. Their identification and characterization in both structural and functional terms therefore represent important steps in the progress of understanding of the neuronal system.

Up to recently, the study of Ca^{2+} stores was carried out almost exclusively by physiological techniques, i.e. by measuring either ionic currents and potential changes at the plasma membrane, or $[Ca^{2+}]_i$ changes in the cytoplasm, the latter by the use of fluorescent Ca^{2+} indicators. Some years ago we considered the possibility of developing a classical cell biological approach, based on the identification of specific store markers, to be revealed by high resolution immunocytochemistry and subcellular fractionation. Because of their functional properties, the markers expressed by the stores could be predicted to include: a Ca^{2+} ATPase, responsible for Ca^{2+} uptake; low affinity-high capacity Ca^{2+} binding protein(s), necessary to accumulate large quantities of the cation with no chance of precipitation of Ca phosphates, and to release this Ca^{2+} rapidly when needed; and one or more Ca^{2+} channels, regulated by intracellular messengers and/or processes, to establish direct pathways across the limiting membrane to the cytoplasm. These molecules have indeed been identified, and their distribution and properties investigated especially in one type of neuron, chosen for its high degree of expression of our markers, the Purkinje neuron of the cerebellum. In the rest of this communication we will summarize our present knowledge on this system, focussing in particular on one species, the chicken. This species has been investigated in greater detail because of its expression in Purkinje neurons of a Ca^{2+} storage protein, calsequestrin [2], believed up to recently to be specific of the striated muscle. In addition to calsequestrin, chicken Purkinje neurons express an abundant Ca^{2+} ATPase different from the isoform of the plasma membrane [3] and two types of intracellular channels, one regulated by inositol 1,4,5-triphosphate (IP_3), the other sensitive to caffeine and ryanodine (Ry) [2,4–6], referred to here as the IP_3 and Ry receptors. In the laboratory, adequate antibodies have been available to the first 3 components, while the Ry receptor has been investigated only by specific binding. We have observed [7] that the Ca^{2+} ATPase is widely distributed in the various regions of the Purkinje neuron: the cell body, dendrites up to the spines and also the axon. In all these regions the enzyme is located in the membranes of the ER and, in addition, also of a population of small vacuoles and tubules of moderate electron density. These structures were found to contain high concentrations of calsequestrin and, because of this property, were classified as calciosomes [7]. The latter nomenclature was proposed a few years ago to indicate structures particularly equipped for the storage of Ca^{2+} [8]. ER cisternae, on the other hand, contain only small amounts of calsequestrin but are endowed with IP_3 receptors, concentrated in peculiar stacks of smooth-surfaced, evenly-spaced cisternae [4,5]. Recently, dual immunogold labeling of cryosections prepared from pellets of submicrosomal fractions has revealed that also part of the calciosomes express the IP_3 receptor, while the others are recovered in subfractions enriched in the Ry receptor and might therefore express the latter channel [5]. These observations demonstrate that Ca^{2+} stores of neurons are more complex and heterogenous than previously envisaged. At the moment we are convinced that calciosomes play an important role for at least 2 reasons:

1. They are equipped to accumulate large amounts of Ca^{2+}, thus they can sustain relatively long responses when activated;
2. They appear to be endowed with either one of the channels and may thus respond to both IP_3 generation and $[Ca^{2+}]_i$ increase.

The latter is a type of response observed initially in the heart that has been described also in neurons [9]. Moreover, calciosomes appear to be strategically located within Purkinje neurons (e.g., at the entrance of dendritic spines) and this can be of importance from the physiological point of view.

In addition to calciosomes, the ER certainly participates in Ca^{2+} homeostasis of Purkinje neurons. However, because of their low complement of calsequestrin, the cisternae of this system are expected to accumulate only relatively small amounts of calcium. The large number of IP_3 receptors expressed by ER cisternal stacks might be functionally in excess. Indeed, the role of these structures could be more that of an IP_3 receptor reservoir than of an active, rapidly-exchanging Ca^{2+} store [4].

References

1. Meldolesi J, Madeddu L and Pozzan T (1990) Biochim. Biophys. Acta 1055: 130–140.

2. Volpe P, Alderson-Lang BH, Madeddu L, Damiani E, Collins JH and Margreth A (1990) Neuron 5: 713–721.
3. Kaprielian Z, Campbell AM and Fambrough DM (1989) Mol. Brain Res. 6: 55–60.
4. Satoh T, Ross CA, Villa A, Supattapone S, Pozzan T, Snyder S and Meldolesi J (1990) J. Cell. Biol. 111: 615–624.
5. Volpe P, Villa A, Damiani E, Sharp A, Podini P, Snyder SH and Meldolesi J (1991) EMBO J. (submitted).
6. Ellisman MH, Deerinck TJ, Ouyang Y, Beck CF, Tanksley SJ, Walton PD, Airey JA and Sutko JL (1990) Neuron 5: 135–146.
7. Villa A, Podini P, Clegg DO, Pozzan T and Meldolesi J (1991) J. Cell. Biol. 113 (in press).
8. Volpe P, Krause KH, Hashimoto S, Zorzato F, Pozzan T, Meldolesi J and Lew D (1988) Proc. Natl. Acad. U.S.A. 85: 1091–1095.
9. Lipscombe D, Madison DV, Poenie M, Reuter H, Tsien RW and Tsien RY (1988) Neuron 1: 355–365.

© 1991 Elsevier Science Publishers B.V. All rights reserved.
Biological Psychiatry, Volume 2. G. Racagni et al., editors.

α_3, β_4, and α_5 human nicotinic receptor subunits genes: Genetic linkage, chromosomal localization and differential expression in neuronal and non-neuronal cells

B. Chini[1], P. Tarroni[1], F. Rubboli[1], E. Raimondi[2] and F. Clementi[1]

[1]Department of Medical Pharmacology, CNR Center of Cytopharmacology, University of Milan, Milan; and [2]Department of Genetics and Microbiology, University of Pavia, Pavia, Italy

Nicotinic acetylcholine receptors (AChR) are key molecules that mediate chemical communications between cells in various parts of the body: at the neuromuscular junction, in autonomic ganglia and in several areas of the brain.

Neuronal AChRs are cationic channels gated by nicotinic agonists which are made up of 2 types of subunit: a subunit which is the ACh binding subunit or α subunit, and a subunit which does not bind cholinergic ligands and is thus called the structural, or β subunit. Several structural and ACh binding subunits have been cloned and their combination has been proved to create different subtypes of functional nAChRs which are differently responsive to the snake venom toxins, neuronal bungarotoxin (NBT) and α-bungarotoxin (αBgtx) (for a recent review see [1]).

Moreover, α-bungarotoxin binding sites which do not seem to possess any agonist-gated ionic channels are present in neurons. Recently, an α_5 subunit has been cloned which might be involved in the formation of αBgtx binding proteins which do not form nicotine-gated channels: this subunit is functionally inactive when expressed in Xenopus oocytes [2,3] and synthetic peptides, constructed on the basis of its cDNA sequence bind αBgtx [4].

The precise functions of the different groups of nicotinic receptors present in the CNS have still to be defined, although they have been shown to be involved, through pre- and postsynaptic action, in the control of temperature, neuronal excitability, memory, motor functions and hormone secretion [1]. Moreover, there is evidence that the nicotinic cholinergic system is impaired in aging, and to a greater extent in Alzheimer's disease [5].

Few data exist on the primary structure of human neuronal nicotinic subunits or their localization in the human brain [6,7]. For this reason, we initiated a study aimed at isolating and cloning human nicotinic receptors, concentrating on the human IMR32 neuroblastoma cell line since it expresses both nicotinic receptors and αBgtx binding sites which are apparently unrelated to ionic channels [8].

Cloning and expression of α_3, α_5 and β_4 subunits in IMR32 cells

An IMR32 cDNA library in λgt 10 (kindly provided by Dr. H. Soreq) was screened using ^{32}P-labeled probes encoding rat α and β neuronal nicotinic receptor subunits (a gift from Dr. J. Boulter and S. Heinemann) in order to isolate the human nicotinic subunits present in IMR32 cells. Using this approach, we identified the cDNA coding for the α_3, α_5 and β_4 nicotinic receptor subunits, which exhibited all of the basic characteristics of nicotinic receptor subunits (Fig. 1).

The expression of the human subunits in IMR32 neuroblastoma cells was investigated by Northern blot analysis, under high stringency conditions. λIMR2A, the human probe for α_3, detected 1 band of 3.5 kb. The full-length IMR α_5 cDNA probe detected 5 bands. Two transcripts, 2.7 kb and 2.1 kb in size, were more abundant, whereas the 4.8 kb, 1.6 kb and 1.3 kb transcripts were less expressed. The λMRβ421 clone coding for human β_4 identified a major transcript with a size of 3.1 kb (Fig. 1).

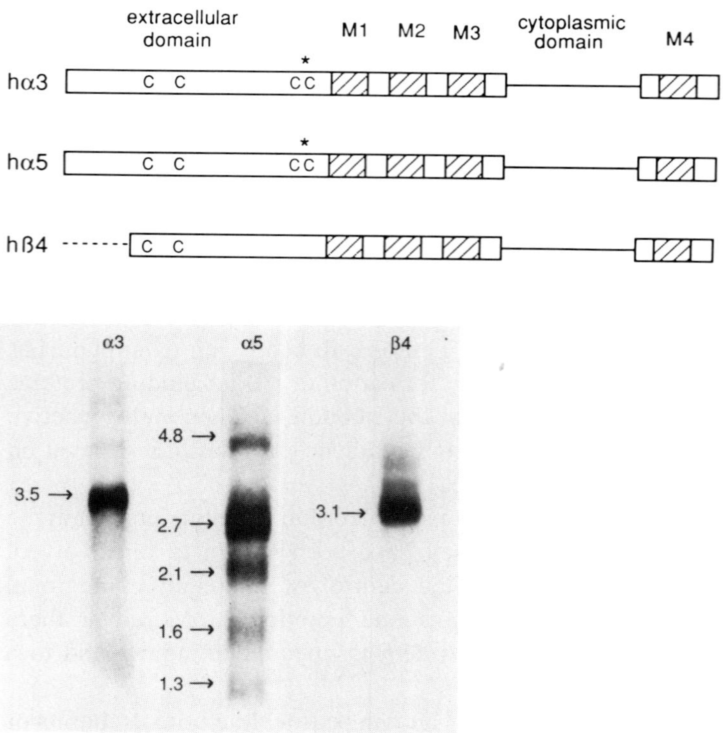

Fig. 1. Top: Schematic representation of deduced amino acid sequences of the α_3, α_5 and β_4 human nicotinic receptor subunits. M1, M2, M3, and M4 represent the putative membrane spanning regions, CC indicates the pair of cysteines conserved in all the nicotinic subunits, C*C indicates the pair of cysteines conserved in all the α type nicotinic subunits. The dashed line indicates the uncloned region of the β_4 human nicotinic receptor subunit. Bottom: Northern blot analysis of α_3, α_5 and β_4 transcripts in IMR32 neuroblastoma cells. Poly (A)+ mRNA was extracted from IMR32 cells and electrophoresed in agarose-formaldehyde gels (10 µg per line), transferred to nylon membranes and hybridized in high stringency conditions with full-length cDNA probes for the α_3 and α_5 subunits, and with a cDNA clone encoding part of the β_4 subunit.

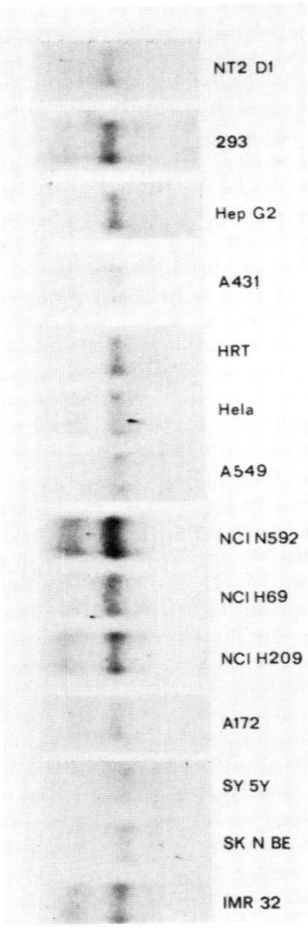

Fig. 2. Northern blot analysis of α_5 transcripts in neuronal and non-neuronal human cell lines. Total RNA was extracted from cells at confluency, electrophoresed in an agarose-formaldehyde gel (30 μg per line), transferred to a nylon membrane and hybridized in high stringency conditions with the full-length cDNA probe encoding the α_5 subunit.

Chromosome localization of human subunits genes

In rat and chick it has been reported that the α_3, α_5 and β_4 genes form a gene cluster and are transcribed with convergent polarity [2,3]. We have isolated several genomic clones for studying the organization of the α_3, β_4 and α_5 genes in the human genome. By Southern blot and restriction mapping analysis of two overlapping genomic clones, we have demonstrated that the α_3, β_4 and α_5 human genes are also organized in a cluster. Furthermore, in situ hybridization on metaphase chromosomes allowed the α_3, β_4 and α_5 human genes to be localized to the same locus on chromosome 15.

Human α_5 and α_5 subunit expression in neuronal and non-neuronal cell lines

The expression of the human α_5 subunit was then studied by Northern blot analysis of total RNA extracted from a number of human cell lines in culture derived from neuroblastoma (IMR32, SY5Y, SK-N-BE), glioblastoma (A172), small cell lung carcinoma (SCLC) (NCI-H-20, NCI-H-6, NCI-N-592), lung (A549), rectal (HRT) and vulvar carcinoma (HeLa, A431), hepatoma (HepG2), embryonic kidney (293) and teratocarcinoma cells (NT2/D1). Despite their different embryological origin, all of these cell lines contained at least 2 major α_5 transcripts of 2.7 kb and 2.1 kb (Fig. 2). We conclude that the human α_5 subunit is expressed in several cultured cell lines of both neuronal and non-neuronal origin.

Different results were obtained using the human α_3 nicotinic subunit. In this case, a 3.5 kb transcript was detected in the neuroblastoma cell lines (IMR32, SY5Y, SK-N-BE), as well as in the SCLC cell lines (NCI-H-20, NCI-H-6, NCI-N-592), but none of the other non-neuronal cell lines expressed any transcripts of the human α_3 subunit (not shown). The results of this distribution study show that, while α_3 gene expression is confined to neuronal or neuroendocrine cell lines, the α_3 gene is actively transcribed in all of the tested cell lines. This suggests that the α_5 subunit might also be involved in assembling αBgtx binding proteins in non-neuronal cells. Moreover, the presence of α transcripts in a number of cell lines growing in vitro opens up a new perspective on the role of nicotinic subunits outside the nervous system, particularly when it is borne in mind that nicotinic agonists and antagonists have been shown to interfere with the growth of human lung cancer and epithelial thymic cells [9]. The presence of α_5 transcripts in a number of immortalized cells growing in vitro might then be related to the proliferative state of these cells.

References

1. Deneris E, Conolly J, Rogers SW and Duvoisin R (1991) Trends Pharmacol. Sci. 12: 34–40.
2. Boulter J, O'Shea-Greenfield A, Duvoisin RM, Connolly JG, Wada E, Jensen A, Gardner PD, Ballivet M, Deneris ES, McKinnon D, Heinemann S and Patrick J (1990) J. Biol. Chem. 265: 4472–4482.
3. Couturier S, Erkman L, Valera S, Rungger D, Bertrand S, Boulter I, Ballivet M and Bertrand D (1990) J. Biol. Chem. 265: 17560–17567.
4. McLane KE, Wu X and Conti Tronconi BM (1990) J. Biol. Chem. 265: 9816–9824.
5. Perry EK, Perry RH, Smith CJ, Dick DJ, Candy JM, Edwardson JA, Fairbain A and Blessed G (1987) J. Neurol. Neurosurg. Psychiatry 50: 806–809.
6. Fornasari D, Chini B, Tarroni P and Clementi F (1990) Neurosci. Lett. 111: 351–356.
7. Anand R and Lindstrom J (1990) Nucleic Acids Res. 18: 4272.
8. Gotti C, Esparis Ogando A and Clementi F (1989) Neuroscience 32: 759–767.
9. Schuller HM, Nylen E, Park P and Becker KL (1990) Life Sci. 47: 571–578.

© 1991 Elsevier Science Publishers B.V. All rights reserved.
Biological Psychiatry, Volume 2. G. Racagni et al., editors.

Nicotinic acetylcholine receptors in human cortex: Changes in Alzheimer's disease

Ezio Giacobini

Department of Pharmacology, Southern Illinois University School of Medicine, P.O. Box 19230, Springfield, IL 62794, U.S.A.

Nicotinic receptors are multimeric proteins composed of two basic subunits, α and β. Several subtypes of α- and β-subunits have been identified and subunit genes for several species of nicotinic receptors have been isolated. The present model of the nicotinic acetylcholine receptor (nAChR) includes five membrane proteins representing four different types of subunits (α, β, γ and δ) of which the α-subunit represents the binding site of the agonist [1]. Neuronal genes encoding nAChR are multiple, at least seven for the α-subunits and three for the β-subunits. Four cDNAs (α_2, α_3, $\alpha_{4\text{-}1}$ and $\alpha_{4\text{-}2}$) have been cloned in rats [2]. In situ hybridization reveals that each of these cDNAs have a unique pattern of distribution. At least four discrete nicotinic receptor α-subunits have been identified in brain (α_2, α_3, α_4 and α_5) which are closely related to the single α-subunit (α_1) found in skeletal muscle [3–4].

Cholinergic receptors in human brain during normal aging

The few studies available on nicotinic receptors in human brain during aging have been summarized by Nordberg and Winblad [5]. In most studies, individuals over 50 years were considered. Age-related changes in cholinergic receptors suggest different effects of aging on receptor subtypes and regions. Age effects are not as obvious as changes in Alzheimer's disease (AD) [5]. A possible up-regulation of receptors located on target cells of neurons lost with age may be considered as a part of a "normal" process of aging.

Changes in nicotinic receptors in Alzheimer's disease: Binding studies

Numerous studies have reported cholinergic deficits in the brains of patients with AD (for review see [6–8]). Postmortem AD brains show a reduced number of binding sites for various nicotinic ligands. Out of 14 autopsy studies, 11 showed decreases of 32–68% depending on the region and ligand and three showed no change in receptor number. Our studies, based on both autopsy and biopsy materials using nicotine (NIC), showed decreases of 44 and 55%, respectively [6,9].

The decreases in nicotinic binding sites correlate closely with enzymatic (choline acetyltransferase (ChAT) and acetylcholinesterase (AChE)) activity changes, suggesting a possible presynaptic localization of the lesion in AD [6,9–11].

A major consequence of decreased cholinergic receptor function is de-regulation of acetylcholine (ACh) release. Release of ^{3}H-ACh can be measured in frontal cortex slices from human autopsy after short postmortem delay [12] and from biopsies [9]. A significant reduction (50–70%) in the evoked release of ACh has been reported by both laboratories. A combined reduction in ACh release and in a number of nicotinic binding sites in the frontal cortex of AD patients supports the hypothesis of a selective loss of presynaptic nicotinic receptors of AD [11].

Neurotoxins as markers of nicotinic receptors

Kappa-bungarotoxin (BTX), isolated from snake venom, has been shown to be a potent and selective antagonist of neuronal nicotinic receptors and blocks nicotinic synaptic transmission in a variety of neuronal preparations where α-BTX has no effect [13]. Our data on autoradiography of ^{125}I-κ-BTX binding sites shows the highest density in the middle and deep layers of human frontal cortex [14]. We have seen a different regional distribution of ^{125}I-κ-BTX binding sites in the presence of non-labelled (–)-NIC and α-BTX. The regional distribution and the pharmacology of agonist and antagonist binding sites suggest that these subtypes may be present in different neuronal populations, and in both pre- and postsynaptic locations. In our experiments, κ-BTX, but not α-BTX, displaced about 50% of the high and low affinity binding sites of ^{3}H-(–)-NIC and decreased electrically evoked ACh release from rat frontal cortex slices [14]. These results suggest two categories of nicotinic receptors, one κ-BTX insensitive and the other κ-BTX sensitive. The former does not have a κ-BTX binding site. Our data show that, in agreement with the molecular biological data on receptor gene families in mammalian species [15–16], human cortex has at least three categories of nicotinic receptors, each showing specific kinetics of ligand binding, distribution and cellular localization. These three subtypes are all found in the frontal cortex. In addition, we have found that human parietal and temporal lobe and hippocampus exhibit the same binding sites with a different receptor density and distribution. Human hippocampal cortex (CA3) had the highest density of ^{125}I-κ-BTX binding sites.

A decrease in nicotinic but not muscarinic receptors can be correlated with presynaptic changes in AD patients including decreases in ChAT activity [6,9] and a loss of cells in the nucleus basalis of Meynert which project to the cortex [17], suggesting a presynaptic localization.

Immunohistochemical localization of nicotinic receptors

Recently, immunohistochemical techniques have localized nAChRs in the human cerebral cortex at the light- and electron-microscopic level [18–20]. Using the monoclonal antibody WF6 [18,19,21] we studied the cellular distribution of nAChRs in the frontal cortex of AD patients as compared to age-matched and young controls [26].

The immunoprecipitate was found on neuronal perikarya, dendrites and on the postsynaptic thickenings. By contrast, a marked decrease of neurons was observed in the frontal cortex of AD patients, with the immunoprecipitate localized in the postsynaptic densities of synaptic complexes [22].

The cellular distribution of nAChR was studied by us in the frontal cortex (area 10) of AD patients and compared to age-matched and young controls using the monoclonal antibody WF6 and an immunoperoxidase protocol [20]. Significant differences were seen between number of labeled neurons among all three groups tested (young controls > aged controls > Alzheimer cases). These findings together with our previous results [14], indicate that nAChRs in the human cerebral cortex are located both pre- and postsynaptically as in the rat cerebral cortex [18] and are strongly decreased in AD.

Acknowledgements

Supported by NIA AG05416; R.J. Reynolds Tobacco Co. and SIU Central Res. Comm.

References

1. Maelicke A (1988) In: Whittaker VP (ed.) The Cholinergic Synapse – Handbook of Experimental Pharmacology, Vol 86. Springer-Verlag, Berlin, pp. 267–313.
2. Chini B and Clementi F (1989) Neurobiol. Aging 10: 371–374.
3. Goldman D, Deneris E, Luyten W, Kochlar A, Patrick J and Heinemann S (1987) Cell 48: 965–973.
4. Neff P, Oneyser C, Alliod C, Couturier S and Ballivet M (1988) EMBO J 7: 595–601.
5. Nordberg A and Winblad B (1986) In: Fisher A, Hanin I and Lachman C (eds.) Alzheimer's and Parkinson's Disease – Advances in Behavioral Biology, Vol 29. Plenum Press, New York, pp. 95–108.
6. Giacobini E, DeSarno P, Clark B and McIlhany M (1989) In: Nordberg A (ed.) Progress in Brain Research, Vol 79. Elsevier, Amsterdam, pp. 335–343.
7. Giacobini E (1990) J. Neurosci. Res. 27: 548–560.
8. Giacobini E (1990) In: Aquilonius SM and Gillberg PG (eds.) Progress in Brain Research, Vol 84. Elsevier, Amsterdam, pp. 321–332.
9. Giacobini E, DeSarno P, McIlhany M and Clark B (1988) In: Clementi F, Gotti C and Sher E (eds.) Nicotinic Acetylcholine Receptors in the Nervous System – NATO ASI Series H, Vol H25. Springer-Verlag, Berlin, pp. 367–378.
10. Davies P (1979) Brain Res. 171: 319–327.
11. Rossor MN, Garrett NJ, Johnson AL, Mountjoy CQ, Roth M and Iversen LL (1982) Brain 105: 313–330.
12. Nordberg A, Adem A, Nilsson L and Winblad B (1987) In: Dowdall MJ and Hawthorne JN (eds.) Cellular and Molecular Basis of Cholinergic Function. Ellis Horwood, New York, pp. 858–868.
13. Chiappinelli VA (1985) Pharmacol. Ther. 31: 1–32.

14. Sugaya K, Giacobini E and Chiappinelli VA (1990) J. Neurosci. Res. 27: 349–359.
15. Wada E, Wada K, Boulter J, Deneris E, Heinemann S, Patrick J and Swanson LW (1989) J. Comp. Neurol. 284: 314–335.
16. Heinemann S, Boulter J, Deneris E, Connolly J, Gardner P, Wada E, Wada K, Ballivet M, Swanson L and Patrick J (1988) In: Clementi F, Gotti C and Sher E (eds.) Nicotinic Acetylcholine Receptors in the Nervous System – NATO ASI Series H, Vol H25. Springer-Verlag, Berlin, pp. 173–191.
17. Whitehouse PJ, Price DL, Struble RG, Clark AW, Coyle JT and DeLong MR (1982) Science 215: 1237–1239.
18. Schroder H, Zilles K, Maelicke A and Hajos F (1989) Brain Res. 502: 287–295.
19. Schroder H, Zilles K, Luiten PGM, Strosberg A and Aghchi AR (1989) Synapse 4: 319–326.
20. Schroder H, Giacobini, Struble RG, Zilles K and Maelicke A (1991) Neurobiol. Aging (in press).
21. Fels G, Plumer-Wilk R, Schrieber M and Maelicke A (1986) J. Biol. Chem. 261: 15746–15754.
22. Schroder H, Zilles K, Luiten PGM and Strosberg AD (1991) Brain Res. (in press).

© 1991 Elsevier Science Publishers B.V. All rights reserved.
Biological Psychiatry, Volume 2. G. Racagni et al., editors.

Deficits in nicotinic receptors in Alzheimer and Parkinson diseases: Possible significance

Remi Quirion, Isabelle Aubert and Serge Gauthier
Douglas Hospital Research Centre and Department of Psychiatry, Neurology and Neurosurgery, Faculty of Medicine, McGill University, 6875 Blvd. LaSalle, Verdun, Quebec, H4H 1R3, Canada

Introduction

It is now well established that the densities of nicotinic receptor binding sites are markedly decreased in cortical areas and in the hippocampal formation in Alzheimer's disease (AD) [1–9]. We have shown that the binding of [^{3}H]-N-methylcarbamylcholine ([^{3}H]MCC), a highly selective CNS-type nicotinic receptor probe [10–12], is decreased to extents at least comparable to that of muscarinic M_2 sites in Alzheimer's brain tissues [8]. However, it is still not clear if these decrements are specific to AD or if they can be observed in other neurological disorders such as Parkinson's disease (PD). We now report on the status of these receptors in AD as compared to PD, and their possible role as "positive autoreceptors" ensuring the normal functioning of the cortical cholinergic synapse [9,10,13].

Materials and Methods

Human brain tissues were obtained at autopsy from the Douglas Hospital Research Centre Brain Bank. Tissues were processed and neuropathological evaluations were performed as described earlier [8]. Four categories of brains were analyzed, namely AD, PD, PD with AD-type dementia (PD/AD) and neuropathologically normal age-matched controls. Various cortical and subcortical areas were evaluated for comparison. [^{3}H]MCC (84.5 Ci/mmol, New England Nuclear, Boston, MA) binding parameters were determined as described before [8,12] using various concentrations of ligands (0.1–20 nM). The activity of the enzyme choline acetyltransferase (ChAT) was determined as previously described [8] for comparison. Protein content was evaluated by the method of Lowry et al. [14] using bovine serum albumin as standard. Data were analyzed as reported earlier by Araujo et al. [8].

Results and Discussion

As expected, cortical and hippocampal ChAT activities were decreased in AD [1–9]. For example, ChAT values represented approximately 50% of normal control activities in the hippocampal formation of AD patients. Interestingly, ChAT activities were also markedly altered in cortical areas in PD and PD/AD brains. ChAT activities were not significantly altered in striatum and thalamus in any of these disorders.

As shown in Table 1, it is also clear that important losses in nicotinic receptor densities are detected in AD, PD and PD/AD brains. Comparable decrements are observed in these disorders in cortical and hippocampal areas (Table 1). This is in agreement with earlier reports [2,4,5,7,9] and correlates well with losses in ChAT activities.

However, important differences are found in subcortical areas. While maximal densities of [^{3}H]MCC sites are not affected in the striatum and thalamus of AD patients, major deficits were observed in these areas in both PD and PD/AD brains (Table 1). Thus, nicotinic receptor deficits are more broadly distributed in Parkinson-associated disorders.

The finding that similar nicotinic and ChAT deficits are found in cortical and hippocampal areas in AD, PD and PD/AD brains may have implications for the localization of these receptors. Our group has recently suggested that nicotinic receptors may act as positive autoreceptors ensuring the basal release of acetylcholine in cortical areas [10,13]. This would thus explain the concomitant decreases of both nicotinic receptors and ChAT activities observed in cortex and hippocampus in AD and PD brains. However, positive nicotinic autoreceptors are apparently absent from striatal cholinergic interneurons [10,13]. In that region, nicotinic receptors are most likely located on dopaminergic nerve terminals originating from mesencephalic areas [12,15]. This could explain major decrements in nicotinic receptors, but not ChAT activities, observed in striatal areas in PD and PD/AD brains.

Losses in thalamic nicotinic receptors in PD and PD/AD tissues are more difficult to interpret. It does not appear that thalamic cholinergic innervation is markedly altered in PD since normal ChAT activities were observed. It may be that, as in the basal ganglia, nicotinic receptors are present on non-cholinergic

Table 1. Decrements in maximal [^{3}H]MCC receptor binding capacities in AD and PD brains

Region	[^{3}H] Binding (% of controls)			
	Controls	AD	PD	PD/AD
Frontal cortex	100 (5)	41 (7)[a]	45 (6)[a]	37 (7)[a]
Temporal cortex	100 (7)	27 (7)[a]	35 (7)[a]	35 (7)[a]
Hippocampus	100 (10)	39 (10)[a]	49 (12)[a]	61 (10)[a]
Striatum	100 (6)	77 (7)	24 (7)[a]	26 (7)[a]
Thalamus	100 (6)	75 (8)	46 (6)[a]	39 (6)[a]

Data derived from the number of brains given in parentheses. Affinity values (K_d) were not altered in any regions in these various disorders. [a]$P < 0.05$ compared to controls.

elements in thalamic areas. Alternatively, deficits in nicotinic receptor sites may be a more sensitive marker of cholinergic nerve integrity than ChAT activities.

In summary, the maximal densities of [^{3}H]MCC/nicotinic receptor sites are markedly altered in cortical and hippocampal areas in AD, PD and PD/AD tissues. Moreover, decrements in nicotinic binding sites have also been detected in subcortical areas in PD and PD/AD, but not AD, brains. The purported "positive autoreceptor" role of these receptors in cortical areas suggests that their stimulation could enhance acetylcholine release; this possibly leading to improved cognitive functions. This could be an attractive avenue for further research, since positive autoreceptor functions appear to be maintained in the aged brain [16].

References

1. Flynn DD and Mash DC (1986) J. Neurochem. 47: 1948–1954.
2. Nordberg A, Nyberg P and Winbald B (1985) Neurochem. Pathol. 3: 223–236.
3. Whitehouse PJ, Martino AM, Antuono PG, Lowenstein PR, Coyle JT, Price DL and Kellar KJ (1986) Brain Res. 371: 146–151.
4. Whitehouse PJ, Martino AM, Marcus KA, Zweig PM, Singer HS, Price DL and Kellar KJ (1988) Arch. Neurol. 45: 722–724.
5. Whitehouse PJ, Martino AM, Wagster MV, Price DL, Mayeux R, Atack JR and Kellar KJ (1988) Neurology 38: 720–723.
6. Kellar KJ, Whitehouse PJ, Martino-Barrows AM, Marcus K and Price DL (1987) Brain Res. 436: 62–68.
7. Perry EK, Perry RH, Smith CJ, Dick DJ, Candy JM, Edwardson JA, Fairbairn A and Blessed G (1987) J. Neurol. Neurosurg. Psychiatry 50: 806–809.
8. Araujo DM, Lapchak PA, Robitaille Y, Gauthier S and Quirion R (1988) J. Neurochem. 50: 1914–1923.
9. Quirion R, Aubert I, Lapchak PA, Schaum RP, Teolis S, Gauthier S and Araujo DM (1989) Trends Pharmacol. Sci. 10: 80–84.
10. Araujo DM, Lapchak PA, Collier B and Quirion R (1988) J. Neurochem. 51: 292–299.
11. Boksa P and Quirion R (1987) Eur. J. Pharmacol. 139: 323–333.
12. Boksa P, Quik M, Mitchell JB, Collier B, O'Neil W and Quirion R (1989) Eur. J. Pharmacol. 173: 93–108.
13. Araujo DM, Lapchak PA, Collier B and Quirion R (1989) In: Nordberg A, Fuxe K, Holmstedt B and Sundwall A (eds.) Progress in Brain Research. Elsevier, London, pp. 345–352.
14. Lowry OH, Rosebrough NJ, Farr AL and Randall RJ (1951) J. Biol. Chem. 193: 265–275.
15. Giorguieff-Chesselet MF, Kemel ML, Wandscheer D and Glowinski J (1979) Life Sci. 25: 1257–1262.
16. Araujo DM, Lapchak PA, Meaney NJ, Collier B and Quirlon R (1990) J. Neurosci. 10: 3069–3078.

© 1991 Elsevier Science Publishers B.V. All rights reserved.
Biological Psychiatry, Volume 2. G. Racagni et al., editors.

Role of the nicotinic receptor in dementia

Elaine Perry[1], Jennifer Court[1], Paul Whiting[3], James Edwardson[1], David Hughes[1], Richard Barlow[1] and Robert Perry[2]

[1]MRC Neurochemical Pathology Unit; [2]Department of Neuropathology; and [3]Merck, Sharp and Dohme, Harlow, U.K.

Introduction

A key role for the nicotinic receptor in cognitive function is increasingly evident from reports that, jointly with the muscarinic receptor, antagonists impair learning [1] and that in patients with Alzheimer's disease nicotine improves visual perception and attention [2]. It is not yet clear which of the several different neuronal nicotinic receptor subtypes (comprising assemblies of a α and β subunits) is or are involved in these behavioural responses, nor whether potential nicotinic therapy should accordingly be focused. It is, however, well established that in patients with various forms of degenerative dementia there is a substantial loss of high and low affinity nicotine binding together with, at least in Alzheimer's disease, a loss of low affinity kappa-bungaratoxin binding sites [3,4]. The nature of the reduction in the high affinity nicotine binding site in dementia, in terms of microanatomical localization and clinical correlates, has been investigated autoradiographically, together with displacement of the ligand at $\alpha_4\beta_2$ nicotinic receptors (the major brain subtype) expressed in a transfected fibroblast cell line which is being used as a model for screening nicotinic compounds that may be of therapeutic value.

Autoradiographic analysis of human brain

In normal human temporal cortex (Brodmann area 20) – high affinity [^{3}H]-nicotine binding (3 nM) is concentrated in the upper and middle layers (Fig. 1) where a distinct band is often apparent [5]. Although binding is reduced in both Alzheimer's and Parkinson's disease and in dementia of Lewy body type, the residual pattern varies amongst these disorders. The reduction is least extensive in non demented cases and most extensive in demented cases of Parkinson's disease and the normal pattern (including elevation in the upper middle layer) is lost, whereas in Lewy body dementia and in Alzheimer's disease, the receptor reduction occurs more evenly and the normal pattern is retained (Fig. 1). Since Parkinson's disease involves, in addition to a cortical cholinergic also a dopaminergic deficit, the question arises as to whether the nicotinic receptor in this area of cortex is also associated with a non-cholinergic transmitter such as dopamine. The receptor loss was greater in Alzheimer's disease compared with Lewy body dementia and this correlated with the severity of dementia, which is greater in Alzheimer's disease. These results thus suggest that a select population of the cortical nicotinic receptor subtypes, possibly associated primarily with cholinergic innervation, is affected in Alzheimer's disease. Both molecular biological and more refined pharmacological studies are needed to clarify this issue. Although surgical lesioning of the cholinergic input into rat hippocampus is not associated with an alteration in the number or affinity of [^{3}H]-nicotine binding sites, alterations in the α_4 (but not other) subunit mRNA levels suggest that the α_4 ligand binding site may be specifically associated with the cortical cholinergic synapse [6].

Ligand binding to transfected fibroblasts

Since the α_4 subunit predominates in the cerebral cortex and may be associated with the cortical cholinergic system (see above), a model system expressing only

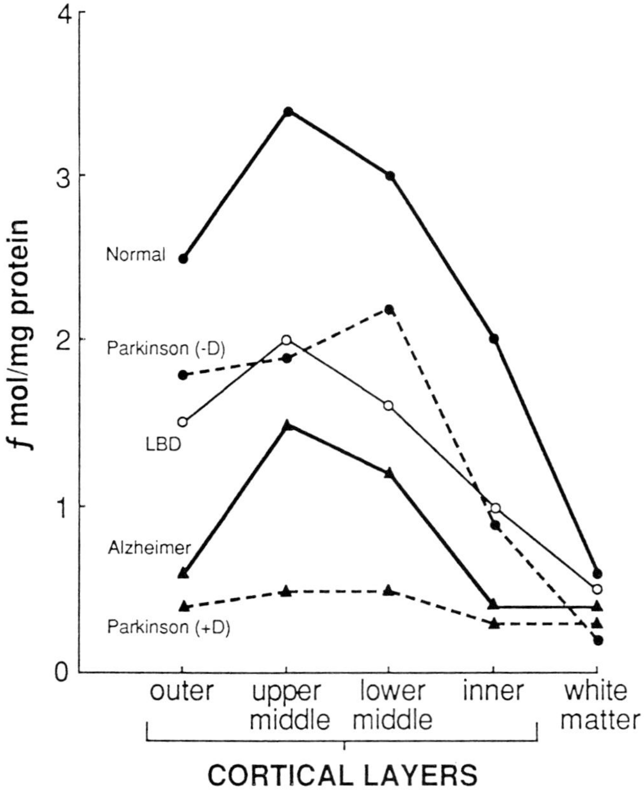

Fig. 1. Autoradiographic distribution of [^{3}H]-nicotine binding in human temporal lobe. Mean values for 5 normal, 4 Parkinson's without (–D) and 4 with (+D) dementia, 9 cases of Lewy body dementia (LBD) and 6 of Alzheimer's disease. Significant differences compared with the normal ($P < 0.05$ or less) in Alzheimer and Parkinson +D groups (all layers) and LBD (lower middle and inner layers).

Table 1. Displacement of [^{3}H]-nicotine from rat cortex and $\alpha_4\beta_2$ transfected fibroblasts

	K (nM)	
	Cortex	Fibroblast
Cytisine	1.7	1.2
Lobeline	72	1.6[a]
Isoarecholone methiodide	23	3.5
Nicotine	11	5.3
β-Pyridylmethyltrimethyl ammonium hydrogen bromide	40	14
Carbachol	586	219
Desoxotetrahydrocytisine	675	257
β-Aminophenylethyltrimethyl iodine	1058	321
Lepodactyline iodide	799	335

K derived from logistic equation as the concentration producing half maximal displacement [8];
[a]For lobeline, but none of the other compounds tested, a lower affinity site, K = 118 nM, was also apparent in fibroblasts.

this α/subunit is clearly of value in searching for selective ligands which may be of therapeutic value. Such a model exists in the fibroblast cell line transfected with α_4 and β_2 subunits [7]. A comparison between membranes prepared from these cells and rat cortex in the ability of a variety of nicotinic ligands to displace 3 nM [^{3}H]-nicotine is provided in Table 1.

These results indicate that, amongst the compounds investigated, not only does cytisine have the highest affinity for the nicotine binding site but it also binds with equal affinity to the fibroblast and cortical membranes, suggesting that this drug may bind more selectively to the α_4-containing subtype than the other ligands. If this finding is substantiated and if it is indeed the α_4 subunit which should be specifically targeted in the treatment of dementia, then cytisine or cytisine-based drugs may be of greater value than nicotine itself. Conversion of cytisine to desoxotetrahydrocytisine (with a view of radiolabelling), however, decreased affinity by over 2 orders of magnitude (Table 1). Further work is now underway to determine the potency of the different nicotinic ligands in terms of their ability to open ion channels in the transfected fibroblasts. There is clearly great scope for including drugs other than nicotine in future studies of the role of the nicotine receptor in the normal CNS and in dementia.

References

1. Riekkinen P, Sirvio J, Aaltonen M and Riekkinen P (1990) Pharmacol. Biochem. Behav. 37: 405–410.
2. Sahakian B, Jones G, Levy R, Gray J and Warburton D (1989) Br. J. Psychiatry 154: 797–800.
3. Perry EK, Smith CJ, Court JA and Perry RH (1990) J. Neural Transm. (P-D Sect.) 2: 149–158.
4. Sugaya K, Giacobini E and Chippinelli VA (1990) J. Neurosci. Res. 27: 349–359.

5. Perry EK, Smith CJ, Perry RH, Johnson M and Fairbairn AF (1989) Neurosci. Res. Commun. 5: 117–124.
6. Miyai I, Veno S, Yorifuji S, Fujimura H and Tarvi S (1990) J. Neural Transm. (Gen. Sect.) 82: 79–91.
7. Whiting P, Schoepfer R, Lindostrom J and Priestly T (1991) (in press).
8. Barlow R and Blake JF (1989) Trends Pharmacol. Sci. 10: 440–441.

© 1991 Elsevier Science Publishers B.V. All rights reserved.
Biological Psychiatry, Volume 2. G. Racagni et al., editors.

Nicotinic receptor deficits in Alzheimer patients: A possible diagnostic marker

Agneta Nordberg
Department of Pharmacology, Uppsala University, Box 591, S-751 24 Uppsala, Sweden

Introduction

Alzheimer's disease, senile dementia of Alzheimer type (AD/SDAT), is a progressive neurodegenerative disease with global deterioration of cognitive function with preservation of many other brain functions. The entity of the disease can be described in terms of clinical symptoms, laboratory investigations and tests during life and neuropathological examination after death. For the definitive diagnosis of AD/SDAT both clinical and histopathological investigations are required. Some lack of agreement exists between histopathological and clinical diagnosis which emphasizes the need for improved diagnostic resolution. From autopsy and biopsy of human brain tissues AD/SDAT has neurochemically been characterized as a disease afflicting numerous neurotransmitters. The cholinergic system, however, shows the most consistent changes and the system also correlates best to cognitive function. There are also current indications that AD/SDAT not only causes changes in the brain but afflicts peripheral non-neural tissues. The aim of this study is to describe the role of the nicotinic receptors in AD/SDAT visualized in vivo by techniques such as positron emission tomography (PET). In addition, changes in peripheral nicotinic receptors on lymphocytes from AD/SDAT patients will be discussed.

Nicotinic receptors in the human brain

Multiple nicotinic receptors exist in the brain. The nicotinic binding sites in human brain have been characterized using various radioactive ligands, mainly ^{3}H-nicotine. The nicotinic agonist binding sites in human brain can be rationalized in terms of super-high, high and low affinity binding sites [1–4]. The existence of multiple nicotinic receptors on the brain is supported by the isolation of a whole family of genes coding for neural nicotinic receptors [5]. The high-affinity nicotinic binding sites show a regional distribution with high content in the thalamus, putamen, caudate nucleus, intermediate in the cortical areas, hypothalamus, cerebellum and low in the hippocampus, medulla oblongata, globus pallidus [4]. Heterogenous intraregional distribution of high affinity nicotinic receptors is observed. Autoradiographical studies performed in the human thalamus reveal high labelling of (–)^{3}H-nicotine in the antero-ventral nucleus of the thalamus and dorso-medial nucleus of thalamus while the labelling is lower in the postero-lateral and postero-ventral nuclei of the thalamus [6]. In attempts to visualize nicotinic receptors in vivo by PET the uptake of ^{11}C-nicotine to the brain has been followed after intravenous injection [7–8]. The distribution of ^{11}C-radioactivity in the brain agrees fairly well with the distribution of nicotinic receptors measured by in vitro receptor binding techniques [4,7,8]. The blood flow marker ^{11}C-butanol shows after intravenous injection a time course in the brain which is much steeper than that for ^{11}C-nicotine. The time course for ^{11}C-nicotine in brain does not solely indicate the blood flow rate, but at least partly a binding profile [9].

Nicotinic receptors in Alzheimer brains

Studies in autopsy brain tissue from patients with AD/SDAT reveal cholinergic presynaptic defects. Marked losses in the number of cortical nicotinic receptors were observed using ^{3}H-nicotine and ^{3}H-acetylcholine by us and others [2,10,11] and have later been reconfirmed by several research groups. A change in the proportion of high to low affinity nicotinic receptors has also been measured in the temporal cortex which suggests a possible interchange in the proportions of nicotinic receptor subtypes [4]. The nicotinic receptor losses are in contrast to the observation of preserved muscarinic receptors in AD/SDAT brains [2,4].

Is it possible to visualize deficits of the nicotinic receptors in human brain in vivo? PET studies of the brain following intravenous injections of the stereoisomers (S)(–)- and (R)(+)-^{11}C-nicotine have shown a markedly reduced uptake of both isomers, especially the (R)(+) form in AD/SDAT patients as compared to age-matched healthy volunteers [8]. The significantly larger difference in uptake between the (S)(–)- and (R)(+)-stereoisomers of ^{11}C-nicotine in AD/SDAT patients might be of diagnostic value [8]. Furthermore, the uptake of (S)(–)-^{11}C-nicotine to brain cortex shows a positive correlation with the Mini-Mental State Examination Score (MMSE) of the patient as revealed by neuropsychological examinations. Interestingly, the difference in uptake of the two stereoisomers of ^{11}C-nicotine seem to be detectable by PET early in the course of the AD/SDAT disease.

Therapeutic strategies and brain nicotinic receptors

The cholinergic hypothesis has been in the focus as one of the major strategies for developing putative drugs in AD/SDAT. The effects of acetylcholinesterase (AChE) inhibitors, like physostigmine and tetra-hydroaminoacridine (THA), have been evaluated mainly by neuropsychological testings in AD/SDAT patients in numerous clinical trials [12,13]. In attempts to visualize by PET, the effects of THA in the brain the uptake of the two stereoisomers of ^{11}C-nicotine has been monitored in

AD/SDAT patients during THA treatment. PET investigations performed in a patient with a mild form of AD/SDAT reveal a normalization of the uptake values for the (R)(+)-^{11}C-nicotine in the frontal and temporal cortices following THA treatment (Nordberg et al., unpublished observations). The uptake of the two ^{11}C-nicotine stereoisomers to the brain was found to be rather equal after 3 weeks of THA treatment. In addition, improvement in neuropsychological testing was observed. The observations support the assumption that inhibition of AChE by THA will increase the content of ACh in the synaptic cleft which will stimulate/ increase/change the nicotinic receptors and thereby increase the cholinergic activity. These findings warrant further exploration.

Nicotinic receptors on lymphocytes from Alzheimer patients

The presence of nicotinic receptors has been demonstrated in human lymphocytes. When nicotinic receptor binding sites are measured in human lymphocytes from individuals of different ages, a significantly increased number of binding sites is observed with increasing age [14]. The number of nicotinic receptors in lymphocytes from AD/SDAT patients is reduced compared to age-matched controls [15]. A significant decrease in the number of nicotinic receptors was also observed in a group of patients with Parkinson's disease but not in patients with multi-infarct dementia (MID) [15]. Nicotinic receptors on lymphocytes have been measured in non-institutionalized as well as institutionalized AD/SDAT patients of different ages. In a younger group of institutionalized AD/SDAT patients (mean age 78 ± 2 years) a significantly decreased number of nicotinic receptors was observed in comparison to non-institutionalized patients, while in an older group of institutionalized AD/SDAT patients (mean age 88 ± 4 years) no significant change in the number of nicotinic receptors was observed compared to controls [14]. These observations support the assumption that AD/SDAT is a heterogenous disease and that the age of onset might define subgroups. Interestingly, we have also observed a tendency towards a decrease in the number of nicotinic receptors with progress of the disease. Furthermore, in AD/SDAT patients with a low number of lymphocyte nicotinic receptors, we have observed that long-term THA treatment will normalize the number of nicotinic receptors to control level. The use of lymphocyte nicotinic receptors as a putative diagnostic marker in AD/SDAT as well as for monitoring drug treatments has to be further evaluated.

Conclusions

The nicotinic receptors in brain are involved in biochemical events observed in neurodegenerative diseases such as AD/SDAT. Monitoring of the nicotinic receptors in brain in vivo by PET and in peripheral lymphocytes by in vitro receptor binding techniques might be valuable tools in the search for early diagnostic markers and for evaluating therapeutic treatment strategies in AD/SDAT.

Acknowledgements

This study was supported by grants from the Swedish Medical Research Council, the Swedish Tobacco Company, Loo and Hans Osterman's Foundation, Stohne's Foundation, Stiftelsen för Gamla Tjänarinnor.

References

1. Nordberg A, Adem A, Nilsson L and Winblad B (1988a) In: Tomlinson B, Pepeu G and Wischik CM (eds.) New Trends in Aging Research, Fidia Research Series, Vol. 15. Liviana Press, Padua, pp. 27–36.
2. Nordberg A, Adem A, Hardy J and Winblad B (1988b) Neurosci. Lett. 86: 317–321.
3. Nordberg A, Adem A, Nilsson L, Romanelli L and Zhang X (1988c) In: Clementi F, Gotti C and Sher E (eds.) Nicotinic Acetylcholine Receptors in the Nervous System, NATO Asi Series, Vol. H25. Springer Verlag, Berlin, pp. 331–350.
4. Nordberg A, Nilsson-Håkansson L, Adem A, Hardy J, Alafuzoff I, Lai Z, Herrera-Marschitz and Winblad B (1989) Prog. Brain Res. 79: 353–362.
5. Patrick J, Boulter J, Deneris E, Wada K, Wada E, Connolly J, Swanson L and Heinemann (1989) Prog. Brain Res. 79: 27–33.
6. Adem A, Singh Jossan S, d'Argy R, Brandt I, Winblad B and Nordberg A (1988) J. Neural Transm. 73: 77–83.
7. Nybäck H, Nordberg A, Långström B, Halldin C, Hartvig P, Åhlin A, Swan C-G and Sedvall G (1989) Prog. Brain Res. 79: 313–319.
8. Nordberg A, Hartvig P, Lilja A, Viitanen M, Amberla K, Lundqvist H, Andersson Y, Ulin J, Winblad B, Långström (1990a) J. Neural Transm. (Sect. P-D) 2: 215–224.
9. Nordberg A, Hartvig P, Lundqvist H, Lilja A, Viitanen M, Amberla K, Ulin J, Winblad B and Långström B (1990b) In: Giacobini E and Becker RE (eds.) Current Research in Alzheimer Therapy – Early Diagnosis. Taylor and Francis, New York, pp. 329–338.
10. Nordberg A and Winblad B (1986) Neurosci. Lett. 72: 115–119.
11. Whitehouse P, Martino AM, Antuono PG, Lowenstein PR, Coyle JT, Price DL and Kellar KJ (1986) Brain Res. 371: 146–151.
12. Thal LJ, Masur DM, Blau AD, Fuld PA and Klauber MR (1989) JAGS 37: 42–48.
13. Gauthier S, Bouchard R, Lamontagne A, Bailey P, Bergman H, Ratner J, Tesfaye Y, Saint-Martin M, Bacher Y, Carrier L, Charbonneau R, Clarfield AM, Collier B, Dastoor D, Gauthier L, Germain M, Kissel C, Krieger M, Kushnir S, Masson H, Morin J, Nair V, Neirinck L and Suissa S (1990) N. Engl. J. Med. 322: 1272–1276.
14. Nordberg, Adem A, Bucht G, Viitanen M and Winblad B (1990c) In: Fowler CJ, Carlsson LA, Gottfries CG and Winblad B (eds.) Biological Markers in Dementia of Alzheimer Type. Smith-Gordon, London, pp. 149–159.
15. Adem A, Nordberg A, Bucht G and Winblad B (1986) Prog. Neuro-Psychopharmacol. Biol. Psychiatry 10: 247–257.

Satellite symposia

© 1991 Elsevier Science Publishers B.V. All rights reserved.
Biological Psychiatry, Volume 2. G. Racagni et al., editors.

Effect of chronic atypical antipsychotic drugs on basal and amphetamine-induced dopamine (DA) release

Junji Ichikawa[1] and Herbert Y. Meltzer[2]
[1]Hokkaido University, Sapporo 060, Japan; and [2]Case Western Reserve University, Cleveland, OH 44106, U.S.A.

Introduction

It has been reported that haloperidol (HAL), a typical antipsychotic drug, which is associated with a relatively higher incidence of extrapyramidal symptoms (EPS), markedly produces depolarization inactivation (DI) in both A9 and A10 regions whereas clozapine (CLOZ), an atypical antipsychotic drug, which is associated with a lower incidence of EPS, produces DI in the A10 but not the A9. Then, it has been generally accepted that neuroleptic-induced DI in the A10 is related to its antipsychotic effect whereas DI in the A9 is causally related to the development of EPS [1]. The authors also suggested that DI in the A9 and the A10 DA cells would alter DA release in neuron terminals in the striatum (STR) and the nucleus accumbens (ACC), respectively.

We have already reported elsewhere [2–4] chronic effects of HAL and CLOZ on basal DA release and metabolism in STR and ACC, and the change of DA release and metabolism in STR and ACC after subsequent challenge with HAL or CLOZ, respectively, using in vivo microdialysis. In the present study, we investigated the effect of d-amphetamine (d-AMP) on DA release and metabolism in both regions after chronic administration of HAL and CLOZ in order to test the possibility that atypical antipsychotic drugs but not typical ones may act on the d-AMP-induced DA release process (so-called carrier-mediated mechanism).

Materials and Methods

Animals and chronic treatment

Male SD rats, 180–200 g at the start of chronic treatment, were used throughout the study. Animals received HAL (0.5 and 2 mg/kg/day) or CLOZ HCl (10 and 20 mg/kg/day) in their drinking water in light-proof drinking bottles. Drugs were dissolved in a minimal amount of 1 M tartaric acid and diluted with deionized water and then adjusted to pH 7.0–7.4 with 1 M $NaHCO_3$.

Drug challenge

HAL (2 mg/kg) and CLOZ (20 mg/kg) were dissolved in a minimal amount of 1 M tartaric acid and administered s.c. to the rats treated with HAL (2 mg/kg/day) and CLOZ HCl (20 mg/kg/day) or vehicle (VEH), respectively. D-AMP HCl (1.0 mg/kg) dissolved in physiological saline (0.9% NaCl) were administered s.c. to the rats treated with HAL (0.5 mg/kg/day) and CLOZ HCl (10 mg/kg/day) or VEH, respectively, after obtaining stable pre-drug basal values in dialysates.

Microdialysis procedure and HPLC analysis of dialysates

On the last day of chronic treatment or on the 2nd day of drug withdrawal after chronic treatment, rats (300–400 g) were anesthetized with chloral hydrate (400 mg/kg, i.p.) and mounted in a stereotaxic frame. The dialysis probe was implanted into either STR (A +1.0, L +3.5, V −5.5) or ACC (A +3.0, L +2.0, V −7.5). The probe was perfused with artificial CSF 24 h after surgery. Dialysates were collected every 30 min into micro-test tubes. Samples were applied directly into HPLC-ECD and analyzed for DA, DOPAC and 5-HIAA. Statistical differences were determined using ANOVA and Tukey's pairwise comparison procedure. A probability of equal to or less than 0.05 was considered significant in this study.

Results

Chronic administration of HAL (2 mg/kg/day) markedly decreased basal extracellular DA (40 and 52% of controls, respectively) and DOPAC (72 and 71%, respectively) in STR and ACC. Chronic administration of a relatively low dose of HAL (0.5 mg/kg/day) also decreased basal extracellular DA (55 and 50% of controls, respectively) and DOPAC (73 and 74% of controls, respectively) in STR and ACC. In sharp contrast, chronic administration of CLOZ (20 mg/kg/day) produced slight but non-significant increases in basal extracellular DOPAC (124% of controls) in STR and had no effect on either DA or DOPAC in ACC. Basal extracellular 5-HIAA were not affected by either treatment in either region.

Chronic HAL administration decreased the HAL-induced increase in extracellular DOPAC (DA metabolism) but not extracellular DA (DA release) in STR, whereas it had no effect on either measure after a challenge dose of HAL in ACC. In sharp contrast, chronic CLOZ administration caused tolerance to the CLOZ-induced increase in DA release and metabolism in ACC, whereas no tolerance or sensitization was observed in STR.

Chronic administration of CLOZ (10 mg/kg/day) enhanced d-AMP-induced increase in extracellular DA in STR whereas it produced an attenuation in d-AMP-induced increase in extracellular DA in ACC. In contrast, chronic administration of HAL (0.5 mg/kg/day) had no effect on d-AMP-induced increase in extracellular DA in either region.

Discussion

The results reported here with HAL and CLOZ illustrate their differential effects on dopaminergic neurotransmission in STR and ACC. The chronic HAL-induced decrease in striatal dopaminergic neurotransmission (reduces basal DA release), together with blockade of postsynaptic D_2 receptors and upregulation of these receptors may contribute to the development of EPS and tardive dyskinesia during chronic HAL treatment. Contrary to this, the slight increase in striatal dopaminergic neurotransmisssion (slightly increased basal DA release) may explain why chronic CLOZ treatment produces few EPS and tardive dyskinesia.

Chronic HAL treatment appears to produce a greater decrease in dopaminergic neurotransmission in ACC which is thought to mediate the antipsychotic effects of neuroleptic drugs, than does CLOZ because of the greater inhibitory effect of HAL on DA release and more profound in vivo DA receptor blockade. However, CLOZ is rather less effective against delusions and hallucinations than HAL or chlorpromazine. This suggests that there may be an optimal level of decrease in dopaminergic neurotransmission in ACC which is exceeded by HAL or that factors other than dopaminergic neurotransmission in ACC influence antipsychotic effects, or both.

Chronic CLOZ enhanced d-AMP-induced DA release in STR, but it attenuated d-AMP-induced DA release in ACC. It is tempting to speculate that the attenuation of AMP-like stimulation of DA release by CLOZ in ACC could contribute to its antipsychotic action. Thus, CLOZ might be a particularly effective treatment for some DA agonist-induced psychoses such as amphetamine or methamphetamine psychosis.

Acknowledgements

The research reported here was supported in part by USPHS MH 41864, MH 41594, GCRC MO1RR00080, the Department of Veterans Affairs and grants from the Cleveland, John Pascal Sawyer and Prentiss Foundations. H.Y.M. is the recipient of a USPHS Research Career Scientist Award MH 47808. We are grateful to Mr. Matthew A. Schreiber, Ms. Elisa K. Caraulia and Dr. Bao-Ling Chai for technical assistance, to Dr. Paul A. Thompson for statistical analysis.

References

1. Chiodo LA and Bunney BS (1985) J. Neurosci. 5: 2539–2544.
2. Ichikawa J and Meltzer HY (1990a) Brain Res. 507: 138–142.
3. Ichikawa J and Meltzer HY (1990b) Eur. J. Pharmacol. 176: 371–374.
4. Ichikawa J and Meltzer HY (1991) J. Pharmacol. Exp. Ther. 256: 348–357.

© 1991 Elsevier Science Publishers B.V. All rights reserved.
Biological Psychiatry, Volume 2. G. Racagni et al., editors.

Clozapine treatment in relation to extrapyramidal functions

J. Gerlach and L. Hansen
St. Hans Hospital, Department P, Roskilde, Denmark

Introduction

One of the salient biochemical features of clozapine is its combined blockade of D_1 and D_2 dopamine receptors. Positron emission tomography of brains of schizophrenic patients treated with clozapine, 300–500 mg/day, has revealed a 40% occupancy of D_1 as well as D_2 receptors, while traditional neuroleptics have a D_2 receptor occupancy of approximately 80% and no or minimal occupancy of D_1 receptors [1]. This unique dopamine receptor binding profile may well be the main factor underlying the beneficial effect of clozapine with respect to extrapyramidal side-effects (EPS) as well as the potent antipsychotic effect, although a specific affinity to the recently-identified D_4 receptor and an anticholinergic effect may also play a role.

In the first part of this paper we shall briefly review the available evidence on the effects and the lack of effects of clozapine in EPS and TD in schizophrenic patients. In the second part, this beneficial effect of clozapine will be analysed on the basis of recent studies of the effect of D_1 and D_2 receptor blockers given alone and in combination to monkeys.

Clozapine and extrapyramidal symptoms in patients

Several papers have indicated that clozapine is associated with an extremely low frequency of EPS, whether dystonia, parkinsonism, akathisia or dyskinesia, whether acute or tardive [2–4]. When such symptoms do arise, akathisia, bradykinesia and tremor may dominate, while dystonia and rigidity is virtually absent. Slow movements and a reduced facial expression (sometimes with a slack jaw and hypersalivation) are the main parkinsonian features which may partly depend on the sedative effects of the drug.

Clozapine may also prove to be an interesting drug in relation to TD, especially with respect to prevention. Clinical experience over 15–20 years suggests that no or extremely few patients have developed TD during/following treatment with this drug [2,4]. Animal studies support this view. However, controlled clinical studies are still needed.

Clozapine may also have a place in the treatment of TD. On the basis of 8 published studies and their own open study, Lieberman et al. [5] found that clozapine had an apparent beneficial effect (50% or greater reduction) upon TD symptoms in 43% of patients with pre-existing TD. The therapeutic effect appeared to be greatest in cases of severe TD, particularly tardive dystonia, and less prominent in patients with typical choreo-athetoid symptoms.

Clozapine may affect TD via different mechanisms:

1. by allowing a spontaneous recovery;
2. by improving the mental state (symptoms such as anxiety and agitation accentuate dyskinesia);
3. by inducing sedation and/or weak parkinsonism; or
4. by a specific antidyskinesia effect (e.g. a D_1 blockade).

Probably all 4 mechanisms are working in varying degree. In the case the of dystonic features, the anticholinergic effect of clozapine may also contribute.

The greatest problem in relation to the treatment of TD with clozapine is the side-effects, especially sedation, confusion and dizziness, which are substantial problems in the treatment of elderly patients. This will often complicate the use of the high doses which may be necessary in the treatment of typical TD.

D_1/D_2 receptor blockade and extrapyramidal symptoms in primates

In order to elucidate the potential advantage of a combined D_1-D_2 receptor blockade, we have studied the effect of D_1 and D_2 antagonists given alone and in combination to Cebus monkeys.

EPS during treatment with D_1/D_2 antagonists in high doses

In drug-naive monkeys, a D_1 antagonist (NNC 756) could be given in extremely high doses (1 mg/kg, i.e. up to 100 times more than a D_2 antagonist, raclopride) without causing dystonia. Only parkinsonism (slow movements and tremor) was seen together with some sedation. The insensitivity to dystonia seen during D_1 antagonist treatment could be transferred to the D_2 antagonist, but during prolonged treatment, the D_2 antagonist resensitized the animal and caused dystonia at low doses. On the other hand, the D_2 antagonist could only be given in low doses (0.01 mg/kg) if dystonia was to be avoided. Following such D_2 antagonist exposure, D_1 antagonists also caused dystonia, until tolerance was re-established.

In these drug-naive monkeys, dyskinesia was seen slightly more frequently and intensively during and following prolonged D_2 antagonist treatment than during/after a corresponding D_1 antagonist treatment.

EPS during treatment with D_1/D_2 antagonists in low doses

In a later study, the same Cebus monkeys were exposed to low and equal doses of the D_1 and D_2 antagonists (0.012 mg/kg). Both drugs produced acute dyskinesia, as did the combination of the two drugs (0.006 mg/kg of each) (no significant difference). This suggests that in previously treated animals, D_1 and D_2 antagonists may produce an identical acute dyskinesia. Although some tolerance to dystonia may develop over time during prolonged treatment with D_1 antagonists, it remains to be determined whether tolerance also may develop to dyskinesia during such treatment or during a combined D_1-D_2 antagonist treatment.

Furthermore, the study revealed that the 3 different treatments caused a decreased arousal (sedation without sleep) of varying degree, the D_1 and the combined D_1-D_2 antagonists being significant more potent than the D_2 antagonist. This D_1 effect may contribute to the therapeutic superiority of clozapine compared to traditional D_2 blocking neuroleptics.

Conclusions

1. One of the main advantages of clozapine is a low propensity to produce EPS and TD.
2. One of the biochemical characteristics of clozapine is the combined low D_1-D_2 dopamine receptor blockade.
3. D_1 antagonists have a lower EPS potential than traditional D_2 neuroleptics, especially concerning dystonia and TD withdrawal.
4. A disturbed balance between dopamine receptors may play a role in TD [6]. Such dysbalance may be avoided by the use of a combined D_1-D_2 receptor blockade.
5. The D_1 component may thus contribute to the favourable EPS profile of clozapine and to the therapeutic effect, while an anticholinergic component may diminish possible parkinsonian symptoms.

References

1. Farde L et al. (1989) Psychopharmacology 99: S28–S31.
2. Poulsen UJ, Noring U, Fog R and Gerlach J (1985) Acta Psychiatr. Scand. 71: 176–185.
3. Casey DE (1989) Psychopharmacology 99: S47–S53.
4. Fitton A and Heel RC (1990) Drugs 40: 722–747.
5. Lieberman JA, Saltz BL, Johns CA, Pollack S, Borenstein M and Kane J (1991) Br. J. Psychiatry 158: 503–510.
6. Gerlach J and Casey DE (1988) Acta Psychiatr. Scand. 77: 369–378.

© 1991 Elsevier Science Publishers B.V. All rights reserved.
Biological Psychiatry, Volume 2. G. Racagni et al., editors.

Limbic-selective antidopaminergic effects of S(+)-aporphines compared to typical and atypical antipsychotic agents in the rat

Ross J. Baldessarini, Alexander Campbell, Silva Yeghiayan and John L. Neumeyer
Departments of Psychiatry and Neuroscience Program, Harvard Medical School, Boston; Laboratories for Psychiatric Research, McLean Hospital, Belmont, MA 02178; and Section of Medicinal Chemistry, School of Pharmacy and Allied Health Professions, Northeastern University, Boston, MA 02115, U.S.A.

Introduction

Antipsychotic agents now in use are virtually all potent antagonists of the D_2 family of dopamine (DA) receptors in limbic portions of forebrain; most also block DA receptors in the extrapyramidal basal ganglia, contributing to typical neurological side-effects that often limit their clinical usefulness. Although there are few innovative principles leading to antipsychotic agents with a low risk of extrapyramidal neurological side-effects [1], plausible strategies include seeking agents with improved limbic selectivity. S(+)-N-n-propylnorapomorphine (NPA) is a D_2-selective agent which can exert apparent DA-*agonistic* effects presynaptically (fully inhibits tyrosine hydroxylase activity) [2] and net *antagonistic* effects postsynaptically (antagonism of behavioral arousal induced by potent DA agonists) [3]; this pattern may reflect low intrinsic agonistic activity and a relatively high presynaptic D_2 receptor reserve. S(+)NPA antagonized both spontaneous locomotor activity and arousal induced by systemic administration of such DA agonists as R(−)-apomorphine or R(−)NPA, but with little effect on stereotyped gnawing behaviors and without inducing catalepsy in the rat. This pattern of responses suggests some selectivity for limbic-over-extrapyramidal anti-DA activity [3].

More directly, representative doses of (+)NPA [4] and other congeners (including its monohydroxy analog S(+)11-OH-NPa [5] and the 10,11-methylenedioxy prodrug S(+)MDO-NPA) [6] potently and selectively blocked behavioral arousal (markedly increased locomotion) induced by exogenous DA unilaterally stereotaxically microinjected into nucleus accumbens septi (limbic target) in rat forebrain; in contrast, the same treatments had very little effect on contralateral head deviation induced by the same dose of DA in corpus striatum (extrapyramidal target). To pursue these striking direct indications of limbic-selective anti-DA effects, we have worked out full dose-effect relationships against DA injected into both brain regions for the several aporphines of interest, and compared them with a standard neuroleptic haloperidol and with the atypical agent cloxapine and its new experimental analog ICI-204,636.

Materials and Methods

DA was injected (at ED_{50} 16 μg) unilaterally into forebrain sites of adult male Sprague-Dawley rats, after pretreatment with a monoamine oxidase inhibitor, through stereotaxically chronically implanted guide cannulae, and behavior was evaluated as described previously in detail [4–6]. Locomotor arousal was monitored electronically after placing DA in the nucleus accumbens septi (a limbic site) and contralateral deviation of the head was assessed quantitatively by observation and timing with a stopwatch after placing DA in the central corpus striatum (an extrapyramidal target); behavioral data were collected for 1 h. Preliminary testing assured that there was neither significant head turning after accumbens injection of DA, nor locomotor arousal after striatal injection. Systemic injections (IP) were given of a range of doses of the representative typical neuroleptic haloperidol (HAL), the atypical antipsychotic agent clozapine (CLZ) and its experimental piperazinyldibenzothiazepine analog ICI-204,636 (ICI), as well as three S(+) aporphines NPA, 10,11-methylenedioxy-NPA (MDO-NPA) and 11-hydroxy-N-n-propylnoraporphine (11-OH-NPa). Data concerning regional anti-DA dose-effect relations were curve-fit by computer assistance to obtain values of median effective inhibitory doses (ID_{50}) ± S.E.M. [3–6], which were compared among test agents on a molar dose basis (μmol/kg, i.p.).

Results

As is summarized in Table 1, the typical neuroleptic DA-antagonist HAL showed high potency and slight *striatal* selectivity against the behavioral effects of intracerebral DA (accumbens ID_{50} 0.24, striatum 0.072 mg/kg; molar ID_{50} ratio 3.3, favoring striatum). The atypical antipsychotic CLZ was less potent against DA in both regions but, paradoxically, showed ever greater striatal selectivity than did HAL (CLZ ID_{50} 37 and 4.2 μmol/kg; ratio 8.8, favoring striatum), while its analog, ICI 204,636 showed intermediate potency and the lowest striatal selectivity of these three neuroleptic agents (ID_{50} 4.1 and 2.0 μmol/kg; ratio = 2.1). In striking

Table 1. Antidopaminergic potency of test agents in rat brain regions

Agent	MW	ID_{50} (μmol/kg) ± S.E.M.		Accumbens/striatal potency ratio
		Accumbens	Striatum	
Haloperidol	376	0.2 ± 0.02	0.07 ± 0.007	0.30
Clozapine	327	36.7 ± 2.3	4.2 ± 0.4	0.11
ICI-204,636	442	4.1 ± 0.4	2.0 ± 0.3	0.49
(+)NPA	332	1.6 ± 0.3	ca. 29 ± 3	ca. 18
(+)MDO-NPA	334	1.3 ± 0.3	ca. 42 ± 4	ca. 32
(+)11-OH-NP	360	0.5 ± 0.1	ca. 35 ± 5	ca. 69

contrast, the S(+)aporphines all induced potent and highly selective antagonism of *limbic* DA with little effect on extrapyramidal injections of DA except at high systemic doses (ID_{50}, accumbens 0.50–1.6, striatal 29–42 μmol/kg); regional ID_{50} ratios were ca. 18–69, favoring the accumbens). The S(+)aporphines showed limbic potency similar to that of HAL and 25–73 times greater than that of CLZ. S(+)11-OH-NPa was 2.7–3.1 times more potent (on a molar dose basis) than the other aporphines against DA in accumbens, and 0.5, 8 and 73 times as potent as HAL, ICI and CLZ.

Discussion

The present results indicate that the S(+)-N-n-propylnoraporphines are potent and regionally highly selective *limbic* DA antagonists. In addition, S(+)11-OH-NPa is known to be orally bioavailable and relatively long-acting [5], as is the methylene-dioxy prodrug of NPA (MDO-NPA) [6] and their oral activity in the present study was nearly identical to that of IP injection (the IP/PO ratio of their ID_{50} values averaged 1.07 ± 0.05). The dose-effect functions for these two groups of drugs yielded significantly dissimilar slopes (averaging −3.3 ± 0.1 for aporphines vs. −1.3 ± 0.2 for the comparison aganets; $t = 9.4$, $P < 0.001$), suggesting that different actions may mediate the limbic effects of the aporphines and the neuroleptics tested. In addition, CLZ not only was much less potent than HAL or the aporphines but, unexpectedly, like HAL showed *extrapyramidal* selectivity. ICI appeared to be pharmacologically similar to CLZ, but was more than twice (2.1 times) as potent vs. limbic-DA.

In conclusion, in addition to the currently reported evidence of their imbic anti-DA selectivity (recently reported in greater detail elsewhere [7]), the S(+)-aporphines have several properties that would be desirable in antipsychotic drug substances. These include their previously reported lack of induction of catalepsy and the oral activity of some of the S(+)aporphines tested [3–6] and the lack of an acute prolactin-elevating effect of S(+)NPA in male rats (unpublished observations). Recently, we found that several weeks of repeated daily treatment with S(+) NPA or 11-OH-NPa failed to induce tolerance to the acute antagonistic effects vs. the DA agonist apomorphine. Accordingly, such aporphine analogs are proposed for development as potential atypical antipsychotic agents with a low risk of extrapyramidal neurological side-effects, and the present methods are proposed for predicting relative limbic vs. extrapyramidal antidopaminergic activity.

Acknowledgements

Supported by USPHS (NIMH) Grants MH-34006, MH-36224 and MH-47370, and a grant from the Bruce J. Anderson Foundation and Stuart-ICI Americas Inc.

Experimental drugs were generously donated by Abbott Labs., McNeil Labs., Sandoz Pharma Ltd., Stuart-ICI Americas Inc. and Research Biochemicals Inc. (RBI).

References

1. Baldessarini RI (1991) In: Birnbaum R, Fava M and Rosenbaum J (eds.) Advances in Behavioral Neurobiology. Mosby-Year Book, Littleton, MA (in press).
2. Booth R, Baldessarini RJ, Kula NS and Neumeyer JL (1990) Mol. Pharmacol. 38: 92–101.
3. Campbell A, Baldessarini RJ, Teicher MH and Neumeyer JL (1986) Psychopharmacology 88: 158–164.
4. Campbell A, Baldessarini RJ, Teicher MH and Neumeyer JL (1985) Neuropharmacology 24: 291–399.
5. Campbell A, Baldessarini RJ, Gao Y, Ram VJ and Neumeyer JL (1990) Neuropharmacology 29: 527–536.
6. Campbell A, Baldessarini RJ, Kula MS, Ram VJ and Neumeyer JL (1987) Brain Res. 403: 393–397.
7. Campbell A, Yeghiayan S, Baldessarini RJ and Neumeyer JL (1991) Psychopharmacology 103: 323–329.

© 1991 Elsevier Science Publishers B.V. All rights reserved.
Biological Psychiatry, Volume 2. G. Racagni et al., editors.

Reversible inhibitors of MAO-A: An introduction

Dargut Kemali
Department of Psychiatry, First Medical School, University of Naples, Italy

Introduced in clinical psychiatry in the late 1950s, monoamine oxidase inhibitors (MAOIs) have gradually fallen from favour in several countries since the 1970s, due to concerns over toxicity and the subsequent need for dietary restrictions.

In some areas, however (especially in the UK and Ireland, but also in Germany and Spain [1]), their use has remained relatively common, mainly for the treatment of the so-called "atypical depressions" (a comprehensive label which probably encompassed conditions and which would be now included among personality or anxiety disorders [2,3]). Moreover, some controlled studies carried out during the 1980s [4,5] have stimulated the use of MAOIs in panic disorder, agoraphobia and social phobia.

The recent development of MAOIs, such as moclobemide, brofaromine and cimoxatone, which are highly selective for the form A of the enzyme (involved in the degradation of serotonin and noradrenaline) and are reversible in action, justifies a reassessment of the role of this class of compounds.

These new drugs are much better tolerated than the older, unselective and irreversible MAOIs. Of special interest is the evidence provided by the oral tyramine test [6] in patients treated with moclobemide: the tyramine sensitivity after two weeks of treatment with 300 mg/day of this drug is of 100–200 mg, whereas the tyramine content in a five-course meal in a European restaurant ranges from 10 to 36 mg [7]. This means that usual quantities of wine and beer are apparently free of risk to patients taking moclobemide and that they only have to avoid aged cheese or exclusive cheese meals [8].

The new MAOIs have been also reported [9] to have a more rapid onset of action and no long-lasting carry-over effects on stopping treatment (which should mean that patients can switch to another antidepressant without a drug-free period).

Clinical research is now expected to clarify the clinical subtypes of depression and/or the subpopulations of depressed patients in which these new "gentle MAOIs" can be proposed as first-choice drugs.

Of special interest, in this connection, are the recent reports of an improvement of cognitive symptoms, not related to the alleviation of depression, in elderly demented patients treated with moclobemide [10,11]. This intriguing effect (which, of course, should be verified in larger, controlled studies), along with the short half-life of the drug and its lack of anticholinergic adverse reactions, may suggest its preferential use in elderly depressives.

References

1. Paykel ES and White JL (1989) Br. J. Psychiatry 155 (Suppl. 6): 9–17.
2. Paykel ES, Parker RR, Rowan PR et al. (1983) Psychol. Med. 13: 131–139.
3. Tyrer PJ (1982) In: Tyrer PJ (ed.) Drugs in Psychiatric Practice. Butterworths, London, pp. 249–279.
4. Liebowitz MR, Quitkin FM, Stewart JW et al. (1988) Arch. Gen. Psychiatry 45: 129–137.
5. Liebowitz MR, Gorman JM, Fyer AJ et al. (1988) J. Clin. Psychiatry 49: 252–257.
6. Simpson GM and DeLeon J (1989) Br. J. Psychiatry 155 (Suppl. 6): 32–37.
7. Da Prada M, Zürcher G, Wuthrich I et al. (1988) Neural Transm. 26 (Suppl.): 31–56.
8. Cooper AJ (1989) Br. J. Psychiatry 155 (Suppl. 6): 38–45.
9. Amrein R, Allen SR, Guentert TW et al. (1989) Br. J. Psychiatry 155 (Suppl. 6): 66–71.
10. Postma JU and Vranesic D (1985) Acta Ther. 11: 1–4.
11. Kummer J, Gündel L and Lorscheid U (1989) Unpublished paper quoted by Amrein R, Allen SR, Guentert TW et al. (1989) Br. J. Psychiatry 155 (Suppl. 6): 66–71.

© 1991 Elsevier Science Publishers B.V. All rights reserved.
Biological Psychiatry, Volume 2. G. Racagni et al., editors.

Moclobemide, an established RIMA antidepressant: In vitro interactions with tyramine

Andrea M. Cesura, Rolf Kettler and Mosé Da Prada
Pharma Division, Preclinical Research, F. Hoffmann-La Roche Ltd., CH-4002 Basel, Switzerland

Introduction

The discovery that 2 structurally and functionally different monoamine oxidase (MAO) enzymes exist, i.e. MAO-type A (MAO-A) and MAO-type B (MAO-B), stimulated the search for reversible and selective MAO-A inhibitor antidepressants with improved safety over previous irreversible and non-selective inhibitors [1,2]. Moclobemide (Aurorix®), a reversible inhibitor of MAO-A (RIMA), has undergone extensive preclinical and clinical investigations over more than 10 years. Convincing evidence has been accumulated to show that moclobemide is totally free of hepatotoxicity [3] and has a greatly reduced liability to lead to sudden long-lasting hypertensive crises (cheese-effect) in response to drugs and foodstuffs compared to any of the irreversible MAO inhibitors of the first generation [3,4].

In contrast to irreversible inhibitors which have a long-lasting activity, the MAO-A inhibition induced by moclobemide in rats lasts only about 24 h, consistent with its reversible mode of inhibition. Moclobemide interacts with low affinity with the MAO-A and its inhibitory effect can be reversed by simply incubating tissue homogenate containing the inhibited enzyme at 37°C [5]. We here report on studies of the interaction between moclobemide and tyramine in vitro using mitochondrial preparations purified from human placenta.

Materials and Methods

Mitochondria from human placenta were prepared as previously described [6]. MAO-A activity was measured radioenzymatically [7] using [^{14}C]-5-hydroxytryptamine (200 μM) as substrate.

Results

In our experimental conditions moclobemide (200 μM) inhibited with a slow time course human placenta MAO-A; maximum inhibition (about 90%) was attained after 2 h incubation (Fig. 1). In the presence of tyramine MAO-A was inhibited less

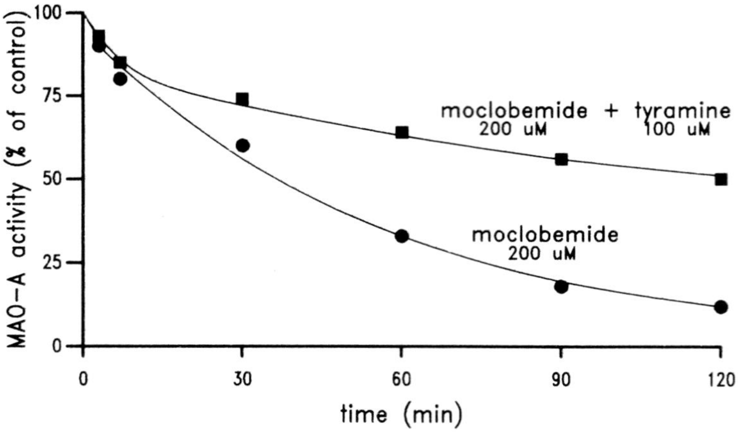

Fig. 1. Time-dependent inhibition of MAO-A activity by moclobemide and prevention by tyramine. Human placental mitochondria were incubated at 37°C in the presence of 200 μM moclobemide alone (circles) or with 200 μM moclobemide plus 200 μM tyramine (squares). At the indicated times, aliquots were sampled and assayed for MAO-A activity.

(about 50% at 2 h), indicating that the substrate tyramine was able to protect the MAO-A active site from the inhibitory effect of moclobemide. In other experiments in which MAO-A was first exposed to moclobemide to result in about 90%

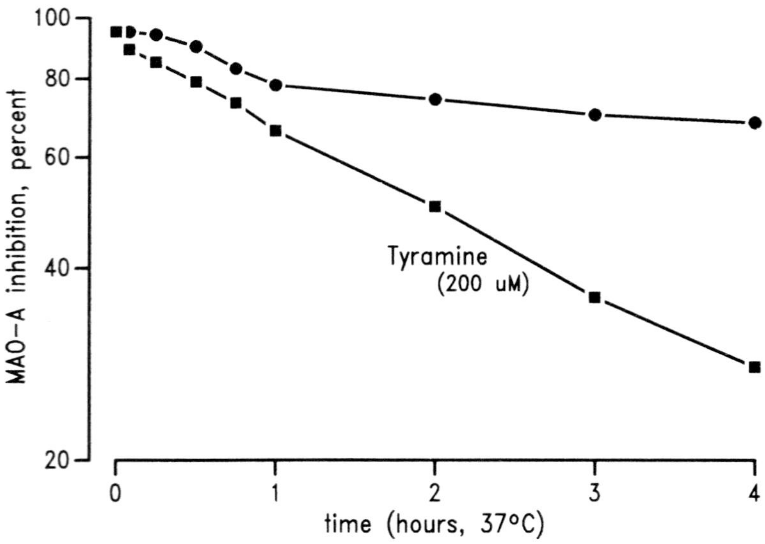

Fig. 2. Effect of tyramine on the reactivation of the moclobemide-inhibited MAO-A. Human placental mitochondria were preincubated for 1 h at 37°C with 200 μM moclobemide. To eliminate the free inhibitor, mitochondria were then centrifuged and rinsed with buffer at 4°C. After resuspension in buffer with (squares) or without (circles) 200 μM tyramine, the mixtures were reincubated at 37°C and aliquots sampled at the indicated times for determination of MAO-A activity.

inhibition of MAO, the enzyme activity recovered by 70% after 4 h incubation in the presence of tyramine (Fig. 2), much more rapidly than in the absence of tyramine.

Discussion

These in vitro experiments show that tyramine is able both to protect MAO-A from the time-dependent inhibition produced by moclobemide and to displace the inhibitor from the MAO-A active site. The low affinity of moclobemide for the enzyme and its competitive interaction with the substrate tyramine appear to be the basis of the negligible tyramine-potentiating effect of moclobemide [2,4].

References

1. Tipton KF, Dostert P and Strolin Benedetti M (eds.) (1984) Monoamine Oxidase and Disease. Prospect for Therapy with Reversible Inhibitors. Academic Press, London.
2. Burrows GD and Da Prada M (eds.) (1989) Reversible MAO-A inhibitors as antidepressants J. Neural Transm. 28 (Suppl.).
3. Schläppi B (1985) Drug Res. 35: 800–803.
4. Youdim MBH, Da Prada M and Amrein R (eds.) (1988) The cheese-effect and new reversible MAO-A inhibitors. J. Neural Transm. 26 (Suppl.).
5. Da Prada M, Kettler R, Keller HH, Burkard WP and Haefely WE (1989) J. Neural Transm. 28 (Suppl.): 5–20.
6. Cesura AM, Bös M, Galva MO, Imhof R and Da Prada M (1990) Mol. Pharmacol. 37: 358–366.
7. Da Prada M, Kettler R, Keller HH, Burkard WP, Muggli-Maniglio D and Haefely WE (1989) J. Pharmacol. Exp. Ther. 248: 400–414.

© 1991 Elsevier Science Publishers B.V. All rights reserved.
Biological Psychiatry, Volume 2. G. Racagni et al., editors.

Drug and enzyme interactions with moclobemide

Brian A. Callingham[1], Massimo Valoti[2] and Pietro Sgaragli[2]
[1]Department of Pharmacology, University of Cambridge, Tennis Court Road, Cambridge, CB2 1QJ, U.K.; and [2]Istituto di Scienze Farmacologiche, Università degli Studi di Siena, Via E.S. Piccolomini, 170, 53100 Siena, Italy

Introduction

It is well known that monoamine oxidase inhibitors (MAOIs) are potentially dangerous and that adverse drug interactions with a wide range of agents can occur [1]. Such is the power of belief that it is widely assumed that the so-called "cheese reaction" is the almost inevitable consequence of inhibition of MAO and, in particular, of MAO-A. As a result, all MAOI are viewed with considerable suspicion and although effective antidepressants in the right hands [2], only a minority of psychiatrists use them as their first choice of therapy [3].

It is against such a background that moclobemide [p-chloro-N-(2-morpholino-ethyl) benzamide], a reversible inhibitor of MAO-A [4] must make its way. It now seems clear that this agent is far less likely to cause the cheese effect than any of the other MAOIs. With tyramine as the pressor challenge, this has been demonstrated with both volunteers and experimental animals [5]. There is, however, one proviso, namely that the tyramine is administered orally or into the lumen of the gastro-intestinal tract. When rats were pre-treated with either moclobemide or tranyl-cypromine, tyramine administered parenterally caused about equal rises in blood pressure in the two groups. In contrast, when the tyramine was given orally the pressor effect was almost non-existent with moclobemide but with tranylcypro-mine it was about as large as before [6]. Could this remarkable difference solely be due to the fact that the inhibition of MAO-A by moclobemide is competitive and readily reversible while that by tranylcypromine is irreversible? Whatever else this observation demonstrates, it clearly shows how important MAOI actions in the gut and liver may turn out to be. In addition, it also brings to attention the possibility that inhibition of other enzymes in gut and liver may be important. Indeed, MAOIs have been reported to inhibit enzymes such as diphosphopyridine nucleotidase, succinic dehydrogenase, guanidine deaminase, spermine oxidase and histaminase (DAO) [7]. It has also been claimed that the MAOIs potentiate the sympatho-mimetic actions of α-methylated monoamines as much as those of unsubstituted amines [7]. However, all this evidence was accumulated from observations made on the MAOIs available several years ago when most in clinical use were either hydrazines or hydrazides and the opprobrium extended to all MAOIs irrespective of their structure.

It seemed important to us, therefore, to re-investigate a small aspect of this early evidence, but with moclobemide as well as some established MAOIs to see if these agents differed in their ability to interact with cytochrome P_{450} as an example of another class of drug-metabolising enzyme.

Materials and Methods

Male rats were anaesthetised with ether and the livers washed through with 50 ml of ice-cold NaCl solution, to remove all blood, via a cannula in the right atrium. The livers were removed and homogenised in ice-cold 0.25M sucrose solution (1:3 w/v). The homogenate was centrifuged at 12,000 g for 20 min to remove debris and mitochondria and the supernatant centrifuged at 100,000 g for 1 h to produce a pellet of microsomes. This pellet was washed and resuspended in a solution containing Tris buffer (10 mM, pH 7.6) together with 1 mM EDTA, 154 mM KCl and 20% glycerol, final concentrations. The suspension was then divided into 1-ml portions and stored in liquid nitrogen until used, following dilution with phosphate buffer (pH 7.6).

The estimation of drug interaction with the microsomal cytochrome P_{450} was undertaken with a Shimadsu UV-160 split-beam spectrophotometer, in which the absorption spectrum of a microsomal suspension with drug is compared in the spectrophotometer with that of a microsomal suspension alone and the difference spectrum displayed.

Results

While iproniazid and phenelzine interacted powerfully with microsomal cytochrome P_{450}, producing typical type II difference spectra, the acetylenic irreversible agent pargyline interacted relatively weakly and mocalobemide hardly at all (Fig. 1). In addition, the resulting spectra for both these inhibitors were similar to type I and did not resemble type II interactions. Increasing the concentration of moclobemide to 1 mm produced only a small change in the difference spectrum. Clorgyline (results not shown) also produced type II difference spectra. The interaction seen with phenelzine was by far the strongest of all the MAOIs tested while that with moclobemide was the weakest.

Discussion

These preliminary data indicate that moclobemide has virtually no affinity for rat liver cytochrome P_{450} in vitro. This, coupled with the fact that the inhibition of MAO-A by moclobemide is both readily reversible and time-dependent, may go some way in accounting for the virtual absence of hypertensive episodes resulting from the oral administration of tyramine. This observation has implications for

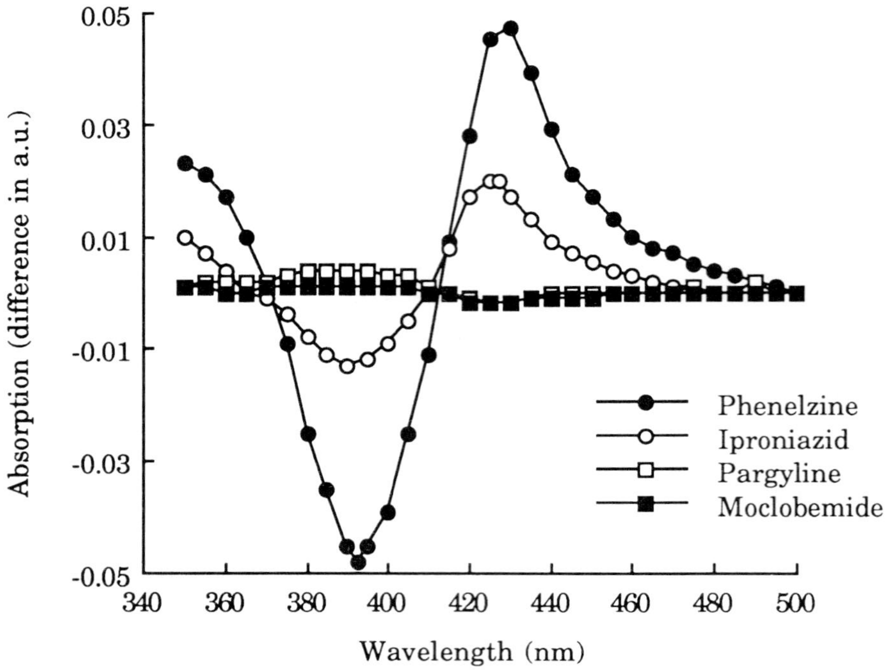

Fig. 1. In vitro interaction between the MAOIs, phenelzine, iproniazid, pargyline and moclobemide and microsomal cytochrome P_{450} from rat liver, indicated by the difference spectrum, measured in a split-beam spectrophotometer, between suspensions of microsomes with and without added MAOI. Readings were taken at 5-nm intervals and plotted against increasing wavelength.

potential interactions with drugs through effects on their breakdown by liver cytochrome P_{450} enzymes in the liver. It is now necessary to demonstrate that moclobemide does not interact with the cytochrome P_{450} and other relevant enzymes of the intestine. It is also important to examine other drug-metabolising enzymes. A potential candidate for study is intestinal peroxidase, which has been shown to catalyse the oxidative ring coupling of tyrosine, α-methyl tyrosine, tyramine and L-dopa [8]. It appears that a full investigation is needed of the effect, or possibly lack of effect, of moclobemide and other new reversible MAOIs on MAO-independent drug metabolism. This would be particularly beneficial if conducted under conditions more closely resembling those that pertain in vivo.

References

1. Griffin JP, D'Arcy PF and Speirs CJ (1988) A Manual of Adverse Drug Interactions, 4th Edn. John Wright, London.
2. Dowson JH (1987) J. Neural. Transm. (Suppl.) 23: 121–138.
3. Paykel ES and White JL (1989) Br. J. Psychiatry 155 (Suppl. 6): 9–17.

4. Keller HH, Kettler R, Keller G and Da Prada M (1987) Arch. Pharmacol. 335: 12–20.
5. Korn A, Da Prada M, Raffesberg W, Allen S and Gasic S (1988) J. Neural Transm. (Suppl.) 26: 57–71.
6. Da Prada M, Zürcher, Wuthrich I and Haefely WE (1988) J. Neural Transm. (Suppl.) 26: 31–56.
7. Bowman WC and Rand MJ (1980) Textbook of Pharmacology, 2nd Edn. Blackwell Scientific Publishers, Oxford, pp. 11.9–11.11.
8. Valoti M, Tipton KF and Sgaragli GP (1990) Proc. Pharmacol. Comm. 22 (Suppl. 2): 586.

© 1991 Elsevier Science Publishers B.V. All rights reserved.
Biological Psychiatry, Volume 2. G. Racagni et al., editors.

Efficacy of reversible inhibitors of MAO-A (RIMA) in various forms of depression

R. Amrein, C. Uchida and M. Stabl
F. Hoffmann-La Roche Ltd., Clin. Research, Basle, Switzerland

Introduction

Moclobemide is a reversible monoamine oxidase inhibitor which preferentially inhibits type-A MAO. Classical MAO-inhibitors are second choice drugs for the therapy of depression because they are considered to be less effective than standard antidepressants. They have mainly been recommended for an ill-defined group of "atypical depression" and are also used with some efficacy in anxiety disorders. Moclobemide as a reversible inhibitor of MAO-A (RIMA) has certainly initiated a new development in the treatment of depression.

In contrast to the classical MAO inhibitors, moclobemide has been shown to be efficacious in a variety of clinical subgroups. The careful analysis of its efficacy in different diagnostic categories and different syndromes is of clinical relevance for selecting patients for treatment. This paper will therefore try to summarize the antidepressant efficacy of moclobemide in:

a) diagnostic subgroups of depression;
b) syndromal subgroups of depression.

Diagnostic subgroups

From a clinical point of view an antidepressant action is relevant if it is present in endogenous depression. Among the latter we can distinguish between unipolar and bipolar disorder.

A clinical study on endogenous depression in inpatients has been carried out by Guelfi and co-workers [1] which dealt with patients who met DSM III criteria for major depression and ICD 9 and Newcastle criteria for endogenous depression. They found a global success rate of 65% in the moclobemide group (n = 62, 300–600 mg/day) and of 15% in the clomipramine group (n = 67, 100–200 mg/day).

There is no doubt that the bipolar subgroup constitutes the hard core of endogenous depressives. There is not much data in the literature on the efficacy of antidepressants in bipolar disorder. It is not that frequent and in many research protocols the bipolar group is excluded.

Pooling double-blind comparative moclobemide trials against standard antidepressants we have obtained efficacy data on 97 bipolar and 530 unipolar depressives treated with moclobemide. These data can be compared to the results obtained with imipramine, clomipramine, desipramine, amitriptyline and "second generation" antidepressants dealing with 78 bipolars and 551 unipolar depressives.

Table 1 shows the results. The baseline values obtained by the Hamilton Depression Rating Scale (17-item version) are similar in all groups. The clinical efficacy (CGI) of moclobemide is comparable in bipolar and unipolar depression. The mild trend toward a lower response in bipolars (60% vs. 66%) is statistically non-significant. Such a trend is more pronounced in patients treated with comparative drugs, which is somewhat surprising (49% vs. 65%).

Syndromal subgroups

Melancholic vs. non-melancholic depression

Five hundred and sixty-eight of 713 (80%) patients with major depression treated with moclobemide met criteria for DSM III-R melancholia (Table 2). Although the melancholic group had a significantly higher baseline Hamilton score (26.6) than the non-melancholic group (21.9), the response of the two groups did not differ statistically, i.e., moclobemide was similarly effective in patients with and without melancholia.

Psychotic vs. non-psychotic depression

Twelve percent of patients with major depression receiving moclobemide were psychotic (Table 3). The baseline Hamilton score was significantly higher (28.3) than that of the non-psychotic group (25.3). A similar difference was found in the patients treated with a comparative standard antidepressant.

Table 1. Bipolar vs. unipolar depression

	Moclobemide		Comparative drugs	
	Bipolar	Unipolar	Bipolar	Unipolar
HAMD 17	26.4 ± 5.9	26.4 ± 5.9	26.6 ± 5.7	26.2 ± 5.7
(n)	(103)	(535)	(84)	(569)
Day 28	11.1 ± 6.6	10.1 ± 7.8	11.0 ± 7.9	10.0 ± 7.0
(n)	(76)	(463)	(58)	(485)
CGI (efficacy)				
% very good/good	59.8	65.5	48.7	64.6
(n)	(97)	(530)	(78)	(551)

Table 2. Melancholic vs. non-melancholic depression

	Moclobemide		Comparative drugs	
	Melancholic	Non-melancholic	Melancholic	Non-melancholic
HAMD 17	26.6 ± 5.5	21.9 ± 5.2	26.2 ± 5.6	21.8 ± 4.8
(n)	(568)	(145)	(559)	(163)
Day 28	10.8 ± 8.1	11.2 ± 6.9	10.3 ± 7.2	11.2 ± 6.8
(n)	(452)	(124)	(464)	(130)
CGI (efficacy)				
% very good/good	59.6	62.7	61.8	55.3
(n)	(559)	(142)	(545)	(159)

As in the case of a standard antidepressant, the response rate to moclobemide tended to be slightly lower in psychotic depression. However, in both cases, the differences were not statistically significant.

Agitated vs. retarded depression

Eight percent of moclobemide patients were agitated and 1% in the group received comparative drugs (Table 4).

The agitated patients responded well to the non-sedative action of moclobemide, although the agitated patients were significantly more depressed according to Hamilton score at baseline ($P < 0.001$).

There was even a trend to a better response in agitated groups, but the differences were statistically non-significant.

Considering the lack of a sedative effect of moclobemide, the tolerance in agitated depression deserves special attention. The classification by item 9 of the

Table 3. Pschotic vs. non-pschotic depression

	Moclobemide		Comparative drugs	
	Psychotic	Non-psychotic	Psychotic	Non-psychotic
HAMD 17	28.3 ± 7.0	25.3 ± 5.5	28.3 ± 7.1	24.9 ± 5.5
(n)	(82)	(631)	(59)	(663)
Day 28	14.4 ± 8.9	10.4 ± 7.6	12.0 ± 7.8	10.4 ± 7.1
(n)	(68)	(508)	(42)	(552)
CGI (efficacy)				
% very good/good	53.7	61.1	56.4	60.7
(n)	(82)	(619)	(55)	(649)

Table 4. Agitated vs. retarded depression (agitated, HAMD item 9 > 2)

	Moclobemide		Comparative drugs	
	Agitated	Retarded	Agitated	Retarded
HAMD 17				
Baseline	30.2 ± 6.4	25.2 ± 5.8	29.9 ± 5.7	25.0 ± 5.8
(n)	(84)	(911)	(74)	(918)
Day 28	12.2 ± 8.5	10.4 ± 7.4	11.1 ± 7.9	10.3 ± 6.9
(n)	(76)	(741)	(58)	(753)
CGI (efficacy)				
% very good/good	75.6	61.2	66.2	60.7
(n)	(82)	(891)	(68)	(885)

Hamilton Score shows a similar tolerance toward moclobemide in agitated and retarded cases. Agitated depressives treated by moclobemide show a significantly better tolerance compared to agitated depressives treated with other antidepressants (Table 5).

Conclusion

This paper has dealt with the question of whether moclobemide is equally effective in certain subgroups of depressives and whether it can compare with standard antidepressant drugs in this respect.

Moclobemide shows the same efficacy in depression as traditional antidepressants, and the efficacy of moclobemide is not confined to either diagnostic subgroups or syndromal subgroups. It is surprising that even agitated depressives responded well to the non-sedative action of moclobemide.

In the study of agitated depressives moclobemide showed better tolerability than other antidepressants.

Table 5. Tolerance: agitated vs. retarded depression (agitated, HAMD item 9 > 2)

	Moclobemide		Comparative drugs	
	Agitated (n = 83)	Retarded (n = 899)	Agitated (n = 71)	Retarded (n = 903)
CGI (tolerance)				
% very good/good	81.9	85.8	71.8	77.1
% poor	7.2	5.5	12.7	9.1

References

1. Lecrubier Y and Guelfi JD (1990) Acta Psychiatr. Scand. 82(360): 18–23.
2. Baumhackl U, Bizière K, Fischbach R, Geretsegger C, Hebenstreit G, Radmayr E and Stabl M (1989) Br. J. Psychiatry 155 (6): 78–83.
3. Casacchia M, Carolei A, Barba C, Frontoni M, Rossi A, Meco G and Zylberman MR (1984) Pharmacopsychiatry 17: 122–125.
4. Guelfi JD, Payan C, Fermanian J, Pédarriosse AM and Manfredi R (1991) Br. J. Psychiatry (accepted for publication).
5. Versiani M, Oggero U, Alterwain P, Capponi R, Dajas F, Heinze-Martin G, Marques CA, Poleo MA, Rivero-Almanzor LE, Rossel L, Schmid-Burgk W and Ucha Udabe R (1989) Br. J. Psychiatry 155(6): 72–77.

© 1991 Elsevier Science Publishers B.V. All rights reserved.
Biological Psychiatry, Volume 2. G. Racagni et al., editors.

Onset of action of moclobemide in clinical trials

Y. Lecrubier[1] and J.D. Guelfi[2]

[1]U 302 Pavilion Clérambault Hôpital de la Salpêtrière 47, Bld de l'Hôpital, 75651 Paris Cedex 13; and [2]Hôpital St Anne 100, rue de la Santé, 75674 Paris, France

For more than 2 decades tricyclic antidepressants (TCA) were considered to be more effective for endogenously depressed patients, while MAOI were more effective in different disorders ranging from anxiety disorders to neurotic and/or atypical depression [1–3]. When these assumptions were tested again with moclobemide, a reversible inhibitor of MAO preferentially inhibiting MAO-A (RIMA), the efficacy of TCA and RIMA appeared to be equivalent both in non-endogenous [4] and in endogenous patients [5]. Another classical claim was the late onset of action of MAOI, 3 weeks, as compared to TCA, 2 weeks. Two French controlled trials comparing moclobemide to clomipramine explored the onset of action of efficacy for both compounds and found this second assumption to be wrong. In a previous preliminary study conducted by R. Rimon and comparing blindly moclobemide to imipramine, a trend for an earlier onset of action in favor of moclobemide had been observed. We describe the methodology and the results concerning the rapidity of action in the 2 French studies.

Onset of action in endogenously depressed patients

This was a 6-week prospective, randomized, double-blind trial comparing moclobemide 450 mg/d to clomipramine 150 mg/d in endogenously depressed patients. For tolerance reasons the dosage of clomipramine was progressively increased during the first week, while the full dose of moclobemide was reached immediately. Patients were included after a 3–7 day washout period; all were inpatients. The diagnosis of endogenous depression was made according to ICD 9 and to the 1971 Newcastle Scale; additionally a MADRS score ≥ 25 had to be present after the washout period. The principal efficacy criterion was the change in the MADRS score. The psychiatrist was asked to determine the day he considered to be that of the onset of efficacy and the day when full efficacy was reached.

One hundred and twenty-nine patients entered the protocol. Fifty-six for moclobemide and 62 for clomipramine were unipolar patients. No relevant difference between treatment groups was observed before treatment. The mean scores of the MADRS for the moclobemide group and the clomipramine group were respectively 14.4 S.D. 10.3 and 16 S.D. 9.6 after 3 weeks and 8.1 S.D. 7.1 and 8 S.D. 7.5 after 6 weeks of treatment. This final low score in endogenously depressed patients is most convincing.

The evaluation of which day was the day of onset was possible in 52 patients (84%) for moclobemide and 61 patients (91%) for clomipramine. The day of the onset of efficacy was 10.1 S.D. 4.7 for moclobemide and 12.8 S.D. 5.1 for clomipramine. This difference was significant ($P < 0.01$). The day when full efficacy was reached in the same patients was 20.8 S.D. 8.3 for moclobemide and 24.7 S.D. 8.2 for clomipramine. The difference was significant ($P < 0.02$).

Onset of action in non-endogenous major depressive episodes

This was a 6-week prospective, randomized, double-blind trial comparing 400–600 mg/d of moclobemide to 100–150 mg/d of clomipramine in major depressive episodes according to DSM III. The trial was continued for 12 weeks in all patients at least moderately improved if they accepted. The dosage of clomipramine was reached after 1 week. Five tablets were proposed with the possibility of decreasing or increasing the dosage of one tablet according to tolerance and efficacy. The washout period was 1 week. Benzodiazepines were forbidden with the exception of patients taking a dosage ≤15 mg/d of diazepam equivalent for a period >3 months without change.

All subjects were outpatients presenting a major depressive episode without melancholia or psychotic features according to DSM III (checklist and video training). Additionally all presented a score ≥17 on the Hamilton Rating Scale for depression (HRS). HRS was the principal efficacy criterion. The same questions concerning the onset and the day of full efficacy were addressed to the psychiatrists.

Twenty psychiatrists recruited 191 patients; 98 were allocated to the moclobemide group and 93 to the clomipramine group. Thirty-five percent of the patients were dysthymic according to DSM III and met criteria for double depression. No relevant difference was observed between treatment groups before treatment. The mean final score was < 10 on the HRS for both treatments and the number of responders (score HRS < 10 or improvement > 50%) was identical, 64%, in both groups. No difference in therapeutic response between treatment groups was observed whether patients were dysthymic or not. The results observed are common for TCA reference compounds in these patients. The onset of action could be determined in 78 patients (80%) for moclobemide and for 78 patients (84%) for clomipramine. The day of the onset of efficacy was 10.6 S.D. 6.1 for moclobemide and 13.2 S.D. 7.7 for clomipramine; the difference was significant ($P < 0.02$). Full efficacy was reached after 25 S.D. 11.1 days for moclobemide and 26.7 S.D. 11.6 days for clomipramine; this trend was not significant.

Moreover, our group developed a scale aimed to measure psychomotor retardation in the depressed (ERD) [6]. For reasons which are beyond the scope of this paper, we consider it to be a more specific measure of depression than most other scales. The improvement observed with the ERD is significantly more important for moclobemide after 1 and 2 weeks and almost reaches significance after 4 weeks of treatment. No difference is observed after 6 and/or 12 weeks. This result is coherent with the results obtained for the onset of action.

Conclusion

Two studies showed moclobemide, a new RIMA, to have an early onset of action, 10 days, both in endogenous and non-endogenous patients. This result is probably relevant if one considers that the reference compound, clomipramine, presented its usual range and onset of efficacy. Although it is not the aim of this paper, it should be stressed that this result was obtained while the tolerance of moclobemide was significantly better in both studies.

However these results may be due to a property of the drug or to the possibility of prescribing the full therapeutic dosage of 450 mg since the first day of treatment due to the good tolerance. A protocol aimed at answering this question and confirming these results is ongoing.

References

1. British Medical Research Council (1965) Br. Med. J. 1: 881–886.
2. Liebowitz MR and Klein DF (1979) Psychiatr. Clin. North Am. 2: 555–575.
3. Tyrer P (1976) Br. J. Psychiatry 128: 354–360.
4. Lecrubier Y and Guelfi JD (1990) Acta Psychiatr. Scand. 360 (Suppl.): 18–23.
5. Guelfi JD, Payan C, Fermanian J, Pedariosse AM and Manfredi R (1991) Moclobemide versus clomipramine in endogenous depression. Br. J. Psychiatry (accepted for publication).
6. Lecrubier Y (1983) In: Widlöcher D (ed.) Le Ralentissement Dépressif. Collection Moduls, PUF, Paris 26–40.

© 1991 Elsevier Science Publishers B.V. All rights reserved.
Biological Psychiatry, Volume 2. G. Racagni et al., editors.

Serotonin in psychiatric illness

Stuart A. Montgomery, Tim Bullock and Naomi Fineberg
Department of Psychiatry, St Mary's Hospital Medical School, London, U.K.

Introduction

The selective 5-HT re-uptake inhibitors provide us with an interesting insight into the role of serotonin in affective disorders. In major depression itself, selective 5-HT re-uptake inhibitors appear to be as effective as conventional TCAs without marked effects on the serotonin system. Indeed, it is one of the puzzles of depression that antidepressants with quite different actions appear to have equal efficacy.

Obsessive-compulsive disorder

There is mounting evidence that in obsessive-compulsive disorder (OCD) only drugs with potent effects on the serotonergic system are effective and that conventional tricyclic antidepressants (TCA) or noradrenaline re-uptake inhibitors are ineffective and similar to placebo. The evidence is now sufficiently strong to indicate that OCD is a specific serotonergic disorder, in contrast to major depression where antidepressants of different pharmacological classes appear to be equally effective.

In the first study to examine the efficacy of potent 5-HT uptake inhibitors in pure OCD without concomitant depression, a strong therapeutic effect was observed indicating a direct antiobsessional effect [1]. This result remained controversial until confirmed later in two large multicentre studies [2]. Other studies which included patients with varying amounts of concomitant depression appeared to demonstrate a similar potent effect, which suggests that the concomitant depression is integral to the OCD.

The depression associated with OCD responds preferentially to potent 5-HT uptake inhibitors and little or not at all to antidepressants without potent serotonin effects, such as nortriptyline or desipramine. Furthermore, the placebo response in those patients with defined OCD and concomitant depression is low and very similar to that seen in pure OCD. It seems therefore that the depression associated with OCD does not behave like conventional depression but instead responds in parallel with the OCD itself.

The implication is that, faced with a patient with major depression and OCD, the most important disorder to treat is the OCD and that the depression associated with OCD should be subsumed diagnostically under OCD. This has important implications for the diagnostic hierarchy of psychiatric illness, suggesting that OCD trumps depression and that OCD, like schizophrenia, should therefore remain above depression in the hierarchy.

Anxiety within depression

Within major depression itself there is now good evidence that selective 5-HT reuptake inhibitors have a particular effect on the anxiety symptoms of depression. Several 5-HT uptake inhibitors have demonstrated efficacy compared with placebo which was not as marked with the comparator antidepressants. This suggests a selective serotonergic component for the anxiety symptoms within depression. It is possible, therefore, that the specific serotonergic phenomenon, which is so visible with OCD, may have a dimensional effect in the anxiety symptoms in depression.

Recurrent brief depression

Major depression is not the only important depressive disorder. Recurrent brief depression (ICD 10 38.10) with 2–4 day profound depressive episodes recurring erratically some 20 times a year is as common and as disruptive a disorder as major obsession [3,4]. There are as yet insufficient studies on recurrent brief depression to be sure, but preliminary data suggest that recurrent brief depression is not responsive to conventional TCAs. There are anecdotal suggestions of efficacy for some 5-HT uptake inhibitors which indicate the possibility that recurrent brief depression is a more pharmacologically selective disorder.

Panic disorder

There is also a suggestion that pure panic may have a selective serotonergic response, although considerably less than with OCD. For example, in the study of den Boer and Westenberg [5] a 5-HT reuptake inhibitor was effective in pure panic without depression, whereas a noradrenaline reuptake inhibitor was not. It is interesting in this regard that panic disorder has a strong overlap with depression, and particularly with recurrent brief depression. Unfortunately, the efficacy studies in panic disorder have not been precise about the presence of recurrent brief depression, so it is not yet possible to comment on the specificity of response of panic disorder and concomitant recurrent brief depression. The overlap of panic disorder with major depression is associated with a response to conventional antidepressants, the most widely studied of which is imipramine. It appears therefore that pure panic caps panic plus depression and that pure panic should also move from the anxiety order category and be placed alongside OCD or OCD with depression as a separate group of disorders with a specific response to serotonergic compounds.

References

1. Montgomery SA (1980) Pharm. Med. 1: 189–192.
2. de Veaugh Geiss J, Landau P and Katz R (1989) Psychiatr. Ann. 19: 97–101.
3. Montgomery SA, Montgomery D, Baldwin D and Green M (1989) Neuropsychobiology 22: 128–134.
4. Angst J, Merinkangas K and Scheidegger P (1990) J. Affective Disord. 19: 87–98.
5. den Boer JA and Westenberg HGM (1988) Int. Clin. Psychopharmacol. 3: 59–74.

© 1991 Elsevier Science Publishers B.V. All rights reserved.
Biological Psychiatry, Volume 2. G. Racagni et al., editors.

The role of sertraline in major depression

Joseph Mendels
Philadelphia Medical Institute, Philadelphia, Pennsylvania, U.S.A.

Major depressive disorder (MDD) continues to present psychiatrists with a challenge and remains a very important public health problem. While there has been progress in the management of MDD, studies suggest that up to 70% of patients with this diagnosis receive either no treatment or inadequate treatment. The costs for this failure are immeasurable human suffering and loss, as well as billions of dollars in inappropriate health care and lost productivity.

There are, of course, a number of reasons for this problem, including ignorance, bias, and prejudice on the part of the patient, the family, and society, as well as the relative failure by many physicians to diagnosis depression and to acknowledge that it is a serious medical disorder that requires aggressive and appropriate treatment.

One major impediment to effective treatment has been the fact that many antidepressant medications have had their potential effectiveness limited because of unpleasant or potentially serious side-effects, resulting in patients not being able to accept a therapeutic dose of the drug or declining to remain on treatment. Consequently, many patients fail to respond or they relapse prematurely.

The recent emergence of a new class of antidepressant medications that block the reuptake of serotonin at receptor sites without significant effects on other central neurotransmitter systems presents us with a fresh opportunity to tackle this critical problem. The serotonin reuptake inhibitors have a very different, and for many patients, more acceptable side-effect profile in that they do not have significant anticholinergic, antihistaminic, or cardiovascular effects.

One of the newer agents in this class of drugs is sertraline. Sertraline is a potent and selective inhibitor of serotonin uptake in the brain as shown by in vitro, ex vivo, and in vivo neurochemical studies. It has negligible binding affinity for dopaminergic, adrenergic and muscarinic receptors. It has been shown to potentiate 5-hydroxytryptophan-induced behaviors in mice, and is active in a number of preclinical tests of antidepressant activity, such as the Porsolt Swim Test ("behavior despair") in mice. It also causes down-regulation and desensitization of the β-adrenoceptor system in rat brain following subacute administration. Chronic administration also produces desensitization of the 5-HT_2 receptor functional system.

A series of clinical studies with sertraline over the past few years have demonstrated that it is an effective antidepressant equivalent to standard tricyclics such as amitriptyline and that its pharmacology, pharmacokinetics and side-effect profile may render it more acceptable to many depressed patients. Of considerable importance is its relative safety in overdose.

A double-blind study was carried out in which sertraline was compared with amitriptyline and placebo in outpatients with major depression [1]. Four hundred and forty-eight patients meeting DSM III criteria for major depression were included in the study. Patients underwent a 1- to 2-week placebo washout period, followed by an 8-week double-blind therapy period during which dose was titrated from 50 to 200 mg for sertraline or 50 to 150 mg for amitriptyline according to toleration. The mean change from baseline in the Hamilton Rating Scale for Depression for evaluable patients was −12.43 for sertraline, −14.06 for amitriptyline, and −8.71 for placebo, with $P < 0.001$ for both active drugs compared with placebo. There was no significant difference in efficacy between sertraline and amitriptyline.

It has also been shown that sertraline, in addition to being effective for patients with major depression as a group, maintains the same level of efficacy in those patients whose depression is more severe or who have the associated syndrome of melancholia. Furthermore, even though sertraline is not significantly sedating, those depressed patients who have concurrent anxiety or insomnia do respond well to it.

The availability of sertraline, the newest representative of an important class of antidepressant medications, promises to add to the increasing range of antidepressant treatments available to the clinician.

Reference

1. Reimherr FW, Chouinard G, Cohn CK et al. (1990) J. Clin. Psychiatry 51 (Suppl. B): 18–27.

© 1991 Elsevier Science Publishers B.V. All rights reserved.
Biological Psychiatry, Volume 2. G. Racagni et al., editors.

Sertraline in a primary care setting

C. Thompson
University of Southampton, Hampshire, U.K.

Sertraline is a member of the selective serotonin reuptake inhibitor class of antidepressants. The relative mildness of side-effects and the low toxicity in overdose of this class of antidepressants suggests that they should be particularly useful in general practice, where the tricyclic antidepressants are often poorly tolerated. Two studies will be reported in which sertraline was administered to patients seen in primary care; the first is a 3-way placebo-controlled trial against dothiepin in 286 depressed patients and the second is a large open study referred to as the SIGMA study (sertraline in general practice, a multicentre assessment) in which the first 1,000 patients' results are available for analysis.

Double-blind study

Patients who met the criteria on DSM III-R for major depressive disorder and who scored at least 22 on the Montgomery Asberg Depression Rating Scale (MADRS) and 4 or more on the Clinical Global Impression (CGI) were treated for 1 week with placebo and then randomized to receive either sertraline (88), dothiepin (93), or placebo (105) for 6 weeks. The sertraline group commenced dosage at 50 mg in the morning, increasing after 2 weeks if there were no signs of improvement and side-effects did not preclude it. The dothiepin group received 75 mg at night, increasing to 150 mg after 2 weeks regardless of improvement if side-effects did not preclude it. Twenty-four sertraline-treated patients increased dosage to 100 mg while all but 15 dothiepin-treated patients increased to 150 mg. This comparison is therefore between a relatively low dose of sertraline and a standard dose of dothiepin.

The mean baseline MADRS score for evaluable patients was between 27 and 28 for all three treatment groups. At the final visit the reduction in MADRS score was 15.6 for sertraline, 13.0 for dothiepin and 13.1 for placebo. The improvement on dothiepin was no greater than on placebo while the group taking sertraline had a significantly greater improvement ($P < 0.05$). In the sertraline group 6 patients suffered nausea and 4 reported headache.These were the most common side-effects. In the dothiepin-treated group the most common side-effects were dry mouth [9] and somnolence [5].

Nine patients in the sertraline group, 13 in the dothiepin group, and 15 in the placebo group were withdrawn. There appeared to be no differences between the groups in the reasons for withdrawal.

This trial demonstrates that dothiepin at a modal dose of 150 mg appears to be no better than placebo in general practice, while a relatively low modal dose of 50 mg sertraline was superior to placebo. There was no statistically significant difference, however, between dothiepin and sertraline.

SIGMA study

This study has a target group size of 3,000. The first 1,002 patients are reported in this preliminary analysis. Patients were entered into the study if they had a depressive illness of at least 2 weeks' duration and that was associated with 5 of the 9 symptoms which make up the DSM III-R criteria for major depressive disorder. The severity of depression was measured at baseline and at follow-up with the MADRS, the CGI, and the self-rated Hospital Anxiety and Depression Rating Scale (HAD). Each patient was treated for 6 weeks with an escalating dose of sertraline starting at 50 mg per day and rising in 50-mg increments every 2 weeks to a maximum of 200 mg, depending upon clinical response and side-effects.

There were 258 male and 744 female patients in the sample. The mean age was 44 years (range 17–85). The current episode of depression had persisted for a mean of 12.8 weeks (range 2–250). There was a previous history of depression in 55% of patients. One hundred and ninety-nine patients (20%) discontinued the study before the end, leaving 871 patients who were evaluable for efficacy. The mean baseline MADRS score was 30.2, and this fell to 10.8 at the end of the treatment period ($P < 0.0001$). All items of the MADRS showed a comparable fall in severity score. The mean baseline CGI score was 4.2, falling to 2.2 at the end of treatment ($P < 0.0001$). The mean HAD depression (D) scale score was 13.7, falling to 7.8 at the end of treatment ($P < 0.0001$) and the A scale score fell from 12.1 to 6.1 ($P < 0.0001$).

Patients with a milder illness at the start of treatment (MADRS score less than 12) also had a significant reduction in severity from 11.1 to 4.6 ($P < 0.001$). Similar improvements were seen in older (over 65 years, n = 95) as in younger patients.

No significant weight gain or change in cardiovascular or biochemical parameters were seen. The most common side-effects were nausea and headache. Somnolence, dizziness, dyspepsia, and diarrhea also occurred.

Fifty-nine percent of evaluable patients remained on 50 mg of sertraline throughout the study, 31% increased to 100 mg, 8% to 150 mg, and 2% to 200 mg.

At the end of the study the overall efficacy was rated as excellent in 39%, good in 35%, fair in 18%, and poor in 8%.

Sixty percent had excellent toleration of the drug, 32% good, 8% fair, and 0.1% (1 patient) poor toleration.

Summary

The studies reported above suggest that sertraline is an effective antidepressant in general practice when the severity of the depression meets criteria for major depressive disorder. At a modal dose of 50 mg it was shown to be more effective than placebo, while in the same study dothiepin at a modal dose of 150 mg failed to demonstrate evidence of effectiveness. For dothiepin, 150 mg is a fairly high dose compared with the practice of most general practitioners [1]. This second large-scale study also demonstrated that in general practice sertraline is a well-tolerated and safe antidepressant, with therapeutic actions over a range of severities of illness and patient ages.

The main side-effects were infrequent, but headache and nausea were seen more commonly than in the placebo group, and these appeared again as the most frequent side-effects in the SIGMA study.

Reference

1. Thompson C and Thompson CM (1989) Hum. Psychopharmacol. 4: 91–102.

© 1991 Elsevier Science Publishers B.V. All rights reserved.
Biological Psychiatry, Volume 2. G. Racagni et al., editors.

Sertraline and the elderly

Louis F. Fabre
The Fabre Clinic, Houston, Texas, U.S.A.

Recent studies in the United States and Europe show that elderly persons (over 60 years of age) are the fastest-growing segment of the population. Unfortunately, elderly persons are more prone to depressive illnesses, with 20% of the elderly suffering significant depressive symptoms and over 50% of the hospitalized elderly showing evidence of depression. Elderly patients often have a variety of medical illnesses for which they are taking medication; they may have compromised cardiovascular, renal, or hepatic functioning that makes the treatment of their depressive illness more difficult than in younger patients. Antidepressant therapies currently available for the elderly are associated with anticholinergic side-effects, cardiotoxicity, and the possibility of severe drug-drug interactions. Sertraline, a new serotonin reuptake inhibitor, may have advantages in the treatment of depression in elderly patients because anticholinergic side-effects are few and severe drug-drug interactions have not been observed.

Two studies of sertraline vs. amitriptyline were carried out: one in the U.S. [1], the other in Europe. Both studies were multicenter, double-blind, flexible-dose studies in which safety and efficacy were compared over 8 weeks, with a 16-week continuation period in the U.S. study. Two hundred and forty-one depressed elderly persons participated in the U.S. and 77 patients were included in an interim analysis in Europe. In both studies, twice as many patients were randomized to sertraline as to amitriptyline. In general, demographic parameters were equivalent. The average age of patients was 71 years, American, and 74 years, European. American patients averaged 10 kg heavier in weight than European patients. Major depression, single episode, without melancholia was the most common diagnosis in the U.S.; major depression, recurrent, with melancholia was the most common diagnosis in Europe. Dosage for sertraline was titrated from 50–200 mg/day and the amitriptyline dosage was 50–150 mg/day unless limited by side-effects.

In both studies, comparable efficacy for sertraline and amitriptyline was shown; both drugs were highly effective in treating depressive symptoms. Between baseline and the final double-blind visit, the average Hamilton Depression Score (HAM-D) decreased by 13.3 points (American) and 12.7 points (European) for the sertraline groups and 14.2 points (American) and 14.0 points (European) for amitriptyline. Other efficacy parameters showed similar results. Side-effect profiles showed more anticholinergic side effects (dry mouth, constipation etc.) for the amitriptyline groups and more nausea for the sertraline groups. In general, American and European studies were similar, but more American patients discontinued the study because of side-effects. In contrast, the European treatment groups had a higher

Table 1. American study – Improvement in primary efficacy variables among evaluable patients

	Sertraline	Amitriptyline	Estimated treatment difference	*P*
HAM-D total score				
Mean baseline values	23.7	25.2		
Mean change from baseline	−13.3	−14.2	1.5	0.10
Mean % change from baseline to last visit	−56.6	−55.9	2.2	0.59
HAM-D depression item (#1) score				
Mean change from baseline to last visit	− 1.8	− 1.7	0	0.95
Clinical global impressions severity score				
Mean change from baseline to last visit	− 1.8	− 1.7	0	0.89
SCL-56 depression factor				
Mean change from baseline to last visit	− 0.44	− 0.34	−0.05	0.64

incidence of discontinuation due to lack of efficacy than the American treatment groups.

Patients doing well in the American study were allowed to continue double-blind for an additional 16 weeks. Seventy-four sertraline and 31 amitriptyline patients participated. Both treatment groups continued to show good efficacy throughout the extension study (HAM-D change from baseline to final visit: sertraline −16.3, amitriptyline −18.7). The side-effect profiles were similar to the 8-week study, with the addition that over the 24-week period sertraline patients lost 0.59 kg and amitriptyline patients gained 2.28 kg.

The results of the efficacy and side-effect profiles of these studies suggest that sertraline is useful in treating geriatric depression, with the low incidence of anticholinergic side-effects being especially important. Fluoxetine has the advantages of the low incidence of anticholinergic side-effects but may not be very useful in the treatment of geriatric depression. Fluoxetine inhibits the cytochrome P-450 enzyme, which is responsible for demethylating, dehydroxylating and desulfoxidating compounds. Drugs metabolized by these pathways may be elevated in patients taking fluoxetine. Fluoxetine may also be problematic in the elderly because of a very long half-life (fluoxetine + active metabolite ≈9 days), requiring 4–6 weeks to be eliminated from the body. Sertraline offers the advantage of no clinically significant inhibition of the cytochrome P-450 enzyme and a half-life of approximately 25 h with no active metabolite.

Sertraline may be a particularly useful drug choice for the treatment of major depression in geriatric patients. It has demonstrated good efficacy, a mild side-effect profile with few anticholinergic effects and a reasonable half-life of approximately 1 day for once-a-day dosing.

Reference

1. Cohn CK, Shrivastava R, Mendels J et al. (1990) J. Clin. Psychiatry 51 (Suppl. B): 28–33.

© 1991 Elsevier Science Publishers B.V. All rights reserved.
Biological Psychiatry, Volume 2. G. Racagni et al., editors.

Sertraline in the prevention of depression

D.P. Doogan
Pfizer Ltd, Sandwich, Kent, U.K.

Sertraline is a novel specific serotonin reuptake inhibitor. Its selective pharmacology allows antidepressant effects without the accompanying side-effects typical of the tricyclic antidepressants.

Studies of up to 8 weeks duration showed the compound to be significantly superior to placebo and to possess similar efficacy to amitriptyline in depressed patients. Sertraline was well tolerated; side-effects were mainly gastrointestinal, without the anticholinergic and cardiovascular side-effects of amitriptyline [1,2]. The present multicentre study was conducted in general practice or in psychiatric outpatients throughout France, Germany, Finland, Austria, Switzerland, the U.K. and Ireland.

Patient population

Outpatients with major depressive disorder (DSM III) were screened. Entry criteria included a minimum score of 17 on the HAM-D, age range of 18–70 years and the absence of significant concurrent medical illness. Concurrent medication of short-acting benzodiazepines was permitted for the control of anxiety or insomnia.

Short-term phase

Design

After a placebo run-in period of 1 week, 467 patients entered an 8-week, open-label treatment phase during which sertraline, 50–200 mg/day, was administered. Assessments were conducted at two-weekly intervals: HAM-D, Clinical Global Impression (CGI) and side-effect interview. Laboratory analyses for hematology and biochemistry were conducted at baseline and week 8.

The dose was commenced at 50 mg O.D. and could be increased at two-weekly intervals to a maximum of 200 mg O.D. if the investigator considered there to be insufficient efficacy without limiting side-effects.

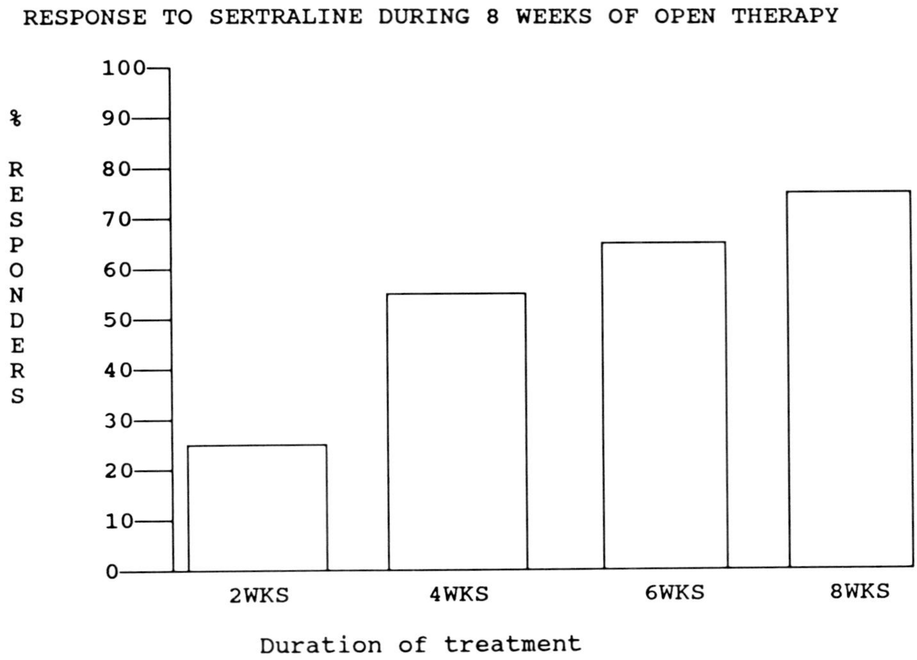

Fig. 1. Responders defined as those patients who achieved a CGI score of very much or much improved during 8 weeks of sertraline therapy.

Results

The overall response rate as judged by CGI improvement (very much or much improved) was 68% at final visit. The time course of antidepressant action was as expected for an antidepressant (Fig. 1). The mean final dose of sertraline was 97 mg.

Continuation phase

Design

Two hundred and ninety-five patients considered to have had a suitable response in the open-label phase were permitted to enter the 44-week second phase of the study. Treatment was double-blind and randomized with 1 patient receiving placebo for every 2 patients receiving sertraline. Dosing was the same range as in short-term. Assessments were conducted every 4 weeks (CGI, side-effects) or 8 weeks (HAM-D). The principal efficacy variable was the relapse rate. This was defined as CGI severity score of 4 or more (at least mildly depressed) for the remainder of the study or discontinuation due to lack of efficacy.

Results

Final dose. The mean final dose of sertraline for this phase of the study was 69 mg.

Withdrawals from treatment. There was a significant difference between sertraline and placebo; 8% of sertraline patients and 41% of placebo patients ($P < 0.0001$) prematurely terminated treatment because of inefficacy.

Relapse/recurrence. Throughout the 44-week treatment period, the relapse rate was significantly higher for placebo patients (46%) than for sertraline patients (13%; $P < 0.001$). The differences were further supported by division of the maintenance phase into 2 parts: weeks 1–16, the relapse phase; and weeks 17–44, the recurrence phase. In weeks 1–16, the relapse rate was 18% on sertraline and 46% on placebo ($P < 0.001$). In weeks 17–44 the recurrence rate (i.e. the emergence of a new depressive episode after being symptom-free for at least 16 weeks) was 9% on sertraline and 22% on placebo ($P < 0.026$).

Side-effects. The level of side-effect reporting was low with little difference between sertraline and placebo. Only 6% of sertraline patients discontinued open-label treatment due to side-effects. Gastrointestinal symptoms (nausea, dyspepsia and abdominal pain) were most frequently reported.

Conclusions

Sertraline, a novel 5-HT reuptake inhibitor, showed clear properties of prevention of both relapse and recurrence of depression in a population of outpatients with major depression (DSM III). This effect was accompanied by good tolerability. These properties together with selective pharmacology make sertraline a valuable new addition to the antidepressant market. These findings are further supported by HAM-D/CGI scores showing a slight improvement with sertraline and deterioration with placebo.

References

1. Reimherr FW, Chouinard G, Cohn CK et al. (1990) J. Clin. Psychiatry 51 (Suppl. B): 18–27.
2. Cohn CK, Shrivastava R, Mendels J et al. (1990) J. Clin. Psychiatry 51 (Suppl. B): 28–33.

© 1991 Elsevier Science Publishers B.V. All rights reserved.
Biological Psychiatry, Volume 2. G. Racagni et al., editors.

A double-blind, multicenter, placebo-controlled study of sertraline in obsessive-compulsive disorder

Guy Chouinard
Louis H. Lafontaine Hospital, 7401, rue Hochelaga, Montreal, Quebec, H1N 3M5; and Allan Memorial Institute, Montreal, Canada

This paper reports the results from the first clinical trial in which sertraline and placebo were compared in the treatment of nondepressed patients with a diagnosis of obsessive-compulsive disorder (OCD). Once considered uncommon, the life-time prevalence of OCD in the adult population is reported to be 3.3%. Until recently, it was considered refractory to treatment. Involvement of serotonin (5-HT) was suggested in the pathogenesis of OCD after clomipramine, a tricyclic noradrenergic and 5-HT reuptake inhibitor, was found effective in treatment of OCD. Sertraline, a new, non-tricyclic, serotonin reuptake inhibitor, was found to have in vitro selectivity for serotonin exceeding that of clomipramine and other SRIs such as fluoxetine, fluovoxamine, and zimelidine.

Eighty-seven patients with a DSM III diagnosis of obsessive-compulsive disorder without depression were entered into a double-blind, placebo-controlled study of the efficacy of sertraline. All patients with a total score of 15 or greater on the Hamilton Depression Scale (24-item, obsessive and compulsive symptom item excluded) or a score of greater than 1 on item 1 (depression) of the scale were excluded to avoid confounding antidepressant effects. After a single-blind, placebo washout period lasting 1 week, patients were randomized to receive either sertraline (50–200 mg) or placebo for 8 weeks, after which sertraline was gradually withdrawn over a 2-week period. A total of 87 patients were randomized, 44 to placebo and 43 to sertraline. The mean age of the patients in both groups was 36–38 years. Triazolam or chloral hydrate was permitted only as necessary. Analyses of the data (2-tailed tests) show that sertraline was significantly more effective than placebo on the Yale-Brown Obsessive-Compulsive Rating total score ($P = 0.05$), the National Institute of Mental Health General Obsessive-Compulsive Rating ($P = 0.026$), the Clinical Global Impression of severity of illness score ($P = 0.047$) and the CGI improvement score ($P = 0.025$). A patient rating instrument, the Maudsley Obsessive-Compulsive Inventory, demonstrated a trend in favour of sertraline but did not reach statistical significance ($P = 0.13$). Results of the Y-BOCS total score, the NIMH score, and the Global Severity and Improvement scores demonstrated a statistically significant superiority of sertraline to placebo. Fifty-six percent of patients on sertraline and 32% on placebo showed "some improvement" during treatment, whereas 25% of patients on sertraline and 11% on placebo were described as "much improved".

A higher than expected placebo response rate (31.8%) was observed at week 8 which may have been due to a number of factors: inclusion of patients with no minimum score on an OCD rating scale (only DSM III diagnosis was required); short length of study; and effective double-blinding of active drug because of the good side-effect profile of sertraline, thus permitting assessment of a true placebo response. Week-by-week changes suggest that symptom relief began soon after the initiation of treatment and continued throughout the treatment period. Results of the Total NIMH Scale and Total Y-BOCS scores, at week 8, support the validity of the observed placebo response. At week 10, when patients were withdrawn from treatment, only those on placebo experienced an immediate rebound in symptomatology. Therefore, placebo ratings at week 10 more accurately represent the placebo response rate than those at week 8. Patients on sertraline improved despite dose reductions, an observation which suggests that continued improvement after 8 weeks could be expected. This finding concurs with results of OCD trials involving fluvoxamine, fluoxetine, and clomipramine, which suggest that prolonged treatment is necessary for optimal results.

In conclusion, sertraline was found to be significantly superior to placebo in the treatment of obsessive-compulsive disorder. Sertraline also demonstrated a better side-effect profile than that reported in studies of clomipramine, with nausea and dyspepsia being the most common effects along with a low incidence of other known serotonergic adverse effects such as nervousness. Clomipramine can cause orthostatic hypotension, peripheral and central anticholinergic effects, weight gain, and cognitive impairment. It is suggested that in future trials of sertraline, prolonged treatment of 12, 24, or even 52 weeks be considered.

© 1991 Elsevier Science Publishers B.V. All rights reserved.
Biological Psychiatry, Volume 2. G. Racagni et al., editors.

Neuropharmacological properties of ondansetron and its potential in treating anxiety and cognitive dysfunction

M.S. Tyers[1], B. Costall[2], A.M. Domeney[2], B.J. Jones[1] C.C. Jordan[1], M.E. Kelly[2], R.J. Naylor[2] and N.R. Oakley[1]

[1]Neuropharmacology Department, Glaxo Group Research Ltd, Hertfordshire; and [2]Postgraduate Studies in Pharmacology, The School of Pharmacy, University of Bradford, U.K.

Introduction

$5\text{-}HT_3$ receptors are located exclusively on neuronal tissue in the peripheral and central nervous systems [1]. It is possible, therefore, that selective antagonists for this receptor may have a use in the treatment of psychiatric and neurological diseases.

In 1979, Glaxo embarked on a programme of research to identify a selective $5\text{-}HT_3$ receptor antagonist. From this programme, ondansetron was selected for further development and in particular for its effects on behaviour.

The $5\text{-}HT_3$ receptor antagonist properties of ondansetron were evaluated in both in vitro and in vivo preparations. In the rat isolated vagus nerve, 5-HT produces concentration-dependent depolarisations via activation of $5\text{-}HT_3$ receptors [2]. Ondansetron causes parallel rightward shifts of the 5-HT concentration-response curve, giving a pA_2 value of 8.1. In binding studies, ondansetron displaced ^3H-GR65630 from $5\text{-}HT_3$ receptor sites with a pK_i of 8.5. Its selectivity for the $5\text{-}HT_3$ receptor, compared with other 5-HT receptors and other neurotransmitter receptor types, has been demonstrated in other isolated tissue preparations in which a concentration of 10 μM had no effect [3].

In the anaesthetized cat, the selective $5\text{-}HT_3$ receptor agonist, 2-methyl-5-HT, induces the Bezold-Jarisch reflex by activation of $5\text{-}HT_3$ receptors on vagal afferents in the cardiac ventricular muscle. This reflex is characterized by a marked but very transient (≈20 s) reflex bradycardia and fall in blood pressure. Both responses are blocked by ondansetron (ED_{50} = 0.42 μg/kg i.v.; 7.0 μg/kg p.o.). Ondansetron has no direct effects on the cardiovascular system, even at the very high dose of 3 mg/kg i.v. and no effects on normal behaviour in several species.

Ondansetron is therefore a potent, highly selective, competitive $5\text{-}HT_3$ receptor antagonist. It is active by the oral route and has a wide therapeutic margin.

Effects of ondansetron in models of anxiety

5-HT has been implicated in the aetiology of anxiety states and in the anxiolytic action of benzodiazepines. Several studies in rodents and primates have shown that ondansetron mimics the disinhibitory properties of the benzodiazepines but lacks their sedative, anticonvulsant and muscle relaxant properties and has no dependence liability [4].

In the social interaction test in the rat, ondansetron, 0.5–100 μg/kg p.o., caused dose-dependent increases in social interaction under experimental conditions of high illumination and unfamiliarity with the test arena. Similar disinhibitory activity was seen for diazepam, 2 mg/kg p.o. (Fig. 1). Ondansetron was also effective in the elevated plus maze in the rat and in the light dark box in the mouse.

In cynomolgus monkeys, ondansetron, 10 and 100 μg/kg p.o., induced disinhibitory behaviour changes similar to those seen with diazepam, 2.5 mg/kg p.o. For example, both drugs reduced provoked and spontaneous aggressive behaviour as well as agitation and restlessness. Diazepam, but not ondansetron, also reduced alertness and motor coordination. Similarly, under mild aversive conditions, marmosets exhibit aggressive and territorial behaviours which are suppressed by ondansetron, 1–100 μg/kg s.c. and diazepam, 25 μg/kg s.c.

Further studies in the mouse and rat have shown that ondansetron, unlike the 5-HT_{1A} agonist buspirone, can suppress the rebound behavioural inhibition which follows withdrawal from chronic treatment with diazepam.

In summary, behavioural studies in animals suggest that ondansetron has potential in treating anxiety disorders in man without associated sedation or dependency.

Effects of ondansetron on cognitive function

Several studies have shown that 5-HT_3 receptors have a modulating influence on neurotransmitter release in the peripheral and central nervous systems. For example, acetylcholine release from parasympathetic nerves in the gastrointestinal tract

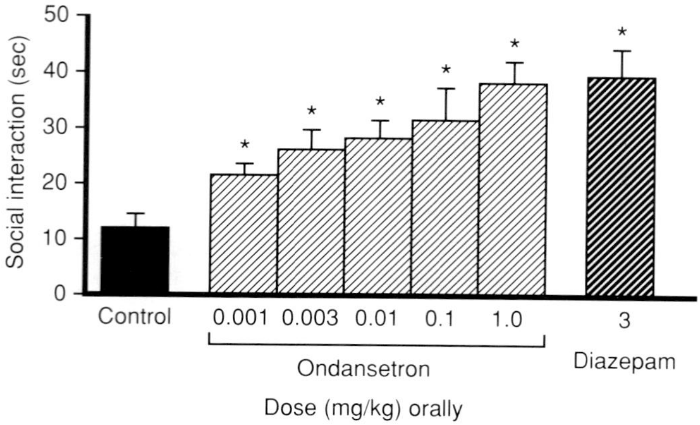

Fig. 1. Effects of ondansetron in the social interaction test in the rat.

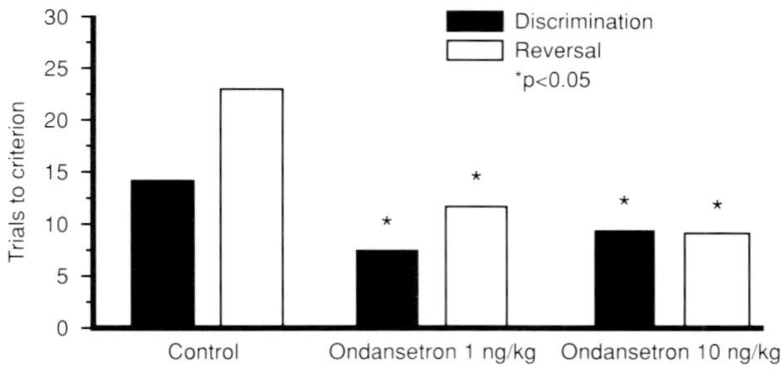

Fig. 2. Effects of ondansetron on cognitive performance in a discrimination reversal task in the marmoset.

is enhanced by 5-HT_3 receptor activation [5]; in addition, dopamine release in the mesolimbic system is reduced by 5-HT_3 receptor blockade [6]. The importance of the cholinergic system in cognitive function is well known. With this background, the effects of ondansetron on cognitive function were evaluated in rodents and primates.

Ondansetron has been shown to enhance cognitive performance in a number of animal models [7]. For example, in a habituation test in mice, ondansetron facilitated performance in young adult and aged animals. In the T-maze reinforced alternation test in rats, ondansetron reversed a scopolamine-induced impairment of performance. Similarly, in an object discrimination and reversal learning task in the marmoset, using the Wisconsin General Test Apparatus, ondansetron improved cognitive performance (Fig. 2).

In further studies, ondansetron has been shown to enhance acetylcholine release in rat isolated entorhinal cortex via 5-HT_3 receptors. This observation provides a rationale for the mechanism of the cognition enhancing action of 5-HT_3 antagonists.

In summary, ondansetron has been shown to have cognitive enhancing effects in several animal models which suggest a therapeutic potential in treating cognitive disorders such as those which occur in geriatric patients (Age Associated Memory Impairment) and in senile dementia.

Conclusions

Ondansetron is a potent and highly selective antagonist at 5-HT_3 receptors with potential for an improved treatment of anxiety disorders and cognitive dysfunction.

References

1. Kilpatrick GJ, Jones BJ and Tyers MB (1987) Nature 330: 746–748.
2. Ireland SJ and Tyers MB (1987) Br. J. Pharmacol. 90: 229–238.

3. Butler A, Hill JM, Ireland SJ et al. (1988) Br. J. Pharmacol. 94: 397–412.
4. Jones BJ, Costall B, Domeney AM et al. (1988) Br. J. Pharmacol. 93: 985–993.
5. Gaddum JH and Picarelli ZP (1957) Br. J. Pharmacol. 12: 323–328.
6. Hagan RM, Butler A, Hill JM et al. (1987) Eur. J. Pharmacol. 138: 303.
7. Barnes JM, Barnes NM, Costall B et al. (1989) Nature 338: 762–763.

© 1991 Elsevier Science Publishers B.V. All rights reserved.
Biological Psychiatry, Volume 2. G. Racagni et al., editors.

Preclinical evidence for the use of ondansetron in schizophrenia and psychoactive substance abuse

B. Costall[1], A.M. Domeney[1], R.M. Hagan[2], M.E. Kelly[1], R.J. Naylor[1], N.R. Oakley[2] and M.B. Tyers[2]

[1]*Postgraduate Studies in Pharmacology, The School of Pharmacy, University of Bradford; and* [2]*Neuropharmacology Department, Glaxo Group Research Ltd., Hertfordshire, U.K.*

Introduction

The aetiological basis of schizophrenia, involving a raised mesolimbic dopamine function, has provided the rationale for the standard treatment with dopamine receptor antagonists [1]. The side-effects of such treatments, caused by blocking both normal as well as abnormal dopamine function, are well known, i.e. extrapyramidal side-effects and endocrine disturbances. For many years, agents have been sought which selectively reduce a raised mesolimbic dopaminergic activity without affecting the nigro-striatal system. The 5-HT_3 receptor antagonist ondansetron has such properties in animal models (Fig. 1).

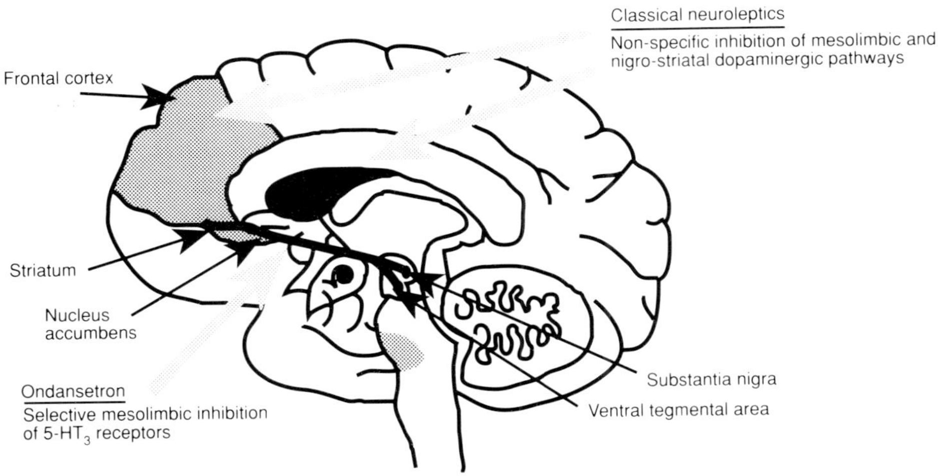

Fig. 1. Dopamine response in human brain. The major systems are the nigro-striatal pathway from the substantia nigra to the striatum and the mesolimbic pathway from the midbrain ventral tegmental area to mesolimbic structures including nucleus accumbens and frontal cortex.

Ondansetron selectively blocks the mesolimbic dopamine system

Animal models were developed to raise mesolimbic dopamine function by the direct injection of amphetamine or infusion of dopamine into the nucleus accumbens/ventral striatum or amygdala of the rat and marmoset brain [2], or by stimulation of the dopamine cell bodies located in the midbrain [3]. All such manipulations produced a common behavioural response of increased locomotor activity, which was inhibited by ondansetron and other 5-HT_3 receptor antagonists. The co-administration of amphetamine with the selective 5-HT_3 receptor agonist, 2-methyl-5-HT, further enhanced the locomotor activity, a response which was inhibited by ondansetron. The 5-HT_3 agonist-antagonist effects are most likely to be mediated via 5-HT_3 receptors which have been shown to be located in limbic brain areas of many species, including man.

An important distinguishing feature of the action of ondansetron, compared with neuroleptics, was its ability to inhibit a raised dopamine function without affecting normal behaviour. Indeed, ondansetron blocked the effects of dopamine excess to return the levels of activity to normal values (Fig. 2). Ondansetron has also failed to produce signs of extrapyramidal or endocrinological disturbance in animals, again confirming the absence of dopamine receptor blockade. A further intriguing finding was that while dopamine receptor supersensitivity developed following chronic neuroleptic treatment, there were no changes in receptor sensitivity following withdrawal from ondansetron treatment. Furthermore, ondansetron was actually capable of preventing or reversing the neuroleptic-induced changes in dopamine receptor sensitivity [2].

The ability of 5-HT_3 receptor antagonists to attenuate hyperactivity implies that 5-HT_3 receptors may normally act to facilitate dopamine function. In this respect, the activation of dopamine cell firing in the ventral tegmental area of the rat brain causes a release of dopamine in the forebrain and increased activity. Both the biochemical and behavioural changes are prevented by ondansetron [4], which is again indicative of a 5-HT_3 receptor involvement that may normally act to increase mesolimbic dopamine function.

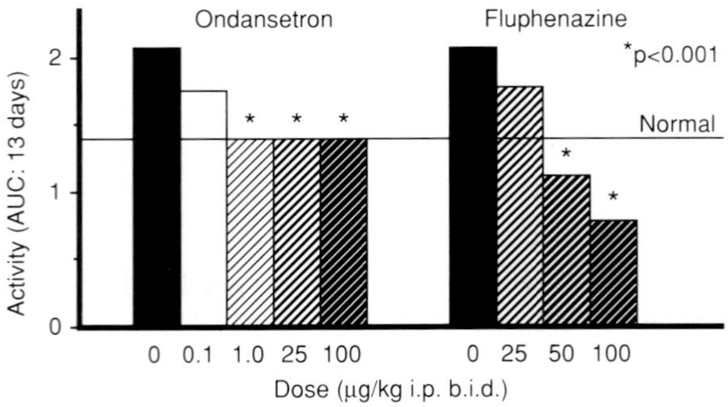

Fig. 2. Abilities of ondansetron and fluphenazine to inhibit the locomotor activity caused by dopamine infusion into the nucleus accumbens of rats.

Ondansetron in the treatment of substance abuse

The ability of 5-HT_3 receptor antagonists to reduce limbic dopamine function may also be relevant to the problems of psychoactive substance abuse. Addictive substances, such as amphetamine, cocaine, nicotine, alcohol and morphine, have rewarding properties in experimental paradigms, such as drug self-administration and conditioned place preference studies. Such rewarding effects have been associated with increases in mesolimbic dopamine function [5]. 5-HT_3 receptor antagonists have been shown to reverse both the rewarding properties of an agent such as ethanol and the associated increase in dopamine release in the nucleus accumbens [4,6].

A number of studies with 5-HT agonists and antagonists and re-uptake inhibitors have implicated 5-HT in the regulation of voluntary alcohol intake in both animals and man. In studies in the marmoset, animals were introduced to and maintained on alcohol in the drinking water which, after 7 days, was then withdrawn [4]. Ondansetron inhibited the behavioural changes that occurred after withdrawal and inhibited the preference for alcohol in a subsequent free choice paradigm (Fig. 3). Ondansetron also decreases alcohol consumption in rats [7]. Similarly, ondansetron and other 5-HT_3 receptor antagonists, inhibit the place preference conditioning to morphine, nicotine and amphetamine [6,8].

Further evidence for an inhibitory effect on the limbic dopaminergic system comes from experiments in which the central stimulant effects of cocaine are attenuated by ondansetron and other 5-HT_3 receptor antagonists in mice [9,10].

Conclusions

There is convincing evidence that mesolimbic dopamine function can mediate behavioural hyperactivity and is involved in reward behaviour. Evidence is being rapidly acquired that ondansetron and other 5-HT_3 receptor antagonists can

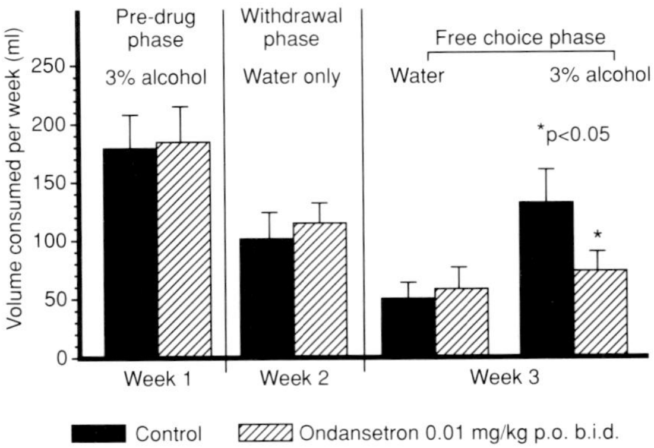

Fig. 3. Effects of ondansetron on alcohol consumption in the marmoset.

attenuate a raised mesolimbic dopaminergic activity without affecting normal behaviour. Such findings have contributed significantly to an understanding of the role of 5-HT in regulating brain function and may have important implications for the development of a novel treatment for schizophrenia and psychoactive substance abuse.

References

1. Costall B and Naylor RJ (1986) In: Bradley PB and Hirsch SR (eds.) The Psychopharmacology and Treatment of Schizophrenia. Oxford Medical Publications, Oxford, pp. 132–165.
2. Costall B, Domeney AM, Naylor RJ and Tyers MB (1987) Br. J. Pharmacol. 92: 881–894.
3. Hagan RM, Butler A, Hill JM et al. (1987) Eur. J. Pharmacol. 138: 303–305.
4. Oakley NR, Jones BJ, Tyers MB et al. (1988) Br. J. Pharmacol. 95: 870P.
5. Wise RA and Bogarth MA (1988) Pharmacol. Biochem. Behav. 17: 239.
6. DiChiara G and Imperato A (1988) Proc. Natl. Acad. Sci. U.S.A. 85: 5247–5248.
7. Sellers EM, Kaplan HL, Lawrin MO et al. (1988) 18th Annual Meeting of the Society for Neuroscience 14 (Part 1): 41.
8. Carboni E, Acquas E, Leone P et al. (1988) Eur. J. Pharmacol. 151: 159.
9. Reith MEA (1990) Eur. J. Pharmacol. 186: 327–330.
10. Van der Hoek GA and Cooper SJ (1990) Psychopharmacology 101: S59.

© 1991 Elsevier Science Publishers B.V. All rights reserved.
Biological Psychiatry, Volume 2. G. Racagni et al., editors.

The clinical psychopharmacology of ondansetron

D.S. Millson and G.C. Preston
Clinical Pharmacology Division, Glaxo Group Research Ltd, Middlesex, U.K.

Introduction

Preclinical studies have demonstrated that ondansetron is a potent selective 5-HT_3 antagonist [1]. The compound is a clinically effective anti-emetic, antagonizing the effects of endogenous 5-HT released during chemotherapy. In addition to its anti-emetic properties, ondansetron is also active in a variety of preclinical models thought to be predictive of therapeutic activity in central nervous system (CNS) disorders. These studies support the hypothesis that 5-HT_3 antagonists have a major influence on "limbic-cortical" circuitry, resulting in beneficial effects as an anxiolytic, antipsychotic, cognitive enhancer and in the treatment of psychoactive substance addiction [2]. Based on this hypothesis, clinical studies in anxiety, geriatric cognitive dysfunction, schizophrenia and psychoactive drug dependence are now in progress.

A variety of clinical pharmacology studies have investigated the safety and tolerability of ondansetron, its pharmacokinetics and clinically important interactions with other drugs (for example benzodiazepines). Throughout these volunteer studies, only minor adverse events have been reported, primarily headache, occurring as frequently on ondansetron as on placebo (about 30% incidence following multiple dosing) and constipation (3% incidence) [3]. Studies have also been conducted to establish the pharmacokinetics of ondansetron in elderly subjects and in special patient groups (e.g. hepatic impairment, renal impairment). Many of these studies were conducted in support of the anti-emesis indication and therefore employed doses in excess of those used (>8 mg b.i.d.) in the CNS clinical trials. Significant differences in ondansetron pharmacokinetics were found in these studies, in that increased exposure occurred due to a predictable reduction in metabolic clearance (e.g. in the elderly). However, because ondansetron is well tolerated and with no evidence for a change in anti-emetic efficacy, no dosage change is considered necessary.

In addition to the above, a number of special studies have been undertaken to support the CNS development of ondansetron.

Effects of ondansetron on psychomotor performance

The effects of ondansetron on psychomotor performance have been assessed in several studies. In one such study [4], 2 doses of ondansetron (1 mg and 8 mg), administered twice daily for 2.5 days to achieve steady state, were compared with multiple doses of placebo and a single dose of lorazepam (2 mg) administered as the last dose after a placebo run-in. The study was a randomized, double-blind, 4-way crossover, involving 12 healthy male volunteers.

Psychomotor performance testing was carried out at baseline prior to dosing and following the fifth and final dose, with assessments at 1, 2, 3 and 7 h post-dose. Four commonly used psychomotor tests (choice reaction time, critical flicker fusion, simulated car tracking and the Sternberg memory scanning task) were employed. Results obtained from this study demonstrated that neither the 1 mg or 8 mg dose of ondansetron administered as repeated oral doses produced any statistically significant effects on the psychomotor tests employed (Fig. 1). In contrast, lorazepam, as expected, did cause a significant impairment, affecting sensory, central and motor function. The authors concluded that there was no evidence that ondansetron produced any objective effects on sedation or psychomotor performance.

Cerebrospinal fluid levels of ondansetron

In order to assess the CNS penetration of ondansetron and to quantify the cerebrospinal fluid (CSF):plasma ratio, a group of volunteer patients who required spinal anaesthesia for genito-urinary surgery received dosing to steady state levels with ondansetron tablets (16 mg) twice daily for 2.5 days prior to spinal anaesthesia (study conducted by K. Simpson, Leeds University, personal communication). The last 16 mg dose of ondansetron was administered 1–8 h (median 3.5 h) prior to the scheduled lumbar puncture. CSF and plasma from blood samples were

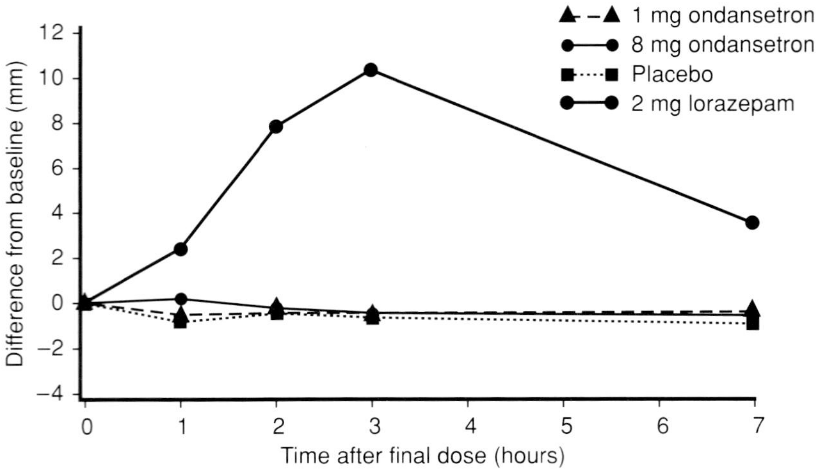

Fig. 1. Mean RMS deviation from simulated car tracking task (n = 12).

both taken at the time of spinal anaesthesia and were assayed by high performance liquid chromatography for ondansetron levels.

In all samples assayed, ondansetron was detected with a mean CSF:plasma ratio of approximately 1:10. There was an appreciable variability in the range of both plasma (39.5–147.0 ng/ml) and CSF (2.6–15.4 ng/ml) ondansetron concentrations. Clearly, ethical considerations precluded the taking of multiple samples, but this study does confirm the penetration of ondansetron into the CNS, with a CSF:plasma partition which would be anticipated from the plasma protein binding (70–76%) and physicochemical characteristics of ondansetron.

Effects of ondansetron on 5-HT-induced flare

The effects of ondansetron [5] on the dermal flare response to intradermal 5-HT injection [6] have been examined in a randomized, double-blind, 4 period cross-over study conducted in 12 healthy subjects. On 4 separate study days, subjects received either placebo or 1 of 3 doses of ondansetron (0.1, 1 or 8 mg) administered intravenously over 10 min. On each occasion, 30 min after the start of the intravenous infusion, subjects received duplicate intradermal injections (0.05 ml) each of placebo and 3 doses of 5-HT (2.5, 40 and 640 μM, administered as serotonin creatinine sulphate) into 8 sites on the back according to a random code. The resulting flare areas were measured at 5 min postintradermal injection.

Log transformed derived responses were subjected to analysis of variance. The effects of ondansetron on the flare response were investigated separately for each level of 5-HT (Fig. 2). The 8 mg dose of ondansetron significantly reduced the flare size in comparison to all levels of 5-HT, whereas at 0.1 mg ondansetron,

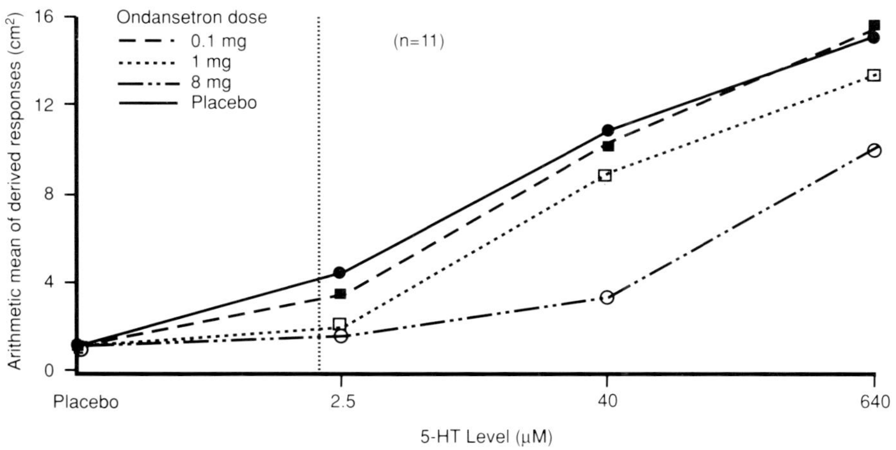

Each subject received three levels of 5-HT and placebo at each dose of ondansetron. Subject 8 has been excluded. Derived flare response is the arithmetic mean of the response at the two sites.

Fig. 2. Effects of intravenous ondansetron on the intradermal response to 5-HT.

reductions were small and not statistically significant. The 1 mg dose reduced the flare response at each level of 5-HT and this was significant at the low and high 5-HT dose levels.

Data from this flare model demonstrate the potency of ondansetron against an exogenous 5-HT_3 mediated peripheral neuronal response in healthy subjects. This model probably underestimates the CNS potency of ondansetron, since the modulation of endogenous 5-HT is likely to be a much less potent challenge to overcome.

Conclusions

The overall conclusions from preclinical data and volunteer studies are that ondansetron, when administered at clinically relevant doses for CNS indications, is safe, well tolerated and produces no overt behavioural changes, psychomotor retardation or sedation.

References

1. Tyers MB, Bunce KT and Humphrey PPA (1989) Eur. J. Cancer Clin. Oncol. 25 (Suppl. 1): S15–S20.
2. Barnes JM, Barnes NM, Costall B et al. (1990) 2nd Iuphar Satellite Meeting on Serotonin, Basel, p. 133.
3. Smith RN (1989) Eur. J. Cancer Clin. Oncol. 25 (Suppl. 1): 547–550.
4. Hall ST and Ceuppens PR (1991) Eur. J. Pharmacol. (in press).
5. Fowler PA, Sweetland J, Lobo D and Thomas M (1991) Presented at the Birmingham 5-HT Club Meeting, July 1991.
6. Fozard J (1984) Neuropharmacology 23: 1473–1486.

© 1991 Elsevier Science Publishers B.V. All rights reserved.
Biological Psychiatry, Volume 2. G. Racagni et al., editors.

Ondansetron in the treatment of anxiety

M.H. Lader
Institute of Psychiatry, London, U.K.

Introduction

Benzodiazepines have dominated the drug treatment of anxiety for three decades. Their hegemony has been challenged by a wide variety of anxiolytic compounds, including partial agonists and inverse agonists acting on the benzodiazepine receptor, compounds chemically non-benzodiazepine though pharmacologically similar, 5-HT_{1A} partial agonists, 5-HT_2 antagonists, 5-HT_3 antagonists, and cholecystokinin antagonists. The benzodiazepine anxiolytics are losing their popularity because of concern over cognitive impairments, abuse potential, and physical dependence on long-term use. However, the introduction of newer compounds takes place against the background of widespread benzodiazepine use with resulting complications.

Ondansetron – Preclinical studies

Ondansetron is active in most, but not all, animal models of anxiolytics. No sedative effects are detectable. In normal volunteers, the pharmacokinetic properties are appropriate for oral administration in twice- or thrice-daily dosage regimens. In contrast to the benzodiazepines, no psychomotor or cognitive impairments have been detected, nor any interactions with alcohol.

Ondansetron – Clinical studies

A major clinical study on anxiety disorder has been completed in the U.K., and another is in progress. Study S3AT05 was a multicentre, double-blind, placebo-controlled, parallel group study with 58 general practitioners enrolling a total of 402 patients. Patients diagnosed as suffering from generalised anxiety disorder as defined in DSM III (with the modification that the anxious mood had been present for 2 weeks or more), and with a HAM-A score of 18 or more and a Montgomery-Asberg Depression Rating Scale (MADRS) score of 20 or less were entered into the study. The patients were randomly allocated to 1 of 4 treatment groups: ondansetron 1 mg t.i.d., ondansetron 4 mg t.i.d., diazepam 2 mg t.i.d., or placebo, for a treatment period of 4 weeks. This was followed by a 2-week withdrawal period during which all patients received placebo. Anxiety was rated weekly using the Hamilton Anxiety Scale (HAM-A) and the Clinical Anxiety Scale (CAS). Depression was rated using the MADRS. The Global Improvement Scale (GIS) was used to measure overall improvement.

The mean total HAM-A scores were reduced for patients in all treatment groups over the 4-week treatment period. Throughout the treatment period, patients receiving ondansetron (4 mg or 1 mg) and diazepam (2 mg) showed lower HAM-A scores than patients receiving placebo. Following 3 weeks of treatment, the mean HAM-A scores for patients in the 4 mg ondansetron and diazepam groups were significantly lower than those in the placebo group ($t = 2.68$, $P < 0.01$ and $t = 2.62$, $P < 0.01$ respectively). After 4 weeks, patients in the 1 mg ondansetron and diazepam groups had significantly lower mean HAM-A scores than those in the placebo group ($t = 2.04$, $P < 0.05$ and $t = 2.47$, $P < 0.02$ respectively).

On the HAM-A, the percentage of patients responding was similar in the three active treatment groups (ondansetron 1 mg t.i.d. 59%; ondansetron 4 mg t.i.d. 57%; diazepam 2 mg t.i.d. 58%) compared with a lower number of patients responding to placebo (45%). On the CAS, the percentage of patients responding was higher in the 2 ondansetron groups (ondansetron 1 mg t.i.d. 59%; ondansetron 4 mg t.i.d. 54%) than in the diazepam (51%) or placebo groups (40%). The ondansetron 1 mg group was significantly better than placebo ($P < 0.05$). On the GIS, the ondansetron 1 mg group performed best, with 50% of responders compared with 43% on ondansetron 4 mg, 48% on diazepam, and 38% on placebo.

It should be noted that the placebo response rate (45% responders and a mean fall of 12.0 points on the HAM-A scale) observed in this study represents a very high placebo response rate, which may mask the effects of ondansetron and diazepam in this study. There was also a trend for patients with prior benzodiazepine use to do better on diazepam than ondansetron, the trend being reversed for benzodiazepine-naive patients.

No rebound anxiety was observed during withdrawal from ondansetron 1 mg or 4 mg, as the HAM-A scores in these 2 groups continued to fall during this period. However, 1 week post-treatment, patients who had been on diazepam showed a mean increase of 2.3 points on the HAM-A scale, representing a significant rebound anxiety ($P < 0.001$) (Fig. 1).

Most adverse events that were reported occurred with similar incidence rates in all treatment groups, but constipation was causally related to treatment with ondansetron (1 mg or 4 mg).

Discussion

The placebo response was very high in this study and it is generally found to be difficult to establish the efficacy of putative anxiolytics under such circumstances. However, some efficacy was demonstrated, slightly more at the 1 mg t.i.d. dose than the 4 mg t.i.d. dose. This accords with the bell-shaped dose-response curve in

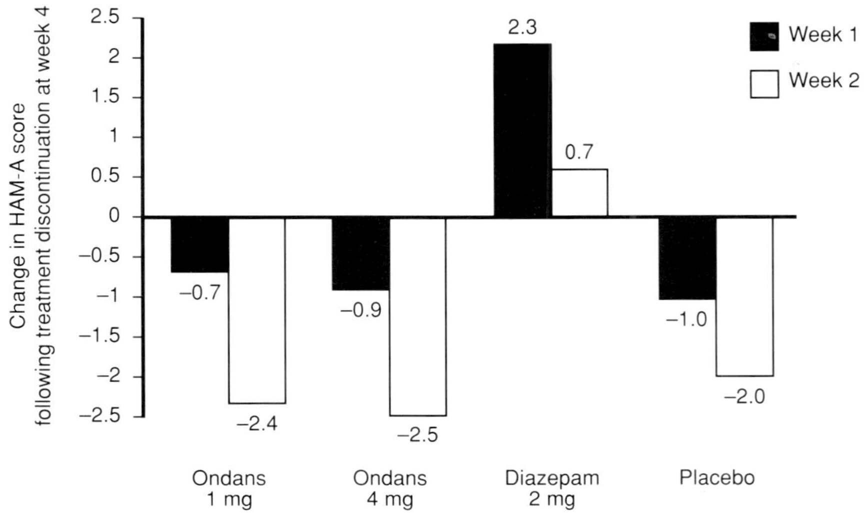

Fig. 1. Rebound anxiety 1 and 2 weeks following withdrawal.

some animal models. Further studies should incorporate a placebo run-in week to facilitate the identification and exclusion of placebo responders. The limited efficacy of diazepam probably reflects the low fixed dose.

The lack of rebound anxiety after ondansetron was striking in comparison to the diazepam-treated group. If replicated, this would suggest a low or absent dependence potential.

Sedation was not seen with ondansetron, the only significant side-effect being constipation. In its intravenous formulation in its licensed indication of emesis, it has proved safe and well tolerated.

Conclusions

Preliminary evidence suggests than ondansetron has anxiolytic activity with few side-effects and no rebound anxiety on discontinuation. It should prove a useful addition to the drug treatment of anxiety.

© 1991 Elsevier Science Publishers B.V. All rights reserved.
Biological Psychiatry, Volume 2. G. Racagni et al., editors.

Effects of ondansetron in age-associated memory impairment

T. Crook[1] and M. Lakin[2]

[1]*Memory Assessment Clinics Inc., Bethesda, Maryland;* [2]*Memory Assessment Clinics Inc., Scottsdale, Arizona, U.S.A.*

Introduction

During the middle and later decades of adulthood, many persons experience problems in performing certain learning and memory tasks that arise in the course of daily life [1]. For example, the ability to learn and remember names of persons to whom one is introduced may decline by 50% or more across the adult life-span, even among intellectually superior individuals [2]. Although such memory problems are so common in later life that they may be described as "normal", they are quite distressing to many older persons, particularly those involved in intellectually demanding activities [3].

Age-associated memory impairment (AAMI) is a diagnostic term applied to healthy, non-demented persons over 50 years of age who have experienced memory loss over the course of adult life [4]. The term was adopted and specific diagnostic criteria were proposed by a National Institute of Mental Heath (NIMH) workgroup in the United States [4].

Preclinical studies

Multiple neurochemical systems have been implicated in AAMI [5], including the serotonergic (5-HT) nervous system [6]. It has been argued [6] that 5-HT exerts an inhibitory influence on learning and memory, possibly via interaction with the cholinergic system [7], and that therapeutic trials with specific 5-HT receptor antagonists would be of interest. Of particular importance in this argument are findings by Costall et al. [8] of dose-dependent improvements in learning and memory performance in marmosets and rodents (in normal animals and in those with experimentally-induced cognitive impairments) treated with the 5-HT_3 antagonist ondansetron. This is supported by in vitro evidence of facilitation by ondansetron of acetylcholine release from slices of rat entorhinal cortex [8].

Clinical study of ondansetron in AAMI

In a clinical study, 232 patients who met the criteria for AAMI were randomly assigned to a 0.01, 0.25, or 1.0 mg b.i.d. dose of ondansetron, or to placebo.

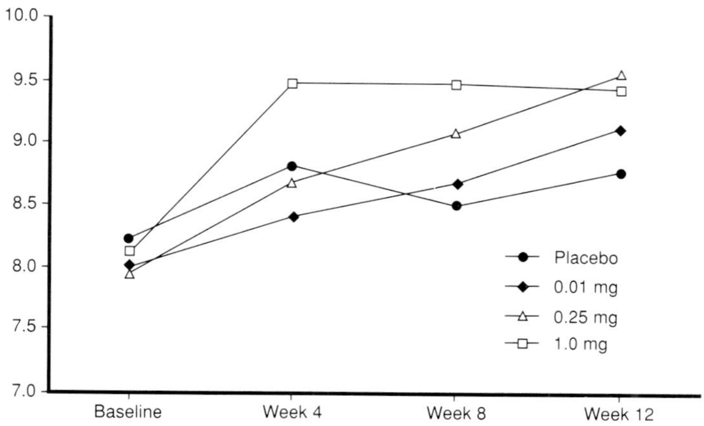

Fig. 1. Effect of ondansetron on name-face association – acquisition.

Patients were treated double-blind for 12 weeks, followed by a 2-week washout period. Assessments were performed at the initiation and termination of treatment, at 4-week intervals during treatment, and at the conclusion of the washout period. Cognitive assessment included a computerised battery of neuropsychological tests related to learning and memory tasks of daily life, as well as behavioural rating scales [9]. Prior to the study five test scores were selected as primary outcome measures. The effects of ondansetron on three of the primary outcome measures are shown in Figs. 1–3.

The results of this study indicate that ondansetron is well tolerated and may affect learning and memory in AAMI. These effects appear to be dose-related in that: a) the 0.01 mg dose was not significantly different from placebo on any of the outcome measures; b) the 0.25 mg dose was most effective at the conclusion of

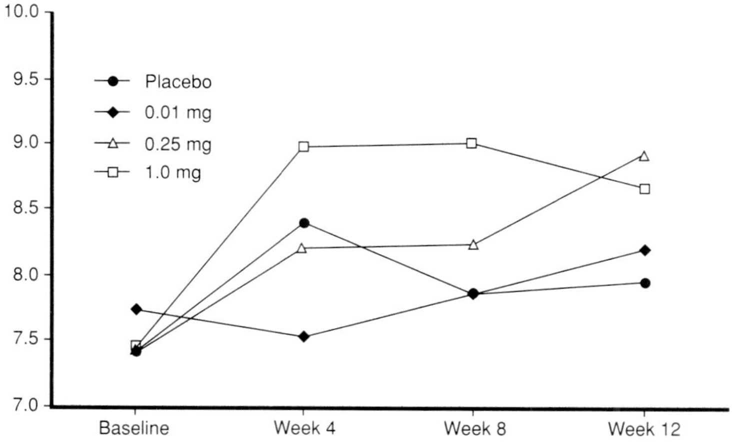

Fig. 2. Effect of ondansetron on name-face association – delayed recall.

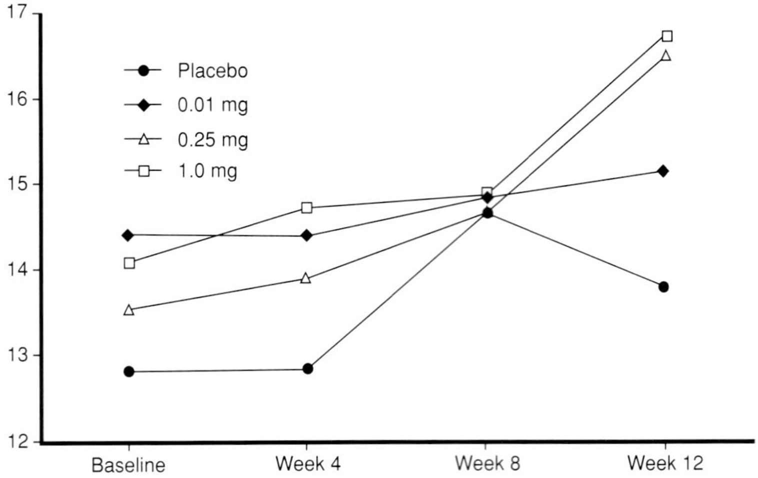

Fig. 3. Effect of ondansetron on facial recognition – number recognised before first error.

treatment, with significant differences apparent on 2 of the 5 primary outcome measures and a clear trend on the third; and c) effects were noted earlier in the course of treatment on the 1.0 mg dose, with significant differences emerging for 2 of the 5 primary variables after 8 weeks of treatment, but without further improvement during the 4 subsequent weeks of treatment. A single trend between the 1.0 mg and placebo groups was seen at the conclusion of treatment.

Conclusions

Overall, the authors concluded that ondansetron was of considerable interest and merits further study as a putative treatment for AAMI and perhaps other adult-onset cognitive disorders.

References

1. Lane F and Snowden F (1989) In: Lovibond P and Wilson P (eds.) Clinical and Abnormal Psychology. Elsevier, North Holland, pp. 365–376.
2. Crook TH and West RL (1990) Br. J. Psychol. 81: 335–349.
3. Crook TH (1989) Sem. Neurol. 9(1): 20–30.
4. Crook TH, Bartus RT, Ferris SH et al. (1986) Dev. Neuropsychol. 2(4): 261–276.
5. McEntee WJ and Crook TH (1990) Neurology 40: 526–530.
6. McEntee WJ and Crook TH (1991) Psychopharmacology 103: 143–149.
7. Fibiger HC, Lepiane FG and Phillips AG (1978) Brain Res. 155: 380–386.
8. Barnes JM, Costall B, Coughlan J et al. (1990) Pharmacol. Biochem. Behav. 35: 955–962.
9. Crook TH, Johnson BA and Larrabee GJ In: Benkert O, Maier W and Rickels K (eds.) Methodology of the Evaluation of Psychotropic Drugs. Springer-Verlag, Heidelberg, Berlin, Germany, pp. 37–55.

© 1991 Elsevier Science Publishers B.V. All rights reserved.
Biological Psychiatry, Volume 2. G. Racagni et al., editors.

Studies of ondansetron in schizophrenia

H.Y. Meltzer
Department of Psychiatry, Case Western Reserve University School of Medicine, Cleveland, Ohio, U.S.A.

Introduction

Over the past 35 years, the conventional dopamine receptor blocking neuroleptics have revolutionized the treatment of acute schizophrenia, although for a significant minority of patients their efficacy falls considerably short of total symptom control. In addition and perhaps more importantly, the chronic administration of conventional neuroleptics has shown itself to be an effective prophylactic treatment for schizophrenia and has enabled many patients to resume useful, productive lives in the community. However, the chronic use of dopamine antagonists seems at best to provide only minimal relief of the negative symptoms of schizophrenia and at worst is associated with the development of disabling movement disorders.

Ondansetron – Preclinical studies

Schizophrenia is thought to be associated with increased dopaminergic activity in the limbic areas of the brain and animal models have been developed in which such an increase can be artificially induced. The common behavioural outcome of all such strategies is an increase in locomotor activity and this response can be inhibited by ondansetron and other 5-HT_3 receptor antagonists as well as by conventional neuroleptics. However, while conventional neuroleptics have a marked effect on normal behaviour in such models, ondansetron is able to inhibit the induced hyperactivity without interfering with normal behaviour and without producing features of extrapyramidal or endocrine disturbance.

Ondansetron – Open studies in schizophrenia

Two open, uncontrolled multicentre studies were performed in the U.K. and the U.S.A. in hospitalized patients with a DSM III diagnosis of acute schizophrenia. One study employed doses of ondansetron of either 4 mg b.i.d., or 8 mg b.i.d. while the other study employed 2 flexible dosing regimens: a low dose regimen with a maximum possible dose of 8 mg b.i.d. and a high dose regimen with a maximum possible dose of 16 mg t.i.d. In these studies, ondansetron appeared to possess antipsychotic activity but, most interestingly, the drug's efficacy appeared to be

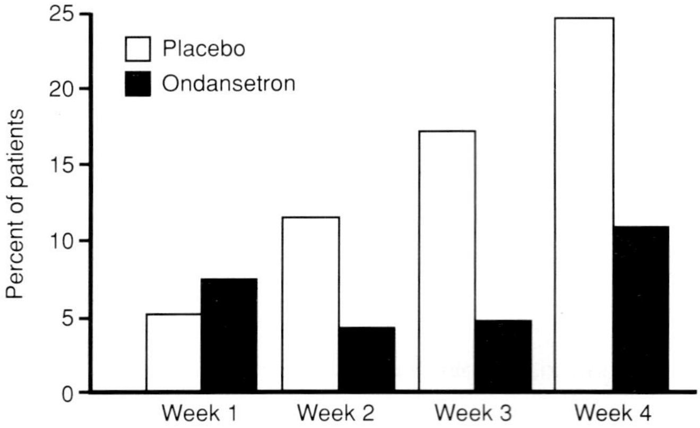

Fig. 1. Need for chlorpromazine at doses ≥1400 mg/week.

inversely related to dose. For this reason, a double-blind placebo-controlled study was undertaken at a dose of 4 mg b.i.d.

Ondansetron – A double-blind placebo-controlled study in acute schizophrenia

One hundred and fourteen DSM III schizophrenic patients from 13 participating centres in the U.K. were randomly assigned to ondansetron 4 mg b.i.d., or placebo, for a 4-week double-blind trial. Chlorpromazine (CPZ) in multiples of doses of 50–100 mg or diazepam was permitted for additional clinical management, if needed. The doses of CPZ were higher in the placebo-treated group (Fig. 1) but 45–50% of patients in both groups did receive some CPZ.

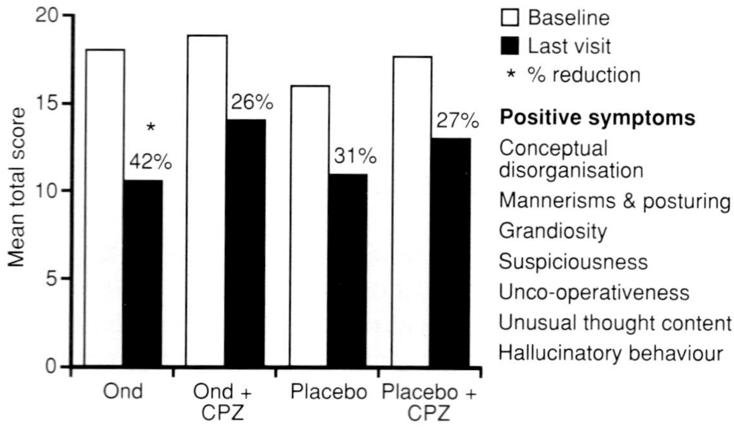

Fig. 2. Total score of BPRS positive symptoms at baseline and week 4 – last visit carried forward.

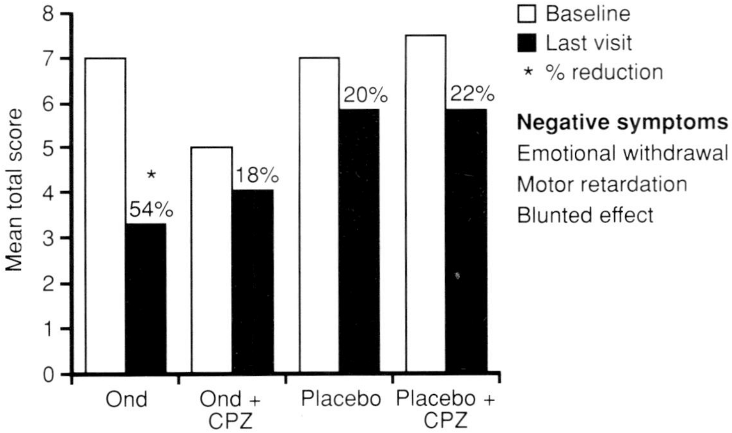

Fig. 3. Total score of BPRS negative symptoms at baseline and week 4 – last visit carried forward.

Thirty-eight of 55 (69.1%) ondansetron and 41 of 59 (69.5%) placebo patients completed the study. Analysis of the total Brief Psychiatric Rating Scale (BPRS), BPRS positive and negative symptoms and the Clinical Global Impression (CGI) using the last value before CPZ carried forward or the last value regardless of CPZ administration did not show a significant drug treatment effect or drug × CPZ interaction. There was also no difference in the proportions of the entire group of patients who responded to ondansetron (30.1%) or placebo (31.6%) with a decrease in BPRS score ≥50%. However, inspection of several measures suggested that the group of patients treated with ondansetron alone may have had a more favourable outcome than the other 3 groups, e.g. in final CGI scores and final BPRS positive and negative symptoms (Figs. 2 and 3). Ondansetron produced no significant extrapyramidal or other side-effects and was well tolerated.

The use of CPZ and diazepam, which was requested by the review boards of the participating centres, clearly compromised the ability of this study to assess the antipsychotic effects of ondansetron. The antipsychotic effect of ondansetron observed in previous open trials could not be definitively confirmed or rejected. Further study of the antipsychotic efficacy of 5-HT_3 antagonists such as ondansetron, using more conventional research designs, is still warranted.

© 1991 Elsevier Science Publishers B.V. All rights reserved.
Biological Psychiatry, Volume 2. G. Racagni et al., editors.

Efficacy of the 5-HT_3 antagonist ondansetron in addictive disorders

E.M. Sellers[1,2,3], M.K. Romach[3], R.C. Frecker[1,2,4] and G.A. Higgins[1]
Departments of Pharmacology[1], Medicine[2] and Psychiatry[3] and Institute of Biomedical Engineering[4], University of Toronto, Clinical Research and Treatment Institute, Addiction Research Foundation, Toronto, Ontario, Canada

Introduction

The substantial progress in the improved treatment of mental disorders over the past 40 years can be ascribed to the development of psychotropic medications. To date, most medications have been developed for their anxiolytic, sedative-hypnotic, antidepressant, or antipsychotic therapeutic potential. However, from a public health perspective, the social, health and economic consequences of alcohol, tobacco and drug addiction constitute a far larger problem.

5-HT_3 receptors and substance abuse

Although the highest levels of central 5-HT_3 receptors are found in the area postrema/nucleus tractus solitarii region, a substantial proportion are found in areas associated with the dopamine-mesolimbic system (e.g. amygdala, nucleus accumbens and olfactory tubercles). Activation of this system may underlie certain aspects of drug reinforcement. Notably, 5-HT_3 receptor antagonists appear to reduce both behaviour and biochemical changes associated with such a functional activation [1]. The 5-HT_3 antagonist ondansetron, may, under certain conditions, reduce free-choice ethanol consumption in rats and marmosets [2,3]. Furthermore, these agents also block the ethanol discriminative stimulus in pigeons, suggesting that some of the subjective effects of ethanol are mediated via this subtype [4]. Also, low concentrations of ethanol may potentiate 5-HT-induced depolarisations at the 5-HT ionophore [5]. Aside from ethanol, 5-HT_3 antagonists appear to modify the discriminative stimulus properties of other abused substances (e.g. morphine, nicotine) since they block the development of place preference conditioning to these treatments [1].

A role for 5-HT_3 receptor antagonists in alleviating the symptoms of withdrawal from various substances of abuse (e.g. opiates, nicotine, ethanol, cocaine) has also become apparent. For instance, ondansetron may ameliorate the behavioural changes seen in rodents following abrupt withdrawal from chronic benzodiazepine, cocaine, nicotine and ethanol treatment. It has also been shown to reduce alcohol intake and anxiety-related withdrawal behaviour in alcohol-dependent marmosets [3]. Recently, the effect of 5-HT_3 receptor antagonists against various behaviours elicited by naloxone-precipitated morphine withdrawal has been studied [6]. While these drugs failed to affect behaviours traditionally associated with withdrawal (e.g. wet dog shakes), they blocked the conditioned place aversion to this treatment.

Based on some of these preclinical observations, several clinical trials have been conducted to examine the effects of 5-HT_3 antagonists in drug abuse and dependence, initially to alcohol and nicotine.

Results

Alcohol abuse and dependence

In a double-blind clinical trial, 71 healthy male alcohol abusers were randomly assigned to receive oral ondansetron 0.25 or 2 mg or placebo twice daily for 6 weeks. Comparison of pretreatment to the last 4 weeks of treatment showed no effect on mean number of drinks/week, drinks on drinking days or abstinent days; however, comparison of pretreatment vs. treatment weeks 1–3 vs. treatment weeks 4–6 vs. post-treatment showed an increasing reduction in ethanol consumption in the 0.25 mg group, e.g. pretreatment minus post-study = −2.6 drinks/day i.e. −30% ($P < 0.05$), which was even more pronounced (37%) if alcohol abusers consuming >10.5 drinks/day were excluded (Table 1) [7]. Since patients entering the study did not have importantly elevated anxiety ratings, no improvements in anxiety or mood could be seen during the study. A significant decrease in urge to drink ($P < 0.05$) was seen in patients receiving ondansetron who also believed that they had received active drug [8].

Smoking

The effects of ondansetron on the smoking behaviour of 200 dependent male smokers were studied in two clinical trials. In both studies, subjects whose smoking behaviour had been well characterised were randomised to placebo or 0.25 mg or 2 mg of oral ondansetron twice daily.

Table 1. Mean (± S.D.) reduction in standard drinks on drinking days

	Placebo	Ondansetron 0.25 mg b.i.d.	Ondansetron 0.20 mg b.i.d.
Weeks 1–3	−1.1 ± 1.0	−1.3 ± 1.9	−0.2 ± 1.3
Weeks 4–6	−1.5 ± 1.5	−2.3 ± 2.0[a]	−0.8 ± 1.4
Post-treatment	−1.2 ± 1.9	−2.8 ± 2.0[a]	−0.7 ± 2.0

[a]$P < 0.05$.

In the first study, 75 subjects were admitted to a clinical research unit during the 2nd week of a 2-week period of drug therapy. The aim of the study was to assess the efficacy of ondansetron in diminishing the intensity of withdrawal resulting from abrupt cessation of nicotine intake. In the second trial, 125 outpatients received drug therapy for a 6-week period during which they were to reduce their level of smoking as much as possible. Smoking intensity (plasma nicotine), physiological and psychological indices of withdrawal, and changes in mood (including anxiety and craving) were measured regularly.

Abstinence from smoking while in hospital was complete (plasma nicotine concentration maintained below 1 ng/ml), and all subjects passed through a phase of rapidly diminishing nicotine withdrawal symptomatology. Drug condition was not a determinant of withdrawal intensity in this trial, nor of the success of either cutting down or quitting in the outpatient trial. Drug side-effects were minimal and confined to occasional headache, facial warmth or flushing, and complaints of mild gastrointestinal upset, including constipation.

Discussion

These data with ondansetron are very encouraging; however, as might be expected with novel compounds with unique preclinical pharmacology, the initial trial results have yielded several unexpected findings.

The size of the decrease in alcohol consumption in the 0.25 mg b.i.d. group (in patients consuming <10.5 drinks/day) is the largest reported for any pharmacological agent for alcohol dependence treatment. A more sustained sociobehavioural treatment component to the treatment programme would undoubtedly increase the size of the effect. The delayed onset in response is not due to an anxiolytic effect in this patient population, and is consistent with a complex effect, possibly on desire to drink, conditioned responses or cognitive processes that enhance self-efficacy. The fact that the lower dose group responded is consistent with the preclinical pharmacology of ondansetron in certain animal models.

Ondansetron had no demonstrable effect on acute nicotine withdrawal (inpatient) or short-term success in achieving abstinence (outpatient). Due to the short duration of drug administration (2–6 weeks), it was not possible to assess effects on long-term recidivism rates. Differential relapse profiles seen after successful inpatient abstinence made it desirable to examine the effects of ondansetron on relapse over a period of 3–12 months, during which time recidivism rates are highest. During the first year of abstinence, patients describe habit and craving (rather than physical withdrawal symptomatology) as primary determinants of relapse.

Conclusions

Ondansetron and other similar medications should have considerable therapeutic potential in the treatment of opiate, alcohol, cocaine, nicotine or other psychoactive use disorders.

What has become apparent from the initial alcohol clinical trials is that the patterns of response (e.g. dose, timing) and mechanism of 5-HT_3 antagonist effects are unique. From a medication development perspective, much more attention than usual will need to be directed towards understanding the human clinical pharmacology of these compounds, and to developing the strategies of use, potentially for application to a wide range of substance use disorders alone and in combination with anxiety disorders.

References

1. Kilpatrick GJ, Bunce KT and Tyers MB (1990) Med. Res. Rev. 10: 441–475.
2. Sellers EM, Kaplan HL, Lawrin MO et al. (1988) 18th Annual Meeting of the Society for Neuroscience 14(1): 41.
3. Oakley NR, Jones BJ, Tyers MB et al. Br. J. Pharmacol. 95: 870P.
4. Grant KA (1990) ISBRA Meeting, Toronto, Ontario, P45.
5. Lovinger DM (1991) Neurosci. Lett. 122: 57–60.
6. Higgins GA, Nguyen P, Joharchi N and Sellers EM (1991) Psychopharmacology (in press).
7. Sellers EM, Romach MK, Toneatto T et al. (1991) 5th World Congress of Biological Psychiatry, Florence, Italy (in press).
8. Toneatto T, Romach MK, Sobell LC et al. (1991) Annual Meeting of the Research Society on Alcoholism, Marco Island, Florida, U.S.A. (in press).

© 1991 Elsevier Science Publishers B.V. All rights reserved.
Biological Psychiatry, Volume 2. G. Racagni et al., editors.

Serotonin receptors and the mechanism of action of antidepressant drugs

Stephen M. Stahl

Department of Psychiatry, University of California, San Diego, and Veterans Affairs Medical Center, 3350 La Jolla Village Drive (116A), San Diego, CA 92161, U.S.A.

Studies of the biochemical mechanism of action of antidepressant drugs show that virtually all drugs, regardless of acute biochemical effects, result in the down-regulation of CNS β_1-adrenergic and serotonin$_2$ (5-HT$_2$) receptor subtypes in rats in a time course which parallels the onset of antidepressant action in patients with major depressive disorder. Other neurotransmitter receptors do not seem to be affected as consistently in this manner by chronic antidepressant treatment, although some evidence is also accruing for 5-HT$_{1A}$ receptor down-regulation by traditional antidepressants, by ECT and by novel putative antidepressant 5-HT$_{1A}$ agonists. Indeed, the specificity of involvement of CNS β-adrenergic and 5-HT receptors in rats is underscored by the observation that an intact serotonergic innervation appears to be required in order for β-adrenergic receptors to be down-regulated by tricyclic antidepressants.

Some experimental evidence challenges the notion that the biochemical mechanism of antidepressant action can by explained by specific neurotransmitter receptor subtype down-regulation. For example, ECT down-regulates CNS β-adrenergic receptors but up-regulates CNS 5-HT$_2$ receptors in rats; agents which are not antidepressants in man can down-regulate 5-HT$_2$ receptors in rats; and some antidepressants which down-regulate 5-HT$_2$ receptors do so in a time course more rapid than their clinical antidepressant actions. Thus, it is not yet established whether receptor down-regulation is the common mechanism of action of antidepressants, or rather, an epiphenomenon. This ultimately requires study of antidepressant action on neurotransmitter receptors in depressed patients themselves.

How can the actions of antidepressants on serotonin receptors be studied in man? Three approaches have been widely employed to study biochemical actions of antidepressants on 5-HT receptors in men: a) postmortem brain studies; b) platelet studies; and c) neuroendocrine studies. Human studies so far have not been able to determine how antidepressants affect 5-HT receptors independently of how depression affects 5-HT receptors. Also, some of the most powerful tools for studying serotonergic functioning in man, namely neuroendocrine studies, largely do not yet allow specific receptor subtypes to be assessed.

Postmortem studies

$5\text{-}HT_2$ receptors have been demonstrated by some but not all investigators to be increased (B_{max}) in autopsy specimens from brains of patients who have committed suicide as well as from brains of patients with depression. Despite some inconsistencies across studies, overall the evidence is quite suggestive for up-regulated $5\text{-}HT_2$ receptors, if not in major depressive disorder, then possibly in subjects who commit suicide, particularly by violent means.

Platelet studies

Similarly, $5\text{-}HT_2$ receptors, also present in platelets, may have increased B_{max} in patients with major depressive disorder and/or with suicidal behavior, although not all investigators agree.

Human neuroendocrine studies

Another method for studying CNS serotonin receptor functioning in patients with major depressive disorder is to measure the secretion of ACTH and prolactin, both of which are controlled in part by serotonergic influence (see below). However, despite a great deal of work in this area, the CNS 5-HT receptor subtype(s) which control plasma prolactin and ACTH concentrations in various neuroendocrine challenge paradigms are not yet well established.

The current literature on 5-HT-related neuroendocrine changes in depressed patients predominantly contains reports utilizing markers of non-selective 5-HT receptor functioning. 5-HTP-induced rises in cortisol are reportedly greater in unmedicated patients with major depressive disorder than in normal controls. Both tryptophan- and fenfluramine-induced increases in plasma prolactin are reportedly blunted in patients with major depressive disorder. Reduced prolactin responses to fenfluramine also correlate with history of suicide attempts and with impulsive aggression in patients with personality disorder independent of depression. It remains to be determined whether these various neuroendocrine observations bear any relationship either to 5-HT receptor subtypes or to findings of up-regulated $5\text{-}HT_2$ receptors in platelets and postmortem brains reported in depressed patients.

Effects of antidepressants on serotonin receptors in man

Postmortem studies

Although not compelling, the data from postmortem brain studies of $5\text{-}HT_2$ receptors provocatively suggest the possibility that CNS $5\text{-}HT_2$ receptors are supersensitive in untreated depressed patients, that they are down-regulated in patients successfully treated with antidepressants, and even that recovered depressives may require chronic down-regulation to maintain their therapeutic effect in the absence of antidepressant drug.

Platelet studies

Relatively little is understood about the response of human platelet 5-HT_2 receptors to chronic treatment with antidepressants. Despite the potential advantage of studying platelet 5-HT_2 receptors in subjects before and after antidepressant treatment, relatively few studies have been performed, and there is no consensus on how antidepressants affect platelet 5-HT_2 receptors independent of disease (i.e. in normal controls), independent of antidepressant clinical response in depressed patients, or under different assay conditions.

Human neuroendocrine studies

Several investigators have begun to study the effects of various antidepressant drugs on 5-HT-related neuroendocrine markers in man. For example, 5-HTP-induced rises in cortisol – which are greater in unmedicated patients with major depressive disorder than in normal controls – are diminished by chronic treatment with tricyclic antidepressants. Acute effects of antidepressants are unknown as are any effects in normal controls. Although these data may suggest that antidepressants are down-regulating 5-HTP-induced rises in cortisol, it is not yet known which 5-HT receptor subtype this phenomenon might represent nor even if 5-HTP is working through 5-HT.

Somewhat the opposite has been observed for both tryptophan- and fenfluramine-induced increases in plasma prolactin. These responses – which are both reportedly blunted in patients with major depressive disorder – are apparently enhanced by chronic treatment with tricyclic antidepressants and by the MAO inhibitor tranylcypromine. The 5-HT-selective reuptake blocker fluvoxamine enhances the prolactin response both acutely (1 week) and chronically (4 weeks) whereas the somewhat selective norepinephrine reuptake blocker desipramine enhances the response at 4 weeks but not as reliably at 1 week. The atypical antidepressants mianserin and trazodone lack this enhancing action with chronic treatment in depressed patients. Actions in drug responders vs. non-responders have not been clearly established, although Price et al. suggest that enhancement of the prolactin response to tryptophan is not clearly correlated with clinical improvement. These studies suggest that some but not all antidepressants enhance the actions of whatever 5-HT receptor(s) control the prolactin response to tryptophan, but that this enhancement is not necessarily a sufficient condition for antidepressant efficacy.

© 1991 Elsevier Science Publishers B.V. All rights reserved.
Biological Psychiatry, Volume 2. G. Racagni et al., editors.

Double-blind, placebo-controlled, parallel-group comparison study of the efficacy and safety of ipsapirone and lorazepam in outpatients with generalized anxiety disorder

Neal R. Cutler[1], John J. Sramek[1], Thomas S. Wardle[1], Neil M. Kurtz[2], Ken B. Kashkin[2] and Allen Heller[2]

[1]California Clinical Trials, 8500 Wilshire Blvd., Lobby Suite, Beverly Hills, California, U.S.A.; and [2]Miles Inc., Pharmaceutical Division, 400 Morgan Lane, West Haven, Connecticut, U.S.A.

Introduction

Generalized anxiety disorder (GAD; DSM III-R) is treated with drugs of the benzodiazepine class which, while effective, have serious adverse effects that affect quality of life and productivity, including sedation, ataxia, amnesia, and confusion. They also cause physical and psychological dependency. Serotonin agonists of the 5-HT_{1A} receptor type have been introduced as a possible alternative therapy for GAD [1,2]. Ipsapirone, a selective serotonin receptor agonist with high affinity for 5-HT_{1A} receptors [3], appears to offer anxiolytic effects without those adverse effects characteristic of the benzodiazepines [4]. With no cardiovascular effects and lacking the effects of a dopamine agonist or antagonist, it in addition may have fewer restrictive adverse effects than the benzodiazepines. To evaluate 5-HT_{1A} receptor agonists as a potential alternative to the benzodiazepines, we compared the efficacy, safety, and tolerance of ipsapirone with those of lorazepam, a short-to-intermediate-acting benzodiazepine, and placebo in patients with GAD.

Clinical Material and Methods

Candidates were selected from among outpatient clinic patients of at least 19 years of age who were being treated for GAD of moderate or greater severity. After giving informed consent to participate in the study, candidates underwent a physical examination including routine laboratory determinations and electrocardiography. Their medical, surgical, and psychiatric histories were evaluated as was performance on a series of psychiatric rating scales, including the Raskin Depression Scale, Covi Anxiety Score, Hamilton Anxiety Scale (HAM-A), Hamilton Depression Scale (HAM-D), Clinical Global Impressions (CGI), and the Zung-Anxiety Self-Rating Scale.

Rigorous medical and psychiatric criteria for exclusion from the study were applied, including any disorder that might compromise the patient's ability to evaluate efficacy and safety of the test medication.

The study population consisted of 90 patients (35 men, 55 women) aged 19 to 56 years (mean 31.2 years). Fecund female subjects participated only if using an acceptable form of birth control.

Patients taking benzodiazepines routinely within 14 days of the initial placebo phase were excluded. Concomitant medications not permitted during the study were: any tranquilizer, tricyclic antidepressants, monoamine oxidase inhibitors, lithium salts, carbamazepine, barbiturates, alcohol, "recreational", drugs, or any other drug that might confound assessment of safety and efficacy.

Patients were randomly assigned to 1 of 3 treatment groups (n = 30). One group (mean age 31.3 years) was assigned to ipsapirone (10–30 mg/d), the second (mean age 28.8 years) to lorazepam (2–6 mg/d), and the third (mean age 33.6 years) to placebo. Both agents and placebo were given as capsules that were all apparently identical. The patients were entered into a single-blind 7-day baseline trial in which all received placebo. Patients not scoring ≥18 on the HAM-A, having >20% reduction in total score on the HAM-A, or scoring ≥8 on the Covi Anxiety Scale or ≥7 on the Raskin Depression Scale were also excluded. Remaining were 26 patients (87%) in the ipsapirone group, 27 (90%) in the lorazepam group, and 24 (80%) in the placebo group.

Patients then received their assigned agent or placebo for 4 weeks in double-blinded fashion. For all groups, dosing began with 1 capsule at bedtime and was increased to 1 capsule 3 times a day by study day 5. The dosage then could be increased to a maximum of 2 capsules 3 times a day at the investigator's discretion. During this period, patients recorded any adverse events they experienced and were evaluated on the psychiatric rating scales weekly in the clinic. The acute 4-week phase of study was followed by a 4-week double-blind extension trial in which 40% (35 of 90) of patients participated. The trial was completed with a 2-week single-blind washout study.

The primary measure of efficacy in the double-blinded trials was the mean change from baseline (pretrial) total HAM-A score. Psychic items tested included anxiety, psychophysiologic symptoms, worry, sleep disturbance, depression, concentration, memory, tension, irritability, and global severity or change. Somatic items included gastrointestinal or cardiac complaints, appetite, faintness, dizziness, headaches, pains, fatigue, and sex functions.

Results

By week 2 of the acute 4-week phase of the trial, both ipsapirone and lorazepam proved significantly ($P < 0.05$) superior to placebo in controlling GAD. Both groups continued to show improvement at the end of week 4 (ipsapirone $P < 0.001$, lorazepam $P < 0.01$). Improvement persisted during the extension phase of the trial (weeks 4–8) and declined during the withdrawal phase (weeks 9–10) to the extent that there were no significant differences in anxiety scores among groups.

Both ipsapirone and lorazepam were tolerated well. Only 3 patients developed

Table 1. Adverse events: overall rates and adverse events of moderate or great severity that led to a reduction in medication during the study period

Adverse event	Ipsapirone (n = 30)		Lorazepam (n = 30)		Placebo (n = 30)	
	Severe	Overall	Severe	Overall	Severe[a]	Overall
Amnesia/confusion	0	1	1	4	0	1
Asthenia	1	9	0	5	1	7
Dizziness	4	22	1	12	0	4
Dry mouth	0	4	0	9	2	6
Nausea	1	12	1	4	1	1
Parasthesias	1	5	0	0	0	0
Somnolence	2	13	7[b]	15	3	7
Total	9	96	10	49	7	26

[a]One each also suffered from thirst, sinusitis, headache, confusion, or taste perversion leading to a reduction in medication during the study period; [b]One severe, 6 moderate.

serious adverse events during the acute phase of the study, 1 with lorazepam (eosinophilia) and 2 with placebo (rash). Adverse events resulting in a reduction of study medication occurred in 9 patients receiving ipsapirone, 10 receiving lorazepam, and 12 receiving placebo. Whereas the adverse event profile of ipsapirone was characterized mainly by dizziness, that of lorazepam was prominently characterized by somnolence. Thirteen patients, including 1 who developed serious adverse events with placebo, were discontinued from the acute study phase prematurely. In the ipsapirone group, 2 patients each developed exclusion criteria or illnesses not related to the study medications. In the lorazepam group, 1 patient each developed adverse experiences or exclusion criteria and 1 was discontinued for noncompliance. In the placebo group, 2 had adverse experiences, 1 developed exclusion criteria, and 3 did not comply with the study protocol.

Discussion

Our results showed an efficacy of ipsapirone (10–30 mg/d) that was comparable to lorazepam (2–6 mg/d) and significantly superior to placebo in treating GAD by as early as week 2 of the trial ($P < 0.05$). While ipsapirone and lorazepam produced a comparable overall incidence of adverse events affecting the nervous system, they presented different profiles. Ipsapirone tended to produce dizziness and paresthesia, whereas lorazepam produced predominantly somnolence and amnesia or confusion. Patients experienced fewer gastrointestinal adverse events with ipsapirone than with lorazepam, with the exception of nausea which was experienced more prominently by patients taking ipsapirone. Overall, it appears that 5-HT_{1A} agonists offer a viable alternative to benzodiazepines in the treatment of GAD and that, particularly with ipsapirone, such compounds may offer fewer restrictions to productivity and quality of life.

References

1. Koe BK (1979) In: Fielding S and Lal H (eds.) Anxiolytics. Futura, N.Y., pp. 173–195.
2. Gray JA (1982) The Neuropsychology of Anxiety. Oxford University Press, N.Y.
3. Peroutka SJ (1985) Biol. Psychiatry 20: 971–979.
4. Hippius H, Engel RR and Laakmann H (1986) Benzodiazepines. Springer-Verlag, Berlin, Heidelberg, New York, Tokyo.

© 1991 Elsevier Science Publishers B.V. All rights reserved.
Biological Psychiatry, Volume 2. G. Racagni et al., editors.

The ipsapirone/5-HT_{1A} receptor challenge in anxiety disorders and depression

K.P. Lesch

Department of Psychiatry, University of Würzburg, Germany; and Laboratory of Clinical Science, NIMH, NIH Clinical Center 10/3D41, Bethesda, MD 20892, U.S.A.

Selective ligands for the 5-HT_{1A} receptor, such as the azapirone ipsapirone, induce hypothermia and neuroendocrine secretion as specific functional correlates of central 5-HT_{1A} receptor activation [1]. The introduction of the ipsapirone challenge paradigm has therefore facilitated the assessment of pre- and postsynaptic 5-HT_{1A} receptor function in psychiatric disorders and its involvement in psychotropic drug effects ([2] and references therein). This paper summarizes studies of 5-HT_{1A} receptor-effector system responsivity in patients with depression (DP), panic disorder (PD), and obsessive compulsive disorder (OCD) as compared with controls. Preliminary investigations of 5-HT_{1A} receptor-mediated function in DP and OCD during chronic treatment with the tricyclic amitriptyline or the 5-HT reuptake inhibitor fluoxetine are also discussed.

Depression

In comparison with controls, patients with DP showed an impaired hypothermic and ACTH/cortisol response to ipsapirone associated with elevated basal cortisol secretion (Table 1). Further, chronic treatment with the tricyclic amitriptyline further reduced already impaired ipsapirone-induced hypothermic responses without affecting ACTH/cortisol release in the depressed patients (Table 2).

The impaired ACTH/cortisol response following 5-HT_{1A} receptor activation by ipsapirone in patients with DP may have resulted from alterations in the setpoint

Table 1. 5-HT_{1A} receptor responsivity in depression, panic disorder and obsessive-compulsive disorder

	Presynaptic 5-HT_{1A})	Postsynaptic 5-HT_{1A})	
	Temperature	ACTH	Cortisol
DP	↓	↓	↓[a]
PD	↓	↓	↓
OCD	↔	↔	↔

↓/↔: Decrease/no change in patients vs. controls; [a]increased basal cortisol secretion.

Table 2. 5-HT_{1A} Responsivity during chronic antidepressant treatment

	Temperature	ACTH	Cortisol
Amitriptyline, DP	↓[a]	↔	↔
Fluxoetine, OCD	↓	↓	↓

↓/↔, Decrease/no change during Rx vs. pre-Rx; [a]decreased response before treatment.

for glucocorticoid (GC)-dependent feedback inhibition at the level of the pituitary and/or hypothalamus, possibly involving dysfunction of the postsynaptic 5-HT_{1A} receptor-effector system complex. However, subsensitivity of both the post- (ACTH/cortisol release) and presynaptic response (hypothermia) to 5-HT_{1A} activation points toward a mechanism of overriding importance. Because basal cortisol secretion was considerably elevated in the depressed patients, the attenuated thermoregulatory and neuroendocrine response to 5-HT_{1A} receptor activation may indicate a GC-dependent subsensitivity of both pre- and postsynaptic 5-HT_{1A} receptor-effector system function.

This finding is in accord with the classical view that the CNS is both the source and the target of neuroendocrine secretion. The demonstration that G proteins are targets of GC action on neurotransmitter systems provided a new dimension to this view. G proteins play a pivotal role in coupling neurotransmitter receptors to various types of intracellular effector systems. 5-HT_{1A} is negatively linked to adenylyl cyclase and positively coupled to a K^+ channel, presumably via a G_i protein. It has been reported that GC increase $G_{s\alpha}$ and decrease $G_{i\alpha}$ concentrations without affecting $G_{o\alpha}$. Therefore, GC may regulate either the expression of the 5-HT_{1A} receptor itself and/or the 5-HT_{1A} receptor-coupled G_i, resulting in altered sensitivity of the postreceptor signal transduction.

Panic disorder

Compared with controls, patients with PD showed an attenuated hypothermic and ACTH/cortisol response following ipsapirone (Table 1). Basal cortisol secretion was not different between controls and patients. Animal models indicate that 5-HT function may be increased during states of anxiety. The attenuated hypothermic response following 5-HT_{1A} receptor activation reflects subsensitivity of the presynaptic 5-HT_{1A} receptor. Hyposensitivity of the presynaptic 5-HT_{1A} receptor-dependent function may give rise to an impaired presynaptic control of 5-HT release, resulting in serotonergic hyperactivity. Alternatively, hyposensitivity of the presynaptic receptor may have a priori been due to a disorder-specific increase in 5-HT activity. In the view of an anxiety-associated increase in 5-HT release, it is conceivable that decreased function of the postsynaptic 5-HT_{1A} receptor also reflects adaptational hyposensitivity as a consequence of increased serotonergic activity in PD.

Obsessive-compulsive disorder

Thermoregulatory and neuroendocrine responses to ipsapirone were not different between controls and patients with OCD (Table 1). These results provide no direct support to the hypothesis that a 5-HT_{1A} receptor-related serotonergic dysfunction may be linked to the pathophysiology of OCD, and point to the need for the evaluation of other 5-HT subsystems.

The ability of ipsapirone to induce hypothermia and ACTH/cortisol release was attenuated during chronic fluoxetine as compared to the pretreatment challenge (Table 2). The decrease of hypothermic and neuroendocrine responses during chronic treatment with fluoxetine, a potent and selective 5-HT reuptake inhibitor, are consistent with the development of adaptive hyporesponsivity of the 5-HT_{1A} receptor-effector system complex. While the classical effect of antidepressants consists of downregulation of 5-HT_2 receptors, increased attention is focussing on the 5-HT_{1A} receptor as a major site of antidepressant action. A reduction in presynaptic 5-HT_{1A} receptor responsivity after chronic administration of a variety of antidepressant treatments has consistently been demonstrated by electrophysiologic, biochemical and behavioral paradigms, while postsynaptically mediated responses appear to be more variable.

The evidence of drug-induced 5-HT_{1A} receptor hyporesponsivity is intriguing in view of reports that this not reflected by a reduction in 5-HT_{1A} receptor binding, neither presynaptically in the raphe nuclei nor at postsynaptic locations such as the hippocampus. The impaired ability of 5-HT_{1A} receptors to desensitize and eventually to up- or downregulate may in part be due to a reduction in phosphorylation sites at the intracellular domains of the receptor structure involved in G protein coupling. Taken together, these findings suggest that the subsensitivity of the 5-HT_{1A} receptor-mediated responses may occur at a level beyond the receptor possibly involving functional alteration of components of the postsynaptic signal transduction pathway (e.g. G proteins, effectors).

Thus, the well-developed pharmacology and molecular biology of receptor-effector system interactions has assisted the demonstration of a complex interrelationship of 5-HT_{1A} receptor, G protein, and effector function in the pathophysiology and treatment of anxiety disorders and depression. Particularly the 5-HT_{1A} receptor and its associated signal transduction components appear to be important targets of psychotropic agents and steroids. The adaptational changes of these components may occur at the level of gene expression and/or post-translational modification involving biochemical mechanisms analogous to the regulation of receptor expression and function. Activation and repression of neural gene expression by protein kinases, transcriptional factors and DNA regulatory elements may therefore be a potential mechanism of 5-HT_{1A} subsystem-related neural plasticity in response to psychotropic drugs and steroids.

References

1. Murphy DL, Lesch KP and Pigott TM (1991) (this volume).
2. Lesch KP (1991) In: Stahl SM, Gastpar M, Keppel Hesselink J and Traber J (eds.) Serotonin 1A Receptors in Depression and Anxiety. Raven Press, New York (in press).

© 1991 Elsevier Science Publishers B.V. All rights reserved.
Biological Psychiatry, Volume 2. G. Racagni et al., editors.

Multicentre study of idebenone vs. placebo in the treatment of cognitive and behavioural disturbances in patients suffering from senile dementia of the Alzheimer type (SDAT)

U. Senin[1], L. Parnetti[1], M. Fioravanti[2], G. Barbagallo-Sangiorgi, L. Bartorelli, V. Bocola, A. Capurso, M. Cuzzupoli, M. Denaro, V. Marigliano and A. Tammaro
[1]Istituto di Gerontologia e Geriatria, Università di Perugia, Perugia; and [2]Istituto di Psicologia, Università di Roma, Rome, Italy

Introduction

Primary degenerative dementias, i.e. Alzheimer's disease, represent more than 50% of all dementia disorders affecting elderly people. Since mental deterioration is the first neurological cause of disability in the aged, effective therapeutic strategies are urgently needed as far as prevention and care are concerned.

Idebenone is a new cerebroactive drug, which has no structural analogy with other neuroactive substances [1]. It acts as a scavenger of free radicals, protecting the mitochondrial membranes from lipid peroxidation and it seems to improve various cerebral functions in different experimental models. Idebenone has shown its efficacy against cerebrovascular pathologies [2,3]. In the present investigation the efficacy and tolerability of idebenone were evaluated in elderly patients suffering from senile dementia of the Alzheimer type (SDAT) of mild to moderate degree.

Materials and Methods

The study included in- and outpatients of both sexes, aged between 65 and 85 years, with 3–11 years of schooling, suffering from senile dementia of the Alzheimer type ranging from mild to moderate in degree, meeting the NINCDS-ADRDA criteria for probable Alzheimer's disease [4]. Other details relative to inclusion criteria are the following: GDS: 2–4; Hachinski Ischaemic Score (mod. by Rosen): <4; MMSE: 11–23; Token test: 17–28; Hamilton Rating Scale for Depression: <24; cerebral CT scan: absence of vascular lesions. Patients with other neurological pathologies or with serious systemic pathologies, with a history of alcohol abuse, suffering from thyroid illnesses, with folate or vitamin B_{12} deficiency, were excluded from the study. The patients were examined at the time of enrollment ($t = -15$), at the beginning of treatment ($t = 0$) and then monthly ($t = 30$, $t = 60$, $t = 90$) until the end of treatment ($t = 120$), and then 4 weeks later ($t = 150$) for the follow-up examinations. At each evaluation time, general and neurological clinical examination, psycho-behavioural and ematochemical evaluations were carried out. The neupsychological instruments for assessing efficacy were: Randt Memory Test; Toulouse-Pieron; GBS Rating Scale for Dementia. All side-effects were recorded according to type, entity, association with the treatment and duration.

Statistical analysis

Differences between treatments were calculated by means of a multivariate analysis of variance between the groups for repeated measurements (MANOVA). Comparisons between groups and within groups were performed using both parametric (for continuous variables) and non-parametric (for non-continuous variables) tests.

Results

One-hundred and two patients (n = 51 idebenone; n = 51 placebo; mean age 76 ± 6 years, 42% male, 58% female) were studied. No difference was detected at baseline between the two groups as far as clinical and neuropsychological details were concerned.

Neuropsychological results

Randt memory test showed a significant improvement of the global mnesic capacities only in the idebenone group. In particular, at t = 120, items assessing acquisition and recall demonstrated a remarkable amelioration both vs. baseline ($P < 0.001$) and vs. placebo group ($P < 0.004$), while they progressively worsened in the placebo group. Toulouse-Pieron test, assessing attention ability, also showed a significant improvement in the idebenone group ($P < 0.003$, t = 120 vs. baseline) whilst a worsening was observed in the placebo group. GBS Rating Scale for Dementia, subscale: "intellectual impairment", in the idebenone group showed a significant improvement of scores already at t = 30 ($P < 0.001$) vs. baseline, while placebo group significantly worsened.

Side-effects and dropout

During the whole period of study, 3 dropouts were recorded in the placebo group – which were judged to be unrelated to treatment – and none in the idebenone group. In both groups some irrelevant side-effects (insomnia, agitation) were documented and considered as feature of the disease under study.

Conclusions

This study on idebenone (45 mg b.i.d. p.o.) administered for 4 months as a therapeutic agent in SDAT patients has shown a consistent pattern of results from the clinical – objective and subjective – evaluation. All patients showed a stabilization and/or an improvement in memory, attention and behavioural control. Further studies will be needed to clarify the persistence of these benefits over a long-term period of treatment.

References

1. Barkworth MF (1985) Arzneim Forsch. 35: 1617–1752.
2. Fioravanti M (1990) In: Agnoli A, Scapagnini U and Zanussi C (eds.) La Neurosenescenza. Excerpta Medica, Amsterdam, The Netherlands, pp. 51–56.
3. Fioravanti M (1990) In: Vakil E, Hoofien D and Grosswasser Z (eds.) Rehabilitation of the Brain Injured. Freund Publishing House Ltd, London, U.K.
4. McKhann G, Drachman D, Folstein M, Ratzman R, Price D and Stadlan EM (1984) Neurology 34: 939–944.

© 1991 Elsevier Science Publishers B.V. All rights reserved.
Biological Psychiatry, Volume 2. G. Racagni et al., editors.

Trends and achievements in neuroimaging research of mental disorders

Alessandro Rossi
Department of Psychiatry, University of L'Aquila, L'Aquila, Italy

Brain imaging refers to a group of relatively new techniques that permits direct observation of the brain in living human beings, making it possible to identify the anatomic, metabolic and neurochemical substrates of mental illness.

These techniques can be roughly separated into two groups: techniques that measure structure and those that measure function. The former methods include CT and magnetic resonance imaging (MRI); these methods permit the study of brain anatomy and possible structural abnormalities. The latter include the measurement of regional cerebral blood flow (rCBF), single photon emission computed tomography (SPECT) and positron emission tomography (PET).

Computed tomography

CT has been used widely in the systematic examination of brain structure in schizophrenia since the first study, 15 years ago, by Johnstone et al. [1]. Early studies more or less agreed that ventricular enlargement characterised a large proportion of patients with schizophrenia. More recently, several studies have signalled caution about the initial enthusiasm. The variations in sampling methods of patients seem to be an increasingly important factor when appropriate control groups are used.

A further shortcoming in the pathophysiological meaning of the lateral ventricular enlargement is that this finding has also been reported in affective disorders, especially of the bipolar type [2].

Magnetic resonance imaging

MRI has become available only in the past 5–6 years and it offers a number of advantages over CT because of its improved visualization precision.

The results of MRS studies on the corpus callosum in schizophrenia are highly inconsistent. More recently, at least three independent studies have reported evidence of structural abnormalities in the temporal lobe of many patients with schizophrenia [3–5].

Preliminary accounts of the application of ^{31}P magnetic resonance spectroscopy

(MRS) in schizophrenia seem to provide additional evidence on the "hypofrontality" in such a disorder. This technique, when combined with MRI, unites anatomical structure, pathological function and biochemistry. The MRS provides a link between the biochemical understanding of disease and the pathophysiology of medicine.

"Functional" brain imaging techniques

The application of these techniques shows that the distribution of functional activity can clarify the physiological and biochemical correlates of mental disorders. Some studies of brain metabolism with PET and rCBF, which is closely related to metabolism, have suggested that activity in the frontal lobes is abnormally low in patients with schizophrenia [6–8].

Conclusion

At present, neuroimaging provides a modest amount of information about the possible pathophysiological mechanisms of major mental illnesses, including structural abnormalities in some forms of schizophrenia. Nonetheless, these premises are encouraging for the future. The mapping of cerebral function in normal subjects with a consequently better understanding of normal structure, physiology and functional organization of the brain will be possible. This will aid in improving the comprehension of mental illnesses.

References

1. Johnstone EC, Crow TJ, Frith CD et al. (1976) Lancet ii: 924–926.
2. Andreasen NC, Swayze VC, Flaum M et al. (1990) Am. J. Psychiatry 147: 893–890.
3. Suddath RL, Casanova M, Goldberg T et al. (1989) Am. J. Psychiatry 146: 464–472.
4. De Lisi LE, Dauphinais ID, Gershon ES et al. (1988) Schizophr. Bull. 14: 185–191.
5. Rossi A, Stratta P, D'Albenzio L et al. (1990) Biol. Psychiatry 27: 61–68.
6. Buchsbaum MS, Ingvar DH, Kessler R et al. (1982) Arch. Gen. Psychiatry 39: 251–259.
7. Wolkin A, Angrist B, Wolf A et al. (1988) Am. J. Psychiatry 145: 251–253.
8. Weinberger D, Berman KF, Illowsky B et al. (1988) Arch. Gen. Psychiatry 45: 609–615.

© 1991 Elsevier Science Publishers B.V. All rights reserved.
Biological Psychiatry, Volume 2. G. Racagni et al., editors.

Psychoneuroendocrine studies in Italy today

F. Brambilla
Ospedale Psichiatrico Pini, Milan, Italy

Introduction

Psychoneuroendocrine studies have been developing in the last years in Italy, an expression of an increasing interest in the link between mental and hormonal physiological and pathological functions. Research has dealt with eating disorders, drug addiction, schizophrenia, depression, panic disorder and psychotropic drug-induced hormonal dysfunctions.

Eating disorders

Investigations have centered on anorexia nervosa (AN). Beta-endorphin (β-EP) secretory pattern, circadian rhythmicity and responses to stimulating-inhibiting agents (CRH, clonidine, domperidone, 5-OH-tryptophan and metoclopramide) have been examined, since opioids are known to intervene in the regulation of eating. GH basal secretion and response to GHRH, TRH, clonidine and insulin-induced hypoglycemia were also examined. The main purpose of this research was to determine whether impairments in specific brain neurotransmitters-neuromodulators, which regulate hormonal functions, could be etiopathogenetically involved in the onset and course of the disease. In this line, GH parameters were used to investigate noradrenergic and acetylcholinergic systems and REP data for the opioid system.

This research was directed by: Prof. V. Coiro (Clin. Med. Int. Univ., Parma); P. Chiodera (Ist. Endocrinol. Univ., Parma); M. Rolla (Clin. Med. Univ., Pisa); F. Cavagnini (Ist. Sci. Med. Univ., Milan); F. Brambilla (Osp. Psichiat., Pini, Milan); C. Bulletti (Dip. Med. Riprodut. Univ., Bologna); D. Nerozzi (Dip. Neurosci. Univ. La Sapienza, Rome); A. Barbarino (Ist. Endocrinol. Univ. Cattolica, Rome); R. Valcavi (Ist. Med. Gen. Endocrinol., Arcispedale, S. Maria, Nuova-Reggio, Emilia); F. Caviezel (Ist. Sci. San Raffaele, Milano).

Drug addiction

The effects of heroin addiction and prolonged methadone consumption on neuro-endocrine secretions were investigated, with the aim of defining the adverse effects of the 2 drugs on hormonal systems; and in the meantime, through the study of these impairments, to clarify the central neurotransmitter-neuromodulator drug-induced alterations as mirrored in the peripheral hormonal data. ACTH, cortisol, β-EP, β-lipotropin, GH, TSH, prolactin, calcitonin, FSH, LH testosterone, dehydroepiandrosterone, dehydrotestosterone, androstenedione, insulin, thyroxine, triiodothyronine basal levels and responses to stimulation and inhibition tests were examined and correlated with duration and severity of addiction.

This research was mainly organized by: Prof. F. Facchinetti et al. (Clin Ostetrica, Ginecol. Univ., Modena); P.P. Vescovi (Clin. Med. Generale Univ., Parma); W. Spagnolli (Div. Med. Istituti Ospedalieri, Trento); F. Tagliaro (Ist. Med. Legale Univ., Verona); G. Ragnii Dip. Ostetrica–Ginecol. Univ., Milan); F. Brambilla (Ospedale Psichiatrico Pini, Milan); S. Lafisca (Ist. Med. Legale, Verona); G. Guerra (Consul. Tossicodipendenze, Osp. Militare, Verona).

Schizophrenia

The psychoendocrine aspects of schizophrenia have been the subject of interest, GH and prolactin responses to various GABAergic agonists have been measured in order to investigate the functional asset of the GABA system in mental disorder (P. Monteleone, Serv. Igiene Ment. USSL 41, Naples; and A. Maj, Ist. Psichol. Med., Psichiatria, Naples).

Vasopressin and TRH were tentatively administered to type II schizophrenic subjects and psychological, neurotransmitter and neuroendocrine parameters were studied in parallel, to assess the mechanism of action of the two hormones in inducing psychological improvement (F. Brambilla, Ospedale Psichiatrico, Pini, Milan).

Concentrations of noradrenaline in the cerebrospinal fluid and of melatonin cortisol, GH, prolactin in plasma, their circadian rhythms and responses to stimulation were also examined (P. Monteleone, Serv. Igiene Ment. USSL 41, Naples; D. Nerozzi, Dip. Neuroscienze Univ. La Sapienza, Rome; and D. Kemali, Ist. Psicol. Med. Psichiat. Univ., Naples), to tentatively clarify the state of activity of neurotransmitter-neuromodulator systems involved in parallel in hormonal and psychological regulation.

Depression

The function of the noradrenergic and GABAergic systems has been investigated by measuring GH responses to GHRH, TRH, baclofen, clonidine, pirenzepine, TSH responses to TRH and dexamethasone suppression test (DST).

The experiments were carried out by: P. Monteleone (Serv. Igiene Ment. USSL 41, Naples); F. Brambilla (Ospedale Psichiatrico, Pini, Milan); V. Coiro (Clin. Med. Int. Univ., Parma); L. Tondo (Clin. Psichiat. Univ., Cagliari).

Panic disorder

Neuroendocrine studies of panic disorder have dealt with GH, MHPG, HVA basal plasma levels and their responses to clonidine stimulation, with ACTH cortisol, β-EP basal plasma levels and their responses to CRH stimulation, with T-lymphocyte β-EP concentrations in basal situation and after CRH stimulation and with responses to the DST. All these endocrine and biochemical data were measured in order to define the status of central noradrenergic-dopaminergic secretory tonus, which controls peripheral hormonal secretion and may be involved in the etiopathogenesis of panic disorder. Moreover, mitogenic responses to phytohaemagglutinin (HPA) were examined before and after CRH stimulation to investigate the influence of ACTH, β-EP and cortisol secretion on the immune system (F. Brambilla, Osp. Psichiat., Pini, Milan).

Effect of psychotropic drugs

The effects of psychotropic drugs administered acutely or chronically to normal subjects or neurologic and psychiatric patients have been studied, with the aim of investigating unwanted side-effects which could interfere with the efficacy of the therapies. Moreover, the neuroendocrine studies could shed light on the central mechanism of action of the drugs. Lithium, carbamezapin, mianserin, diazepam, phenobarbital and sodium valproate effects on hormonal functions were studied by: L. Tondo (Clin. Psichiat. Univ, Cagliari); M. D'Armento (Dip. Endocrinol. Univ. La Sapienza, Rome); L. Murri (Ist. Clin. Neurol. Univ., Pisa); P. Monteleone (Serv. Igiene Ment. USSL 41, Naples); C. Altamura (Clin. Psichiat. I Univ., Milan); D. Kemali (Ist. Psicol. Med. Psichiat. Univ., Naples); V. Coiro (Clin. Med. Int. Univ., Parma); F. Cavagnini (Ist. Sci. Med. Univ., Milan).

© 1991 Elsevier Science Publishers B.V. All rights reserved.
Biological Psychiatry, Volume 2. G. Racagni et al., editors.

Psychopharmacology in Italy: An update

A.C. Altamura
Department of Psychiatry-University of Milan, Milan, Italy

Clinical psychopharmacology in Italy has a relatively long-lasting tradition, since the Italian Association for Neuropsychopharmacology was founded in the mid-1960s and was one of the first in Europe along with the British and Swedish associations. On the other hand, the psychopharmacological interest in this country stems from the well-known attitude of Italian psychiatry, which since the beginning of this century, has been more biologically than psychodynamically oriented.

This paper will deal with the following aspects:
1. main research topics;
2. new drugs development;
3. teaching and training programmes.

Main research topics

Concerning *drug epidemiology*, there is a very active centre in Verona directed by Prof. Tansella and operating since the 1970s. In 2 weeks' prevalence studies performed in the south Verona area in 1980 and 1987 it was shown that the prevalence of psychotropic drug consumption was 13% and 15% respectively. Another finding was that women and patients over 65 years were the most represented among users (18% men and 9% women; 25% patients over 65% years).

Table 1. Main research topics in the field of clinical psychopharmacology: Italy 1991

1. Drug epidemiology;
2. Drug utilization;
3. Clinical pharmacokinetics;
4. Treatment and prophylaxis of affective disorders;
5. Long-term treatment with antipsychotics;
6. The elderly;
7. Clinical trials.

Other:

8. Pharmacogenetics;
9. Diagnostic tools for treatment;
10. Neuroimaging;
11. Clinical neurophysiology (EEG mapping).

Benzodiazepines were the most utilised drugs (78%) and consumption of psychoactive drugs was associated positively to some occupational and family variables. There is another interesting study investigating national trends of prescription of psychotropic drugs between 1975 and 1984 based on the pharmacies selling those drugs [1–5]. *Drug utilization* studies have been performed at Mario Negri Institute in Milan (since the beginning of the 1970s), consisting of research in collaboration with psychiatric hospitals or general medical departments on the utilisation of the psychotropic compounds. At the end of the 1960s at the Institute of Clinical Psychiatry of the University of Pisa, a Center for Clinical Psychopharmacology Data Documentation was established jointly with the National Institute of Mental Health in Bethesda. This initiative had a "major objective", the enhancement of quality of clinical trials with psychopharmacological agents performed internationally by improving and disseminating computer-based data documentation techniques and by offering to the investigators the possibility of utilizing the BLIPS/BDP (Biometric Laboratory Information Processing System/ Data Bank for Psychopharmacology), a standardized data-processing system [6–7].

Concerning *treatment and prophylaxis of affective disorders*, contributions have come from the School of Naples (Professors Kemali and Maj), Pisa (Dr. Placidi) and Rome (Dr. Koukopulos). Published data deal mainly with prediction of response to lithium, use of alternative drugs to lithium (like carbamazepine) or influence of antidepressants on clinical evolution of bipolar syndromes [8–9]. The work of Professor Maj on the use of lithium in the prophylaxis of schizoaffective psychosis deserves special mention [10–12].

Since the mid-1970s studies at the Psychiatric Institute of Milan University have measured neuro-psychotropics, particularly antiepileptic and antidepressant drugs. From the beginning of the 1980s we were also able to measure haloperidol and recently its main metabolite hydroxyhaloperidol, using a combined mass spectrometry liquid chromatography technique. Our research is mainly directed toward the study of drug resistance phenomena, secondary to compliance problems and/or abnormal metabolic patterns. Moreover, we were interested in studying acute kinetic profiles of antidepressants in relation to age, showing that some atypical compounds have kinetic parameters (like $t_{1/2}$, V_d, C_1) affected by age. We also use plasma levels in long-term treatments with antipsychotics like haloperidol decanoate. Recently, investigating tardive dyskinesia in long-institutionalized psychiatric patients, a relationship between age and occurrence and severity of TD has been found. No relationship with previous neuroleptics treatment or ECT or anticholinergic drugs was observed [13–15].

Concerning *clinical trials* in the international literature data, Italian contributions are not very frequent: this can be explained on the basis of two main reasons. The first is that until very recent years novel molecules from the U.S. or European countries reached Italy too late to give rise to clinical trials still of interest. The second reason is that quality of most of these trials is arguable. Finally, concerning topics belonging to other research areas I would like to mention Dr. Tacchini and myself in Milan in the CIDI project, that is a structured diagnostic interview which seems a suitable starting point for any treatment. Moreover, there are pharmacogenetic (Dr. Spina in Messina) [16] and clinical neurophysiology studies in relation to treatment response carried out by Dr. Galderisi in Naples [17] and neuroimaging in Milan (Dr. Vita) [18].

New drugs development

Also in Italy in the last 15 years the search for novel molecules in the field of psychopharmacology have led to the introduction of some original compounds that deserve to be mentioned since they are "Italian" molecules; some of them are now well known and widely investigated in eastern and western countries i.e., drugs for the treatment of depression like trazodone, from Angelini [19]; SAMe, from Bioresearch [20]; and the new drug reboxetine, from Carlo Erba in Milan, a very promising noradrenergic reuptake selective inhibitor. Moreover, there are some other so-called nootropic compounds like acetylcarnitine, from Sigma Tau, phosphatydilserine and gangliosides from Fidia in the treatment of dementias [21–28].

Teaching and training programmes in psychopharmacology

We should distinguish between academic and non-academic programmes: in the first case they are organized by each university for their residents in psychiatry. Concerning academic programmes, at the moment purely theoretical teaching is available, without specific training programmes. This is expected to change in the next few years with unified teaching and training activities for all the countries belonging to the European Community. The non-academic programmes should be organized by the state for clinical psychiatrists.

Again, the majority of these activities are not planned by law but due to personal initiatives, often without any financial support. In this light, the creation of a WHO Italian Centre for Research and Training in Mental Health with the participation of Istituto Superiore di Sanita' Institute of Psychiatry of Naples Verona, Institute Mario Negri and Department of Pharmacology of Milan (Prof. Racagni) could encourage not only psychopharmacological research but also attempt to organize continuous training programmes nationwide in the near future.

References

1. Balestrieri M, Bragagnoli N and Bellantuono C (1991) J. Affective Disord. 21: 45–55.
2. Bellantuono C, Arreghini E, Adami M, Bodini F, Gastaldo M and Micciolo R (1989) Soc. Psychiatry Psychiatr. Epidemiol. 24: 212–218.
3. Bellantuono C, Fiorio R, Williams P, Arreghini E and Cason G (1988). Eur. Arch. Psychiatry Neurol. Sci. 237: 347–350.

4. Fiorio R, Bellantuono C Arreghini E, Leoncini M and Micciolo R (1989) Int. Clin. Psychopharmacol. 4: 7–17.
5. Fiorio R, Bellantuono C, Leoncini M, Montemezzi G, Micciolo R and Williams P (1990) Hum. Psychopharmacol. 5: 195–205.
6. Cassano GB, Conti L, Massimetti G and Levine J (1979) In: Bowers JZ and Velo GP (eds.) Drug Assessment: Criteria and Methods. pp. 253–260.
7. Conti L, Cassano GB, Massimetti G and Levine J (1985) In: Pichot P, Berner P, Wolf and Thau K (eds.) Psychiatry, Vol. 1. Plenum Publ. Co., New York, pp. 173–185.
8. Koukopulos A and Tondo L (1980) In: Johnson FN (ed.) Handbook of Lithium Therapy. MTP Press, Lancaster.
9. Placidi GF, Lenzi A, Lazzerini F, Cassano GB and Akiskal HS (1986) J. Clin. Psychiatry 47: 490–494.
10. Maj M, Pirozzi R and Kemali D (1989) Psychopharmacology 98: 535–538.
11. Maj M (1988) J. Affective Disord. 14: 129–135.
12. Maj M, Starace F, Nolfe G and Kemali D (1986) Pharmacopsychiatry 19: 420–423.
13. Altamura AC, Cavallaro R and Regazzetti MG (1990) Arch. Psychiatry Clin. Neurosci. 240: 9–12.
14. Bell M, Plon L, Bunney W, Potkin G (1988) Am. J. Psychiatry 145: 1110–1114.
15. Altamura AC, De Novellis F, Mauri MC and Gomeri R (1987) Prog. Neuro-Psychopharmacol. Biol. Psychiatry 11: 23–33.
16. Spina E, Steiner E, Dumont E and Dahlqvist R (1989) In: Dahl SG and Gram LF (eds.) Clinical Pharmacology in Psychiatry. Springer Verlag, Berlin.
17. Galderisi S, Mucci A, Di Gregorio MR, Bucci P, Maj M and Kemaly D (1990) J. Eur. Coll. Neuropsychopharmacol.
18. Vita A, Valvassori G, Brambilla S et al. (1989) In: Casacchia M and Rossi A (eds.) MTP Press, Lancaster, pp. 79–90.
19. Altamura AC, Mauri MC, Rudas N, Carpiniello B et al. (1989) Clin. Neuropharmacol. 12: 25–33.
20. Amaducci L and SMID Group (1991). Psychopharmacol. Bull. Vol. 24, 1: 130–134.
21. Loo H, Benjacub K, Rovei V, Altamura AC, Vadrot M and Morselli PL (1980) Br. J. Psychiatry 137: 444–451.
22. Altamura AC, Mauri MC and Guercetti G (1986) Prog. Neuro-Psychopharmacol. Biol. Psychiatry 10: 67–75.
23. Altamura AC and Mauri MC (1985) Br. J. Clin. Pharmacol. 20: 714–716.
24. Altamura AC, Melorio T, Invernizzi G and Gomeri R (1982) Psychopharmacology 78: 380–382.
25. Altamura AC, Melorio T, Invernizzi G, Colacurcio F and Gomeri R (1983) Psychopharmacology 81: 281–285.
26. Altamura AC, Curry SH, Montgomery S and Wiles DH (1985) Psychopharmacology 87: 30–33.
27. Altamura AC, Mauri MC, Cavallaro R and Gorni A (1987). Lancet i: 814–815.
28. Altamura AC, Mauri MC, Cavallaro R, Colacurcio F, Gorni A and Bareggi S (1988) Prog. Neuro-Psychopharmacol. Biol. Psychiatry 12: 689–694.

© 1991 Elsevier Science Publishers B.V. All rights reserved.
Biological Psychiatry, Volume 2. G. Racagni et al., editors.

Trends and achievements in neuropsychophysiological research on mental disorders

S. Galderisi

Department of Psychiatry, First Medical School, University of Naples, Naples, Italy

Selected Italian investigations on schizophrenic, mood and anxiety disorders, based on neurophysiological and neuropsychological testing, will be briefly reviewed and discussed.

Sleep EEG studies

The Pisa group, led by Maggini et al., confirmed the finding of a reduced REM latency and stage 4 duration in depression, but also demonstrated that similar alterations of sleep structure can be found in manic and schizophrenic patients, as well as in elderly normals, coming to the conclusion that neither parameter can be considered a biological marker of endogenous depression [1]. They also cautioned against unrealistic expectations concerning the diagnostic value of sleep characteristics in the individual subject, emphasizing its utility in the investigation of pathophysiological mechanisms underlying different biological subtypes within diagnostic categories. A similar trend has characterized the work of the Milan group (Pugnetti et al.).

Waking QEEG studies

Scarone et al. (Milan) have devoted much attention to α reactivity in schizophrenia and have come to the conclusion that it represents a sensitive measure of the schizophrenic process and probably a trait-dependent characteristic [2]. The same group has also investigated hemispheric lateralization of QEEG abnormalities in schizotypal patients as well as in subchronic and chronic schizophrenics during cognitive activation, reporting different lateralization patterns of β activity among the groups, and speculating that a bilateral increase might be specific to the early phase of schizophrenia or its premorbid stage [3]. The Naples group (Kemali et al.) has reported bilateral increase of β relative power in drug-free schizophrenics and a positive correlation between this activity and noradrenaline levels in the cerebrospinal fluid, lending support to the hyperarousal theory of schizophrenia. Our investigations on relationships between QEEG and structural abnormalities demonstrated different neurophysiological profiles in patients with and without enlarged lateral ventricles [4]. More recently, EEG mapping studies by the same group have confirmed the presence in drug-free schizophrenics of increased slow and fast activities and of decreased α, but have not supported claims of either frontal predominance of δ activity or temporal localization of increased fast activity. The role of neuroleptics in the genesis of these abnormalities has also been excluded by demonstrating their partial normalization after haloperidol treatment [5]. Moreover, it has been shown that in schizophrenics both baseline and drug-induced QEEG characteristics are related to clinical responsivity to drug treatment.

Event-related potential (ERP) studies

Mainly the late ERP components, linked to cognitive activity, have been studied. Romani et al. (Pavia) confirmed the largely reported finding of a P300 amplitude reduction in medicated schizophrenics and also found an increase of its latency, associated with poor performance on several neuropsychological tests; neither P300 abnormalities, nor neuropsychological performance was related to CT scan measures [6]. A reduced amplitude of P300 for auditory stimuli in schizophrenics was also reported by Scrimali et al. (Catania) [7]. In drug-free schizophrenics we found abnormal hemispheric lateralization of P300 and other late positive components of the ERPs recorded during visual verbal stimuli recognition; abnormalities were partly reversed by neuroleptic treatment [8]. Rizzo et al. (Rome) have provided interesting contributions on the dopaminergic modulation of ERP negative late components and have reported on their utility in the study of phobic disorders [9].

Neuropsychological studies

Scarone et al., Rossi's and our group have contributed to this research area. All of us have been investigating schizophrenics' performance on the Luria Nebraska Neuropsychological Battery (LNNB). A poorer performance was observed in patients with structural brain abnormalities [10]. All groups failed, however, to find statistically significant correlations between LNNB and morphological variables. The Milan group suggests that the impairment picked up by the battery is not only an index of organic brain damage, but is influenced by other variables, in particular educational level. The LNNB localization scales showed bilateral involvement in schizophrenics and depressives [11], and no impairment in obsessive patients [12]. Our group has also studied schizophrenic and obsessive-compulsive patients using tests aimed to evaluate left and right fronto-hippocampal and temporo-hippocampal functioning; results are compatible with a left fronto-temporo-hippocampal deficit in schizophrenics [13] and a right frontal impairment in obsessive patients.

Conclusion

On the whole, Italian research on neuropsychophysiology of mental disorders has been characterized by a cautious attitude toward clinical implications of findings. Neither QEEG, nor neuropsychological testing have been claimed to represent diagnostic tools, but both have generally been regarded as non-invasive instruments in the study of pathogenetic mechanisms of these disorders, in the search for possible biological markers and in the attempt to improve clinical subtyping within diagnostic categories.

References

1. Maggini C, Guazzelli M, Pieri M, Lattanzi L, Ciapparelli A, Massimetti G and Rossi G (1986) New Trends Exp. Clin. Psychiatry II: 93–101.
2. Colombo C, Gambini O, Macciardi F, Locatelli M, Calabrese G and Scarone S (1989) In: Casacchia M and Rossi A (eds.) Schizophrenia: A Psychobiological View. Kluwer Academic Publishers, Lancaster, pp. 119–124.
3. Scarone S, Gambini O, Colombo C, Cattaneo R, Bellodi L and Pugnetti L (1987) In: Flor-Henry P, Gruzelier J and Takahashi R (eds.) Laterality, Psychopathology and Cerebral Dynamics. Elsevier, Amsterdam, pp. 115–124.
4. Kemali D, Galderisi S and Maj M. (1988) In: Giannitrapani D and Murri L (eds.) The EEG of Mental Activities. Karger, Basel, pp. 69–181.
5. Galderisi S, Mucci A, Mignone ML, Maj M and Kemali D (1991) Schizophr. Res. (in press).
6. Romani A, Merello S, Gozzoli L, Zerbi F, Grassi M and Cosi V (1987) Br. J. Psychiatry 151: 506–513.
7. Scrimali T, Grimaldi L and Rapisarda V (1988) Res. Commun. Psychol. Psychiatry Behav. 13: 3–16.
8. Kemali D, Galderisi S, Maj M, Mucci A and Di Gregorio M (1991) Int. J. Psychophysiol. 10: 225–230.
9. Rizzo PA, Spadaro M, Albani G and Morocutti C (1983) Neuropsychobiology 9: 73–77.
10. Kemali D, Maj M, Galderisi S, Salvati A, Starace F, Valente A and Pirozzi R (1987) Psychiatr. Res. 21: 137–149.
11. Bellini L, Gambini O, Palladino F and Scarone S (1988) Acta Psychiatr. Scand. 78: 242–246.
12. Bellini L, Massironi R, Palladino F, Locatelli M, Gambini O and Scarone S (1989) Res. Commun. Psychol. Psychiatry Behav. 14: 73–82.
13. Kemali D, Maj M, Galderisi S, Monteleone P and Mucci A (1987) Neuropsychobiology 17: 30–34.

© 1991 Elsevier Science Publishers B.V. All rights reserved.
Biological Psychiatry, Volume 2. G. Racagni et al., editors.

Trends and achievements in genetics of mental disorders

Enrico Smeraldi and Fabio Macciardi

Istituto Scientifico H San Raffaele, Department of Neurosciences, University of Milano School of Medicine, via L. Prinetti 29, 20127 Milan, Italy

Psychiatric genetics in Italy did not meet with a great interest in the academic world, at least in this last half-century, despite a remarkable relevance and several interesting findings in the field. Since the pioneering work of Rudin, Slater and Kallmann (to quote just some of the pioneers), a dramatic amount of knowledge has been accumulated, giving rise to the modern genetics of complex characters. Moreover, in recent years, the introduction of recombinant DNA technology has allowed an enormous variability of DNA among individuals to be analyzed systematically, leading to the development of new strategies, such as the use of restriction fragment length polymorphisms (RFLPs) and other DNA variants as markers. These, in turn, have led to notable success in identifying the chromosomal region and sometimes the exact gene too, for several disorders characterized by a clear Mendelian pattern of transmission. Schizophrenia, however, as well as affective disorders and anxiety disorders to some extent, are part of a large group of diseases – including hypertension, many metabolic disorders and many cancers – which show strong evidence of genetic influence, but often display non-Mendelian segregation (Fig. 1).

Several strategies have been suggested for handling the complex task of understanding the genetics of mental disorders that are synthetically represented by association and linkage methodologies. Preliminary work, however, is needed to

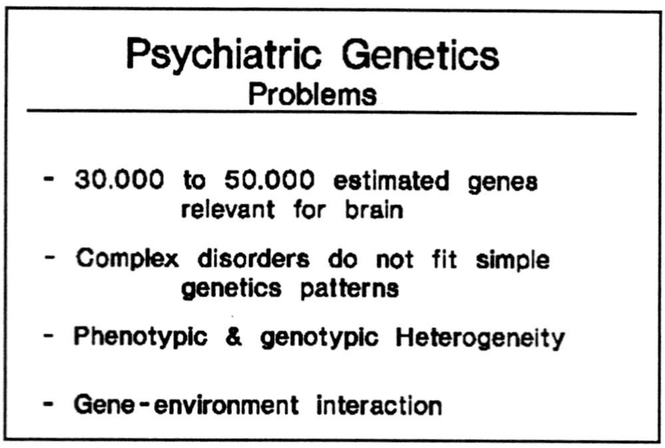

Fig. 1. Problems in genetics of mental disorders.

PSYCHIATRIC GENETICS
PROJECTS

INTERNATIONAL COLLABORATION

ESF: Human Genome Linkage Mapping
to localize genes of brain interest
Toronto: Candidate genes
Linkage Analysis with tandem repeats

Fig. 2.

cope with some key features of psychiatric disorders, such as defining the diagnostic boundaries for psychiatric diseases and searching for genetic models allowing for an appropriate description of the observed inheritance pattern: logic, for example, it could be shown that a 2-locus model for schizophrenia is highly better than the traditional single major locus (SML) [1,2].

Additional problems are associated with the task of identifying and collecting informative families for genetic analyses. Therefore it is easy to understand that collaborative efforts are required to successfully confront these issues and to give a pace to the studies (Fig. 2). Among the various collaborations, the network for molecular neurobiology of mental illnesses organized by the European Science Foundation represents a hallmark for genetic studies on schizophrenia and affective disorders. Our department has been selected as the Italian representative, together with the Florence group, and initial investigations are already underway (Fig. 3).

European Science Foundation
Partecipating Groups & Chromosomal Allocation

Country	P.I.	Chromosome(s)
ITALY	Smeraldi	6, 11p, 17q (7, 8q, 13)
	Sorbi	4, 6, 19, 21
GERMANY	(2 groups)	2, 18, 19
FRANCE	Mallet	9, 10, 20
U.K.	(4 groups)	3, 5, 11q, 12, 21, 22, X
BELGIUM	(2 groups)	1, 17,
DK+FINLAND	(2 groups)	1, 15, 16

Fig. 3.

PSYCHIATRIC GENETICS
PROJECTS

MOLECULAR GENETICS

DRD2, DRD1 & DRD4 genes in Schizophrenia and Delusional Disorders

Hypotheses of biological determinants in congnitive defects for Schizophrenia: role of chromosome 21

Linkage analysis for early onset Familial Alzheimer Disease (FAD): Chromosome 21

Gerstmann-Strausler Disease: differential diagnosis from FAD by PCR techniques for the PrP Protein on chromosome 20

Fig. 4. Molecular projects under development.

A sustained effort will be required for the ESF project to be completed: several large pedigrees have been selected within the various countries participating in the project and a systematic search among the whole human genome is now moving on.

Alternative strategies could also be followed: historically, we have been among the first groups studying genetics of complex disorders, suggesting some ideas that still hold true [3–5].

Projects under development encompass both formal and molecular genetics: whereas the former are highly specialized and require both mathematical and statistical skills [6]; the latter apparently appear to be of more immediate comprehension (Fig. 4).

In conclusion, a great amount of work on the genetics of mental disorders is now more feasible than in the past and is almost in progress; methods and techniques of psychiatric genetics are also becoming more sophisticated, and fruitful application of this field demands both an excellent psychiatric and genetic background.

References

1. Risch N (1990) Am. J. Hum. Genet. 46: 222–228.
2. Smeraldi E and Macciardi F (1991) This volume.
3. Smeraldi E, Negri F, Melica A and Scorza-Smeraldi R (1978) Tissue Antigen 12: 270–274.
4. Smeraldi E, Morabito A, Macciardi F et al. (1986) Clin. Genet. 30: 157–166.
5. Smeraldi E, Lucca A, Macciardi F and Bellodi L (1988) Hum. Genet. 76: 138–140.
6. Macciardi F and Morabito A (1990) In: Atti del II Congr. Naz. dell'Associazione Italiana di Statistica Medica e Programmazione Socio-Sanitaria. Pavia, pp. 343–350.

Index of authors

Volume 2

Subject index

Volume 2